THE ENCYCLOPEDIA OF WORLD
MILITARY AIRCRAFT

THE ENCYCLOPEDIA OF WORLD
MILITARY AIRCRAFT

Edited by David Donald and Jon Lake

BARNES
&NOBLE
BOOKS
NEW YORK

This edition published by Barnes & Noble, Inc.,
by arrangement with Amber Books Ltd
2000 Barnes & Noble Books

M 10 9 8 7 6 5 4 3 2 1

ISBN: 0-7607-2208-0

Copyright © 2000 Aerospace Publishing Ltd

This material was previously published in 1996 in the
World Air Power Journal.

Editorial and design by
Amber Books Ltd
Bradley's Close
74–77 White Lion Street
London N1 9PF

Editors: David Donald and Jon Lake
Illustrations: Chris Davey, Grant Race, Mark Styling, John Weal

Printed in Italy

Introduction

The *Encyclopedia of World Military Aircraft* covers all
the aircraft that are in current service with the
military air arms around the world, presenting
detailed technical, service and operator information
on each individual type.

The encyclopedia arranges the aircraft types in
alphabetical order according to the current, or most
recent, manufacturer. A complete index is
provided, arranged by manufacturer, designation
and common name.

Further information on all current military aircraft,
and regular updates as situations change, is provided
in the quarterly publication *World Air Power Journal*,
available from the addresses opposite.

Aeritalia (FIAT/Alenia) G91R/T

Alenia
Via E. Petrolini 2
I-00197 Roma, Italy

NATO's need for a light fighter and tactical support aircraft led to the formulation of a specification in December 1953. Circulated to West European industry in early 1954, it brought a number of proposals, that from the Italian manufacturer Fiat finally being selected. This came after the prototypes (the first of them flown on 9 August 1956) had taken part in technical evaluation trials at Brétigny, France, in 1957. There the **Fiat G91** demonstrated it could satisfy NATO requirements and also have the ability to operate, with or without stores, from semi-prepared airstrips.

The initial production version was the single-seat G91 ground-attack fighter with fixed armament of four 0.5-in (12.7-mm) Colt-Browning machine-guns (two mounted on each side of the cockpit). Four underwing pylons were provided for 500-lb (227-kg) bombs, tactical nuclear weapons, Nord 5103 AAMs, rocket pods and machine-gun pods. Operational evaluation of the G91 began with 103ᵃ Squadriglia of the **Aeronautica Militare Italiana** during February 1959. During the development of the G91 the role of high-speed tactical reconnaissance was not ignored, resulting in the **G91R/1,** first flown during 1959. This was essentially a standard G91 with a shortened nose section mounting three 70-mm focal length Vinten cameras (forward-looking and oblique) suitable for high-speed low-level photography by day; vertical coverage from high altitude is also possible. The G91R/1 was adopted by the AMI and two examples were evaluated by the USAF. Subsequent versions included the similar **G91R/1A,** differing by installation of improved navigation aids as in the G91R/3;

the **G91R/1B,** similar to the G91R/1A but with a reinforced structure, landing gear and equipment changes; the similar **G91R/3,** built to **Luftwaffe** specifications with two 30-mm cannon, Doppler radar and a position and homing indicator; and, finally, the **G91R/4,** basically a G91R/3 but with R/1 armament and some equipment changes. Two G91R/3s and one G91T/1 trainer were evaluated by the US Army in 1961 as tactical support aircraft for operation from unprepared airstrips.

European service

The G91R and its corresponding trainer variant, the G91T, has served with three European air arms. The Federal German Luftwaffe received a total of 344 G91R/3s (74 built by Fiat and 270 licence-built in Germany), all of which were phased out of service in the mid-1980s. In addition, 24 ex-Luftwaffe G91Ts were operated at Husum by civilian contractor Condor Flugdienst to provide target facilities for the West German air force. These were supplanted in 1992 by the Pilatus PC-9. The **Portuguese air force** was allocated G91R/4s under the US MAP scheme and has used the type in its African wars. Forty ex-GAF G91R/3s and at least 10 G91T trainers were also acquired and were given a secondary air-defence capability with AIM-9L missiles. All Portuguese G91s were phased out in late 1993, following replacement by A-7Ps and F-16A/Bs. The sole surviving G91R/T operator is the AMI, which continues to operate 50 G91T trainers for the final stage of pilot training before conversion to an operational type. All AMI G91Rs were retired in April 1992.

Aeritalia (Fiat/Alenia) G91T

Wing: span 8.60 m (28 ft 3 in); aspect ratio 4.46; area 16.42 m² (176.74 sq ft)
Fuselage and tail: length 11.67 m (38 ft 3.5 in); height 4.45 m (14 ft 7.25 in); wheel track 2.82 m (9 ft 3 in); wheel base 3.51 m (11 ft 6.25 in)
Powerplant: one Fiat-built Rolls-Royce (Bristol Siddeley) Orpheus Mk 803 rated at 5,000 lb st (22.24 kN) dry
Weights: operating empty 3865 kg (8,521 lb); normal take-off 5500 kg (12,125 lb); maximum take-off 6050 kg (13,338 lb)
Fuel and load: internal fuel 2100 litres (555 US gal); external fuel up to two 520- or 260-litre (137- or 69-US gal) drop tanks; maximum ordnance 680 kg (1,500 lb)
Speed: maximum level speed 'clean' at 5,000 ft (1525 m) 556 kt (640 mph; 1030 km/h); cruising speed at optimum altitude 350 kt (403 mph; 650 km/h)
Range: ferry range 1,000 nm (1,152 miles; 1854 km) with drop tanks; typical combat radius 173 nm (199 miles; 320 km) on a

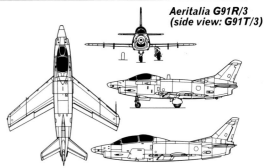

Aeritalia G91R/3 (side view: G91T/3)

hi-lo-hi attack mision
Performance: maximum rate of climb at sea level 6,000 ft (1830 m) per minute; climb to 13,125 ft (4000 m) in 4 minutes 30 seconds; service ceiling 40,000 ft (12190 m); take-off distance to 50 ft (15 m) 4,760 ft (1451 m) at maximum take-off weight; landing distance from 50 ft (15 m) 2,200 ft (671 m) at normal landing weight

A handful of G91Ts remain in service with the AMI. They are still used for advanced training purposes with 60ᵃ Brigata at Amendola.

Aeritalia (Fiat/Alenia) G91Y

Whereas the original Fiat G91R was a single-engined fighter-bomber and tactical reconnaissance aircraft produced to a NATO specification, the **Aeritalia G91Y** (or 'Yankee' as it is unofficially known) was developed for the **Italian air force.** Compared with the G91R, which was retired in Italy during 1984, the 'Yankee' differs fundamentally in having two J85 afterburning turbojets side-by-side in a revised fuselage, these providing 60 per cent more thrust for only a small increase in weight. In order to increase combat radius, one engine can be shut down during the cruise phase of a mission. Fuel capacity of the fuselage and inner wing tanks is 3200 litres (704 Imp gal), but drop tanks may be carried on the four underwing pylons, giving a ferry range of 3500 km (2,175 miles). The G91Y retains the three-camera nose and two internal 30-mm DEFA cannon of later-model G91Rs, but is capable of carrying an increased warload. This includes provision for 1,000-lb (454-kg) bombs, 750-lb (340-kg) napalm tanks, four 7 x 2-in rocket packs, four 28 x 2-in rocket packs or four 5-in rocket containers. A more sophisticated avionics fit comprises position and homing indicator, twin axis gyro platform, Doppler radar ranger, air-data computer radar altimeter and electronic head-up display (HUD).

With the emphasis on STOL performance, the aircraft has provision for JATO rocket bottles which can halve the required take-off run, and an airfield arrester hook for use with SATS (Short Airfield for Tactical Support) installations. Operating from a semi-prepared surface, the aircraft will unstick in 914 m (3,000 ft) and land (unassisted) from 15 m (50 ft) in 600 m (1,970 ft). With the obvious exception of the engine compartment, the G91Y's airframe is based on the earlier G91T two-seat trainer, although accommodation is provided for a pilot only in an armoured, air-conditioned, pressurised cockpit fitted with a Martin-

Baker zero-zero ejection seat. The wing has 38° sweepback, full-span slats and electrically-actuated slotted flaps. Two airbrakes are hinged beneath the centre fuselage, and engine replacement entails removal of the rear fuselage, with the variable-incidence trimming tailplane. The first of two prototypes was flown on 27 December 1966. An order for 20 pre-series aircraft was followed by contracts for a further 53 production examples but, in the event, production ended at the 67th aircraft. A projected **G91YT** two-seat trainer was not developed, and the sole **G91YS** was demonstrated to the Swiss air arm without success.

Deliveries to the **AMI**'s 8° Stormo at Cervia began in May 1970 for a single oversized squadron (101° Gruppo), while 32° Stormo (13° Gruppo) at Brindisi re-equipped from August 1973, assigning some of its aircraft an anti-shipping strike role and decorating them with sharksmouth markings. It was originally envisaged that the G91Y would be gradually replaced by the AMX from 1987. However, delays with the service introduction of the latter type have meant that the above units were still opera-

tional on the G91Y in early 1994. The G91Y will remain in service with the AMI until 1998, and from 1993 the fleet received the overall grey scheme worn by the AMX.

Aeritalia (Fiat/Alenia) G91Y

Wing: span 9.01 m (29 ft 6.5 in); aspect ratio 4.475; area 18.13 m² (195.16 sq ft)
Fuselage and tail: length 11.67 m (38 ft 3.5 in); height 4.43 m (14 ft 6 in); tailplane span 4.00 m (13 ft 1.5 in); wheel track 2.04 m (9 ft 8 in); wheel base 3.56 m (11 ft 8 in)
Powerplant: two General Electric J85-GE-13A each rated at 2,720 lb st (12.10 kN) dry and 4,080 lb st (18.15 kN) with afterburning
Weights: empty equipped 3900 kg (8,598 lb); normal take-off 7800 kg (17,196 lb); maximum take-off 8700 kg (19,180 lb)
Fuel and load: internal fuel 3200 litres (845 US gal); external fuel up to two 520-litre (137-US gal) drop tanks; maximum ordnance 4,000 lb (1814 kg)
Speed: maximum level speed 'clean' at 30,000 ft (9145 m) 560 kt (645 mph; 1038 km/h) and at sea level 600 kt (691 mph; 1111 km/h); cruising speed at 35,000 ft (10670 m) 432 kt (497 mph; 800 km/h)
Range: ferry range 3500 km (1,889 nm; 2,175 miles) with drop tanks; typical combat radius 600 km (324 nm; 373 miles) on a lo-lo-lo attack mission with a

2,910-lb (1320-kg) warload
Performance: maximum rate of climb at sea level 17,000 ft (5180 m) per minute with afterburning or 7,000 ft (2135 m) per minute without afterburning; climb to 42,000 ft (12200 m) in 4 minutes 30 seconds with afterburning or 11 minutes 0 seconds without afterburning; service ceiling 41,000 ft (12500 m); take-off run 4,000 ft (1219 m) on a hard runway at 8700 kg (19,180 lb), or 3,000 ft (914 m) on a semi-prepared runway at 7000 kg (15,432 lb), or 1,500 ft (457 m) on a semi-prepared runway at maximum take-off weight with JATO boost; take-off distance to 50 ft (15 m) 6,000 ft (1829 m) on a hard runway at 8700 kg (19,180 lb), or 4,500 ft (1372 m) on a semi-prepared runway at 7000 kg (15,432 lb), or 2,500 ft (762 m) on a semi-prepared runway at maximum take-off weight with JATO boost; landing distance from 50 ft (15 m) 1,970 ft (600 m) at normal landing weight

The 'Yankee' was a considerable improvement over the original G91, on account of its twin engines. The type still serves the AMI in some numbers although it is slowly being replaced by the AMX. The aircraft is employed in the close support and reconnaissance roles, able to carry a variety of unguided air-to-ground weaponry and equipped with cameras in the nose.

Aermacchi (Lockheed) AL.60 Conestoga/Trojan

Aermacchi SpA
Via Sanvito Silvestro 80
CP 246, I-21100 Varese, Italy

All the design work on this aircraft was carried out in the United States by Lockheed, which first flew the prototype in 1959. Financial considerations persuaded the company to offer the type for licensed construction abroad. Lockheed-Azcarte in Mexico built 18 as the **LASA-60** in 1960, for the **Fuerza Aérea Mexicana**, but the chief licensee was Italy's Aermacchi. With room for six people in the cabin and good rough-field performance, the **AL.60** was also suitable for the casevac role. The original aircraft was improved to become the **AL.60C** by uprating the engine and adding a parachute door. It was this version, with its associated tail-wheel undercarriage, which was eventually sold, as the **AL.60C-5 Conestoga**, to the **Central African Republic** (these are probably the only types left in service) and **Mauretania**. A second modified version, the **AL.60F-5 Trojan**, was sold to the **Rhodesian Air Force** but with the original tricycle undercarriage.

SPECIFICATION

Aermacchi (Lockheed) AL.60F-5 Conestoga
Wing: span 11.99 m (39 ft 4 in); aspect ratio 7.35; area 19.55 m² (210.44 sq ft)
Fuselage and tail: length 8.80 m (28 ft 10.5 in); height 3.30 m (10 ft 10 in); tailplane span 4.59 m (15 ft 0.5 in); wheel track 2.84 m (9 ft 4 in)
Powerplant: one Textron Lycoming IO-720-A1A rated at 400 hp (298 kW)

Weights: empty 2,394 lb (1086 kg); operating empty 2,731 lb (1239 kg); maximum take-off 4,500 lb (2041 kg)
Fuel and load: internal fuel 345 litres (91.1 US gal); external fuel none; maximum payload 1,440 lb (653 kg)
Speed: maximum level speed 'clean' at sea level 135 kt (156 mph; 251 km/h); maximum cruising speed at 10,000 ft (3050 m) 125 kt (144 mph; 232 km/h); economical cruising speed at 5,000 ft (1525 m) 94 kt (108 mph; 174 km/h)
Range: 560 nm (645 miles; 1037 km)
Performance: maximum rate of climb at sea level 1,085 ft (331 m) per minute; service ceiling 13,615 ft (4150 m); take-off run 645 ft (196 m) at maximum take-off weight; take-off distance to 50 ft (15 m) 1,100 ft (335 m) at maximum take-off weight; landing distance from 50 ft (15 m) 845 ft (258 m) at normal landing weight

A few AL.60C-5s were supplied to the Central African Republic for utility transport duties. These are still in service.

Aermacchi MB-326

Design of the **Aermacchi MB-326** two-seat basic trainer was started by Dr Ing. Ermanno Bazzocchi in 1954, and the first of two prototypes flew on 10 December 1957. This aircraft had a 7.78-kN (1,750-lb) thrust Bristol Siddeley (now Rolls-Royce) Viper 8 turbojet, but the second prototype, and 15 pre-production aircraft ordered for the Aeronautica Militare Italiana (AMI), used the 11.12-kN (2,500-lb) thrust Viper 11 engine as standard. The AMI received the first of 85 of these jet trainers (designated MB-326 in its initial form) in February 1962, in addition to the 15 pre-production aircraft. Intended for all stages of flying training, the basic airframe is simple, robust and has tandem two-seat accommodation in a pressurised cabin equipped with lightweight ejection seats.

The MB-326 has been built in many variants and clearly had potential for use in a light attack role. Such capability was offered by Aermacchi on the **MB-326A** with six underwing hardpoints for a variety of external stores, but the AMI at that time had no requirement for such an aircraft. However, orders for similar aircraft were received from **Ghana** (nine **MB-326F**) and Tunisia (eight **MB-326B**), and four unarmed **MB-326D** trainers were built as pilot trainers for Alitalia. The **MB-326H** with full armament provisions was assembled or licence-built in Australia by Commonwealth Aircraft Corporation as the **Commonwealth CA-30** for the Royal Australian Air Force (87) and Navy (10). Last of the early versions were 135 of a total of 151 aircraft known as the **Impala Mk 1 (MB-326M)** assembled or licence-built in the Transvaal by Atlas Aircraft Corporation for the South African air force. Sixteen complete aircraft (MB-326M) were delivered by Macchi from June 1966,

and 40 of the first Atlas-assembled aircraft contained Italian components. All Impala Mk 1s were powered by the uprated Viper Mk 540 engine of the MB-326G.

The more powerful Viper 20 engine was introduced in early 1967; combined with a strengthened airframe in the **MB-326G** prototype, the improved type had double the weapon load of earlier versions. It was built as the **MB-326GB** for the Argentine navy (eight) and the air forces of Zaïre (17) and Zambia (22); EMBRAER in Brazil licence-built 182 similar **MB-326GC** aircraft for the air forces of Brazil (167 **AT-26 Xavante**), Paraguay (nine) and Togo (six). Eleven ex-Brazilian EMB-326GBs were delivered to the Argentine navy air command in 1983. Aermacchi provided for the AMI six **MB-326E** aircraft with basically the MB-326GB airframe but the Viper 11 engine, and converted six earlier MB-326s to the same configuration. The final two-seat version was the **MB-326L** advanced trainer, based upon the single-seat MB-326K; two were supplied to Dubai and four to the Tunisian air force.

The delivery of the final EMB-326 in February 1983 completed MB-326 production, at the 761st aircraft.

SPECIFICATION

Aermacchi MB-326GB
Wing: span 10.854 m (35 ft 7.25 in) over tip tanks
Powerplant: one Rolls-Royce (Bristol Siddeley) Viper 20 Mk 540 rated at 15.17 kN (3,410 lb st)
Weights: basic operating 5,640 lb (2558 kg); normal take-off 9,805 lb (4447 kg); maximum take-off 11,500 lb (5216 kg)
Fuel and load: internal fuel 1392 litres (368 US gal); external fuel up to two 332-litre (88-US gal) drop tanks

Speed: maximum level speed 'clean' at optimum altitude 468 kt (539 mph; 867 km/h); cruising speed at optimum altitude 430 kt (495 mph; 797 km/h)
Range: ferry range 1,320 nm (1,520 miles; 2446 km) with drop tanks; combat radius 350 nm (403 miles; 648 km) on a hi-lo-hi attack mission with a 1,695-lb (769-kg) warload, or 70 nm (81 miles; 130 km) on a hi-lo-hi attack mission with a 4,000-lb (1814-kg) warload, or 50 nm (57 miles; 92 km) on a hi-lo-hi attack mission with 11-minute loiter with 1,700-lb (771-lb) warload
Performance: maximum rate of climb at sea level 3,550 ft (1082 m) per minute at 10,500 lb (4763 kg) or 3,100 ft (945 m) per minute at maximum take-off weight; climb to 10,000 ft (3050 m) in 3 minutes 10 seconds at 10,500 lb (4763 kg) or in 4 minutes at maximum take-off weight; service ceiling 39,000 ft (11890 m) at 10,500 lb (4763 kg); take-off run 2,100 ft (640 m) at 10,500 lb (4763 kg) or 2,770 ft (844 m) at

maximum take-off weight; take-off distance to 50 ft (15 m) 2,840 ft (866 m) at 10,500 lb (4763 kg) or 4,630 ft (1411 m) at maximum take-off weight; landing distance from 50 ft (15 m) 2,810 ft (856 m) at 9,250 lb (4195 kg)

OPERATORS

Two-seat trainer versions remain in service with the following air arms in 1994:
Argentine navy air command (16), Royal Australian Air Force (66), Brazil (50 – described separately under EMBRAER EMB-326 Xavante), Dubai (five), Ghana (five), Italy (44 MB-326, three MB-326D and six MB-326E), Paraguay (seven), South Africa (115 – described separately under Atlas Impala), Togo (four), Tunisia (12), Zaïre (nine) and Zambia (10).

Aermacchi MB-326

Below: The MB-326 had some success on the export market, where Tunisia was one of the early customers, buying eight MB-326Bs for advanced training. Here five of them fly a training sortie over the desert.

Right: Having been replaced on advanced training units, Australia's remaining MB-326Hs are used for fighter support, including attack lead-in training. This aircraft is assigned to No. 76 Sqn.

Aermacchi MB-326K

Early use of the two-seat MB-326 had shown that the aircraft was an excellent and stable weapons platform, as evinced by the light attack variants. It seems surprising, therefore, that it was not until 22 August 1970 that the manufacturer flew the first **Aermacchi MB-326K** prototype, a single-seater for ground attack or close air support powered by the Viper 20 Mk 540 of the late-production MB-326 family.

From the outset, it had been intended to provide even more power for production aircraft, and the second prototype introduced the 17.79-kN (4,000-lb) thrust Viper 632-43 engine. This made it possible to add more potent armament, in the form of two electrically operated 30-mm DEFA cannon installed in the lower forward fuselage, with 125 rounds per gun. The increased fuselage volume gained by elimination of the second seat provided space for the ammunition drums for the cannon, additional fuel tankage, and the avionics formerly located in the nose. In most other respects the airframe was similar to that of the MB-326GB, but some additional localised structural reinforcement was introduced to cater for the increased stress of low-level manoeuvres, and for this latter reason hydraulically servo-powered ailerons were also provided. Six underwing pylons were provided for carriage of up to 4,000 lb (1814 kg) of external stores, comprising bombs, napalm containers, AS11 or AS12 ASMs, machine-gun and Minigun pods, MATRA 550 AAMs and launchers for 37-mm, 68-mm, 100-mm, 2.75-in or 5-in rockets. In addition, a four-camera tactical reconnaissance pod could be carried on the port inner station without affecting the weapons capability of the other five wing pylons.

Export orders

Although the test and development programme proceeded without major problems, there was a gap of almost two years before the first order was finalised for three MB-326Ks to provide Dubai with a counter-insurgency flight. Later deliveries included three more for Dubai, with others for the air forces of Ghana (six), Tunisia (eight) and Zaïre (six). In 1974 Aermacchi delivered to South Africa seven MB-326Ks in component form, followed by 15 more sets in the following year for assembly by Atlas Aircraft Corporation. Since that time Atlas has continued to build the type under licence as the **Impala Mk 2** (described separately), which retains the Viper 20 Mk 540 powerplant. The MB-326K currently serves with **Dubai** (three), **Ghana** (four), **Tunisia** (seven) and **Zaïre** (six).

SPECIFICATION

Aermacchi MB-326K

Wing: span 10.15 m (33 ft 3.6 in) without tip tanks and 10.85 m (35 ft 7 in) with tip tanks; aspect ratio 6.08; area 19.35 m² (208.29 sq ft)
Fuselage and tail: length 10.673 m (35 ft 0.25 in); height 3.72 m (12 ft 2 in); tailplane span 4.164 m (13 ft 8 in); wheel track 2.485 m (8 ft 2 in); wheel base 4.157 m (13 ft 7.5 in)
Powerplant: one Rolls-Royce (Bristol Siddeley) Viper Mk 632-43 rated at 18.79 kN (4,000 lb st) dry thrust
Weights: empty equipped 2964 kg (6,534 lb); normal take-off 4211 kg (9,285 lb); maximum take-off 5897 kg (13,000 lb)
Fuel and load: internal fuel 1660 litres (438.5 US gal); external fuel up to two 340-litre (90-US gal) drop tanks; maximum ordnance 4,000 lb (1814 kg)
Speed: maximum level speed 'clean' at 5,000 ft (1525 m) 480 kt (553 mph; 890 km/h) and at 30,000 ft (9145 m) with underwing weapons 370 kt (426 mph; 686 km/h)
Range: ferry range more than 2130 km (1,149 nm; 1,323 miles) with drop tanks; combat radius 145 nm (167 miles; 268 km) on a lo-lo-lo attack mission with a 2,822-lb (1280-kg) warload, or 70 nm (81 miles; 130 km) on a lo-lo-lo attack mission with a 4,000-lb (1814-kg) warload, or 400 nm (461 miles; 742 km) on a hi-lo-hi visual reconnaissance mission with two drop tanks, or 560 nm (645 miles; 1038 km) on a hi-lo-hi photo-reconnaissance mission with one camera pod and two drop tanks
Performance: maximum rate of climb at sea level 6,500 ft (1981 m) per minute; climb to 36,000 ft (10975 m) in 9 minutes 30 seconds; service ceiling 47,000 ft (14325 m); take-off run 2,200 ft (671 m) at 12,000 lb (5443 kg); take-off distance to 50 ft (15 m) 3,000 ft (914 m) at 12,000 lb (5443 kg)
g limits: -3.5 to +7.33

The attack version of Aermacchi's jet trainer did not prove as successful in export terms. Dubai led the way with an order for three MB-326Ks, a figure later doubled. Three of these are still in service, serving on counter-insurgency duties. For these they carry two 30-mm cannon and a variety of stores underwing.

Aermacchi MB-339

From experience gained by nearly 800 of its highly-successful MB-326 jet trainers in 12 air forces, including licensed production in Australia, Brazil and South Africa, Aermacchi developed a successor version with 13-in (33-cm) stepped rocket-boosted SICAMB/Martin-Baker Mk 1T-10F zero-zero ejection seats to improve the instructor's rear cockpit view, plus pressurisation in a new and deeper forward fuselage. After reviewing available powerplants, including new small turbofans and even twin-engine installations, Aermacchi elected to stay with the time-honoured Rolls-Royce Viper turbojet, despite its higher fuel consumption, because of its low first cost, good 'hot-and-high' performance and proven reliability. The uprated Viper 632-43 – developed and produced jointly by Rolls-Royce and Fiat Avi-

Serving as Italy's advanced trainer, the MB-339A offers good performance at low cost. The AMI fleet is being resprayed in light grey, with high-conspicuity panels.

azione – was selected for the **MB-339**, with 4,000 lb (17.8 kN) of take-off thrust and a better specific fuel consumption.

In April 1983, following earlier installation in the second prototype, flight trials also started in an MB-339 (MM54502/I-GROW) of the still more potent Viper 680-43, developing 450 lb (2 kN) more thrust from minor compressor modifications. This was intended for the projected **MB-339B** and single-seat **MB-339K** light ground-attack fighter.

With the same basic airframe aft of the rear cockpit as the MB-326, the MB-339 has a 25 per cent bigger fin, plus twin rear ventral strakes to balance the deeper forward fuselage, and a new wing leading-edge profile. Its also has hydraulic servo-operated ailerons for flight operations up to about Mach 0.86. For weapons training or light ground-attack roles, for which six Argentine navy **MB-339AA**s were used operationally in 1982 against British forces in the Falklands, up to 4,000 lb (1814 kg) of external stores may be carried on six underwing pylons, including two 30-mm (1.18-in) DEFA cannon. The MB-339 has also been cleared to operate with the AIM-9L/P Sidewinder AAMs.

Italian service

Two MB-339 prototypes preceded AMI orders for 100 production aircraft, the first (MM588/I-NOVE) initially flying on 12 August 1976 from the Venegono factory airfield. The MB-339 entered AMI service at the SVBIA flying school at Lecce in August 1989. Nineteen from the overall AMI purchase of 100, with tip-tanks removed and known as **MB-339PAN**s, also equipped from 1982 the 313º Gruppo Pattuglia Aerobatica Nazionale, better known as the 'Frecce Tricolori', the renowned Italian national aerobatic team. Between February 1981 and the late 1980s, eight specially-equipped **MB-339RM**s operated with the 8th Sqn of the 14th Radio Aids and Elec-

Malaysia purchased 12 MB-339As to replace its elderly Canadair CL-41s operating in the advanced training role with No. 3 Flying Training Centre at Kuantan. The MB-339s also undertake weapons training for the RMAF.

tronic Warfare Wing at Pratica di Mare.

In conjunction with Lockheed, Hughes and Rolls-Royce, Aermacchi is offering a version of the prototype Viper 680-powered MB-339B for the US JPATS joint basic trainer competition. This type, known as the **T-Bird II** (described separately), incorporates bigger wing-tip tanks and is fitted with an RB.582-01 Viper turbojet derated by some 1.8 kN (404 lb) to around 17.8 kN (4,000 lb) for reduced life-cycle costs. I-RAIB, a new prototype to this standard, made its initial flight on 8 April 1992 following abandonment of earlier JPATS plans for a twin P&WC JT15D-powered **MB-339D**.

SPECIFICATION

Aermacchi MB-339A

Wing: span 10.858 m (35 ft 7.5 in) over tip tanks; aspect ratio 6.1; area 19.30 m² (207.74 sq ft)
Fuselage and tail: length 10.972 m (36 ft 0 in); height 3.994 m (13 ft 1.25 in); elevator span 4.08 m (13 ft 4.75 in); wheel track 2.483 m (8 ft 1.75 in); wheel base 4.369 m (14 ft 4 in)
Powerplant: one Piaggio-built Rolls-Royce (Bristol Siddeley) Viper Mk 632-43 rated at 17.79 kN (4,000 lb st) dry
Weights: empty equipped 3125 kg (6,889 lb); operating empty 3136 kg (6,913 lb); normal take-off 4400 kg (9,700 lb); maximum take-off 5895 kg (12,996 lb)
Fuel and load: internal fuel 1100 kg (2,425 lb);

external fuel up to two 325-litre (86-US gal) drop tanks; maximum ordnance 2040 kg (4,497 lb)
Speed: never exceed speed 500 kt (575 mph; 926 km/h); maximum level speed 'clean' at 30,000 ft (9145 m) 441 kt (508 mph; 817 km/h) and at sea level 485 kt (558 mph; 898 km/h)
Range: ferry range 1,140 nm (1,311 miles; 2110 km) with drop tanks; range 950 nm (1,094 miles; 1760 km); combat radius 320 nm (368 miles; 593 km) on a hi-lo-hi attack mission with four Mk 82 bombs and two drop tanks, or 212 nm (244 miles; 393 km) on a hi-lo-hi attack mission with six Mk 82 bombs, or 275 nm (317 miles; 510 km) on a hi-lo-hi attack mission with two 30-mm cannon pods, two rocket launchers and two drop tanks, or 305 nm (351 miles; 565 km) on a hi-lo-hi attack mission with four rocket launchers and two drop tanks, or 165 nm (190 miles; 306 km) on a hi-lo-hi attack mission with six rocket launchers, or 200 nm (230 miles; 371 km) on a lo-lo-lo attack mission with four Mk 82 bombs and two drop tanks, or 146 nm (168 miles; 271 km) on a lo-lo-lo attack mission with six Mk 82 bombs, or 190 nm (219 miles; 352 km) on a lo-lo-lo attack mission with two 30-mm cannon pods, two rocket launchers and two drop tanks, or 193 nm (222 miles; 358 km) on a lo-lo-lo attack mission with four rocket launchers and two drop tanks, or 123 nm (142 miles; 228 km) on a lo-lo-lo attack mission with six rocket launchers; endurance 3 hours 45 minutes with drop tanks or 2 hours 50 minutes on internal fuel
Performance: maximum rate of climb at sea level 6,595 ft (2010 m) per minute; climb to 30,000 ft (9145 m) in 7 minutes 6 seconds; service ceiling 48,000 ft (14630 m); take-off run 1,525 ft (465 m) at

normal take-off weight or 3,000 ft (914 m) at maximum take-off weight; landing run 415 m (1,362 ft) at normal landing weight
g limits: -4 to +8

OPERATORS

Total MB-339A production stood at 161in late 1993.

One hundred and one **AMI** MB-339As (including 19 PANs) were delivered between 1979-87 and operate mainly with the 212°/213° Gruppi of the 61ª Brigata Aerea at Lecce Galatina for all AMI basic training. Export customers have included the **Argentine navy** (10), **Dubai** air wing (seven), and the air forces of **Ghana** (two), **Malaysia** (13), **Nigeria** (12), and **Peru** (16).

The MB-339 has sold well in many corners of the world. Nigeria bought a dozen to satisfy its advanced and weapons training requirements.

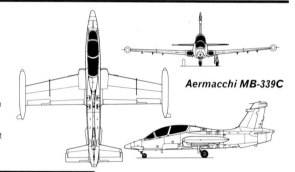

Aermacchi MB-339A (side view: MB-339K)

Aermacchi **MB-339C**

Development of a relatively low-cost lead-in fighter trainer version of the MB-339 with advanced nav/attack systems and provision for ground and naval strike roles started in the mid-1980s, in collaboration with such companies as GEC Avionics in the UK and Kaiser Electronics in the US. Studies were initiated at the request of the AMI, which was interested in the possibility of supplementing its Tornado fleet with simpler aircraft to maintain combat proficiency for lower costs, for which Aermacchi proposed an MB-339 upgrade originally designated the **MB-340**.

For optimum cost effectiveness, equipment such as a Litton LR80 twin-gyro inertial platform, GEC Avionics 620K tactical area navigation system and a commercial ARINC 429 databus were selected in preference to more complex hardware, other items including a GEC AD-660 Doppler velocity sensor, Kaiser Sabre HUD/WAC, a stores management system by Logic of Italy, a FIAR/Ericsson P.0702 laser rangefinder, Aeritalia TV Maverick-compatible multi-function CRT display, Elettronica ELT-156 RWR and Honeywell radar altimeter.

The **MB-339C** was equipped to operate with such stand-off weapons as Maverick, Marte 2, AS34 Kormoran and laser-guided bombs. Powered by a Rolls-Royce Viper Mk 680-43 as used in the MB-339B prototype, developing some 14 per cent more thrust than the Viper 632-43 in the MB-339A, and with revised nose contours and bigger tip-tanks, the MB-339C prototype made its initial flight on 17 December 1985.

The AMI was originally reported in early 1989 to be the launch customer for the MB-339C with a requirement for 20 for operational and continuation training, the first production aircraft having made its initial flight on 8 November 1988. However, the sole customer to date for the MB-339C has been the **Royal New Zealand Air Force** from a NZ$266 million (US$157 million) order for 18 in May 1990, to replace the BAC Strikemasters of No. 14 Sqn at Ohakea. Despite defence economies in New Zealand, which at one time threatened the contract with cancellation before Aermacchi agreed to accept seven of the

RNZAF Strikemasters in part exchange, deliveries started with the airlifting of the first three aircraft to Christchurch on 9 March 1991, followed by the remainder in 1992-93, including some which flew in.

Following a 1986 Italian government contract to integrate the OTO Melara Marte 2A anti-ship missile with the MB-339 to give the AMI trainer fleet a secondary wartime role attacking fast patrol boats, detected by Atlantic ASW/MR aircraft transmitting target co-ordinates and launch data, Aermacchi started trials with this weapon on a prototype **MB-339AM** (MM54554) on 24 April 1991. These were largely concluded by late 1992, after successful launches of the Marte Mk 224 AShM from the MB-339AM at the Salto di Quirra NATO firing range in Sardinia, qualifying the MB-339C for an additional operational capability.

SPECIFICATION

Aermacchi MB-339C

generally similar to the Aermacchi MB-339A except in the following particulars:
Wing: span 11.22 m (36 ft 9.75 in) over tip tanks
Fuselage and tail: length 11.24 m (36 ft 10.5 in)
Powerplant: one Piaggio-built Rolls-Royce (Bristol Siddeley) Viper Mk 680-43 rated at 4,400 lb st (19.57 kN) dry thrust
Weights: empty equipped 3310 kg (7,297 lb); normal take-off 4635 kg (10,218 lb); maximum take-off 6350 kg (13,999 lb)
Fuel and load: internal fuel 1388 kg (3,060 lb)
Speed: maximum level speed 'clean' at sea level 487 kt (560 mph; 902 km/h)
Range: ferry range 1,187 nm (1,367 miles; 2200 km) with drop tanks; standard range 1,060 nm (1,221 miles; 1965 km);

combat radius 170 nm (196 miles; 315 km) on a lo-lo-lo attack mission with four Mk 82 bombs, or 270 nm (311 miles; 500 km) on a hi-lo-hi attack mission with four Mk 82 bombs
Performance: maximum rate of climb at sea level 7,300 ft (2225 m) per minute; climb to 30,000 ft (9145 m) in 6 minutes 42 seconds

Aermacchi MB-339C

WEAPON OPTIONS

Six underwing hardpoints can carry up to 1814 kg (4,000 lb) of stores. Four inboard pylons stressed for up to 454 kg (1,000 lb) each; two outboard pylons for 340 kg (750 lb) each. Stores can include various free-fall bombs and rocket pods, cluster bombs, flares or missile armament. RNZAF aircraft equipped for AGM-65 Maverick air-to-ground missiles and AIM-9 Sidewinder IR-homing air-to-air missiles. MATRA Magic optional for air-to-air role.

Two Macchi gun pods are offered, one housing a 30-mm DEFA 553 cannon with 120 rounds, the other accommodating a 12.7-mm AN/M-3 machine-gun with 350 rounds.
Reconnaissance pod with four 70-mm Vinten cameras optional.

New Zealand's 'Macchis' have replaced Strikemasters in the advanced and weapons training role. They could also be used in an emergency wartime offensive role.

Aermacchi MB-339K

The successful reception of the MB-339A trainer encouraged Aermacchi to adopt for this version a treatment similar to that for the two-seat MB-326/single-seat MB-326K. The company developed a single-seat **Aermacchi MB-339K** which it named **Veltro 2**, perpetuating the name given to Macchi's M.C.205V Veltro (greyhound), regarded as the best Italian fighter/fighter-bomber of World War II. However, this name was dropped in 1989.

The development process was characterised by the adoption of a new forward fuselage with single-seat accommodation. The increased fuselage volume provided room for avionics stowage, increased fuel and the installation of internally-mounted DEFA cannon. In other respects the MB-339K differs little from its two-seat counterpart, but for customers who might require more sophistication a wide range of optional avionics is available, including an ECM jammer pod, plus head-up and/or TV

display. The prototype (I-BITE), built as a private venture, had the standard licence-built Viper Mk 632-43 turbojet as its powerplant. This aircraft was flown for the first time on 30 May 1980 and subsequently displayed at the SBAC Farnborough air show in September of that year. No orders have been announced to date, and this may be because potential customers feel there is insufficient capability/performance improvement with respect to the MB-339A and MB-339C.

Aermacchi has subsequently developed an upgraded version incorporating changes to the powerplant, avionics system and equipment. In addition to its more powerful (19.79-kN/4,450-lb thrust) Viper 680-43 turbojet, the introduction of a nav/attack system (incorporating inertial navigation, a stores management system, a weapon-aiming computer and HUD) could make this aircraft more attractive for both training and combat use.

SPECIFICATION

Aermacchi MB-339K

Wing: span 11.22 m (36 ft 9.75 in) over tip tanks; aspect ratio 6.1; area 19.30 m² (207.75 sq ft)
Fuselage and tail: length 10.85 m (35 ft 7 in); height 3.994 m (13 ft 1.25 in); elevator span 4.08 m (13 ft 4.75 in); wheel track 2.483 m (8 ft 1.75 in); wheel base 4.369 m (14 ft 4 in)
Powerplant: one Rolls-Royce Viper Mk 680-43 rated at 4,400 lb st (19.57 kN) dry
Weights: empty equipped 3245 kg (7,154 lb); normal take-off 5050 kg (11,133 lb); maximum take-off 6350 kg (13,999 lb)
Fuel and load: internal fuel 1582 kg (3,488 lb) with circular-section tip tanks; external fuel up to two 325-litre (86-US gal) drop tanks; maximum ordnance 1935 kg (4,266 lb)
Speed: never-exceed speed 500 kt (575 mph; 927 km/h); maximum level speed 'clean' at sea level 486 kt (560 mph; 900 km/h)
Range: combat radius 340 nm (391 miles; 630 km) on

The MB-339K programme has resulted only in this prototype. The single-seat attack version has two internal 30-mm cannon.

a hi-lo-hi attack mission with a 1088-kg (2,400-lb) warload, or 205 nm (236 miles; 380 km) on a lo-lo-lo attack mision with a 1088-kg (2,400-lb) warload
Performance: maximum rate of climb at sea level 7,875 ft (2400 m) per minute; service ceiling 46,000 ft (14020 m); take-off run 1,900 ft (579 m at normal take-off weight or 2,985 ft (910 m) at maximum take-off weight; landing run 1,475 ft (450 m) at normal landing weight
g limits: -4 to +8

Aermacchi/Lockheed MB-339 T-Bird II

Aermacchi was one of the first of the world's jet trainer manufacturers to answer the USAF and USN Statement of Operational Need for the Joint Primary Aircraft Training System (JPATS). In 1989 the company signed a co-operation agreement with Lockheed and Hughes to produce a version of the MB-339 modified to comply with the American service requirements. This includes an improved cockpit, new avionics and a strengthened canopy, together with some engine changes. Rolls-Royce, which joined the team in 1990, has offered the 17.79-kN (4,000-lb st) RB582 engine instead of the MB-339C's Viper 680

powerplant. In addition, the airframe will undergo some structural changes to enable it to meet the required service life of 14,400 hours with limits of +6g/-3g. The first production orders for more than 700 aircraft are expected in 1994 and, should the MB-339 emerge as the winner, the prime American airframe contractor will be Lockheed, which would also hold the manufacturing licence. Hughes would be responsible for the simulators and the overall training system.

Lockheed is Aermacchi's partner for the JPATS competition, offering a USAF-optimised MB-339.

*Aero Vodochody Akciová
CR-250 70 Odolena Vodo
Czech Republic*

Aero L-29 Delfin

Designed by a team under the leadership of Z. Rublic and K. Tomas to supersede the piston-engine trainers then in service with the Czech air force, the **Aero XL-29** prototype was flown for the first time on 5 April 1959. Following the flight of a second prototype in mid-1960, a small pre-production batch built for service evaluation was flown in competition with the P.Z.L. Mielec TS-11 Iskra and Yakovlev Yak-30 during 1961. The XL-29's excellent all-round performance resulted in the type being selected as the standard trainer for all Warsaw Pact air forces, with the exception of Poland, which opted to retain the nationally-designed and built TS-11. A mid-wing monoplane with retractable tricycle landing gear, the XL-29 prototype had flown initially under the power of a Bristol Siddeley Viper turbojet, but the second adopted the Czech-

Resplendent after overhaul at the Aero factory is an Egyptian air force L-29. The type serves in small numbers on basic training duties.

designed Motorlet M 701 turbojet, and this latter powerplant was selected for production aircraft.

A straightforward design, simple to fly and easy to operate, the **L-29 Delfin** (dolphin) has docile handling characteristics and can be operated from grass, sand or water-logged strips. Pupil and instructor are seated in tandem on synchronised ejection seats, and there is underwing provision for the carriage of light armament for training purposes. The first L-29s began to enter service in 1963, and when production ended in 1974 some 3,600 had been built. On the face of it, this large-scale manufacture may seem surprising, but this trainer was procured also for the Soviet air force (its L-29s gaining the NATO reporting name **'Maya'**), which accounted for over 2,000 of the production total. In addition to procurement for Bulgaria, Czechoslovakia, East Germany, Hungary, Romania and the USSR, L-29s were exported to several countries, including Afghanistan, Egypt, Guinea, Indonesia, Iraq, Nigeria, Syria and Uganda.

L-29s probably remain active in **Bulgaria**, **Czechoslovakia**, **Egypt**, **Iraq**, **Mali**, **Nigeria**, **Romania** and **Syria**. The L-29 has recently become available as a 'warbird' and has been sold in small numbers to private owners in the USA.

There have been just two variants of the type, the first being the single-seat **L-29A Delfin Akrobat**, built in only small numbers for aerobatic use, and a dedicated attack version designated **L-29R** which appeared only in prototype form.

SPECIFICATION

Aero L-29 Delfin 'Maya'

Wing: span 10.29 m (33 ft 9 in); aspect ratio 5.35; area 19.85 m²
Fuselage and tail: length 10.81 m (35 ft 5.5 in); height 3.13 m (10 ft 3 in); tailplane span 3.34 m (10 ft 11.5 in); wheel track 3.44 m (11 ft 3.5 in); wheel base 3.90 m (12 ft 9.5 in)
Powerplant: one Motorlet M 701c 500 rated at 8.73 kN (1,962 lb st) dry

Weights: empty equipped 2364 kg (5,212 lb); normal take-off 3280 kg (7,231 lb); maximum take-off 3540 kg (7,804 lb)
Fuel and load: internal fuel 1050 litres (277.4 US gal); external fuel up to two 150-litre (39.6-US gal) drop tanks; maximum ordnance 200 kg (441 lb)
Speed: maximum level speed 'clean' at 5000 m (16,405 ft) 655 km/h (353 kt; 407 mph) and at sea level 620 km/h (335 kt; 385 mph); cruising speed at 5000 m (16,405 ft) 545 km/h (294 kt; 339 mph)
Range: ferry range 894 km (482 nm; 555 miles) with drop tanks; range 640 km (345 nm; 397 miles) with standard fuel; endurance 2 hours 30 minutes with drop tanks or 2 hours 0 minutes with standard fuel
Performance: maximum rate of climb at sea level 840 m (2,756 ft) per minute; climb to 5000 m (16,405 ft) in 8 minutes and to 10000 m (32,810 ft) in 25 minutes; service ceiling 11000 m (36,090 ft); take-off run 550 m (1,805 ft) at normal take-off weight from a paved runway; take-off distance to 25 m (82 ft) 950 m (3,117 ft) at normal take-off weight on a grass runway; landing distance from 25 m (82 ft) 900 m (2,953 ft) at normal landing weight on a grass runway; landing run 440 m (1,444 ft) at normal landing weight on a paved runway

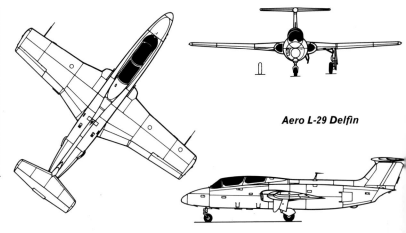

Aero L-29 Delfin

Aero **L-39 Albatros**

The evolution of a successor to the extensively built L-29 Delfin began about three years after that aircraft entered production. Designed by a team under the leadership of Dipl Ing. Jan Vlcek, the new type's development proceeded under close co-operation with the USSR which, subject to adequate performance, expected to adopt it to supersede the L-29 as its standard jet trainer. A key to much enhanced performance was adoption of the Ivchenko AI-25 turbofan engine, of practically double the power output of the Motorlet turbojet in the L-29; the achievement of full compatibility of this engine with an airframe of similar overall dimensions to the L-29 brought delays in design finalisation. The second of the first three prototypes (the first and third being used for structural test) was flown initially on 4 November 1968, and was joined later in the development programme by four other flying prototypes. It was not until late 1972 that a production go-ahead confirmed the **Aero L-39 Albatros** as a successor to the L-29 in the air forces of the USSR, Czechoslovakia and East Germany. Full service trials were conducted during 1973 and the L-39 began to enter service, initially with the Ceskoslovenské Letectvo, in early 1974.

A cantilever low-wing monoplane with retractable tricycle landing gear, the L-39 offers a significant improvement in performance over its predecessor (Mach 0.83 maximum speed, compared with the L-29's Mach 0.75). Tandem seating (on zero-height ejection seats in the L-39C) is retained, but naturally with the rear (instructor's) seat elevated to improve his view forward. Simultaneously, this enables the lower-placed front cockpit to slope downward towards a finely-pointed nose that reduces drag and contributes to enhanced performance.

Structure

Construction is modular, the airframe being broken down into only three major sub-assemblies (wing, fuselage and rear fuselage/tail unit) to facilitate major maintenance and overhaul. The entire wing, except for the moving surfaces, is in one piece, including the permanent tip tanks, and the swept fin is integral with the rear fuselage; the latter is removable to provide easy access to the engine for servicing. Including detachable items such as nosecone, control surfaces, landing gear and canopies, the entire L-39 airframe consists of little more than a couple of dozen basic components. This enables any unit to be replaced quickly and easily; plenty of access panels are pro-

vided for reaching individual systems or installations.

A first-class all-round view is available from both pressurised cockpits, and dual controls are, of course, standard. The rear seat is removed in the L-39ZO, presumably providing space, if required, for avionics or an additional fuel tank. A small auxiliary power unit (APU), in the form of a compressed-air turbine and generator, makes the aircraft independent of ground power sources for engine starting, fuel flow or other services.

More than 2,800 L-39s have been produced, including the **L-39C** basic and advanced trainer, **L-39V** target tug, **L-39ZO** weapons trainer with reinforced wings and four underwing weapon stations, and the **L-39ZA** for ground attack and reconnaissance, adding reinforced landing gear and an underfuselage gun pod to the L-39ZO. The **L-39ZE** is a version for Thailand with Elbit avionics.

SPECIFICATION

Aero L-39ZO Albatros

Wing: span 9.46 m (31 ft 0.5 in); aspect ratio 4.4 geometric or 5.2 including tip tanks; area 18.80 m² (202.37 sq ft)

Fuselage and tail: length 12.13 m (39 ft 9.5 in); height 4.77 m (15 ft 7.75 in); tailplane span 4.40 m (14 ft 5 in); wheel track 2.44 m (8 ft 0 in); wheel base 4.39 m (14 ft 4.75 in)

Powerplant: one ZMDB Progress (Ivchyenko) AI-25TL rated at 16.87 kN (3,792 lb st) dry

Weights: empty equipped 3540 kg; normal take-off 4525 kg (9,976 lb); maximum take-off 4700 kg (10,362 lb)

Fuel and load: internal fuel 824 kg (1,816 lb) plus provision for 156 kg (344 lb) in two 180-litre (48-US gal) non-jettisonable tip tanks; external fuel up to 544 kg (1,199 lb) in two 420-litre (110-US gal) drop tanks; maximum ordnance 1000 kg (2,200 lb)

Speed: never-exceed speed at 11000 m (36,090 ft) 850 km/h (459 kt; 528 mph); maximum level speed 'clean' at 5000 m (16,405 ft) 407 kt (755 km/h; 466 mph) and at sea level 388 kt (720 km/h; 447 mph)

Range: ferry range 1750 km (944 nm; 1,087 miles) with drop tanks; standard range 1100 km (593 nm; 683 miles) with internal fuel; endurance at 7000 m (22,975 ft) 3 hours 50 minutes with drop tanks or 2 hours 30 minutes with internal fuel

Performance: maximum rate of climb at sea level 1260 m (4,134 ft) per minute; climb to 5000 m (16,405 ft) in 5 minutes 0 seconds; service ceiling 11000 m (36,090 ft); take-off run 530 m (1,740 ft) at normal take-off weight; landing run 650 m (2,135 ft) at normal landing weight

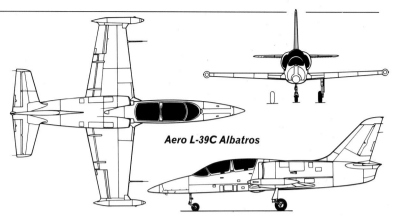

Aero L-39C Albatros

g limits: -4 to +8 operational and +12 ultimate at 4200 kg (9,259 lb)

OPERATORS

Large numbers of L-39s remain in service in Russia (L-39C) and other republics of the former USSR, and in Afghanistan (L-39C), Algeria (L-39ZA), Bulgaria (L-39ZA), Congo, Cuba (L-39C), Czechoslovakia (L-39C, V, ZA and ZO), Egypt (L-39ZO), Ethiopia (L-39C), Hungary (L-39ZO), Iraq (L-39ZO), Libya (L-39ZO), Nicaragua (L-39C and ZO), Nigeria (L-39ZA), North Korea, Romania (L-39 ZA), Syria (L-39ZA and ZO), Thailand (L-39ZE) and Vietnam (L-39C). The former East Germany's L-39ZOs and L-39Vs were retired on reunification and several have now been sold.

Above: One of the roles of the L-39 is target-towing. This East German L-39V has the KT-04 target towed from the centreline, with a winch in the rear cockpit.

Below: Twenty-four unarmed L-39C trainers were delivered to the Republic of Vietnam in 1980/81. They are based at Nha Trang with the 910th 'Julius Fucik' Training Regiment.

Aero L-39MS/L-59 Albatros

Development of the **L-39MS** began in the early 1980s and aimed to remedy the original aircraft's perceived lack of thrust. The first prototype (X-22, registered OK-184) made its maiden flight on 30 September 1986, and was followed by two further prototypes (X-24 and X-25). The designation changed to **L-59** for production.

Compared to the standard L-39, the L-59 is a much more capable aircraft with a strengthened airframe, new avionics (including a head-up display) and a new, more powerful engine, developed jointly by Lotarev in the USSR and ZVL in Czechoslovakia. The DV-2 is a 21.57-kN (4,850-lb) turbofan and fits into the existing L-39 engine bay, making retrofit to existing aircraft a real possibility. The L-59 also has new lightweight flaps, untabbed ailerons and fully powered elevators, and has a revised undercarriage with new brakes. Externally, the L-59 is identifiable by its more pointed nosecone and reshaped fin-tip. The first production L-59 flew on 1 October 1989. Six L-39MS aircraft serve with **Slovakia**.

Forty-eight L-59s, equipped with US avionics, have been ordered by **Egypt** for a reported $200 million, and deliveries began on 29 January 1993. Twelve similar aircraft have been ordered by **Tunisia**. Optimistically, a Garrett TFE731-4-powered development of the L-59, designated **L-139**, has been proposed as a contender to meet the USAF's JPATS requirement for a jet trainer. Also projected in 1994 is the **L-159**, a single-seat light fighter/attack derivative with a 2722-kg (6,000-lb) weapon load and Mach 0.85 capability using a Garrett F124, Rolls-Royce Adour or CDV-2 turbofan.

following particulars:
Wing: span 9.54 m (31 ft 3.5 in) including tip tanks
Fuselage and tail: length 12.20 m (40 ft 0.25 in)
Powerplant: one ZMDB Progress DV-2 rated at 21.57 kN (4,850 lb st) dry
Weights: empty equipped 4150 kg (9,149 lb); normal take-off 5510 kg (12,147 lb) as a trainer; maximum take-off 5700 kg (12,566 lb) with external stores from a grass strip
Fuel and load: internal fuel 1200 kg (2,645 lb) including two tip tanks; external fuel up to 544 kg (1,199 lb) in two 350-litre (92.5-US gal) drop tanks; maximum ordnance 1290 kg (2,844 lb)
Speed: maximum level speed 'clean' at 5000 m (16,405 ft) 876 km/h (473 kt; 544 mph)
Range: ferry range at 9000 m (29,530 ft) 1500 km (809 nm; 932 miles) with drop tanks
Performance: maximum rate of climb at sea level 1560 m (5,118 ft) per minute; service ceiling 11730 m (38,485 ft); take-off run 620 m (2,034 ft) at maximum take-off weight; landing run 650 m (2,135 ft) at normal landing weight

Above: The L-39MS/59 is an attempt to breathe life back into the Albatros design. A more powerful and economic turbofan is at the heart of the update, and can be retrospectively applied to L-39s.

Below: The first customer for the L-59 is Egypt, which has bought 48 for the Air Force Academy. These L-59Es are equipped with ventral gun pod and four wing pylons for the weapons training role.

SPECIFICATION

Aero L-59 (originally L-39MS)
generally similar to the Aero L-39C except in the

Aérospatiale (Potez/Fouga) CM 170 Magister/CM 175 Zéphyr

Notable as the first jet trainer to enter service anywhere in the world, and for its use of a butterfly tail, the Magister was designed to meet a French air force specification. Three prototypes were built by the Fouga company, where Pierre Mauboussin had already pioneered the application of small jet engines to light aircraft and powered gliders. Following the first flight of the

Fouga CM 170 Magister prototype on 23 July 1952, orders were placed in June 1953 for 10 pre-production aircraft and then in January 1954 for quantity production for the French air force.

In 1958, the Potez group took over responsibility for Fouga activities and continued CM 170 Magister production and development. This activity was, in turn, taken

over by Sud-Aviation in April 1967, and production of the Magister continued into 1970, by which time the company had been absorbed into Aérospatiale. First flown on 7 July 1954, the pre-production Magister was to **CM 170-1** standard, as were the early production aircraft, the first of which flew on 29 February 1956.

Production of the CM 170 in France

totalled 622 to meet orders from the French air force (400) and navy (32) and the air forces of Austria (18), Belgium (48), Brazil (seven), Cambodia (four), Congo Leopoldville (six), Finland (20), the Federal Republic of Germany (62), Israel (18) and Lebanon (four). In addition, Flugzeug Union Sud in Germany built 188, Valmet in Finland built 62 and IAI in Israel built 36, bringing overall production including prototypes to 921.

Improved variants

The initial production model, CM 170-1, had Marboré IIA engines, replaced in the **CM 170-2** by uprated Marboré VICs. Martin-Baker ejection seats under a modified canopy, and an increased fuel capacity, were features of the **CM 170-3**, first flown on 8 June 1964 and later redesignated **CM 173 Super Magister**. For the Aéronavale, the carrier-capable **CM 175 Zéphyr**, based on the CM 170-1, had an arrester hook among other changes. The first of two prototypes flew on 30 May 1959, and of 30 examples produced about 12 remain in service with 59 Escadrille at Hyères.

Some 150 Magisters remain with the Armée de l'Air, used by Division des Vols 5/312 at Salon de Provence for initial flight training of career officers, and for miscellaneous duties including communications/liaison in base flights and at squadron level. Similarly, about 12 remain with the Force

Six elderly Magisters still form the most potent equipment available to the Irish Air Corps. They are based at Baldonnel with the Light Strike Squadron, part of No. 1 Support Wing.

Left: The Magister still takes an important place in the Armée de l'Air training organisation. This example serves with the Ecole de l'Air.

Right: Initial carrier training for Aéronavale students is undertaken on the CM 175 Zéphyr, serving with Escadrille 59S at Hyères.

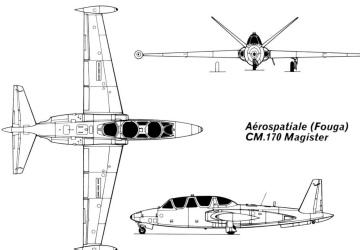

Aérospatiale (Fouga) CM.170 Magister

Aérienne Belge for communications and continuation flying.

Withdrawal from service of Magisters by the other original purchasers – except perhaps Lebanon, where two or three may remain flyable – led to acquisition of small quantities of CM 170s by several other air forces, for use as basic trainers and/or in the light attack role, for which gun and rocket pods or bombs could be carried. The Israeli Defence Force/Air Force remains a major Magister user, having added nine ex-Belgian and possibly other secondhand examples to its original purchase/production of 82. Between 1981 and 1986, some 80 in all were modernised by Bedek Division of IAI to have Marboré VI engines, new avionics and other upgrades, being then renamed **Tzukit** (Thrush) (described separately) in the Advanced Multi-mission Improved Trainer (AMIT) programme.

SPECIFICATION

Aérospatiale (Potez/Fouga) CM 170-1 Magister
Wing: span 11.40 m (37 ft 5 in) without tip tanks and 12.15 m (39 ft 10 in) with tip tanks; aspect ratio 7.51; area 17.30 m² (186.22 sq ft)
Fuselage and tail: length 10.06 m (33 ft 0 in); height 2.80 m (9 ft 2 in); tailplane span 4.38 m (14 ft 4.5 in); wheel track 3.80 m (12 ft 6.75 in); wheel base 4.49 m (14 ft 9 in)
Powerplant: two Turboméca Marboré IIA each rated at 3.92 kN (882 lb st) dry
Weights: empty equipped 2150 kg (4,740 lb); normal take-off 2850 kg (6,283 lb) without tip tanks and 3100 kg (6,834 lb) with tip tanks; maximum take-off 3200 kg (7,055 lb)
Fuel and load: internal fuel 730 litres (193 US gal) plus provision for 250 litres (66 US gal) in two non-jettisonable tip tanks, or for 460 litres (121.5 US gal) in two non-jettisonable ferry tip tanks; external fuel none; maximum ordnance 100 kg (220 lb)
Speed: maximum level speed 'clean' at 9000 m (29,525 ft) 715 km/h (386 kt; 444 mph) and at sea level 650 km/h (350 kt; 403 mph)
Range: ferry range 1200 km (648 nm; 746 miles) with auxiliary fuel; range 925 km (499 nm; 575 miles) with standard fuel; endurance 2 hours 40 minutes with tip tanks or 1 hour 55 minutes with standard fuel
Performance: maximum rate of climb at sea level 1020 m (3,346 ft) per minute; service ceiling 11000 m (36,090 ft); take-off run 655 m (2,149 ft) at 3100 kg (6,834 lb); take-off distance to 15 m (50 ft) 930 m (3,051 ft) at 3100 kg (6,834 lb)

OPERATORS

Current or recent users, sometimes as a result of deals that have involved French, German, Brazilian, Austrian and Israeli surplus aircraft, are Algeria (equipping two squadrons for light attack role), Bangladesh (for FTS at Jessore), Cameroon (counter-insurgency role), Gabon (used by Presidential Guard), Ireland (light strike, advanced training and aerobatic team), Libya (training), Morocco (light attack and training), El Salvador (light attack), Senegambia (basic training), and Togo (training). The major user remains France, aircraft serving with both air force and navy in the training and liaison roles.

Aérospatiale (Sud-Est/Sud) SE 310 Caravelle

Aérospatiale SNI
37 Boulevard Montmorency
F-75781 Paris Cedex 16, France

The Aérospatiale (Sud-Aviation) Caravelle was the world's first rear-engined airliner, making its maiden flight in May 1955. This 80-seat, short/medium-range, twin-engined passenger transport has been used by only a few military operators including Argentina (three **VIN**s), the Central African Republic (one **III**) and Yugoslavia (one VIN). Sweden's National Defence Research Institute operated two Series IIIs for ECM and Elint use. Serving until 1993, they were replaced by two Gulfstream IV SRAs to serve with F16M. Nine Caravelles were operated from 1962 by the **French air force** for VIP transport/liaison duties (two IIIs, one **VIR**, one **10R** and three **IIR**s), flight test research (one ex-VIP III), avionics research (one VIR) and as a SNECMA M53 engine testbed (one III). By early 1994, all French Caravelles had been retired, except for the sole Series 10R VIP/liaison transport operating from Orly, and two Caravelles operated by the CEV.

SPECIFICATION

Aérospatiale (Sud-Aviation) SE 310 Caravelle III
Wing: span 34.30 m (112 ft 6 in); aspect ratio 8.02; area 146.70 m² (1,579.12 sq ft)
Fuselage and tail: length 32.01 m (105 ft 0 in); height 8.72 m (28 ft 7 in); tailplane span 10.60 m (34 ft 9 in); wheel track 5.21 m (17 ft 0 in); wheel base 11.79 m (38 ft 7 in)
Powerplant: two Rolls-Royce Avon RA.29 Mk 527 each rated at 11,400 lb st (50.71 kN) dry
Weights: manufacturer's empty 24185 kg (53,318 lb); operating empty 27210 kg (59,987 lb); maximum take-off 46000 kg (101,411 lb)
Fuel and load: internal fuel 19000 litres (5,019 US gal); external fuel none; maximum payload 8400 kg (18,519 lb)
Speed: maximum cruising speed at 7620 m (25,000 ft) 805 km/h (434 kt; 500 mph); economical cruising speed at 10675 m (35,000 ft) 725 km/h (391 kt; 450 mph)
Range: 1845 km (995 nm; 1,146 miles) with a 7620-kg

(16,799-lb) payload or 1700 km (917 nm; 1,056 miles) with maximum payload
Performance: take-off run 1830 m (6,004 ft) at maximum take-off weight; landing run 1800 m (5,906 ft) at normal landing weight

Believed to be the last military Caravelle, this aircraft serves with ET 3/60 at Paris-Orly. It works on ministerial transport duties.

Aérospatiale (Sud-Est/Sud)
SA 313B/SA 318C Alouette II

The Alouette (lark) family of general-purpose helicopters originated with the three-seat SE 3120, which first flew on 31 July 1952. A product of the Société Nationale de Constructions Aéronautiques du Sud-Est (SNCASE), it was powered by a 149-kW (200-hp) Salmson 9NH radial piston engine and was aimed largely at the agricultural market. A complete redesign to utilise the 269-kW (360-shp) Turboméca Artouste I turboshaft resulted in the SE 3130 **Alouette II**, flown on 12 March 1955. French certification on 2 May 1956 cleared the way

The German army has been a staunch Alouette II operator, this example wearing a scheme to celebrate 25 years of service.

Aérospatiale (Sud-Est) SA 313B/SA 318C Alouette II

for production deliveries, and the designation changed to **SE 313B** soon after, when SNCASE merged into Sud-Aviation (which, in turn, was incorporated into Aérospatiale in 1970). Production aircraft used the Artouste IIC6 turboshaft.

Further evolution of the basic helicopter produced the SE 3140 with a 298-kW (400-shp) Turboméca Turmo II turboshaft, no production of which ensued, and then the SA 3180 with an Astazou IIA, flown on 31 January 1961. As the **Alouette II Astazou**, this was certificated in France in February 1964, production aircraft taking the designation **SA 318C** and deliveries commencing in 1965.

Large-scale production

Among the first production types to demonstrate the tremendous versatility of a small, multi-role helicopter in both civil and military spheres, the Alouette II achieved unprecedented levels of production for a European rotary-wing aircraft. Its 'bug-eye' glazed cabin seated up to five – pilot and passenger in front and three passengers abreast behind. An open fuselage structure carried the fuel tank immediately behind the cabin, the powerplant and, on the aft extension, the tail rotor. A skid-type landing gear was standard, with retractable wheels for ground manoeuvring, and high skids, wheels or pneumatic floats as options. A rescue hoist was available, with 120-kg (265-lb) capacity, and listed roles included flying crane, liaison, observation, training, agricultural work, photographic survey, and ambulance (with two stretchers). In the military role, rockets, guns or air-to-surface missiles could be carried.

Production ended in 1975 with a total of 1,305 built.

SPECIFICATION

Aérospatiale SA 318C Alouette II Astazou
Rotor system: main rotor diameter 10.20 m (33 ft 5.625 in); tail rotor diameter 1.91 m (6 ft 3 in); main rotor disc area 81.71 m² (879.58 sq ft); tail rotor disc area 2.87 m² (30.84 sq ft)
Fuselage and tail: length overall, rotors turning 12.10 m (39 ft 8.5 in) and fuselage 9.75 m (31 ft

11.75 in) with tail rotor turning; height overall 2.75 m (9 ft 0 in); skid track 2.22 m (7 ft 3 in)
Powerplant: one 530-shp (395-kW) Turboméca Astazou IIA derated to 360 shp (268 kW)
Weights: empty 890 kg (1,961 lb); maximum take-off 1650 kg (3,638 lb)
Fuel and load: internal fuel 580 litres (153.25 US gal); external fuel none; maximum payload 600 kg (1,323 lb)
Speed: maximum level speed at sea level 205 km/h (110 kt; 127 mph); maximum cruising speed at sea level 180 km/h (97 kt; 112 mph)
Range: 720 km (388 nm; 447 miles); endurance 5 hours 18 minutes
Performance: maximum rate of climb at sea level 396 m (1,300 ft) per minute; service ceiling 3300 m (10,825 ft); hovering ceiling 1550 m (5,085 ft) in ground effect and 900 m (2,955 ft) out of ground effect

OPERATORS

Among well over 120 users of the Alouette II (military and civil) in nearly 50 countries, Germany was the largest, with the Heeresfliegertruppen taking 226 SA 313Bs and 54 SA 318Cs from 1959. Some 50 remain in service with four Army Aviation Support Squadrons (HFS) at Celle, Rotenburg and Rheine, with a like number for training at the Army Aviation Weapons School, Bückenburg. Other military users of the Alouette II, mostly in small numbers, include Belgium, Benin, Cameroon, the Central African Republic, Congo Republic, Djibouti, Dominican Republic, France, Guinea-Bissau, Ivory Coast, Lebanon, Morocco, Portugal, Senegal, Sweden, Switzerland, Togo, Tunisia and Turkey.

The Alouette II is becoming quite rare in French army (ALAT) service, but a number are retained for regional defence force work and for training.

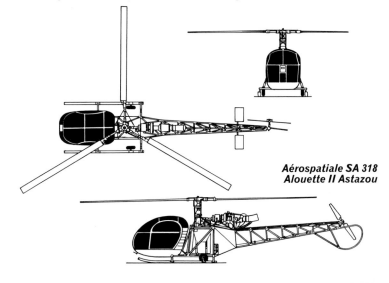

Aérospatiale SA 318 Alouette II Astazou

Aérospatiale (Sud) **SA 316/SA 319 Alouette III**

Aérospatiale helicopter division became Eurocopter France on 16 January 1992

The reliability and sales success of the Alouette II prompted Sud-Aviation to initiate development of an advanced version. The incorporation of a more powerful turboshaft engine and improved aerodynamics was considered essential to give greater payload capability and enhanced performance and, at the same time, the opportunity was taken to introduce new equipment. Initially designated **SE 3160**, the prototype **Alouette III** incorporated a larger and more enclosed cabin than that of its predecessor, able to carry a pilot and six passengers with baggage holds for luggage and parcels, or a pilot and six equipped troops. In a casevac role two stretchers and two sitting casualties or medical attendants could be accommodated behind the pilot or, alternatively, the six seats could easily be removed for the carriage of cargo; there was also provision for an external sling for loads of up to 750 kg (1,653 lb).

The prototype was flown for the first time on 28 February 1959 and early production examples followed in 1961. The initial production **SA 316A** helicopter, built for home and export markets, became the subject of a licence agreement with Hindustan Aeronautics Ltd in India. Subsequent development produced the main production **SA 316B**, first flown on 27 June 1968, which introduced the Turboméca Artouste IIIB turboshaft with uprated main and tail rotor transmissions, and was able to carry more payload. HAL-built versions are known as **Chetak** in Indian Air Force service. Last of the Artouste-powered Alouette IIIs was the **SA 316C**, built in only small numbers with an Artouste IIID engine. The SA 316B was also the subject of licence agreements with the Swiss Federal Aircraft Factory, and ICA-Brasov in Romania where the type was produced until 1989. The Romanian version, of which 230 examples were built, is desig-

Portugal was a major purchaser of the Alouette III, buying over 140. Around 30 are still in service, used mainly for utility transport but also for training.

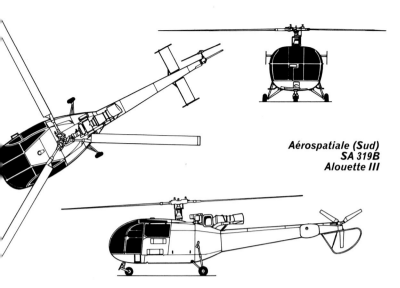

*Aérospatiale (Sud)
SA 319B
Alouette III*

nated **IAR 316B**. This formed the basis of the **IAR-317 Skyfox**, a dedicated gunship variant (both described separately).

The capability of the SA 316B soon led to two-seat military versions deployed in a variety of roles, with a range of weapon options that made them suitable for light attack and ASW. As with the Alouette II, a version was introduced with the Turboméca Astazou turboshaft, this being the **SA 319B** Alouette III with a 649-kW (870-shp) Astazou XIV derated to 447 kW (600 shp). A total of 1,453 Alouettes of all versions was built by Aérospatiale.

The Rhodesian air force operated two specialised versions of the Alouette III in support of quick-reaction units to intercept terrorist forces. The **G-Car** four-troop transport was armed with two side-mounted Browning machine-guns, whereas the **K-Car** was a dedicated gunship variant with a single 20-mm Mauser cannon mounted in the cabin and firing to port.

Limited production continues in India, where 322 examples of the Chetak had been produced by HAL by March 1991.

SPECIFICATION

Aérospatiale (Sud) SA 319B Alouette III Astazou
Rotor system: main rotor diameter 11.02 m (36 ft 1.75 in); tail rotor diameter 1.91 m (6 ft 3.25 in); main rotor disc area 95.38 m² (1,026.68 sq ft); tail rotor disc area 2.87 m² (30.84 sq ft)
Fuselage and tail: length overall, rotors turning 12.84 m (42 ft 1.5 in) and fuselage 10.03 m (32 ft 10.75 in); height to top of rotor head 3.00 m (9 ft 10 in); wheel track 2.60 m (8 ft 6.25 in)
Powerplant: one 870-shp (649-kW) Turboméca Astazou XIV derated to 600 shp (447 kW)
Weights: empty 1140 kg (2,513 lb); maximum take-off 2250 kg (4,960 lb)
Fuel and load: internal fuel 575 litres (152 US gal); external fuel none; maximum payload 750 kg (1,653 lb)
Speed: maximum level speed 'clean' at sea level

220 km/h (118 kt; 136 mph); maximum cruising speed at sea level 197 km/h (106 kt; 122 mph)
Range: 605 km (326 nm; 375 miles) with six passengers
Performance: maximum rate of climb at sea level 270 m (885 ft) per minute; hovering ceiling 3100 m (10,170 ft) in ground effect and 1700 m (5,575 ft) out of ground effect

OPERATORS

The Alouette III is currently operated by the air forces of Angola, Argentina (navy), Austria, Belgium (navy), Burkina Faso, Burundi, Cameroon, Chile (navy), Congo, Ecuador, El Salvador, Equatorial Guinea, France (all three air arms), Gabon, Ghana, Guinea, Guinea-Bissau, Indonesia, Iraq, Ireland, Lebanon, Libya (all three air arms), Malawi, Malaysia, Mexico (all three air arms), Mozambique, Myanmar, Netherlands, Nicaragua, Pakistan (all three air arms), Peru (army and navy), Portugal, Romania, Rwanda, Serbia, South Africa, Spain, Suriname, Switzerland, Tunisia, United

With high installed power and a good-sized cabin, the Alouette III has proved popular in the search and rescue role. The Dutch aircraft were replaced in this role by Bell 412s in 1994.

Arab Emirates (Abu Dhabi), Venda, Venezuela, Zaïre and Zimbabwe.
HAL-built Chetaks are operated by Ethiopia, India (all three air arms), Nepal and the Seychelles.

In peacetime ALAT Alouette IIIs are used for training and general transport, but in wartime would be used to form offensive units.

Aérospatiale (Sud) **SA 315 Lama**

Following an Indian armed forces requirement, design of the **Aérospatiale Lama** was begun in late 1968. Externally resembling the Alouette II, the Lama is in effect a 'hot-and-high' variant of the SE 313B. The required performance is derived by combining features of the Alouette II and III; the Lama has the Alouette II's airframe (with some reinforcement) and dynamic components of the SA 316 Alouette III, including the rotor system and Artouste IIIB powerplant.

The SA 315B prototype flew on 17 March 1969 and production was launched simultaneously in France (where the name Lama was adopted) and India (with the name **Cheetah**). In Brazil, Helibras assembled the Lama, using French components, as the **HB 315B Gavião**. This version is operated by the **Bolivian air force** and the **Brazilian navy**.

French production of the SA 315B ended by 1991 with a total of 407 delivered. Production in India, where the first Cheetah flew on 6 October 1972, was initially for the **Indian Air Force**, equipping Nos 659-662 AOP/liaison squadrons. Since 1987, these units have been part of the **Indian Army Air Corps**. Current production of the Cheetah by HAL at Bangalore stands at 197 examples, including 20 assembled from French components. Lamas continue to fly with the air arms of **Angola**, **Argentina** (air force and army), **Cameroon**, **Chile** (air force and army), **Ecuador**, **El Salvador**, **Peru** (army) and **Togo**.

SPECIFICATION

Aérospatiale SA 315B Lama
Rotor system: main rotor diameter 11.02 m (36 ft

1.75 in); tail rotor diameter 1.91 m (6 ft 3.25 in); main rotor disc area 95.38 m² (1,026.69 sq ft); tail rotor disc area 2.87 m² (30.84 sq ft)
Fuselage and tail: length overall, rotors turning 12.91 m (42 ft 4.25 in) and fuselage 10.23 m (33 ft 6.25 in); height overall 3.09 m (10 ft 1.75 in); skid track 2.38 m (7 ft 9.75 in)
Powerplant: one 858-shp (640-kW) Turboméca Artouste IIIB derated to 542 shp (404 kW)
Weights: empty 1021 kg (2,251 lb); normal take-off 1950 kg (4,299 lb); maximum take-off 2300 kg (5,071 lb)
Fuel and load: internal fuel 575 litres (152 US gal); external fuel none; maximum payload 1135 kg (2,502 lb)
Speed: never-exceed speed at sea level 210 km/h (113 kt; 130 mph); maximum cruising speed at optimum altitude 192 km/h (103 kt; 119 mph)
Range: 515 km (278 nm; 320 miles)
Performance: maximum rate of climb at sea level

The Cheetah is a HAL-built Lama, used widely by India for mountain work. The type features raised skids for better ground clearance on rough terrain.

330 m (1,083 ft) per minute; service ceiling 5400 m (17,715 ft); hovering ceiling 5050 m (16,565 ft) in ground effect and 5600 m (15,090 ft) out of ground effect

Aérospatiale (Sud) **SA 321 Super Frelon**

To meet requirements of the French armed services for a medium transport helicopter, Sud-Aviation flew the prototype **SA 3200 Frelon** (hornet) on 10 June 1959. Powered by three Turboméca Turmo IIIB turboshaft engines, the SA 3200 had large external fuel tanks that left the interior clear for a maximum 28 troops, and a swing-tail fuselage to simplify loading cargo. Development was terminated in favour of a larger and more capable helicopter designed

in conjunction with Sikorsky in the USA, and with Fiat in Italy producing the main gearbox and transmission. What was to become Europe's largest production helicopter clearly shows Sikorsky influence, the rotor system being of Sikorsky design, and with its watertight hull suitable for amphibious operation. Two military prototypes of the Super Frelon were built, the SA 3210-01 troop transport flown on 7 December 1962, and the SA 3210-02 maritime version for

The Aéronavale Super Frelons were previously used for ASV and ASW work, but now they are used primarily for transport duties, including vertical replenishment of ships under way. The type serves with 32F at Lanvéoc, 33F at St Mandrier and 20S also at the latter base.

Aérospatiale (Sud) SA 321 Super Frelon

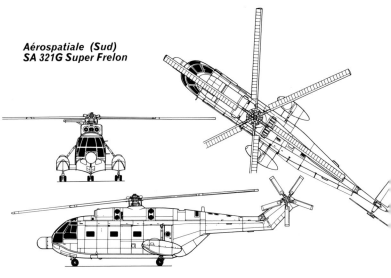

Aérospatiale (Sud) SA 321G Super Frelon

Libya purchased both maritime and transport Frelon variants. This is one of the latter, distinguished by its sand and green camouflage.

the Aéronavale on 28 May 1963.

Four pre-production aircraft were built under the new designation **SA 321**. These were followed in October 1965 by an initial production series of 16 **SA 321G** ASW helicopters for the Aéronavale, which received a further 10 (including three pre-production models). This variant was identifiable by having a small stabilising float incorporating Sylphe surveillance radar mounted to the support structure of each main unit of the tricycle landing gear (later removed). Apart from ship-based ASW missions, the SA 321G also carried out sanitisation patrols in support of 'Rédoutable'-class ballistic missile submarines. Some were modified with nose-mounted targeting radar for AM39 Exocet missiles, giving an ASV capability. Five **SA 321Ga** cargo-carrying versions, originally used in support of the Pacific nuclear test centre, were transferred to assault support duties. The 20 surviving Aéronavale Super Frelons are currently assigned to transport duties including com-

mando transport, vertical replenishment of ships at sea and civilian support duties such as SAR. Six **SA 321GM**s fitted with Omera ORB-32WAS radar were delivered to Libya in 1980-81. The SA 321G was modified for air force and army service by removal of stabilising floats and external fairings on each side of the lower fuselage. Designated **SA 321H**, a total of 16 examples was delivered from 1977 to the Iraqi air force with Omera ORB-31D radar and AM39 Exocet ASMs. These aircraft were used in the Iran-Iraq conflict and the 1991 Gulf War, in which at least one example was destroyed.

The maritime variant was followed by the **SA 321F** commercial airliner for 34-37 passengers, and the commercial **SA 321J** intended for use as a 27-seat passenger transport, as a cargo carrier with a 4000-kg (8,818-lb) internal or 5000-kg (11,023-lb) external load, or for other utility purposes such as fire fighting. This version was later superseded by the **SA 321Ja** operating at a higher gross weight. The naval air arm of the **People's Republic of China** received 16 aircraft fitted with Omera ORB-31D targeting radar. Non-amphibious military export versions included 12 **SA 321K**

transports for Israel, 16 similar **SA 321L** transports for South Africa (retired in 1991) and eight **SA 321M** SAR/logistical support helicopters for Libya.

When French production ended in 1983 a total of 99 Super Frelons had been built. Production continues in China under licence-agreement as the **Changhe Z-8** (described separately). Eight survivors of the examples delivered to Israel were re-engined with GE T58 turboshafts (for performance improvement and commonality with Israel's CH-53 fleet) and later sold to Argentina.

SPECIFICATION

Aérospatiale (Sud) SA 321G Super Frelon
Rotor system: main rotor diameter 18.90 m (62 ft 0 in); tail rotor diameter 4.00 m (13 ft 1.5 in); main rotor disc area 280.55 m² (3,019.93 sq ft); tail rotor disc area 12.57 m² (135.27 sq ft)
Fuselage and tail: length overall, rotors turning 23.03 m (75 ft 6.625 in), fuselage 19.40 m (63 ft 7.8 in), and 17.07 m (56 ft 0 in) with main rotor blades and tail folded; height overall 6.76 m (22 ft 2.25 in), and 4.94 m (16 ft 2.5 in) with main rotor blades and tail folded; wheel track 4.30 m (14 ft 1 in); wheel base

6.56 m (21 ft 6.25 in)
Powerplant: three Turboméca Turmo IIIC3 each rated at 1100 kW (1,475 shp) or, in later helicopters, three Turboméca Turmo IIIC7 each rated at 1201 kW (1,610 shp)
Weights: empty 6863 kg (15,130 lb); maximum take-off 12500 kg (27,557 lb) in earlier helicopters or 13000 kg (28,660 lb) in later helicopters
Fuel and load: internal fuel 3975 litres (1,050 US gal) plus provision for 1000 litres (264 US gal) of auxiliary fuel in two cabin tanks; external fuel up to two 500-litre (132-US gal) auxiliary tanks; maximum payload 5000 kg (11,023 lb)
Speed: never-exceed speed at sea level 275 km/h (149 kt; 171 mph); maximum cruising speed at sea level 248 km/h (134 kt; 154 mph)
Range: 1020 km (550 nm; 633 miles) with a 3500-kg (7,716-lb) payload; endurance 4 hours
Performance: maximum rate of climb at sea level 300 m (984 ft) per minute; service ceiling 3100 m (10,170 ft); hovering ceiling 1950 m (6,400 ft) in ground effect

OPERATORS

Argentina (SA 321K), China (SA 321G and Z-8), France (Aéronavale SA 321G/SA 321 Ga), Iraq (SA 321H), Libya (SA 321GM/SA 321M).

Aérospatiale (Nord) N 262 Frégate

With its design origins in the piston-engined Max Holste MH-250 Super Broussard which flew on 20 May 1959, the definitive **Nord N 262 Frégate** differed in having a pressurised, circular-section fuselage. The powerplant comprised two Turboméca Bastan turboprops, as introduced by Max Holste in the MH-260 prototype (flown on 29 July 1960) and the 10 pre-production slab-sided MH-260s. After Nord had assumed responsibility for further development of the light transport for military and civil use, the N262 prototype first flew on 24 December 1962.

The first production aircraft flew on 8 June 1964 and Nord went on to build a total of 110 in several versions, production being completed after Nord was absorbed into Aérospatiale in 1970. Principal military users are the **French air force**, which bought five new-build **N 262A** and 24 **N 262D** Frégates plus other used aircraft, and the French navy, which acquired 25 new and secondhand. For the Armée de l'Air, five **N 262AEN**s fly in the training role to instruct navigators with GE 316 'Toulouse', for which purpose they are fitted with OMERA ORB-32 radar, Crouzet Oméga 600 navigation equipment and TACAN, with consoles for four students and three instructors. Other N 262s fly with several training and transport squadrons (ETE 41, 43, 44),

while most of the 24 original 262Ds serve in the light transport role with ET 1/65 'Vendôme' at Villacoublay.

The **Aéronavale** uses its Nord 262s as multi-engine trainers for co-pilots converting to the Atlantique, this being the responsibility of 55S, the Ecole de Perfectionnement sur Multimoteurs in Corsica. Navigation and flight engineer training is given by 56S at Nîmes/Garons, using **Nord 262E** conversions of the 262A with appropriate equipment. Three Nord 262Es also are used for inshore surveillance by 2S from Lann-Bihoué. Elsewhere, **Angola** continues to fly four ex-civil Nord 262As acquired in 1980, and the **Burkina-Faso** air force has two **N 262C** Frégates, but Gabon retired its three aircraft in 1990.

SPECIFICATION

Aérospatiale (Nord) N 262 Frégate Series D
Wing: span 22.60 m (74 ft 1.75 in); aspect ratio 9.10; area 55.79 m² (600.54 sq ft)
Fuselage and tail: length 19.28 m (63 ft 3 in); height 6.21 m (20 ft 4 in); tailplane span 8.80 m (28 ft 10.5 in); wheel track 3.13 m (10 ft 9 in); wheel base 7.23 m (23 ft 9 in)
Powerplant: two Turboméca Bastan VII each rated at 1,145 ehp (854 ekW)
Weights: basic empty 6200 kg (13,668 lb); operating

empty 7225 kg (15,928 lb); maximum take-off 10800 kg (23,810 lb)
Fuel and load: internal fuel 2000 litres (528 US gal) plus provision for 570 litres (151 US gal) of optional fuel; external fuel none; maximum payload 3075 kg (6,779 lb)
Speed: maximum level speed 'clean' at optimum altitude 418 km/h (226 kt; 260 mph); maximum and economical cruising speed at optimum altitude 408 km/h (221 kt; 254 mph)
Range: 2400 km (1,295 nm; 1,491 miles) with

maximum fuel or 1450 km (782 nm; 901 miles) with 26 passengers
Performance: maximum rate of climb at sea level 420 m (1,378 ft) per minute; service ceiling 8690 m (28,510 ft); take-off run 570 m (1,870 ft) at maximum take-off weight; take-off distance to 10.7 m (35 ft) 1070 m (3,510 ft) at maximum take-off weight; landing distance from 15 m (50 ft) 530 m (1,740 ft) at normal landing weight

Large numbers of Nord 262s remain in French service on both training and transport tasks. The Aéronavale uses this aircraft for communications work.

Aérospatiale (SOCATA) TB 30B Epsilon

Aérospatiale (SOCATA)
12 rue Pasteur
F-92150 Suresnes, France

SOCATA, Aérospatiale's light-aircraft subsidiary, began development in 1977 of a military basic trainer based on its TB 10 Tobago four/five-seat lightplane. Redesigned to meet a specification drawn up by the Armée de l'Air for a tandem trainer, the new design was proposed in **Aérospatiale TB 30A** and **TB 30B** versions with engines of 194 kW (260 hp) and 224 kW (300 hp), respectively. The TB 30B gained a development contract in 1979, and the first prototype was flown on 22 December 1979. The second prototype, flown on 12 July 1980, introduced the increased span, rounded wingtips, redesigned rear fuselage and tail which had been finalised for production **TB 30B Epsilon** aircraft. Following completion of the development programme, the first production aircraft was flown on 29 June 1983.

Of all-metal construction, the Epsilon has retractable tricycle landing gear, a large aft-sliding canopy and a cockpit layout and flying characteristics that are intended to prepare pupils for the Dassault-Breguet/Dornier Alpha Jet. Fully aerobatic and stressed for *g* limits of +6.7 and -3.35, the Epsilon has a Christen fuel system to permit up to two minutes of inverted flight. On 6 January 1982, before the development programme was completed, the **Armée de l'Air** ordered 150 for delivery at the rate of 30 per year. Two initial production batches were approved in 1982, each covering 30 aircraft. The Epsilon duly entered service with the Centre d' Expériences Aériennes Militaires (CEAM) at Mont-de-Marsan on 29 July 1983 to establish the training syllabus. Epsilons began to equip Groupement Ecole (GE) 315 at Cognac/Chateaubernard in June 1984, this unit eventually receiving 150 Epsilons by late 1989. GE 315 is the Basic

Flying School (Ecole de Formation Pilotage de Base) and receives direct-entry aircrew for a 23-week course involving 66½ hours. Four Flying Instruction Squadrons (EIV – Escadron d'Instruction en Vol) are partnered by the Instructors School (Ecole des Moniteurs) providing a 73-hour course.

Export orders for the Epsilon have been restricted to two customers. The **Portuguese air force** took delivery from 1989 of 18 Epsilons assembled locally by OGMA. These aircraft are operated by Esquadra 104 at Sintra. An armed version of the Epsilon was ordered by the **Togolese air force** in late 1984. This version is equipped with four underwing hardpoints, carrying a total of 300 kg (661 lb) of stores with pilot only, or 200 kg (441 lb) with two crew. Three aircraft were delivered in 1986 and were followed by a single attrition replacement in 1987.

SPECIFICATION

Aérospatiale TB 30B Epsilon
Wing: span 7.92 m (25 ft 11.75 in); aspect ratio 7.0; area 9.00 m² (96.88 sq ft)
Fuselage and tail: length 7.59 m (24 ft 10.75 in); height 2.66 m (8 ft 8.75 in); tailplane span 3.20 m (10 ft 6 in); wheel track 2.30 m (7 ft 6.5 in); wheel base 1.80 m (5 ft 10.75 in)
Powerplant: one Textron Lycoming AEIO-540-L1B5D rated at 300 hp (224 kW)
Weights: empty equipped 932 kg (2,055 lb); maximum take-off 1250 kg (2,755 lb)
Fuel and load: internal fuel 150 kg (331 lb); external fuel none; maximum ordnance 300 kg (661 lb)
Speed: never-exceed speed 520 km/h (281 kt; 323 mph); maximum level speed 'clean' at sea level 378 km/h (204 kt; 236 mph); cruising speed at 1830 m (6,005 ft) 358 km/h (193 kt; 222 mph)

Range: 1250 km (675 nm; 777 miles); endurance 3 hours 45 minutes
Performance: maximum rate of climb at sea level 564 m (1,850 ft) per minute; service ceiling 7010 m (23,000 ft); take-off run 410 m (1,345 ft) at maximum take-off weight; take-off distance to 15 m (50 ft) 640 m (2,100 ft) at maximum take-off weight; landing distance from 15 m (50 ft) 440 m (1,444 ft) at normal landing weight; landing run 250 m (820 ft) at normal landing weight

Portugal has 18 Epsilons for its basic training needs with Esq 104. The aircraft were assembled locally by OGMA.

Epsilon of GE 315, used for basic training.

Aérospatiale (SOCATA) TB 31 Omega

Aérospatiale's SOCATA light aircraft division developed as a private venture a turboprop version of its TB 30 Epsilon piston-engined basic trainer (of which 172 had been delivered to the French, Portuguese and Togo air forces from 1989), mainly to meet Armée de l'Air requirements for an eventual Fouga Magister replacement. The prototype Epsilon 01 was initially used as a flying testbed for the first 450-shp (335-kW) Turboméca TP319 turboprop, flat-rated to 350 shp (261 kW), to replace the original 300-hp (224-kW) Textron Lycoming AEIO-540-LIB5D flat-six piston-powerplant in an extensively-revised nose cowling with a chin intake. Initially fitted with a three-bladed Ratier-Figeac composite propeller, the **Turbo Epsilon** made its first flight in this form on 9 November 1985 but, after extensive engine development, underwent further modifications to emerge in 1989 as the **TB 31 Omega**.

Apart from installation of a developed 488-shp (364-kW) TP319-1A2 Arrius turboprop, derated to 360 shp (268 kW) and driving a Hartzell propeller, the Omega featured a new two-piece moulded canopy for improved cockpit visibility and room for stepped twin Martin-Baker 15FC lightweight zero-height/60-kt ejection seats if required, plus EFIS instrumentation and an additional dorsal fin. Despite a successful flight-test programme, which began on 30 April 1989 and confirmed the Omega's substantial increase in performance, French government preference for the much bigger and more powerful EMBRAER Tucano has so far inhibited SOCATA from launching production of the TB 31.

SPECIFICATION

Aérospatiale TB 31 Omega
Wing: span 7.92 m (25 ft 11.75 in); aspect ratio 6.97; area 9.00 m² (96.88 sq ft)
Fuselage and tail: length 7.81 m (25 ft 7.5 in); height 2.68 m (8 ft 9.5 in); wheel track 2.30 m (7 ft 6.5 in); wheel base 1.80 m (5 ft 10.75 in)
Powerplant: one 364-kW (488-shp) Turboméca TP 319 IA2 Arrius derated to 268 kW (360 shp)
Weights: empty equipped 860 kg (1,896 lb);

maximum take-off 1450 kg (3,197 lb)
Fuel and load: internal fuel 222 kg (489 lb); external fuel none; maximum ordnance 300 kg (661 lb)
Speed: never-exceed speed 595 km/h (321 kt; 370 mph); maximum level speed 'clean' at 4875 m (16,000 ft) 519 km/h (280 kt; 322 mph); maximum cruising speed at 3050 m (10,000 ft) 434 km/h (234 kt; 269 mph); economical cruising speed at optimum altitude 354 km/h (191 kt; 220 mph)
Range: 1308 km (706 nm; 813 miles)

The Omega remains in prototype form, having been developed from the piston-engined Epsilon.

Performance: maximum rate of climb at sea level 640 m (2,100 ft) per minute; service ceiling 9145 m (30,000 ft); take-off distance to 15 m (50 ft) 570 m (1,870 ft) at maximum take-off weight
g **limits:** -3.5 to +7

Aerostar (Yakovlev) Yak-52

Aerostar SA
9 Condorilor Street
R-5500 Bacau, Romania

Together with its single-seat Yak-50 counterpart, the two-seat **Yak-52** was developed by the Yakovlev OKB in Moscow to provide the Soviet air force with a successor for the Yak-18 primary trainer. First flown in 1976 (after the first Yak-50), the Yak-52 proved successful and its production was assigned to the IAv factory at Bacau in Romania. Production began there in 1979, the first Yak-52 flying at Bacau early in 1980. Deliveries to the **Soviet Union**

began later in 1980 and, by June 1992, IAv had completed 1,600 Yak-52s, virtually all for the former Soviet air force, with production continuing.

The fully-aerobatic Yak-52 features tandem seating. All three wheels of the tricycle undercarriage remain fully exposed when retracted, to give a measure of protection in the event of wheels-up landings. The Yak-52 is powered by the 268-kW (360-hp) Vedeneyev M-14P radial engine, but

Aerostar has also flown a developed prototype, known as the **Condor**, with a 300-hp (224-kW) Lycoming AEIO-540-L1B5D piston engine and redesigned tail unit.

The name of the company responsible for the factory has now changed to Aerostar SA, and the designation is rendered as **Iak-52**. In addition to the former Soviet air forces, the type is in widespread use with the **Romanian air force**. Twelve were purchased by **Hungary** in 1994.

SPECIFICATION

Aerostar (Yakovlev) Yak-52
Wing: span 9.30 m (30 ft 6.25 in); aspect ratio 5.77; area 15.00 m² (161.5 sq ft)
Fuselage and tail: length 7.75 m (25 ft 5 in); height 2.70 m (8 ft 10.25 in); wheel track 2.72 m (8 ft 10.75 in); wheel base 1.86 m (6ft 1.25 in)
Powerplant: one 268-kW (360-hp) VMKB (Vedeneyev) M-14P nine-cylinder air-cooled radial

Aerostar (Yakovlev) Yak-52

Weights: empty 1015 kg (2,238 lb); maximum take-off 1305 kg (2,877 lb)
Fuel and load: internal fuel 100 kg (220 lb); external fuel none
Speed: never-exceed speed 360 km/h (194 kt; 223 mph); maximum level speed at sea level 285 km/h (154 kt; 177 mph); maximum level speed at 1000 m (3,280 ft) 270 km/h (145 kt; 167 mph)
Range: 500 km (270 nm; 310 miles) at 500 m (1,640 ft), maximum fuel and 20 min. reserves
Performance: maximum climb rate at sea level

600 m (1,970 ft) per minute; service ceiling 4000 m (13,125 ft); take-off run 180-200 m (591-657 ft); landing run (flaps up) 285 km/h (935 m); landing run (flaps down) 260 m (853 ft)
g limits: -5 to +7

The Yak-52 is used in huge numbers by the air forces of the former Soviet Union, although production is undertaken in Romania.

Aérostructure (Fournier) RF-10

First flown on 6 March 1981, the **RF-10** was designed in France by René Fournier as a continuation of a series of motor-gliders and ultra-light aircraft based on classic sailplane design. Generally similar to the RF-9, the RF-10 introduced an all-composite structure with a carbon-fibre main spar and more powerful 59.5-kW (80-hp) Limbach L2000-LOI flat-four engine. After completing a second prototype, Fournier sold rights in the RF-10 to Aérostructure SARL, which put the type into production, with a T-tail replacing the low-mounted tailplane of the prototypes. The first production RF-10 flew on 10 May 1984 and about a dozen were built, of which four were procured by the **Portuguese air force** to serve with No. 802 Squadron at the Air Force Academy, at Sintra, to allow career officers to go solo prior

to embarking on their flying training course. Rights in the RF-10 were subsequently acquired by AeroMot in Porto Alegre, Brazil, with a view to series assembly/manufacture as the **AMT-100 Ximango**.

SPECIFICATION

Aérostructure (Fournier) RF-10
Wing: span 17.47 m (57 ft 3.75 in); aspect ratio 16.3; area 18.70 m² (201.29 sq ft)
Fuselage and tail: length 7.89 m (25 ft 10.75 in); height 1.03 m (6 ft 4 in)
Powerplant: one Limbach L 2000 EOI rated at 80 hp (59.5 kW)
Weights: empty 600 kg (1,323 lb); maximum take-off 800 kg (1,764 lb)
Fuel and load: internal fuel 90 litres (23.8 US gal); external fuel none

Speed: maximum cruising speed at optimum altitude 200 km/h (108 kt; 124 mph); economical cruising speed at optimum altitude 180 km/h (97 kt; 112 mph); maximum gliding speed 245 km/h (133 kt; 153 mph) in smooth air and 180 km/h (97 kt; 112 mph) in rough air
Performance: maximum rate of climb at sea level 150 m (492 m) per minute; best glide ratio 30 at

Several air arms operate motor gliders for initial training. Portugal has four RF-10s.

100 km/h (54 kt; 62 mph); minimum sink rate 0.96 m (3.15 ft) per second at 90 km/h (49 kt; 56 mph)
g limits: -2.6 to +5.3

Aerotec T-23 Uirapuru

Designed as a private venture by two Brazilian engineers, the original **A-122 Uirapuru** was flown on 2 June 1965 with an 80.5-kW (108-hp) Lycoming O-235-C1 flat-four engine. The basic type was adopted by the **Brazilian air force** to replace its Fokker S.11 and S.12 primary trainers, with an order for 30, subsequently increased to 70. Designated **T-23**, the first of these flew on 23 January 1968, with a 119.5-kW (160-hp) Lycoming O-320-B2B engine. An update produced the **A-132 Uirapuru II** which flew on 26 February 1981 as the **T-23B**, later the **YT-17 Tangara**.

Planned production of 100 T-23Bs did not take place, but some features of the Uirapuru II were incorporated in 45 T-23s in 1979/80. Six Tangaras were completed in 1986 for sale to the **Bolivian air force**, which previously had procured 18 T-23 Uirapurus; a dozen of the latter, plus the A-132s, remain in service at the Military Aviation College at Santa Cruz. The only other

sale was to **Paraguay**, where eight (of about 20 procured, including a dozen ex-Brazilian air force) provide basic training at the Air Force Academy at Campo Grande. The T-23 was retired as a primary trainer by the Brazilian air force in 1980, a few remaining on strength for miscellaneous duties.

SPECIFICATION

Aerotec A-132 Uirapuru
Wing: span 8.50 m (27 ft 10.75 in); aspect ratio 5.33; area 13.50 m² (145.32 sq ft)
Fuselage and tail: length 6.60 m (21 ft 8 in); height 2.70 m (8 ft 10 in); tailplane span 2.80 m (9 ft 2.25 in); wheel track 2.40 m (7 ft 10.5 in); wheel base 1.53 m (5 ft 0.25 in)
Powerplant: one Textron Lycoming O-320-B2B rated at 160 hp (119.5 kW)
Weights: empty 515 kg (1,135 lb); operating empty 540 kg (1,190 lb); maximum take-off 840 kg (1,852 lb)
Fuel and load: internal fuel 140 litres (37 US gal)

plus provision for 100 litres (26.4 US gal) of auxiliary fuel in two tip tanks; external fuel none; maximum ordnance none
Speed: maximum level speed 'clean' at sea level 122 kt (140 mph; 225 km/h); maximum cruising speed at 5,000 ft (1525 m) 100 nm (115 miles; 185 km/h)
Range: 432 nm (497 miles; 800 km) with standard fuel; endurance 4 hours
Performance: maximum rate of climb at sea level 240 m (787 ft) per minute; service ceiling 4500 m

Its days as a primary trainer long over, the Aerotec T-23 nevertheless continues in Brazilian service as a hack. Bolivia and Paraguay do still use the type in its original role.

(14,765 ft); take-off run 200 m (656 ft) at maximum take-off weight; landing run 180 m (590 ft) at normal landing weight

Aerotek NGT

Although described by its manufacturer, Aerotek, a division of the South African CSIR (Council for Scientific and Industrial Research), as a composites technology demonstrator, the **NGT (New Generation Trainer)** was conceived primarily in response to an anticipated South African Air Force request for a successor to the veteran North American Harvard trainer.

Originally known as **Project Ovid**, the NGT was initiated in 1986 as an exercise in Kevlar/glass-fibre construction, and a prototype entered flight test on 29 April 1991. In the same performance category as the Pila-

tus PC-7, the NGT is claimed to be cheaper and easier to build and maintain owing to its all-composite construction. Of classic vertically-staggered tandem-seat configuration, the NGT has a one-piece, sideways-opening acrylic perspex framed canopy embodying a rollover bar. Powered by a 750-shp (559-kW) Pratt & Whitney Canada PT6A-25 turboprop, it is fully aerobatic. Evaluation against

the PC-7, P.Z.L. 130 Turbo Orlik, EMBRAER Tucano and Aérospatiale Omega resulted in a SAAF order for the PC-7 Mk II, which is essentially a PC-9 with a de-rated engine. Renamed the **Atlas/Denel Ace**, a second prototype became the subject of an international marketing campaign in 1993. Production aircraft will be lengthened to accept engines of up to 1,600 shp (1193 kW).

Agusta A 109

*Agusta SpA
Via Giovanni Agusta 520,
I-21017 Cascina Costa di Samarate, Italy*

Agusta, one of Italy's earliest aircraft manufacturers, became involved in helicopter construction in 1952, after acquiring a licence for the Bell Model 47, and still has licence agreements with Bell. Growing experience in helicopter design/construction led to the Agusta A 109, the company's first own-design helicopter to enter large-scale

production. The initial A 109 was powered by a single 515-kW (690-shp) Turboméca Astazou XII, but was revised in 1967 to use two 276-kW (370-shp) Allison 250-C14 turboshafts. The planned military utility A 109B was abandoned in 1969; instead, Agusta concentrated on the eight-seat civil A 109C Hirundo (swallow), the first of three proto-

types (NC7101) flying on 4 August 1970. However, it was 1976 before deliveries began of production aircraft, then redesignated A 109A. This model soon proved a commercial success, being used not only as a light passenger transport, but also as an air ambulance, for freight carriage and for search and rescue. Several air arms pro-

cured the type in small numbers for liaison and utility transport. Of four bought by Argentina, two were captured by the United Kingdom during the Falklands War and pressed into service with 7 Regiment, Army Air Corps, at Netheravon, later augmented by two more. These are used primarily to support SAS special operations with 8

Left: The Italian army adopted the A 109 to fulfil a variety of roles, including liaison, scouting and light attack.

Right: Wearing a civil-style scheme, this is one of the captured A 109s used by the British Army for support of Special Forces (SAS) operations.

Flight, flying mostly from Hereford.

From September 1981 the basic civil model was redesignated **A 109A Mk II** following modifications including uprated transmission, a new tail rotor driveshaft, a structurally redesigned tailboom and detailed cockpit improvements. In 1989, a 'wide body' **A 109C** version with uprated transmission was introduced, featuring a more roomy and comfortable cabin. One example was delivered to 31° Stormo of the **AMI** for the President of Italy.

Military development

The A 109 clearly had greater military potential, and was developed to fill a variety of military roles, including scout, aeromedical evacuation and attack. The **Aviazione Leggera dell'Esercito** (Italian army) procured 24 **A 109EOA** (Elicottero d'Osservazione Avanzata) helicopters powered by the Allison 250-C20R, delivered during 1988. These feature sliding cabin doors for rapid access, roof-mounted SFIM M334-25 daylight sight with boresighted CILAS laser rangefinder and a variety of armament options, the latter carried on two outrigger pylons either side of the main cabin. Further militarisation resulted in fixed landing gear, ECM equipment and crashworthy fuel system being fitted.

Agusta currently offers the **A 109CM** as its principal military model, similar to the A 109EOA but with a wider range of options, including different sights. The **Belgian army** is the only customer so far (designation **A 109BA**), having acquired 18 in scout configuration and 28 for the anti-armour role. The scouts feature a Saab Helios roof-mounted observation sight, while the anti-tank helicopters have a Saab/ESCO HeliTOW 2 sight and provision for eight Hughes TOW-2A anti-armour missiles. The A 109BAs are assembled in Belgium by SABCA, and feature cable-cutters.

With an eye on African and Middle East markets, more recent development has been concentrated on the multi-role 'hot-and-high' **A 109K**, with uprated transmission, a lengthened nose to house increased avionics and detail improvements. First flight of the A 109K took place in April 1983 and current orders stand at 15 **A 109K2**s for the Swiss mountain rescue service. Military versions are the **A 109KM** land-based version, with fixed landing gear and sliding cabin doors, and the similar **A 109KN** naval version, which adds shipborne capability and maritime weapons. More than 500 A 109s of all versions have been delivered to date.

Agusta A 109EOA

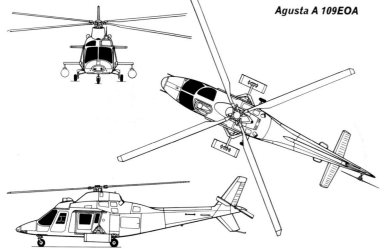

WEAPON OPTIONS

Four hardpoints on lower fuselage sides allow the carriage of many different stores, including 7.62-mm or 12.7-mm machine-gun pods, 70-mm or 80-mm rocket launchers, up to eight TOW anti-tank missiles and Stinger air-to-air missiles. The A 109 can also carry light UAV (unmanned air vehicles), and in the maritime strike role can launch anti-ship missiles. Machine-guns can be pintle-mounted in the doors.

SPECIFICATION

Agusta A 109KM

Rotor system: main rotor diameter 11.00 m (36 ft 1 in); tail rotor diameter 2.00 m (6 ft 6.75 in); main rotor disc area 95.03 m² (1,022.96 sq ft); tail rotor disc area 3.143 m² (33.83 sq ft)

Fuselage and tail: length overall, rotors turning 13.05 m (42 ft 9.75 in) and fuselage 11.106 m (36 ft 5.25 in); height to top of fin 3.30 m (10 ft 10 in); stabiliser span 2.88 m (9 ft 5.5 in); wheel track 2.45 m (8 ft 0.5 in); wheel base 3.535 m (11 ft 7.25 in)

Powerplant: two Turboméca Arriel IK each rated at 700 shp (522 kW) for take-ff and 585 shp (436 kW) for continuous running

Weights: empty 1595 kg (3,517 lb); maximum take-off 2850 kg (6,283 lb)

Fuel and load: internal fuel 700 litres (185 US gal); external fuel none

Speed: maximum level speed 'clean' at sea level 140 kt (161 mph; 259 km/h); maximum cruising speed at sea level 144 kt (166 mph; 266 km/h)

Range: 537 km (289 nm; 333 miles)

Performance: maximum rate of climb at sea level 1,740 ft (530 m) per minute; service ceiling 20,000 ft (6095 m); hovering ceiling 18,500 ft (5640 m) in ground effect and 11,000 ft (3350 m) out of ground effect

Belgium has purchased 28 A 109BAs for the anti-armour role, complete with eight TOW launchers and roof-mounted sight. A further 18 aircraft are in scout configuration.

Agusta **A 129 Mangusta**

Conceived for an **Italian army** requirement in the mid-1970s as the first night/all-weather light attack helicopter to incorporate a fully computerised and redundant integrated management system for a minimum crew workload, the first of five prototype **A 129**s (MM.590/E.I.901), powered by two Piaggio-built Rolls-Royce Gem Mk 2-1004D turboshaft engines, made its initial flight on 11 September 1983. All five were flying by March 1986, and the first production A 129 of an initial batch of 15 from a requirement for 60 was scheduled for delivery to Italian army aviation (ALE) before the end of 1987. The first five **Mangusta**s were not delivered to the ALE centre at Viterbo, however, until July 1990, for operational trials and training, and although further deliveries of about 1.5 per month were reported to the 1° RALE 'Antares' Army Light Aviation Wing at the same base, only two operational squadrons appear to be planned within ALE's 49° Gruppo Squadroni 'Capricorno' in the 5° Army Aviation Region at Casarsa.

Deliveries were also delayed through funding problems for the full ALE requirement of 60 Hughes/Emerson/Saab Heli-TOW systems, plus 20 more as spares. Normal armament comprises up to 2,645 lb (1200 kg) of external stores on four stub-wing pylons, including up to eight TOW-2A, HOT or six Hellfire ATMs, Stinger, Mistral or AIM-9 AAMs, 52 70-mm (2.75-in) or 81-mm (3.18-in) SNIA-BPD rockets, and 7.62-, 12.7-or 20-mm (0.3-, 0.5- or 0.787-in) gun pods, in conjunction with Honeywell IHADSS night-vision goggles, and eventually a helmet-mounted sight. Qualification trials have been completed with a Lucas chin turret mounting a 12.7-mm (0.5-in) machine-gun, although this is not currently planned for AMI use.

On 8 October 1986 preliminary agreement was reached in an MoU by the governments of Britain, Italy, the Netherlands and Spain to study an advanced version of the A 129 known as the Joint European Helicopter **Tonal**, as a prospective European Light Attack Helicopter (LAH). The Tonal would feature more power, new high-speed rotor blades, an increase in take-off

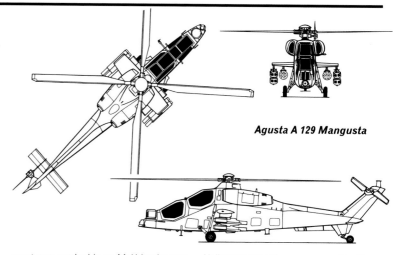

Agusta A 129 Mangusta

weight from 9,039 lb (4100 kg) to about 9,900 lb (4490 kg), a retractable landing gear contributing towards a 20 kt (23 mph; 37 km/h) level speed increase to about 160 kt (183 mph; 296 km/h), and IR-imaging TriGAT ATMs instead of Hughes TOW missiles. After protracted feasibility, cost and definition studies, rejection of Tonal full-scale development plans by the UK MoD's Equipment Policy Committee in June 1990, following UK and Dutch preference for the MDH AH-64, ended further European interest in this programme.

Tonal would have been similar in size and weight to the US Army's LHX scout/attack helicopter (now the T800-powered RAH-66 Comanche), for which competing submissions were made by Agusta of an A 129 Light Battlefield Helicopter powered by two 1,200-shp (894-kW) Allison/Garrett LHTEC T800 turboshaft engines for improved 'hot-and-high' performance. A Mangusta prototype started flying with these engines in October 1988, and was demonstrated to the United Arab Emirates shortly before the 1991 Gulf War. Agusta also proposed a 10-

12 passenger or 3,527-lb (1600-kg) payload, T800-powered, 11,000-lb (4990-kg) **A 139** utility version of the A 129, for which a collaborative programme had been discussed with Japan and Australia, and agreed in 1989 with TEA and Techint in Argentina, together with a naval attack development with anti-ship missiles. Neither of these projects, however, has so far materialised.

Scout version

At ALE's request, for possible third-batch procurement of another 30, Agusta produced plans for a scout/attack version (Elicottero da Esplorazione Scorta) of the A 129 for escort and anti-helicopter roles, fitted with a chin-mounted power turret for a 12.7-mm (0.5-in) or 15.5-mm (0.61-in) machine-gun and provision for air-to-air missiles and a mast-mounted sight. If the batch is not procured, 20 of the original aircraft will become convertible to the scout configuration. Interest has been expressed in acquiring A 129s by Iran, which in mid-1991, according to the Italian Foreign Minister, was prepared to sign a $154 million order

for an unspecified number, plus help from Italy with overhauling its fleet of Bell and Boeing Chinook helicopters.

WEAPON OPTIONS

On the stub wings are four hardpoints, each stressed for 300 kg (660 lb). Each pylon can be elevated 2° and depressed up to 10° to maximise missile envelope. Standard Italian army armament configuration consists of eight TOW 2A anti-tank missiles in four-round launchers on the

outboard pylons, aimed with a Saab/ESCO HeliTOW sight system, with either gun pods or rocket launchers on the inboard. Gun pods can be of 7.62-mm, 12.7-mm or 20-mm calibre, while rockets are either 70-mm or 81-mm weapons. For a rocket attack mission, a 19-tube launcher is carried on the inboard pylon, and a seven-tube launcher on the outboard. Anti-armour missile options include up to six Hellfires or eight HOT. Air-to-air missiles (two) can be Stinger, Sidewinder, Mistral or Javelin. A mast-mounted sight is an option for the scout version, and anti-ship missiles could be carried.

SPECIFICATION

Agusta A 129 Mangusta
Rotor system: main rotor diameter 11.90 m (39 ft 0.5 in); tail rotor diameter 2.24 m (7 ft 4.25 in); wing span 3.20 m (10 ft 6 in); main rotor disc area 111.22 m² (1,197.20 sq ft); tail rotor disc area 3.94 m² (42.42 sq ft)
Fuselage and tail: length overall, rotors turning 14.29 m (46 ft 10.5 in) and fuselage 12.275 m (40 ft 3.25 in); height overall 3.35 m (11 ft 0 in) and to top of fin 2.65 m (8 ft 8.25 in); stabiliser span 3.00 m (9 ft 10 in); wheel track 2.20 m (7 ft 3.5 in); wheel base 6.955 m (22 ft 9.75 in)
Powerplant: two Rolls-Royce Gem 2 Mk 1004D each rated at 825 shp (615 kW)
Weights: empty equipped 2529 kg (5,575 lb); maximum take-off 4100 kg (9,039 lb)
Fuel and load: internal fuel 750 kg (1,653 lb); maximum ordnance 1200 kg (2,645 lb)
Speed: dash speed 170 kt (196 mph; 315 km/h); maximum level speed at sea level 140 kt (161 mph; 259 km/h); maximum cruising speed at optimum altitude 135 kt (155 mph; 250 km/h)
Range: combat radius 100 km (54 nm; 62 miles) for a 90-minute patrol; maximum endurance 3 hours
Performance: maximum rate of climb at sea level 2,150 ft (655 m) per minute; hovering ceiling 12,300 ft (3750 m) in ground effect

Above and right: The A 129 Mangusta is now taking its place as Italy's primary anti-armour weapon system. It has been deployed to Somalia as part of the UN peace-keeping force.

Agusta (Elicotteri-Meridionali/Boeing Vertol) CH-47C Chinook

A licence for production of the **CH-47C** in Italy was acquired from Boeing Vertol by Elicotteri Meridionali, and was subsequently continued by Agusta when EM became part of the latter group. Of a total of 95 Chinooks ordered by Iran, all but the first 22 were to have been from the Italian production line, but deliveries from the latter actually comprised 10 helicopters prior to the revolution, followed by six in 1979 and eight in 1981, all for the **Islamic Republic of Iran** army aviation. The **Italian army**

light aviation force has acquired a total of 30 CH-47Cs, including two flown on behalf of the SNPC. Italian production also provided Chinooks to **Egypt** (15), **Libya** (20) and **Morocco** (nine).

Agusta's licence for Chinook marketing covers the Mediterranean and Middle East region. Among the customers for the CH-47C was Egypt, which took 15 for army support.

Agusta (SIAI-Marchetti) S.211

D eveloped as a private-venture basic jet trainer, the **S.211** also has a light attack capability, bestowed by four underwing hardpoints for a total combined load of 660 kg (1,455 lb). First flown on 10 April 1981, it has been adopted by four air forces: **Singapore**, **Brunei**, **Haiti** and the **Philippines**, with aircraft for the last-mentioned assembled locally by PADC. Similarly, Singa-

pore Aerospace was responsible for assembly of 24 of an initial batch of 30 aircraft, which serve with Nos 131 and 132 Squadrons to provide advanced flying train-

The S.211 is one of the prime contenders for the JPATS competition, with Grumman acting as the US contractor.

Of the 18 S.211s for the Philippines, four were built in Italy and the remainder assembled locally from kits. They are split between these training aircraft and camouflaged aircraft for light attack.

ing at RAAF Pearce in Australia. The Royal Brunei armed forces, air wing, purchased four. The Haitian air corps ordered a similar number but has now disposed of its S.211s. A version of the S.211 with an improved nav/attack system has been planned, as has one with an uprated JT15D engine and increased fuel capacity.

SPECIFICATION

Agusta (SIAI-Marchetti) S.211
Wing: span 8.43 m (27 ft 8 in); aspect ratio 5.1; area 12.60 m² (135.63 sq ft)
Fuselage and tail: length 9.31 m (30 ft 6.5 in); height 3.80 m (12 ft 5.5 in); tailplane span 3.96 m (13 ft 0 in); wheel track 2.29 m (7 ft 6 in); wheel base 4.02 m (13 ft 2.25 in)
Powerplant: one Pratt & Whitney JT15D-4C rated at 2,500 lb st (11.12 kN) dry
Weights: empty equipped 1850 kg (4,078 lb); normal take-off 2750 kg (6,063 lb) as a trainer; maximum take-off 3150 kg (6,944 lb) as an attack warplane
Fuel and load: internal fuel 622 kg (1,371 lb); external fuel up to 390 kg (860 lb) in two 270-litre (71.3-US gal) drop tanks; maximum ordnance 660 kg (1,455 lb)

Speed: never-exceed speed 400 kt (460 mph; 740 km/h); maximum cruising speed at 25,000 ft (7620 m) 360 kt (414 mph; 667 km/h)
Range: ferry range 1,340 nm (1,543 miles; 2483 km) with drop tanks; combat radius 300 nm (345 miles; 556 km) on a hi-lo-hi attack mission with four rocket

launchers, or 125 nm (144 miles; 231 km) on a lo-lo-lo attack mission with four rocket launchers; endurance 3 hours 24 minutes
Performance: maximum rate of climb at sea level 4,200 ft (1280 m) per minute; service ceiling 40,000 ft (12190 m); take-off run 1,280 ft (390 m) at 2500 kg

(5,511 lb); take-off distance to 50 ft (15 m) 1,680 ft (512 m) at 2500 kg (5,511 lb); landing distance from 50 ft (15 m) 2,313 ft (705 m) at normal landing weight; landing run 1,185 ft (361 m) at normal landing weight
g limits: -3 to +6 at normal take-off weight or -2.5 to +5 at maximum take-off weight

Agusta-Bell **AB 204**

Having forged links with the Bell company through licence-production of the Bell 47 from 1954, Agusta in Italy went on to produce several hundred examples of the Bell 204B, equivalent to the US Army's UH-1B, starting in 1961. As the **AB 204**, Italian-built machines were supplied for military and civil use in the utility role, with up to 11 seats (including pilot) and provision for cargo-carrying, stretchers or slung loads. Optional powerplants were the 1,150-shp (858-kW) Lycoming T53-L-9, 1,200-shp (895.5-kW) Bristol Siddeley Gnome and 1,325-shp (989-kW) General Electric T58-GE-3 turboshaft. Pontoons could replace the skids for water/swamp operations.

Agusta also developed the **AB 204AS** for naval ASW operation, with radar, sonar, long-range tanks and provision to carry two Staffel of Helicopter Wing III in the **Austrian army**, in the **Swedish army** medium helicopter squadron (using the local designation **Hkp 3C**), in the **Turkish gendarmerie**, and in the **Yemen Arab Republic**. The AB 204AS was purchased originally by the Italian and Spanish navies, now out of service, but a few remain in **Turkish naval aviation** service.

Austria flies eight AB 204Bs with HG III at Hörsching, these having received a refurbishment.

SPECIFICATION

Agusta-Bell AB 204AS
Rotor system: main rotor diameter 48 ft 0 in (14.63 m); tail rotor diameter 8 ft 6 in (2.59 m); main rotor disc area 1,809.56 sq ft (168.11 m²); tail rotor disc area 56.74 sq ft (5.27 m²)
Fuselage and tail: length overall, rotors turning 57 ft 0 in (17.37 m) and fuselage 41 ft 7 in (12.67 m); height overall 12 ft 7.25 in (3.84 m); stabiliser span 9 ft 4 in (2.84 m); skid track 8 ft 8 in (2.64 m)
Powerplant: one General Electric T58-GE-3 rated at

1,290 shp (962 kW)
Weights: empty equipped 6,480 lb (2939 kg); maximum take-off 9,500 lb (4309 kg)
Fuel and load: internal fuel 242 US gal (916 litres); external fuel none
Speed: maximum cruising speed at sea level 90 kt (104 mph; 167 km/h)
Range: operational radius 60 nm (69 miles; 111 km) for a 1.67-hour sonar search patrol

Agusta-Bell AB 204
generally similar to the Agusta-Bell AB 204AS except in the following particulars:
Rotor system: main rotor diameter 44 ft 0 in (13.41 m) or 48 ft 0 in (14.63 m); main rotor disc area 1,520.53 sq ft (141.26 m²) or 1,809.56 sq ft (168.11 m²)

Fuselage and tail: length overall, rotors turning 55 ft 0 in (16.76 m) or 57 ft 0 in (17.37 m)
Powerplant: one Textron Lycoming T53-L-11A rated at 1,100 shp (820 kW), or General Electric T58-GE-3 rated at 1,290 shp (962 kW), or Rolls-Royce Gnome H.1200 rated at 1,250 shp (932 kW)
Weights: empty equipped about 4,610 lb (2091 kg); normal take-off 8,510 lb (3860 kg)
Speed: maximum level speed 'clean' at sea level 104 kt (120 mph; 193 km/h); maximum cruising speed at sea level 96 kt (110 mph; 177 km/h)
Range: range 340 nm (392 miles; 630 km); endurance 4 hours
Performance: maximum rate of climb at sea level 1,400 ft (427 m) per minute; hovering ceiling 10,000 ft (3050 m) in ground effect and 4,500 ft (1370 m) out of ground effect

Agusta-Bell **AB 205**

Matching development by Bell of its Model 205 as an enlarged Model 204, Agusta put the **AB 205** into production in 1964 and went on to build several hundred for military and civil use. Like its US counterpart, the AB 205 differed from the AB 204 in having a longer cabin to accommodate up to 14 troops plus a pilot, and was powered by an uprated engine. Normally

unarmed, the AB 205 could have a pintle-mounted machine-gun in the cabin, firing through the door, or air-to-ground missiles mounted externally each side of the cabin. Also standard on the AB 205 was the 48-ft (14.63-m) main rotor, replacing the 44-ft (13.41-m) rotor used on the AB 204, although Agusta had also used the larger rotor on its AB 204AS. Later production in

Italy focused on the **AB 205A-I** version with a number of small improvements, and higher operating weights. Agusta also prototyped twin-engined versions of the type, as the **AB 205BG** with a pair of Gnome H 1200s and the **AB 205TA** with two Turboméca Astazous, but these did not achieve production.

Substantial use of the AB 205 continues, although production ended in 1988, the largest single operators being the **Turkish army**, which has some 130, in addition to about 50 used by the Turkish gendarmerie.

Turkey is one of the few users to have operated AB 205As in the gunship role, this helicopter serving elsewhere primarily as a transport, for SAR and for training. The Italian army flies more than 100 AB 205As (as **EM-2**s) and has provided detachments in support of the UN in Lebanon, Namibia and Kurdistan, and for the EC Monitor Mission in the former Yugoslavia. Both the **Greek army** and **Greek air force** are substantial users, the latter's No. 358 Mira providing flights for SAR and VIP flights at various bases. Others using AB 205As for transport/ utility tasks are the **Iranian army** and **navy, Moroccan air force, Sultan of Oman air force** (No. 14 Sqn), **Royal Saudi AF** (Nos 12 and 14 Sqns), **Republic of Singapore AF** (Nos 120 and 123 Sqns), **Tanzania, Tunisia** (No. 31 Sqn), **Turkish army, Ugandan air force, Zambia,** and **Zimbabwe** (No. 7 Sqn), which operates the type as the **Cheetah.** Zimbabwe made extensive use of the Cheetah for anti-guerrilla operations. In **Spain,** the air force's Esc 783/Ala 78 has a few remaining in service for IFR training, designated **HE.10B.**

SPECIFICATION

Agusta-Bell AB 205
Rotor system: main rotor diameter 48 ft 3.5 in (14.72 m); tail rotor diameter 8 ft 6 in (2.59 m); main rotor disc area 1,831.61 sq ft (170.16 m2); tail rotor disc area 56.74 sq ft (5.27 m2)
Fuselage and tail: length overall, rotors turning 57 ft 2.75 in (17.98 m) and fuselage 41 ft 11 in

(12.78 m); height overall 14 ft 8 in (4.48 m); stabiliser span 9 ft 4 in (2.84 m); skid track 8 ft 6.5 in (2.60 m)
Powerplant: one 1,400-shp (1044-kW) Textron Lycoming T53-L-13 derated to 1,250 shp (932 kW) for take-off and 1,100 shp (820 kW) for continuous running
Weights: empty 4,800 lb (2177 kg); normal take-off 8,510 lb (3860 kg); maximum take-off 9,500 lb (4309 kg)
Fuel and load: internal fuel 220 US gal (833 litres); external fuel none; maximum payload 3,000 lb (1361 kg)
Speed: maximum level speed at sea level 120 kt (138 mph; 222 km/h); maximum cruising speed at optimum altitude 110 kt (127 mph; 204 km/h)
Range: 313 nm (360 miles; 580 km); endurance 3 hours 48 minutes
Performance: maximum rate of climb at sea level 1,800 ft (549 m) per minute; service ceiling 15,000 ft (4575 m); hovering ceiling 17,000 ft (5180 m) in ground effect and 11,000 ft (3355 m) out of ground effect

The yellow band around this 358 Mira AB 205 marks it as one of the Greek air force's SAR helicopters. They have a secondary VIP role.

Agusta-Bell **AB 206 JetRanger**

Of the total of more than 7,000 JetRangers of all versions built, about 1,000 were contributed by Agusta, which began production of the **AB 206A** at the end of 1967 in continuation of its long-standing licence-agreement with Bell. The **AB 206B** was added in 1972, with uprated engine, and Agusta adopted the designations **AB 206A-1** and **B-1** for optimised military variants that incorporated features of the US Army OH-58A Kiowa, including the high-skid landing gear option, increased rotor diameter, local strengthening of the airframe, additional access doors and provision for armament.

The **Italian army** purchased 150 AB 206s, starting with 16 in a basically civil configuration for training, designated **ERI-2** by the army. The original 317-shp (236.5-kW) Allison 250-C18 engines were subsequently replaced by the more powerful 250-C20 model, helicopters with these engines continuing in service as **AB 206A-2**s. As **ERI-3**s, the remainder for the Italian army were AB 206A-Is, but these also have now been fitted with -C20 engines and features of the JetRanger III/OH-58C, taking the designation **AB 206C-1.** They serve the army's Aviazione Leggera in the Elicot-

teri do Ricoynizione (reconnaissance helicopter) role, distributed in 16 of the ERI squadrons at bases throughout Italy.

Austria's Luftstreitkräfte bought 12 AB 206A-1s for training and SAR use, in 2 Staffel of Hubschraubergeschwader 1 at Tulln, and the **Royal Saudi Air Force** had 20 for training use by Nos 12 and 14 Squadrons at Taif. **Morocco** retains in service some 20 of the 25 JetRangers acquired, which included 20 of the AB 206B version to supplement five AB 205As bought in 1975. **Sweden** operates the AB 206A under the designation **Hkp 6A.** Nineteen JetRangers are on charge for liaison, observation and spotting duties, while seven Hkp 6As are used by the Swedish navy as part of the anti-submarine force with one torpedo, or three depth charges, as offensive capability. The **Iranian air force** continues to be a major operator of the JetRanger, with over 80 AB 206A/Bs used for liaison duties; further examples are used in a similar role by the navy (10) and air force (two).

Smaller quantities of the Italian-built JetRanger serve in **Greece** (two with No. 358 Mira Elikopteron for SAR and VIP flights, and over 15 with the army), **Libya**

(five used by the army), **Malta** (one AB 206A for coastal duties and SAR), **Oman** (three AB 206B used by No. 14 Sqn at Seeb), the Amiri Guard air wing, **Sharjah** (three AB 206B), the **Spanish army** (four AB 206A-1, transferred from the air force, as **HR.12A**s at the Centro de Ensenanza de las FAMET for training), **Tanzania** (two AB 206B), **Uganda** (four operated by the police), and **Yemen Arab Republic** (six).

SPECIFICATION

Agusta-Bell AB 206B JetRanger
Rotor system: main rotor diameter 33 ft 4 in (10.16 m); tail rotor diameter 5 ft 2 in (1.57 m); main rotor disc area 872.66 sq ft (81.07 m2); tail rotor disc area 20.97 sq ft (1.95 m2)
Fuselage and tail: length overall, rotors turning 39 ft 2 in (11.94 m) and fuselage 31 ft 2 in (9.50 m); height overall 9 ft 6.5 in (2.91 m); stabiliser span 6 ft 5.25 in (1.96 m); skid track 6 ft 3.5 in (1.92 m)
Powerplant: one 400-shp (298-kW) Allison 250-C20 derated to 317 shp (236 kW)
Weights: empty 1,504 lb (682 kg); normal take-off

3,200 lb (1452 kg) with an internal payload; maximum take-off 3,350 lb (1519 kg) with an external payload
Fuel and load: internal fuel 76 US gal (288 litres); external fuel none; maximum payload 1,200 lb (544 kg)
Speed: maximum level speed at sea level 122 kt (140 mph; 226 km/h); maximum cruising speed at optimum altitude 116 kt (133 mph; 214 km/h)
Range: 363 nm (418 miles; 673 km); endurance 4 hours
Performance: maximum rate of climb at sea level 1,360 ft (415 m) per minute; service ceiling more than 20,000 ft (6,095 m); hovering ceiling 11,325 ft (3450 m) in ground effect and 5,800 ft (1770 m) out of ground effect

Malta's small helicopter force includes this AB 206A, donated by the Libyan government.

Agusta-Bell **AB 212**

Production of the Bell 212 in Italy followed quickly upon development in the US of this twin-engined derivative of the Bell 205, undertaken in the first instance to meet USAF and Canadian Forces requirements. In essence, the Bell 212 (and AB 212) comprised the Model 205 airframe mated with the PT6T-3 Turbo Twin-Pac powerplant, comprising paired PT6 turboshafts. In its accommodation and equipment options, the **AB 212** closely resembled the AB 205A-I, with enhanced performance.

Following the precedent set with the AB 204AS, Agusta alone developed an anti-submarine warfare version of the AB 212, for which extensive modifications were made, particularly to the equipment. In the ASW role, a Bendix AN/AQS-15B/F sonar is the basic sensor, whereas the ASV version has Ferranti Seaspray search radar; both are fully instrumented for all-weather operations by day and night from the decks of small ships. For SAR, a hydraulically-operated external hoist is fitted. The normal crew

comprises three or four, with provision for up to seven passengers with two pilots, or four stretcher patients and an attendant.

Agusta built more than 100 **AB 212ASW**s for seven operators, of which the largest is the Italian navy, with 60. Of these, the first 12 had MEL ARI-5955 radar and the remainder MM/APS-705 matched to Aérospatiale AS12 ASMs. As the navy's standard shipboard helicopter aboard its destroyers and frigates, the AB 212ASW carries a pair of Mk 44, Mk 46 or MQ44 homing torpedoes, AS12s or Sea Killer 2 ASMs. Greece uses 14 of the ASWs, including three for ECM and the others from two 'Elli'-class frigates, while five with the Peruvian navy are used for reconnaissance. Spain's 10 AB 212ASWs, with AS12 and machine-gun armament, are used by Tercera Escuadrilla (Eslla 003) from the assault transport *Galicia* for close support duties. The Turkish navy bought 12, with Sea Spray radar and Sea Skua ASMs, to fly from 'Yavuz'-class frigates. Venezuela has six with OTO-Melara Sea Killer armament for

its Esc Aero Antisubmarino 3, based at Puerto Cabello, to serve from 'Sucre'-class frigates.

A 1983 contract covered the sale of 10 AB 212ASWs to Iraq, but this was placed under embargo and discussions for their release were finally ended by the Iraqi inva-

sion of Kuwait. Approximately 20 AB 212ASWs were ordered for the Iranian navy in early 1974 with provision for AS12 wire-guided missiles (these ASMs were used to attack Gulf shipping in 1985-86). The helicopters suffered from poor serviceability and are probably non-operational.

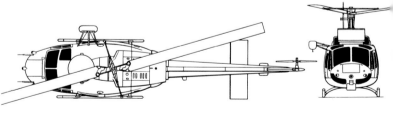

Agusta-Bell AB 212ASW

SPECIFICATION

Agusta-Bell AB 212ASW

Rotor system: main rotor diameter 48 ft 0 in (14.63 m); tail rotor diameter 8 ft 6 in (2.59 m); main rotor disc area 1,808.52 sq ft (168.10 m2); tail rotor disc area 56.74 sq ft (5.27 m2)

Fuselage and tail: length overall, rotors turning 57 ft 1in (17.40 m) and fuselage 42 ft 4.75 in (12.92 m); height overall 14 ft 10.25 in (4.53 m) and to top of rotor head 12 ft 10 in (3.91 m); stabiliser span 9 ft 4.5 in (2.86 m); skid track 8 ft 8 in (2.64 m)

Powerplant: one Pratt & Whitney Canada PT6T-6 Turbo Twin Pac rated at 1,875 shp (1398 kW)

Weights: empty equipped 3420 kg (7,540 lb); maximum take-off 5070 kg (11,177 lb) for the ASW mission with Mk 46 torpedoes, or 4973 kg (19,961 lb) for the ASV mission with AS12 missiles, or 4937 kg (10,883 lb) for the SAR mission

Fuel and load: internal fuel 1021 kg (2,250 lb) plus provision for auxiliary fuel in a cabin tank, plus provision for 356 kg (785 lb) of auxiliary fuel in one cabin and two external tanks; maximum ordnance 490 kg (1,080 lb)

Speed: never-exceed speed 130 kt (150 mph; 240 km/h); maximum level speed 'clean' at sea level

Distinguished by the large search radar above the cabin and large array of ESM antennas around the nose, the AB 212ASW is Italy's principal maritime helicopter. It can launch the Sea Killer missile in the anti-ship role.

106 kt (122 mph; 196 km/h); maximum cruising speed at optimum altitude 100 kt (115 mph; 185 km/h) with armament

Range: ferry range 360 nm (414 miles; 667 km) with auxiliary fuel; range 332 nm (382 miles; 615 km) on an ASV mission with AS12 missiles; maximum endurance 5 hours 0 minutes; typical endurance 4 hours 7 minutes on an ASV mission with AS12

Performance: maximum rate of climb at sea level 1,300 ft (396 m) per minute; hovering ceiling 10,500 ft (3200 m) in ground effect and 1,300 ft (396 m) out of ground effect

OPERATORS

Substantial numbers of AB 212s serve in military roles. In Austria, the air force has two squadrons of 12 each, serving in Hubschraubergeschwader I (Helicopter Wing) at Tulln and

Hubschraubergeschwader III at Hörsching, in the utility and transport role. The Italian air force has more than 30 divided between 208° Gruppo, 72° Stormo at Frosinone for training, and 85° Gruppo, 15° Stormo at Ciampino for SAR, and several of the 600-series squadrons that provide communications for the operational units at base level. Fifteen AB 212s in the Italian army serve (as EM-3s) in two squadrons (Nos 520 and 530) fulfilling the transport role at

Pontecagnano and Fontanarossa, respectively, with two on detachment to the Malta Helicopter Flight. For training and support missions, some 30 AB 212s obtained by Saudi Arabia serve in Nos 12 and 14 Squadrons at Taif. Other users include the Dubai police air wing (one), Lebanon (up to seven), Morocco (seven), Somalia (four, of which two for VIP), Spanish army (six), Sudan (11), the Yemen Arab Republic (six) and Zambia (two).

Agusta-Bell AB 412 Grifone

Collaborating closely with Bell, Agusta launched production of the **Model 412** in civil guise in 1981, after prototype testing in the US had begun with a first flight in August 1979. A further extrapolation of the design that had begun with the Model 204 (AB 204) in 1956, the Model 412 was, in effect, the Model 212 (AB 212) with a four-bladed rotor replacing the two-bladed rotor previously favoured for all Bell/Agusta-Bell production helicopters. Like the Model 212, the Model 412 depended for propulsion on the Pratt & Whitney Canada Turbo Twin Pac turboshafts.

Having put the civil **AB 412** into production, Agusta proceeded to evolve a military variant, which it named the **Grifone** (griffon) and flew for the first time in August 1982. With the needs of Italian military and quasi-military services particularly in view, the Grifone was designed to cope with a wide variety of roles that could include direct fire support and area suppression with one or two side-mounted cannon; scouting and reconnaissance with rocket pods and cable cutters; air defence with AAMs or other weapons; assault transport carrying up to 14 combat-equipped troops; and battlefield support. Subsequently, a maritime model was evolved for SAR, surveillance, mission monitoring, etc., for which it was provided with a 360° search radar on the roof, FLIR and TV sensors, four-axis autopilot and a special navigation system.

Special features of the Grifone include a strengthened undercarriage to absorb higher landing impacts, energy-absorbing armour-protected seats, armour for selected airframe areas, cabin floor fittings to provide for a wide variety of attachments for seats, stretchers, internal hoist or other special equipment, crash-attenuating seats for up to 14 troops in the personnel transport role, and an option for the installation of IR emission-reduction devices on the engine exhaust pipes.

In **Italy**, the AB 412 is now used by no fewer than six military and government agencies, including the national forest service and national fire service. A major user is the Carabinieri, with 20, while the SNPC (National Civilian Protection Service) agency has four or more.

Under Italian navy control, the coast guard has a growing fleet, with 24 in prospect ultimately. The largest single user in Italy is the army (Esercito Italiano), which has 30 to date – with more to come – under the designation **EM-4**, indicating the fourth type of Elicottero Multiruolo, or multi-role helicopter. Principal units flying the EM-4s are the 511 and 512 squadrons at Viterbo as part of 51° Gruppo Squadroni EM 'Leone' and one of the squadrons of 49° GSEM Capricornon at Casara.

Agusta also sold two Grifones to the **Uganda army air force**, which uses them in an armed anti-guerrilla role, and 12 to the **Air Force of Zimbabwe**, including

As one would expect, the largest operator of the AB 412 is the Italian army, which flies the type on assault transport/utility duties.

two equipped for VIP/ambulance missions. Other operators include the **Finnish coast guard** (two), the **Dubai air wing** (three), **Lesotho** (two) and the **Venezuelan army** (two).

SPECIFICATION

Agusta-Bell AB 412 Grifone

Rotor system: main rotor diameter 46 ft 0 in (14.02 m); tail rotor diameter 8 ft 6 in (2.59 m); main rotor disc area 1,661.90 sq ft (154.40 m2); tail rotor disc area 56.75 sq ft (5.27 m2)

Fuselage and tail: length overall, rotors turning 56 ft 0 in (17.07 m) and fuselage 42 ft 4.75 in (12.92 m); height overall 14 ft 2.25 in (4.32 m) with tail rotor

turning and to top of rotor head 1 ft 9.5 in (3.29 m); stabiliser span 9 ft 4.5 in (2.86 m); skid track 8 ft 6 in (2.59 m)

Powerplant: one 1,800-shp (1342-kW) Pratt & Whitney Canada PT6T-3B Turbo Twin Pac flat-rated at 1,400 shp (1044 kW) for take-off and 1,130 shp (843 kW) for continuous running

Weights: empty equipped 6,263 lb (2841 kg); maximum take-off 11,905 lb (5400 kg)

Fuel and load: internal fuel 330 US gal (1250 litres) plus provision for two 20- or 90-US gal (76- or 341-litre) auxiliary tanks; external fuel none; maximum payload 5,050 lb (2291 kg)

Speed: never-exceed speed at sea level 140 kt (161 mph; 259 km/h); maximum cruising speed at sea level 122 kt (140 mph; 226 km/h) and at 1500 m (4,920 ft) 125 kt (144 mph; 232 km/h); endurance at 4,920 ft (1500 m) 4 hours 12 minutes

Range: 434 nm (500 miles; 805 km) with standard fuel

Performance: maximum rate of climb at sea level 1,437 ft (438 m) per minute; service ceiling 17,000 ft (5180 m); hovering ceiling 4,100 ft (1250 m)

Agusta-Sikorsky AS-61

Under licence from Sikorsky, Agusta put the SH-3D Sea King into production in Italy in 1967, and began delivery in 1969 to the **Aviazione per la Marina Militare Italiana**. Production of up to 38 for the Italian navy included several variants with different equipment standards, the final batch matching US Navy SH-3H Sea Kings. They serve with the 1° and 3° Grupelicot. Also operating Agusta-built Sea Kings in the ASW role are the **Argentine navy** (four), **Brazilian navy** (nine) and **Peruvian navy** (five).

As the **AS-61A-4**, Agusta built a derivative of the SH-3D in the logistic and VIP transport role. This variant was sold to the

Italian air force (two), **Iraq** (six), **Iran** (two), **Egypt** (two), the **Royal Saudi air force** (one) and to the **Venezuelan army**, which bought four. Equivalent to the USAF's HH-3F SAR helicopter, the **AS-61R Pelican** was built by Agusta for the Italian air force, which initially acquired 20 and ordered 15 more in 1992. The AMI's AS-61Rs are being upgraded with new RWRs, chaff/flare dispensers and a dark green camouflage colour scheme. Two were deployed in 1993 to Somalia to aid the United Nations effort. Specifications for the Agusta-built S-61 variants are similar to those for their Sikorsky equivalents.

The armed AS-61R is used by the Italian air force for combat rescue duties. This is one of two aircraft deployed to Somalia.

SPECIFICATION

Agusta-Sikorsky AS-61R Pelican

Rotor system: main rotor diameter 62 ft 0 in (18.90 m); tail rotor diameter 10 ft 4 in (3.15 m); main rotor disc area 3,019.07 sq ft (280.47 m2); tail rotor disc area 83.86 sq ft (7.79 m2)

Fuselage and tail: length overall, rotors turning 73 ft 0 in (22.25 m) and fuselage 57 ft 3 in (17.45 m); height overall 18 ft 1in (5.51 m) and to top of rotor head 16 ft 1 in (4.90 m); wheel track 13 ft

4 in (4.06 m); wheel base 17 ft 1 in (5.21 m)

Powerplant: two General Electric T58-GE-100 each rated at 1,500 shp (1118 kW)

The AS-61 is a licence-built version of the Sea King, principally produced for the Italian navy's ASW force. This Exocet-armed example flies with Brazil. A derivative was produced without ASW equipment for the utility transport role.

Weights: empty 13,250 lb (6010 kg); normal take-off 21,240 lb (9634 kg); maximum take-off 22,050 lb (10002 kg)
Fuel and load: internal fuel 1,116 US gal (4225 litres); external fuel none; maximum payload 8,000 lb (3629 kg)

Speed: maximum level speed at sea level 141 kt (162 mph; 261 km/h); maximum cruising speed at sea level 130 kt (150 mph; 241 km/h); economical cruising speed at sea level 75 kt (86 mph; 139 km/h) for maximum endurance
Range: range 770 nm (886 miles; 1427 km); radius 50 nm (57 miles; 92 km) on a SAR mission with a 5-hour loiter, or 240 nm (276 miles; 445 km) on a utility mission to collect 24 fully equipped troops; endurance 8 hours 0 minutes
Performance: maximum rate of climb at sea level 1,340 ft (408 m) per minute; service ceiling 11,100 ft (3385 m); hovering ceiling 7,200 ft (2195 m) in ground effect

AIDC **AT-3 Tsu Chiang**

Known to the Republic of China air force as the **Tsu Chiang**, the **AIDC AT-3** tandem two-seat basic trainer provides the initial 120-hour jet course at the service's academy at Kang Shan, Taiwan. The first military jet aircraft developed on Taiwan to achieve series production, the AT-3 was initiated in 1975 by the Aero Industry Development Centre (AIDC), and the first of two (**XAT-3**) prototypes entered flight test on 16 September 1980. Contracts were subsequently placed on behalf of the RoCAF for 60 production aircraft, the first of which was flown on 6 February 1984, with the last being delivered by early 1990.

The AT-3 is of conventional construction, the one-piece carry-through wing being a multi-spar light alloy structure with heavy-plate machined skinning and the fuselage being a light alloy semi-monocoque. The crew is accommodated in zero-zero ejection seats under individual manually-operated canopies, all fuel is carried in two rubber-impregnated nylon bladder fuselage tanks, and provision is made for an aerial target system to be carried on the fuselage centre-line and on outboard wing pylons.

In the late 1980s, Smiths Industries was appointed prime contractor for a programme to convert 20 AT-3 trainers for the close air support role, trials with two prototype conversions commencing in 1989. The basic training version was retrospectively designated **AT-3A**, and the converted close air support variant became the **AT-3B**. The conversion included installation of a Westinghouse AN/APG-66 radar and fire control system, and the AT-3B has a manually-adjustable gunsight and a camera in the forward cockpit. A weapons bay beneath the rear cockpit can accommodate a variety of stores, including quick-change, semi-recessed machine-gun packs. A centreline pylon is stressed for a 2,000-lb (907-kg) ordnance load, two inboard wing pylons are each stressed for a 1,400-lb (635-kg) load, and the two outboard pylons are each stressed for 600 lb (272 kg). In addition, wingtip launch rails can be fitted for AAMs. The maximum external stores load of the AT-3B is 6,000 lb (2721 kg). This type equips one RoCAF unit, No. 71 Squadron of the 443rd TFW at Tainan.

An attack version designated **A-3 Lui Meng** was developed in the late 1980s, featuring similar armament to the AT-3B, but with a single-seat cockpit. Two prototypes were built, but development was probably halted in favour of the AT-3B.

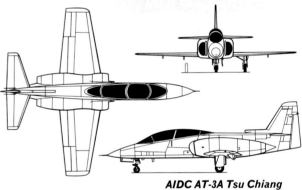

SPECIFICATION

AIDC AT-3B Tsu Chiang
Wing: span 10.46 m (34 ft 3.75 in); aspect ratio 5.0; area 21.93 m² (236.06 sq ft)
Fuselage and tail: length 12.90 m (42 ft 4 in) including probe; height 4.36 m (14 ft 3.75 in); tailplane span 4.83 m (15 ft 10.25 in); wheel track 3.96 m (13 ft 0 in); wheel base 5.49 m (18 ft 0 in)
Powerplant: two Garrett TFE731-2-2L each rated at 3,500 lb st (15.57 kN) dry

Above: The AT-3 represents a considerable achievement for the Taiwanese aerospace industry, developing its own advanced trainer. The standard AT-3A serves with the air force academy at Kangshan, also equipping the display team.

AIDC AT-3A Tsu Chiang

Weights: empty equipped 8,500 lb (3856 kg); normal take-off 11,500 lb (5216 kg); maximum take-off 17,500 lb (7938 kg)
Fuel and load: internal fuel 2,800 lb (1270 kg); external fuel up to 1,950 lb (884 kg) in two 150-US gal (568-litre) drop tanks; maximum ordnance 6,000 lb (2722 kg)
Speed: maximum level speed 'clean' at 36,000 ft (10975 m) 488 kt (462 mph; 904 km/h) and at sea level 485 kt (558 mph; 898 km/h); cruising speed at 36,000 ft (10975 m) 476 kt (548 mph; 882 km/h)
Range: 1,230 nm (1,416 miles; 2279 km) with standard fuel; endurance 3 hours 12 minutes
Performance: maximum rate of climb at sea level 10,100 ft (3078 m) per minute; service ceiling 48,000 ft (14625 m); take-off run 1,500 ft (458 m) at maximum take-off weight; take-off distance to 50 ft (15 m) 2,200 ft (671 m) at maximum take-off weight; landing distance from 50 ft (15 m) 3,100 ft (945 m) at normal landing weight; landing run 2,200 ft (671 m) at normal landing weight

Left: Camouflaged Tsu Chiangs undertake weapons training for the ROCAF. The similar AT-3B has a sophisticated weapons system for light strike duties, including internal weapons bay for the carriage of gun packs, underwing pylons and APG-66 radar. These potent aircraft serve with No. 71 Squadron.

AIDC T-CH-1 Chung Tsing

Possessing a close resemblance to the North American T-28, the **AIDC T-CH-1** tandem two-seat basic trainer was developed in the early 1970s by the AIDC at Taichung, Taiwan, to meet a Republic of China air force requirement. The first military aircraft of indigenous Taiwanese design to achieve production status, the T-CH-1 prototype was first flown on 23 November 1973. The production of 50 T-CH-1s was begun in 1976, with deliveries being concluded in 1981.

Powered by a 1,450-shp (1082-kW) Textron Lycoming T53-L-701 turboprop licence-manufactured in Taiwan, the T-CH-1 entered service at the RoCAF academy at Kang Shan in 1977, remaining standard basic training equipment until the introduction of a new flying training syllabus in which part of the spectrum covered by the T-CH-1 was taken over by the Beech T-34C and the remainder by the AT-3.

Progressively phased out of academy service from 1985, the T-CH-1 was adapted for the weapons training task, equipping No. 72 Squadron of the 1st Tactical Fighter Wing based at Tainan where some 20 examples now remain as **A-CH-1**s. Although the T-CH-1 was not fitted with armament during its service at the academy, all aircraft of this type had been built with wing hardpoints and their adaptation to A-CH-1 weapons trainer standard was thus facilitated. A few, designated **R-CH-1**, have a reconnaissance camera fitted in the lower fuselage.

Fuselage and tail: length 10.26 m (33 ft 8 in); height 3.66 m (12 ft 0 in); tailplane span 5.56 m (18 ft 3 in); wheel track 3.86 m (12 ft 8 in); wheel base 2.39 m (7 ft 10 in)
Powerplant: one Textron Lycoming T53-L-701 rated at 1,450 ehp (1081 kW)
Weights: empty equipped 5,750 lb (2608 kg); normal take-off 7,500 lb (3402 kg); maximum take-off 11,150 lb (5057 kg)
Fuel and load: internal fuel 255 US gal (963 litres); external fuel none
Speed: never-exceed speed 370 kt (426 mph; 685 km/h); maximum level speed 'clean' at 15,000 ft (4570 m) 320 kt (368 mph; 592 km/h); maximum cruising speed at 15,000 ft (4570 m) 220 kt (253 mph; 407 km/h); economical cruising speed at 15,000 ft (4570 m) 170 kt (196 mph; 315 km/h)
Range: 1,085 nm (1,249 miles; 2010 km)
Performance: maximum rate of climb at sea level 3,400 ft (1036 m) per minute; service ceiling 32,000 ft (9755 m); take-off run 480 ft (146 m) at 7,600 lb (3477 kg); take-off distance to 50 ft (15 m) 800 ft (244 m) at 7,600 lb (3477 kg); landing distance from 50 ft (15 m) 1,250 ft (381 m) at normal landing weight; landing run 600 ft (183 m)

SPECIFICATION

AIDC T-CH-1 Chung Tsing
Wing: span 12.19 m (40 ft 0 in); aspect ratio 6.0; area 25.18 m² (271.00 sq ft)

The T-CH-1 is notable as Taiwan's first indigenous military aircraft. Although replaced in the training role, a handful still fly coastal patrol work.

Wearing tactical camouflage, this is an R-CH-1, featuring a camera.

AIDC Ching-Kuo

Taiwan's ambitious programme to develop an advanced fighter to replace its fleet of F-5s and F-104s began in 1982, after the US government placed an embargo on the sale of the Northrop F-20 and any comparable fighter. The same restrictions were not placed on technical assistance, however, and US aerospace companies have collaborated closely with AIDC to develop an indigenous fighter and weapons system. The overall programme, codenamed An Hsiang (Safe Flight), has been managed through four subsidiary programmes for airframe, engines, avionics and armament systems.

The airframe (which bears a passing resemblance to an F-16/F/A-18 hybrid) was developed with assistance from General Dynamics in the Ying Yang (Soaring Eagle) programme and has a design fatigue life of 8,000 flying hours. The prototypes and first 160 production aircraft were to be powered by two Allied-Signal/Garrett TFE-1042-70 (F125) turbofans. These are afterburning versions of the Garrett TFE73, developed under the Yun Han (Cloud Man) programme. These develop 4,820 lb st dry and 8,340 lb st with afterburning (21.44 and 37.09 kN). More powerful versions of the F125 or General Electric J101 were considered for later aircraft. Avionics have been developed by a team led by Smiths Industries under a programme codenamed Tien Lei (Sky Thunder), and the primary missile armament has been developed in the Tien Chien (Sky Sword) programme. The aircraft is equipped with a new Golden Dragon GD-53 multi-mode pulse-Doppler radar based on the GE AN/APG-67 (V) developed for the F-20 but incorporating some technology from the Westinghouse AN/APG-66 (used by the F-16A). The aircraft also has a Honeywell H423 inertial navigation system, and Bendix/King multi-function and head-up displays.

Of conventional all-metal construction (although a progressively increasing proportion of composites will be introduced on production aircraft), the **Ching-Kuo** is of conventional configuration, albeit with wing/fuselage blending. Elliptical intakes are located below long LERXes for good high-Alpha performance. The pilot sits on a Martin-Baker Mk 12 ejection seat, under a blown canopy, and behind a single-piece windscreen. The pressurised cockpit is fitted with a sidestick controller, *à la* F-16, a wide-angle HUD, and three multi-function look-down displays. The aircraft has an internal 20-mm M61A1 cannon beneath the port LERX, and has two underfuselage and two underwing hardpoints, in addition to its wingtip missile launch rails. These will carry a variety of indigenous missiles, including the IR-homing Sky Sword I, the longer-range SARH Sky Sword II (two in tandem recesses under the fuselage only) or three Hsiung Feng II (Male Bee II) anti-ship missiles.

First flight

The first of three single-seat prototypes, 77-8001, made its maiden flight on 28 May 1989, but was seriously damaged in a take-off accident on 29 October. The second prototype (78-8002) flew on 27 September 1989 but was lost in a fatal crash caused by vibration during transonic acceleration on 12 July 1990. The third prototype (78-8003), with modified engine intakes, made its maiden flight on 10 January 1990, and was followed by the fourth prototype, the first two-seater (79-8004), on 10 July 1990.

There was originally a requirement for 256 aircraft, some of which would be two-

The fourth prototype Ching-Kuo was the first of the two-seaters, and was finished in the tactical camouflage adopted by operational aircraft. General Dynamics assisted with the design.

SKY SWORD II MISSILE

Although not carried on this aircraft, the Sky Sword II is a weapon developed for the Ching-Kuo. Carried in a tandem pair in recessed bays beneath the fuselage, the Sky Sword II is a semi-active radar homing missile similar to the AIM-7 Sparrow. However, the wing and fin planform is considerably different, with both sets of surfaces being heavily cropped, perhaps to fit the confines of the Ching-Kuo airframe. As with the Sky Sword I, the present status is unclear, as Taiwan has ordered both MICA and AIM-7 missiles from France and the United States.

SKY SWORD I MISSILE

Resembling an AIM-9 Sidewinder, the Tien Chien (Sky Sword) I missile is a closely-related infra-red-guided air-to-air missile carried on the wingtip launch rails of the Ching-Kuo, or from outboard wing pylons. Few details are available as to the differences between it and the AIM-9, and it is likely that the missile has all-aspect capability and active laser fusing. The first test firing was in April 1986 from an F-5, with production starting in 1989. The status of the programme is unclear, as Taiwan has ordered both Magic 2 and AIM-9s as part of its Mirage 2000-5 and F-16 buys.

seat trainers, and some of which could be configured for anti-shipping duties. The sum of $10 billion has been allocated to the programme, and unit cost of a bare flyaway aircraft is estimated at $30 million. The aircraft is named after a former President of Taiwan, Chiang Ching-Kuo.

The first of 10 pre-production aircraft was rolled out on 9 March 1992, and this introduced new enlarged engine intakes, a small ventral fin and tubular RWR fairings on the LERXes. Deliveries to the air force began earlier than the expected date of January 1994. On 10 February 1993 the first 'Seed' squadron publicly unveiled its aircraft at Chin Chuan Kang air base, which included two production single-seaters (81-8007 and 81-8008) and two production two-seaters (81-8006 and 81-8010). Also present and apparently on charge were the rebuilt first prototype and the fourth prototype. In March 1993 the country's legislature announced that procurement would be limited to only 130 aircraft, to equip two, instead of the planned four, wings.

WEAPON OPTIONS

In addition to the internal M61A1 20-mm Vulcan cannon, weapons identified with the Ching-Kuo include the GBU-12 227-kg (500-lb LGB), the CBU-87 Rockeye, the AGM-65B TV Maverick ASM, the AIM-9P Sidewinder IR-homing AAM and the indigenous Sky Sword I and Sky Sword II AAMs. The Sky Sword I closely resembles an AIM-9B or AIM-9D (though with wider span tailfins), while the Sky Sword II is similar to the AIM-7 Sparrow in appearance. For the anti-shipping role, the Ching-Kuo will be armed with three indigenous Hsiung Feng II sea-skimming anti-ship missiles. One of the two-seaters has been noted with an extra pair of underwing pylons accommodating a pair of F-5E-style 1040-litre (275-US gal) external fuel tanks.

SPECIFICATION

AIDC Ching-Kuo
Wing: (estimated) span over wingtip missile rails 8.53 m (28 ft 0 in)
Fuselage and tail: (estimated) length including probe 14.48 m (47 ft 6 in)
Powerplant: two ITEC (Garrett/AIDC) TFE1042-70 (F125) each rated at 6,025 lb st (26.80 kN) dry and 9,460 lb st (42.08 kN) with afterburning
Weights: normal take-off 9072 kg (20,000 lb)
Fuel and load: (estimated) internal fuel 1950 kg (4,300 lb)
Speed: maximum level speed 'clean' at 36,000 ft (10975 m) more than 688 kt (792 mph; 1275 km/h)
Performance: maximum rate of climb at sea level 50,000 ft (15240 m) per minute; service ceiling 55,000 ft (16760 m)
g limits: +6.5

AIDC Ching-Kuo

Despite considerable technical problems which have affected the programme, Taiwan's single-minded determination to produce an indigenous fighter has borne fruit, with the Ching-Kuo entering service in 1993. With Western arms embargoes being lifted, the need for large numbers has been reduced (Taiwan purchasing F-16s and Mirage 2000s), but the programme still stands at a respectable 130 airframes.

ANTI-SHIP MISSILE

For the anti-ship role the Ching-Kuo will carry three Hsiung Feng (Male Bee) II missiles, one under the centreline and one under each inboard wing pylon. The missile is reported to have been developed from the Israeli Gabriel, although the AGM-84 Harpoon may be the basis. It is similar in configuration to the AGM-84, with a small turbofan engine providing a range in the order of 50 miles (80 km).

SYSTEMS

Internal fuel capacity is 2517 litres (665 US gal). The undercarriage is by Menasco, and the ECS by AiResearch. Honeywell supplied the INS, and Bendix/King the two head-down and one head-up displays.

CONTROLS

The Lear Astronics fly-by-wire system controls large all-moving tailerons, rudder and near full-span flaperons. Leading-edge slats are also tied to the system for maximum combat agility.

ATTACK WEAPONRY

This two-seater is shown carrying the AGM-65 Maverick, used for precision attack of hardened targets. The main use of this missile is in the anti-armour role. A wide variety of bombs and cluster bombs can be carried.

EJECTION SEAT

The Ching-Kuo crew sit on Martin-Baker Mk 12 zero-zero ejection seats.

RADAR

The radar is a modified APG-67 known as the Golden Dragon 53. It has a range of 150 km (93 miles) and can operate in both air and sea search modes.

POWERPLANT

The Ching-Kuo features two ITEC (Garrett/AIDC) TFE1042-70 turbofans, equipped with full-authority digital controls. Plans for an improved performance engine were cancelled.

Airbus Industrie A310

Airbus Industrie
1 Rond Point Maurice Bellonte
F-31707 Blagnac Cedex, France

The **Airbus A310** short/medium-haul commercial transport was flown as a prototype for the first time on 3 April 1982. The first military order was placed early in 1990, comprising one aircraft for delivery to the **Royal Thai air force** in September 1991 for governmental transportation tasks. In the following year, the German **Luftwaffe** began to take delivery of three A310s originally flown by the defunct East German Interflug airline. Fitted with military communications equipment, these supplemented Boeing 707-320Cs operated by the special air missions squadron (FBS) at Köln/Bonn for VIP transportation and other support tasks. Similarly, the **Canadian Forces** adopted the A310 as a replacement for its five elderly Boeing 707s (CC-137s) used by No. 437 Sqn, with the purchase of three used A310s (designated **CC-150 Polaris**) from Canadian Airlines International in 1992/93 and an option on two more for 1993/94. One of the CC-150s was fitted with VIP interior, and was sold as part of a cost-cutting drive. The others may be subject to a tanker conversion. In 1992, France's **Armée de l'Air** became a customer for two used A310s, to replace DC-8s operated by ET 3/60 'Esterel'.

SPECIFICATION

Wing: span 144 ft 0 in (43.89 m); aspect ratio 8.8; area 2,357.30 sq ft (218.99 m²)
Fuselage and tail: length 153 ft 1 in (46.66 m);
height 51 ft 10 in (15.80 m); tailplane span 53 ft 4.25 in (16.26 m); wheel track 31 ft 6 in (9.60 m); wheel base 49 ft 10.75 in (15.21 m)
Powerplant: two General Electric CF6-80C2A2 each rated at 53,500 lb (237.98 kN) dry thrust or Pratt & Whitney PW4152 each rated at 52,000 lb (231.31 kN)

The Thais were the first to put the A310 into military colours, one being employed on VIP transport. France and Canada have followed since.

dry thrust
Weights: manufacturer's empty 158,380 lb (71840 kg) with CF6 engines or 158,250 lb (71781 kg) with PW4152 engines; operating empty 176,859 lb (80222 kg) with CF6 engines or 176,753 lb (80174 kg) with PW4152 engines; maximum take-off 337,305 lb (153000 kg) with options at 346,125 lb (157000 kg) and 361,560 lb (164,000 kg)
Fuel and load: internal fuel 108,112 lb (49039 lb); external fuel none; maximum payload 74,472 lb (33780 kg) with CF6 engines or 74,582 lb (33,830 kg) with PW4152 engines
Speed: maximum cruising speed between 31,000 and 41,000 ft (9450 and 12500 m) Mach 0.8
Range: range with 218 passengers 4,420 nm (5,090 miles; 8191 km) with CF6 engines or 4,400 nm (5,065 miles; 8155 km) with PW4152 engines
Performance: take-off field length 7,900 ft (2408 m) at maximum take-off weight with CF6 engines or 7,300 ft (2225 m) at maximum take-off weight with PW4152 engines; landing field length 4,850 ft (1479 m) at maximum landing weight with CF6 engines or 5,100 ft (1555 m) at maximum take-off weight with PW4152 engines

Airtech (CASA/IPTN) CN.235

Following on from the success of the Model 212 Aviocar, CASA joined forces with IPTN (Industri Pesawat Terbang Nusantara) on a 50/50 basis to begin development of a larger, more efficient transport for both civil and military use, under the joint company Airtech. Development work began on the **CN.235** in 1980, and prototypes were simultaneously constructed in both countries. Spain's ECT-100 flew first on 11 November 1983, followed by PK-XNC in Indonesia on 30 December. IPTN delivered its first aircraft on 15 December 1986, and CASA followed on 4 February 1987. A licence-assembly agreement has been reached with TAI of Turkey, which may lead to full Turkish production.

The standard military transport **CN.235M** is tailored to short-range cargo/trooping missions, exhibiting the accepted layout of high-set wing, circular-section pressurised fuselage, upswept rear fuselage with rear loading ramp, tall fin and main undercarriage in sponsons on the side of the fuselage. The wing incorporates powerful high-lift devices for STOL operation, and the undercarriage is designed for operation from semi-prepared surfaces. Power initially came from the General Electric CT7-7A turboprops, fitted to the first 30 **CN.235 Series 10** aircraft, but is now provided by the CT7-9C engine in the current **Series 100** production machines, each powerplant being rated at 1,750 shp (1305 kW) for take-off with an emergency reserve.

Typically a crew consists of pilot, co-pilot and a loadmaster, and standard accommo-

Morocco operates six CN.235Ms on general transport duties, and a single example on VIP work. The type has achieved excellent military sales.

dation is provided for 48 troops or 46 paratroops. A roller cargo system can be installed and other options include electronic warfare equipment, 24 litters and four attendants in the medevac role or maritime patrol. For the latter role Airtech has developed the **CN.235MPA Persuader**, which features a lengthened nose housing search radar (APS-504), forward-looking infra-red and electronic surveillance equipment. Six underwing hardpoints are provided for the carriage of torpedoes or Exocet anti-ship missiles.

SPECIFICATION

Airtech (CASA/IPTN) CN.235M Series 100
Wing: span 25.81 m (84 ft 8 in); aspect ratio 11.3; area 59.10 m² (636.17 sq ft)
Fuselage and tail: length 21.353 m (70 ft 0.75 in); height 8.177 m (26 ft 10 in); tailplane span 11.00 m (36 ft 1 in); wheel track 3.90 m (12 ft 9.5 in); wheel base 6.919 m (22 ft 8.5 in)
Powerplant: two General Electric CT7-9C each flat-rated at 1,750 shp (1305 kW) without automatic power reserve or 1,870 shp (1394.5 kW) with automatic power reserve
Weights: operating empty 8800 kg (19,400 lb); maximum take-off 16500 kg (36,376 lb)
Fuel and load: internal fuel 4230 kg (9,325 lb); external fuel none; maximum payload 5000 kg

(11,023 lb) or maximum ordnance 3500 kg (7,716 lb)
Speed: maximum level speed 'clean' at sea level 240 kt (276 mph; 445 km/h); maximum cruising speed at 15,000 ft (4570 m) 248 kt (286 mph; 460 km/h)
Range: range 2,350 nm (2,706 miles; 4355 km) with a 3600-kg (7,936-lb) payload or 810 nm (932 miles; 1501 km) with maximum payload
Performance: maximum rate of climb at sea level 1,900 ft (579 m) per minute; service ceiling 26,600 ft (8110 m); take-off distance to 50 ft (15 m) 4,235 ft (1290 m) at maximum take-off weight; landing distance from 50 ft (15 m) 2,530 ft (772 m) at normal landing weight; landing run 1,306 ft (398 m) at normal landing weight

The CN.235 is useful for both passenger and cargo transport. This example wears French colours and the markings of EET 6/330, based at Mont-de-Marsan.

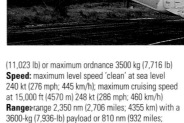

OPERATORS

Military sales have been brisk, to Botswana (two), Brunei (three MPAs), Chile (three for use on wheel/ski undercarriage), Ecuador (two), France (eight), Gabon (one), Indonesia (32 and six MPAs), Ireland (one M and two MPAs), Malaysia (32), Morocco (six transports and one VIP), Panama (one), Papua New Guinea (two), Saudi Arabia (two transports and two VIP), South Korea (12) Spain (18 transports, two VIP and six MPAs), Turkey (52, including 50 assembled by TAI) and United Arab Emirates (seven).

Alenia (Aeritalia/Lockheed) F-104ASA

Alenia
Via E. Petrolini 2
I-00197 Roma, Italy

Following the completion in March 1979 of the 246th and last of the GE J79-J1Q-engined **Lockheed F-104S Starfighter** interceptors developed and built under licence by Aeritalia, including 40 for the **Turkish air force**, an upgrade programme was launched in 1981 for 153 of 206 originally delivered to **Italy**'s AMI. These then equipped some six air defence squadrons (9°, 10°, 12°, 18°, 21°, 23° Gruppi), plus the OCU (20° Gruppo), and

one strike squadron (102° Gruppo). With Aeritalia (amalgamated with Selenia in late 1990 as the Alenia group) as prime contractor, the AMI's ASA (Aggiornamento Sistema d'Arma, or armament system modernisation) programme was planned to upgrade the low-level interception capabilities of the F-104S, as well as improving its air-to-ground performance.

Main changes, costing in all some $528 million, included replacement of the original

NASARR R21G/H fire-control radar by the FIAR R21G/M1 Setter non-coherent Doppler version with automatic frequency changing and improved detection and illumination capability over ranges of up to about 22 nm (25 miles; 40 km). The addition of a moving target indicator to the original R21G, in conjunction with a new processor and the introduction of the Selenia Aspide Mk 1A semi-active monopulse radar-guided development of its original AIM-7E Sparrow AAM, con-

fers look-down/shoot-down capability over a maximum range of around 19 nm (22 miles; 35 km).

Unlike the F-104S, the associated on-board guidance equipment for the Aspide was miniaturised so that the gun bay of the **F-104ASA** can again fulfil its function of housing the 20-mm T171E3 six-barrelled Vulcan rotary cannon of the F-104G. For ground-attack roles, the F-104ASA is equipped with AN/ALQ-70 or AN/ALQ-73

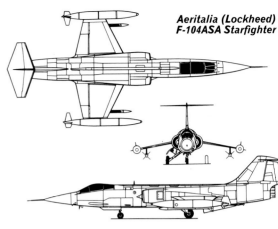

Aeritalia (Lockheed) F-104ASA Starfighter

Left: An operational F-104ASA in the markings of 36° Stormo. The ASA has an internal cannon.

ECM systems. New avionics also included more generator power, a four-digit NATO IFF, a new altitude reporting system and an improved weapons computer, plus provision for the all-aspect AIM-9L Sidewinder AAM in place of the original rear-attack only AIM-9B. The F-104ASA also features an

A development F-104ASA carries a Selenia Aspide air-to-air missile for a test launch. The Aspide is an Italian development of the AIM-7E Sparrow.

improved computer for the automatic low-speed pitch control system, which limits excessive angles of attack.

ASA enters service

After flight testing, which started in July 1983, the first 'production' F-104ASA was accepted on 19 November 1986 at Turin-Caselle by Cdte Canetto from the AMI's Reparto Sperimentale Volo (RSV, flight test centre) at Pratica di Mare. The 100th example had been completed by early 1990 and the 147th and last was redelivered in late

1991. Under economies planned for the AMI at that time as part of defence budget cuts following the collapse of Communism in the Eastern Bloc were disbandment of two of the remaining seven F-104ASA squadrons, leaving five in operation, plus the OCU, with 130 Starfighters on establishment (plus reserves), pending their eventual replacement by a similar number of European Fighter Aircraft early in the next century. Studies were made for further F-104S/ASA improvements through a proposed Operational Capacity Extension (ECO) programme, including a completely new radar, a head-up display and an air-refuelling probe, to extend Italian Starfighter service lives beyond the originally-planned 2005, in the event of delays to the EFA programme. The most basic service life extension, put forward by the Italian Defence Minister in late 1992, would necessitate fitting a new INS, a partial rewiring and the provision of new wings to 99 of the surviving 143 F-104ASAs to allow their continued operation until their planned replacement, for an overall cost, including operation, of some $135 million. Considerable political opposition has been expressed to these proposals, although $40 million was included in the 1993 defence budget for further F-104ASA upgrades. Such plans may now have been abandoned. RAF Tornados have been leased as interim air defence aircraft pending delivery of the Eurofighter EFA 2000,

SPECIFICATION

Alenia (Aeritalia) F-104ASA

Wing: span 21 ft 11 in (6.68 m) without tip tanks; aspect ratio 2.45; area 196.10 sq ft (18.22 m²)
Fuselage and tail: length 54 ft 9 in (16.69 m); height 13 ft 6 in (4.11 m); tailplane span 11 ft 11 in (3.63 m); wheel track 9 ft 8 in (2.74 m); wheel base 15 ft 0.5 in (4.59 m)
Powerplant: one General Electric J79-GE-19 rated at 11,870 lb st (52.80 kN) dry and 17.900 lb st (79.62 kN) with afterburning
Weights: empty 6760 kg (14,903 lb); normal take-off 9840 kg (21,693 lb); maximum take-off 14060 kg (30,996 lb)
Fuel and load: internal fuel 3392 litres (896 US gal); external fuel up to 2770 litres (732 US gal) in two 740-litre (195-US gal) drop tanks and two 645-litre (170-US gal) tip tanks; maximum ordnance 3400 kg (7,495 lb)
Speed: never-exceed and maximum level speed 'clean' at 36,000 ft (10975 m) 1,259 kt (1,450 mph; 2333 km/h), and at sea level 790 kt (910 mph; 1464 km/h); maximum cruising speed at 36,000 ft (10975 m) 530 kt (610 mph; 981 km/h)
Range: ferry range 2920 km (1,576 nm; 1,814 miles) with drop tanks; combat radius 1247 km (673 nm; 775 miles) with maximum fuel
Performance: maximum rate of climb at sea level 55,000 ft (16764 m) per minute; climb to 35,000 ft (10670 m) in 1 minute 20 seconds; service ceiling 58,000 ft (17680 m); take-off run 2,700 ft (823 m) at normal take-off weight with two AIM-7 Sparrow AAMs; landing run 2,500 ft (762 m)

Alenia (Aeritalia/Fiat) G222

The **Aeritalia Fiat G222** proposal was drawn up to meet the outlines of NATO's Basic Military Requirement Four (NBMR4) of 1962, which sought to develop a practical V/STOL transport for service with NATO air forces. Although a number of

advanced proposals came from several manufacturers, none was deemed sufficiently practical or attractive to gain even a prototype contract. However, the Aeronautica Militare Italiana believed that Fiat's proposal could prove a useful transport, if

finalised as a more conventional design in terms of powerplant and aerodynamics, and in 1968 signed a contract for two **G222TCM** prototypes and a static test airframe. Their manufacture was delayed by two successive total redesigns, and it was not until 18 July 1970 that the first prototype (MM582) was flown, the second (MM583) following on 22 July 1971. These began operational evaluation with the AMI on 21 December 1971, highly successful tests resulting in a contract for 44 production G222s, the first of them flown on 23 December 1975.

Italian production

From the outset other major Italian manufacturers were involved in the programme,

with Aermacchi responsible for the outer wings, CIRSEA for the landing gear, Piaggio for the wing centre-section, SIAI-Marchetti for the tail unit, and Aeritalia for the fuselage and for final assembly and testing. The G222 continues in production and has been built in several versions. These include the G222 standard military transport which serves with the armed forces of **Argentina, Dubai, Italy, Nigeria, Somalia** and **Venezuela**; the **G222R/M** (Radio Misure) for radio/radar calibration; the **G222SAA** (Sistema Aeronautico Antincendio) fire-fighter with equipment to disperse water or fire retardants; the **G222T** (Rolls-Royce Tyne-powered version) for the **Libyan Arab air force** which designates it **G222L**; and the electronic warfare

Chrysler/Alenia C-27A Spartan

A few of the AMI's G222s are assigned to special duties. This is a G222RM of the 8° Gruppo at Pratica di Mare, equipped for radio and navigation aid calibration. Other versions fly firefighting (G222SAA) and Elint missions.

G222VS (Versione Speciale). **Thailand** has six transports on order.

In August 1990, the **USAF** selected the Alenia (which took over Aeritalia) G222 as its RRITA (Rapid-Response Intra-Theater Airlifter) following extensive evaluation. The aircraft, designated **C-27A Spartan**, are procured from Alenia by Chrysler, the prime US contractor, and modified for USAF operations by installation of mission-specific communications, navigations and mission systems. An initial order for five aircraft led to a fleet of 10 C-27As, stationed at Howard AFB, Panama, to support US Southern Command operations in Latin America. Total deliveries of all versions, including the C-27A, stands at 100 in early 1994.

SPECIFICATION

Alenia (Aeritalia/Fiat) G222
Wing: span 28.70 m (94 ft 2 in); aspect ratio 10.05; area 82.00 m² (882.67 sq ft)
Fuselage and tail: length 22.70 m (74 ft 5.5 in); height 9.80 m (32 ft 1.75 in); tailplane span 12.40 m (40 ft 8.25 in); wheel track 3.668 m (12 ft 0.5 in); wheel base 6.23 m (20 ft 5.25 in)
Powerplant: two Fiat-built General Electric T64-GE-P4D each flat-rated at 3,400 shp (2535 kW)
Weights: empty equipped 15400 kg (33,951 lb); operating empty 15700 kg (34,612 lb); maximum take-off 28000 kg (61,728 lb)
Fuel and load: internal fuel 9400 kg (20,723 lb); external fuel none; maximum payload 9000 kg (19,841 lb)
Speed: maximum level speed 'clean' at 4575 m (15,010 ft) 292 kt (336 mph; 540 km/h); economical cruising speed at 6000 m (19,685 ft) 237 kt (273 mph; 439 km/h)

Range: ferry range 2,500 nm (2,879 miles; 4633 km); range 740 nm (852 miles; 1371 km) with maximum payload or 1,350 nm (1,555 miles; 2502 km) with 36 litters and four attendants
Performance: maximum rate of climb at sea level 520 m (1,706 ft) per minute; climb to 4500 m (14,765 ft) in 8 minutes 35 seconds; service ceiling 7620 m (25,000 ft); take-off run 662 m (2,172 ft) at maximum take-off weight; take-off distance to 15 m (50 ft) 1000 m (3,281 ft) at maximum take-off weight; landing distance from 15 m (50 ft) 775 m (2,543 ft) at maximum landing weight; landing run 545 m (1,788 ft)

The Chrysler C-27 is a G222 fitted out in the US for service with the 24th Wing. It provides theatre transport for Southern Command, being able to land at most Central and South American airfields.

American Aircraft Corporation **Penetrator**

Late in 1991, AAC unveiled a prototype of its modified Bell UH-1D Iroquois, adapted for the assault and transport roles and named **Penetrator**. This prototype retains the 1,150-shp (858-kW) Avco Lycoming T53-L-13 turboshaft, transmission and rotor system of the UH-1. The Penetrator has a new all-composite fuselage with tandem seating for the pilot (front) and gunner, the latter controlling a 20-mm cannon, two machine-guns, two forward-firing 37-mm rocket pods and up to eight missiles. Only the missiles and some rocket launchers are carried externally on stub wings, other weaponry being mounted internally. Two pintle-mounted machine-guns are carried in the cabin, which accommodates up to 10 troops, and any production-model Penetrators will have retractable landing gear in place of the prototype's UH-1-style skids.

The Penetrator is based on the proven power/dynamic system of the Bell UH-1.

AMX International **AMX**

AMX development, started formally in April 1978 when Aeritalia and Aermacchi combined their resources to meet AMI requirements for an advanced multi-purpose strike/reconnaissance aircraft, received extra impetus in 1980 when Brazil joined the programme. A common specification, including good short-field performance, high subsonic operating speeds and advanced nav/attack systems, allowed initial agreement in July 1981 for the joint procurement of 266 aircraft. These comprised 79 AMXs for Brazil and 187 for Italy, plus six prototypes, from Aeritalia, Aermacchi and EMBRAER production lines (with relative programme shares of 46.5, 23.8 and 29.7 per cent), as well as licensed-construction of the AMX's 11,030-lb (49.07-kN) thrust Rolls-Royce Spey Mk 807 turbofan. An extra development AMX (A11) later flew (from April 1991) with a Spey 807A uprated to 13,500 lb (60.05 kN) for take-off, while Rolls-Royce has offered the new RB.168-821 Spey with a demonstrated 30 per cent bench-test thrust increase over the Mk 807.

AMX-A01 (MMX594) first flew at Aeritalia's Turin-Caselle factory flight-test centre in May 1984, the first of two Brazil-assembled prototypes (A04/YA-1-4200 and A06) following in October 1985 at São dos Cam-

The first Italian aircraft served with the RSV, the AMI's test and trials unit at Pratica di Mare.

AMX International AMX

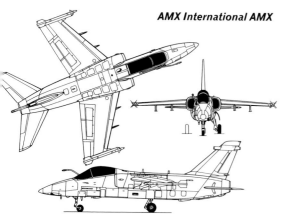

The AMX-T has few airframe changes compared to the single-seater. The second cockpit occupies the space vacated by the forward fuel tank, and combat capability remains the same, albeit with reduced range. The AMX-T is proposed as the basis for an electronic warfare/reconnaissance variant armed with anti-radiation missiles.

pos. Although the first Italian prototype crashed fatally on only its fifth take-off after an engine problem on 1 June 1984, development was concluded by four more prototypes in Italy and in Brazil.

Design features include HOTAS, Litton Italia INS, head-up and head-down digital data displays, digital databus, active and passive ECM, and provision for air refuelling. By mid-1989, programme totals had increased to 317 aircraft, with the addition of 51 two-seat **AMX-T**s to replace the Fiat G91Ts of the AMI's 201°/204° Gruppi of the advanced training wing at Amendola within the 60ª Brigata Aerea (redesignated the 32° Stormo at the same base in September 1992). Retaining the same dimensions and full combat capabilities as the single-seat AMX, the trainer version replaces a fuel bay behind the original cockpit with a second Martin-Baker Mk 10L ejection seat, with some reduction in range. The first of three AMX-T prototypes (MM55024) initially flew in Italy on 14 March 1990, although funding problems delayed first flight of the Brazilian two-seat prototype (TA-1 5650) until 14 August 1991. Radar-equipped versions of the AMX-T are also under development in Brazil and Italy for enhanced all-weather, ECR and maritime strike roles, with SMA/Tecnasa's SCP-01 Scipio installation favoured for all AMXs in the former country and FIAR's Grifo-F possibly replacing some of AMX's standard Elta/FIAR range-only radar in the latter. Trials have been completed in Italy for this version with Aérospatiale's AM39 Exocet radar-guided anti-ship missile by Aermacchi's Grifo-equipped AMX-T prototype. Other radars, notably the Westinghouse APG-66, are also envisaged for the AMX.

In the reconnaissance role the AMX can either carry external photo or IR pods, or can be equipped with any one of three pallets developed by Aeroelectronica for internal carriage in the forward fuselage.

By April 1992, Alenia, Aermacchi and EMBRAER had delivered 60 of 136 AMXs then funded by the AMI to equip five attack/reconnaissance squadrons, plus 37 of the required 51 AMX-Ts and 13 of 56 AMXs ordered by the FAB. First operational squadron to receive the AMX, in 1989, was the AMI's 103° Gruppo of the 51° Stormo CB (fighter-bomber wing) at Treviso/Istrana in north-eastern Italy. They were followed by the 132° Gruppo CR/3° Stormo (reconnaissance squadron) at Villafranca, and the 14° Gruppo/2° Stormo, also at Istrana. If funding permits, other AMI units to re-equip with 187 AMXs will comprise 102° Gruppo/5° Stormo at Rimini, 28° Gruppo/3° Stormo at Villafranca, 101° Gruppo/8° Stormo at Cervia, and 13° Gruppo/32° Stormo at Brindisi.

In Brazil, the 1st Sqn of the 16th Aviation Group (1°/16° GAv) has been operating more than a dozen AMX (**A-1**) attack aircraft from Santa Cruz, Rio de Janeiro since the first operational example was delivered on 17 October 1989. Total Brazilian AMX procurement currently remains at 79, including 14 two-seat AMX-T (**TA-1**) operational trainers, to equip four or five attack squadrons. With each of the three integrated production lines now producing about one aircraft per month, AMX International is actively pursuing possible export sales. The planned purchase in late 1990 by the Royal Thai air force, as the first overseas customer, of 26 AMXs and 12 AMX-Ts costing some $590 million, plus over $150 million for spares and technical support, was cancelled in February 1992 through funding problems for the 10-year budget commitment involved.

AMX International AMX

The '51' nosecode and cat-and-mouse fin badge identify this aircraft as one of those delivered to the first operational AMX unit, the 103° Gruppo, 51° Stormo at Istrana. This squadron was previously equipped with the Aeritalia G91R and had been based at Treviso. The aircraft wears an overall grey colour scheme – unusual for a dedicated ground attack aircraft – and new-style roundels with reduced-conspicuity white ring. The aircraft is depicted carrying four low-drag general-purpose bombs on the inboard pylons and two ballute-retarded bombs on the outboard pylons. The centreline mounts a reconnaissance pod, and wingtip AIM-9L Sidewinders complete the fit.

UNDERCARRIAGE
The hydraulically retracted undercarriage is designed by Messier-Hispano-Bugatti, but is built in Italy by ERAM (main gear) and Magnaghi (nose gear). The mainwheels rotate through 90° during the retraction cycle to lie flat in the undersides of the air intakes.

The AMX is designated A-1 by the Brazilian air force. This aircraft, the first Brazilian production TA-1 two-seater, wears the 'SC' code for Santa Cruz air base and serves with 1° Esquadrão of 16° Grupo de Aviação.

WORK-SHARE

The AMX originated from an AMI requirement for a G91/F-104G replacement issued in 1977. Aermacchi was already working with EMBRAER on the similar A-X requirement to replace Brazil's AT-26 Xavantes, and began working with Aeritalia (now Alenia) on the Italian air force requirement. Alenia is the programme leader, with 46.7 per cent of the share, and responsible for fuselage centre section, radome, fin, rudder, elevators, spoilers and flaps. Aermacchi has 23.6 per cent of the programme, and builds the forward fuselage, canopy and tailcone, and integrates the gun and avionics. EMBRAER accounts for the remaining 29.7 per cent, and constructs air intakes, wing, slats, pylons, external fuel tanks and reconnaissance pallets. The Brazilian factory is also responsible for the rear cockpit and systems integration on the AMX-T. The single-source component manufacture leads to assembly lines in both Italy and Brazil to satisfy local demands.

POWERPLANT

The Rolls-Royce Spey Mk 807 is built under licence by a consortium consisting of Fiat, Piaggio and Alfa Romeo Avia, in association with the Brazilian Companhia Eletro-Mecanica (CELMA). The engine develops 49.1 kN (11,030 lb) thrust, and is based on the Spey Mk 101 used in the Buccaneer. An option to uprate the powerplant to Mk 807A standard is possible with the use of Spey Mk 202 (RAF Phantom) components.

WEAPON OPTIONS

Internal armament comprises a 20-mm six-barrelled M61A1 Vulcan cannon with 350 rounds in Italian AMXs and two 30-mm cannon in the Brazilian aircraft. External stores of up to 3800 kg (8,377 lb) are carried on one fuselage, four underwing and two wingtip weapons pylons. The centreline and inboard wing pylons are each stressed to carry 907 kg (2,000 lb), while the outboard is stressed for 454 kg (1,000 lb). The wingtip rails are for infra-red guided air-to-air missiles (AIM-9 Sidewinder for Italy or MAA-1 Piranha for Brazil). Triple bomb carriers can be mounted on the inboard wing pylons and twin bomb carriers on the other stations. In addition to free-fall bombs, cluster munitions and unguided rockets,

A well-laden AMX displays the double bomb carrier on the centreline pylon. The wing has large slats on the leading edge, and large flaps. The small ailerons are augmented by overwing spoilers.

stores may include laser-guided munitions linked with such targeting pods as the GEC Ferranti TIALD or Thomson-CRT Defense ATLIS 2 or CLDP, electro-optical guided weapons and anti-ship missiles (trials with Exocet undertaken in 1991). Trials have also been completed with the CASMU Skyshark stand-off weapons dispenser, while recce equipment comprises either a visual-spectrum fuselage pack or Oude Delft Orpheus IR linescan pod. Two-seater also capable of being fitted for the electronic warfare role.

SPECIFICATION

AMX International AMX

Wing: span 8.874 m (29 ft 1.5 in) excluding wingtip missile rails and 10.00 m (32 ft 9.75 in) over wingtip AAMs; aspect ratio 3.75; area 21.00 m² (226.05 sq ft)

Fuselage and tail: length 13.575 m (44 ft 6.5 in); height 4.576 m (15 ft 0.25 in); tailplane span about 5.20 m (17 ft 0.75 in); wheel track 2.15 m (7 ft 0.75 in); wheel base 4.74 m (15 ft 6.5 in)

Powerplant: one Fiat/Piaggio/Alfa Romeo Avio/CELMA-built Rolls-Royce Spey RB.168 Mk 807 rated at 11,030 lb st (49.06 kN) dry

Weights: operating empty 6700 kg (14,771 lb); normal take-off 9600 kg (21,164 lb); maximum take-off 13000 kg (28,660 lb)

Fuel and load: internal fuel 2790 kg (6,151 lb); external fuel up to 1732 kg (3,818 lb) in two 1000-litre (264-US gal) or two 500-litre (132-US gal) drop tanks; maximum ordnance 3800 kg (8,377 lb)

Speed: maximum level speed 'clean' and maximum cruising speed at 36,000 ft (10975 m) 493 kt (568 mph; 914 km/h)

Range: ferry range 1,800 nm (2,073 miles; 3336 km) with two 1100-litre (290-US gal) drop tanks; combat radius 300 nm (345 miles; 556 km) on a lo-lo-lo attack mission with a 2,000-kg (907-kg) warload, or 480 nm (553 miles; 889 km) on a hi-lo-hi attack mission with a 2,000-lb (907-kg) warload, or 285 km (328 miles; 528 km) on a lo-lo-lo attack mission with a 6,000-lb (2722-kg) warload, or 500 nm (576 miles; 926 km) on a hi-lo-hi attack mission with a 6,000-lb (2722-kg) warload

Performance: maximum rate of climb at sea level 10,250 ft (3124 m) per minute; service ceiling 42,650 ft (13000 m); take-off run 2,070 ft (631 m) at 10750 kg (23,699 lb) increasing to 3,220 ft (982 ft) at maximum take-off weight; take-off distance to 50 ft (15 m) 4,730 ft (1442 m) at maximum take-off weight; landing distance from 50 ft (15 m) 2,470 ft (753 m) at maximum landing weight
g limits: -4 to +8

COCKPIT

The cockpit is covered by a one-piece sideways-hinging canopy, and one-piece wrap-around windshield which combine to give excellent visibility. The pilot sits on a Martin-Baker Mk 10L zero-zero ejection seat. The aircraft has an advanced cockpit to reduce pilot workload, with an OMI/Selenia head-up display. This is complemented by an Alenia head-down multi-function display which can present TV/IR and synthetic map images. The functions are controlled by HOTAS (hands on throttle and stick).

Antonov **An-2 'Colt'**

WSK-PZL Mielec
ul. Ludwego Wojska Polskiego 3
PL-39-300, Poland

One of the last biplanes in production, the **An-2** remains in widespread military service, mainly as a utility transport and hack, although a handful may remain in use in the special forces insertion/support role, notably with North Korea. First flown on 31 August 1947 as the **SKh-1**, the An-2 proved popular with civil and military customers, and more than 5,000 were built at Kiev before production finally ceased in about 1965 (though a small number of An-2Ms were built until the early 1970s). Licensed production in China (which has now ceased) began in 1957, where approximately 1,500 were produced as **Harbin Y-5s**. PZL Mielec in Poland commenced licensed production in 1960, and has since produced almost 12,000 more. With a production run exceeding 18,000 aircraft, the unspectacular An-2 has been one of the great post-war success stories.

When the An-2 appeared in 1947, it was treated with some derision in the West and was regarded as an anachronistic and near-obsolete curio, destined for a very short lifespan. The unfashionable biplane configuration was chosen quite deliberately, however, with the new Antonov OKB willingly accepting drag penalties in order to exploit the configuration's many advantages – chiefly impeccable low-speed handling characteristics, agility and useful STOL performance. The aircraft's ruggedness and easy maintainability were also enhanced by a simple, straightforward engineering approach.

Despite its appearance, the An-2 did incorporate a host of modern features, including its full-span slats and electrically-actuated double-slotted trailing-edge flaps. Designed primarily for agricultural use, the An-2 has also seen service as a fire-bomber, light transport (**An-2-P, An-2T , An-2TP**) freighter, paratroop transport (**PZL An-2TD**), glider tug, air ambulance (**PZL An-2S**), survey platform, navigation trainer, meteorological research aircraft (**An-2ZA**) and even as a light bomber. Later improved agricultural versions include the **PZL An-2R**.

Acting as transports and make-shift bombers, An-2s were of crucial importance to the Croatian air force in the fighting that followed its secession from Yugoslavia in 1991.

and **An-2M**. A turbine-engined derivative, the **An-3**, did not reach production because of delays in availability of the selected engine. The type remains in large-scale service with a large number of air forces, with some on charge with most of Russia's Frontal Aviation regiments as hacks. The basic An-2 also serves as the basis for the proposed new **Delaero T-101 Gratch** utility monoplane, shown in mock-up form (in floatplane configuration) at the 1992 Moscow Aeroshow.

OPERATORS

Afghanistan
Albania (Harbin Y-5)
Angola
Azerbaijan
Byelorussia
Bulgaria
China (Harbin Y-5, Fong Shou 2 Harvester)
Croatia
Cuba
Czech Republic
Egypt
Georgia
Iraq
Laos
Latvia
Mali
Mongolia
Nicaragua
North Korea (Harbin Y-5)
Poland
Romania
Russia
Slovakia
Tadjikistan
Turkmenistan
Ukraine
Uzbekistan
Vietnam

SPECIFICATION

PZL Mielec (Antonov) An-2P

Wing: span, upper 18.18 m (59 ft 7¼ in); lower 14.24 m (46 ft 8½ in); aspect ratio, upper 7.6, lower 7.1
Fuselage and tail: length overall, tail up 12.74 m (41 ft 9½ in); height, tail up 6.10 m (20 ft 0 in); wheel track 3.36 m (11 ft ¼ in)
Powerplant: one 1,000-hp (746-kW) PZL Kalisz ASz-621R (licence-built ASh-62)
Weights: empty 3450 kg (7,605 lb); maximum fuel 900 kg (1,984 lb); maximum take-off 5500 kg (12,125 lb)
Fuel and load: internal fuel 12,000 litres (317 US Gal, 264 Imp Gal)
Speed: maximum level speed at 1750 m (5,740 ft) 139 kt (258 km/h, 160 mph); economic cruising speed 100 kt (185 km/h, 115 mph)
Range: at 1000 m (3,280 ft) with payload of 500 kg (1,102 lb) 900 km (485 nm, 560 miles)
Performance: maximum rate of climb at sea level 210 m per min (689 ft per min); service ceiling 4400 m (14,425 ft)|

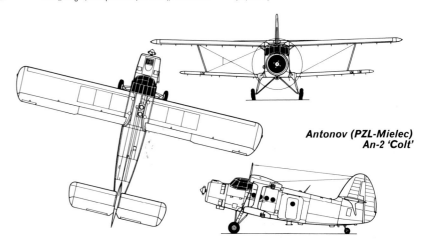

*Antonov (PZL-Mielec)
An-2 'Colt'*

Antonov **An-8 'Camp'**

The twin-engined forerunner of the An-10, and of the Kiev-based bureau's better-known An-12 'Cub', remains in small-scale use with both Aeroflot and the **Russian air force** (and perhaps the air arms of some other former Soviet republics). Designed to meet a VVS requirement for a rear-loading tactical transport, and an Aeroflot require-

ment for a 42-48 seat passenger/freighter, the **An-8** first flew during late 1955, and Western sources usually indicate a production run of about 100. No new An-8s were ever delivered to Aeroflot, production being devoted to the military, which later passed examples on. Until recent years, the type was widely regarded as retired, but in the

early 1990s small numbers have been discovered still active in support roles, around Moscow and in the hands of Aeroflot's former Far East Division. In the light of the efforts being made to dispose of remaining An-12s by the former Soviet Union, in favour of more modern types, serviceability of the An-8 must be extremely low.

Antonov **An-10/An-12 'Cub'**

Usually regarded as the 'Soviet C-130', the **An-12** is similar to the Hercules in many respects. Designed as a high-wing, four-engined, rear-loading military freighter, the Ukrainian-built aircraft has had considerable sales success in both civilian and military markets, and has been adapted to fulfil a variety of other roles. The prototype An-12 made its maiden flight during 1958. It is estimated that more than 900 were built at Kiev before production ceased during 1973, and more have been produced in China under the designation **Shaanxi Y-8**.

Developed from the passenger-carrying **An-10** (which was itself a stretched, four-engined derivative of the An-8, with a pressurised circular-section fuselage), the An-12 was designed from the start as a military transport and civilian freighter, with a rear-loading ramp like that of the An-8, and a

partly-pressurised cabin forward of the main portion of the freight compartment. Unlike the C-130, the An-12 lacks an integral rear-loading ramp, with the upswept rear fuselage instead consisting of a pair of longitudinally-split inward-opening doors and a third upward-opening door aft.

Designated **'Cub'** by NATO's Air Standards Co-ordinating Committee, the An-12 has been produced in several versions. The **An-12BP** is the basic military freighter, although the very earliest aircraft, which had a smaller undernose radome and other detail differences, may have had a different designation. All basic freighter variants are known to NATO simply as 'Cubs'.

Large numbers of military An-12s have been converted to perform other roles (and some production 'special duties' An-12s may also have been manufactured). Factory

As a result of fatigue cracking in the main spar, the Indian An-12 fleet was reduced and finally withdrawn in 1993. Ten survivors were advertised for sale along with a stock of engines. Their replacement came, at first, in the shape of the Il-76, and more recently a C-130 Hercules buy has been proposed.

and air force designations for these shadowy aircraft remain unknown, and not all have separate NATO reporting names, although most remain in active front-line use with the successors to the Soviet air force. The first 'special duties' An-12 identified by NATO had blade antennas on the

forward fuselage, plus other minor changes, and was a dedicated Elint platform. It is possible that this **'Cub-A'** was an interim type, since most Elint 'Cubs' encountered in recent years have had more extensive modifications. One such aircraft had prominent 'carrot' fairings on the fin and wingtips.

The **'Cub-B'**, which remained, until recently, in front-line service (even with the Russian air force in former East Germany), is a more obvious Elint conversion, with two prominent radomes under the belly and a host of other blade antennas. Some of these aircraft have been encountered in full Aeroflot livery and, during the 1970s, others may have worn Egyptian markings. **'Cub-C'** is understood to be a dedicated ECM platform, with palletised electrical generators and control equipment, and possibly chaff-cutters and dispensers in the cabin. Externally, the 'Cub-C' can be identified by the array of antennas on its underside, the cooling scoops and heat exchanger outlets fore and aft of the wing, and the bulged, ogival tailcone which replaces the normal gun turret. There have been suggestions that these 'stand-off' jamming platforms had a primary role of neutralising NATO air defence and surface-to-air missile radars.

The most recently identified version of the An-12, **'Cub-D'**, is a second ECM platform, with a different equipment fit and characterised by huge external pods on the lower 'corners' of the forward fuselage and on each side of the base of the tailfin. Unconfirmed reports suggest the existence of an airborne command post version of the An-12, which may have seen service during the Indo-Pakistan war, but details of its appearance are unavailable.

In addition to these aircraft, large numbers of An-12s have been converted as one-off test and research platforms, including a meteorological research aircraft, ejection seat test aircraft, avionics testbeds (SSSR-11417, -11700), icing rigs, and engine testbeds. In the latter category an Egyptian 'Cub' flew with its port inner engine replaced by a Helwan E-300 turbojet, developed for a stillborn indigenous fighter. A

Soviet An-12 (SSSR-11916) may have acted as a prototype for a proposed maritime reconnaissance and ASW variant.

OPERATORS

Although replacement, in the Soviet Union, by the jet-powered Ilyushin Il-76 began in 1974, sizeable numbers remain in service with the VTA and Aeroflot's fleet of 'Cubs' could also be commandeered. The An-12's main future role lies in the many 'special missions' conversions. Elsewhere, existing users are rapidly retiring their An-12s from use. In India, replacement by the Il-76 is underway and all surviving An-12s have been withdrawn and advertised for sale. Polish aircraft have also been retired. Surviving operators include the Czech Republic, Egypt, Ethiopia, Sri Lanka (Y-8), Ukraine and Yemen, while some aircraft may still be active in Iraq and Sudan.

SPECIFICATION

Antonov An-12BP 'Cub-A'

Wing: span 38.00 m (124 ft 8 in); aspect ratio 11.85; area 121.70 m² (1,310.01 sq ft)

Fuselage and tail: length 33.10 m (108 ft 7.25 in); height 10.53 m (34 ft 6.5 in); tailplane span 12.20 m (40 ft 0.25 in); wheel track 5.42 m (17 ft 9.5 in); wheel base 10.82 m (35 ft 6 in)

Powerplant: four ZMDB Progress (Ivchyenko) AI-20K each rated at 4,000 ehp (2983 kW)

Weights: empty 28000 kg (61,728 lb); normal take-off 55100 kg (121,473 lb); maximum take-off 61000 kg (134,480 lb)

Fuel and load: internal fuel 18100 litres (4,781 US gal); external fuel none; maximum payload 20000 kg (44,092 lb)

Speed: maximum level speed 'clean' at optimum altitude 777 km/h (419 kt; 482 mph); maximum cruising speed at opimum altitude 670 km/h (361 kt; 416 mph)

Above: This modified An-12 is an ejection seat testbed, firing seats from a modified tail housing. Note the camera pods under the wingtips.

The Sri Lankan air force's sole heavylift asset was a pair of Y-8s, provided as part of substantial Chinese assistance. One was lost in July 1992.

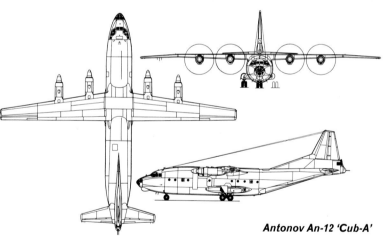

Antonov An-12 'Cub-A'

Range: 5700 km (3,075 nm; 3,542 miles) with maximum fuel or 3600 km (1,942 nm; 2,237 miles) with maximum payload

Performance: maximum rate of climb at sea level 600 m (1,969 ft) per minute; service ceiling 10200 m (33,465 ft); take-off run 700 m (2,297 ft) at maximum take-off weight; landing run 500 m (1,640 ft) at normal landing weight

---

Antonov **An-14 'Clod'**

Known as the **Pchelka** (Little Bee) to its manufacturers, the **An-14**, which first flew on 15 March 1958, was produced between 1965 and 1975 as a light twin-engined utility aircraft which could be flown by pilots of limited experience. While the launch of the An-14 was heralded with great fanfare, it then suffered eight years of redesign until true production could begin. The aircraft can accommodate a pilot and seven passengers, or a pilot, six stretchers

and an attendant. Access is via clamshell doors at the rear. About 300 were built and military customers included Bulgaria, East Germany, the Republic of Guinea, and the USSR.

Four An-14s may remain active in **Guinea**, but the type's main importance is that it formed the basis of the turboprop **An-14M** prototype of 1969, which eventually became the An-28 'Cash', built by PZL Mielec in Poland.

SPECIFICATION

Antonov An-14 Pchelka 'Clod'

Wing: span 21.99 m (72 ft 2 in); aspect ratio 12.15; area 39.72 m² (427.56 sq ft)

Fuselage and tail: length 11.36 m (37 ft 3 in); height 4.63 m (15 ft 2.5 in); tailplane span 5.00 m (16 ft 4.75 in); wheel track 3.60 m (11 ft 9.75 in); wheel base 3.71 m (12 ft 2 in)

Powerplant: two ZMDB Progress (Ivchyenko) AI-14RF each rated at 300 hp (224 kW)

Weights: empty 2600 kg (5,732 lb); maximum take-off 3270 kg (7,209 lb)

Fuel and load: internal fuel 385 litres (101 US gal);

external fuel none; maximum payload 720 kg (1,587 lb)

Speed: maximum level speed 'clean' at 1000 m (3,280 ft) 222 km/h (120 kt; 138 mph); normal cruising speed at 2000 m (6,560 ft) 180 km/h (97 kt; 112 mph)

Range: 800 km (353 nm; 407 miles) with maximum fuel, or 715 km (386 nm; 444 miles) with a 550-kg (1,212-lb) payload, or 650 km (351 nm; 404 miles) with maximum payload

Performance: maximum rate of climb at sea level 306 m (1,004 ft) per minute; service ceiling 4500 m (14,764 ft); take-off run 100 m (328 ft) at maximum take-off weight; take-off distance to 15 m (50 ft) 200 m (656 ft) at max take-off weight; landing distance from 15 m (50 ft), 300 m (984 ft) at normal landing weight; landing run 70 m (230 ft), at normal landing weight

Antonov **An-22** 'Cock'

Antonov Design Bureau
1 Tupolev Street
Kiev 252062, Ukraine

When the **An-22** prototype appeared at the 1965 Paris air show, only months after its 27 February 1965 maiden flight, it generated a storm of interest. Then the largest aircraft in the world, the An-22 weighed in at an astonishing 246-tonne maximum take-off weight and yet enjoyed relatively good take-off performance, despite a higher wing loading than any other military transport. This was achieved by the combination of powerful 11186-kW (15,000-shp) Kuznetsov NK-12MA turboprops whose prop wash was forced over highly effective double-slotted flaps which covered almost two thirds of the trailing edge.

In many respects, the An-22 is little more than a scaled-up An-12, with a new tail unit with twin endplate fins to give better control characteristics in asymmetric flight, and to avoid an excessive aircraft height. Like the An-12, it has a pressurised forward compartment (with the flight deck and 28 or 29 passengers) and an unpressurised main cargo hold. Unlike the An-12, though, it does have an integral rear loading ramp, plus four travelling gantries and two winches for loading heavy cargo. The undercarriage, which consists of twin nosewheels and three twin-wheel levered suspension units per side, is designed to allow off-runway operation. Three separate nose radars allow all-weather operation and accurate navigation over huge distances. Tyre pressures can be adjusted from the cockpit to optimise the undercarriage for landing weight and runway surface.

Until the introduction of the An-124, the An-22 was the only Soviet transport capable of carrying main battle tanks, and the 45 left in service (of perhaps 100 produced) are kept extremely busy. A handful of An-22s are used for externally carrying outsized cargoes (mainly An-124 wings). Most wear **Aeroflot** colours, but a handful seem to be

The bulk of Russian An-22s wear Aeroflot colours, though one aircraft has been seen wearing a three-tone green and brown camouflage scheme, with Soviet air force red stars. Twenty are based at Tver/Kalinin air base, 100 miles (160 km) north west of Moscow, alongside a number of An-12s.

permanently allocated to the **VTA** and at least one wears three-tone camouflage colours. Even the Aeroflot aircraft seem to undertake regular military tasking. Some reports suggest that the new **Ukrainian air force** may operate a small number of An-22s, but this cannot be confirmed.

SPECIFICATION

Antonov An-22 Antei 'Cock'
Wing: span 64.40 m (211 ft 4 in); aspect ratio 12.02; area 345.00 m² (3,713.67 sq ft)
Fuselage and tail: length about 57.92 m (190 ft 0 in); height 12.53 m (41 ft 1.5 in)
Powerplant: four KKBM (Kuznetsov) NK-12MA each rated at 15,000 shp (11186 kW)
Weights: empty equipped 114000 kg (251,323 lb); maximum take-off 250000 kg (551,146 lb)
Fuel and load: internal fuel 43000 kg (94,797 lb); external fuel none; maximum payload 80000 kg (176,367 lb)
Speed: maximum level speed 'clean' at optimum altitude 740 km/h (399 kt; 460 mph); cruising speed at optimum altitude 520 km/h (281 kt; 323 mph)
Range: 10950 km (5,909 nm; 6,804 miles) with a 45000-kg (99,206-lb) payload and maximum fuel or 5000 km (2,776 nm; 3,197 miles) with maximum payload
Performance: service ceiling 7500 m (24,605 ft); take-off run 1300 m (4,260 ft) at maximum take-ff weight; landing run 800 m (2,620 ft) at normal landing weight

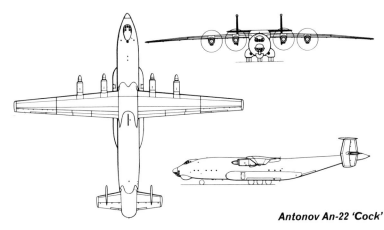

Antonov An-22 'Cock'

Antonov **An-24** 'Coke'

The **An-24** made its maiden flight on 20 December 1959, and was designed to meet an Aeroflot requirement for a turbine-engined replacement for the piston-engined Il-14s, Il-12s and even Li-2s (Soviet DC-3 copies) which operated on the airline's extensive network of local routes. Heavier, and with larger engines than the contemporary and largely equivalent Fokker F27, the export success of the An-24 was limited by its higher operating costs, although its robustness, strength and take-off performance widened its appeal to military customers. A total of 1,100 An-24s was built by the time production finished in 1978, but production continued in China, where the aircraft is designated **Xian Y-7** (described separately).

The basic **An-24V** seated 28-40 passengers, while the 1967 **An-24V Series II** seated 50. Substitution of a Tumanskii RU-19-300 turbojet for the gas turbine APU in the rear of the starboard engine nacelle resulted in the **An-24RV**, which enjoyed much improved take-off performance. Dedicated freighters, with the passenger door removed, and a freight access hatch in the underside of the rear fuselage, were the **An-24T** and **An-24RT** (with jet APU). The freight hatch hinged inwards from its rear edge, and small strakes on each side of the rear fuselage replaced the single centreline ventral fin of the standard An-24. An **An-24P** was evaluated for the firefighting role. Improved Chinese variants are designated **Y-7-100** and **Y-7-200A/B**. Most military An-24s are used for passenger and especially VIP transport duties, but overall the type has not enjoyed the sales success of the dedicated An-26 freighter and tactical transport.

OPERATORS

Afghanistan: 1 (VIP)
Angola: 3
Bulgaria: 8
China: 20 (An-24/Y-7)
Congo: 3/2 (An-24V/RV)
Cuba: 3
Czech Republic: 3 (An-24RV)
Hungary: 2 (An-24RV)
Iraq: 10
Mali: 2
Mongolia: 18 (An-24V/RV)
North Korea: 10
Romania: 10 (An-24RT/RV)
Slovakia: 3 (An-24RV)
Sudan: 5 (WFU)
Ukraine:
Vietnam: 12 (WFU)
Yemen: 3 (An-24V)

SPECIFICATION

Antonov An-24T 'Coke'
Wing: span 29.20 m (95 ft 9.5 in); aspect ratio 11.77; area 72.46 m² (779.98 sq ft)
Fuselage and tail: length 23.53 m (77 ft 2.5 in); height 8.32 m (27 ft 3.5 in); tailplane span 9.08 m (29 ft 9.5 in); wheel track 7.90 m (25 ft 11 in); wheel base 7.89 m (25 ft 10.5 in)
Powerplant: two ZMDB Progress (Ivchyenko) AI-24A each rated at 2,550 ehp (1678 kW)
Weights: empty 14060 kg (30,996 lb); operating empty 14968 kg (32,998 lb); maximum take-off 19800 kg (43,651 lb)
Fuel and load: internal fuel 4760 kg (10,494 lb); external fuel none; maximum payload 4612 kg (10,168 lb)
Speed: normal cruising speed at 6000 m (19,685 ft)

The An-24, like this Hungarian An-24V, is a dedicated passenger aircraft with fixed seats. Freight and paradropping duties are exclusively the preserve of the An-26.

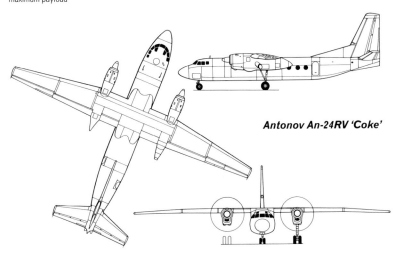

450 km/h (243 kt; 280 mph); economical cruising speed at 7000 m (22,965 ft) 450 km/h (243 kt; 280 mph)
Range: 3000 km (1,619 nm; 1,864 miles) with a 1612-kg (3,554-lb) payload, or 640 km (345 nm; 397 miles) with maximum payload

Performance: service ceiling 8400 m (18,520 ft); take-off run 640 m (2,100 ft) at maximum take-off weight; landing distance from 15 m (50 ft) 1590 m (5,217 ft) at normal landing weight; landing run 880 m (1.903 ft) at normal landing weight

Antonov An-24RV 'Coke'

Antonov An-26 'Curl'

Although derived from the Antonov An-24, the **An-26** is a new design with a host of new features and improvements. The most obvious of these is a new rear loading ramp, which forms the underside of the upswept rear fuselage when closed, but which can be slid forward along tracks on each side of the underside of the fuselage to lie directly under the cabin, clear of the open hatch. This is especially useful when loading directly from a truck or for air-dropping. The actuators for the mechanism which slides the ramp forward are enclosed in prominent fibreglass fairings on each side of the rear fuselage, directly ahead of deep strakes which 'enclose' the more sharply swept rear fuselage. These improve airflow around the rear fuselage, which is particularly important when air-dropping loads. However, the nature of their construction (fibreglass) means they are easily damaged, a fact somewhat at odds with the An-26's role as a tactical transport.

All An-26s are fitted with a Tumanskii RU-19A-300 turbojet in the rear of the starboard engine nacelle. As well as acting as an APU, this can be used as a take-off booster and for increasing performance at other times. Many An-26s are also fitted with a large observation 'bubble' on the port side of the forward fuselage, replacing the normal navigator's window. This can be used in conjunction with an OPB-1R optical sight for accurately delivering air-dropped loads or paratroops. The Chinese-built **Xian Y7H** is described separately.

Less obvious is the fact that the An-26 has a fully-pressurised cargo hold (the first Soviet transport aircraft so equipped), or that on all but the earliest aircraft the belly has been toughened to withstand the erosion and abrasion which go hand-in-hand with rough field operation. A sheet of 'bimetal', with a titanium skin overlying aluminium alloy, protects the under-surfaces from debris. Other improvements adopted at the same time included more powerful AI-24T engines, and increased diameter (to 3.9 m/12.8 ft) AN-72T constant-speed, fully feathering four-bladed propellers. Since 1980, many An-26 engines have been upgraded to AI-24VT standard, giving a power output of 2103 ekW (2,820 ehp).

Internally, the An-26 features an electrically- or manually-operated conveyor flush with the cabin floor, while the later **An-26B** has roll gangs (panels fitted with rollers) which can be swung up against the cabin walls when not in use. These allow three standard freight pallets (weighing 1400 kg/4,041 lb and measuring 2.44 x 1.46 x 1.6 m/8 x 4.79 x 5.25 ft) to be unloaded, and another three loaded, by two men within 30 minutes. The hold can accommodate cargo up to 2.1 m (6.88 ft) wide and 1.5 m (4.92 ft) high, including a variety of commonly-used Warsaw Pact/Eastern Bloc vehicles. An electrically-powered mobile winch of 2000-kg (4,409-lb) capacity runs along rails on the cabin ceiling. In all An-26 versions, the interior can be reconfigured within 30 minutes

as a transport, with tip-up seats along the cabin sides to seat 38-40 passengers, or for casevac with 24 stretchers. Parachute static line points are fitted as standard.

The An-26 has mechanical controls, with electrical trim tabs on the servo-assisted ailerons and rudder. The flaps (single-slotted inboard, double-slotted outboard) are hydraulically actuated, as are the cargo ramp, emergency escape doors, forward-retracting undercarriage, nosewheel steering system and the brakes. The aircraft has two separate but interconnected fuel systems, with 5500 kg (12,125 lb) of fuel in integral tanks in the centre-section and five bag-type tanks in each wing. A single pressure refuelling point is located in the starboard engine nacelle, with gravity refuelling points above each tank area. An inert gas fire suppression system is incorporated.

A small number of An-26s have been converted as Elint/Sigint/EW platforms. These bear the NATO reporting name **'Curl-B'**, and have a profusion of swept blade antennas above and below the cabin. Painted as standard transports and often operating from the same bases, these aircraft remain in use with the Russian air force, including units based in former East Germany. Former East German special-duties An-26s were designated **An-26ST** (sometimes reported as **An-26SM** for calibration and **An-26M** for Elint). Similarly modified An-26s are in Czech service also.

An even more active combat role has been undertaken by Angolan and Mozambique An-26s, which have been fitted with bomb racks for use as makeshift COIN aircraft. These bomb racks are fitted on the fuselage, below the trailing edge of the wingroot. Some An-26s (most notably those used in Afghanistan) have had chaff/flare dispensers pylon-mounted in the same, or a very similar, position.

In line with other Antonov twins (most notably the An-32), a fire-bombing version of

the An-26 has also been developed, utilising tanks along the fuselage, under the wing.

OPERATORS

Production ended after about 1,000 had been built, mostly for military operators who currently include Afghanistan, Angola, Bangladesh, Benin, Bulgaria, Cape Verde, China, Cuba, Congo, Czech Republic, Germany, Ethiopia, Guinea Bissau, Hungary, Iraq, Laos, Libya, Madagascar, Mali, Mongolia, Mozambique, Nicaragua, Poland, Romania, Russia, Serbia, Slovakia, Ukraine, Vietnam, Yemen and Zambia. Two hundred were built for Aeroflot and a handful more for other civilian users. The Y-7H-500 remains in production. The An-26 was replaced on the line by the An-32.

SPECIFICATION

Antonov An-26B 'Curl-A'
Wing: span 29.20 m (95 ft 9.5 in); aspect ratio 11.7; area 74.98 m² (807.10 sq ft)
Fuselage and tail: length 23.80 m (78 ft 1 in); height 8.575 m (28 ft 1.5 in); tailplane span 9.973 m (32 ft 8.75 in); wheel track 7.90 m (25 ft 11 in); wheel base 7.651 m (25 ft 1.25 in)
Powerplant: two ZMDB Progress (Ivchyenko)

AI-24VT each rated at 2,820 ehp (2103 kW) and one Soyuz (Tumanskii) RU-19A-300 rated at 7.85 kN (1,765 lb st) dry
Weights: empty 15400 kg (33,950 lb); normal take-off 23000 kg (50,705 lb); max take-off 24400 kg (53,790 lb)
Fuel and load: internal fuel 5500 kg (12,125 lb); external fuel none; maximum payload 5500 kg (12,125 lb)
Speed: maximum level speed at 5000 m (16,400 ft) 540 km/h (292 kts/336 mph); maximum level speed at sea level 510 km/h (275 kts/317 mph); cruising speed at 6000 m (19,685 ft) 440 km/h (237 kt; 273 mph)
Range: range 2550 km (1,376 nm; 1,585 miles) with maximum fuel or 1100 km (593 nm; 683 miles) with maximum payload
Performance: max rate of climb at sea level 480 m (1,575 ft) per minute; service ceiling 7500 m (24,605 ft); take-off run 780 m (2,559 ft) at max take-off weight; take-off distance to 15 m (50 ft) 1240 m (4,068 ft) at max take-off weight; landing distance from 15 m (50 ft) 1740 m (5,709 ft) at normal landing weight; landing run 730 m (2,395 ft) at normal landing weight

This Antonov An-26 'Curl-B' Elint aircraft was operational with the Group of Soviet Forces in Germany, flying from Sperenburg, near Berlin. Its antenna farm comprises 10 aerials, with an improved blade-aerial IFF above the nose.

Right: An An-26 formerly operated by the Soviet Northern Group of Forces at Legnica, Poland.

Below: Nominally on charge with the civil airline Hang Khong Vietnam, these An-26s flew from Tan Son Nhut airbase.

Antonov **An-30 'Clank'**

Based on the airframe of the An-24RT freighter, and first flown in 1974, the **An-30** is a dedicated photographic and survey platform, with appropriate role equipment and a completely redesigned forward fuselage. It replaced a similarly modified version of the Ilyushin Il-14. A considerably raised cockpit gives access to the new glazed nose which accommodates the relocated navigator's compartment. There are few other structural changes (although some cabin windows are deleted) and the aircraft could theoretically be reconfigured for passenger or cargo duties by removing survey equipment and by fitting cover plates over the camera apertures, which are normally covered by remotely-controlled doors.

The An-30 is spacious, and a toilet, buffet and crew rest area with armchairs and couches is provided for the crew of seven (pilot, co-pilot, navigator, engineer, radio operator and two photographers), together with a darkroom and film storage area. The last two facilities account for the removal of the cabin windows.

The An-30 can carry a variety of mapping and survey equipment, including magnetometers (for mineral surveys) and microwave radiometers for surveying ice build-up, snow cover, flooding, soil type or seasonal changes of vegetation. More commonly, the An-30 can carry a variety of optical cameras (both vertical and oblique) in fixed or gyro-stabilised mountings. An extremely accurate navigation computer maintains the pre-programmed course, altitude and speed. A cloud-seeding version, the **An-30M 'Sky Cleaner'** has been

Romania was one of the few export customers for the specialised An-30 survey aircraft.

developed to disperse granular carbon dioxide to increase rain and snowfall, or fight fires.

Production of the An-30 has been very limited and only a handful serve in the air forces of **Russia**, **Bulgaria**, the **Czech Republic**, **Hungary**, **Romania** and, perhaps, **Ukraine** and **Vietnam**.

SPECIFICATION

Antonov An-30 'Clank'
Wing: span 29.20 m (95 ft 9.5 in); aspect ratio 11.4; area 74.98 m² (807.10 sq ft)
Fuselage and tail: length 24.26 m (79 ft 7 in); height 8.32 m (27 ft 3.5 in); tailplane span 9.09 m (29 ft 10 in); wheel track 7.90 m (25 ft 11 in); wheel base 7.65 m (25 ft 11.25 in)
Powerplant: two ZMDB Progress (Ivchyenko) AI-24VT each rated at 2,820 ehp (2103 kW) and one Soyuz (Tumanskii) RU-19A-300 rated at 7.85 kN (1,764 lb st)
Weights: operating empty 15590 kg (34,369 lb); maximum take-off 23000 kg (50,705 lb)
Fuel and load: internal fuel 6200 litres (1,638 US gal); external fuel none
Speed: maximum level speed 'clean' at optimum altitude 540 km/h (292 kt; 336 mph); cruising speed at 6000 m (19,685 ft) 430 km/h (232 kt; 267 mph)
Range: 2630 km (1,419 nm; 1,634 miles) with maximum fuel
Performance: service ceiling 7300 m (23,950 ft) without APU and 8300 m (27,230 ft) with APU; take-off run 710 m (2,330 ft) at maximum take-off weight; landing run 670 m (2,198 ft) at normal landing weight

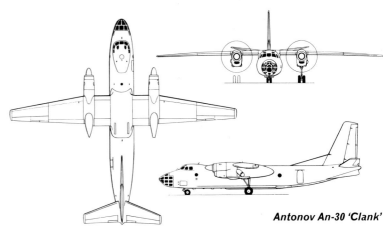

Antonov An-30 'Clank'

Antonov **An-32 'Cline'**

The **An-32** replaced the An-26 in production, and is designed to offer improved take-off performance, ceiling and payload, especially under 'hot-and-high' conditions. It retains the superb cargo ramp of the An-26, and has an increased capacity (3000 kg/6,615 lb) internal winch. Removable roller conveyors aid air-dropping or the extraction of loads by drag-parachute. The cabin can accommodate up to 50 passengers, 42 paratroops, or 24 stretcher patients and three attendants. The normal crew consists of pilot, co-pilot and navigator, with provision for a flight engineer.

Although the An-32 was originally offered with a choice of powerplant, all production aircraft are fitted with the 3812-ekW (5,112-ehp) Ivchenko AI-20D series 5, similar to (but more powerful than) the engine used by the An-12 and Il-18. These are mounted above the wing to give greater clearance for the increased-diameter propellers, reduce the danger of debris ingestion, and decrease noise levels in the cabin. The overwing position, however, results in very deep nacelles because the bulk of the An-26's original nacelle has been retained to accommodate the improved main undercarriage units when retracted. The overwing portion of the nacelle extended back only to about mid-chord on the An-32 prototype, but extends back almost to the trailing edge of

the original underwing nacelle on production aircraft. The 'turbojet APU' of the An-26 and some An-24 versions has been replaced by a simple TG-16M APU in the tip of the starboard landing gear fairing.

Besides these aerodynamic refinements, the undercarriage extension/retraction mechanism, and the de-icing, air conditioning, electrical and engine starting systems have all been improved. The improvements to the An-32 have been extremely successful, producing an aircraft which can operate from airfields with elevations of up to 4500 m (14,750 ft) above sea level, and which has set a host of world records for payload-to-height, and sustained altitude.

In 1993 the first **An-32B** was seen boasting uprated powerplants with approximately 200-shp (149-kW) extra power available per engine. At the Paris air show that same year, Antonov demonstrated the **An-32P** (Protivopozharny) water-bomber, named **Firekiller**. Like the similar An-26 conversion it features side-mounted tanks with a total capacity of 8000 kg (17,635 lb), though those of the An-32 are substantially larger and faired on. Flares are carried to induce artificial precipitation over fires. However, the tanks have to be refilled on the ground, necessitating specialised pumping equipment, and radius of action is quoted at a mere 150 km (93 miles).

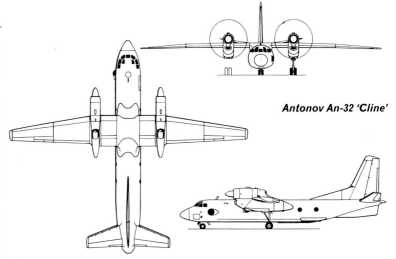

Antonov An-32 'Cline'

OPERATORS

The An-32 has already attracted a number of military customers, including the USSR (it is as yet unclear exactly which independent republics have taken over former Soviet An-32s), Afghanistan, Bangladesh, Cuba, India, Mongolia, Peru and Tanzania. It is unclear whether orders from Cape Verde, Nicaragua and São Tomé are from military or civilian customers. India's

order for 95 was to have been met by licence-production of the aircraft, which has the local name **Sutlej**, but this plan fell through and India's aircraft are Soviet built, albeit with a high content of indigenous equipment and avionics. In addition to the basic transport version of the An-32, fire-fighting, fisheries protection, air ambulance and agricultural versions have been offered for sale, while Peru's 15 An-32s have two bomb racks on each side of the fuselage, below the wings.

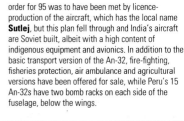

Left: Several 'tropical' operators, such as the Bangladesh (seen here) and the Peruvian air forces, have traded in their An-26s for more powerful An-32s.

Right: India too appreciates the An-32's good 'hot-and-high' performance, relying on six squadrons of the type for all of its tactical transport needs. The Antonov design was selected in 1979 in preference to the Aeritalia G222, DHC-5 Buffalo, and ex-RAF Andover C.Mk 1s.

Antonov An-32 'Cline'
Wing: span 29.20 m (95 ft 9.5 in); aspect ratio 11.7; area 74.98 m² (807.10 sq ft)
Fuselage and tail: length 23.78 m (78 ft 0.25 in); height 8.75 m (28 ft 8.5 in); tailplane span 10.23 m (33 ft 6.75 in); wheel track 7.90 m (25 ft 11 in); wheel base 7.651 m (25 ft 1.25 in)
Powerplant: two ZMDB Progress (Ivchyenko) AI-20DM Series 5 each rated at 5,112 ehp (3812 kW)
Weights: empty 16800 kg (37,037 lb); maximum take-off 27000 kg (59,524 lb)
Fuel and load: internal fuel 5445 kg (12,004 lb); external fuel none; maximum payload 6700 kg (14,771 lb)
Speed: maximum cruising speed at 8000 m (26,245 ft)

530 km/h (286 kt; 329 mph); economical cruising speed at 8000 m (26,245 ft) 470 km/h (254 kt; 292 mph)
Range: 2500 km (1,349 nm; 1,553 miles) with a 3700-kg (8,157-lb) payload or 2000 km (1,070 nm; 1,243 miles) with maximum payload
Performance: service ceiling 9500 m (31,170 ft); take-off run 760 m (2,495 ft) at maximum take-off weight; take-off distance to 15 m (50 ft) 1200 m (3,940 ft) at maximum take-off weight; landing run 470 m (1,542 ft) at normal landing weight

An-32s, particularly Ukranian air force examples, are becoming increasingly involved in UN duties. This former-Soviet aircraft was engaged in relief flights in Africa.

Antonov An-70T

Development of the **An-70** began during the early 1980s, to enter production during 1988, but this was delayed by funding problems. Slightly larger than the proposed Euroflag, and considerably smaller than the C-17, the **An-70T** takes the An-12's place, but with modern technology (including a Mil-Std 1553B databus, SKI-77 HUD and Cat IIIB landing aids), powerful engines and advanced aerodynamics. The aircraft is equipped with a fly-by-wire control system with three digital and six analog channels. Antonov have also developed an innovative back-up hydraulic/electro-magnetic control system. Increased use of composites by Antonov is in evidence, as the An-70T features carbon fibre tail assemblies.

At a ceremony at its Kiev factory, Antonov rolled out the first An-70 on 20 January 1994. Present at the roll-out was VVS Commander-in-Chief Col Gen. Piotr Deinkin, reinforcing hopes for a substantial purchase by the Russian air force. Two thirds of all research and development funding was provided by the defence ministry of the former Soviet Union (project breakdown is 63 per cent Russian, 21 per cent Ukrainian and 16

per cent among the other Republics). Ninety-five per cent of components are currently sourced in Russia, but Ukraine's share of these would rise to 13 per cent once production is underway. A prototype flew during June 1994 with series production undertaken both at Kiev, Ukraine, and Samara, Russia. Overall span is 44.06 m (114 ft 6¼ in), length is 40.25 m (132 ft ¼ in) and height is 16.120 m (52 ft 10 in). The cockpit is laid out for three, including a flight engineer. The cargo hold is pressurised and air-conditioned, but has no provision for any seating, barring two loadmasters in the forward fuselage. The crew door is positioned in the port forward fuselage, and there is no rear door, which excludes any future paradropping option. Maximum payload, using the ramp, is pegged at 30000 kg (66,135 lb), with maximum take-off weight an estimated 123000 kg (271,165 lb). The 10440-kW (14,000-hp) Zaporozhye Progress D-27 propfan is fitted with highly distinctive Stupino SV-27 contra-rotating propellers. Each engine drives eight 4.5-m (14-ft 7-in) blades in the first stage and six in the second, and all are of curved scimitar profile and

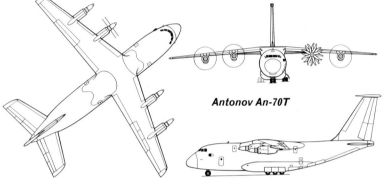

Antonov An-70T

feature electric de-icing. Estimated cruising speed will be 400 kt (740 km/h; 460 mph) at an altitude of 9500 m (31,000 ft). Operating from runways of 1800-2000 m (5,900-6,500 ft), the aircraft's maximum range will be 2,700 nm (5000 km/3107 miles). The An-70 will also be capable of rough field operations from strips as short as 600 m (1,970 ft).

The An-70T is intended for a life of 45,000 flying hours or 20,000 cycles, and is operable for 3,500 hours per year, with seven to eight man maintenance hours per

flight hour. Funding has passed to the Ukrainian government, and the Antonov OKB is actively courting interest in the aircraft, which could even be produced to fulfil the RAF's requirement for a C-130 replacement. An uninvited bid for the RAF's proposed Hercules replacement has been tendered under the designation **An-77**.

In March 1994 Antonov signed a joint venture with Daewoo, of South Korea, to build a new transport aircraft, based on the An-70T.

Antonov An-72 'Coaler-A', 'Coaler-C'

The **An-72** was developed as a turbofan-powered STOL transport to replace the turboprop An-26. The first of two prototypes made its maiden flight on 22 December 1977 and these, together with eight pre-series aircraft also built at Kiev, were given the reporting name **'Coaler-A'** by NATO's Air Standards Co-ordinating Committee. Series production at Kharkov was of a slightly modified aircraft with extended outer wing panels, a lengthened fuselage, no ventral fins and other detail changes. This initial production version was designated **An-72A**. This was codenamed **'Coaler-C'** because it appeared after the West had seen the long-span wing and lengthened fuselage on the An-74, which was allocated the 'Coaler-B' reporting name.

Because their aircraft flew for the first time only 17 months after the superficially similar Boeing YC-14, Antonov was unfairly accused of directly copying the US aircraft. There were certainly similarities, with a high wing, T-tail and high-mounted turbofan engines which discharged over the upper surface of the wing, using the Coanda effect in which jet exhaust is entrapped by

When the An-72 appeared at Farnborough in 1984, it was among the first Soviet aircraft to do so. When Antonov brought the An-72P to the 1992 show, it wore Ukrainian air force markings.

the extended flaps and thereby dramatically increases lift. The high-set wing, traditional on Soviet freighters, gives an unobstructed freight hold and eases production, while the high-set engines allow upper-surface blowing, as described above, but also minimise FOD ingestion problems.

The An-72's cargo ramp is little changed from that fitted to the An-32, and owes nothing to Western design practices. Telescopic struts fold down from the rear of each undercarriage fairing to support the rear fuselage when the ramp is swung forward under the belly for direct loading. The

undercarriage itself is similarly novel, and optimised for operation from semi-prepared strips, with low-pressure tyres, twin nose-wheels and main units which consist of two tandem trailing arms, each with a single mainwheel.

The An-72 has been built in several versions. The **An-72A** is a dedicated freighter equipped to handle standard international containers. The **An-72S** is an executive transport with the cabin split into

Antonov An-72 'Coaler-A' and 'Coaler-C'

three compartments, the forward compartment housing the galley, toilets and wardrobe, with baggage, a three-seat sofa and a work table in the next compartment (or alternatively the sofa and three pairs of armchairs), and with 12 pairs of armchairs in the rear compartment. The An-72S can be reconfigured as a freighter, or as a 38-seat transport with tip-up seats along the cabin sides, or as an air ambulance with eight stretcher patients.

The latest version of the aircraft is the **An-72P**, a dedicated maritime surveillance platform and the most obviously military version of the aircraft to date. Operational aircraft wear a smart three-tone camouflage, and are armed with a GSh-23L 23-mm cannon in the starboard undercarriage fairing, and underwing rocket pods. A novel system of bombs carried on an internal hoist has been displayed, and the An-72P is currently being offered with a range of anti-ship missiles, torpedoes and depth charges. The aircraft features an advanced inertial navigation system, linked to on-board cameras which allow it to photograph target ships and record their exact position with great accuracy. Prominent bulged 'eyeball' windows aft of the flight deck give a better field of view. SFP-2A flares are carried for night photography. Linked to the autopilot, the navigation system can also automatically fly a wide variety of search patterns, and can be used to calculate the speed and course of its targets. The An-72P has an endurance in excess of five hours with a cruising speed of between 160 and 190 kt (295 and 350 km/h; 183 and 217 mph) at an altitude of 1000 m (3,300 ft). Antonov has now entered into a partnership with several Israeli firms, offering the An-72P with much improved systems. The deal, announced at

The An-72P appeared at the 1992 MosAero show, at Zhukhovskii, with a far more military air than on other occasions. The aircraft is in service with Russia's Border Guards.

the 1994 Asian Aerospace Show, at Singapore, has been struck with IAI and its subsidiaries. Elta have supplied an EL/M 2022A surveillance radar, and Elisra an improved ESM system. El-Op are responsible for a new stabilised, large-aperture, high-resolution all-weather sensor fit. The An-72P's current sensor fit includes A-86P lateral and oblique cameras for daytime use, and UA-47 vertical nightime cameras. A TV system is fitted beneath the port undercarriage faring. The cameras are housed under the tail, alongside the photo-flash ejection system. The An-72P retains the pressurised fuselage of the transport version and can accommodate up to 40 folding passenger seats. Alternatively, 22 fully-equipped paratroops can be carried.

A typical eight-hour maritime mission could survey an area of 120x140 km (10,440 sq mile), with the aircraft flying from the centre of the search area outwards. covering a swatch of 20 km. Three Antonov An-72Ps (of a total of eight ordered) entered

service with a **Russian Border Guards** unit based on the Pacific coast during July 1992, finding a Japanese fishing boat illegally operating in Russian territorial waters on their first operational mission.

SPECIFICATION

Antonov An-72A 'Coaler-C'
Wing: span 31.89 m (104 ft 7.5 in); aspect ratio 10.31; area 98.62 m² (1,061.57 sq ft)
Fuselage and tail: length 28.07 m (92 ft 1.25 in); height 8.65 m (28 ft 4.5 in); wheel track 4.15 m (13 ft 7.5 in); wheel base 8.12 m (26 ft 7.75 in)
Powerplant: two ZMDB Progress (Lotarev) D-36 each rated at 63.74 kN (14,330 lb st) dry, but to be replaced by two ZMDB Progress (Lotarev) D-436 each rated at 73.62 kN (16,550 lb st) dry
Weights: empty 19050 kg (41,997 lb); maximum take-off 34500 kg (76,058 lb) from a 1800-m (5,906-ft) runway, or 33000 kg (72,751 lb) from a 1500-m (4,921-ft) runway, or 27500 kg (60,626 lb) from a

1000-m (3,281-ft) runway
Fuel and load: internal fuel 12950 kg (28,549 lb); external fuel none; maximum normal payload 10000 kg (22,046 lb)
Speed: maximum level speed 'clean' at 10000 m (32,810 ft) 705 km/h (380 kt; 438 mph); cruising speed at 10000 m (32,810 ft) between 550 and 600 km/h (297 and 324 kt; 342 and 373 mph)
Range: range 4800 km (2,590 nm; 2,980 miles) with a 7500-kg (16,534-lb) payload or 800 km (430 nm; 497 miles) with maximum payload
Performance: service ceiling 11800 m (38,715 ft); take-off run 930 m (3,052 ft) at maximum take-ff weight; take-off distance to 10.7 m (35 ft) 1170 m (3,840 ft) at maximum take-off weight; landing run 465 m (1,525 ft) at normal landing weight

The An-72P's primary armament is a twin-barrelled GSh-23L 23-mm cannon and a pair of underwing UV-32M rocket pods. It can also carry four 100-kg (220-lb) bombs, which can be dropped through the rear ramp.

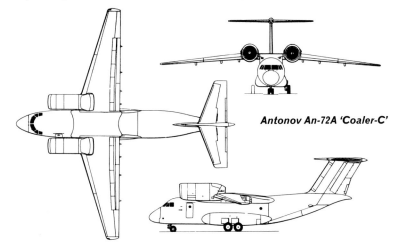

Antonov An-72A 'Coaler-C'

Antonov **An-74** 'Coaler-B' and 'Madcap'

The original **An-74** was a dedicated polar version, optimised for operation in the Arctic and Antarctic and designed to replace ageing Ilyushin Il-14s then in use for supporting Arctic scientific stations, Antarctic expeditions, and for observing and monitoring ice flows and ice build-up. Because it was the first version noted in the West after the original short-winged, short-fuselage prototypes and pre-series aircraft, it received the reporting name **'Coaler-B'**, whereas it was in fact a development of the series production An-72A which received the later reporting name 'Coaler-C'.

The An-74 had the same basic airframe as the production An-72, although there are two blister observation windows aft of the flight deck and at the front of the cabin on

the port side, and a larger radome whose underside does not follow the contours of the forward fuselage, giving a pronounced 'droop'. The aircraft carries a flight crew of five, with a pilot, co-pilot, flight engineer, radio operator and dedicated navigator, and is fitted with an advanced inertial navigation suite. Fuel capacity is significantly increased and provision is made for a wheel/ski landing gear to be fitted for operations from snow.

The An-74 'Coaler-B' made its Western debut at the Paris air show in 1987. Since then, despite the plethora of versions that have been announced, few examples have been noted.

The An-74 has spawned a family of variants, only some of which have the prominent nose radome of the basic aircraft, but most of which seem to have the observation blisters. The **An-74A** is a basic passenger/freighter, which is said to retain the larger nose of the basic aircraft. The **An-74T** (designated **An-74T-100** with navigator station) is a dedicated freighter with an internal winch, roller equipment and cargo mooring points, as well as provision for air-dropping cargo and static lines for paratroops. The **An-74TK** is a convertible cargo/passenger variant, with 52 folding passenger seats or a mix of passengers and freight, or all-cargo options. When a navigator station is provided the aircraft is designated **An-74TK-100**. The **An-74P-100** is a business aircraft or military VIP transport with a navigator's station (indicated by the -100 suffix) and a three-compartment interior similar to that of the **An-72S**. Telephone and fax facilities are included as standard, along with video entertainment and a refrigerator and bar. The forward compartment has four armchair seats in pairs, each pair separated by a work table, while the central compartment has a three-seat sofa to starboard, two more armchairs, and another table. The rear compartment has another three-seat sofa and two pairs of armchairs, bringing accommodation to 16.

At least one An-74 (SSSR-780151) was modified to serve as a prototype AEW platform. With a rotodome atop a new forward-swept fin and rudder, the aircraft may have been intended as a lower-cost AWACS system for the export market, or to augment the larger Ilyushin A-50 'Mainstay' in Soviet service or perhaps even as a shipborne AEW aircraft for the aircraft-carrier *Tbilisi* (now *Kuznetsov*). Development is understood to have been abandoned, perhaps in favour of the Yakovlev Yak-44, but not before NATO assigned the reporting name **'Madcap'**.

Production of the basic Antonov An-72, the An-72P and the An-74A, An-74TK, An-74TK-100 and An-74P-100 continues at the rate of about 20 per year (from the same assembly line) at their parent company's Kharkov plant. By early 1994 approximately 150 Antonov An-72 and An-74s had been completed. Further improved variants are likely to appear, and there are plans to re-engine the An-72 and An-74 with more powerful 73.53-kN (16,535-lb) ZMKB Progress (Lotarev) D-436K turbofans.

SPECIFICATION

Antonov An-74 'Coaler-B'
generally similar to the Antonov An-72A 'Coaler-C' except in the following particulars:
Range: 5300 km (2,860 nm; 3,293 miles) with a 1500-kg (3,307-lb) payload or 1,150 km (620 nm; 715 miles) with maximum payload

Above: The An-74 was intended for Arctic operations and many wore the high-visibility red scheme of Aeroflot's Polar Directorate.

Below: The only freely available picture of 'Madcap' (SSSR-780151), taken in 1987 during a visit by President Gorbachev to Antonov.

Antonov **An-124 Ruslan ('Condor')**

Only a handful of the (approximately) 40 **An-124**s delivered by early 1994 are assigned directly to the VTA, wearing full military markings, but other Aeroflot aircraft are frequently employed on military tasks. Named after Pushkin's legendary giant, the **Ruslan** is in many respects comparable to the slightly smaller Lockheed C-5 Galaxy, which has a very similar configuration. The An-124 remains the world's largest production aircraft (only the one-off An-225 is bigger), and has set a series of world records, most notably exceeding by 53 per cent the C-5's payload to 2000 m.

Designed to meet **Aeroflot** and **Soviet air force** (**VVS**) Long-Range Transport Aviation (VTA) requirements for an An-22 replacement, the An-124 has an upward-hinging 'visor-type' nose (with a folding nose ramp) and an enormous set of rear loading doors (with a three-part folding ramp) which allow simultaneous loading or unloading from both ends, or allow vehicles to be 'driven through'. The rear loading doors consist of the ramp, which can be locked in an intermediate position to allow direct loading from a truckbed, with an upward-hinging centre panel and downward-hinging clamshell doors behind.

The vast, constant-section cargo hold has a titanium floor with roll gangs and retractable cargo tiedown points, and is lightly pressurised, with a fully-pressurised upper passenger deck for up to 88 people. For ease of loading the aircraft can be made to 'kneel' in a nose-down position by retracting the nosewheels and supporting the nose of the aircraft on retractable feet. This gives the cargo hold a slope of 3°.

No simple, crude flying juggernaut, the An-124 has fly-by-wire controls and a supercritical wing, and makes extensive use of composite materials for weight saving. The aircraft is capable of carrying virtually any load, including all Soviet main battle tanks, helicopters and other military equipment. In an emergency, passengers can be carried in the partially pressurised main hold, and in 1990 an An-124 carried 451 Bangladeshi refugees (evacuated from Amman to Dacca during the Gulf crisis) using a foam rubber lining in the hold in lieu of seats.

SPECIFICATION

Antonov An-124 Ruslan ('Condor')
Wing: span 73.30 m (240 ft 5.75 in); aspect ratio 8.56; area 628.00 m² (6,759.96 sq ft)
Fuselage and tail: length 69.10 m (226 ft 8.5 in); height 20.78 m (68 ft 2.25 in)
Powerplant: four ZMDB Progress (Lotarev) D-18T each rated at 229.47 kN (51,587 lb st) dry
Weights: operating empty 175000 kg (385,802 lb); maximum take-off 405000 kg (892,857 lb)
Fuel and load: internal fuel 230000 kg (507,055 lb); external fuel none; maximum payload 150000 kg (330,688 lb)
Speed: maximum cruising speed at optimum altitude 865 km/h (467 kt; 537 mph); normal cruising speed at 10000 m (32,810 ft) between 800 and 850 km/h (432 and 459 kt; 497 and 528 mph)
Range: range 16500 km (9,140 nm; 10,523 miles) with maximum fuel and 4500 km (2,430 nm; 2,796 miles) with maximum payload
Performance: balanced take-off field length 3000 m (9,843 ft) at maximum take-off weight; landing run 800 m (2,625 ft) at maximum landing weight

The An-124's strategic importance lay in its ability to carry items such as main battle tanks, whole SAM systems and even the SS-20 mobile IRBM.

Antonov An-124 Ruslan ('Condor')

Antonov An-225 Mriya 'Cossack'

Despite high-profile appearances at a number of international air shows and a headline-grabbing series of 106 world records, the **An-225 Mriya** (**Dream**) remains something of an enigma. Reportedly developed to replace the pair of Mya-sishchev VM-T Atlants in use for carrying outsize loads, particularly those associated with the Soviet space programme's Energia rockets, the sole An-225 made its maiden flight on 21 December 1988, and flew with the Buran space shuttle on its back on 13 May 1989, visiting the Paris air show in the same year. Until recently, however, it apparently languished in storage, losing engines and other components to active An-124s. The VM-Ts remain active, and reports suggest that further VM-Ts may be produced through conversion of surplus 'Bisons'. Ambitious plans for the An-225, including a production run and leasing deal, as a launcher for Britain's (now defunct) HOTOL recoverable spacecraft seem to have fallen through, despite the huge potential.

The first aircraft to fly with a gross weight in excess of 1,000,000 lb (453600 kg), the An-225 is an ingenious derivative of the An-124 designed to offer a 50 per cent improvement in payload and maximum take-off weight. This was achieved by providing a stretched fuselage, six engines instead of four and seven pairs of wheels per side instead of five, plus redesigning the dihedral tailplane with endplate fins, deleting the rear loading ramp and increasing wingspan. The latter modification relieves airflow problems when carrying external loads. All controls are fly-by-wire. A second aircraft began to take shape on the line alongside standard An-124s in the early 1990s, but it remains unfinished and unwanted.

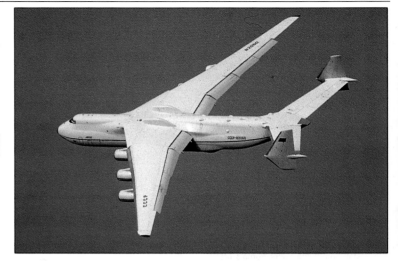

SPECIFICATION

Antonov An-225 Mriya 'Cossack'
Wing: span 88.40 m (290 ft 0 in); aspect ratio 8.63; area 905.00 m2 (9,741.66 sq ft)
Fuselage and tail: length 84.00 m (275 ft 7 in); height 18.20 m (59 ft 8.5 in); tailplane span 32.65 m (107 ft 1.5 in); wheel track 8.84 m (29 ft 0 in); wheel base 29.10 m (95 ft 9.5 in)
Powerplant: six ZMDB Progress (Lotarev) D-18T each rated at 229.47 kN (51,587 lb st) dry
Weights: maximum take-off 600000 kg (1,322,275 lb)
Fuel and load: internal fuel 300000+ kg (661,376+ lb); external fuel none; maximum payload 250000 kg (551,146 lb)
Speed: maximum cruising speed at optimum altitude 850 km/h (458 kt; 528 mph); normal cruising speed at

optimum altitude 700 km/h (378 kt; 435 mph)
Range: range 15400 km (8,310 nm; 9,570 miles) with maximum fuel or 4500 km (2,428 nm; 2,796 miles) with maximum payload
Performance: take-off balanced field length 3500 m (11,483 ft) at maximum take-off weight

The An-225 has re-emerged from a period of storage and is once more being promoted by the Antonov bureau as a unique heavylift aircraft. Plans to build further examples remain in abeyance.

ASTA (GAF) Nomad/Searchmaster

*ASTA Defence
Private Bag 4, Avalon Airport, Lara
Victoria 3212, Australia*

The **ASTA** (Aerospace Technologies of Australia (PTY) Ltd, previously Government Aircraft Factory) **Nomad** was the product of a mid-1960s effort to provide Australia with an indigenous twin-engined STOL utility aircraft with military and civil potential. The aircraft was built in **N22** and **N24** versions with different fuselage lengths. The basic N22 (and **N22B** with increased weights) seated 12, whereas the N24 could accommodate 17. Military transport and maritime surveillance versions were marketed under the names **Missionmaster** and **Searchmaster**, respectively. The former has wing hardpoints and load-bearing drop-doors in the cabin floor; the latter carries search radar, either Bendix RDR-1400 in the nose (**Searchmaster B**) or Litton APS-504(V)2 in an undernose radome (**Searchmaster L**).

Production of the Nomad series ended in 1984 with 170 built, including 40 **N24A**s, which first flew on 23 July 1971. The **Australian Army Aviation Corps** uses 10 N22s, distributed equally between No. 173 (GS) Squadron and the School of Army Aviation, both based at Oakey. Two other N22s support the **RAAF**'s Aircraft Research and Development Unit, alongside one N24A. The **Philippine air force** is another user of the transport Nomad, having acquired 12 Missionmasters for the 223rd Tactical Squadron in the 220th Heavy Airlift Wing, later supplemented by four Searchmasters.

For the counter-insurgency role, the **Royal Thai air force** has a total of 22 N22B Missionmasters, shared between Nos 461 and 462 Squadrons in 46 Wing at Phitsanulok and No. 605 in 6 Wing at Don Muang. Acquired in 1982/83, some were

immediately pressed into service as gunships (possibly with cabin-mounted machine-guns) to replace ageing AC-47s. Searchmasters are used by the **Indonesian navy**'s Skwadron Udara 800, which has received a total of 18, including 12 B and six L models. With Australian aid, the **Papua New Guinea** defence force has received up to seven assorted models and is operating both the Searchmaster B and Searchmaster L for EEZ patrols.

SPECIFICATION

ASTA (GAF) N22B Searchmaster L
Wing: span 54 ft 2.3 in (16.52 m); aspect ratio 9.11; area 324.00 sq ft (30.10 m2)
Fuselage and tail: length 41 ft 2.4 in (12.56 m); height 18 ft 1.5 in (5.52 m); tailplane span 17 ft 8.4 in

(5.39 m); wheel track 9 ft 6 in (2.90 m); wheel base 12 ft 3 in (3.73 m)
Powerplant: two Allison 250-B17C each rated at 420 shp (313 kW)
Weights: manufacturer's empty 4,613 lb (2092 kg); maximum take-off 9,100 lb (4127 kg)
Fuel and load: internal fuel 1,770 lb (803 kg) plus provision for 580 lb (263 kg) of auxiliary fuel; external fuel none; maximum ordnance 2,000 lb (907 kg)
Speed: normal cruising speed at optimum altitude 168 kt (193 mph; 311 km/h)
Range: 730 nm (841 miles; 1353 km)
Performance: maximum rate of climb at sea level 1,460 ft (445 m) per minute; service ceiling 21,000 ft (6400 m); take-off run 730 ft (223 m) at maximum take-off weight; take-off distance to 50 ft (15 m) 1,180 ft (360 m) at maximum take-off weight; landing distance from 50 ft (15 m) 1,340 ft (408 m) at normal landing weight; landing run 695 ft (212 m) at normal landing weight

In 1976, 12 Nomads were delivered to the Philippines, and 10 are still in use. They operate from Mactan AFB alongside C-130s.

Searchmasters were built in two versions until the line closed in 1984: the N.22SB (7) and the N.22SL (13). This example serves with the Australian Customs Service.

Atlas XH-1 Alpha

*Atlas Aviation (PTY) Ltd (a division of Denel)
PO Box 11, Kempton Park 1620, Transvaal
Republic of South Africa*

The Atlas Alpha is a one-off systems demonstrator, developed to support South Africa's indigenous attack helicopter programme, and is based on the airframe, engine rotor and transmission system of the Alouette III. Atlas was awarded a contract to develop the aircraft in March 1981, and it made its first flight on 27 February 1986. A new narrow fuselage accommodated tandem cockpits for pilot and gunner, with a single-barrelled 20-mm cannon under the nose, aimed via the gunner's helmet-mounted sight. The aircraft was given a new tail unit and tailwheel undercarriage.

SPECIFICATION

Atlas Alpha XH-1
Rotor system: main rotor diameter 11.02 m (36 ft 1.75 in); tail rotor diameter 1.91 m (6 ft 3.25 in); main rotor disc area 95.38 m2 (1,026.68 sq ft); tail rotor disc area 2.87 m2 (30.84 sq ft)
Powerplant: one 649-kW (870-shp) Turboméca Artouste IIIB flat-rated at 425 kW (570 shp)
Weights: empty 1400 kg (3,086 lb); maximum take-off 2200 kg (4,850 lb)
Speed: maximum level speed 'clean' at optimum altitude 210 km/h (113 kt; 130 mph); maximum

cruising speed at optimum altitude 185 km/h (100 kt; 115 mph)
Range: combat radius 275 km (148 nm; 171 miles)
Performance: maximum rate of climb at sea level 245 m (804 ft) per minute; service ceiling 3200 m (10,500 ft); hovering ceiling 2880 m (9,450 ft) in ground effect and 1520 m (4,985 ft) out of ground effect

Derived from the Alouette III, the XH-1 served as a weapons testbed for the Atlas Rooivalk. It led to the XTP-1 Beta (a converted Puma) and, ultimately, the XH-2 Rooivalk.

Atlas Oryx (Gemsbok) and XTP-1 Beta

South Africa was a major customer for the French-built Aérospatiale Puma, taking delivery of an estimated 70 SA 330F/J/L Pumas, eventually equipping or partly equipping Nos 15, 16, 18, 19, 22, 30 and 31 Squadrons. Attrition and defence economies reduced the force to three squadrons (15, 19 and 31) by early 1993, and substantial numbers of Pumas are now in storage. Improvements and upgrades to the aircraft began early in its career, Atlas soon building up considerable experience and expertise with the type, and in order to circumvent UN sanctions manufactured frequently required items such as tyres, transparencies, acrylic floor panels, gearboxes, engine hot sections, and rotor blades. It also manufactured newly-designed components optimised for SAAF requirements, including fuel tanks and armoured seats.

The first major upgrade programme resulted in the **XTP-1 Beta**, which featured extended engine intake filters, denoting installation of the Super Puma's Makila turboshafts, and with a tail unit similar to that fitted to the AS 532 Cougar. These modifications were later disclosed to be intended for retrofit across the Puma fleet, whereas the other modifications, which gave the aircraft its XTP- (Experimental Test Platform) designation, were not. These modifications included a long air data probe projecting from the port side of the cockpit, and stub wings mounted on the cabin sides, and apparently requiring the cabin doors to

be 'sealed shut'. The wings each carried two articulated pylons, capable of carrying 18-round 68-mm rocket pods. A 20-mm GA1 cannon was installed in a ventral turret (with a 1,000-round magazine) and was aimed by helmet-mounted sight.

Originally the XTP-1 was expected to form the basis of a gunship conversion of the Puma, but in fact it was a systems and weapons testbed, marking a further step towards the indigenous Rooivalk attack helicopter (described separately). The aircraft was later used as the basis of a low-cost alternative to the Rooivalk, and several stub-winged, cannon-armed Pumas entered operational evaluation during mid-1990. These had wingtip launch rails for the IR-homing Darter or Viper AAM, and a laser designator for the 'Swift' anti-tank missile. Atlas offered a range of four Puma gunships. Using detachable weapons pylons (so that aircraft could easily be reconfigured to a troop-carrying role, with 12 armoured seats), the most basic Option 1 saw the addition of a Kentron TC-20 ventral gun turret and helmet-mounted sights for the crew. Option 2 involved fitting four 68-mm rocket launchers. Aircraft modified to Option 3 standard added a nose-mounted Kentron HSOS (Helicopter Stabilised Optronic Sight) to the rocket armament. The 'full spec' Option 4 Oryx gunship will be equipped with ZT-3 Swift laser-guided anti-tank missiles. Option 3 and 4 aircraft are currently undergoing development.

The XTP-1's tail and (Makila) engine modifications, together with a new Super Puma style nose radome, formed the basis of the **Oryx**, originally known as **Gemsbok**, upgrade. The Oryx cockpit is also configured for single pilot operations. Pumas converted to this standard have replaced the SAAF's ageing Super Frelon, and entered service from 1988, with Nos 19 and 31 Squadrons.

SPECIFICATION

Atlas Oryx

Rotor system: main rotor diameter 15.00 m (49 ft 2.5 in); tail rotor diameter 3.04 m (9 ft 11.5 in); main rotor

The South African Air Force operates much-modified SA 330 Pumas in the shape of the re-engined, radar-equipped Atlas Oryx.

disc area 176.71 m2 (1,902.20 sq ft); tail rotor disc area 7.26 m2 (78.13 sq ft)
Fuselage and tail: length overall, rotors turning 18.15 m (59 ft 6.5 in) and fuselage 14.06 m (46 ft 1.5 in); height overall 5.14 m (16 ft 10.5 in) and to top of rotor head 4.38 m (14 ft 4.5 in); wheel track 2.38 m (7 ft 10.75 in); wheel base 4.045 m (13 ft 3 in)
Powerplant: two Turboméca Makila 1A1 each rated at 1400 kW (1,877 shp) for take-off and 1184 kW (1,588 shp) for continuous running
Fuel and load: external fuel up to two 350-litre (92.5-US gal) auxiliary tanks

Atlas XH-2/CSH-2 Rooivalk

The **Rooivalk** (Red Kestrel) programme continues despite defence cuts which once threatened the **SAAF** requirement for the aircraft. Development of an indigenous attack helicopter began in 1981 and involved the XH-1 Alpha and XTP-2 Beta as concept-proving and systems testbeds. The definitive Rooivalk prototype, originally designated **XH-2** (XH for Experimental Helicopter), made its maiden flight on 11 February 1990, and was later redesignated **CSH-2** (Combat Support Helicopter) and later still **XDM** (experimental development model). A second prototype, the **ADM** (advanced development model) flew soon afterwards, tasked with avionics and weapons development. Externally this differed from the first prototype in having a cropped 'tailfin', although the first prototype was later modified to a similar external configuration.

Although it looks like an entirely new aircraft, the Rooivalk is based on a degree of reverse engineering of the Aérospatiale Puma, using the same Turboméca Turmo IV engines (albeit slightly uprated), and the same rotor. The fuselage is entirely new, incorporating some composite structural components, with stepped tandem cockpits for pilot (rear) and co-pilot/gunner (front). Crew positions are reversed in the second prototype, which retains full dual controls and with the same three CRT displays and a HUD in each cockpit. The cockpits are covered by canopies formed from flat-plate or single curvature sheets to minimise glint. The engines are mounted on the sides of the fuselage, further aft than on the Puma, to give the pilot a better field of view, and this has dictated a redesign of the transmission system.

A nose-mounted, gyro-stabilised turret contains an automatic target detection and tracking system which incorporates a laser rangefinder, FLIR and TV camera, and the

two crewmen each have helmet-mounted sights. The cockpit is NVG-compatible, and night/all-weather capability is improved by twin redundant mission computers, twin weapon-aiming computers and a Doppler-based navigation system with moving map displays.

The Rooivalk is heavily armed, with an indigenous Armscor GA-1 Rattler 20-mm cannon turret mounted under the nose. An alternative XC-30 turret, containing a 30-mm DEFA 553 cannon, is also said to be a possibility. The cannon is backed up by weapons carried on the four underwing pylons. These can accommodate an 18-round 68-mm rocket launcher, or four-round launchers for the Atlas Swift laser-guided ATM. Air-to-air missiles can be carried on the wingtips. Rockets and missiles were test fired from a number of Puma testbeds before live firings from the Rooivalk were made during early 1994.

Provision is made for IR jammers and other ECM equipment, and the airframe is well protected by armour. If the aircraft

takes a catastrophic hit, the crewmen's energy-absorbing seats have a high degree of crashworthiness.

The full production standard Rooivalk will differ from the prototypes in a number of important respects. The pilot will be seated behind the WSO, unlike the arrangement in the ADM. Improved IR exhaust suppressers (pointing directly up into the rotor disc) will be fitted, together with enlarged sponson cheeks (similar to those on the AH-64C and AH-64D) housing avionics and ammunition. A pair of external seats can be fitted to these, allowing a Rooivalk to pick up the

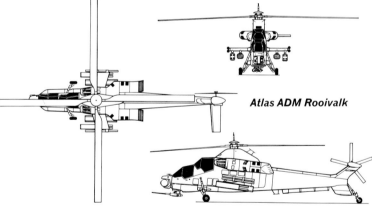

Atlas ADM Rooivalk

Visible on the ADM Rooivalk (to the rear) are its IR exhaust suppressors, weapons fit and revised rotor masthead.

crew of a downed helicopter, or to transport special forces soldiers.

The South African Minister of Defence has announced in Parliament that the Air Force will receive four aircraft for evaluation and indoctrinal/tactical development, and an order has since been placed for some 12 aircraft for at least one squadron. The aircraft's future can only really be secured by a major export order. With this in mind, Atlas have begun an intense marketing effort, which included displaying the demonstrator at the 1993 Dubai air show. The aircraft has been offered to Britain to fulfil the Army Air Corps requirement for a next-generation attack helicopter, and in April, Atlas were formally invited to tender for the requirement. The variant offered to Britain is known simply as the 'Kestrel', and differs from the intended SAAF production standard in having a new SWIM sight and a new weapons system, with provision for Short Starstreak missiles and NATO-type rockets. It will also have redesigned exhaust suppressors. This configuration will be adopted

The first aircraft, the XDH, is still a vital part of the Rooivalk programme, having amassed over 300 flying hours.

by the SAAF if finances and international sanctions permit. There have been some rumours that an export order, for a reported five aircraft, was placed during May 1991, and there have been discussions with a number of overseas partners regarding possible joint development and production.

SPECIFICATION

Atlas CSH-2 Rooivalk
Rotor system: main rotor diameter 15.08 m (49 ft 5.7 in)
Powerplant: two uprated Atlas-built Turboméca Turmo IV (Topaz) turboshafts
Weights: normal take-off 7200 kg (15,873 lb); maximum take-off 8000 kg (17,637 lb)
Speed: never exceed speed 170 kt (195 mph; 315 kt); maximum cruising speed at optimum altitude 145 kt (167 mph; 269 km/h)

Range: ferry range 720 nm (829 miles; 1335 km) with auxiliary fuel; range 507 nm (584 miles; 940 km) with standard fuel; endurance 7 hours 22 minutes with auxiliary fuel

Performance: maximum rate of climb at sea level 2,700 ft (823 m) per minute; service ceiling 20,500 ft (6250 m); hovering ceiling 13,800 ft (4205 m) in ground effect and 11,800 ft (3600 m) out of ground effect

Atlas **Impala**

In the mid-1960s **South Africa** finalised a contract with Aermacchi for a variant of the M.B.326GB which would be suitable for advanced training and the counter-insurgency (COIN) role. Designated **M.B.326M**, an initial 16 kits were supplied by Aermacchi, these being assembled by Atlas Aircraft at Kempton Park, Transvaal, the first of them being flown on 11 May 1966. The next 30 kits were less complete, requiring Atlas to fabricate a percentage before assembly, after which an additional 105 were built by Atlas, the last of these aircraft being completed in 1974. These duly entered service with the South African Air Force, which designated the type the **Atlas Impala Mk 1**, equipping first the Flying Training School at Langebaanweg. Impala Mk 1s are used by No. 83 Jet Flying School at Langebaanweg for streaming of jet- and transport-assigned pilots. The two-seat trainer is also the mount of the 'Silver Falcons', the five-ship aerobatic display team of the SAAF, which is co-located with No. 83 JFS. The SAAF currently operates 115

This Atlas Impala Mk 2, operated by the South African Air Force's No. 85 Air Combat School, was painted to resemble a gannet (the unit badge) for the school's 25th anniversary celebrations in September 1992.

Impala Mk 1s (of a total of 151 examples delivered).

Development by Aermacchi of the single-seat **M.B.326K** trainer/ground-attack aircraft was of considerable interest to South Africa, which acquired a licence for the type. Atlas production began (as with the M.B.326M two-seat trainer) by assembly of seven Italian-built kits, progressing to almost 90 per cent manufacture in South Africa. The first of the assembled aircraft entered service with the SAAF on 22 April 1974, being designated **Impala Mk 2**. These differ from the Aermacchi M.B.326K in minor details, primarily by retaining the same powerplant as the Impala Mk 1 instead of the more powerful version of the Rolls-Royce Viper of the M.B.326K.

A mixture of Impala Mks 1 and 2 equips Nos 5, 6, 7 and 8 Squadrons of the ACF (reserve) in the COIN/advanced training role. Impala Mk 2s are also used in the streaming

of future Cheetah pilots. The aircraft of No. 7 Squadron provide six-month single-seat conversion training as a prelude to transfer to No. 85 Combat Flying School at Pietersburg, where wingman and flight leader courses are undertaken. Selection for a squadron Cheetah (see entry below) posting is only considered after a minimum of 700 Impala hours.

It is believed that 100 Impala Mk 2s were eventually received by the SAAF, of which 75 are still in service. In addition to their current training roles, they have been exten-

sively used in South Africa's bush wars in Angola and Namibia, where the main tasks were ground-attack/close-support and aerial reconnaissance.

SPECIFICATION

Aermacchi M.B.326KM (Atlas Impala Mk 2)
generally similar to the Aermacchi M.B.326K except in the following particulars
Powerplant: one Rolls-Royce (Bristol Siddeley) Viper 20 Mk 540 rated at 3,410 lb st (15.17 kN) dry thrust

Atlas **Cava**

The indigenous Cava programme has now been abandoned, and is unlikely to be resurrected. The aircraft was an all-new

design based on the airframe of the Mirage III, using the upgraded wing of the Cheetah, but with a fly-by-wire control system and powered by the SNECMA Atar 9K-50 engine. A twin-engined version, using the same powerplant, was also proposed. The aircraft were to have been newly built, not

conversions of existing Mirage IIIs or Cheetahs, and would therefore have enjoyed a long fatigue life, and the potential of a long production run, not restricted by airframe availability. The aircraft was primarily intended for air-to-ground operations as a replacement for the dwindling fleet of Buc-

caneers and Canberras and eventually for the Mirage F1s. A change of regime in South Africa, coupled with the reduction of tension in the area, have combined to put the future of the aircraft (and indeed of any indigenous fighter programme) in some doubt.

Atlas **Cheetah**

Since November 1977 **South Africa** was been prevented by arms embargoes from procuring advanced aircraft. The SAAF therefore attached a high priority to a mid-life update for survivors of the 74 Mirage IIIs received during 1963-70. The upgrade was revealed on 16 July 1986 with the unveiling of a two-seat Mirage IIID2Z, redesignated **Atlas Cheetah**. The Cheetah benefits from Israeli technology (not officially verified) and closely resembles the IAI Kfir.

Aerodynamic modifications include Kfir-style small nose side-strakes (to prevent yaw departure at high AOA), dog-tooth outboard leading-edge extensions, short fences replacing leading-edge slots, canards and fixed wing leading-edge droop. Two-seaters also have curved strakes below the cockpit along the lower fuselage.

Structural modifications are centred around increasing the minimum life of the wing main spar (originally set at 800 hours). Several progressive stages of modification are proposed, reducing fatigue problems and providing life extension of up to 1,250 hours (for a complete refurbishment with a newly-manufactured main spar).

Two-seaters and R2Zs are powered by an Atar 9K50 engine, for which Atlas has a manufacturing licence. Other conversions retain SNECMA Atar 9C/9D turbojets. Retention of the Atar engine is indicated by the absence of the large dorsal airscoop and smaller overfuselage airscoops of the Kfir (which is powered by the heavier, more powerful GE J79). Installation of the 9K50 (in the two-seaters) involves modifications to the inlets and fuselage frames; the R2Z already had this engine. The installation of an IFR probe permits take-off with a lower fuel load and a correspondingly higher warload. The probe is mounted to starboard immediately aft of the cockpit. In addition, a

The cruciform braking chute used by the Cheetah D has the advantages of ease of manufacture and packing over more common round chutes. Cheetah Ds were initially assigned to the SAAF's No. 89 CFS, but in recent times the fleet has been passed on to No. 2 Squadron.

single-point pressure refuelling system is fitted, enabling times to be reduced (a maximum of five minutes for a clean aircraft).

The performance improvements include a reduction in specific fuel consumption (four per cent), take-off distance (10-20 per cent), minimum speed (100 KIAS), time-to-height and increased SEP, sustained load factor and sustained turn rate (15 per cent). The canards permit MTOW to be increased by 700 kg (1,545 lb) for a penalty of under five per cent in level acceleration time and maximum level speed. The uprated engine also allows a possible growth in payload/fuel capability or MTOW.

The Cheetah introduces a new ECS providing adequate cooling for the revised avionics. The avionics upgrade may be based on the Elbit System 81 (or possibly upgraded System 82) weapons delivery and navigation system fitted to the Kfir C2 (or C7). The HUD, CTU (Computer Terminal Unit) and ACDP (Armament Control and Display Panel) function via a MIL-STD-1553B databus and allow for pre-flight programming and HOTAS pilot operation. The nav/attack system includes an inertial system and options include a helmet-mounted sight (of indigenous, or Israeli, origin) and a radar altimeter. The Kfir-type drooped nose houses an Elta EL/M-2001B I/J-band radar ranging unit. Like Kfirs, the Cheetah features a fuselage plug ahead of the windscreen to accommodate the extra avionics. An Israeli AOA sensor vane is fitted to the port side of the forward fuselage. Self-protection systems include an SPS-2000 RWR system with antennas in the nose and in the fin trailing edge (replacing the Mirage III ILS aerials) and a possible jammer system in the former rocket motor fairing.

The Cheetah DZ differs primarily from the EZ by having a longer nose (like that of the Kfir-T) with more pronounced droop, housing displaced avionics from the spine. An undernose fairing directly aft of the pitot boom contains two radar warning antennas and a large cooling intake.

Fixed armament of the Cheetah comprises two 30-mm DEFA cannon. All weaponry of the Cheetah has been officially stated to be of South African origin, including Armscor V3B Kukri/V3C Darter dogfight missiles. Air-to-ground weapons include AS30 ASMs (which also form the basis of a reported smart weapon with an indigenous designator pod), cluster bombs, rockets and combined fuel/rocket pods. Two Kfir-C7-type stores pylons have been introduced directly ahead of the wing/engine intake trunking.

The first Cheetah conversions comprised eight IIID2Z trainers to two-seat **Cheetah D** standard. Declared operational in 1987, the DZs were initially operated by No. 89 Combat Training School and may have a pathfinder role for the **Cheetah Es**. The SAAF has a total of 16 Mirage IIIDZ and D2Z two-seaters available for conversion. For economic reasons, conversions to Cheetah EZ standard may be limited to 14 surviving Mirage IIIEZ and four IIIR2Z single-seaters. These aircraft retain their original Atar 09C-3 or 9K50 powerplants and the reconnaissance models will retain recce capability. These initially equipped No. 5 Squadron, but were passed to No. 2 when it retired the Mirage IIICZs, IIIBZ s and IIIRZs operated by No. 2 ('Cheetah') Squadron at Hoedspruit which were considered not viable for conversion and were ultimately retired from service in 1990.

In April 1992, a further upgraded version of the Cheetah was revealed. Based on the single-seat Mirage IIIR2Z, this prototype features an advanced combat wing which reduces drag and increases lift. The wing also permits an increase in wing fuel tankage in its fixed leading edge and additional wing-tip missile stations. The modifications allow a 15 per cent increase in sustained turn performance, improved handling qualities for a small weight penalty, an increase in MTOW of 700 kg (1,545 lb) and a 55-nm (63-mile/101-km) improvement in tactical radius. There have been reports that IAI and Elta are further modifying the 12 lowest-houred Cheetah Es under a $1.8 billion programme, with a new Elta EL/M-2035 radar and more powerful engines taken from retired Mirage F1CZs, which may themselves receive Russian engines.

SPECIFICATION

Atlas Cheetah EZ

Wing: span 8.22 m (26 ft 11.6 in); aspect ratio1.94; area 34.80 m2 (374.60 sq ft); canard foreplane span 3.73 m (12 ft 3 in); canard foreplane area 1.66 m2 (17.87 sq ft)
Fuselage and tail: length including probe 15.65 m (51 ft 4.25 in); height 4.55 m (14 ft 11.25 in); wheel track 3.20 m (10 ft 6 in); wheel base 4.87 m

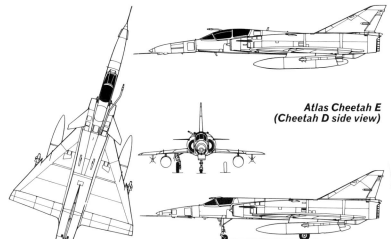

*Atlas Cheetah E
(Cheetah D side view)*

(15 ft 11.7 in)
Powerplant: one SNECMA Atar 9C rated at 41.97 kN (9.436 lb st) dry and 60.80 kN (13,668 lb st) with afterburning or, more probably, one SNECMA Atar 9K-50 rated at 49.03 kN (11,023 lb st) dry and 70.82 kN (15,873 lb st) with afterburning
Fuel and load: internal fuel 2288 litres (5,044 US gal); external fuel up to two 1700-, 1300-, 1100- or 625-litre (449-, 343-, 291- or 165-US gal) drop tanks; maximum ordnance about 4000 kg (8,818 lb)
Speed: maximum level speed 'clean' at 12000 m (39,370 ft) 2338 km/h (1,262 kt; 1,453 mph); maximum cruising speed at 11000 m (36,090 ft) 956 km/h (516 kt; 594 mph)

Above: Sometimes erroneously referred to as the Cheetah C, prototype aircraft No. 855 is the Mirage IIIR2Z Cheetah conversion and the first to carry the Advanced Combat Wing. This features a drooped leading edge, and plans exist for a wingtip launch rail.

Below: This Cheetah E wears the (toned-down) Pegasus badge of No. 5 Squadron, but all the SAAF's Cheetahs are now assigned to No. 2 Squadron.

Avions de Transport Régional ATR 42/52/72

Avions de Transport Régional
1 Allé Pierre Nadot
F-31712 Blagnac Cedex, France

A joint effort of Aérospatiale and Alenia, the ATR family serves the regional airline market. Two basic aircraft are available, the PW120 turboprop-powered **ATR 42** offering 40-50 seats, and the **ATR 72** offering 64-74 seats and PW124 power. An MPA version (**Petrel**) with nose search radar was proposed, but has found no buyers. Only one standard aircraft has been sold to the military: an **ATR 42F** freighter with port-side cargo door and strengthened floor to **Gabon**. Risk-sharing partners are now being sought for the rear-loading **ATR 52C Milfreighter**, a developed ATR-72-210.

SPECIFICATION

ATR 42F
Wing: span 24.57 m (80 ft 7.5 in); aspect ratio 11.08; area 54.50 m² (586.65 sq ft)

Fuselage and tail: length 22.67 m (74 ft 4.5 in); height 7.586 m (24 ft 10.75 in); elevator span 7.31 m (23 ft 11.75 in); wheel track 4.10 m (13 ft 5.5 in); wheel base 8.78 m (28 ft 9.75 in)
Powerplant: two Pratt & Whitney Canada PW120 each flat-rated at 1,800 shp (1342 kW)
Weights: operating empty 10285 kg (22,674 lb); maximum take-off 16700 kg (36,817 lb)
Fuel and load: internal fuel 4500 kg (9,921 lb); external fuel none; max payload 5375 kg (11,850 lb)
Speed: never exceed speed 250 kt (287 mph; 463 km/h) CAS; maximum cruising speed at 17,000 ft (5180 m) 267 kt (307 mph; 495 km/h); economical cruising speed at 25,000 ft (7620 m) 243 kt (279 mph; 450 km/h)
Range: 2,160 nm (2,487 miles; 4000 km) with a 2900-kg (6,393-lb) freight payload, or 1,250 nm (1,439 miles; 2316 km) with a 3800-kg (8,377-lb) freight payload or 42 passengers, or 540 nm (622 miles; 1000 km) with maximum freight payload

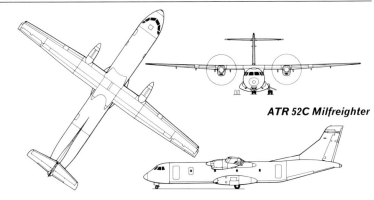

ATR 52C Milfreighter

Performance: maximum rate of climb at sea level 2,100 ft (640 m) per minute; maximum operating altitude 25,000 ft (7620 m); balanced take-off field

length 3,576 ft (1090 m) at maximum take-off weight; landing field length 3,380 ft (1030 m) at maximum landing weight

---

Ayres **Turbo-Thrush (NEDS)**

Ayres Corporation
PO Box 3090, One Rockwell Ave, Albany
Georgia 31708-5201, USA

E volved from the long line of proven Turbo-Thrush agricultural aircraft for use as a **Narcotics Eradication Delivery System** (**NEDS**), the two-seat **Ayres S2R-T65/400** was developed specifically for use by the State Department's International Narcotics Matters Bureau. Intended to dispense 'Roundup' herbicide from a hopper ahead of the cockpit, the NEDS Turbo-Thrush flies Operation Roundup narcotics plantation eradication missions in Colombia, Belize, Guatemala, Mexico, Myanmar and Thailand, targeting cocaine and marijuana.

The NEDS Turbo-Thrush, 19 examples of which were ordered by the **United States**

State Department between 1983 and 1985, has an armoured tandem two-seat cockpit, armour around its turboprop engine and a self-sealing fuel tank (additional to normal wing tankage) in a bullet-proof structure. Underwing hardpoints are fitted and theoretically allow gun or rocket pods to be carried.

SPECIFICATION

Ayres Turbo-Thrush S2R-T65 NEDS
Wing: span 44 ft 5 in (13.54 m); aspect ratio 6.04; area 326.60 sq ft (30.34 m²)

Fuselage and tail: length 33 ft 0 in (10.06 m); height 9 ft 2 in (2.79 m); tailplane span 17 ft 0 in (5.18 m); wheel track 9 ft 0 in (2.74 m); wheel base 8 ft 11 in (2.74 m)
Powerplant: one Pratt & Whitney Canada PT6A-65AG rated at 1,376 shp (1026 kW)
Weights: empty 3,600 lb (1633 kg) with standard hopper or 3,900 lb (1769 kg) with optional hopper; normal take-off 8,200 lb (3719 kg) with standard hopper or 8,500 lb (3856 kg) with optional hopper
Fuel and load: internal fuel 228 US gal (863 litres) plus provision for 20 US gal (75.7 litres) of auxiliary fuel in a bulletproof fuselage tank; external fuel none

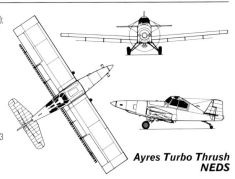

Ayres Turbo Thrush NEDS

Ayres **V-1-A Vigilante**

D eveloped as a low-cost surveillance and close-support aircraft based on the Turbo-Thrush NEDS, the **V-1-A Vigilante** was evolved in co-operation with the **US State Department** and in association with the **US Army** Electro-Optical Survivability Program. The prototype, first flown in May 1989, performed night surveillance trials along the Texas and Arizona borders on behalf of the US Border Patrol, successfully detecting groups of illegal immigrants.

Intended for marketing primarily in Latin America and North Africa, the Vigilante's turboprop has exhaust suppression and a hush kit. Its features include a two-seat armoured cockpit, a self-sealing auxiliary fuel tank, four standard NATO wing hardpoints and three stores stations under the fuselage. Stores may include 500-lb (227-kg) bombs, 2.75-in (70-mm) rockets, gun pods containing weapons ranging in calibre from 7.62 mm to 20 mm, and a variety of anti-armour missiles, sea mines and torpedoes.

SPECIFICATION

Ayres V-1-A Vigilante
generally similar to the Ayres Turbo-Thrush S2R-T65 NEDS except in the following particulars:
Fuselage and tail: tailplane span 16 ft 9 in (5.11 m); wheel base 17 ft 5 in (5.31 m)
Weights: empty 4,900 lb (2223 kg); maximum take-off 10,500 lb (4762 kg)
Fuel and load: external fuel 2,800 lb (1270 kg) in drop tanks; maximum ordnance 4,500 lb (2041 kg)
Speed: never exceed speed and maximum level speed clean at optimum altitude 191 kt (220 mph; 354 km/h); maximum cruising speed at optimum altitude 200 kt (230 mph; 370 km/h); economical cruising speed at optimum altitude 150 kt (173 mph; 178 km/h)
Range: ferry range 1,750 nm (2,015 miles; 3243 km) with drop tanks; range 900 nm (1,036 miles; 1667 km) with standard fuel; endurance 7 hours with standard fuel
Performance: maximum rate of climb at sea level

3,500 ft (1067 m) per minute; service ceiling 25,000 ft (7620 m); take-off run 1,250 ft (381 m) at maximum take-off weight; landing run 750 ft (229 m) at maximum landing weight

In its surveillance role the V-1-A can carry a Honeywell, Lockheed or Texas Instruments FLIR, Lockheed/Kollmorgen LLLTV and even a Honeywell IRLS.

Beech **Model 23/Musketeer III**

Beech Aircraft Corporation
9709 East Central, Wichita
Kansas 67201-0085, USA

F irst flown on 23 October 1961, the Beech Model 23 Musketeer was later adopted for primary tuition by two air arms, the **Mexican air force** and the Air Command of the **Canadian Forces**. The former procured 20 of the 112-kW (150-hp) Avco Lycoming O-320-E2C-powered Musketeer III (Sport) trainers in 1970, and the latter obtained 21 134-kW (180-hp) O-360-A4K-powered Beech Musketeer III (Sundowner) aircraft in 1981. The Canadian Musketeers were employed as **CT-134**s at No. 3 FTS at Portage la Prairie and gave place in mid-1992 to Slingsby T-67

Fireflies supplied by a private contractor (Canadair). The Mexican aircraft remain in service with the Escuela Militar de Aviación at Zapopán.

The Musketeer was awarded its type certificate in February 1972. Initially a two-seat design, it was developed into a 200-hp (149-kW), six-seat aircraft with retractable undercarriage. Nearly 4,000 of all versions have been built, but military sales have been slight. This is a Canadian example, now retired.

SPECIFICATION

Beech Model C23 Sundowner
Wing: span 32 ft 9 in (9.98 m); aspect ratio 7.5; area 146.00 sq ft (13.57 m²)
Fuselage and tail: length 25 ft 8.5 in (7.84 m); height 8 ft 3 in (2.51 m); tailplane span 10 ft 8 in (3.25 m);

wheel track 11 ft 10 in (3.61 m); wheel base 6 ft 4 in (1.93 m)
Powerplant: one Textron Lycoming IO-360-A4J rated at 180 hp (134 kW)
Weights: basic empty 1,425 lb (646 kg); maximum take-off 2,450 lb (1111 kg)
Fuel and load: internal fuel 60 US gal (227 litres); external fuel none; maximum ordnance none

Speed: maximum level speed 'clean' at sea level 131 kt (151 mph; 243 km/h); maximum cruising speed at 7,000 ft (2135 m) 124 kt (143 mph; 230 km/h); economical cruising speed at 10,000 ft (3050 m) 107 kt (123 mph; 198 km/h)
Range: 747 nm (860 miles; 1384 km)
Performance: maximum rate of climb at sea level 888 ft (271 m) per minute; service ceiling 13,650 ft

(4160 m); take-off run 1,132 ft (345 m) at maximum take-off weight; take-off distance to 50 ft (15 m) 1,883 ft (574 m) at maximum take-off weight; landing distance from 50 ft (15 m) 1,493 ft (455 m) at normal landing weight; landing run 746 ft (227 m) at normal landing weight

Beech **Model 33/Bonanza**

Derived from the V-tailed Model 35, the **Model 33 Bonanza** differed in having a conventional tail, and was first flown on 14 September 1959 as the **Debonair**. Manufactured almost continuously since then, the Model 33 Bonanza has been adopted by a number of air arms in both standard **F33A** and aerobatic **F33C** forms. Of these, the **Mexican air force** has more than 30 F33Cs remaining from batches of 20 acquired in 1975 and 22 in 1986. These aircraft serve at the Escuela Militar de Aviación at Zapopán. The **Islamic Republic of Iran air force** may fly the survivors of 18 F33As and 27 F33Cs procured prior to the revolution of February 1979. The **Spanish air force** has 18 F33s with its 42 Grupo de Ensenanza at Getafe and half a dozen with the San Javier air academy, remaining from 12 F33As and 29

F33Cs originally purchased, and several of six F33Cs obtained in 1979 remain with the air arm of the **Ivory Coast**. Bonanzas are additionally flown by the air forces of **Haiti**, **Israel** and **Paraguay**.

SPECIFICATION

Beech Model F33A Bonanza
Wing: span 33 ft 5.5 in (10.20 m); aspect ratio 6.2; area 181.00 sq ft (16.81 m²)
Fuselage and tail: length 25 ft 6 in (7.77 m); height 8 ft 3 in (2.51 m); tailplane span 12 ft 2 in (3.71 m); wheel track 9 ft 6.75 in (2.91 m); wheel base 7 ft 5.75 in (2.27 m)
Powerplant: one Teledyne Continental IO-520-B rated at 285 hp (213 kW)
Weights: empty 2,000 lb (907 kg); maximum take-off 3,400 lb (1542 kg)

Production of the first Model 35 Bonanza commenced in 1946. Spain operates the IO-520-B-powered F33A and C under the designation E.24A and B.

Fuel and load: internal fuel 44 US gal (166.5 litres) plus provision for 30 US gal (113.5 litres) of auxiliary fuel; external fuel none; maximum ordnance none
Speed: maximum level speed 'clean' at sea level 182 kt (209 mph; 336 km/h); maximum cruising speed at 6,000 ft (1980 m) 174 kt (200 mph; 322 km/h); economical cruising speed at 10,000 ft (3050 m) 135 kt (156 mph; 251 km/h)
Range: ferry range 851 nm (980 miles; 1577 km);

range 433 nm (499 miles; 803 km)
Performance: maximum rate of climb at sea level 1,136 ft (346 m) per minute; service ceiling 17,500 ft (5335 m); take-off run 1,091 ft (333 m) at maximum take-off weight; take-off distance to 50 ft (15 m) 1,873 ft (571 m) at maximum take-off weight; landing distance from 50 ft (15 m) 1,500 ft (457 m) at normal landing weight; landing run 792 ft (242 m) at normal landing weight

Beech **Model 45 T-34A/B Mentor**

Derived from the Model 35 Bonanza commercial light cabin monoplane of 1945, the Beech **Model 45 Mentor** tandem two-seat trainer was first flown as a prototype on 2 December 1948. Early in 1950, the USAF initiated the selection process for a primary tuitional aircraft, evaluating three Model 45s as **YT-34s**. On 4 March 1953, the Beech trainer was announced the winning contender and ordered into production as the **T-34A**, the **USAF** eventually procuring 350 from the parent company and 100 from Canadian Car and Foundry. Deliveries to the USAF's Air Training Command began in 1954, in which year the **US Navy**, too, elected to adopt the Mentor as standard primary training equipment, deliveries of 423 similar **T-34Bs** commencing on 17 December 1954. In 1955 the Model 73 Jet Mentor, developed from the Model 45 but powered by a YJ69 turbojet, first flew. It was soon abandoned in favour of the increasingly popular T-34.

Canadian Car and Foundry also manufactured 25 Mentors for the **Royal Canadian Air Force** (24 of these subsequently being transferred to **Turkey**), and 75 were assembled by the FMA at Cordoba for the **Argentine air force** (which also received 15 from the parent company), while Fuji in **Japan** built 124 under licence for the

national Air Self-Defence Force and 36 for the **Philippine air force**. In addition, the parent company exported T-34s to Japan (18), **Chile** (66), **Colombia** (41), **Mexico** (four), **El Salvador** (three) and **Venezuela** (41). The US government also supplied T-34s through the Military Assistance Program to **Spain** and **Saudi Arabia**. The Mentor became redundant in USAF service in 1960 with the introduction of all-through jet training while, in the US Navy, the Mentors were progressively phased out in favour of the **T-34C Turbo Mentor** (described separately) through the late 1970s and early 1980s. A small number of Mentors are still operated as hacks in support of recruitment efforts.

Of more than 1,300 Mentors manufactured, approximately 120 of these trainers – each averaging some 35 years of age – remain standard primary tuitional equipment with the air forces of Argentina, Colombia, **Dominica**, El Salvador, the Philippines, Turkey (air force and navy), **Uruguay** and Venezuela.

SPECIFICATION

Beech Model 45 (T-34A/B Mentor)
Wing: span 32 ft 10 in (10.01 m); aspect ratio 6.07;

area 177.60 sq ft (16.50 m²)
Fuselage and tail: length 25 ft 10 in (7.87 m); height 9 ft 7 in (2.92 m); wheel track 9 ft 6.5 in (2.91 m)
Powerplant: one Continental O-470-13 or, in T-34B, one Continental O-470-4, both rated at 225 hp (168 kW)
Weights: empty 2,055 lb (932 kg); normal take-off 2,600 lb (1179 kg); maximum take-off 2,900 lb (1315 kg)
Fuel and load: internal fuel 50 US gal (189 litres); external fuel none; ordnance none
Speed: maximum level speed 'clean' at sea level 163 kt (188 mph; 302 km/h); maximum cruising speed at 10,000 ft (3050 m) 145 kt (167 mph; 269 km/h)

Beech T-34B Mentor

Range: 667 nm (770 miles; 11238 km)
Performance: maximum rate of climb at sea level 1,210 ft (369 m) per minute; service ceiling 21200 ft (6465 m)

The Mentor was licence-built by Fuji, in Japan, and was supplied to the Philippine air force in its T-34A form.

Beech **Model 45 (T-34C) Turbo Mentor**

In March 1973, almost 20 years after the service had selected the Model 45 as its standard primary trainer under the designation T-34B, the US Navy sought a single type of aircraft to replace both the *ab initio* Beech trainer and the North American T-28B and T-28C onto which students progressed from the T-34B. To meet this requirement, and under US Navy contract, Beech began adaptation of the basic Model 45 design to take a derated PT6A-25 turboprop, converting two T-34Bs to take this powerplant as **YT-34Cs**, the first of these flying on 21 September 1973.

After an extended development programme, in April 1975 the USN ordered production of the **T-34C Turbo Mentor**. Since its earliest days in US Navy service the Turbo Mentor has been referred to as the 'Tormentor', and it is still the first aircraft encountered by prospective naval pilots. Successive contracts brought the total produced to 352 by April 1984, of which 19 were built as attrition replacements, with the final deliveries in April 1990. An armed version built solely for export carries the designation **T-34C-1.**

OPERATORS

The majority of USN T-34Cs are used in the primary training role and approximately 200 aircraft are shared by Training Wing Five's three squadrons: VT-2, VT-3 and VT-6 at Whiting Field, FL. Training Wing Four at Corpus Christi, TX, operates a smaller fleet of some 70 T-34Cs in a similar role; these aircraft being assigned to VT-27. VT-10 of Training Wing Six at Pensacola, FL, operates 20 aircraft to give limited flight instruction to naval flight officers.

In addition, the Turbo Mentor is operated in very limited numbers by USN fleet training units VA-42

(equipped with the A-6 Intruder), VFA-125 (F/A-18 Hornet), LAW-1 (F/A-18) and USMC attack squadron VMFAT-101 (F/A-18), on range clearance and spotting duties. VF-43 has at least three T-34Cs as spin trainers. One early production Turbo Mentor was assigned to permanent test duties at Patuxent River as an NT-34C. Six T-34Cs were transferred from US Navy stocks to the US Army to serve as chase and photographic aircraft for the Airborne Special Operations Test Board at Fort Bragg until replaced by Pilatus PC-9s (since disposed of also). It is intended to replace this veteran design with whatever aircraft is selected to fulfil the JPATS requirement, but probably not before fiscal year 2000.

Beech also built for export 129 T-34C-1 armament systems training models of the US Navy's T-34C, these being capable of forward air control and strike training missions in addition to basic flying tuition.

Beech T-34C Turbo Mentor

This variant was supplied to the Argentine navy (15), the Ecuadorian air force (20), the Ecuadorian navy (three), the Gabonese Presidential Guard (four), the Indonesian air force (25), the Moroccan air force (12), the Peruvian navy (seven), the Nationalist Chinese air force (40) and the Uruguayan navy (three). A civil version is known as the Turbine Mentor 34C, six trainers of this type having been supplied to the Algerian national pilot training school in 1979.

SPECIFICATION

Beech T-34C Turbo Mentor
Wing: span 33 ft 4 in (10.16 m); aspect ratio 6.2; area 179.6 sq ft (16.69 m²)
Fuselage and tail: length 28 ft 8.5 in (8.75 m); height 9 ft 7 in (2.92 m); tailplane span 12 ft 2 in (3.71 m); wheel track 9 ft 8 in (2.95 m); wheel base 7 ft 11 in (2.41 m)
Powerplant: one Pratt & Whitney Canada PT6A-25 rated at 715 shp (533 kW)

The T-34C is becoming increasingly popular as a hack and range safety aircraft with various US Navy FRS. This Turbo Mentor wears the colours of VF-124 'Gunfighters', the West Coast FRS.

Weights: empty 2,960 lb (1342 kg); maximum take-off 4,300 lb (1950 kg)
Fuel and load: internal fuel 130 US gal (492 litres); external fuel none; maximum ordnance none
Speed: never exceed speed 280 kt (322 mph; 518 km/h); maximum cruising speed at 17,000 ft (5180 m) 214 kt (246 mph; 396 km/h)
Range: 708 nm (814 miles; 1311 km) at 180 kt (207 mph; 333 km/h) at 20,000 ft (6095 m), or 427 nm (491 miles; 790 km) at 181 kt (208 mph; 335 km/h) at 1,000 ft (305 m)
Performance: maximum rate of climb at sea level 1,480 ft (451 m) per minute; service ceiling more than 30,000 ft (9145 m); take-off run 1,155 ft (352 m) at 4,210 lb (1588 kg); take-off distance to 50 ft (15 m)

1,920 ft (586 m) at 4210 lb (1588 kg); landing distance from 50 ft (15 m) 1,795 ft (547 m) at maximum landing

weight; landing run 740 ft (226 m) at maximum landing weight

Beech **Model 50/Twin Bonanza/L-23/U-8 Seminole**

The first post-World War II US light twin-engined aircraft to attain quantity production, the **Model 50 Twin Bonanza** six-seater first flew on 15 November 1949. Various examples of the progressively-refined series models were procured in small quantities for utility and liaison tasks

by several air forces. In addition, the **US Army** adopted the Twin Bonanza as the **L-23A Seminole**, 55 of which were followed by 40 examples of the generally similar **L-23B**. In November 1956 the US Army began to accept 85 **L-23D**s based on the commercial Model E50 and, during 1956

and 1958, the 93 surviving L-23As and Bs were remanufactured to the same standard with 340-hp (253-kW) Lycoming O-480-1 engines. Six Model D50s with 295-hp (220-kW) GO-480-G2D6 were acquired as **L-23E**s. In 1962, the L-23D and E were respectively redesignated **U-8D** and **U-8E**,

the last of these veterans being phased out of US Army service in the 1980s. One Twin Bonanza ostensibly remains in the inventory of the **Haitian air corps** and another continued in service until recently with the **Pakistan air force** alongside more modern Beech B55 Barons.

Beech **Model Baron 55/T-42 Cochise**

A development of the Model 95 Travel Air with two 260-hp (194-kW) Continental IO-470-L engines and swept vertical tail surfaces, the four/five-seat **Model 95-55**, or **Baron 55**, first flew on 29 February 1960. An optional sixth seat was introduced with the **Baron A55**, available from January 1962. The Baron was built in large numbers primarily for civil use in successively upgraded series (**B55**, **C55**, **D55** and **E55**), the provision of a 30-in (76-cm) longer cabin and 285-hp (213-kW) IO-520-C engines late in 1969 resulting in the **Baron 58**. Production continued until the early 1990s.

The Baron was procured for utility and liaison roles by various military forces and, in February 1965, was chosen by the **US Army** for use as a twin-engined instrument trainer. Seventy examples of the **Baron B55B** were ordered as the **T-42A Cochise**, five of these being for Military

Assistance Program delivery to **Turkey**.

Some 20 T-42As are currently included in the inventory of the US Army Reserve at Cairns Army Airfield, and three remain with the Turkish army. Various models of the Baron 55 and 58 serve with the **Argentine army** (two), the **Mexican navy** (three), the **Haitian air corps** (one), and the air forces of **Brazil** (one), **Paraguay** (one), **Spain** (five – local designation **E.20**) and **Togo** (two).

SPECIFICATION

Beech Baron Model D55
Wing: span 37 ft 9.75 in (11.52 m); aspect ratio 7.2; area 199.20 sq ft (18.51 m²)
Fuselage and tail: length 29 ft 0 in (8.84 m); height 9 ft 3 in (2.82 m); tailplane span 15 ft 11.25 in (4.86 m); track 9 ft 7 in (2.92 m); wheel base 8 ft 0 in (2.44 m)

Powerplant: two Teledyne Continental IO-520-C each rated at 285 hp (212 kW)
Weights: empty 3,075 lb (1395 kg); maximum take-off 5,300 lb (2404 kg)
Fuel and load: internal fuel 112 US gal (424 litres) standard or 142 US gal (536 litres) optional; external fuel none
Speed: maximum level speed clean at sea level 210

kt (242 mph; 390 km/h); maximum cruising speed at 7,000 ft (2135 m) 200 kt (230 mph; 370 km/h); economical cruising speed at 10,000 ft (3050 m) 169 kt (195 mph; 314 km/h)
Range: 993 nm (1,143 miles; 1840 km)
Performance: maximum rate of climb at sea level 1,670 ft (510 m) per minute; service ceiling 20,900 ft (6370 m); take-off run 596 ft (182 m) at maximum take-off weight; take-off distance to 50 ft (15 m) 968 ft (295 m) at maximum take-off weight; landing distance from 50 ft (15 m) 1,414 ft (431 m) at normal landing weight; landing run 868 ft (265 m) at normal landing weight

The Beech B55 Baron was a six-seat development of the A55, with a longer nose and increased MTOW. Nearly 2,000 were built.

Beech **Model 65/80/Queen Air (Excalibur Queenaire)**

A direct-growth version of the Model 50 Twin Bonanza embodying basic fuselage redesign, the **Model 65 Queen Air** was first flown on 28 August 1958. With a crew of one or two and accommodation for four to seven passengers, the Model 65 Queen Air or Queen Air 65 was ordered for evaluation by the **US Army**. The first example flew as the **L-23F Seminole** in January 1959. Subsequent contracts placed by the service brought total procurement of the L-23F to 68 aircraft. The type was redesignated as the **U-8F** in 1962, following rationalisation of all service designations.

The Queen Air 65 was also adopted by **Japan's Maritime Self-Defence Force** for navigational and communications tasks, 19 being delivered from 1963 and known as the **B-65 Umibato** (Sea Dove). The JMSDF Queen Air 65s were later supplemented by nine **Queen Air A65**s introduced by the Beech company in 1966, featuring swept vertical tail surfaces

similar to those first employed by the Model 65-80 Queen Air 80, which had entered production in 1962. The A65 also embodied increased fuel capacity. Five of the JMSDF's Queen Airs were transferred to the Air Self-Defence Force in March 1980 and currently remain with that service. Only two are still included in the inventory of the JMSDF, and these have relinquished their training role.

The **Queen Air 80** introduced a 300-lb (136-kg) weight increase – raising MTOW to 8,000 lb (3629 kg) and resulting in the numerical suffix – and IGSO-540-A1A engines. First flown on 22 June 1961, the Queen Air 80 was succeeded in 1964 by the **A80** with a modest wing span increase and certification for up to 11 passengers. With more minor changes, the **B80** followed in 1966, and the Queen Air 80 series proved popular with Latin American military services and is serving with the air forces of **Colombia** (four), **Dominica** (three), **Peru** (15), **Uruguay** (five) and **Venezuela** (four).

The air component of the **Ecuadorean army** operates two examples. The Queen Air 80 is also operated by **Israel's Heyl Ha'Avir**, which has some 20 for the twin-engine conversion role.

Beech designed the Queen Air to accommodate two main seating arrangements. The Airliner Package comprised seven seats with a baggage compartment. The Executive Package sat four passengers.

The Colombian air force operates a wide range of transports, from a Boeing 707 to the DHC-3 Otter. This is a Beech 65-B80 Queen Air attached to the liaison fleet of CACOM-3 at Barranquilla.

During 1981-83, the US Army purchased 11 ex-commercial Queen Air 65s, which, like the essentially similar aircraft originally built, were designated U-8F Seminole. More than 40 U-8Fs currently remain in service with Army Reserve and National Guard units after conversion to **Excalibur Queenaire 800** standard. This involved fitting new Lycoming IO-720 powerplants driving metal Hartzell props, revised engine nacelle design and a new exhaust system.

SPECIFICATION

Beech Queen Air Model A65

Wing: span 45 ft 10.5 in (13.98 m); aspect ratio 7.6; area 277.06 sq ft (25.73 m²)

Fuselage and tail: length 35 ft 6 in (10.82 m); height 14 ft 2.5 in (4.33 m); tailplane span 17 ft 2.75 in (5.25 m); wheel track 12 ft 9 in (3.89 m); wheel base 12 ft 3.5 in (3.75 m)

Powerplant: two Textron Lycoming IGSO-480-A1E6

each rated at 340 hp (253.5 kW)

Weights: empty 4,960 lb (2249 kg); maximum take-off 7,700 lb (3493 kg)

Fuel and load: internal fuel 214 US gal (811 litres) standard or 264 US gal (1000 litres) optional; external fuel none

Speed: maximum level speed 'clean' at 12,000 ft (3660 m) 208 kt (239 mph; 385 km/h); maximum cruising speed at 15,000 ft (4570 m) 186 kt (214 mph; 344 km/h); economical cruising speed at 15,000 ft (4570 m) 149 kt (171 mph; 275 km/h)

Range: range 1,442 nm (1,660 miles; 2671 km) with optional fuel

Performance: maximum rate of climb at sea level 1,300 ft (396 m) per minute; service ceiling 31,300 ft (9540 m); take-off run 1,180 ft (360 m) at maximum take-off weight; take-off distance to 50 ft (15 m) 1,560 ft (475 m) at maximum take-off weight; landing distance from 50 ft (15 m) 1,750 ft (533 m) at normal landing weight; landing run 1,330 ft (405 m) at normal landing weight

Beech 90 King Air/U-21 Ute/T-44

One Queen Air 80 airframe was fitted with 500-hp (372-kW) Pratt & Whitney Canada PT6A-6 turboprops and flown on 15 May 1963, subsequently being delivered to the US Army as the NU-8F. The definitive model, which was developed from the NU-8F, featured a pressurised cabin and was first flown on 20 January 1964.

In October 1966, the **US Army** adopted an unpressurised version of the King Air as the **U-21A Ute** with 550-hp (409-kW) PT6A-20 engines. The first example flew in March 1967 and a total of 161 was eventually procured. The U-21A utility aircraft could accommodate 10 combat troops, six command personnel, or three stretcher patients and three seated casualties. Some 60 were adapted for various Elint tasks, designations ranging from **RU-21A** to **RU-21E** according to the equipment and powerplant installed. Many of these were upgraded to **RU-21H** standard with new wingtips and undercarriage, and this sub-type preponderates among the 40-plus RU-21s remaining in US Army service. About a dozen others have been reconverted to the utility role to join approximately 100 surviving U-21s.

In 1976, a **US Navy** advanced turboprop pilot training aircraft requirement was met by an off-the-shelf purchase of the **King Air 90** as the **T-44A**. This tuitional model entered service in 1977, with procurement totalling 61 aircraft for service at NAS Cor-

pus Christi, TX, with squadrons VT-28 and VT-31. A modestly stretched version of the basic King Air appeared in 1969. With a 4-ft 2-in (1.27-m) longer fuselage, a reduced wing span and 680-hp (507-kW) PT6A-28 engines, this **Model 65-100 King Air 100** had a crew of two and carried 13 passengers. Five examples were delivered to the US Army as **U-21Fs**.

The King Air has been exported to a number of military services. The Model 65-90 is included in the air forces of **Bolivia**, **Colombia** (**C90**), **Ecuador** (**E90**), **Mexico** (and Mexican navy), **Peru** (**C90**) and **Thailand** (**E90**). The C90 version is operated additionally by the **Venezuelan army** and **navy**. Twenty-five **TC90** and **UC90** King Airs have been acquired by the **Japanese Maritime Self-Defence Force** for transport and multi-engine training, replacing Queen Air 65s. The larger Model 65-100 serves with the air forces of **Chile** (in the photo-survey role), **Ivory Coast** and **Morocco**. The **Jamaican Defence Force Air Wing** operates one King Air 100 for maritime patrol and transport duties.

SPECIFICATION

Beech King Air Model C90A

Wing: span 50 ft 3 in (15.32 m); aspect ratio 8.6; area 293.94 sq ft (27.31 m²)

Fuselage and tail: length 35 ft 6 in (10.82 m); height 14 ft 3in (4.34 m); tailplane span 17 ft 3 in (5.26 m); wheel track 12 ft 9 in (3.89 m); wheel base 12 ft 3 in (3.73 m)

Powerplant: two Pratt & Whitney Canada PT6A-21 each rated at 550 shp (410 kW)

Weights: empty 6,580 lb (2985 kg); maximum take-off 10,100 lb (4581 kg)

Fuel and load: internal fuel 384 US gal (1454 litres); external fuel none

Speed: maximum cruising speed at 12,000 ft (3660 m) 241 kt (278 mph; 448 km/h) and at 16,000 ft (4875 m) 247 kt (284 mph; 457 km/h)

Range: 1,277 nm (1,470 miles; 2336 km)

Performance: maximum rate of climb at sea level 2,000 ft (610 m) per minute; service ceiling 28,900 ft (8810 m); take-off run 1,885 ft (574 m) at maximum take-off weight; take-off distance to 50 ft (15 m) 2,577 ft

Beech T-44A Pegasus

(785 m) at maximum take-off weight; landing distance from 50 ft (15 m) 2,078 ft (633 m) at maximum landing weight with propeller reversal; landing run 1,036 ft (316 m) at maximum landing weight with propeller reversal

To the US Navy, the Beech T-44A is known as the Pegasus. All examples currently in service are based at NAS Corpus Christi, flown by Training Wing Four.

Beech Model 99

The prototype of the **Beech Model 99**, when flown for the first time during July 1966, represented the largest aircraft to be manufactured in quantity by the company. Intended for operators of commuter airlines, it was a low-wing monoplane powered by twin turboprop engines. The roomy fuselage incorporated a flight deck with side-by-side seats for pilot and co-pilot, and the cabin was equipped with easily removable seats in a 15-passenger high-density layout. A double-width door was optional, to simplify the loading of cargo, and a movable cabin divider was available so that the aircraft could operate in an all-passenger, all-cargo or combined passenger/cargo role. Initial reaction was favourable and there were plans to build 100 units per year by mid-1968 to meet strong initial demand.

Such enthusiasm was not ultimately justified and it was not until 2 May 1968 that the first production aircraft was delivered to Commuter Airliners Inc. in the USA. When production of what was then designated the **B99 Airliner** was suspended in 1977, a total of only 164 had been built.

Of this total, small numbers entered military service, and some of these were acquired secondhand. The Beech 99 was purchased by **Thailand** and **Peru**, the type remaining in service only with the Royal Thai army, which operates a single example for transport duties. By far the largest user is **Chile**, which had nine **Beech 99As** built as new. Three aircraft are used as liaison and general transports, with one example configured for VIP duties. The transports serve with 10 Grupo at Merino Benitez.

Political friction with Argentina has led to modification of the remaining aircraft for electronic surveillance work. These serve with Grupo No. 2's Escuadrilla de Guerra Electronica at Los Cerillos. Three examples, known as **Petrel Alfa**, have been configured with surveillance radar for maritime patrol missions. The remaining aircraft, named **Petrel Beta**, are fitted with an ENAER ITATA electronic intelligence suite and are employed for classifying Argentina's radar systems. This enables determination of an electronic order of battle and development of countermeasures.

SPECIFICATION

Beech Model B99

Wing: span 45 ft 10.5 in (13.98 m); aspect ratio 7.51; area 279.70 sq ft (25.98 m²)

Fuselage and tail: length 44 ft 6.75 in (13.58 m); height 14 ft 4.25 in (4.37 m); tailplane span 22 ft 4.5 in

(6.82 m); wheel track 13 ft 0 in (3.96 m); wheel base 17 ft 11.75 in (5.48 m)

Powerplant: two Pratt & Whitney Canada PT6A-28 each rated at 680 shp (507 kW)

Weights: empty equipped 5,777 lb (2620 kg); maximum take-off 10,900 lb (4944 kg)

Fuel and load: internal fuel 368 US gal (1393 litres); external fuel none

Speed: maximum cruising speed at 16,000 ft (4875 m) 244 kt (281 mph; 452 km/h)

Range: 1,019 nm (1,173 miles; 1887 km)

Performance: maximum rate of climb at sea level 2,090 ft (637 m) per minute; service ceiling 26,215 ft (8020 m); take-off run 1,660 ft (506 m) at maximum take-off weight; take-off distance to 50 ft (15 m) 2,480 ft (756 m) at maximum take-off weight; landing distance from 50 ft (15 m) 2,793 ft (851 m) at normal landing weight without propeller reversal or 1,810 ft (552 m) at normal landing weight with propeller reversal; landing run 1,317 ft (401 m) at normal landing weight without propeller reversal or 850 ft (259 m) at normal landing weight with propeller reversal

Beech King Air 100/Super King Air 200/C-12

The **Beech King Air 100** was based on the King Air 90 but incorporated a 50-in (127-cm) fuselage stretch, two extra cabin windows, larger tail, increased MTOGW and a twin-wheel main undercarriage. Nearly 400 were built and several found their way into military service. The **Super King Air 200** evolved from the King Air 100 as an even more enlarged, more powerful derivative of the latter, a pro-

totype flying on 27 October 1972. Introducing a T-tail, increased wing span, extra fuel and improved pressurisation, the Super King Air was adopted by all US armed services, with more than 300 currently active.

The first three production Super King Airs were delivered in 1974 to the **US Army** as **RU-21J** (later redesignated **C-12L**) electronic warfare and intelligence-gathering equipment testbeds. In the same year, stan-

dard Super King Airs were obtained off-the-shelf as staff transports by all four US armed services simultaneously, the US Army and **USAF** aircraft being assigned the designation **C-12A**, and those for the US Navy and **Marine Corps** (with cargo doors, more powerful engines and high flotation undercarriages) being designated as **UC-12B**. All versions were given the name **Huron**.

The C-12A Huron was powered by 750-shp (560-kW) Pratt & Whitney Canada PT6A-38 turboprops and had provision for two pilots and eight passengers, the first of 60 entering US Army service in July 1975. The USAF received 30 identical aircraft. The Army later adopted the PT6A-41 engine for its C-12As, purchasing 14 additional aircraft with this powerplant as **C-12Cs**. Twenty-nine of the USAF's C-12As were retrofitted

Beech King Air 100/Super King Air 200/C-12

with similar PT6A-42 engines as **C-12E**s.

Further production for the US Army comprised 55 **C-12D**s with side cargo doors, high flotation undercarriages and provision for wingtip tanks. Six of these were delivered (as **UC-12D**s) to the Army National Guard and six more to the USAF, while 18 were converted to **RC-12D Guardrail** (described seperately) Elint configuration. Five examples of this variant were for FMS supply to **Israel** and the remainder for the US Army, which purchased six more under a May 1983 contract. These were followed in 1986 by a US Army purchase of nine basically similar **RC-12K**s with PT6A-67 engines, large cargo door and oversize wheels, deliveries of this model continuing through 1992 against follow-on contracts.

Deliveries of the Super King Air 200 to the USAF as an operational support aircraft under the designation **C-12F** began in May 1984, these having side cargo doors and payload choices including two casualty litters plus attendants. Forty were purchased by the USAF after an initial five-year lease, six were supplied to the Air National Guard and 17 were delivered to the US Army. The designation **UC-12B** was applied to 49 Super King Air 200s ordered off-the-shelf for the US Navy, with a further 17 going to the US Marine Corps. The US Navy also obtained 12 **UC-12F**s (equivalent to the C-12F) and these, together with the UC-12Bs, became **UC-12M**s from 1987.

SPECIFICATION

Beech C-12F

Wing: span 54 ft 6 in (16.61 m); aspect ratio 9.8; area

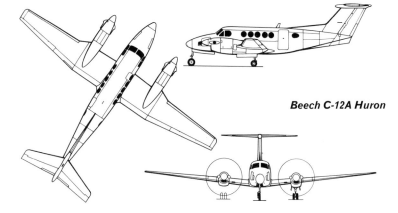

Beech C-12A Huron

303.0 sq ft (28.15 m²)
Fuselage and tail: length 43 ft 9 in (13.34 m); height 15 ft 0 in (4.57 m); tailplane span 18 ft 5 in (5.61 m); wheel track 17 ft 2 in (5.23 m); wheel base 14 ft 11.5 in (4.56 m)
Powerplant: two Pratt & Whitney Canada PT6A-42 each rated at 850 shp (634 kW)
Weights: operating empty 8,060 lb (3656 kg); maximum take-off 12,500 lb (5670 kg)
Fuel and load: internal fuel 3,645 lb (1653 kg); external fuel none; maximum payload 2,647 lb (1201 kg)
Speed: never exceed speed 259 kt (298 mph; 480 km/h) IAS; maximum level speed at 25,000 ft (7620 m) 294 kt (339 mph; 545 km/h); maximum cruising speed at

25,000 ft (7620 m) 289 kt (336 mph; 536 km/h); economical cruising speed at 25,000 ft (7620 m) 282 kt (325 mph; 523 km/h)
Range: 1,965 nm (2,263 miles; 3641 km)
Performance: maximum rate of climb at sea level 2,450 ft (747 m) per minute; service ceiling more than 35,000 ft (10670 m); take-off run 1,856 ft (566 m) at maximum take-off weight; take-off distance to 50 ft (15 m) 2,579 ft (786 m) at maximum take-off weight; landing distance from 50 ft (15 m) 2,074 ft (632 m) at normal landing weight with propeller reversal or 2,845 ft (867 m) without propeller reversal; landing run 1,760 ft (536 m) at normal landing weight

The US Navy and Marine Corps purchased the UC-12B, a military version of the Super King Air A200C, with PT6A-41s and a rear cargo door.

Standard civil Super King Airs have been widely adopted as staff/VIP transports. This is one of three aircraft operated by the Swedish air force.

Beech **RC-12**

Versions of the U-21 configured for battlefield Sigint missions have served the **US Army** well for many years. The natural heir is the Beech RC-12, based on the Super King Air 200 airframe. Several versions are in use, the first of which was the **RC-12D**, which was produced under the programme name **Improved Guardrail V**. Thirteen of this variant were built, mostly for service with the 1st and 2nd Military Intelligence Battalions in Germany. With cabin windows faired over, the cabin of the RC-12D is packed with electronic recording equipment largely aimed at the gathering of Comint. The RC-12D operates in minimally-manned configuration, onboard receivers collecting and locating hostile communications, and relaying the data via a downlink to ground vehicles for further analysis and dissemination to ground commanders. RC-12Ds are characterised by a wide array of dipole and blade antennas, and large wingtip pods housing ESM.

Two similar versions are the **RC-12G**, of which three were delivered with higher gross weights and Sanders-installed electronics equipment, and the **RC-12H**, six of which were delivered to the 3rd Military Intelligence Battalion operating in Korea. These again have higher gross weights, but have the same ESL-installed Improved Guardrail V equipment as the RC-12D.

The current major model is the **RC-12K Guardrail Common Sensor**, which combines the Comint mission of the RC-12D with the Elint mission previously undertaken

The RC-12K succeeds the RU-21H and RC-12D as the US Army's prime D/F and voice intercept intelligence-gathering platform. This programme dates from the Korean War and the current aircraft were heavily utilised during Operation Desert Storm. Improved Guardrail aircraft are fitted with the Guardrail/Common Sensor System (G/CSS) combining a Comint and Elint sensor fit. They also carry the ASE/ACS self-protection jamming fit.

by the Grumman RV-1D. Thirty-four are on order for the US Army, and deliveries began to Europe. These aircraft feature even larger numbers of aerials than their predecessors, with radar receivers having been added. The **RC-12N** is believed to be a similar version with some upgrades. In 1995/96 the US Army will introduce the **RC-12P** into the Guardrail fleet but, beyond its name, little has been made public about this aircraft.

In addition to the US Army **Special Electronic Mission Aircraft (SEMA)**, there are two **US Navy** King Air versions with the RC-12 designation. Both are configured as **RANSAC** (range surveillance aircraft) platforms, and are distinguished by having a large radome under the centre-section. The two **RC-12F**s are employed at the Barking Sands Missile Range Facility in the Hawaiian islands, and a similar number of **RC-12M**s fly with the Naval Air Warfare Center/Weapons Division (formerly Pacific Missile Test Center) at NAS Point Mugu, CA, and with the base flight at NS Roosevelt Roads, PR. Their chief task is to clear the maritime ranges before missiles tests.

SPECIFICATION

Beech RC-12D

Wing: span 57 ft 10 in (17.63 m)
Powerplant: two Pratt & Whitney Canada PT6A-41 each rated at 850 shp (634 kW
Weights: empty 7,334 lb (3327 kg)
Fuselage and tail: length 43 ft 9 in (13.34 m); height 15 ft 0 in (4.57 m); tailplane span 18 ft 5 in (5.61 m); wheel track 17 ft 2 in (5.23 m); wheel base 14 ft

11.5 in (4.56 m)
Fuel and load: internal fuel 3,540 lb (1606 kg); maximum payload more than 2,300 lb (1043 kg)
Speed: maximum level speed at 14,000 ft (4265 m) 260 kt (299 mph; 481 km/h); maximum cruising speed at 30,000 ft (9145 m) 236 kt (272 mph; 438 km/h)
Range: at maximum cruising speed 1,584 nm (1,824 miles; 2935 km)
Performance: service ceiling 30,900 ft (9420 m); take-off distance to 50 ft (15 m) 2,850 ft (869 m); landing distance from 50 ft (15 m) 2,514 ft (766 m)

Beech Super King Air 300/350

Following the success of its 200 series, Beech introduced the **Super King Air 300/350** series to continue the sales drive. The **King Air 300LW** is an improved Series 200, and this led to the **Super King Air 350**, which featured a stretched fuselage accommodating up to 12 passengers in standard configuration, useful for the staff transport/liaison mission. The 350 is also characterised by its drag-reducing winglets.

Raytheon undertook the conversion of the prototype 350 to **RC-350 Guardian** standard for the signals intelligence mission. In addition to ALQ-142 ESM equipment in wingtip pods and Watkins-Johnson communications intelligence receiver in an underbelly radome, the RC-350 also has accurate navigation gear including laser INS and GPS, and a secure datalink. As yet there are no military orders for the Guardian, which closely resembles the RC-12 in its mission and equipment, despite an impressive six-plus hour loiter time on-station. The government of **Morocco** operates a single Super King Air 300 for VIP duties.

This heavily retouched photograph illustrates Beechcraft's planned special mission Super King Air 350/RC-350 Guardian.

Beech Model 1900/C-12J

The **Beech Model 1900** commuter transport evolved as a stretched derivative of the Super King Air 200. The first Model 1900 flew on 3 September 1982, and made provision for a crew of either one or two on the flight deck and standard accommodation for 19 passengers. The Model 1900, of which only three examples were built, gave place to the **Model 1900C** as the standard production variant, differing only in having a starboard rear cargo door. This was powered by two 820-kW (1,100-shp) Pratt & Whitney Canada PT6A-65B turboprops, as was also the succeeding series version, the **Model 1900C-1** with a wet wing and redesigned fuel system. Production of the Beech 1900C ceased in 1991 after delivery of a total of 225 examples. A 'biz-prop' version, the **1900C/C-1 Exec-Liner**, was developed but fewer than 10 were sold, to civilian customers only.

The Model 1900C-1 was the first to receive military orders, a contract being placed in March 1986 by the **USAF** for six examples. Delivered from September 1987 as **C-12J**s, these replaced C-131s with the Air National Guard as mission support aircraft. From January 1988, 12 Model 1900C-1s were delivered to the **Republic of China air force**, the last of these being delivered in late 1989, and these serve with the VIP Transport Squadron of the Sungshan air base command. Eight were ordered for delivery to the **Egyptian air force** from 1989. Of these, six were delivered with electronic surveillance equipment and the remaining two, intended for maritime surveillance, were fitted with Litton search radar and Motorola side-looking airborne multi-mode radar (SLAMMR) and Singer-manufactured ESM equipment.

The Model 1900C was superseded in production by the **Model 1900D**. This version introduces a cabin with 28.5 per cent increased volume, swept tail surfaces with tailplane ventral fins, winglets, twin ventral strakes to improve directional stability and rear fuselage stabilons (additional fixed tail surfaces) to improve centre of gravity range. No military orders have yet been received.

The USAF and RoCAF operate the Beech 1900 in its intended transport role. The heavily modified Egyptian aircraft boast extensive aerial arrays.

Beech 400/T-1A Jayhawk

Entering service in increasing numbers, the **Beech T-1A Jayhawk** provides the **USAF** with advanced training for aircrew destined for multi-engine tanker/transport aircraft. It is the first aircraft type to be delivered for the SUPT (Specialized Undergraduate Pilot Training) system, which is being implemented to make the USAF's aircrew training more efficient and to cover a shortfall in T-38 capability, the Talon previously being responsible for all advanced training. The arrival of the T-1A in the TTTS (Tanker/Transport Training System) role allows the advanced training of crews for large aircraft on a system more compatible with their intended operational aircraft (KC-10, KC-135 and C-17).

From the outset, the US Air Force was looking for an 'off-the-shelf' design. Proposals from British Aerospace, Cessna and Learjet were considered by the US Air Force before Beech was awarded the contract in February 1990, this also covering simulator and a syllabus as part of an overall package.

The Jayhawk is based on the **Beechjet 400**, itself based on the Mitsubishi Diamond biz-jet. The Jayhawk differs from its civil counterpart by having increased fuel capacity with single-point refuelling, strengthened leading edges and windscreen for low-level birdstrike protection, and increased air-conditioning capability. The Jayhawk also features six fewer cabin windows in total, plus strengthened wing carry-through structure and engine attachment points to meet low-level flight stresses. The cabin-mounted avionics (relocated from the nose) include Rockwell Collins five-tube EFIS, turbulence-detection radar and TACAN with air-to-air capability.

For the SUPT role the aircraft carries instructor (right) and student (left) pilots, with a third observer/second student seat immediately behind. The cabin has four seats for passenger carriage or for additional students awaiting instruction.

When Beech acquired the Diamond design from Mitsubishi, they built 65, progressed to the improved Model 400A then developed the 400T (T-1A) for the TTTS programme, then sold it back to Japan.

Beech 400/T-1A Jayhawk

The first production T-1A took to the air at Wichita, Kansas, on 5 July 1991, and the first was formally handed over to the US Air Force on 17 January 1992. Instructor training began in March 1992 with the 64th FTW at Reese AFB, with the first student courses beginning in September. By early 1994, 148 Jayhawks had been ordered, with an eventual total of 180 planned.

Both name and designation duplicate those of other US aircraft: T-1A was the post-1962 designation of the Lockheed T2V SeaStar, while the HH-60J Coast Guard helicopter is also known as the Jayhawk.

In a somewhat ironic move, by early 1994 the **Japan Air Self-Defence Force** had also taken delivery of three Beech **400T**s (equivalent to the T-1A) for its Kawasaki C-1 pilot training. The Beech 400T features thrust-reversers, extra fuel and regeared trim (to simulate a heavier aircraft). Three more are on order.

The Jayhawk features several changes over standard Beechjets. Featuring an additional fuel tank and a new fuel system, a strengthened undercarriage and only three windows (as opposed to six) 148 aircraft are currently on order. First deliveries went to Reese AFB.

SPECIFICATION

Beech T-1A Jayhawk
Wing: span 43 ft 6 in (13.25 m); aspect ratio 7.5; area 241.40 sq ft (22.43 m²)
Fuselage and tail: length 48 ft 5 in (14.75 m); height 13 ft 9 in (4.19 m); tailplane span 16 ft 5 in (5.00 m); wheel track 9 ft 4 in (2.84 m); wheel base 19 ft 3 in (5.86 m)
Powerplant: two Pratt & Whitney Canada JT15D-5B each rated at 2,900 lb st (12.9 kN) dry
Weights: operating empty 10,115 lb (4588 kg);

maximum take-off 15,780 lb (7157 kg)
Fuel and load: internal fuel 4,904 lb (2224 kg); external fuel none; maximum payload 2,400 lb (1089 kg)
Speed: never exceed speed Mach 0.785; maximum level speed at 29,000 ft (8840 m) 461 kt (531 mph; 854 km/h); typical cruising speed at 39,000 ft (11890 m) 447 kt (515 mph; 828 km/h); long-range cruising speed at 41,000 ft (12495 m) 388 kt (447 mph; 719 km/h)
Range: 1,930 nm (2,222 miles; 3575 km) with four passengers
Performance: maximum operating altitude 41,000 ft (12495 m); take-off distance to 35 ft (10.7 m) 3,950 ft (1204 m) at maximum take-off weight; landing distance from 50 ft (15 m) 2,830 ft (862 m) at maximum landing weight

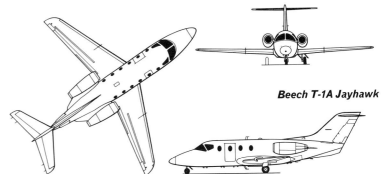

Beech T-1A Jayhawk

Bell **Model 47/H-13 Sioux**

The comparatively small number of company personnel who witnessed on 8 December 1945 the first flight of the prototype **Bell Model 47**, a small two-seat utility helicopter, could not have expected that when production by Bell and its licensees ended well over 5,000 would have been built. However, the Model 47 was not only to prove a classic design, it was also the first helicopter to gain an Approved Type Certificate, and on 8 March 1946 was issued the first commercial helicopter licence (NC-1H) granted by the United States Civil Aeronautics Administration. It quickly proved both its reliability and simplicity of operation, and in 1947 the **USAAF** began procurement for evaluation of 28 improved Model 47A helicopters with the 157-hp (117-kW) Franklin O-335-1 piston engine. Of these, 15 were designated **YR-13**, three **YR-13A** models were for cold-weather trials, and the balance of 10 went to the US Navy as **HTL-1** trainers. In 1948 the US Army ordered the Model 47, acquiring 65 under the designation **H-13B**; all US Army versions were subsequently named **Sioux**. Later variants included the H-13B (15 conversions) to carry external

stretchers (redesignated **H-13C**); the two-seat **H-13D** with stretcher carriers and Franklin O-335-5 engines; the three-seat but similar dual-control **H-13E**; the **H-13G** which added a small elevator; and the **H-13H** with 250-hp (186-kW) Lycoming VO-435 engine. Some H-13Hs were used by the USAF, which also acquired two as **H-13J** helicopters for Presidential use, powered by derated VO-435 engines. The designation **H-13K** covered two trial H-13Hs with larger rotors and 225-hp (168-kW) Franklin 6VS-335 engines. In 1962 US Army H-13E/G/H/K Sioux were redesignated with prefix O, for observation; similarly, USAF H-13H/J helicopters were prefixed U, for utility. Later versions were the three-seat **OH-13S**, and the **TH-13T** instrument trainer. US Navy procurement included 12 **HTL-2** and nine **HTL-3** helicopters, but the **HTL-4** was the first major version; it was followed by the **HTL-5** (with O-335-5 engine), **HTL-6** (with elevator), **HTL-7** all-weather instrument trainer, and **HUL-1** for ice-breaking ships. In 1962 the HTL-4/6/7 and HUL-1 became, respectively, **TH-13U/M/N** and **UH-13P**.

Also licence-built by Agusta in Italy and Kawasaki in Japan, and by Westland Heli-

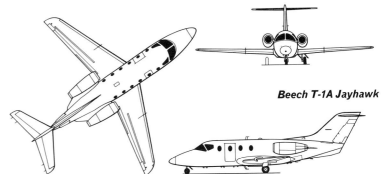

This Royal Malaysian Air Force Bell 47G is an ex-Indonesian aircraft and one of the few surviving US-built Model 47s still in service.

copters (under sub-licence from Agusta) as the **AB 47G-2** for the British army, Bell's Model 47 has seen widescale use by armed forces around the world. Today, numbers are dwindling, but an ever decreasing number still serve in the training or 'hack' roles with smaller air arms.

SPECIFICATION

Bell Helicopter Textron Model 47G-3B-2A
Rotor system: main rotor diameter 37 ft 2.5 in (11.32 m); tail rotor diameter 5 ft 10.125 in (1.78 m); main rotor disc area 1,082.49 sq ft (100.56 m²); tail rotor disc area 26.82 sq ft (2.49 m²)
Fuselage and tail: length overall, rotors turning 43 ft

7.5 in (13.30 m) and fuselage 31 ft 7 in (9.63 m); height overall 9 ft 3.875 in (2.84 m) to top of rotor head; skid track 7 ft 6 in (2.29 m)
Powerplant: one Textron Lycoming TVO-435-F1A rated at 280 hp (209 kW)
Weights: empty 2,893 lb (858 kg); maximum take-off 2,950 lb (1338 kg)
Fuel and load: internal fuel 57 US gal (216 litres); external fuel none; maximum payload 1,000 lb (454 kg)
Speed: maximum level speed at sea level 91 kt (105 mph; 169 km/h); recommended cruising speed at 5,000 ft (1525 m) 73 kt (84 mph; 135 km/h)
Range: 215 nm (247 miles; 397 km)
Performance: maximum rate of climb at sea level 990 ft (302 m) per minute; service ceiling 19,000 ft (5790 m); hovering ceiling 17,700 ft (5385 m) in ground effect and 12,700 ft (3870 m) out of ground effect

Bell **Model 204/UH-1 Iroquois**

Bell Helicopter Textron Inc.
PO Box 482, Fort Worth, Texas 76101
USA

In the early 1950s the **US Army** unveiled its requirement for a helicopter with a primary casevac mission, but suitable also for utility use and as an instrument trainer. In 1955 the design submitted by Bell was announced the winner, three prototypes of the **Bell Model 204** being ordered under the designation **XH-40**. The first of these (55-4459) was flown initially on 22 October 1956, its 825-shp (615-kW) Lycoming XT53-L-1 turboshaft engine, derated to 700 shp (522 kW), making it the first turbine-powered aircraft to be acquired by the US Army. The XH-40s were followed by six **YH-40** service trials aircraft with small changes,

the most important being a 1.0-ft (30.5-cm) fuselage 'stretch'. When ordered into production, the designation **HU-1A** was allocated, the HU prompting the 'Huey' nickname that survived the 1962 redesignation to **UH-1**, and which became far better known than the official title of l**Iroquois.** Initial production version was the HU-1A, with a crew of two, plus two passengers or two stretchers, and with the T53-L-1 engine. It was followed by the **HU-1B** with revised main rotor blades and an enlarged cabin seating two crew, plus seven passengers or three stretchers; early production helicopters had the 960-shp (716-kW)

Lycoming T53-L-5, late-production machines the 1,100-shp (820-kW) T53-L-11. In 1962, the HU-1A and HU-1B were redesignated **UH-1A** and **UH-1B** respectively, and in 1965 the UH-1B was superseded in production by the **UH-1C.**

Other military versions included the USMC's **UH-1E** (with rescue hoist, rotor brake and special avionics, and initially with a TAT-101 chin turret housing two 7.62-mm M60 machine-guns) and 20 similar dual-control-equipped **TH-1E** trainers; the USAF's 120 **UH-1F**s used for ICBM site support and 26 similar **TH-1F** trainers (both with uprated 1,290-shp/962-kW) General Electric

T58-GE-3 engines, and an increased-diameter Bell 540 rotor, 27 US Navy search and rescue **HH-1K**s (similar to the UH-1E but with a 1,400-shp/1044-kW) T53-L-13 engine and improved avionics, 90 **TH-1L** (training) and eight **UH-1L** (utility) both Navy versions of the UH-1E with T53-L-13 engine; and the US Army **UH-1M** with INFANT low-light-level TV equipment (three acquired for evaluation). In addition to production for the US armed forces, The Model 204B was extensively licence-built for both civil and military use by Agusta in Italy as the **Agusta-Bell AB 204** (described separately) and by Fuji in Japan, the latter also developing the

Fuji-Bell 204B-2 with increased engine power and a tractor tail rotor. In **Japanese Ground Self-Defence Force** service it was known as the **Hi'yodori** (meaning Bulbul – a type of finch).

OPERATORS

Austria: AB 204
Brazil: UH-1D
Indonesia: AB 204
Japan: UH-1B
Panama: UH-1B
Singapore: UH-1B
South Korea: UH-1B
Spain: UH-1C (HU.8)
Sweden: AB 204B (Hkp 3B)
Thailand: UH-1A, UH-1B
Uruguay: UH-1B
Yemen: AB 204B

SPECIFICATION

Bell Helicopter Textron Model 204 (UH-1C)
Rotor system: main rotor diameter 44 ft 0 in (13.41 m); tail rotor diameter 8 ft 6 in (2.59 m); main rotor disc area 1,520.53 sq ft (141.26 m2); tail rotor disc area 56.74 sq ft (5.27 m2)
Fuselage and tail: length overall, rotors turning 53 ft 0 in (16.15 m) and fuselage 42 ft 7 in (12.98 m); height

overall 12 ft 7.25 in (3.84 m); stabiliser span 9 ft 4 in (2.84 m); skid track 8 ft 8 in (2.64 m)
Powerplant: one Textron Lycoming T53-L-11 rated at 1,100 shp (820 kW)
Weights: empty 5,071 lb (2300 kg); maximum take-off 9,500 lb (4309 kg)
Fuel and load: internal fuel 242 US gal (916 litres) plus provision for 350 US gal (1325 litres) of auxiliary fuel in a fuselage tank; external fuel none; maximum payload 3,000 lb (1361 kg)
Speed: maximum level and maximum cruising speed 'clean' at sea level 129 kt (148 mph; 238 km/h); economical cruising speed at 5,000 ft (1525 m) 124 kt (143 mph; 230 km/h)
Range: ferry range 332 nm (382 miles; 615 km) with auxiliary fuel
Performance: maximum rate of climb at sea level 1,400 ft (427 m) per minute; service ceiling 11,500 ft (3505 m); hovering ceiling 10,600 ft (3230 m) in ground effect and 10,000 ft (3050 m) out of ground effect

Bell Helicopter Textron Model 204 (UH-1E)
generally similar to the Model 204 (UH-1C Iroquois) except in the following particulars:
Weights: empty 5,055 lb (2292 kg); maximum take-off 9,500 lb (4309 kg)
Fuel and load: max payload 4,000 lb (1814 kg)
Speed: maximum level speed at sea level 140 kt (161 mph; 259 km/h); maximum cruising speed at sea level 120 kt (138 mph; 222 km/h)
Range: 248 nm (286 miles; 460 km)

Twenty-four Bell 204B Iroquois were delivered to Austria, though these have now largely been replaced by 24 Bell 212s. Eight 204Bs remain.

The hardworking Hkp 3Bs (AB 204Bs) of the Flygvapen (Swedish air force) are tasked mainly with SAR duties at bases throughout the country.

Performance: maximum rate of climb at sea level 1,849 ft (563 m) per minute; service ceiling 21,000 ft

(6400 m); hovering ceiling 15,800 ft (4815 m) in ground effect and 11,800 ft (3595 m) out of ground effect

Bell **Model 205/UH-1D/H** Iroquois

Production of the Model 204 for the US armed services totalled some 2,500 examples, and Bell proposed an improved **Bell Model 205** to the US Army in 1960. A contract followed in July 1960 for seven service evaluation **YUH-1D** helicopters. These retained the Lycoming T53-L-11 turboshaft, but differed from the Model 204 by having a larger-diameter main rotor, and a lengthened fuselage for a pilot and 12-14 troops, or six stretchers and a medical attendant, or 4,000 lb (1814 kg) of freight. Additionally, the Model 205 featured increased fuel capacity and provision was made for auxiliary fuel. The prototype was flown on 16 August 1961 and the type was ordered into production for the US Army under the designation **UH-1D**, the first example being delivered on 9 August 1963. A total of 2,008 UH-1Ds was built for the US Army, followed by the generally similar **UH-1H**, which differed by introducing an uprated 1,400-shp (1044-kW) T53-L-13 turboshaft; final production of the UH-1H (40 for the Turkish army) occurred in 1986.

Variants of the Model 205 include three **EH-1H** ECM conversions from the UH-1H (with many more planned before the intended 'Quick Fix' ECM/Elint mission was taken over by the Sikorsky EH-60A), four **JUH-1H** testbeds for the radar intended for the EH-60B SOTAS, and some **220 UH-1V** medevac/rescue conversions from UH-1Hs, carried out by the US Army Electronics Command. One **EH-1X** was produced by marrying the airframe of an EH-1 jammer with the engine and IR jammer of an AH-1. Other military versions of the Model 205, generally similar to the UH-1H, have included 10 **CUH-1H** operational trainers for the Canadian Armed Forces (designated **CH-118**) and 30 **HH-1H** rescue helicopters for the USAF. Production of the UH-1H for the US Army totalled 3,573 examples, and it is planned to retain large numbers in service into the 21st century.

Under a product improvement programme, the US Army's Hueys have gained new avionics and equipment, and new composite main rotor blades are to be introduced, as well as Doppler navigation and an improved cockpit. Further radical upgrading seems increasingly likely. The US Army

requirement for 491 LUHs (Light Utility Helicopters) is unlikely to be funded, so many are pressing for the National Guard to take over the role with upgraded UH-1s or a new off-the-shelf type (the Vought Panther 800, MDH Explorer and Bell OH-58D all having been suggested). Thus, the Guard might gain more UH-1s to be upgraded alongside the 200 aircraft it already wants to replace or rebuild. Many export customers are also looking to upgrade their ageing Hueys.

Three companies are offering different UH-1 upgrades, all centred around re-engining the aircraft and upgrading its dynamic system. Avionics improvements are also incorporated and costs work out at between $750,000 and $1,000,000 per aircraft. Bell Helicopter itself offers the **UH-1HP Huey II** with an upgrade to the existing T53-13B engine (bringing it to T53-703 standard) during overhaul. This increases power by 400 shp (300 kW) and extends TBO by 600

hours (to 3,000 hours). If the 'new' engine is then derated to 13B levels, the airframe and dynamic system improvements necessary to use the extra power can be added in stages. All of these use existing Model 212 and UH-1N components, and include a strengthened tailboom, a tractor tail rotor, an uprated drive train and a 1,290-shp (960 kW) transmission, and the Model 212 main rotor hub and blades. The prototype first flew in August 1992. Gross weight is increased to 10,500 lb (4750 kg), allowing the aircraft to carry a 3,000-lb (1350-kg) payload over 200 nm (230 miles/370 km), where the original UH-1 would only carry 1,000 lb (450 kg). The T53-703 is marginally more fuel efficient than the original powerplant, offering a slight increase in range.

The fact that the Huey II carries Bell's 'seal of approval' has not deterred other companies from offering their own upgrades. Global Helicopter is promoting

the **Huey 800,** which replaces the T53 with an LHTEC T800-800 engine with an integral inlet particle separator and full authority digital engine controls. Engine life is extended to over 6,000 hours. Power output is actually reduced slightly, to 1,300 shp (985 kW), but the new engine is significantly lighter and much more fuel efficient. Power is not increased so the new aircraft requires no dynamic system changes, and the unchanged gross weight means that no airframe strengthening is necessary, although a speed reduction gearbox does need to be fitted. Range is increased dramatically, although maximum payload is not significantly increased. The prototype Huey 800 flew on 15 June 1992.

UNC Helicopter's upgraded aircraft is designated **UH-1/T700 Ultra Huey** and uses the same airframe/dynamic system improvements as the Huey II, but with a 1,900-shp (1400-kW) General Electric T700-GE-701C engine, with a life of 5,000 hours. The new engine requires a speed reduction gear box and vertical strip engine instruments, as found on the H-60. Performance

The Pakistan army was already operating helicopters of Soviet (Mil Mi-8), French (Sud Alouette III) and Romanian (CNIAR Lama) origin when it received its first American type in the form of the UH-1H. Six were delivered after the disastrous floods of 1973, with the strict proviso that they should be used only for humanitarian work. Allocated to No. 6 Emergency Relief Sqn they were later joined by 10 ex-Iranian AB 205As with No. 21 Sqn.

Bell Model 205/UH-1D/H Iroquois

benefits are almost identical to those enjoyed by the Huey II, though with better fuel burn figures.

In addition to military exports by Bell, a multi-role utility helicopter for both civil and military use has been extensively licence-built by Agusta in Italy as the **Agusta-Bell AB 205** (described separately); Fuji in Japan remains the only current production source of the Model 205 under the designation **HU-1H**. (The **AB 205A** and the improved **Advanced Model 205A-1** model are described separately.) Dornier in Germany completed 352 equivalent to the UH-1D model, which serve with the Luftwaffe and Heeresfliegertruppen, and in Taiwan AIDC built 118 similar to the UH-1H for the Chinese Nationalist army.

OPERATORS

Argentina: UH-1D, UH-1H
Australia: UH-1H
Bahrain: AB 205A-1
Bangladesh: AB 205A-1
Bolivia: UH-1H
Brazil: UH-1D, UH-1H
Brunei: B 205A-1
Canada: UH-1H (CH-118)
Chile: UH-1D, UH-1H
Colombia: UH-1H
Dominican Republic: B 205A-1
Dubai: B 205A-1
El Salvador: UH-1H
Germany: UH-1D
Greece: AB 205A, UH-1H
Guatemala: UH-1D
Honduras: UH-1H
Iran: AB 205A
Italy: AB 205
Jamaica : B 205
Japan: UH-1H, UH-1 Kai
Mexico: AB 205A-1, UH-1H
Morocco: AB 205A-1

Myanmar/Burma: UH-1H
New Zealand: UH-1H
Oman: AB 205A-1
Pakistan: AB 205, UH-1H
Panama: UH-1H
Peru: AB 205A-1
Philippines: UH-1H
Saudi Arabia: AB 205
Singapore: B 205, UH-1H
South Korea: UH-1H
Spain: UH-1H (HU.10B)
Taiwan/Republic of China: UH-1H
Tanzania: AB 205A
Thailand: UH-1H
Tunisia: AB 205A-1
Turkey: AB 205A, UH-1H
Uganda: AB 205
United Arab Emirates: B 205A
US Army UH-1H – chiefly special mission variants
Uruguay: UH-1H
Venezuela: UH-1D
Zambia: AB 205A
Zimbabwe: AB 205A

SPECIFICATION

Bell Helicopter Textron Model 205
Rotor system: main rotor diameter 48 ft 0 in (14.63 m); tail rotor diameter 8 ft 6 in (2.59 m); main rotor disc area 1,809.56 sq ft (168.11 m2); tail rotor disc area 56.74 sq ft (5.27 m2)
Fuselage and tail: length overall, rotors turning 57 ft 9.625 in (17.62 m) and fuselage 41 ft 10.25 in (12.77 m); height overall 14 ft 5.5 in (4.41 m) with tail rotor turning, and to top of rotor head 11 ft 9.75 in (3.60 m); stabiliser span 9 ft 4 in (2.84 m); skid track 9 ft 6.5 in (2.91 m)
Powerplant: one Textron Lycoming T53-L-13 rated at 1,400 shp (1044 kW)
Weights: empty equipped 5,210 lb (2363 kg); basic operating 5,557 lb (2520 kg) in the troop-carrying role; normal take-off 9,039 lb (4100 kg); maximum take-off 9,500 lb (4309 kg)
Fuel and load: internal fuel 223 US gal (844 litres)

The Huey II is Bell's own entrant in the race for lucrative UH-1 upgrade contracts. Combining many of the advances found in the Model 212, it faces competition from the UNC Ultra Huey and Global Helicopter's Huey 800.

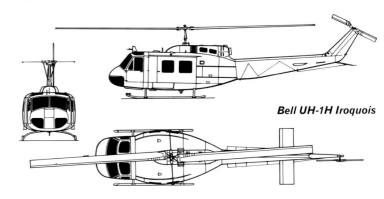

Bell UH-1H Iroquois

plus provision for 511 US gal (1935 litres) of auxiliary fuel in two tanks; external fuel none; maximum payload 3,880 lb (1759 kg)
Speed: never exceed, maximum level, maximum cruising and economical cruising speed at 5,700 ft (1735 m) 110 kt (127 mph; 204 km/h)

Range: 276 nm (318 miles; 511 km)
Performance: maximum rate of climb at sea level 1,600 ft (488 m) per minute; service ceiling 12,600 ft (3840 m); hovering ceiling 13,600 ft (4145 m) in ground effect and 4,000 ft (1220 m) out of ground effect

Bell **Model 206 JetRanger/TH-67/206L LongRanger**

The **Bell Model 206A JetRanger** was derived substantially from Bell's losing HO-4 submission for the **US Army's** LOH competition. The JetRanger was fundamentally the same as the **OH-4A** (formerly HO-4) prototypes, except for modifications to provide seating for five. Flown on 10 January 1966 it was certificated nine months later as a general-purpose light helicopter. It was also built under licence by Agusta as the **AB 206** (described separately).

Bell began development of an improved version of the Model 206A in early 1971. The resulting **Model 206B JetRanger II** replaced the Model 206A in production, and introduced a more powerful 400-shp (298-kW) Allison 250-C20 turboshaft engine. The installation of this engine involved only minor airframe modification and made it possible for Bell to offer kits for the upgrading of earlier Model 206s to Model 206B standard.

Production of the JetRanger II ended in 1977 when it was replaced by the **Model 206B JetRanger III**. This introduced a

420-shp (313-kW) Allison 250-C20B turboshaft, derated to 317 shp (236 kW), which offered further improved performance. Manufacture was transferred in early 1987 to Bell's Mirabel plant in Canada, where production continues.

The JetRanger was subsequently sold, ostensibly in civil guise, to numerous military air arms. Current operators comprise **Brazil, Brunei, Chile, Colombia, Cyprus, Ecuador, Guatemala, Guyana, Indonesia, Israel, Ivory Coast, Mexico, Myanmar, Pakistan, Peru, South Korea, Sri Lanka, Thailand, United Arab Emirates** (Abu Dhabi) and **Venezuela.** The JetRangers are used in a variety of duties, primarily for training and liaison, but also for observation and VIP transport. The Chilean navy operates the **206AS** ASW variant armed with torpedoes. In March 1993 the US Army again selected the JetRanger, this time in the form of the JetRanger III-derived **TH-67 Creek** as its **NTH** (New Training Helicopter). Against bids from Eurocopter

(Astar/Ecureuil), Grumman/Schweizer/UNC (TH-330) and Enstrom (TH-28), Bell won an initial order for 29 aircraft (company designation **TH206**), with an eventual requirement for up to 102, with options on a further 55. Deliveries to Fort Rucker, Alabama, replacing existing UH-1s, commenced on 15 October 1993.

Bell developed a medium-lift version under the designation **Model 206L-1 LongRanger**. This retained the powerplant of the JetRanger III, but incorporated a fuselage stretch of 2 ft 1 in (0.63 m) to accommodate a total of five passengers and an increased cabin capacity of 83 cu ft (2.35 m3). A double door in the port side of the fuselage simplifies the loading of bulky cargo. Other improvements included the

use of an advanced main rotor, plus introduction of the company's patented Noda-Matic suspension system giving reduced cabin vibration levels.

Deliveries of the LongRanger commenced in 1975, superseded in mid-1978 by the **Model 206L-2 LongRanger II**. This differed by having an uprated Allison 250C-20B turboshaft with a maximum continuous rating of 489 shp (365 kW) and higher-rated transmission. The **Model 206L-3 LongRanger III** was introduced in 1981 and featured a 650-shp (485-kW)

The US Army's TH-67 (Bell TH206) will carry a pilot and student in the cockpit, with a second trainee observing by CCTV in the cabin.

Standard 'off-the-shelf' Bell JetRangers, like this Brunei air force example, are popular training helicopters and a useful transport asset.

Allison 250-C30P engine and detail modifications. The **206L-4 LongRanger IV** remains the current production variant at Mirabel and has been joined by the **206LT TwinRanger**, a newly developed twin-engined conversion. All Canadian-built Bells (except those bound for Canada) are sold to the parent company at Ft Worth for resale on the US and world market.

Military operators of the LongRanger comprise **Bangladesh**, **Cameroon**, **Guatemala**, **Mexico**, **United Arab Emirates** (Dubai air wing and Ras Al-Khaimah Mobile Force) and the **Venezuelan army**. The aircraft are used primarily for liaison/communications and exclusively non-combat duties.

In 1980 Bell began development of a military **Bell Model 206L TexasRanger**, which has not proceeded beyond a demonstration aircraft. Powered by a 500-shp (373-kW) Allison 250-C28B turboshaft, it incorporates the fuselage of the **Model 206L LongRanger** to seat a pilot and up to six passengers, but for anti-armour/armed reconnaissance sorties it has side-by-side armoured seats for the pilot and weapons operator. Weapons include air-to-air or TOW missiles, or two pods containing folding-fin rockets or 7.62-mm (0.3-in) machine-guns. Industrias Cardoen of Chile has developed a modified armed version of the LongRanger as the **Cardoen CB 206L-III** (described separately).

By 1994, overall production by Bell of members of the Model 206 family was considerably in excess of 7,000 examples. Italian production, for civil and military use, exceeds 1,000 aircraft.

SPECIFICATION

Bell Helicopter Textron Model 206B JetRanger III
Rotor system: main rotor diameter 33 ft 4 in (10.16 m); tail rotor diameter 5 ft 5 in (1.65 m); main rotor disc area 872.65 sq ft (81.07 m²); tail rotor disc area 23.04 sq ft (2.14 m²)
Fuselage and tail: length overall, rotors turning 38 ft 9.5 in (11.82 m) and fuselage 31 ft 2 in (9.50 m) including tailskid; height overall 9 ft 6.5 in (2.91 m)

and to top of fin 8 ft 4 in (2.54 m); stabiliser span 6 ft 5.75 in (1.97 m); skid track 6 ft 3.5 in (1.92 m)
Powerplant: one 420-shp (313-kW) Allison 250-C20J flat-rated at 317 shp (236 kW)
Weights: empty 1,635 lb (742 kg); maximum take-off 3,200 lb (1451 kg)
Fuel and load: internal fuel 91 US gal (344 litres); external fuel none; maximum payload 1,500 lb (680 kg)
Speed: never exceed speed at sea level 122 kt (140 mph; 225 km/h); maximum cruising speed 'clean' at 5,000 ft (1525 m) 116 kt (134 mph; 216 km/h)
Range: 404 nm (465 miles; 748 km)
Performance: maximum rate of climb at sea level 1,260 ft (384 m) per minute; service ceiling 13,500 ft (4115 m); hovering ceiling 12,800 ft (3900 m) in ground effect and 8,800 ft (2680 m) out of ground effect

Bell **Model 206/OH-58A/B/C Kiowa**

In 1960 the **US Army** launched a design competition for a new Light Observation Helicopter (LOH). The requirement was for a helicopter suitable not only for an observation role but for missions that included casevac, close support, photo-reconnaissance and light transport. The specification called for a four-seat helicopter, carrying a 400-lb (180-kg) payload at a cruising speed of approximately 120 mph (190 km/h). The competition elicited responses from 12 manufacturers, from which Bell, Hiller and Hughes were each contracted to build five prototypes for competitive evaluation. Hughes' HO-6 (later OH-6) contender was subsequently declared the winner and was chosen by the US Army. Nevertheless, convinced of the merit of its losing **HO-4** submission, Bell built a new five-seat prototype as the **Bell Model 206A JetRanger** (described separately).

In 1967 the US Army, worried by the delivery rate and rising costs of the OH-6A, reopened its LOH competition; on 8 March 1968 the Bell Model 206A was declared the winner and ordered into production as the **OH-58A Kiowa**. Deliveries to the US Army began on 23 May 1969, and over five years a total of 2,200 was procured. The **Canadian Armed Forces** also acquired 74 as **COH-58A** (later designated **CH-136 Kiowa**) helicopters. An additional US Army contract for 74 was issued in January 1973 to replace those supplied to Canada. This Canadian order was followed in 1980 by 14 JetRanger III (designated **CH-139**) helicopter trainers.

Licence-production over an eight-year period was also undertaken by Commonwealth Aircraft Corporation in Australia. A total of 56 helicopters, essentially similar to the JetRanger II, was produced as the **Model 206B-1 Kiowa**. Twelve helicopters were supplied by Bell and 44 were manufactured under a co-production agreement. CAC was responsible for final assembly, with avionics and powerplant of US origin. Forty-three survive with the **Australian army**, locally named **Kalkadoon**. Twelve Kiowas were also delivered to the **Austrian army** in 1976 under the designation **OH-58B**. These are operated by 3 Staffel of Hubschraubergeschwader 1 at Tulln, with a detachment at Klagenfurt.

On 30 June 1976 the US Army awarded Bell a development contract to convert one OH-58A to improved **OH-58C** standard. This version introduced a flat glass canopy to reduce glint, an uprated Allison T63-A720 turboshaft developing 420 shp (313 kW) and an installation for infra-red suppression. The final OH-58C configuration also included a new instrument panel, improved avionics and improved maintenance features. In addition, two OH-58As were modified to OH-58C standard for pre-production flight testing by the US Army and Bell. Production modification of 435 OH-58As to

OH-58C standard began in March 1978 and was completed in March 1985. Israeli Aircraft Industries completed an additional 150 conversions for the US Army in Germany.

Bell began delivery in September 1985 of kits for an improved tail rotor configuration for retrofitting to OH-58As and OH-58Cs. This modification increases the available tail rotor thrust, thus increasing directional controllability (such as uncommanded yaw at low speeds experienced during nap-of-the-earth (NOE) flying). The improved **OH-58D** scout is described in a separate entry.

SPECIFICATION

Bell Helicopter Textron Model 206A/OH-58A Kiowa
Rotor system: main rotor diameter 35 ft 4 in (10.77 m); tail rotor diameter 5 ft 2 in (1.57 m); main

rotor disc area 980.52 sq ft (91.09 m²); tail rotor disc area 20.97 sq ft (1.95 m²)
Fuselage and tail: length overall, rotors turning 40 ft 11.75 in (12.49 m) and fuselage 32 ft 3.5 in (9.84 m); height overall, rotors turning 9 ft 6.5 in (2.91 m); stabiliser span 6 ft 5.25 in (1.96 m); skid track 6 ft 3.5 in (1.92 m)
Powerplant: one Allison T63-A-700 rated at 317 shp (236.5 kW)
Weights: empty equipped 1,583 lb (718 kg); maximum take-off 3,000 lb (1361 kg)
Fuel and load: internal fuel 73 US gal (276 litres); **Speed:** never exceed speed 130 kt (150 mph; 241 km/h); maximum cruising speed at sea level 106 kt (122 mph; 196 km/h); economical cruising speed at sea level 102 kt (117 mph; 188 km/h); loiter speed, for maximum endurance, 49 kts (91 km/h; 56 mph)
Range: maximum range at sea level with reserves 260 nm (299 miles; 481 km); endurance at sea level, no reserves 3 hours 30 minutes
Performance: maximum rate of climb at sea level 1,780 ft (543 m) per minute; service ceiling 19,000 ft (5790 m); hovering ceiling 13,750 ft (4190 m) in ground effect and 9,000 lb (2745 m) out of ground effect

Right: The Royal Australian Navy dubbed its Bell B 206B-1 Kiowas 'Battle Budgies'. The same legend was applied to armed AS 555 Squirrels serving in the Persian Gulf.

Left: To the Canadian Armed Forces the Kiowa is the CH-135. This float-equipped example also sports cable-cutters, above and below the cockpit, like most Kiowas worldwide.

Bell **Model 206/TH-57 SeaRanger**

The **US Navy** showed little interest in the US Army's light observation OH-58 Kiowa, but with a requirement identified in 1967 for a light turbine primary training helicopter it was decided, if possible, to procure an off-the-shelf aircraft. On 31 January 1968 the US Navy ordered from Bell 40 examples of a basically standard **Model 206A JetRanger II**; these differed only by having US Navy avionics and the optional

dual controls installed. Designated **TH-57A SeaRanger**, they were delivered during 1968 to training squadron HT-8 at NAS Whiting Field, Milton, FL. Utilised for the transition phase of helicopter training, the TH-57A served until the late 1980s. Today, almost all A models have been retired, although a few examples are still flown by the Naval Air Warfare Center/Aircraft Division at Patuxent River, MD, on test duties.

Initial helicopter training for both US Navy and Marine Corps aircrew is now accomplished on two developed variants of the TH-57A. Expanding requirements have led to 51 new production **TH-57B** primary trainers, the last of which was delivered in late 1985; these are based on the later **Model 206B JetRanger III**, and primarily differ from the TH-57A by having uprated Allison 250-C20 turboshafts, flat rated at

317 shp (236 kW), in addition to minor detail improvements. The TH-57B does retain, however, the dual controls of the TH-57A. Concurrent with the acquisition of the TH-57B, the US Navy ordered the **TH-57C**, a new production advanced instrument trainer, in January 1982. Also based on the JetRanger III, these are somewhat more sophisticated machines and feature full IFR instrumentation, thus allowing mastery of more complex skills in anticipation of moving on to operational type helicopters such as the SH-60B Seahawk and AH-1 SeaCobra. The initial order for 55 examples was

Bell Model 206/TH-57 SeaRanger

eventually raised to 89, the last of which was delivered in December 1984.

The SeaRanger serves exclusively with Training Wing Five at Whiting Field, FL. The TH-57B model is assigned to HT-8 and is operated as a primary and intermediate helicopter trainer. Following the initial six-week course, student pilots are subsequently assigned to HT-18, which operates the TH-57C model, for a 13-week advanced phase.

SPECIFICATION

Bell Helicopter Textron Model 206A (TH-57C SeaRanger)
Rotor system: main rotor diameter 33 ft 4 in (10.16 m); tail rotor diameter 5 ft 2 in (1.57 m); main rotor disc 873.0 sq ft (81.10 m2); tail rotor disc area 20.97 sq ft (1.95 m2)
Fuselage and tail: length overall, rotors turning 38 ft 9.5 in (11.82 m) and fuselage 31 ft 2 in (9.50 m); height 9 ft 6.5 in (2.91 m); stabiliser span 6 ft 5.25 in (1.96 m)
Powerplant: one 420-shp (313-kW) Allison 250-C20J flat-rated to 317 shp (236 kW)
Weights: empty 1,852 lb (840 kg); maximum take-off 3,350 lb (1520 kg)

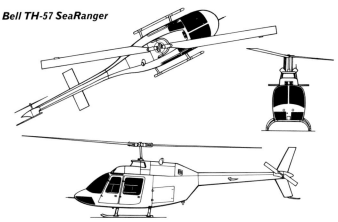

Bell TH-57 SeaRanger

Fuel and load: internal fuel 76 US gal (288 litres)
Speed: never exceed speed 122 kt (140 mph; 225 km/h); maximum and economical cruising speed at sea level 115 kt (133 mph; 214 km/h)
Range: 458 nm (527 miles; 848 km)

Performance: max rate of climb at sea level 1,540 ft (469 m) per minute; service ceiling above 20,000 ft (6095 m); hovering ceiling 12,700 ft (3870 m) in ground effect, 6,000 ft (1830 m) out of ground effect

The US Navy's TH-57Bs are charged with basic rotary training, while the advanced classes of HT-18 are also allocated TH-57Cs.

Bell **Model 209/AH-1F/S HueyCobra**

Produced in 1965 as a private project, the **Bell Model 209 HueyCobra** was intended to fulfil an urgent requirement for an 'interim' armed helicopter escort pending service entry of the AAFSS winner (the AH-56). The latter project subsequently foundered, while Bell produced some 1,100 **AH-1G Cobra**s for the US Army.

Post-Vietnam, the Cobra was upgraded to carry TOW missiles, resulting in conversion of some to **AH-1Q** standard. This was underpowered and a sequence of improvements was initiated, intended to upgrade engine and transmission, armament, avionics, cockpit and rotors, all of which would culminate in a common standard known as **AH-1S(MC)**. This was never fully achieved and left the Army with a range of airframes all designated 'S' but in different modification states. In 1989 redesignations renamed the MC **AH-1F**, and the less advanced versions as **AH-1P**, **AH-1E** and **AH-1S**. The AH-1F is the current production configuration and so applies to most exports.

Unchanged structurally from the prototype to date, F models and all but the earliest S airframes are distinguishable by the 'flat-plate' canopy and nose turret for the M65 TOW sighting system. A modified aft cowling and prominent exhaust suppressor are also distinctive. A Lycoming T53-L-703 turboshaft rated at 1,800 shp (1342 kW) drives the K-747 composite rotor. This unit retains the characteristics of Bell's original 540 semi-rigid 'teetering' rotor but is lighter, with a much-improved life. The Dash 747 blade is distinguished by its tapered tips.

The updated cockpit is NVG-compatible with a HUD for the pilot, a new stores management system and a comprehensive nav/comms fit. The co-pilot's panel is dominated by the TOW sight so he is provided with 'sidestick' cyclic and collective controls. Extensive armour is provided around the seats and cockpit to give some protection from small-arms fire. Further upgrades centred on a four-bladed rotor and new stability augmentation system are available, adding 1,000 lb (454 kg) to the payload.

Notable items (along with the squadron badge) visible on this Israeli AH-1F are the low-speed sensor probe between the cockpits, bulge for the laser tracker (not fitted) forward of the rotor mast, exhaust suppressor, Kaiser HUD and wire cutters behind the cockpit.

Pakistani army AH-1s are spread between two squadrons, Nos 31 and 32, both based at Multan. All aircraft retain their standard US Army olive drab finish. Deliveries began in 1984. Despite the current US arms embargo, Pakistan is believed to have obtained further AH-1s during 1993, perhaps from a third party.

WEAPON OPTIONS

Primary armament is the TOW missile, four of which can be carried on each outboard pylon; 2.75-in FFARs with a variety of warheads are carried inboard in either seven- or 19-shot pods. Gun pods remain a seldom-seen option. Secondary armament is the M197 triple-barrelled 20-mm cannon in a chin turret. As part of the original AH-1S (later AH-1E) stage 2 upgrade, aircraft were fitted with this weapon along with a new wing stores management system, the Enhanced Cobra Armament System (ECAS). A maximum of 750 rounds can be carried and the gun, together with the M65 'bucket', can be slaved to the crew helmet sight system. The gun has a field of fire of 110° on either side of the nose, an elevation of 20.5° and a maximum depression of 50°. Accuracy of the ballistic weapons is greatly enhanced by an air data system (by GEC Avionics) supplying information to a weapons computer. Some aircraft are now receiving the CNITE thermal imaging system which provides a full night capability, and trials are underway to qualify the aircraft for Stinger missiles. Provision has also been made for a laser spot tracker.

Bell AH-1F Cobra

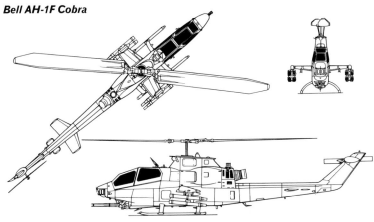

Passive defence starts with a special paint designed to be non-reflective of both visible and IR spectrum light. A suppressor cools and diffuses the exhaust plume and the Dash 747 blade reduces radar signature compared with the previous metal unit. Radar warning receivers give cockpit indication of hostile emissions. A laser detector has been trialled but is not currently fitted. Active defence is entrusted to a radar countermeasures/jammer set and the AN/ALQ-144 IR jammer. Army Cobras do not normally carry chaff/flare dispensers.

OPERATORS

The largest user of the AH-1F/S remains the US Army, with some 800 airframes still in service. Ninety-nine were built to Modernised AH-1S between 1979 and 1986, while 378 were rebuilt to the new standard from November 1979 to June 1982. This total includes 42 TAH-1S trainers. A handful of AH-1S aircraft (with the early canopy and XM-28 turret) remain in use, as well as some AH-1Ps (with XM-28 turret) and AH-1Es (which lack the low-speed sensor probe and some avionics equipment). The F is licence-built in Japan and has been exported to Jordan, South Korea, Pakistan, Israel, Thailand and, most recently, to Turkey.

Israel: AH-1F (30)
Japan: AH-1F (88 with 70 funded)
Jordan: AH-1F (24)
Pakistan: AH-1F (20 plus 10 options)
South Korea: (42 plus 28 options)
Thailand: AH-1F (4)
Turkey: AH-1S Mod/AH-1F (unknown)

Since the 1970s Turkish Army Aviation (Türk Kara Havaciligi) has had a requirement for an attack helicopter. Initially a $50 million order was placed for six Bell AH-1S in 1983, but no confirmation of delivery was ever announced. However, the Turkish army has joined the ranks of Cobra operators, flying an unknown number of single-engined AH-1Fs alongside its twin-engined ex-USMC AH-1Ws.

SPECIFICATION

Bell Helicopter Textron Model 209 (AH-1F HueyCobra)
Rotor system: main rotor diameter 44 ft 0 in (13.41 m); tail rotor diameter 8 ft 6 in (2.59 m); main rotor disc area 1,520.23 sq ft (141.26 m²); tail rotor disc area 56.75 sq ft (5.27 m²)
Wing: span 10 ft 9 in (3.28 m)
Fuselage and tail: length overall, rotors turning 53 ft

1 in (16.18 m) and fuselage 44 ft 7 in (13.59 m); height to top of rotor head 13 ft 5 in (4.09 m); stabiliser span 6 ft 11 in (2.11 m); skid track 7 ft 0 in (2.13 m)
Powerplant: one 1,800-shp (1342-kW) Textron Lycoming T53-L-703 transmission limited to 1,290 shp (962 kW) for take-off and 1,134 shp (845 kW) for continuous running
Weights: operating empty 6,598 lb (2993 kg); normal take-off 9,975 lb (4524 kg); maximum take-off 10,000 lb (4536 kg)
Fuel and load: internal fuel 259 US gal (980 litres);

external fuel none
Speed: never exceed speed 170 kt (195 mph; 315 km/h) in TOW configuration; maximum level speed at optimum altitude 123 kt (141 mph; 227 km/h) in TOW configuration
Range: 274 nm (315 miles; 507 km)
Performance: maximum rate of climb at sea level 1,620 ft (494 m) per minute; service ceiling 12,200 ft (3720 m); hovering ceiling 12,200 ft (3720 m) in ground effect

Bell **Model 209/AH-1W SuperCobra**

The lineage of the Whiskey model Cobra can be traced directly back to the Model 209 prototype and subsequent **AH-1G** service variant. Developed for the USMC, the **AH-1J** was essentially a twin-engined AH-1G to which was added the M197 20-mm turreted gun. Development thereafter followed its own path via the improved Iranian **AH-1J**, the **KingCobra** demonstrator, and the stretched **AH-1T** models.

The AH-1W had its origins in a paper proposal to the Iranian air force for an upgraded AH-1T with T-700 engines. A demonstrator (c/n 161022) was built and flown as the **'AH-1T+'** to qualify the engines. This aircraft accumulated various modifications and improvements until it fully represented the production aircraft, by which time it was known as **SuperCobra**. The designation **AH-1W** was adopted as the first production airframe was rolled out for the USMC.

That the 'W' airframe is fundamentally unchanged from the 'T' is amply demonstrated by the fact that nearly 50 (from a total built of only 57) of the Ts are being rebuilt to incorporate the W improvements and will be indistinguishable from new-build. Compared to other Cobra variants, the T/W airframe features a lengthened tail boom and forward fuselage plug to accommodate the 48-ft (14.63-m) diameter/2-ft 9-in (0.84-m) chord main rotor, and to maintain aircraft CG. The tail fin is truncated in the manner of the Huey. Aside from the obvious redesign of the engine cowlings, the other external airframe change is the 'cheek bulge', which, together with a starboard shift of the ammunition box, allowed the TOW 'black boxes' to be moved from the tail boom.

T700-GE-401 turboshafts, each rated at 1,690 shp (1260 kW), are currently used, giving the Cobra one of the best thrust/weight ratios of any current attack helicopter and ensuring single-engine safety. Future upgrades will take the current 14,750 lb (6691 kg) gross weight to 16,000 lb (7258 kg). The two-bladed teetering rotor is retained at present, but a more advanced four-bladed design has been flown and par-

tially qualified, resulting in the **AH-1(4B) W Viper** designation. The USMC intends that it will be incorporated eventually.

The AH-1W forms the basis of the **Cobra Venom** offered by Bell and GEC to meet the British Army Air Corps' need for a battlefield helicopter. A new avionics suite incorporates night vision and all-weather sensors, with an autonomous navaid fit and digital mapping, colour CRT displays. It will also be Hellfire equipped, as standard.

During Operation Desert Storm AH-1Ws from HMLA-169, -269, -367, and -369 were deployed, with the two former units land-based and the remaining two sea-based. Flying with the 1st Marine Expeditionary Force from the start of the ground offensive on 24 February 1991, they provided air support for the advancing Marines, including an engagement at Al Jaber airfield which claimed 60 Iraqi tanks. Whiskey Cobras were deployed to Somalia in 1993. However, in 1993/94 a sizeable portion of the fleet was grounded with fatigue problems.

WEAPON OPTIONS

The Whiskey is qualified for most of the stores in the USMC inventory. Uniquely, it has a dual main armament, TOW or AGM-114 Hellfire ATGMs, which can be carried simultaneously if required. Up to four 19-round LAU-61A, LAU-86A, LAU-68A/A, LAU-68B/A, or seven-round LAU-69A rocket pods can be carried. All pods utilise 2.75-in Hydra 70 rockets. The AIM-9L

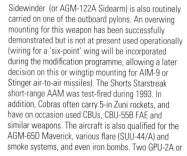

AH-1Ws from four USMC units saw action during Desert Storm. They were involved in the fighting for Khafji and later employed their Hellfire capability for the first time.

Sidewinder (or AGM-122A Sidearm) is also routinely carried on one of the outboard pylons. An overwing mounting for this weapon has been successfully demonstrated but is not at present used operationally (wiring for a 'six-point' wing will be incorporated during the modification programme, allowing a later decision on this or wingtip mounting for AIM-9 or Stinger air-to-air missiles). The Shorts Starstreak short-range AAM was test-fired during 1993. In addition, Cobras often carry 5-in Zuni rockets, and have on occasion used CBUs, CBU-55B FAE and similar weapons. The aircraft is also qualified for the AGM-65D Maverick, various flare (SUU-44/A) and smoke systems, and even iron bombs. Two GPU-2A or

In 1990 the first of five former US Marine Corps AH-1W SuperCobras was delivered to the Turkish army. These were joined by at least a further five aircraft in 1993, to complement the AH-1s already in service. These Cobras have seen action in the fighting against Kurdish rebels on Turkey's southern borders. Turkish AH-1Ws do not carry the 'hot brick' IR jammer above the engines but do carry chaff and flare dispensers on the weapons pylons.

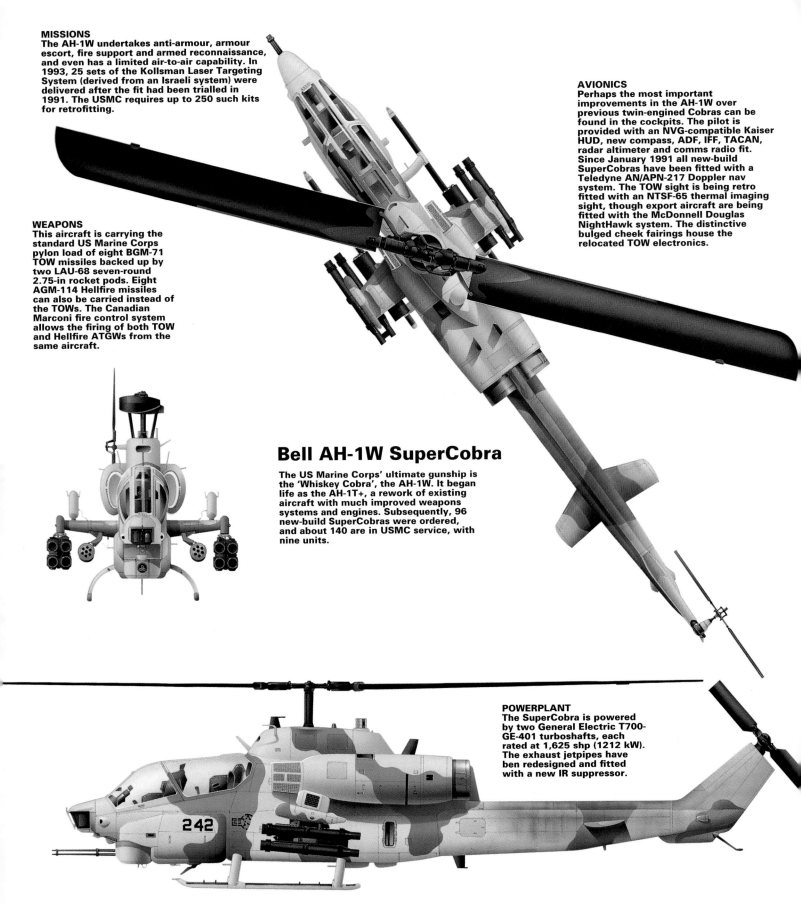

MISSIONS
The AH-1W undertakes anti-armour, armour escort, fire support and armed reconnaissance, and even has a limited air-to-air capability. In 1993, 25 sets of the Kollsman Laser Targeting System (derived from an Israeli system) were delivered after the fit had been trialled in 1991. The USMC requires up to 250 such kits for retrofitting.

AVIONICS
Perhaps the most important improvements in the AH-1W over previous twin-engined Cobras can be found in the cockpits. The pilot is provided with an NVG-compatible Kaiser HUD, new compass, ADF, IFF, TACAN, radar altimeter and comms radio fit. Since January 1991 all new-build SuperCobras have been fitted with a Teledyne AN/APN-217 Doppler nav system. The TOW sight is being retro fitted with an NTSF-65 thermal imaging sight, though export aircraft are being fitted with the McDonnell Douglas NightHawk system. The distinctive bulged cheek fairings house the relocated TOW electronics.

WEAPONS
This aircraft is carrying the standard US Marine Corps pylon load of eight BGM-71 TOW missiles backed up by two LAU-68 seven-round 2.75-in rocket pods. Eight AGM-114 Hellfire missiles can also be carried instead of the TOWs. The Canadian Marconi fire control system allows the firing of both TOW and Hellfire ATGWs from the same aircraft.

Bell AH-1W SuperCobra

The US Marine Corps' ultimate gunship is the 'Whiskey Cobra', the AH-1W. It began life as the AH-1T+, a rework of existing aircraft with much improved weapons systems and engines. Subsequently, 96 new-build SuperCobras were ordered, and about 140 are in USMC service, with nine units.

POWERPLANT
The SuperCobra is powered by two General Electric T700-GE-401 turboshafts, each rated at 1,625 shp (1212 kW). The exhaust jetpipes have ben redesigned and fitted with a new IR suppressor.

SUU-11A/A gun pods can also be fitted. Finally, the pylons are 'plumbed' for either 100-US gal (378-litre) ferry or 77-US gal (291-litre) combat fuel tanks.

As mentioned previously, the Cobra mounts the M197 cannon in a General Electric A/A49E-7(V4) turret as standard. This is qualified to fire the depleted uranium rounds used in the Navy's Phalanx close-in defence system for greater effectiveness out to ranges in excess of 1.8 miles (3 km). Both the turret gun and the M-65 sight system can be slaved to either crewman's helmet sight system. Seven hundred and fifty rounds are carried aft of the turret, and while the maximum rate of fire is 650 rpm, the gun is limited to single bursts of 16 rounds. An upgrade programme is

underway which will provide a night targeting system incorporating FLIR and laser designation/range finding. This is extremely significant as it means that the aircraft has a true night capability and can designate targets either for its own weapons or those carried by fixed-wing aircraft. Countermeasures systems consist of AN/APR-44 and AN/APR-39 passive radar warning and detector systems, while active countermeasures include AN/ALE-39 chaff/flare dispensers and an AN/ALQ-144 IR jammer.

Installation of the NTS has provided the opportunity to make considerable cockpit improvements. The front panel will be enlarged and improved. The addition of new multi-function displays,

a HUD, improved ANVIS displays and a radar altimeter will mean that both crewmen will have full access to navigation and communication information. Other improvements include a five-point seat harness with inflatable head and body restraints to increase survivability.

OPERATORS

The USMC is the primary user of the AH-1W and will eventually receive 230 (including the rebuilt Tango model). These will equip the Marine Corps' light attack squadrons (HMLAs 167, 267, 367, 169, 269 and

369), the training squadron (HMT-303), and two reserve units (HMAs 773 and 775). Two HMLs may also receive Cobras (771 and 776). In March 1994 Bell withdrew 60 of the USMC's 128 aircraft, having discovered serious salt water corrosion of their main rotors. The AH-1Ws concerned had chalked up over 1,000 flying hours, and all rotors with over 400 hours now require attention. Foreign SuperCobra operators are Turkey (which is using five ex-USMC airframes on a loan basis pending delivery of a further five new-build machines), and Thailand, which took delivery of its first example in March 1993. Thailand had signed letter of acceptance in February 1992 for 18 AH-1W aircraft plus 24 options.

SPECIFICATION

Bell Helicopter Textron Model 209 (AH-1W SuperCobra)
Rotor system: main rotor diameter 48 ft 0 in (14.63 m); tail rotor diameter 9 ft 9 in (2.97 m); main rotor disc 1,809.56 sq ft (168.11 m²); tail rotor disc area 74.7 sq ft (6.94 m²)

Wing: span 10 ft 7 in (3.23 m); aspect ratio 3.74
Fuselage and tail: length overall, rotors turning 58 ft 0 in (17.68 m) and fuselage 45 ft 6 in (13.87 m); height overall 14 ft 2 in (4.32 m) and to top of rotor head 13 ft 6 in (4.11 m); stabiliser span 6 ft 11 in (2.11 m); skid track 7 ft 0 in (2.13 m)
Powerplant: two 1,625-shp (1212-kW) General Electric T700-GE-401 transmission, limited to a total of 2,032 shp (1515 kW) for take-off and 1,725 shp

(1286 kW) for continuous running
Weights: empty 10,200 lb (4627 kg); maximum take-off 14,750 lb (6691 kg)
Fuel and load: internal fuel 304.5 US gal (1153 litres); external fuel up to four 77-US gal (291-litre) or two 100-US gal (379-litre) drop tanks; maximum ordnance 2,466 lb (1119 kg)
Speed: never exceed speed 190 kt (219 mph; 352 km/h); maximum level speed 'clean' at sea level 152

kt (175 mph; 282 km/h) or at optimum altitude 150 kt (173 mph; 278 km/h)
Range: 343 nm (395 miles; 635 km) with standard fuel
Performance: maximum rate of climb at sea level, one engine out 800 ft (244 m) per minute; service ceiling more than 12,000 ft (3660 m); hovering ceiling 14,750 ft (4495 m) in ground effect and 3,000 ft (914 m) out of ground effect

Bell **Model 212/UH-1N**

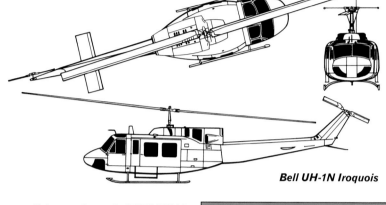

Following negotiations in early 1968 between Bell Helicopters, the Canadian government and Pratt & Whitney Canada, it was mutually agreed to initiate a jointly-funded programme covering the development of a twin-turbine version of the Bell Model 205/UH-1H Iroquois (described separately). Selected as powerplant for this new venture was the PT6T Turbo Twin-Pac. It comprised two turboshaft engines mounted side-by-side to drive a single output shaft through a combining gearbox. An advantage was provided by sensing torquemeters in the gearbox which, in the event of an engine failure, could signal the still-operative turbine to develop either emergency or continuous power in order that the flight could be concluded in safety.

Adaptation of the initial production PT6T-3 Turbo Twin-Pac to the airframe of the Bell Model 205 proceeded without serious problems, and the first deliveries of the resulting **Bell Model 212** helicopters to the US Air Force began during 1970 under the tri-service designation **UH-1N**. The USAF acquired a total of 79 UH-1Ns, which saw service worldwide in support of Special Operations Force counter-insurgency activities. A larger number went to the US Navy and Marine Corps, which by 1978 had received a total of 221. Those of the US Marine Corps include two UH-1Ns converted to **VH-1N** VIP transports, plus six built as new to this configuration. The Canadian Armed Forces acquired 50 Bell 212s, the first of them handed over on 3 May 1971 and the last of them being delivered just over a year later. These were designated initially **CUH-1N**, but have since been redesignated **CH-135 Twin Huey**.

The improved safety offered by the Twin-Pac powerplant made this helicopter attractive to companies providing support to offshore gas/oil operations, and while Bell soon had a commercial **Twin Two-Twelve** in full-scale production, it also built small numbers of military helicopters for other nations. Agusta in Italy soon acquired a licence for the Model 212, producing the **AB 212** (described separately) for civil and military customers, and has developed a specialised maritime version as the AB 212ASW.

Lebanon: AB 212
Libya: AB 212
Malta: AB 212
Mexico: B 212
Morocco: AB 212
Panama: UH-1N, B 212
Philippines: UH-1N
Saudi Arabia: AB 212
Singapore: B 212
South Korea: B 212
Spain: AB 212 (HU.18B), AB 212ASW
Sri Lanka: B 212
Sudan: AB 212
Thailand: B 212
Tunisia: UH-1N
Turkey: AB 212, AB 212ASW
Uganda: B 212
Venezuela: AB 212ASW
Yemen: AB 212
Zambia: B 212

USAF: HH-1N, UH-1N, VH-1N
USMC: UH-1N, VH-1N
USN: HH-1N

SPECIFICATION

Bell Helicopter Textron Model 212 (UH-1N Iroquois)
Rotor system: main rotor diameter 48 ft 2.25 in (14.69 m) with tracking tips; tail rotor diameter 8 ft 6 in (2.59 m); main rotor disc area 1,871.91 sq ft (173.90 m²); tail rotor disc area 56.74 sq ft (5.27 m²)
Fuselage and tail: length overall, rotors turning 57 ft 3.25 in (17.46 m) and fuselage 42 ft 4.75 in (12.92 m); height overall 14 ft 10.25 in (4.53 m) and to top of rotor head 12 ft 10 in (3.91 m); stabiliser span 9 ft 4.5 in (2.86 m); skid track 8 ft 8 in (2.64 m)
Powerplant: one 1,800-shp (1342-kW) Pratt & Whitney Canada T400-CP-400 flat rated to 1,290 shp (962 kW) for take-off and 1,130 shp (842 kW) for continuous running
Weights: empty 6,143 lb (2787 kg); maximum take-off 11,200 lb (5080 kg)
Fuel and load: internal fuel 215 US gal (814 litres);

external fuel none; maximum payload 5,000 lb (2268 kg) externally or 4,000 lb (1814 kg)internally
Speed: never exceed speed at sea level 140 kt (161 mph; 259 km/h); maximum cruising speed at sea level 123 kt (142 mph; 230 km/h); economical cruising speed at sea level 100 kt (115 mph; 185 km/h)
Range: range 227 nm (261 miles; 420 km)
Performance: maximum rate of climb at sea level 1,320 ft (402 m) per minute; service ceiling 14,200 ft (4330 m); hovering ceiling 11,000 ft (3355 m) in ground effect

Right: The bright red UH-1Ns of VXE-6 (Antarctic Development Squadron 6) 'Puckered Penguins' operate alongside LC-130 Hercules of the same unit in support of US bases in the Antarctic.

Bell UH-1N Iroquois

Sri Lanka received 12 Bell 212s, nine of which have been fitted out as gunships. Three wear an IR-reflecting olive drab paint scheme but carry no nose radar.

Below: The Philippine air force has two VIP-configured Bell 212s on strength. The smartly painted aircraft are fitted out with much-improved radio equipment, and weather radar under the nose.

OPERATORS

Argentina: B 212
Austria: AB 212
Bangladesh: B 212
Brunei: B 212 Twin Pac
Canada: UH-1N (CH-135 Twin Huey)
Chile: B 212
Dominican Republic: B 212
Dubai: B 212
Ecuador: B 212
El Salvador: B 212
Ghana: B 212
Greece: B 212, AB 212, AB 212ASW
Guatemala: B 212
Guyana: B 212
Iran: AB 212, AB 212ASW
Iraq: AB 212ASW
Israel: AB 212
Italy: AB 212, AB 212ASW
Japan: B 212

Bell Model 214/Isfahan

Evolved via the Huey Plus (a privately-funded, improved version of the Model 205), the **Model 214A** 16-seat utility helicopter was, in late 1972, the subject of a major Iranian contract (worth upwards of $575,000,000). Featuring a more powerful engine to cater for high ambient temperatures, a larger main rotor and a strengthened airframe, the Model 214A was first flown on 13 March 1974. Two hundred and eighty-seven were delivered to **Iran**, primarily for use by the air component of the army as a troop carrier and supply transport helicopter, the Model 214A being assigned the name **Isfahan** in Iran. Isfahan (Esfahan) is an ancient town in central Iran, and was also home to the Iranian Army helicopter training school. It is uncertain how many Model 214A Isfahan helicopters remain in the inventory of the Islamic Republic of Iran army aviation, or the level of serviceability of those still considered operable, but more than 100 may still be active. Iranian Bell 214s were heavily involved in the fighting against Iraq as troop transports, alongside surviving CH-47Cs. Throughout the bitter fighting of the first Gulf war the Iranian aircraft faced Iraqi gunship Bell 214STs. Forty-five of these had been delivered to Saddam Hussein's forces from 1985, ostensibly for the civilian Ministry of Communications and Transport.

Iran was also the recipient of 39 **Model 214C** helicopters equipped for SAR tasks. A commercial derivative of the basic helicopter was designated **Model 214B** and dubbed **BigLifter**. The latter was subsequently sold in small numbers to several military operators, including **Dubai**,

Prime mover behind the Bell 214's development was the Shah's Imperial Iranian Air Force. Two hundred and eighty-seven B 214As were ordered and a deal for a further 400 Isfahans had been signed when the 1978 revolution halted everything. This is the Philippine air force's sole Bell 214 in formation with a UH-1H.

Ecuador, **Oman** and the **Philippines**, all of which have small numbers in their respective inventories. The Iranian requirement for a transport version of the Bell 214 led to the development of a completely new version, the Model 214ST.

SPECIFICATION

Bell Helicopter Textron Model 214B BigLifter
Rotor system: main rotor diameter 50 ft 0 in (15.24 m); tail rotor diameter 9 ft 8 in (2.95 m); main rotor disc area 1,963.49 sq ft (182.41 m2); tail rotor disc area 73.39 sq ft (6.82 m2)
Powerplant: one 2,930-shp (2185-kW) Textron Lycoming T5508D flat-rated at 2,050 shp (1528 kW) for take-off and 1,850 shp (1379.5 kW) for continuous running
Weights: maximum take-off 16,000 lb (7257 kg)
Fuel and load: external fuel none; maximum payload 7,000 lb (3175 kg)
Speed: maximum cruising speed at optimum altitude 140 kt (161 mph; 259 km/h)

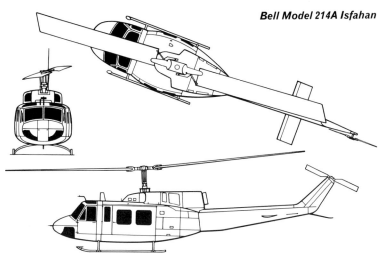

Bell Model 214A Isfahan

Bell Model 214ST

Despite retention of the type number of the preceding Model 214A, the **Model 214ST** possesses little commonality with the earlier helicopter, being twin-engined, with a stretched fuselage, composite rotor blades of greater diameter, and numerous other changes. The Model 214ST (the suffix originally signified Stretched Twin, then **SuperTransport**) was designed to an Iranian requirement calling for increased capacity, higher safety margins and improved 'hot-and-high' performance by comparison with the Model 214A Isfahan.

Plans for licence assembly of the Isfahan in Iran were changed when Bell proposed the more capable Model 214ST, the programme being revised to cover only 50 examples of the former and 350 of the latter. Bell initiated construction of three prototypes but, before the first of these flew on 21 July 1979, the Islamic revolution occurred and the licence plan was abandoned.

Having identified a market for a medium-lift helicopter in the Model 214ST category, Bell continued development and, in November 1979, launched production of a series of 100 aircraft, delivering the last in 1990. Of these, the majority found military customers, principal of which was the **Iraqi air force** which procured 45 during 1987-88. Other current operators of the Model 214ST are the air wing of the **Royal Brunei armed forces** (one), the air forces of **Oman**, **Peru** and **Venezuela** (each with three), and the **Royal Thai armed forces**, comprising the air force and army (each with two) and the navy (five).

SPECIFICATION

Bell Helicopter Textron Model 214ST
Rotor system: main rotor diameter 52 ft 0 in (15.85 m); tail rotor diameter 9 ft 8 in (2.95 m); main rotor disc area 2,123.71 sq ft (197.29 m2); tail rotor disc area 73.39 sq ft (6.82 m2)

Fuselage and tail: length overall, rotors turning 62 ft 2.25 in (18.95 m) and fuselage 49 ft 3.5 in (15.02 m); height overall 15 ft 10.5 in (4.84 m); skid track 8 ft 8 in (2.64 m) or wheel track 9 ft 3.5 in (2.83 m)
Powerplant: two General Electric CT7-2A each rated at 1,625 shp (1212 kW)
Weights: empty 9,445 lb (4284 kg); maximum take-off 17,500 lb (7938 kg)
Fuel and load: internal fuel 435 US gal (1647 litres) plus provision for 174 US gal (658 litres) of auxiliary fuel in two cabin tanks; external fuel none; maximum payload more than 7,700 lb (3493 kg)
Speed: maximum cruising speed at 4,000 ft (1220 m) 140 kt (161 mph; 259 km/h)
Range: ferry range 550 nm (633 miles; 1019 km) with auxiliary fuel; range 463 nm (533 miles; 858 km) with standard fuel
Performance: maximum rate of climb at sea level 1,780 ft (543 m) per minute; service ceiling 4,800 ft (1460 m) with one engine out; hovering ceiling 6,400 ft (1950 m) in ground effect

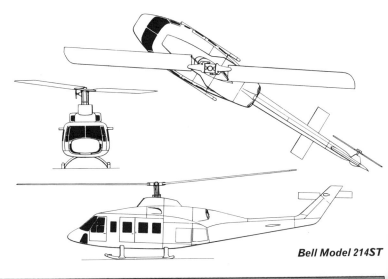

Bell Model 214ST

The Imperial Iranian Air Force took a decision in the mid-1970s to establish a sizeable air cavalry force, under the influence of US experience in Vietnam. This led to significant orders for types such as the Bell AH-1 and the initiation of a whole new type in the form of the Bell 214 Isfahan. The Bell 214ST design was led by the Iranian requirement and resulted in a $575 million contract, which was cancelled in 1978. Small numbers of B 214STs were sold elsewhere. The Royal Thai navy bought five Model 214STs from Bell in 1986, with deliveries taking place the following year. They operate alongside ASW Bell 212s and transport UH-1Hs.

Bell Model 230

An upgraded derivative of the Model 222, the **Model 230** light utility and transport helicopter is being offered for both military and commercial tasks. The responsibility of Bell's Canadian company at Mirabel, Quebec, the Model 230 was first flown on 12 August 1991, both first and second prototypes being converted Model 222s. Accommodating up to 10 persons, it is powered by two 700-shp (522-kW) Allison 250-C30G2 turboshafts and is available in both fixed-skid and retractable-wheel versions. Variants currently proposed include a medevac model with extra storage capacity for medical equipment, rupture-resistant fuel cells and self-sealing fuel fittings. It is anticipated that military models will have provision for externally-mounted weaponry. In 1993 one much modified aircraft was leased to the **Chilean navy**, which has several classes of helicopter-capable vessels, for SAR duties. Equipped with a hoist, Honeywell Primus 700 radar, Spectrolab SX-16 Nitesun searchlight, thermal imager, EFIS cockpit with GPS nav system, HUD and auxiliary fuel tanks it is also fitted out with an Indal ASIST deck landing system.

The twin-engined Bell 230 is the successor to Bell's Model 222, and is available with either a retractable wheeled undercarriage or skids. It is aimed primarily at the VIP and air ambulance market.

SPECIFICATION

Bell Helicopter Textron Model 230 Utility
Rotor system: main rotor diameter 42 ft 0 in (12.80 m); tail rotor diameter 6 ft 10.75 in (2.10 m); main rotor disc area 1,385.44 sq ft (128.71 m²); tail rotor disc area 37.35 sq ft (3.47 m²)
Fuselage and tail: length overall, rotors turning 50 ft 5.5 in (15.38 m) and fuselage 42 ft 6.75 in (12.97 m); height overall 12 ft 0.25 in (3.66 m) on skids; skid track 7 ft 10 in (2.39 m)
Powerplant: two Allison 250-C30G2 each rated at 700 shp (522 kW) for take-off and 622 shp (464 kW) for continuous running, or two Textron Lycoming LTS 101750C-1 each rated at 684 shp (510 kW)
Weights: manufacturer's empty 4,950 lb (2245 kg); maximum take-off 8,400 lb (3810 kg)
Fuel and load: internal fuel 246 US gal (931 litres) plus provision for 48 US gal (182 litres) of auxiliary

fuel; maximum payload 2,800 lb (1270 kg)
Speed: maximum cruising speed at sea level 137 kt (158 mph; 254 km/h); economical cruising speed at sea level 134 kt (154 mph; 248 km/h)

Range: range 379 nm (436 miles; 702 km)
Performance: service ceiling 15,000 ft (4570 m); hovering ceiling 12,300 ft (3750 m) in ground effect and 7,300 ft (2225 m) out of ground effect

Bell Model 406CS Combat Scout

A lighter and simplified export derivative of the US Army's OH-58D Kiowa (Model 406 AHIP) two-seat scout and attack helicopter, the **Model 406CS Combat Scout** entered flight test in June 1984, and that year entered a fly-off competition in **Saudi Arabia**. Retaining the main rotor, tail rotor and transmission of the OH-58D, and a similar powerplant, the Combat Scout was a nevertheless downgraded version of the OH-58D, as export of the mast-mounted sight, Hellfire missile and specialist cockpit electronics was prohibited. Armament choices include two GIAT 20-mm cannon pods, a quartet of TOW 2 or Hellfire anti-armour missiles, or combinations of Stinger missiles, 70-mm rockets, 7.62-mm or 12.7-mm guns. The Combat Scout successfully performed air-to-air combat trials, flown at NAS Patuxent River in 1987.

The Combat Scout is equipped with a SFENA hybrid cockpit with conventional instrumentation and electronic displays for TOW missiles and communications control. Other features include a roof-mounted Saab-Emerson HeliTOW sight with a folding overhead direct-view optics tube, folding rotor blades and tailplane, and a squatting undercarriage to facilitate rapid loading and redeployment from C-130 transports. Further upgrades are planned, including TOW armament, laser ranger and designator and an increase in gross weight of 500 lb (227 kg).

During autumn 1988, an order was placed on behalf of the Royal Saudi Land Forces Army Aviation Command for 15 Combat Scouts, these being delivered from June 1990. The first flight of a Saudi aircraft was made by Col Homood Al-Reshoodi at Arlington on 2 February of that year. These aircraft have frequently been referred to as **MH-58D**s, but this is inaccurate. Five of the 15 aircraft are now equipped with TOW missiles.

The Bell 406 was a result of the US Army's Advanced Helicopter Improvement Program of 1979. Having produced the OH-58D, Bell offered the downgraded Combat Scout for the export market. This is the company demonstrator, armed with a pair of GIAT M621 20-mm cannon.

Powerplant: one Allison 250-C30R rated at 650 shp (485 kW)
Weights: empty 2,271 lb (1030 kg); maximum take-off 5,000 lb (2268 kg)
Fuel and load: internal fuel 120 US gal (454 litres);

external fuel none; maximum payload 1,500 lb (680 kg)
Speed: never exceed speed 130 kt (150 mph; 241 km/h); maximum level speed 'clean' at optimum altitude 125 kt (144 mph; 232 km/h); max cruising speed at optimum altitude 120 kt (138 mph; 222 km/h)

Range: 218 nm (251 miles; 404 km); endurance 2 hours 48 minutes
Performance: hovering ceiling 20,500 ft (6250 m) in ground effect and 14,500 ft (4420 m) out of ground effect

SPECIFICATION

Bell Helicopter Textron Model 406CS Combat Scout
Rotor system: main rotor diameter 35 ft 0 in (10.67 m); tail rotor diameter 5 ft 5 in (1.65 m); main rotor disc area 962.00 sq ft (89.37 m²); tail rotor disc area 23.04 sq ft (2.14 m²)
Fuselage and tail: length overall, rotors turning 42 ft 2 in (12.85 m) and fuselage 34 ft 4.75 in (10.48 m); height overall 12 ft 10.625 in (3.93 m); stabiliser span 7 ft 6 in (2.29 m); skid track 6 ft 2 in (1.88 m)

The OH-58D was a cautious (pre-Reagan era) attempt to find a no-frills armed scout to complement the AH-64 force. The Bell 406CS has so far attracted only one customer, the Royal Saudi Land Forces, to back up its newly delivered Apaches. Taiwan is interested in acquiring the Combat Scout also, but only if it comes equipped with the Hellfire/mast-mounted sight combination, which does away with the 406CS's raison d'être.

Bell Model 406 (AHIP)/OH-58D Kiowa/Kiowa Warrior

In September 1981, the **Bell Model 406** proposal won the Army Helicopter Improvement Program (AHIP) to develop a near-term scout helicopter, capable of intelligence gathering and surveillance duties, in addition to the support of attack helicopters and directing artillery fire. After Bell was awarded a development contract, the first of five **OH-58D** prototypes made its first flight on 6 October 1983. Development and operational test programmes were conducted by the US Army at Yuma and Edwards AFB, and were completed in February 1985.

The Model 406 thus introduced a mast-mounted sight (developed by McDonnell Douglas Astronautics in association with Northrop's Electro-Mechanical Division), specialised avionics and a cockpit control and display sub-system developed by Sperry Flight Systems. In addition, the two-bladed rotor of the OH-58A was replaced with a four-bladed soft-in-plane rotor with composite blades, main rotor head yoke and elastomeric bearings.

Initial plans envisaged upgrading of 592 US Army OH-58As to 'D' standard in 1985-1991, but have been progressively reduced to the current total of 315 examples, with a further 12 Gulf War attrition replacements. Deliveries of two OH-58Ds commenced in December 1985, with the first Europe-based delivery taking place in June 1987. Under Operation Prime Chance, 15 OH-58Ds were modified from September 1987 for operations against Iranian fast-patrol boats in the Persian Gulf. Provision

The needle-nose and treated windscreen identify the Optimized Aircraft, or 'stealthy' OH-58D. Eighteen of these specialist conversions fly with the 82nd Airborne Division's 1/17th Cavalry.

was made for Stinger and Hellfire missiles, in addition to 12.7-mm (0.50-in) machine-guns and seven-tube rocket pods.

The armament options of the Prime Chance OH-58Ds have been retained for an armed OH-58D, designated **Kiowa Warrior**, to which standard 243 planned OH-58Ds are to be modified. The major modifications include an integrated weapons pylon, uprated engine and transmission, increased gross weight, RWR, IR jammer, laser warning receiver, tilting vertical fin, integrated avionics and a lightened structure. Newly-converted Kiowa Warriors were delivered from the 208th aircraft in May 1991 and were delivered initially to 'C' and 'D' Troops of 4-17 Aviation, US Army.

Eighty-one Kiowa Warriors are to be modified further as **Multi-Purpose Light Helicopter** (MPLH). This version features squatting landing gear and quick-fold rotor blades, horizontal stabiliser and tilting fin for

An OH-58D launches Hydra-70 rockets. These weapons provide capability against soft targets, and are often used in conjunction with gun pods.

transportation in C-130s and speedy deployment for use by US Army rapid reaction forces. Later modifications envisaged include provision for a cargo hook for a slung load of up to 2,000 lb (907 kg) and fittings for external carriage of four stretchers or six troop seats. A further Kiowa Warrior upgrade is also offered by Bell, this version featuring new avionics including a FLIR,

DEFENCES
The OH-58D is fitted with various threat warning systems. These include APR-44(V)3 radar warning receiver, AVR-2 laser detection set and APR-39(V)1 radar warning. The principal anti-missile defence is the ALQ-144 infra-red countermeasures set. To counter small arms fire, the OH-58D uses nap-of-the-earth flying so that it is exposed for as short a time as possible.

10553

UNITED STATES ARMY

THUGS

THUGS

GRANT RACE

AIR TRANSPORTABILITY
Some Kiowa Warriors are completed with collapsible skids, folding stabiliser and fin, removable wire-cutter and MMS support frame for rapid air transportability in C-130s or C-141s.

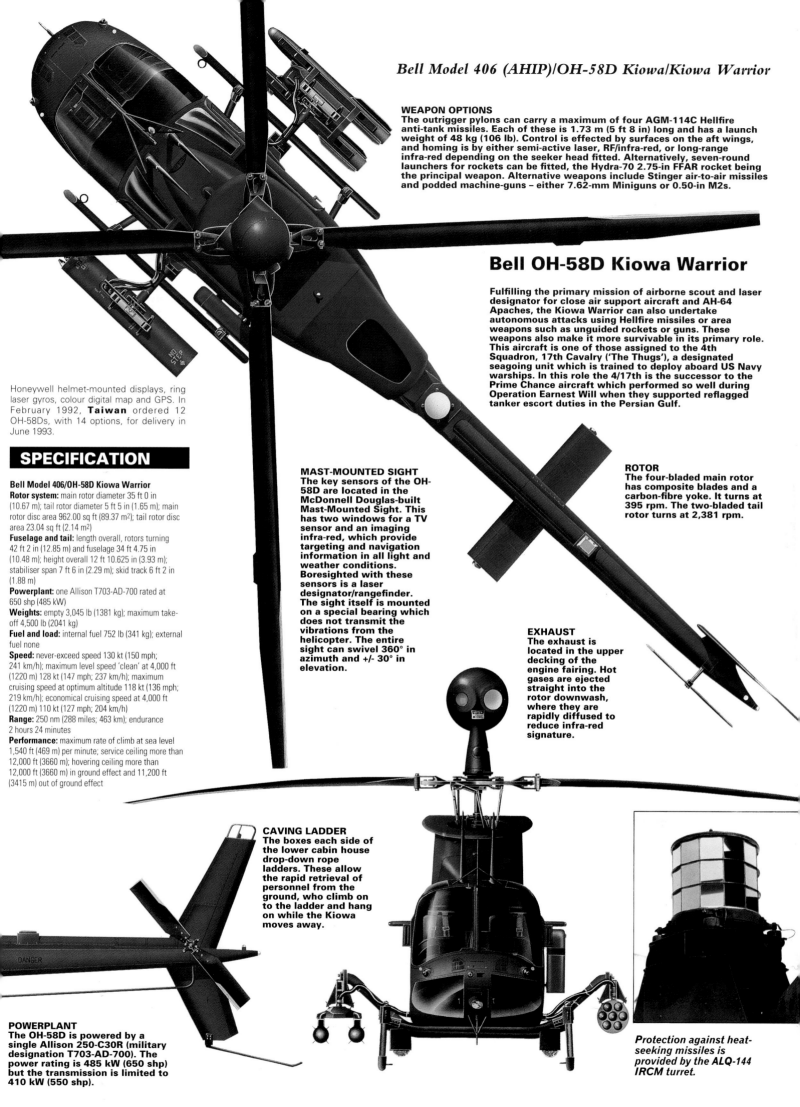

Bell Model 406 (AHIP)/OH-58D Kiowa/Kiowa Warrior

WEAPON OPTIONS
The outrigger pylons can carry a maximum of four AGM-114C Hellfire anti-tank missiles. Each of these is 1.73 m (5 ft 8 in) long and has a launch weight of 48 kg (106 lb). Control is effected by surfaces on the aft wings, and homing is by either semi-active laser, RF/infra-red, or long-range infra-red depending on the seeker head fitted. Alternatively, seven-round launchers for rockets can be fitted, the Hydra-70 2.75-in FFAR rocket being the principal weapon. Alternative weapons include Stinger air-to-air missiles and podded machine-guns – either 7.62-mm Miniguns or 0.50-in M2s.

Bell OH-58D Kiowa Warrior

Fulfilling the primary mission of airborne scout and laser designator for close air support aircraft and AH-64 Apaches, the Kiowa Warrior can also undertake autonomous attacks using Hellfire missiles or area weapons such as unguided rockets or guns. These weapons also make it more survivable in its primary role. This aircraft is one of those assigned to the 4th Squadron, 17th Cavalry ('The Thugs'), a designated seagoing unit which is trained to deploy aboard US Navy warships. In this role the 4/17th is the successor to the Prime Chance aircraft which performed so well during Operation Earnest Will when they supported reflagged tanker escort duties in the Persian Gulf.

Honeywell helmet-mounted displays, ring laser gyros, colour digital map and GPS. In February 1992, **Taiwan** ordered 12 OH-58Ds, with 14 options, for delivery in June 1993.

SPECIFICATION

Bell Model 406/OH-58D Kiowa Warrior
Rotor system: main rotor diameter 35 ft 0 in (10.67 m); tail rotor diameter 5 ft 5 in (1.65 m); main rotor disc area 962.00 sq ft (89.37 m²); tail rotor disc area 23.04 sq ft (2.14 m²)
Fuselage and tail: length overall, rotors turning 42 ft 2 in (12.85 m) and fuselage 34 ft 4.75 in (10.48 m); height overall 12 ft 10.625 in (3.93 m); stabiliser span 7 ft 6 in (2.29 m); skid track 6 ft 2 in (1.88 m)
Powerplant: one Allison T703-AD-700 rated at 650 shp (485 kW)
Weights: empty 3,045 lb (1381 kg); maximum take-off 4,500 lb (2041 kg)
Fuel and load: internal fuel 752 lb (341 kg); external fuel none
Speed: never-exceed speed 130 kt (150 mph; 241 km/h); maximum level speed 'clean' at 4,000 ft (1220 m) 128 kt (147 mph; 237 km/h); maximum cruising speed at optimum altitude 118 kt (136 mph; 219 km/h); economical cruising speed at 4,000 ft (1220 m) 110 kt (127 mph; 204 km/h)
Range: 250 nm (288 miles; 463 km); endurance 2 hours 24 minutes
Performance: maximum rate of climb at sea level 1,540 ft (469 m) per minute; service ceiling more than 12,000 ft (3660 m); hovering ceiling more than 12,000 ft (3660 m) in ground effect and 11,200 ft (3415 m) out of ground effect

MAST-MOUNTED SIGHT
The key sensors of the OH-58D are located in the McDonnell Douglas-built Mast-Mounted Sight. This has two windows for a TV sensor and an imaging infra-red, which provide targeting and navigation information in all light and weather conditions. Boresighted with these sensors is a laser designator/rangefinder. The sight itself is mounted on a special bearing which does not transmit the vibrations from the helicopter. The entire sight can swivel 360° in azimuth and +/- 30° in elevation.

ROTOR
The four-bladed main rotor has composite blades and a carbon-fibre yoke. It turns at 395 rpm. The two-bladed tail rotor turns at 2,381 rpm.

EXHAUST
The exhaust is located in the upper decking of the engine fairing. Hot gases are ejected straight into the rotor downwash, where they are rapidly diffused to reduce infra-red signature.

CAVING LADDER
The boxes each side of the lower cabin house drop-down rope ladders. These allow the rapid retrieval of personnel from the ground, who climb on to the ladder and hang on while the Kiowa moves away.

POWERPLANT
The OH-58D is powered by a single Allison 250-C30R (military designation T703-AD-700). The power rating is 485 kW (650 shp) but the transmission is limited to 410 kW (550 shp).

Protection against heat-seeking missiles is provided by the ALQ-144 IRCM turret.

Bell Model 412

The success of the Bell Model 212 Twin Two-Twelve in both civil and military use led the company to consider how to improve its performance. Reliable and useful though it is, the Model 212 nevertheless has a sea-level maximum cruising speed of only 100 kt (115 mph; 185 km/h) and a maximum range of 261 miles (420 km). The aim was to increase both these parameters, as well as other aspects of performance, without any major structural change to the airframe or the introduction of an entirely different powerplant. With these factors in mind, two new production Model 212s were taken to serve as prototypes for the new helicopter.

As a beginning, the standard Pratt & Whitney Canada PT6T-3B Turbo Twin Pac of the Model 212 gave way to the PT6T-3B-1 version, which differs only by being rated to produce a maximum 1,400 shp (1044 kW) for take-off. To increase range the standard fuel capacity was increased from 215 US gal (814 litres) to 330 US gal (1249 litres). The most significant change was the introduction of a new advanced-technology foldable four-bladed main rotor, comprising a new hub with elastomeric bearings and rotor blades of composite construction. These blades each have a glass-fibre spar and, apart from a Nomex honeycomb filler between the spar and blade trailing edge, the basic blade is entirely of glass-fibre with a titanium abrasion strip and a stainless steel tip cap. Not only was this combination expected to give the desired performance improvements, but static testing had suggested that the new rotor would eliminate most of the induced vibration, avoiding costly structural changes to introduce a nodal suspension system.

The two **Bell Model 412** prototypes were flown first in 1979 and gained VFR and IFR certification in 1981, on 9 January and 13 February respectively. The first production deliveries were made in January 1981, and Bell is continuing production for both civil and military customers.

Norway operates the Bell 412SP Arapaho with 720 Skvadron. This example is seen operating from a portable landing pad. The Norwegians bought 18, of which 17 were assembled locally.

In 1989 Bell transferred its production to Quebec in Canada, although many components are still made at Fort Worth. Further developments are the **Bell 412SP**, which introduced increased gross weight and fuel capacity, itself superseded by the **Bell 412HP** with improved transmission. These variants have accounted for the majority of military sales, including a 1992 order from the Canadian Forces covering 100 examples as the **CH-146 Griffon**. IPTN manufactures the type under licence in Indonesia as the **NBell-412**, while Agusta continues its tradition of Bell licence-production by building the **AB 412**. The Italian company has developed its own **Grifone** (described separately), a dedicated military variant.

SPECIFICATION

Bell Helicopter Textron Model 412SP
Rotor system: main rotor diameter 46 ft 0 in (14.02 m); tail rotor diameter 8 ft 6 in (2.59 m); main rotor disc area 1,661.90 sq ft (154.40 m²); tail rotor disc area 56.74 sq ft (5.27 m²)
Fuselage and tail: length overall, rotors turning 56 ft

0 in (17.07 m) and fuselage 42 ft 4.75 in (12.92 m); height overall 14 ft 2.25 in (4.32 m) with tail rotor turning and to top of rotor head 10 ft 9.5 in (3.29 m); stabiliser span 9 ft 4.5 in (2.86 m); skid track 8 ft 6 in (2.59 m)
Powerplant: one 1,800-shp (1342-kW) Pratt & Whitney Canada PT6T-3B-1 Turbo Twin Pac flat-rated at 1,400 shp (1044 kW) for take-off and 1,130 shp (843 kW) for continuous running
Weights: empty 6,470 lb (2935 kg); maximum take-off 11,900 lb (5397 kg)
Fuel and load: internal fuel 330 US gal (1249 litres) plus provision for 164 US gal (621 litres) of auxiliary fuel; external fuel none
Speed: never-exceed speed at sea level 140 kt (161 mph; 259 km/h); maximum cruising speed at sea level 124 kt (143 mph; 230 km/h)
Range: 375 nm (432 miles; 695 km) with maximum payload
Performance: maximum rate of climb at sea level 1,350 ft (411 m) per minute; service ceiling 16,300 ft (4970 m); hovering ceiling 9,200 ft (2805 m) in and out of ground effect

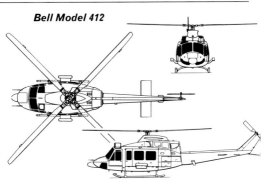

Bell Model 412

OPERATORS

Military versions of the Bell 412 are operated by Bahrain, Botswana, Canada, Colombia, Guatemala, Guyana, Honduras, Indonesia, Lesotho, Norway, Peru, Slovenia, South Korea, Sri Lanka, Thailand, Uganda, Venezuela and Zimbabwe, with the prospect of further sales.

Bell/Boeing V-22 Osprey

From research started by Bell with the tilt-rotor XV-3 in 1951 and Vertol in 1956 with the first tilt-wing VZ-2 (V-76) prototype, followed by Bell's development from 1973 of the highly successful XV-15 proof-of-concept tilt-rotor demonstrator, Bell Helicopter Textron and Boeing Vertol joined forces in the early 1980s to scale up and develop the XV-15 for the Joint Services Advanced Vertical Lift Aircraft (formerly JVX) programme. Combining the vertical lift capabilities of a helicopter with the fast-cruise (275 kt) forward flight efficiencies of a fixed-wing turboprop aircraft, the resulting **V-22 Osprey**, powered by tip-mounted 6,150-shp (4588-kW) Allison T406-AD-500 turboshaft engines driving three-bladed prop-rotors through interconnected drive shafts in nacelles which could be swivelled through 97.5°, was the subject of a US Navy-managed full-scale development contract awarded in June 1985.

Workshare

This included six prototypes, plus several static test airframes, for which Bell was responsible for design and construction of the wing, nacelles, transmissions, rotor and hub assemblies, and integration of the government-furnished engines. Boeing handled the fuselage, empennage, overwing fairings and avionics integration. Composite materials account for 59 per cent of the V-22's airframe weight. Both companies will compete for the major share of any future production lots. Initial joint service requirements were for 913 Ospreys, mostly for the US Army and **Marine Corps**, comprising 552 **MV-22A** USMC assault versions each carrying up to 24 fully-armed troops, as Boeing CH-46 replacements; 231 similar vari-

The first and second prototype V-22s in translational flight. The Osprey will revolutionise assault transport if it eventually succeeds in the budgetary battlefield.

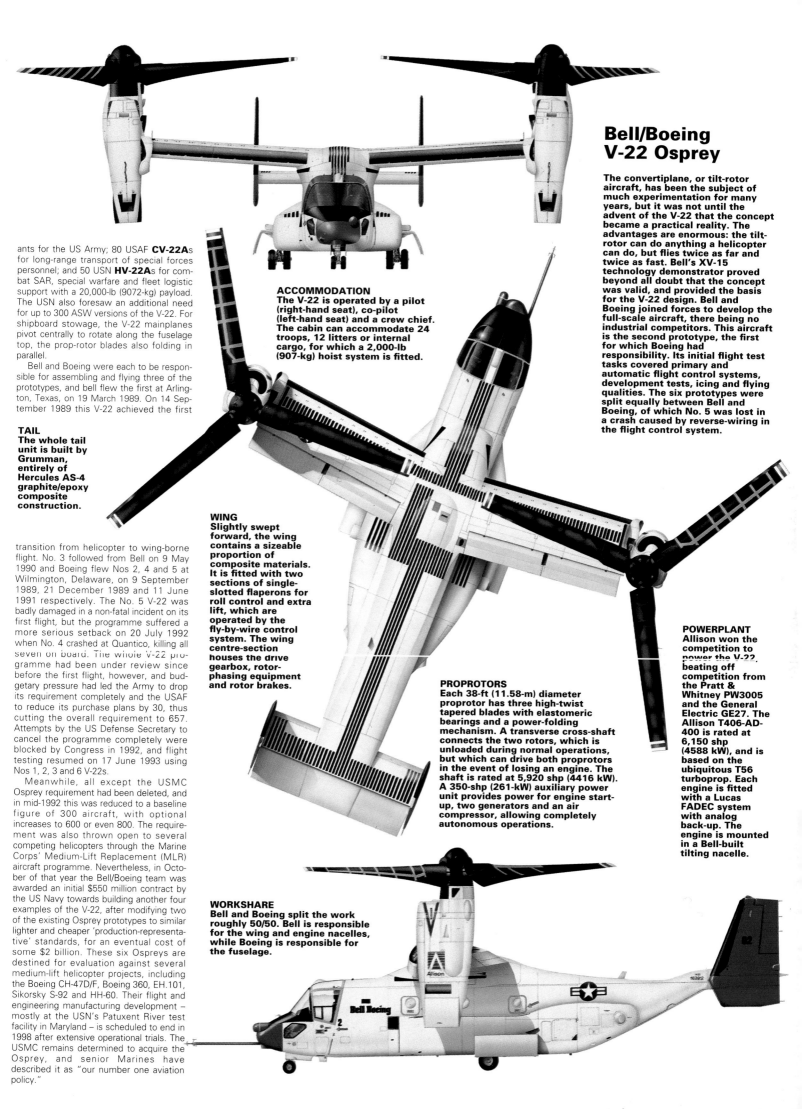

Bell/Boeing
V-22 Osprey

The convertiplane, or tilt-rotor aircraft, has been the subject of much experimentation for many years, but it was not until the advent of the V-22 that the concept became a practical reality. The advantages are enormous: the tilt-rotor can do anything a helicopter can do, but flies twice as far and twice as fast. Bell's XV-15 technology demonstrator proved beyond all doubt that the concept was valid, and provided the basis for the V-22 design. Bell and Boeing joined forces to develop the full-scale aircraft, there being no industrial competitors. This aircraft is the second prototype, the first for which Boeing had responsibility. Its initial flight test tasks covered primary and automatic flight control systems, development tests, icing and flying qualities. The six prototypes were split equally between Bell and Boeing, of which No. 5 was lost in a crash caused by reverse-wiring in the flight control system.

ants for the US Army; 80 USAF **CV-22A**s for long-range transport of special forces personnel; and 50 USN **HV-22A**s for combat SAR, special warfare and fleet logistic support with a 20,000-lb (9072-kg) payload. The USN also foresaw an additional need for up to 300 ASW versions of the V-22. For shipboard stowage, the V-22 mainplanes pivot centrally to rotate along the fuselage top, the prop-rotor blades also folding in parallel.

Bell and Boeing were each to be responsible for assembling and flying three of the prototypes, and bell flew the first at Arlington, Texas, on 19 March 1989. On 14 September 1989 this V-22 achieved the first

ACCOMMODATION
The V-22 is operated by a pilot (right-hand seat), co-pilot (left-hand seat) and a crew chief. The cabin can accommodate 24 troops, 12 litters or internal cargo, for which a 2,000-lb (907-kg) hoist system is fitted.

TAIL
The whole tail unit is built by Grumman, entirely of Hercules AS-4 graphite/epoxy composite construction.

transition from helicopter to wing-borne flight. No. 3 followed from Bell on 9 May 1990 and Boeing flew Nos 2, 4 and 5 at Wilmington, Delaware, on 9 September 1989, 21 December 1989 and 11 June 1991 respectively. The No. 5 V-22 was badly damaged in a non-fatal incident on its first flight, but the programme suffered a more serious setback on 20 July 1992 when No. 4 crashed at Quantico, killing all seven on board. The whole V-22 programme had been under review since before the first flight, however, and budgetary pressure had led the Army to drop its requirement completely and the USAF to reduce its purchase plans by 30, thus cutting the overall requirement to 657. Attempts by the US Defense Secretary to cancel the programme completely were blocked by Congress in 1992, and flight testing resumed on 17 June 1993 using Nos 1, 2, 3 and 6 V-22s.

Meanwhile, all except the USMC Osprey requirement had been deleted, and in mid-1992 this was reduced to a baseline figure of 300 aircraft, with optional increases to 600 or even 800. The requirement was also thrown open to several competing helicopters through the Marine Corps' Medium-Lift Replacement (MLR) aircraft programme. Nevertheless, in October of that year the Bell/Boeing team was awarded an initial $550 million contract by the US Navy towards building another four examples of the V-22, after modifying two of the existing Osprey prototypes to similar lighter and cheaper 'production-representative' standards, for an eventual cost of some $2 billion. These six Ospreys are destined for evaluation against several medium-lift helicopter projects, including the Boeing CH-47D/F, Boeing 360, EH.101, Sikorsky S-92 and HH-60. Their flight and engineering manufacturing development – mostly at the USN's Patuxent River test facility in Maryland – is scheduled to end in 1998 after extensive operational trials. The USMC remains determined to acquire the Osprey, and senior Marines have described it as "our number one aviation policy."

WING
Slightly swept forward, the wing contains a sizeable proportion of composite materials. It is fitted with two sections of single-slotted flaperons for roll control and extra lift, which are operated by the fly-by-wire control system. The wing centre-section houses the drive gearbox, rotor-phasing equipment and rotor brakes.

PROPROTORS
Each 38-ft (11.58-m) diameter proprotor has three high-twist tapered blades with elastomeric bearings and a power-folding mechanism. A transverse cross-shaft connects the two rotors, which is unloaded during normal operations, but which can drive both proprotors in the event of losing an engine. The shaft is rated at 5,920 shp (4416 kW). A 350-shp (261-kW) auxiliary power unit provides power for engine start-up, two generators and an air compressor, allowing completely autonomous operations.

POWERPLANT
Allison won the competition to power the V-22, beating off competition from the Pratt & Whitney PW3005 and the General Electric GE27. The Allison T406-AD-400 is rated at 6,150 shp (4588 kW), and is based on the ubiquitous T56 turboprop. Each engine is fitted with a Lucas FADEC system with analog back-up. The engine is mounted in a Bell-built tilting nacelle.

WORKSHARE
Bell and Boeing split the work roughly 50/50. Bell is responsible for the wing and engine nacelles, while Boeing is responsible for the fuselage.

Bell/Boeing V-22 Osprey

The No. 1 V-22 in helicopter flight. This regime is controlled by normal rotary wing controls with cyclic and collective. As the aircraft translates to horizontal flight, the system automatically decreases these signals to the rotor swashplates, and increases those to the standard fixed-wing flying surfaces.

SPECIFICATION

Bell/Boeing V-22 Osprey
Wing and rotors: rotor diameter, each 38 ft 0 in (11.58 m); width overall, rotors turning 84 ft 6.8 in (25.78 m) and with rotors folded 18 ft 5 in (5.61 m); rotor disc area, total 2,268.23 sq ft (210.72 m2)
Wing: span 50 ft 11 in (15.52 m) including nacelles; aspect ratio 6.77; area 382.00 sq ft (35.59 m2)
Fuselage and tail: length, fuselage excluding probe

57 ft 4 in (17.47 m); height over fins 17 ft 7.8 in (5.38 m) and overall with nacelles vertical 20 ft 10 in (6.35 m); tailplane span over fins 18 ft 5 in (5.61 m); wheel track 15 ft 2 in (4.62 m); wheel base 21 ft 7.5 in (6.59 m)
Powerplant: two Allison T406-AD-400 each rated at 6,150 shp (4586 kW) for take-off and 5,890 shp (4392 kW) for continuous running
Weights: empty equipped 31,886 lb (14463 kg); normal mission take-off 47,500 lb (21545 kg) for VTO and 55,000 lb (24947 kg) for STO; maximum take-off

60,500 lb (27442 kg) for STO
Fuel and load: internal fuel 13,700 lb (6215 kg) standard and 30,074 lb (13641 kg) with self-ferry cabin tanks; maximum internal payload 20,000 lb (9072 kg); maximum external payload 10,000 lb (4536 kg) on a single hook or 15,000 lb (6804 kg) on two hooks
Speed: maximum cruising speed at optimum altitude 300 kt (345 mph; 556 km/h) in aeroplane mode; maximum cruising speed at sea level 100 kt (115 mph; 185 km/h) in helicopter mode and 275 kt (316 mph; 509 km/h) in aeroplane mode; maximum forward

speed with maximum slung load 200 kt (230 mph; 370 km/h)
Range: ferry range 2,100 nm (2,418 miles; 3892 km) after STO at 60,500 lb (27442 kg); tactical range 1,200 nm (1,382 miles; 2224 km) after VTO at 44,619 lb (21146 kg) with 12,000-lb (5443-kg) payload, or 1,800 nm (2,075 miles; 3336 km) after STO at 55,000 lb (24947 kg) with 20,000-lb (9072-kg) payload
Performance: service ceiling 26,000 ft (7925 m); take-off run less than 500 ft (152 m) at normal STO weight

Bellanca **Citabria**

A product of the Aeronca company with its origins in the wartime L-3 Grasshopper, the Model 7 Champion became a Bellanca property in 1970 after it had been further developed by Champion Aircraft Corp. An aerobatic version was named **Citabria** ('Airbatic' reversed), and in 1979 an order for 40 of these was placed by the Turkish army to serve as primary trainers. Known as the **Citabria 150S**, the chosen model was the Model 7GCBC powered by a 150-hp

(112-kW) Lycoming O-320-A2D engine. The Citabrias continue in service at the main army aviation base at Güverncinlik.

The Turkish army operates the Citabria in the primary trainer role and it is also used to screen potential students. The aircraft serve with the army aviation school.

Beriev **Be-6 'Madge'**

Beriev OKB
Taganrog Aviation Scientific-Technical Complex
Instrumentalniy Toupic 347927, Taganrog, Russia

Designed in 1945, and first flying in 1947, the Beriev LL-143 prototype was developed into the **Be-6** flying-boat, which first flew in 1949 and was assigned the NATO reporting name **'Madge'**. The aircraft was of classic Beriev design, with a long boat hull, gull wings and high-set engines. Power came from two Shvetsov ASh-73 radials. Initial production aircraft had a twin NS-23 cannon installation in the tail, but this gave way later to a MAD boom. Other weapons were a twin NS-23 dorsal barbette, and a bow-mounted single NS-23. Mines, depth charges or torpedoes could be carried. The 'Madge' remained in Soviet service into the 1970s, on second-line duties However, a small number were supplied to **China,** and it is believed that 10 of these continue to serve in the ASW role from the base at Tuandao.

Beriev **Be-12 Tchaika 'Mail'**

Developed as a successor to the Beriev Be-6, the **Be-12 Tchaika** (seagull) was designed primarily as an ASW and maritime patrol aircraft, although as land-based aircraft like the Il-38 and Tu-142 have taken over this role, SAR operations have become increasingly important.

Despite its anachronistic appearance, the Be-12 is a capable aircraft, and between 1964 and 1983 broke or set all 44 FAI world records for turboprop amphibians and flying-boats. The prototype first flew in 1960, probably after competitive evaluation against the same bureau's jet-powered Be-10 'Mallow'.

The Be-12 is of very similar configuration and appearance to the 1949-vintage Be-6 flying-boat, with a cranked (gullwing) cantilever high wing, with considerable dihedral on the inner panels and slight anhedral on the outer wings. A 3124-kW (4,190-ehp) Ivchenko AI-20D turboprop is mounted on the top of each wing at the highest point, giving the AV-681 four-bladed propellers maximum clearance. The tailplanes also have considerable anhedral, and are tipped by vertical endplate fins. The aircraft has a single-step metal monocoque hull, with strakes on each side of the forward fuselage to minimise the amount of spray

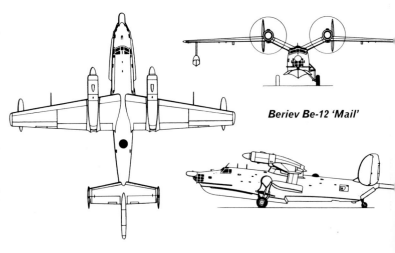

Beriev Be-12 'Mail'

The elderly Be-12 serves the Russian navy on coastal patrols. These cover ASW, SAR and fishery protection.

thrown up on take-off and landing. For operations from land, the Be-12 has a retractable tailwheel undercarriage, with the single mainwheels retracting upwards to lie flush in the sides of the hull. The five-man crew consists of pilot, co-pilot, navigator, radar operator and MAD operator.

A small search radar is carried, with a thimble radome directly above the glazing of the navigator's nose station, and there is a prominent magnetic anomaly detector 'stinger' projecting aft from the tailcone. The aircraft has an internal weapons bay in the hull, immediately aft of the step, and has two underwing pylons under each outer wing panel, and can reportedly also carry rocket rails farther outboard. Armament would usually consist of homing torpedoes and depth charges.

About 70 of the 100-200 Be-12 Tchaika amphibians built remain in service with the air forces of the **Russian Northern Fleet,** and almost certainly with the **Ukrainian** successor to the old Black Sea Fleet. About a dozen may also remain active with the **Vietnam People's Army Air Force,** and a handful more with **Syria,** serving on SAR and patrol duties.

Seven ex-AV-MF Be-12s were returned in 1993 to Taganrog for conversion to new roles. Two are serving as the prototypes for a proposed water-bomber, with twin water scoops behind the step, extra drop doors in the hull just behind the cockpit, and small overflow portholes in the upper fuselage

above all the water tanks. Three 1.5-ton tanks are fitted in the former rear weapons bay, and a single 3-ton tank in the stores position behind the cockpit. The 7½-ton load can be dropped simultaneously, or sequentially from fore and aft doors to cover a larger area. The Be-12's agility and powerful engines make it extremely suitable for the firefighting role, and Beriev expects an order in 1993 for six aircraft for service in the Russian Far East. A third aircraft is serving as the prototype for a cargo aircraft,

with an enlarged hatch and all ASW equipment removed.

SPECIFICATION

Beriev Be-12 Tchaika 'Mail'
Wing: span 29.71 m (97 ft 5.75 in); aspect ratio 8.4; area 105.00 m² (1,130.25 sq ft)
Fuselage and tail: length 30.17 m (99 ft 0 in); height 7.00 m (22 ft 11.5 in)
Powerplant: two ZMDB Progress (Ivchyenko) AI-20D

each rated at 3,124 ekW (4,190 ehp)
Weights: empty 21700 kg (47,840 lb); maximum take-off 31000 kg (68,342 lb)
Fuel and load: external fuel none; maximum ordnance about 5000 kg (11,023 lb)
Speed: maximum level speed 'clean' at optimum altitude 608 km/h (328 kt; 378 mph); normal operating speed at optimum altitude 320 km/h (173 kt; 199 mph)
Range: ferry range 7500 km (4,047 nm; 4,660 miles)
Performance: maximum rate of climb at sea level 912 m (2,990 ft) per minute; service ceiling 11280 m (37,000 ft)

Beriev **A-40 Albatros 'Mermaid'**

Development of the **A-40** began during 1983 as a successor to the Be-12 'Mail' in the ASW, maritime patrol, minelaying and secondary SAR roles. The prototype made its first flight during December 1986, and it became known to the West during 1987. In 1988 the director of US naval intelligence revealed that the provisional reporting name **'TAG-D'** (the fourth new experimental aircraft spotted at Taganrog) had been allo-

cated to a new amphibian photographed by a US satellite. On 20 August 1989 the prototype made a flypast at the Aviation Day display at Tushino, and articles about the aircraft (described as being for SAR duties, and attributed to designer Alexei K. Konstantinov) began to appear in the Soviet press. The second prototype finally made the type's Western debut at the 1991 Paris air show at Le Bourget, by which time the

Beriev Design Bureau had been renamed as the Taganrog Aviation Scientific-Technical Complex, named after G. M. Beriev.

The A-40 is the largest amphibian ever built, and is of completely modern design. A pair of Perm/Soloviev D-30KPV turbofan engines is mounted on pylons above the wingroot, just aft of the trailing edge. An RD-60K turbojet take-off booster is fitted inside each pylon, with its nozzle usually

covered by a vertically split 'eyelid'. The wings themselves, along with small strakes on the nose, protect the engine intakes from spray.

The single-step hull is of revolutionary design, described by its creators as the world's first 'variable rise bottom', with unique double chines. This sets new standards of stability and controllability in the water and gives smaller *g* forces on take-off and landing. Small wedges help the aircraft to 'unstick'. The aircraft has a large stores bay in the hull, aft of the step, and the large pods which form the wingroots accommodate electronic equipment as well as the retracted four-wheel main undercarriage bogies. Slim ESM pods are carried on the wingtips, above the stabilising floats. A flight crew of eight would be carried, consisting of two pilots, a flight engineer, a radio operator, a navigator and three observers/equipment operators.

The basic A-40 ASW/patrol amphibian will probably bear the service designation **Be-44** (which may have been the subject of a lapsed 10-aircraft order for the **CIS navy**) if it ever enters production. The aircraft forms the basis for a number of as-yet unflown variants. A minimum-change SAR version, stripped of ASW equipment and without ESM wingtips, is designated **Be-42.** This will have a nine-man crew, with an additional technician and the three observer/operators replaced by medical attendants. The aircraft would carry two LPS-6 life rafts, blood transfusion equipment, ECG machines and other surgical equipment. Up to 54 survivors could be accommodated, entering the aircraft via two side hatches, each equipped with mechanised ramps. Searchlights and IR sensors

An impressive view of an A-40 Albatros launching during a test flight. The aircraft has excellent water characteristics, and good performance once it is airborne.

The A-40's strange configuration results from the conflicting demands of operations from both water and land. The engines are mounted high above the fuselage to avoid spray ingestion.

Fuselage and tail: length 43.839 m (143 ft 10 in) including probe; height 11.066 m (36 ft 3.75 in); tailplane span 11.87 m (38 ft 11.5 in); wheel track 4.96 m (16 ft 3.25 in); wheel base 14.835 m (48 ft 8 in)
Powerplant: two PNPP 'Aviadvigatel' (Soloviev) D-30KPV each rated at 117.68 kN (26,455 lb st) dry and two Klimov RD-60K each rated at 24.52 kN (5,511 lb st) dry
Weights: maximum take-off about 86000 kg (189,594 lb)
Fuel and load: internal fuel 35000 kg (77,160 lb); external fuel none; maximum ordnance 6500 kg (14,330 lb)
Speed: never-exceed speed 650 km/h (350 kt; 404 mph); maximum level speed 'clean' at 6000 m (19,685 ft) 760 km/h (410 kt; 472 mph); maximum cruising speed at 6000 m (19,685 ft) 720 km/h (388 kt; 447 mph)
Range: 5500 km (2,967 nm; 3,417 miles) with maximum fuel or 4100 km (2,212 nm; 2,547 miles) with maximum payload
Performance: maximum rate of climb at sea level 1800 m (5,906 ft) per minute with one engine inoperative; service ceiling 9700 m (31,825 ft); take-off run 1000 m (3,281 ft) at maximum take-off weight; take-off distance to 15 m (50 ft) 1100 m (3,609 ft) at maximum take-off weight; landing distance from 15 m (50 ft) 1450 m (4,757 ft) at normal landing weight; landing run 900 m (2,953 ft) at normal landing weight

would be used for locating survivors. The first Be-42 is already under construction, but the status of an order for 10 by the CIS navy (which originally wanted 10 ASW Be-44s) is very uncertain. The **Be-40P** is a projected 105-seat passenger aircraft, and the **Be-40PT** a mixed passenger and cargo aircraft carrying between 37 and 70 people plus freight. The **Be-200** is a scaled-down version, powered by a pair of Lotarev D-436T turbofans and with passenger, cargo, ambulance and SAR versions projected.

SPECIFICATION

Beriev A-40 Albatros 'Mermaid'
Wing: span 41.62 m (136 ft 6.5 in); aspect ratio 8.6; area 200.00 m² (2,152.85 sq ft)

Boeing **B-52G Stratofortress**

*Boeing Defense and Space Group
PO Box 3999, Seattle
WA 98124, USA*

Backbone of Strategic Air Command until the organisation's demise on 31 May 1992, the mighty B-52 has been an icon of US military strength for nearly 40 years, having first entered service in June 1955. In today's streamlined **Air Combat Command**, the type still plays an important part in the power projection force, while also retaining its nuclear deterrent function. By the end of 1994 only the B-52H will be left in service.

One hundred and ninety-three **B-52Gs** were built, these introducing integral wing tanks and a shorter fin compared to earlier variants. Defensive armament remained as four 0.50-in machine-guns in a remotely-controlled turret, although in October 1991 the gunner was removed from the crew as an economy measure. Eighty G models remained in service in early 1993, but during the year most were retired to the boneyard.

In the initial ACC structure, B-52Gs served with the 2nd, 42nd, 93rd, 366th, 379th and 416th Bomb Wings. Power projection was the principal role for these veterans, using their enormous range and load-carrying ability to haul conventional bomb-loads to any point on the globe. Desert Storm missions were all assigned to the G model. Some aircraft were converted to carry 12 AGM-86 cruise missiles on the wing pylons, principally for the nuclear role with the AGM-86B. However, the conventional warhead AGM-86C is now in use,

launched operationally for the first time on the opening night of Desert Storm. Non-cruise configured B-52Gs were assigned a maritime role, including the launch of Harpoon anti-ship missiles. In the Gulf War these aircraft operated as free-fall bombers.

Internal configuration

Internally the B-52G has a large weapons bay occupying the central fuselage, which is capable of accommodating clips of conventional weapons or free-fall nuclear devices. The crew area is arranged on two levels, the lower deck housing the en route navigator and radar navigator/bombardier, while the upper deck has the two pilots and the electronic warfare officer, the latter facing

backwards in a seat next to the vacated gunner's position. Four main undercarriage units are staggered to retract sideways into the fuselage, and outriggers are provided in the tips of the drooping wings to maintain stability. The B-52G is well protected by numerous ECM systems, and two under-nose blisters house LLLTV and FLIR sen-

The B-52G is fast disappearing from service as Air Combat Command shrinks to a manned bomber force consisting of the B-52H and B-1B, with a 'silver bullet' fleet of B-2s. The 366th Wing at Mountain Home was the last user of the G model, receiving B-1Bs in 1994.

In its twilight years, the B-52G has become closely associated with conventional weapons. Here the load is low-drag general-purpose bombs, of which a great number can be carried. In the maritime role the B-52 can sow mines.

sors, which are used with terrain-avoidance radar to provide low-level penetration capability in bad weather or at night.

With the reduction in threat posed by the former Soviet Union, the nuclear deterrent requirement is considerably reduced, releasing B-52Hs to assume many of the conventional tasks previously undertaken by the B-52G. Consequently, the G model will be out of service by the mid-1990s. The final unit is the 366th Wing, the US Air Force's power projection unit headquartered at Mountain Home AFB, Idaho. This unit controls the 34th Bomb Squadron, stationed at Ellsworth AFB, SD (previously March AFB, CA). The squadron is converting to the B-1B, the first two of a planned six having been delivered by May 1994.

WEAPON OPTIONS

Tail turret with four 0.50-in machine-guns (not currently used), internal bomb bay and inboard wing pylons for carriage of offensive load. Up to 20 AGM-86 ALCM can be carried, eight internally and three on each wing pylon. Internal carriage for 'clip' of four B83 free-fall nuclear weapons. In the conventional role the B-52G can be configured with the Heavy Stores Adaptor Beam on the wing hardpoints so that nine 2,000-lb class Mk 84 bombs can be carried under each wing, with a further 27 internally. Alternatively 27 750-lb class M117 or 1,000-lb class Mk 83 bombs can be carried internally, with a further 24 on wing pylons fitted with the redundant Hound Dog pylon and multiple ejector racks. AGM-86C conventional-warhead cruise missiles provide long-range stand-off attack capability, and the AGM-142 Have Nap EO-guided missile can be carried on the HSABs. This missile has

a stand-off range of 80 km (50 miles) and features a 896-kg (1,975-lb) high-explosive warhead.

SPECIFICATION

Boeing B-52G Stratofortress
generally similar to the B-52H except in the following particulars:
Powerplant: eight Pratt & Whitney J57-P-43WB each rated at 13,750 lb st (61.16 kN) dry
Weights: maximum take-off more than 488,000 lb (221357 kg)
Range: range more than 6,513 nm (7,500 miles; 12070 km)
Performance: service ceiling 40,000 ft (12190 m)

Right: The B-52Gs of the 366th Wing have been issued with the AGM-142 EO/IR-guided Have Nap stand-off missile. This allows the B-52 to hit targets with great accuracy but without having to penetrate heavily-defended air space.

Boeing **B-52H Stratofortress**

Based on the preceding B-52G version, the **Boeing B-52H** was intended to serve as a carrier for the Douglas GAM-87A Skybolt air-launched ballistic missile under development in the early 1960s. The most significant of the changes for this mission was to ensure that the B-52H would be able to penetrate enemy air space at low level, below radar coverage, which required extensive structural modification to ensure the airframe would be able to withstand the effects of low-level turbulence. The changes were barely visible externally, but two other modifications were to provide external features that allowed identification. One of the early-build B-52Gs (57-6471) had flown in July 1960 as a testbed for the Pratt & Whitney TF33-P-1 turbofan, and more powerful versions of the same engine were installed in revised cowlings to enhance performance of the B-52H, giving a range increase of almost one third by comparison with the B-52G. The last externally noticeable change was replacement of the four 12.7-mm (0.5-in) machine-guns in the tail turret of the B-52G with a Vulcan cannon with six 20-mm barrels. Internal changes for the new role brought revised ECM equipment and the provision of terrain-avoidance radar.

A total of 102 B-52H Stratofortresses

was built, the first (60-006) being flown on 6 March 1961. Within 16 months, in June 1962, the last of them had been completed; six months later President John F. Kennedy cancelled the Skybolt programme for which the B-52H had been developed. Since that time the aircraft has been subject of many update programmes, which have added improved avionics, ECM protection and the ALQ-151 Electro-optical Viewing System (EVS). B-52Hs were configured to carry 20 AGM-86B cruise missiles (12 under the wing pylons and eight on an internal rotary launcher), and were employed mainly in the stand-off nuclear missile launch role until 1991, when the force began to adopt a wider brief including conventional bombing tasks. In the same time-frame, the H model began to be equipped with the AGM-129

Advanced Cruise Missile, a stealthy successor to the AGM-86. Further weapon options include AGM-86C conventional-warhead cruise missiles, B61 or B83 free-fall nuclear

Above: Operating in the conventional role, this B-52H is from the 5th Bomb Wing, seen participating in a Red Flag exercise.

A 416th BW B-52H displays the unique undercarriage arrangement of the Stratofortress. The tail gun may be replaced by Stinger missiles.

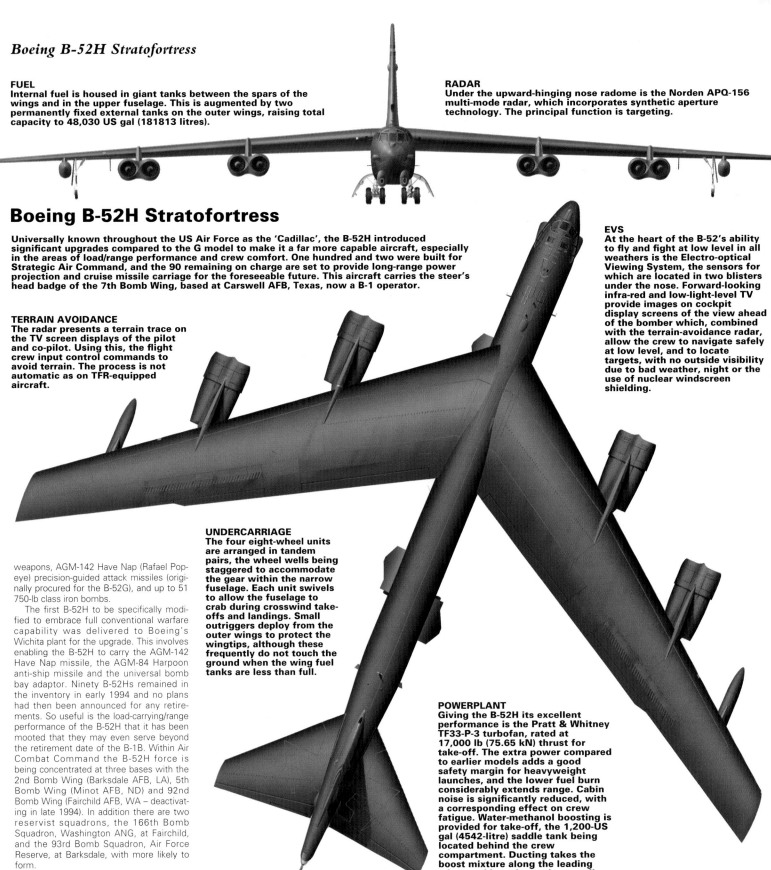

Boeing B-52H Stratofortress

FUEL
Internal fuel is housed in giant tanks between the spars of the wings and in the upper fuselage. This is augmented by two permanently fixed external tanks on the outer wings, raising total capacity to 48,030 US gal (181813 litres).

RADAR
Under the upward-hinging nose radome is the Norden APQ-156 multi-mode radar, which incorporates synthetic aperture technology. The principal function is targeting.

Boeing B-52H Stratofortress

Universally known throughout the US Air Force as the 'Cadillac', the B-52H introduced significant upgrades compared to the G model to make it a far more capable aircraft, especially in the areas of load/range performance and crew comfort. One hundred and two were built for Strategic Air Command, and the 90 remaining on charge are set to provide long-range power projection and cruise missile carriage for the foreseeable future. This aircraft carries the steer's head badge of the 7th Bomb Wing, based at Carswell AFB, Texas, now a B-1 operator.

TERRAIN AVOIDANCE
The radar presents a terrain trace on the TV screen displays of the pilot and co-pilot. Using this, the flight crew input control commands to avoid terrain. The process is not automatic as on TFR-equipped aircraft.

EVS
At the heart of the B-52's ability to fly and fight at low level in all weathers is the Electro-optical Viewing System, the sensors for which are located in two blisters under the nose. Forward-looking infra-red and low-light-level TV provide images on cockpit display screens of the view ahead of the bomber which, combined with the terrain-avoidance radar, allow the crew to navigate safely at low level, and to locate targets, with no outside visibility due to bad weather, night or the use of nuclear windscreen shielding.

UNDERCARRIAGE
The four eight-wheel units are arranged in tandem pairs, the wheel wells being staggered to accommodate the gear within the narrow fuselage. Each unit swivels to allow the fuselage to crab during crosswind take-offs and landings. Small outriggers deploy from the outer wings to protect the wingtips, although these frequently do not touch the ground when the wing fuel tanks are less than full.

weapons, AGM-142 Have Nap (Rafael Popeye) precision-guided attack missiles (originally procured for the B-52G), and up to 51 750-lb class iron bombs.

The first B-52H to be specifically modified to embrace full conventional warfare capability was delivered to Boeing's Wichita plant for the upgrade. This involves enabling the B-52H to carry the AGM-142 Have Nap missile, the AGM-84 Harpoon anti-ship missile and the universal bomb bay adaptor. Ninety B-52Hs remained in the inventory in early 1994 and no plans had then been announced for any retirements. So useful is the load-carrying/range performance of the B-52H that it has been mooted that they may even serve beyond the retirement date of the B-1B. Within Air Combat Command the B-52H force is being concentrated at three bases with the 2nd Bomb Wing (Barksdale AFB, LA), 5th Bomb Wing (Minot AFB, ND) and 92nd Bomb Wing (Fairchild AFB, WA – deactivating in late 1994). In addition there are two reservist squadrons, the 166th Bomb Squadron, Washington ANG, at Fairchild, and the 93rd Bomb Squadron, Air Force Reserve, at Barksdale, with more likely to form.

POWERPLANT
Giving the B-52H its excellent performance is the Pratt & Whitney TF33-P-3 turbofan, rated at 17,000 lb (75.65 kN) thrust for take-off. The extra power compared to earlier models adds a good safety margin for heavyweight launches, and the lower fuel burn considerably extends range. Cabin noise is significantly reduced, with a corresponding effect on crew fatigue. Water-methanol boosting is provided for take-off, the 1,200-US gal (4542-litre) saddle tank being located behind the crew compartment. Ducting takes the boost mixture along the leading edges and into the engine nacelles.

ECM
The B-52 is comprehensively equipped to handle hostile radar threats. Equipment includes an ALT-28 jammer in a fairing on top of the nose, ALQ-117 deception jammers facing sideways from the nose, ALQ-172 deception jammer forward of the gun-control radar and clusters of aerials for the ALQ-155 system under the forward and rear fuselage. Radar warning receivers are located in the tailcone and in blisters on the sides of the vertical fin.

CREW
The B-52H crew consists of two pilots and an electronic warfare officer on the upper deck, with a navigator and bombardier/radar navigator on the lower deck. The former gunner's station is now vacant.

WEAPON OPTIONS

In the nuclear role the B-52H can carry 20 cruise missiles (eight internally on rotary launcher and six under each wing pylon). These can either be AGM-86B ALCM or AGM-129 Advanced Cruise Missiles. Free-fall weapons such as B61 or B83 remain an option, but this capability is at present entrusted to the B-1 fleet (with B-2 assuming the role in the future). Conventional weapons are the same as for B-52G, namely AGM-86C cruise missiles, AGM-142 Have Nap and AGM-84 Harpoon. Free-fall bombs can be carried on HSABs or Hound Dog pylons,

to a maximum of 51 750-lb class weapons. Alternatives to general-purpose bombs include cluster munitions and mines. The M61A1 Vulcan 20-mm cannon in the tail turret is no longer used, and may be replaced by a Stinger air-to-air missile launcher.

SPECIFICATION

Boeing B-52H Stratofortress
Wing: span 185 ft 0 in (56.39 m); aspect ratio 8.56; area 4,000.00 sq ft (371.60 m²)
Fuselage and tail: length 160 ft 10.9 in (49.05 m); height 40 ft 8 in (12.40 m); tailplane span 55 ft 7.5 in

(16.95 m); wheel track 8 ft 3 in (2.51 m); wheel base 50 ft 3 in (15.48 m)
Powerplant: eight Pratt & Whitney TF33-P-3 each rated at 17,000 lb st (75.62 kN) dry
Weights: maximum take-off 505,000 lb (229088 kg)
Fuel and load: internal fuel 299,434 lb (135821 kg) plus provision for 9,114 lb (4134 kg) in two 700-US gal (2650-litre) non-jettisonable underwing tanks; external fuel none; maximum ordnance about 50,000 lb (22680 kg)
Speed: maximum level speed 'clean' at high altitude 516 kt (595 mph; 957 km/h); cruising speed at high altitude 442 kt (509 mph; 819 km/h); penetration speed at low altitude between 352 and 365 kt

These B-52Hs wear the 'Seattle Seahawks' badge of the 92nd Bomb Wing, based at Fairchild AFB, Washington. The aircraft are armed with AGM-86B ALCMs, six being carried on each wing pylon with a further eight inside.

(405 and 420 mph; 652 and 676 km/h)
Range: more than 6,865 nm (10,000 miles; 16093 km)
Performance: service ceiling 55,000 ft (16765 m); take-off run 9,500 ft (2896 m) at maximum take-off weight

Boeing **C-135**

Eight hundred and twenty of the C-135 family were built, all but 12 being for **USAF** service. Although the KC-135 tankers were the principal variants, 45 were built as **C-135A** (15) or **C-135B** (30) transports, with tanking equipment deleted. Several of these remain in limited service on specialised transport or test duties.

Having spent many years with the 89th MAW on staff transport duties, this C-135B is one of a small fleet assigned to general duties with the 55th Wing at Offutt AFB, where most 'special' C-135s are gathered.

J57 turbojets powered the C-135A, and only two of these remain in service under this designation, used by the 4950th Test Wing of Air Force Materiel Command and as a command transport/trials aircraft by the 55th Reconnaissance Wing. Further C-135A aircraft still serve as transports, upgraded to **C-135E** standard with TF33 turbofans and wide-span tailplanes, one flying with the 4950th TW and one operated by the 552nd AW&CW on behalf of the Commander, Space Command.

C-135Bs were built with TF33 turbofans and wide-span tailplanes from the outset, and a small number remains in service in

their original form, one serving with the 55th Wing on staff transport duties. The **C-135C** designation applies to three **WC-135B** weather reconnaissance aircraft which reverted to transport status. Most of the other C-135Bs were converted to various special mission variants following their service with Military Airlift Command.

SPECIFICATION

Boeing C-135A
Wing: span 130 ft 10 in (39.88 m); aspect ratio 7.04; area 2,433.00 sq ft (226.03 m²)
Fuselage and tail: length 136 ft 3 in (41.53 m); height 41 ft 8 in (12.70 m); tailplane span 40 ft 3 in (12.27 m); wheel base 46 ft 7 in (14.20 m)
Powerplant: four Pratt & Whitney J57-P-59W each

rated at 13,750 lb st (61.16 kN) dry
Weights: operating empty 106,306 lb (48220 kg); maximum take-off 316,000 lb (143335 kg)
Fuel and load: internal fuel 189,702 lb (86047 kg); external fuel none; maximum payload 83,000 lb (37650 kg)
Speed: maximum level speed at high altitude 530 kt (610 mph; 982 km/h); cruising speed at 35,000 ft (10670 m) 462 kt (532 mph; 856 km/h)
Range: ferry range 7,990 nm (9,200 miles; 14806 km); operational radius 3,000 nm (3,455 miles; 5560 km) to offload 24,000 lb (10886 kg) of fuel or 1,000 nm (1,151 miles; 1854 km) to offload 120,000 lb (54432 kg) of fuel
Performance: maximum rate of climb at sea level 1,290 ft (393 m) per minute; service ceiling 45,000 ft (13715 m); typical take-off run 10,700 ft (3261 m) increasing to 14,000 ft (4267 m) under 'hot and high' conditions at maximum take-off weight

Boeing **KC-135A/Q Stratotanker**

On 15 July 1954, Boeing's famous Model 367-80 prototype took to the air for the first time at the company's Renton plant. The four-jet swept-wing transport provided the basis for the prolific Model 707 civil airliner and Model 717 (C-135) tanker-transport families, and also set the design philosophy which extended throughout Boeing's hugely successful airliner dynasty.

In September 1955 Boeing received the first order for the **KC-135A** tanker, following successful trials with the 'Dash Eighty' prototype configured with a Boeing-designed flying boom under the rear fuselage. The first tanker (55-3118) flew from Renton on 31 August 1956, piloted by 'Dix' Loesch and 'Tex' Johnston. Flight tests revealed no serious flaws and the KC-135A entered service with the 93rd Air Refueling Squadron on 28 June 1957.

Seven hundred and thirty-two KC-135s were built in a long and efficient production run. The first 582 aircraft were built with a short fin, but from the 583rd today's taller fin was introduced to make the aircraft more stable during take-off, a feature retro-fitted to all machines. An early modification was the addition of strengthening straps around the rear fuselage to dampen jet-induced resonance.

Internal configuration

Internally, the KC-135A features integral wing tanks between the spars, and further tanks in the lower lobe of the fuselage, making a total of 22. The main cabin provides a considerable volume for cargo carriage, for which a side-loading cargo door is fitted. Alternatively, seating can be provided for 80 troops. A crew of four comprises two pilots, a navigator and a boom operator. The latter is called upon to act as loadmaster and to aid the flight crew in navigation and with checklists, in addition to his primary task.

This is performed from a prone position in a fairing under the rear of the aircraft, from where the boomer has an excellent view of the boom and the receiver aircraft. A small control column is provided which is linked to control surfaces on the end of the boom. Further controls are provided for extending and retracting the boom, and the boomer also operates director lights which provide positional information for receiver pilots. The fuel system is managed by the co-pilot from a console between the two pilots.

Fifty-six of the tankers were converted as **KC-135Q**s, which featured additional navigation and communications equipment for the support of the now-retired Lockheed SR-71 fleet. These carried high-flashpoint JP-7 fuel in addition to the regular JP-4/5 used by the tanker itself. They remained capable of refuelling other receivers, but the JP-7 tanks had to be purged before they could carry regular fuel. Today the Q models are often involved in supporting F-117 operations, and are in the process of being re-engined to **KC-135T** standard (described separately). Other early tanker variants were the **C-135F** (a designation applied to 12 KC-135As which were supplied to France), and the **KC-135D**, four of which were converted from RC-135A survey aircraft.

Between 1975 and 1988, Boeing replaced the lower wing skins of all surviving KC-135s to extend their useful lives to beyond 2020. Work also began on re-engining a large portion of the fleet to replace the noisy and thirsty J57 engines.

Two major re-engining programmes reduced the numbers of KC-135As in the inventory considerably, and in 1993/94 large numbers were retired to AMARC at Davis-Monthan AFB, AZ. In early 1994 the only front-line units still operating the original J57-engined 'stovepipe' tankers were the 71st Air Refueling Squadron, 19th Air Refueling Wing at Barksdale AFB, LA, (inactivating 1994), 350th ARS/43rd ARW at Beale AFB, CA, and the 917th ARS/43rd ARW at Dyess AFB, TX. Each squadron was operating 15 KC-135Qs. Six KC-135As remained with the 93rd ARS, the training unit at Castle AFB, but were due for imminent retirement, while the training function was to transfer (with KC-135Rs) to Altus AFB, OK, under the auspices of Air Education and Training Command.

With the KC-135A retired to the boneyard, and the KC-135Q fleet being cycled through Boeing Wichita for conversion to KC-135T standard, the days of the 'stovepipe' are all but over.

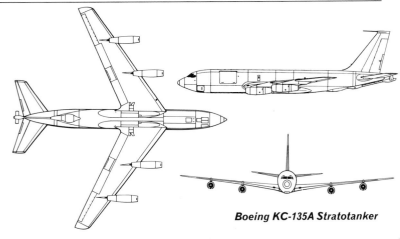

Boeing KC-135A Stratotanker

SPECIFICATION

Boeing KC-135A Stratotanker
Wing: span 130 ft 10 in (39.88 m); aspect ratio 7.04; area 2,433.00 sq ft (226.03 m²)
Fuselage and tail: length 136 ft 3 in (41.53 m);
height 41 ft 8 in (12.70 m); tailplane span 40 ft 3 in (12.27 m); wheel base 46 ft 7 in (14.20 m)
Powerplant: four Pratt & Whitney J57-P-59W each rated at 13,750 lb st (61.16 kN) dry
Weights: operating empty 106,306 lb (48220 kg); maximum take-off 316,000 lb (143335 kg)
Fuel and load: internal fuel 189,702 lb (86047 kg); external fuel none; maximum payload 83,000 lb (37650 kg)
Speed: maximum level speed at high altitude 530 kt (610 mph, 982 km/h); cruising speed at 35,000 ft (10670 m) 462 kt (532 mph, 856 km/h)
Range: ferry range 7,990 nm (9,200 miles; 14806 km); operational radius 3,000 nm (3,455 miles; 5560 km) to offload 24,000 lb (10886 kg) of fuel or 1,000 nm (1,151 miles; 1854 km) to offload 120,000 lb

Having previously supported SR-71 operations, the KC-135Qs are often used to refuel Lockheed F-117s. The specialist aircraft are the last to undergo the F108 re-engining.

(54432 kg) of fuel
Performance: maximum rate of climb at sea level 1,290 ft (393 m) per minute; service ceiling 45,000 ft (13715 m); typical take-off run 10,700 ft (3261 m) increasing to 14,000 ft (4267 m) under 'hot-and-high' conditions at maximum take-off weight

The 'stovepipe' KC-135As are now retired from service. This example wears 379th BW markings.

Boeing **KC-135D/E Stratotanker**

Of the two re-engining programmes for the KC-135, the least ambitious was that to upgrade the KC-135A tankers of the Air National Guard and Air Force Reserve (together with a small number of special mission EC/RC/NKC-135 aircraft) with turbofans.

Large numbers of surplus 707 airliners were purchased by the US Air Force, and stripped of their JT3D (military designation TF33) engines for fitment to the tankers. At the same time the wide-span tailplanes of the airliners were also fitted to the tankers to maintain stability with the greater thrust of the new engines.

Fitment of the TF33s provides several important improvements over the J57. The greater thrust allows the **KC-135E** to operate on far greater safety margins than previously possible, and to use shorter runways. The fan engines are more efficient, offering cost-saving and greater fuel offloads on similar mission profiles. Noise pollution is considerably reduced, a major factor for Guard units operating from civilian airports, and lastly the TF33s incorporate thrust-reversers for greater landing safety.

Over one hundred and sixty ANG and AFRES KC-135s underwent the 'E' conver-

sion, including the four **KC-135D**s (although these retain their original designation), and were joined by 21 special mission aircraft. Current units are:

Air Force Reserve – 63rd ARS/434th ARW (Selfridge ANGB), 314th ARS/434th ARW (McClellan AFB) and 336th ARS/452nd ARW (March AFB);

Air National Guard – 168th ARS/Alaska ANG (Eielson AFB, operates all four KC-135Ds in addition to KC-135Es), 197th ARS/Arizona ANG (Sky Harbor IAP, Phoenix), 196th ARS/California ANG (March AFB), 108th ARS/Illinois ANG (O'Hare ARFF, Chicago), 117th ARS/Kansas ANG (Forbes Field, Topeka), 132nd ARS/Maine ANG (Bangor ANGB), 133rd ARS/New Hampshire ANG (Pease AFB – converting to KC-135R), 141st ARS and 150th ARS/New Jersey ANG (McGuire AFB), 146th ARS and 147th ARS/Pennsylvania ANG (Greater Pittsburgh IAP), 151st ARS/Tennessee ANG (McGhee Tyson AP, Knoxville), 191st ARS/Utah ANG (Salt Lake City IAP) and 116th ARS/Washington ANG (Fairchild AFB – converting to B-52H). Three more ANG tanker squadrons were due to form in 1994: 106th ARS/Alabama, 136th ARS/New York and 173rd ARS/Nevada.

SPECIFICATION

Boeing KC-135E Stratotanker
generally similar to the KC-135A
Powerplant: four Pratt & Whitney JT3D-3B each rated at 18,000 lb st (80.07 kN) dry

The KC-135E (and similar KC-135D illustrated) forms the main equipment of the Air National Guard and Air Force Reserve tanker units. The TF33 turbofans give increased performance and greater efficiency compared to the old J57s.

Boeing **KC-135R/T/C-135FR Stratotanker**

In 1980 Boeing announced a major upgrade programme for the KC-135 involving the fitment of high bypass-ratio turbofans to offer far greater fuel efficiency, noise reduction and operational flexibility. Under the company designation **KC-135RE**, the first conversion took to the air on 4 August 1982.

Designated **KC-135R** in service (the second time this had been applied, having previously been used by a reconnaissance variant of the KC-135A), the re-engined and

The KC-135R is the mainstream type in the USAF's tanker fleet, although further conversions have been cancelled. In addition to the obvious re-engining, the KC-135R has an APU added to allow autonomous operations. Most serve with CONUS units, but squadrons are assigned to PACAF (909th ARS at Kadena – illustrated) and USAFE (351st ARS at RAF Mildenhall).

upgraded tanker is now the mainstay of the US Air Force's tanker fleet, and as more conversions are completed more units are dispensing with their older variants in favour of the KC-135R.

CFM International's CFM56 engine (military designation F108) was chosen for the KC-135R, offering 22,000 lb (97.86 kN) of thrust. This allows an increase in maximum take-off weight and an increase in fuel carriage. An APU is fitted, characterised by intake and exhaust ports on the port side of the rear fuselage, which allows the KC-135R to undertake autonomous operations from austere locations. Many other systems are also upgraded during the conversion.

Air Force delivery

First delivery (to SAC's 384th Air Refueling Wing) took place in July 1984, and the 200th was delivered in April 1990. Three hundred and six conversions have been funded so far, with the prospect of the programme continuing to cover most of the

active-duty tanker fleet. The surviving 11 C-135Fs delivered to France were also upgraded under this programme, becoming **C-135FR**s, and were subsequently fitted with Adèle radar warning receivers and underwing pods for probe-and-drogue work.

Related variants include the **KC-135R(RT)**, the designation applied to a small number of aircraft fitted with a refuelling receptacle. Most of these are ex-special mission or trials aircraft. These have been joined by the survivors of the 56 KC-135Q aircraft, which are being fitted with refuelling receptacles as they undergo the re-engining conversion to emerge as **KC-135T**s, with a primary role of supporting F-117 attack aircraft and other covert programmes. A feasibility study has also been undertaken to fit the KC-135R with wing pods for the refuelling of probe-equipped aircraft from other US or foreign services. At present, this is only possible by fitting a short hose/drogue assembly to the end of the boom, as originally practised by

the French C-135FR aircraft.

Active-duty US Air Force units were first in line to receive the new tanker, but in 1991 the KC-135Rs were delivered to the Air National Guard. By 1994 five squadrons had re-equipped, with a sixth (Hawaii) being established to provide refuelling coverage for the Pacific islands. Following the 1 June 1992 reshuffle of Air Force units, KC-135R assignments remained roughly along the previous SAC lines, but were soon dramatically altered as all but the 366th Wing aircraft were transferred to Air Mobility Command and the two reservist organisations.

SPECIFICATION

Boeing KC-135R Stratotanker
generally similar to the KC-135A except in the following particulars:
Powerplant: four CFM International F108-CF-100 each rated at 22,000 lb st (97.86 kN) dry
Weights: maximum take-off 322,500 lb (146284 kg)
Fuel and load: internal fuel 203,288 lb (92210 kg)
Range: operational radius 2,500 nm (2,879 miles; 4633 km) to offload 150 per cent more fuel than the KC-135A

Boeing KC-135R/T/C-135FR Stratotanker

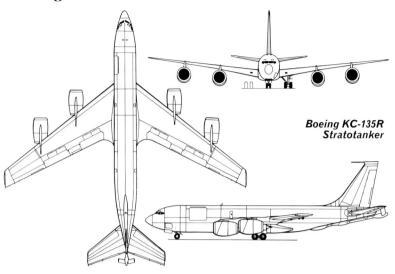

Boeing KC-135R Stratotanker

French C-135FR aircraft have been fitted with Adèle RWR, with distinctive antennas above the flight deck and on the fin.

The following were KC-135R and C-135FR assignments in early 1994:

Air Combat Command – 22nd ARS/366th Wing (Mountain Home AFB – to get KC-10s in 1995)
Air Mobility Command – 19th ARW: 99th and 912th ARS (Robins AFB), 11th and 306th ARS (Altus AFB)
22nd ARW: 384th ARS (McConnell AFB) – one more squadron to form
43rd ARW: 91st and 97th ARS (Malmstrom AFB), 28th ARS (Ellsworth AFB), 43rd and 92nd ARS (Fairchild AFB – 92nd ARW to form in 1994), 906th ARS (Minot AFB)
319th ARW: 905th ARS (Grand Forks AFB - one more squadron to form)
380th ARW: 310th and 380th ARS (Plattsburgh AFB), 42nd ARS (Loring AFB – deactivating), 509th ARS (Griffiss AFB)
398th OG: 93rd ARS (Castle AFB – KC-135 training unit. The task will move to Altus in 1994)
Pacific Air Forces – 906th ARS/18th Wing (Kadena AB, Okinawa)
US Air Forces in Europe – 351st ARS/100th ARW (RAF Mildenhall, England)
Air Force Reserve – 72nd and 74th ARS/434th ARW (Grissom AFB). 77th and 465th ARS to convert in 1994.
Air National Guard – 153rd ARS/Mississippi ANG (Key Field, Meridian), 133rd ARS/New Hampshire ANG (Pease ANGB), 145th ARS and 166th ARS/Ohio ANG (Rickenbacker ANGB), 126th ARS/Wisconsin ANG (General Mitchell IAP, Milwaukee) and 203rd ARS/Hawaii ANG (Hickam AFB)
Armée de l'Air – Escadre de Ravitaillement en Vol 93 (HQ and ERV 1/93 'Aunis' at Istres, ERV 2/93 'Sologne' at Avord and ERV 3/93 'Landes' at Mont-de-Marsan)

Boeing EC-135

Under various EC-135 designations, the US Air Force flies a small fleet of aircraft dedicated to the airborne command post mission. As the Cold War has ended, this mission has assumed far less importance than in previous times, and the inventory has been reduced accordingly. EC-135s were previously assigned to theatre commanders, in addition to the major US Air Force commands, but are now centrally maintained by the 2nd Air Command and Control Squadron of the 55th Wing at Offutt AFB, with detachments made to commands who need their services.

Originally developed to provide an airborne command post for SAC's nuclear retaliation forces, the EC-135 fleet is equipped with comprehensive communications equipment, which allows the airborne commander to link with national command authorities, theatre forces, other airborne command posts (such as the Navy's TACAMO fleet) and with his assets on the ground. A trailing wire aerial deploys from the EC-135's belly, while the airframe is liberally covered with aerials for a wide range of frequency coverage. New to the aircraft is the ARC-208(V) Milstars satellite communications antenna, housed in a large dorsal fairing on some aircraft.

Backbone of the 2nd ACCS fleet is the **EC-135C** variant, which was previously dedicated to SAC support. Other similar variants are the **EC-135H**, **J**, **P** and **Y**, which were previously given a theatre assignment. The **EC-135A**, **G** and **L** are radio relay platforms used to extend the effective range of the main command post. By late 1992 most of the EC-135A/G/H/L and P aircraft were in open storage at Davis-Monthan AFB, along with two EC-135Cs and an EC-135J. Among future plans is the complete retirement of the USAF EC-135 fleet, with command post functions being performed by the US Navy's E-6 Mercury.

Further aircraft in the series include two **EC-135K** aircraft, which are used to provide navigation support to fighter deployments, and four **EC-135E** range support/test aircraft. The latter fly with the 4950th Test Wing, and are fitted with a telemetry-receiving dish antenna in a bulbous nose radome.

Four of the 55th Wing's EC-135Cs are equipped with the Milstars satcom antenna on the spine.

Boeing EC-135C
Wing: span 130 ft 10 in (39.88 m); aspect ratio 7.04; area 2,433.00 sq ft (226.03 m²)
Fuselage and tail: length 136 ft 3 in (41.53 m); height 41 ft 8 in (12.70 m); tailplane span 45 ft 3 in (13.79 m); wheel base 45 ft 8 in (13.92 m)
Powerplant: four Pratt & Whitney TF33-P-9 each rated at 18,000 lb st (80.07 kN) dry
Weights: basic empty 102,300 lb (46403 kg); maximum take-off 299,000 lb (135626 kg)
Fuel and load: internal fuel 189,702 lb (86047 kg); external fuel none
Speed: maximum level speed at 25,000 ft (7620 m) 535 kt (616 mph; 991 km/h); cruising speed at 35,000 ft (10670 m) 486 kt (560 mph; 901 km/h)
Range: ferry range 4,910 nm (5,654 miles; 9099 km); operational radius 2,325 nm (2,677 miles; 4308 km)

Boeing NC/NKC/OC/WC-135

Under various designations, including **NC-135A**, **NKC-135A** and **NKC-135E**, the US Air Force operates a fleet of grossly modified C-135 airframes on development and trials work, mostly with the 4950th Test Wing at Wright-Patterson AFB, OH. The type of work performed by these aircraft is highly varied, but includes staff transport, refuelling tests with new aircraft types, airborne laser trials, weightlessness training for astronauts (the 'vomit comets' serving with NASA), and numerous programmes involving the testing of airborne equipment and space technology. A large portion of their work has been in support of the SDI programme. A single NKC-135A serves with the 55th Wing on command support transport duties.

Two further NKC-135A aircraft serve with the Fleet Electronic Warfare Support Group of the US Navy, maintained and flown by Chrysler at Waco, TX. These operate alongside a single DC-8, providing realistic electronic warfare environments for naval ships on exercise, and are consequently fitted with a wide range of jammers, resulting in numerous external fairings and antennas.

Unconnected with the test fleet, the **WC-135B** is a meteorological aircraft previously operated by the US Air Force's 55th Weather Reconnaissance Squadron at McClellan AFB, CA. Ten C-135B transports were converted to this standard, identified by having air scoops on either side of the fuselage. Today six of these aircraft remain in service, gathered with other C-135 specials at Offutt AFB with the 55th Wing. Two retain the WC-135B designation, while one has been redesignated the **TC-135B** to act as a crew trainer for the remaining three aircraft, which have been modified as **OC-135B**s for the 'Open Skies' reconnaissance mission. These have a series of photographic sensors installed, including a

Among the work undertaken by the NKC-135 test fleet is inflight refuelling trials. Shown here refuelling an Edwards AFB B-52 is an NKC-135E.

Chrysler operates two NKC-135As on behalf of the US Navy from Waco Field, alongside the single Douglas EC-24. These aircraft are packed with jammers to create a hostile ECM environment for fleet exercises.

KA-91A panoramic camera for medium-altitude work, and two KS-87 oblique cameras and a single KS-87 vertical camera for low-altitude photography. The OC-135Bs can accommodate 38 crew, including maintenance personnel, foreign representatives and members of the On-Site Inspection Agency, the organisation responsible for providing sensors and linguists for the 'Open Skies' verification sorties. The OC-135Bs and TC-135B are assigned to the 24th Reconnaissance Squadron.

SPECIFICATION

Boeing NKC-135A
Wing: span 130 ft 10 in (39.88 m); aspect ratio 7.04; area 2,433.00 sq ft (226.03 m²)

The USAF's latest C-135 variant is the OC-135B, a dedicated platform for 'Open Skies' arms treaty verification flights. The aircraft is equipped with a battery of cameras.

Fuselage and tail: length 136 ft 3 in (41.53 m); height 41 ft 8 in (12.70 m); tailplane span 40 ft 3 in (12.27 m); wheel base 46 ft 7 in (14.20 m)
Powerplant: four Pratt & Whitney J57-P-59W each rated at 13,750 lb (61.1 kN) dry
Weights: operating empty 123,000 lb (55793 kg); maximum take-off 270,000 lb (122472 kg)
Fuel and load: internal fuel 189,702 lb (86047 kg); external fuel none
Speed: maximum level speed at high altitude 530 kt (610 mph; 982 km/h); cruising speed at 35,000 ft (10670 m) 462 kt (532 mph; 856 km/h)
Range: ferry range 7,990 nm (9,200 miles; 14806 km);

typical operational range 4,400 nm (5,057 miles; 8154 km)
Performance: maximum rate of climb at sea level

1,290 ft (393 m) per minute; service ceiling 41,000 ft (12495 m); typical take-off run 10,700 ft (3260 m) at maximum take-off weight

Boeing **RC/TC-135**

From an early date, the Boeing C-135 was recognised as an excellent airframe for various special missions. One of these was strategic reconnaissance, using the aircraft's capacious cabin to house large amounts of electronic equipment. Designated RC-135, several versions of reconnaissance Stratotankers are used today.

All RC-135s serve with the 55th Wing at Offutt AFB, previously the headquarters of Strategic Air Command, from where they are detached on a global basis to cover areas of the world where intelligence-gathering is required. Regular detachments are made to RAF Mildenhall in England, Souda Bay on Crete, Kadena AB on Okinawa and Shemya AB on the Aleutians.

Among the current versions are three dedicated to general Sigint gathering. All feature large amounts of electronic recording and analysing equipment on board, and have many aerials on the airframe. All three have slab-sided cheek fairings where many of the side-facing antennas are grouped. These serve the Automatic Elint Emitter Locator System (AEELS), which gathers signals from across the frequency spectrum, sifts out those of particular interest and

Fourteen RC-135s are Rivet Joint aircraft, eight being RC-135Vs (illustrated) and six being RC-135Ws. These are the backbone of the Sigint-gathering fleet.

relays data to operator stations in the cabin. Many other antennas, notably the farm of 'MUCELS' under the fuselage, supply data for other systems.

Two aircraft are to **RC-135U** standard, these characterised by cheek fairings and additional fairings in the chin, boomer, wingtip, tailcone and fin-top positions. Until 1991 they were fitted with 'towel rail' antennas above the cheek fairings, but these have been removed. Known as **Combat Sent** aircraft, the pair of RC-135Us is believed to have special purposes within the Sigint fleet, and may also be used to trial new equipment.

Eight aircraft are to **RC-135V Rivet Joint** standard, and six are the essentially similar **RC-135W** variant. These are the workhorses of the Sigint fleet, and are distinguished by having extended 'thimble' noses and large plate aerials under the centre-section. External differences between the two variants are restricted to a lengthened cheek fairing on the W model, which also lacks auxiliary air intakes on its engine pods. A related variant is the **TC-135W**, which is based at Offutt to provide crew training for the RC-135U/V/W fleet. This has the 'thimble' nose and cheek fairing, but does not have mission equipment.

An altogether more specialised role is undertaken by two **RC-135S Cobra Ball** aircraft which normally operate from Shemya. In addition to 'thimble' noses, elec-

Above: Two RC-135U Combat Sent aircraft serve with the 55th Wing. They have now had the fuselage side 'towel rail' removed.

Below: The TC-135W is used as an aircrew trainer for the RC-135U/V/W. The 55th Wing also flies TC-135B and TC-135S trainers.

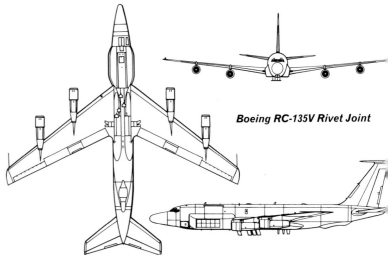

Boeing RC-135V Rivet Joint

Two RC-135S Cobra Balls fly with the 55th Wing. Their role is to record foreign missile tests, but they may be assigned a 'Scud'-hunting theatre missile reconnaissance role.

tronic receivers mounted in cheek fairings and a teardrop-shaped fairing on the aft fuselage, these have large circular windows in the fuselage for the photography of foreign missile tests. The equipment is known as the Real Time Optical System (RTOS). The wings and engine nacelles on the starboard side were painted black to reduce glare for re-entry vehicle photography (in the process of being removed), while the aerials are used to gather telemetry data from the

test launches and re-entries.

Telint (telemetry intelligence) is the role of the RC-135S, and it serves with the 24th Reconnaissance Squadron. With the decrease in foreign ICBM tests following the end of the Cold War, the Cobra Balls may adopt a theatre role spotting battlefield missiles. This is in response to the difficulties caused by the Iraqi 'Scud' missiles during the Gulf War. Until February 1993 the pair was augmented by the sole **RC-135X Cobra Eye**, which had a single camera window behind a sliding door for missile photography, and fewer antennas. A single **TC-135S**, without mission equipment, provides aircrew training for the Telint fleet.

The RC-135 fleet has consistently proved

of great value, both as a strategic reconnaissance tool during peacetime and as a more tactical asset during times of tension. The 55th Wing has been highly active in all the world's troublespots, and played an instrumental part in Desert Storm and subsequent operations in the Gulf. Two more airframes are earmarked for conversion to

RC-135W standard to swell the 'Rivet Joint' fleet.

SPECIFICATION

Boeing RC-135/TC-135
generally similar to the Boeing KC-135E Stratotanker

Boeing **C-137/C-18**

Derived from the same Model 367-80 prototype as the KC-135, the Boeing 707 proved to be one of the most successful airliners of all time, with 916 sales of civil models. 707s in **USAF** service received the C-137 designation, and comprised three 707-153s delivered in 1959 as **VC-137A**s. These were subsequently re-engined with TF33 turbofans, becoming **VC-137B**s in the process. The 'V' was dropped from the prefix in the late 1970s. The trio is still in use with the 89th Airlift Wing at Andrews AFB, and has been joined by four more aircraft.

The first pair were 707-353Cs procured for use as Presidential transports under the **VC-137C** designation. On replacement by the VC-25As currently in use as 'Air Force One' aircraft, the two C-137s joined the first three on general staff and VIP transport duties. In the late 1980s, two more C-137Cs were added to the 89th Airlift Wing fleet. In 1991 a 707-355C was issued to Central Command as a transport under the **EC-137D** designation (used for the second time, having previously been applied to the test aircraft for the E-3 programme).

Under the designation **C-18A**, eight ex-American Airlines Boeing 707s were purchased in 1981 for the 4950th Test Wing fleet at Wright-Patterson AFB, OH (subsequently moved to Edwards AFB, CA). Two were left in their original configuration, although one was broken up for spares and

the other used for general trials and training work. Of the other six, four were modified to **EC-18B** standard, for the **ARIA** (Advanced Range Instrumentation Aircraft) role, which involves the fitment of a large steerable telemetry-receiving antenna in a giant nose radome, as fitted to the EC-135E. The final pair are equipped as **EC-18D** Cruise Missile Mission Control Aircraft, with APG-63 radar (as fitted to the F-15) and telemetry receiver.

SPECIFICATION

Boeing C-137C
Wing: span 145 ft 9 in (44.42 m); aspect ratio 7.056; area 3,010.00 sq ft (279.63 m2)
Fuselage and tail: length 152 ft 11 in (46.61 m); height 42 ft 5 in (12.93 m); tailplane span 45 ft 9 in (13.94 m); wheel track 22 ft 1 in (6.73 m); wheel base 59 ft 0 in (17.98 m)
Powerplant: four Pratt & Whitney TF33 (JT3D-3) each rated at 18,000 lb st (80.07 kN) dry
Weights: maximum take-off 327,000 lb (148325 kg)
Fuel and load: internal fuel 23,855 US gal (90299 litres); external fuel none; maximum payload 51,615 lb (23413 kg)
Speed: maximum level speed at high altitude 545 kt (628 mph; 1011 km/h); maximum cruising speed at 25,000 lb (7620 m) 520 kt (599 mph; 964 km/h); economical cruising speed at optimum altitude 478 kt (550 mph; 886 km/h)
Range: 6,610 nm (7,611 mph; 12248 km)

A few C-137s remain in service with the 89th Airlift Wing on VIP transport duties.

Below: The EC-18B has a telemetry receiver antenna in the giant nose radome for supporting missile tests.

Performance: maximum rate of climb at sea level 3,550 ft (1082 m) per minute; service ceiling 42,000 ft (12800 m); take-off distance to 35 ft (10.7 m) 10,350 ft

(3155 m) at maximum take-off weight; landing distance from 50 ft (15 m) 5,930 ft (1807 m) at normal landing weight

Boeing **E-3 Sentry**

The **Boeing E-3 Sentry** is the West's principal AWACS (airborne warning and control system) platform. Using the airframe of a Boeing 707-320B airliner and a massive payload of radar and electronic sensors, the E-3/AWACS is a flying headquarters for C³I (command, control, communications and intelligence), employed near a combat zone to monitor aircraft and missiles and to direct friendly warplanes.

On a typical mission, an E-3, which has

an unrefuelled endurance of 11 hours, routinely refuels and stays aloft for up to 18 hours, carrying a crew of 20 including 16 mission specialists such as weapon controllers, radar operators and communications specialists. Heart of the AWACS system is its Westinghouse AN/APY-2 Overland Downlook Radar (ODR) which, with other sensors and instrumentation, is mounted in a saucer-like rotodome mounted on two 3.35-m (11-ft) struts above

the rear fuselage. The AN/APY-2 replaced the AN/APY-1 system from the 25th aircraft onwards and is fitted to all export E-3s. The deep circular rotodome is some 9.14 m (30 ft) in diameter, weighs 1540 kg (3,395 lb) and is canted 2.5° downward. In operation, the dome rotates six times per minute. The radar is capable of tracking up to 600 low-flying aircraft.

The **EC-137D** prototype for the AWACS series first flew on 5 February 1972. The first E-3 Sentry, of a total of 34 (including two EC-137Ds) procured by the **USAF**, made its maiden flight on 31 October 1975, and following completion of full-scale devel-

opment in 1976, the first operational example was delivered to the 552nd AC&CW at Tinker AFB, OK, in March 1977. IOC (initial operating capability) was gained in April 1978 and E-3s assumed a US continental air defence role in January 1979. Since then, AWACS aircraft have been involved in all American combat operations in Grenada (1983), Lebanon (1983), Panama (1989) and Iraq (1991).

Twenty-two **E-3A** and two EC-137D aeroplanes, collectively termed 'core' aircraft when they were standardised in the late 1970s, were upgraded to **E-3B** standard. The first was converted by Boeing,

Boeing E-3D Sentry AEW.Mk 1

After a protracted procurement programme, including the development and cancellation of the Nimrod AEW.Mk 3, the RAF was eventually able to retire its vintage Shackletons in 1991. Seven Sentry AEW.Mk 1s were procured for No. 8 Squadron at RAF Waddington, which supports the NATO Airborne Early Warning Force, itself an E-3 operator. RAF aircraft have been active on Deny Flight operations over Bosnia.

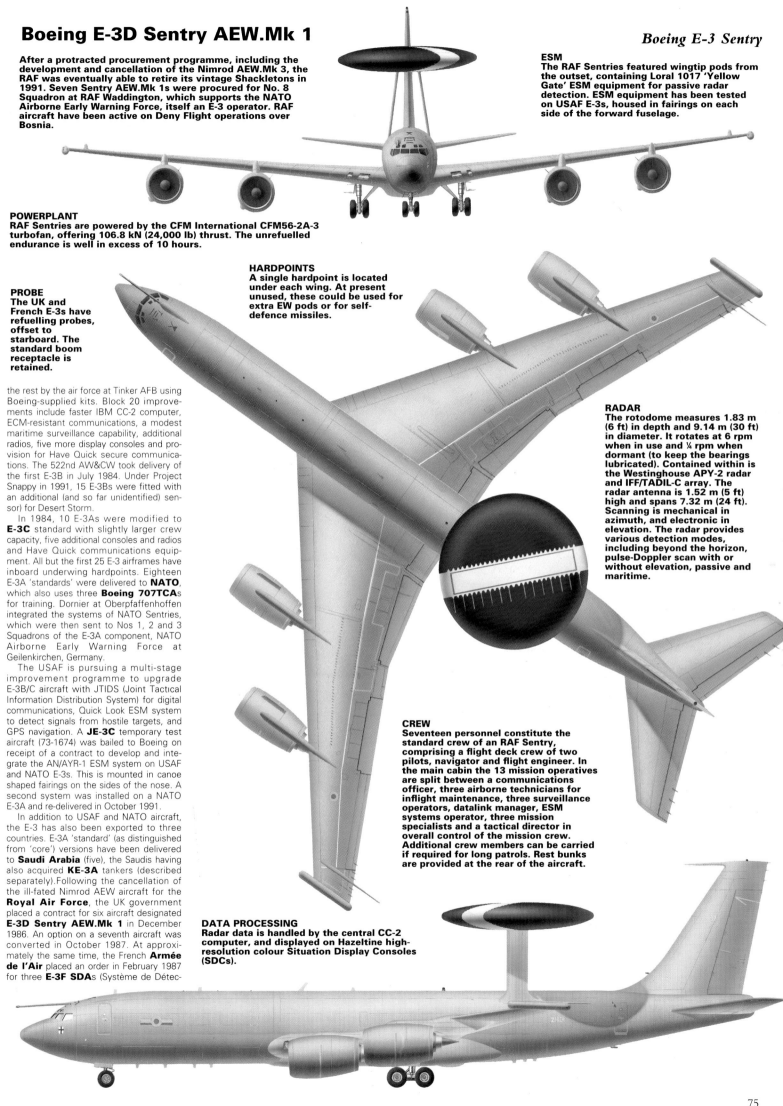

ESM
The RAF Sentries featured wingtip pods from the outset, containing Loral 1017 'Yellow Gate' ESM equipment for passive radar detection. ESM equipment has been tested on USAF E-3s, housed in fairings on each side of the forward fuselage.

POWERPLANT
RAF Sentries are powered by the CFM International CFM56-2A-3 turbofan, offering 106.8 kN (24,000 lb) thrust. The unrefuelled endurance is well in excess of 10 hours.

HARDPOINTS
A single hardpoint is located under each wing. At present unused, these could be used for extra EW pods or for self-defence missiles.

PROBE
The UK and French E-3s have refuelling probes, offset to starboard. The standard boom receptacle is retained.

the rest by the air force at Tinker AFB using Boeing-supplied kits. Block 20 improvements include faster IBM CC-2 computer, ECM-resistant communications, a modest maritime surveillance capability, additional radios, five more display consoles and provision for Have Quick secure communications. The 522nd AW&CW took delivery of the first E-3B in July 1984. Under Project Snappy in 1991, 15 E-3Bs were fitted with an additional (and so far unidentified) sensor) for Desert Storm.

In 1984, 10 E-3As were modified to **E-3C** standard with slightly larger crew capacity, five additional consoles and radios and Have Quick communications equipment. All but the first 25 E-3 airframes have inboard underwing hardpoints. Eighteen E-3A 'standards' were delivered to **NATO**, which also uses three **Boeing 707TCA**s for training. Dornier at Oberpfaffenhoffen integrated the systems of NATO Sentries, which were then sent to Nos 1, 2 and 3 Squadrons of the E-3A component, NATO Airborne Early Warning Force at Geilenkirchen, Germany.

The USAF is pursuing a multi-stage improvement programme to upgrade E-3B/C aircraft with JTIDS (Joint Tactical Information Distribution System) for digital communications, Quick Look ESM system to detect signals from hostile targets, and GPS navigation. A **JE-3C** temporary test aircraft (73-1674) was bailed to Boeing on receipt of a contract to develop and integrate the AN/AYR-1 ESM system on USAF and NATO E-3s. This is mounted in canoe shaped fairings on the sides of the nose. A second system was installed on a NATO E-3A and re-delivered in October 1991.

In addition to USAF and NATO aircraft, the E-3 has also been exported to three countries. E-3A 'standard' (as distinguished from 'core') versions have been delivered to **Saudi Arabia** (five), the Saudis having also acquired **KE-3A** tankers (described separately).Following the cancellation of the ill-fated Nimrod AEW aircraft for the **Royal Air Force**, the UK government placed a contract for six aircraft designated **E-3D Sentry AEW.Mk 1** in December 1986. An option on a seventh aircraft was converted in October 1987. At approximately the same time, the French **Armée de l'Air** placed an order in February 1987 for three **E-3F SDA**s (Système de Détec-

RADAR
The rotodome measures 1.83 m (6 ft) in depth and 9.14 m (30 ft) in diameter. It rotates at 6 rpm when in use and ¼ rpm when dormant (to keep the bearings lubricated). Contained within is the Westinghouse APY-2 radar and IFF/TADIL-C array. The radar antenna is 1.52 m (5 ft) high and spans 7.32 m (24 ft). Scanning is mechanical in azimuth, and electronic in elevation. The radar provides various detection modes, including beyond the horizon, pulse-Doppler scan with or without elevation, passive and maritime.

CREW
Seventeen personnel constitute the standard crew of an RAF Sentry, comprising a flight deck crew of two pilots, navigator and flight engineer. In the main cabin the 13 mission operatives are split between a communications officer, three airborne technicians for inflight maintenance, three surveillance operators, datalink manager, ESM systems operator, three mission specialists and a tactical director in overall control of the mission crew. Additional crew members can be carried if required for long patrols. Rest bunks are provided at the rear of the aircraft.

DATA PROCESSING
Radar data is handled by the central CC-2 computer, and displayed on Hazeltine high-resolution colour Situation Display Consoles (SDCs).

A USAF E-3 approaches a KC-135. USAF E-3s proved their worth in Desert Storm, during which they controlled all coalition attacks.

tion Aéroportée). An order for a fourth aircraft was added later, but options on a further two E-3s were droppped in 1988. Both European versions differ markedly from other E-3s, with Boeing giving each nation a 130 per cent industrial offset. The primary difference is the replacement of TF33 turbofans with 106.8-kN (24,000-lb st) CFM56-2A-3 turbofans, and installation of an upper forward fuselage-mounted SOGERMA inflight-refuelling probe in additon to the refuelling receptacle. RAF aircraft also have wingtip-mounted Loral 1017 'Yellow Gate' ESM pods. The RAF's first E-3D (ZH101) was first flown on 11 September 1989, and made its initial flight in fully-equipped mode in 5 January 1990. It preceded the French E-3F which first flew on 27 June 1990. The last RAF aircraft was the ultimate Boeing 707 airframe produced, after which the production line was closed, forcing Japan to opt for an AEW version of the much newer twin-engined Boeing 767, using essentially E-3C equipment. Planned improvements for the E-3 include the Block 30/35 programme

Designated JE-3C, this aircraft was bailed back to Boeing for integration of an ESM system, with antennas mounted in two fuselage bulges and an undernose fairing.

with radar improvements, an upgrade of JTIDS to TADIL-J standards, improved memory and compatibility with GPS. A further improvement may be funded, which will give a radar upgrade for USAF aircraft, with new processors and displays and pulse compression for enhanced performance against small targets.

France's four E-3F Sentries are similar to those of the RAF, except that they lack the wingtip ESM pods. The E-3Fs serve with EDA 36, and are the only aircraft assigned to the French air defence command CAFDA. They are based at Avord.

SPECIFICATION

Boeing E-3C Sentry
Powerplant: four Pratt & Whitney TF33-P-100/100A turbofans each rated at 93.41 kN (21,000 lb st)
Dimensions: wing span 145 ft 9 in (44.42 m); length 46.61 m (152 ft 11 in); height 12.73 m (41 ft 9 in); wing area 283.35 m² (3,050.00 sq ft)
Weights: operating empty 77996 kg (171,950 lb); maximum take-off 147420 kg (325,000 lb)
Performance: maximum level speed at high altitude 853 km/h (530 mph; 460 kt); operating ceiling 8840 m (29,000 ft); operational radius 1612 km (1,002 miles; 870 nm) for a 6-hour patrol without flight refuelling; endurance more than 11 hours without flight refuelling

Boeing KE-3

The **Boeing KE-3A/B** is an air-refuelling tanker for **Saudi Arabia**. Eight 'new build' KE-3A models were delivered to the Royal Saudi air force in 1987 under the Peace Shield programme and are operated by the RSAF's No. 18 Squadron at Riyadh.

Manufactured with the E-3A Sentry AWACS aircraft, and using the same Boeing 707-320B airframe, the KE-3A has a dedicated tanker mission and lacks AWACS sensors or capability. Although other countries operate tanker versions of the veteran 707, none employs the KE-3 designation.

As part of its ongoing military build-up, Saudi Arabia would like to obtain seven further KE-3As to refuel its F-15s and Tornados. Prompted by Israel's dual-role use of the Boeing 707 as a tanker and intelligence gatherer, the RSAF is also expected to add an Elint function with cabin consoles.

Since the 707 production line will not be reopened, additional KE-3s will be obtained by purchasing and modifying existing 707s. At the beginning of 1993, a single, previously-owned 707 airframe was being modified by E-Systems at Greenville, TX, to become the RSAF's first **KE-3B** tanker.

SPECIFICATION

Boeing KE-3A
Wing: span 145 ft 9 in (44.42 m); aspect ratio 7.056; area 3,050.00 sq ft (283.35 m²)
Fuselage and tail: length 152 ft 11 in (46.61 m); height 41 ft 9 in (12.73 m); tailplane span 45 ft 9 in (13.94 m); wheel track 22 ft 1 in (6.73 m); wheel base 59 ft 0 in (17.98 m)

Powerplant: four CFM International CFM56-2A2 each rated at 24,000 lb st (106.76 kN) dry
Weights: maximum take-off 342,000 lb (155131 kg)
Fuel and load: internal fuel 23,855 US gal (90299 litres) plus provision for 5,030 US gal (19040 litres) of transfer fuel in in the rear lower cargo hold; external fuel none
Speed: never-exceed speed Mach 0.95; maximum

Despite the designation KE-3A, the aircraft is simply a tanker 707 powered by CFM56 turbofans.

level speed at high altitude 460 kt (530 mph; 853 km/h)
Range: operational radius 1,000 nm (1,151 miles; 1853 km) to offload 123190 lb (55878 kg) of fuel

Boeing E-4

Based on the successful 747-200B airframe, the **E-4B** serves the **United States** as an AABNCP (Advanced Airborne National Command Post). The main purpose is to provide an aerial platform for the national command authority during time of (nuclear) war, from which the President and his key staff can lead the chain of command of the nation and its forces. Known alternatively as the National Emergency Airborne Command Post (NEACP, inevitably 'kneecap', or in popular parlance the 'Doomsday Plane'), four E-4Bs serve with the 1st Airborne Command and Control Squadron of the 55th Wing, headquartered at Offutt AFB, NE, but with one aircraft always deployed to an airfield near to the President's location when he is overseas. The practice of maintaining one E-4B on alert at Andrews AFB near the White House was discontinued in the late 1980s as global tensions reduced.

Using the 747-200B airframe, the E-4B is adapted internally for its mission. Five operating compartments on the main deck are a flight crew station (the E-4 carrying two complete crews of aircraft commander, co-pilot, navigator and flight engineer), NCA area (equivalent to a 'flying White House Situation Room'), conference room, battle staff area and C3I area, from where the communications equipment is operated. The top deck provides crew rest facilities.

Hardening against electro-magnetic pulse and thermal shielding from nuclear blast is incorporated, and the comprehensive communications suite covers the frequency range. A feature of the E-4B is the SHF (super high frequency) communications aerial in a large dorsal fairing, and the capability to break in to civilian radio/TV networks for direct broadcasts to the population.

Inflight refuelling is possible through a receptacle mounted in front of the flight deck, and the systems of the E-4B are optimised for long endurance. A minimum requirement of 72 hours aloft is accepted, and the mission could theoretically last for a week. Barring other malfunctions, the limiting factor is the availability of lubrication for the engines.

Three of the four aircraft were delivered as **E-4A**s in late 1974 following a first flight on 13 June 1973. Initially the equipment was that ripped from the aircraft's predecessor, the EC-135J. The fourth aircraft was

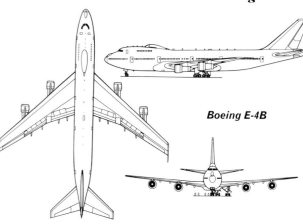

Boeing E-4

Boeing E-4B

In terms of communications, the E-4B is the best-equipped aircraft in the world.

completed as an E-4B, and was first delivered in December 1979 with vastly updated systems including SHF, better engines and revised accommodation. The E-4As were subsequently upgraded to this standard.

SPECIFICATION

Boeing E-4B

Wing: span 195 ft 8 in (59.64 m); aspect ratio 6.96; area 5,500.00 sq ft (510.95 m²)
Fuselage and tail: length 231 ft 4 in (70.51 m); height 63 ft 5 in (19.33 m); tailplane span 72 ft 9 in (22.17 m); wheel track 36 ft 1 in (11.00 m); wheel base

84 ft 0 in (25.60 m)
Powerplant: four General Electric F103-GE-100 (CF6-50E2) each rated at 52,500 lb st (233.53 kN) dry
Fuel and load: internal fuel 331,565 lb (150395 kg); external fuel none
Speed: maximum level speed at 30,000 ft (9145 m) 523 kt (602 mph; 969 km/h)
Range: ferry range 6,800 nm (7,830 miles; 12600 km);

mission endurance 12 hours without flight refuelling or 72 hours with flight refuelling
Performance: cruise ceiling 45,000 ft (13715 m); take-off distance to 35 ft (10.7 m) less than 10,820 ft (3298 m) at maximum take-off weight; landing field length 6,920 ft (2109 m) at maximum landing weight

---

Boeing **E-6 Mercury**

Procured to replace the Lockheed EC-130Q Hercules, the **E-6A Mercury** performs the TACAMO (Take Charge And Move Out) role, maintaining communications links with the **US Navy**'s ballistic missile submarine force. Two US Navy squadrons are active with the aircraft.

A decision to acquire a new TACAMO platform was taken as the Hercules airframes were getting old, and the Lockheed aircraft did not offer much endurance. On 29 April 1983 Boeing was given the contract to develop TACAMO II, and naturally chose its Model 707 airframe, offering commonality with the E-3 Sentry. CFM F108 turbofans were chosen for outstanding fuel efficiency, resulting in ultra-long endurance while on patrol, which can be further extended by inflight refuelling.

The first E-6A took to the air at Renton, WA, on 19 February 1987. Flight trials revealed a flaw in the structure which caused part of the fin to be lost in a high-speed dive. With suitable remedies, the first pair of E-6s was delivered to NAS Bar-

An E-6A displays the two trailing wire aerials (TWAs) which deploy from the tailcone and rear fuselage. These are for VLF communications.

ber's Point on 2 August 1989. The name **Hermes** was initially assigned, but this was changed to Mercury.

Internally the E-6 is arranged in three sections, comprising a forward crew area with eight rest bunks for spare crew members, galley and other facilities. Over the wing is the mission compartment, with five communications stations. In the rear is the equipment compartment, with access for inflight maintenance. The Mercury is packed with communications equipment operating across the frequency spectrum. Three VHF/UHF and five HF radio systems are carried and UHF satellite communications antennas are housed in the wingtip pods (along with ALR-66(V)4 ESM antennas), with prominent HF probes underneath. All communications equipment is secure against eavesdropping, and is hardened against the effects of EMP.

Principal task of the E-6 is to provide a link between various national and military commands, including the Presidential Boeing E-4B, and the US Navy's submarines. In order to communicate with the subs, the E-6 uses two trailing wire antennas which deploy from the tailcone (4,000 ft/1220 m long) and under the rear fuselage (26,000 ft/ 7925 m long). When the aircraft flies in a

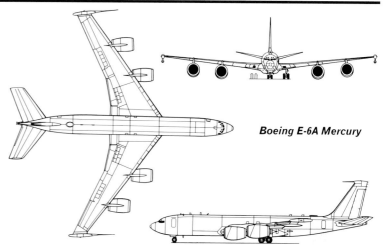

Boeing E-6A Mercury

tight orbit, the aerials hang vertically, allowing VLF communications to be transmitted to submarines, which have a towed aerial array.

Training support

Training for the Mercury fleet is undertaken at Waco, TX, by civilian contractor Chrysler using two standard 707s with E-6 cockpit systems. VQ-3 (initially 'Tacamopac' but now known as 'Iron Men') was the first operator, and deliveries followed to East

Coast operator VQ-4 'Shadows' in early 1991. Each squadron is assigned eight aircraft. As part of the rationalisation of US command assets, both squadrons have consolidated under Strategic Wing One at Tinker AFB, OK, where they enjoy central maintenance with the USAF's E-3 Sentry fleet. Further cost-saving may be possible in an era of reduced threat by moving the USAF's strategic command post function aboard the E-6s and retiring the current fleet of EC-135Cs.

Boeing E-6 Mercury

SPECIFICATION

Boeing E-6A Mercury
Wing: span 148 ft 2 in (45.16 m); aspect ratio 7.2; area 3,050.00 sq ft (283.35 m²)
Fuselage and tail: length 152 ft 11 in (46.61 m); height 42 ft 5 in (12.93 m); tailplane span 45 ft 9 in (13.94 m); wheel track 22 ft 1 in (6.73 m); wheel base 59 ft 0 in (17.98 m)
Powerplant: four CFM International F108-CF-100 (CFM56-2A-2) each rated at 22,000 lb st (97.9 kN) dry
Weights: operating empty 172,795 lb (78378 kg); maximum take-off 342,000 lb (155128 kg)
Fuel and load: internal fuel 155,000 lb (70308 kg); external fuel none
Speed: dash speed at optimum altitude 530 kt (610 mph; 981 km/h); maximum cruising speed at 40,000 ft (12190 m) 455 kt (523 mph; 842 km/h)
Range: mission range 6,350 nm (7,307 miles; 11760 km) without flight refuelling; operational radius 1,000 nm (1,152 miles; 1854 km) for a patrol of 10 hours 30 minutes without flight refuelling, or of 28 hours 54 minutes with one flight refuelling, or of

72 hours with multiple flight refuellings; endurance 15 hours 24 minutes without flight refuelling
Performance: service ceiling 42,000 ft (12800 m); patrol altitude between 25,000 and 30,000 ft (7620

and 9145 m); maximum effort take-off run with fuel for 2,500 nm (2,875 miles; 4630 km) 2,400 ft (732 m); maximum effort take-off distance 5,400 ft (1646 m); landing run 2,600 ft (793 m) at max landing weight

Initially based on both East and West Coasts, the E-6 fleet is now centrally located at Tinker AFB, Oklahoma, alongside USAF E-3s.

Boeing 707

*Boeing Commercial Airplane Group
PO Box 3707, Seattle,
WA 98124-2207, USA*

USAF versions of this popular airliner are described under the C-137/C-18 entry, but many others are in service with air arms as transports, tankers and special mission aircraft. Transport tasks include both passenger and cargo carriage, and some aircraft can be reconfigured for either. Tanker conversions are usually restricted to wingtip refuelling pods, although KC-135-style flying booms or fuselage HDUs (hose-drum units) have been installed on some tankers. Special mission aircraft are used by Israel and South Africa, who have several versions of Sigint-gathering aircraft, radar reconnaissance aircraft and jamming platforms based on the 707 airframe, some of them with RC-135-style antenna arrays.

In alphabetical order, the current military users are: **Argentina** has two **707-372C**s and three **707-387B**s serve with 1 Escuadrón de Transporte at BAM El Palomar, Buenos Aires, used for general transport tasks although they were pressed into long-range maritime patrol duties during the Falklands War. **Australia** flies a single **707-368C** on transport duties, and three of four **707-338C**s converted to tanker standard by ASTA with Flight Refuelling Ltd

An Israeli 707 in full tanker configuration, with Sargent Fletcher 34-000 wingtip pods and a fuselage boom. Other Israeli aircraft feature electronic intelligence/command post equipment.

(FRL) Mk 32 wing pods (the fourth was lost in a fatal crash). They serve with No. 34 Sqn, RAAF, at Fairbairn. **Brazil** operates two **707-324C**s and two **707-345C**s, all converted to tanker status with Beech 1800 wing pods. Service designation is **KC-137**. **Canada** flew five **707-347C**s (local designation **CC-137**) on transport duties with No. 437 Sqn, RCAF, at Ottawa. Two have been converted to tankers with Beech 1800 wing pods, while the other three have been retired in favour of Airbus A310s.

Chile has four 707s, a **-321B** and **-330B** for staff transport, and a **-351C** and **-385C** for freight duties. **Colombia** flies a single **707-373C** on transport flights from Bogotá-El Dorado. **Germany**'s Köln-Bonn-based Flugbereitschaftsstaffel has four **707-307C**s for passenger transport, although these may be converted to tankers from 1995. **India** flies two **707-337C**s with the Aviation Research Centre at Palam. **Indonesia** has a single **707-3M1C** flying on long-range VIP missions. **Iran** received 14 new-build **707-3J9C**s, four of which were completed by Boeing as tankers with booms and Beech 1800 wing pods. One further **707-386C** has been added, and further tanker conversions may have been undertaken.

Israel operates a large fleet of aircraft, some sources suggesting a number of 17, although only four **-328**s, three **-329**s, one **-328B**, two **-331C**s, two **-344C**s and a **-3H7C** are positively identified. Most have

Boeing Model 707-320C (C-137C)

been modified to various standards by IAI's Bedek Aviation Division. At least six are tankers, with Sargent Fletcher 34-000 wing pods and centreline booms. Several Sigint versions have been noted, including a dual-role Sigint/tanker platform with wing pods and Elta EL/L-8300 Sigint system on board, with corresponding aerials and main cabin configured for operator stations. An unknown number have the Elta Phalcon

L-band conformal phased-array radar system scabbed on to the fuselage sides (described separately under IAI/Elta). Further machines retain a transport function, and it is believed that there is an active jamming system. IAI retains several withdrawn airframes which may be the subject for further special mission conversions.

Italy has recently joined the ranks of 707 operators, and now flies four **707-382B** tankers, converted by Alenia with Sargent Fletcher 34-000 wing pods and a Flight Refuelling 480C fuselage HDU. **Morocco** flies a single transport **707-3W6C**, which was the last civil 707 built and originally constructed as the **707-700** with CFM56

The Beech 1800 is one of three types of pod fitted to 707 tankers, seen here on a Brazilian KC-137. The drogue is trailed from a section which hinges down from the pod.

engines, and a **707-138B** tanker with Beech 1800 wing pods. **NATO** relieves the pressures on its E-3A Sentry fleet by employing three **707-329C**s for crew training, these based at Geilenkirchen in Germany. **Pakistan** has a **707-340C** for freight carriage, and a **707-351C** for VIP transport. **Peru** has recently acquired a single **707-323C** tanker, with FRL wing pods fitted by IAI.

Saudi Arabia stands alone in operating the **KE-3A** variant (described separately), which is a pod- and boom-equipped tanker powered by CFM56 engines. These serve with 18 Squadron alongside E-3A AWACS platforms. **South Africa** has recently added four 707s to its inventory, which are believed to include two Phalcon-equipped radar platforms and two dual-role Sigint/tanker aircraft, all fitted out by IAI. **Spain**'s single examples of **707-331B**, **-331C** and **-368C** are locally designated **T.17**, and two are configured with Sargent Fletcher 34-000 wing pods. **Venezuela** has a pair of **707-394C** tankers, both converted by IAI with SFC pods and fuselage boom. The former **Yugoslavia** now operates a single ex-Ugandan Airlines **707-324C**, which was seized on 31 August 1991 while it was allegedly on an arms supply flight.

Several other nations also fly the 707 on government transport tasks, but with civil registrations. These are Abu Dhabi, Dubai, Egypt, Libya, Saudi Arabia, Togo and Zaïre. There is every likelihood of more 707s joining air arms as they are retired from commercial service, and conversions to tanker and special mission configurations will continue, mostly under the auspices of IAI.

SPECIFICATION

Boeing Model 707-320B
Wing: span 145 ft 9 in (44.42 m); aspect ratio 7.06; area 3,010.00 sq ft (279.64 m2)
Fuselage and tail: length 152 ft 11 in (46.61 m); height 42 ft 5 in (12.93 m); tailplane span 45 ft 9 in (13.94 m); wheel track 22 ft 1 in (6.73 m); wheel base 59 ft 0 in (17.98 m)
Powerplant: four Pratt & Whitney JT3D-9/3B each rated at 18,800 lb st (80.07 kN) dry
Weights: operating empty 138,385 lb (62771 kg) standard or 140,524 lb (63740 kg) optional; maximum take-off 327,000 lb (148325 kg) standard or 333,600 lb (151315 kg) optional
Fuel and load: internal fuel 23,855 US gal (90299 litres); external fuel none; maximum payload 51,615 lb (23413 kg) standard or 54,476 lb (24709 kg) optional
Speed: maximum level speed 'clean' at optimum altitude 545 kt (627 mph; 1010 km/h); maximum cruising speed at 25,000 ft (7620 m) 521 kt (600 mph; 966 km/h); economical cruising speed at optimum altitude 478 kt (550 mph; 886 km/h)
Range: range 6,610 nm (7,611 miles; 12249 km) with maximum fuel or 5,350 nm (6,161 miles; 9914 km) with maximum payload
Performance: maximum rate of climb at sea level 3,550 ft (1082 m) per minute; service ceiling 42,000 ft (12800 m); take-off distance to 35 ft (10.7 m) 10,350 ft (3155 m) at maximum take-off weight; landing distance from 50 ft (15 m) 5,930 ft (1807 m) at normal landing weight; landing run 2,455 ft (750 m)

Above: Italy's four tankers have SFC 34-000 wing pods, but also have a Flight Refuelling HDU in the lower rear fuselage.

Below: India is among the users of unmodified 707s, which are used on both passenger and cargo transport duties.

Boeing 720

The Model 720 was developed by Boeing as a short/medium-haul derivative of the successful 707 airliner. It was shorter, and featured a reduced-strength structure and revised aerodynamics. Only one aircraft serves in military colours, an ex-Northwest 720-051B flying with the Presidential Flight of the **Republic of China Air Force**. It was purchased in 1971, and flies with a luxury interior fitting from Sungshan Air Base, outside the capital, Taipei.

Believed to be the only military 720, this aircraft flies with Taiwan's Presidential Flight. A civil-registered aircraft is used for engine tests by Pratt & Whitney.

Boeing 727/C-22

As the **Boeing 727** was one of the world's most popular airliners, with 1,832 built, it is no surprise that small numbers have found their way into military service, mostly in a passenger transport role. Additionally, the governments of several other nations operate the 727 on similar tasks but in civil markings.

In US service, the 727 is designated **C-22**, this covering six aircraft of three variants. The **C-22A** was a single 727-030 which had previously served with Lufthansa and the FAA, before being purchased for US Southern Command. It has been withdrawn from use at Davis-Monthan AFB. Four **C-22B**s were ex-National/Pan Am Srs 100s, purchased by the US Air Force in 1985. These flew on behalf of the Air National Guard Bureau with Det 1, 121st TFW, DC ANG at Andrews AFB, MD. The detachment has been raised to squadron level as the 201st Airlift Squadron, and the four continue their staff transport mission, internally configured with 24 leather first-class seats and 66 fabric seats, all rear-facing. The single **C-22C** is an ex-Singapore Airlines 727-212 which flies from Andrews AFB on behalf of Central Command.

SPECIFICATION

Boeing Model 727-200 (C-22C)
Wing: span 108 ft 0 in (32.92 m); aspect ratio 7.07; area 1,700.00 sq ft (157.93 m2)
Fuselage and tail: length 153 ft 2 in (46.69 m); height 34 ft 0 in (10.36 m); tailplane span 35 ft 9 in (10.90 m); wheel track 18 ft 9 in (5.72 m); wheel base 63 ft 3 in (19.28 m)
Powerplant: three Pratt & Whitney JT8D-9A each rated at 14,500 lb st (64.50 kN) dry
Weights: operating empty 102,900 lb (46675 kg); maximum take-off 209,500 lb (95027 kg)
Fuel and load: internal fuel 8,090 US gal (30623 litres); external fuel none; maximum payload typically 40,000 lb (18144 kg)
Speed: maximum level speed 'clean' at 20,500 ft (6250 m) 540 kt (622 mph; 1001 km/h); maximum cruising speed at 24,700 ft (7530 m) 520 kt (599 mph; 964 km/h); economical cruising speed at 30,000 ft (9145 m) 470 kt (541 mph; 871 km/h)
Range: range 2,362 nm (2,720 miles; 4392 km) with a 27,500-lb (12474-kg) payload or 2,160 nm (2,487 miles; 4003 km) with maximum payload
Performance: initial cruise ceiling 33,000 ft (10060 m); take-off distance to 35 ft (10.7 m) 9,200 ft (2804 m) at maximum take-off weight; landing distance from 50 ft (15 m) 4,690 ft (1430 m) at normal landing weight

OPERATORS

In addition to the United States, other military operators are Belgium (one remaining of two **727-29C**s bought from SABENA serves with 21 Smaldeel/Escadrille but is due for sale), Mexico (one **727-51** of Presidential Flight and three **727-14**s), New Zealand (two **727-22C**s serving with No. 40 Sqn at Whenuapai), Panama (one **727-44**) and Taiwan (two **727-109**, one **727-109C** and one **727-121C** with VIP squadron at Sungshan AB).

Boeing Model 727-200

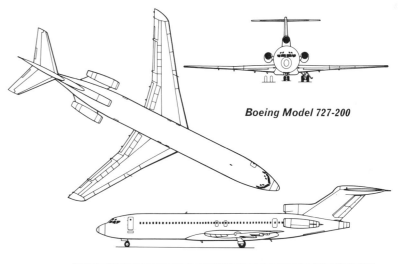

Taiwan flies a quartet of Boeing 727s with its VIP squadron. All operators of the type use it purely as a passenger transport.

Boeing 737/CT-43

Boeing's **Model 737** is the world's best-selling airliner, and has notched up over 3,000 sales. Apart from two special military variants, surprisingly few serve with air forces in staff transport roles.

The major military variant is the **CT-43A**, originally delivered as the **T-43A**. This is a dedicated navigation trainer for the **US Air Force**. Derived from the **737-200**, the CT-43 has a standard flight deck, but with the main cabin configured for 12 student navigators, four advanced students and three instructors. Each station has a complete range of navigation instruments, allowing students to plot courses and monitor the aircraft's path during each mission. The stations are arranged in bays along the starboard side of the cabin, the port side being a walkway which also contains sighting platforms for portholes in the ceiling for celestial navigation using sextants.

Nineteen navigation trainers were delivered from July 1973 to the 323rd Flying Training Wing at Mather AFB, CA, the remainder having moved to Randolph AFB, TX. One aircraft was seen operating in Europe with civilian registration, allegedly on CIA business. It then joined the 58th MAS at Ramstein, from where it flew on regular duties. Three ex-USAF CT-43s now serve with Las Vegas-based EG&G, ferrying personnel to test-sites in Nevada.

The other four aircraft were diverted to Air National Guard support duties, initially with Det 1, 121st TFW, DC ANG at Andrews AFB (two aircraft) and Det 1, 140th TFW, Colorado ANG at Buckley ANGB (two aircraft). The latter took over the East Coast aircraft in the 1980s, and in 1992 upgraded to squadron status as the 200th Airlift Squadron. It has two tasks: to provide navigation training for cadets at the USAF Academy at Colorado Springs, and to provide general staff transport for West Coast ANG units.

Indonesia was the only customer for the second military variant, the **737-200**

The T-43 was originally procured for the navigation training role, with a cabin given over to navigator stations. Some aircraft were subsequently converted for transport use, and the type redesignated CT-43 to reflect the new tasking.

Surveiller. The main features of this maritime reconnaissance variant are two blade antennas on the upper fuselage forward of the fin, each 16 ft (4.87 m) in length. These serve a Motorola SLAMMR (side-looking airborne modular multi-mission radar), which can spot a small ship in heavy seas at a range of 115 miles (185 km) from an altitude of 30,000 ft (9150 m). The interior retains seating for 14 in first class and 88 in tourist class, allowing the 737s to be used for standard passenger transport tasks. Three aircraft were delivered to the TNI-AU's 32 Skwadron at Malang. Other aircraft in military service are civilian variants, the **Series 300** featuring a lengthened fuselage and CFM56 engines.

OPERATORS

In addition to those flying with the USAF and Indonesia, other 'airliner' 737s in military service fly with Brazil (two **737-2N3**s), India (two **737-2A8 Advanced** with Air Headquarters Communications Squadron at Palam), South Korea (one **737-3Z8**), Mexico (one **737-112** and one **737-247**), Thailand (one **737-2Z6 Advanced** and one **737-3Z6** with the Royal Flight at Bangkok-Don Muang) and Venezuela (one **737-2N1 Advanced**).

SPECIFICATION

Boeing Model T-43A (737-200)
Wing: span 93 ft 0 in (28.35 m); aspect ratio 8.8; area 980.00 sq ft (91.05 m²)
Fuselage and tail: length 100 ft 0 in (30.48 m);

height 37 ft 0 in (11.28 m); tailplane span 36 ft 0 in (10.97 m); wheel track 17 ft 2 in (5.23 m); wheel base 37 ft 4 in (11.38 m)
Powerplant: two Pratt & Whitney JT8D-9 each rated at 14,500 lb st (64.4 kN) dry
Weights: operating empty 60,210 lb (27311 kg); maximum take-off 115,500 lb (52391 kg)
Fuel and load: internal fuel 5,151 US gal (19498 litres) plus provision for 800 US gal (3028

litres) of auxiliary fuel; external fuel none; maximum payload 34,790 lb (15780 kg)
Speed: never-exceed speed at 20,000 ft (6095 m) 545 kt (628 mph) 1010 km/h); maximum level speed at 23,500 ft (7165 m) 59 kt (586 mph; 943 km/h); maximum cruising speed at 22,600 ft (6890 m) 500 kt (576 mph; 927 km/h)
Range: range 2,600 nm (2,994 miles; 4818 km); endurance 6 hours
Performance: maximum rate of climb at sea level 3,760 ft (1146 m) per minute; take-off distance to 35 ft (10.7 m) 6,700 ft (2042 m) at 109,000 lb (49442 kg); landing distance from 50 ft (15 m) 4,300 ft (1311 m)

Indonesia is the only user of the 737 Surveiller, equipped with side-looking radar for maritime patrol.

Boeing 747/C-19/VC-25

The **Boeing 747**, acclaimed as an airline pioneer, has proven highly adaptable to military roles. Derivatives of the 747 serve as VIP transports (the **United States**, **Japan**) and as dual-role cargo/tanker aircraft (**Iran**). Conceived as a military aircraft for the requirement which produced the Lockheed C-5A Galaxy in the late 1960s, the 747 was developed by Boeing as a departure in commercial airliners, introducing the 'wide body' and carrying 400 or more passengers. The first Boeing 747 flew on 9 February 1969. Variants, including long-range and 'stretched' versions, are credited with nothing less than a revolution, bringing air travel to vast numbers into the first time. A civilian **747-123** is used by NASA as a 'piggy-back' transport for the Space Shuttle orbiter.

American-owned 747 airliners are part of

the Civil Reserve Aircraft Fleet which is impressed into military service when needed to supplement USAF Air Mobility Command. The designation **C-19A** was applied to a military **747-200** once planned for a single Air National Guard squadron but never purchased.

The designation **VC-25A** applies to two specially-equipped Boeing **747-200B** presidential aircraft, referred to as 'Air Force One' when the President is on board. The VC-25A can carry president and staff, with 70 passengers and 23 crew members, 7,140 miles (11490 km) without refuelling.

Iran acquired three **747-100** tanker-transports and four **747F** freighters for military use. Two **747-47C**s were delivered to Japan as VIP transports and have been operated by the Japan Air Self-Defence Force since 1 April 1992.

SPECIFICATION

Boeing Model 747-200F
Wing: span 195 ft 8 in (59.64 m); aspect ratio 7.0; area 5,500.00 sq ft (510.95 m²)
Fuselage and tail: length 231 ft 10 in (70.66 m); height 63 ft 5 in (19.33 m); tailplane span 72 ft 9 in (22.17 m); wheel track 36 ft 1 in (11.00 m); wheel base 84 ft 0 in (25.60 m)
Powerplant: four Pratt & Whitney JT9D-7R4G2 each rated at 54,750 lb st (243.54 kN) dry, or General Electric CF6-50E2 (F103-GE-102) each rated at 52,500 lb st (233.53 kN) dry, or General Electric CF6-80C2 each rated at 56,700 lb st (252.21 kN) dry, or Rolls-Royce RB211-524D4-B each rated at 53,110 lb st (236.24 kN) dry
Weights: operating empty 342,200 lb (155219 kg) with JT9D engines, or 345,700 lb (156807 kg) with CF6-50 engines, or 348,300 lb (157986 kg) with CF6-80 engines, or 351,100 lb (159256 kg) with RB211 engines; maximum take-off 775,000 lb (351525 kg) with options at 785,000 lb (356070 kg), 800,000 lb (362875 kg), 820,000 lb (371945 kg) and 833,000 lb (377840 kg)
Fuel and load: internal fuel 364,400 lb (165289 kg)

The JASDF operates a pair of 747-400s on governmental transport duties.

Two 747s serve as Presidential transports, designated VC-25A.

with JT9D and RB211 engines, or 361,870 lb (164141 kg) with both CF6 engine variants; external fuel none; maximum payload 247,800 lb (112400 kg) with JT9D , or 244,300 lb (110812 kg) with CF6-50, or 348,300 lb (109633 kg) with CF6-80, or 238,900 lb (108363 kg) with RB211
Speed: maximum level speed 'clean' at 30,000 ft (9145 m) between 522 and 530 kt (601 and 610 mph; 967 and 981 km/h) depending on engine type
Range: ferry range 7,900 nm (9,091 miles; 14630 km) with JT9D engines, or 7650 nm (8,803 miles; 8426 km) with CF6-50 engines, or 8,300 nm (9,551 miles; 15371 km) with CF6-80 engines, or 7,950 nm (9,148 miles; 14723 km); range with a 200,000-lb (90720-kg) payload 4,700 nm (5,408 miles; 8704 km) with JT9D engines, or 4,550 nm (5,236 miles; 8426 km) with CF6-50 engines, or 4,900 nm (5,639 miles; 9075 km) with CF6-80 engines, or 4,650 nm (5,351 miles; 8612 km) with RB211 engines
Performance: cruise ceiling 45,000 ft (13715 m); take-off distance to 35 ft (10.7 m) at 833,000 lb (377840 kg) 10,400 ft (3170 m) with JT9D engines, or 10,800 ft (3292 m) with CF6-50 engines, or 10,100 ft (3078 m) with CF6-80 engines, or 10,350 ft (3155 m) with RB211 engines; landing field length 6,170 ft (1881 m) at 564,000 lb (255825 kg) increasing to 6,930 ft (2112 m) at 630,000 lb (285765 kg)

Boeing 757

The **Boeing 757** is a third-generation workhorse for commercial carriers. The first aircraft, a Boeing 757-200, flew on 18 February 1982. The type has good potential for the military passenger-carrying role; the **Fuerza Aérea Mexicana** operates a **757-225** delivered in October 1987 and returned to the US in March 1988 for conversion to a presidential aircraft. One also serves with **Argentina**. Boeing uses the prototype for testing F-22 systems, currently being modified to **'Catfish'** configuration with an F-22 nose and a wing section above the flight deck to test conformal avionics.

SPECIFICATION

Boeing Model 757-200
Wing: span 124 ft 10 in (38.05 m); aspect ratio 7.8; area 1,994.00 sq ft (185.24 m²)
Fuselage and tail: length 155 ft 3 in (47.32 m); height 44 ft 6 in (13.56 m); tailplane span 49 ft 11 in (15.21 m); wheel track 24 ft 0 in (7.32 m); wheel base 60 ft 0 in (18.29 m)
Powerplant: two Rolls-Royce 535C each rated at 37,400 lb st (166.36 kN) dry, or Pratt & Whitney PW2037 each rated at 38,200 lb st (169.92 kN) dry, or Rolls-Royce 535E4 each rated at 40,100 lb (178.37 kN) dry, or Pratt & Whitney PW2040 each rated at 41,700 lb st (185.49 kN) dry
Weights: operating empty 126,060 lb (57180 kg) with 535E engines, or 125,750 lb (57039 kg) with PW engines; maximum take-off 250,000 lb (113395 kg)
Fuel and load: internal fuel 11,253 US gal (42597 litres); external fuel none; maximum payload 57,530 lb (26096 kg)
Range: range 3,820 nm (4,399 miles; 7070 km) with 535E engines, or 4,000 nm (4,603 miles; 7408 km) with PW engines

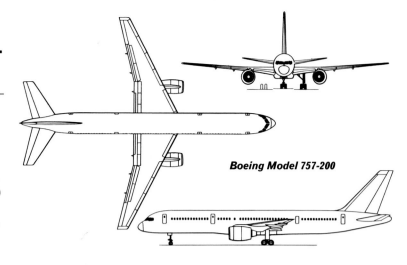

Boeing Model 757-200

Performance: initial cruise ceiling 38,970 ft (11880 m) with 535 engines, or 38,300 ft (11675 m) with PW engines; take-off field length at maximum take-off weight 7,000 ft (2134 m) with 535E engines, or 9,160 ft (2792 m) with PW2037 engines, or 6,950 ft (2118 m) with PW2040 engines; landing field length at maximum landing weight 4,630 ft (1411 m) with 535E engines, or 4,790 ft (1460 m) with PW engines

Boeing 767

The **Boeing 767** is a third-generation jetliner sharing features with the 757 but with a wider-body fuselage. The US Army operates the prototype Boeing 767-200 (no military designation) with a dorsal cupola, giving the aircraft a 'humpbacked' configuration. It was converted as the Airborne Optical Adjunct laboratory with a unique long-wavelength infra-red sensor as part of the Air Defence Initiative and the Strategic Defense Initiative programmes. The extra keel area forward is compensated for by a pair of enormous ventral fins.

Boeing is promoting the **767-200ER** as an AWACS platform, and plans are well advanced to supply two AWACS 767s to **Japan** under the designation **E-767**. Japan has an eventual requirement for four large AWACS platforms, but did not act on this before the E-3 production line closed. Two Boeing 767s will therefore be built at Seat-tle and then flown to Wichita for structural modifications in January 1995. They will then return to Seattle for equipment installation and flight test (a seven-month process) before being handed over to the JASDF from January 1998.

SPECIFICATION

Boeing Model 767-200
Wing: span 156 ft 1 in (47.57 m); aspect ratio 7.9; area 3,050.00 sq ft (283.35 m²)
Fuselage and tail: length 159 ft 2 in (48.51 m); height 52 ft 0 in (15.85 m); tailplane span 61 ft 1 in (18.62 m); wheel track 30 ft 6 in (9.30 m); wheel base 64 ft 7 in (19.69 m)
Powerplant: typically two Pratt & Whitney JT9D-7R4D or General Electric CF6-80A each rated at 48,000 lb st (213.51 kN) dry
Weights: manufacturer's empty 164,800 lb (74752 kg)

The prototype 767 is used as an airborne laboratory for strategic defence programmes.

with JT9D engines or 163,900 lb (74344 kg) with CF6 engines; operating empty 178,400 lb (80921 kg) with JT9D engines or 177,500 lb (80512 kg) with CF6 engines; maximum take-off 300,000 lb (136078 kg)
Fuel and load: internal fuel 112,725 lb (51131 kg); external fuel none; maximum payload 43,200 lb (19595 kg)
Speed: maximum cruising speed at optimum altitude Mach 0.80
Range: range 3,160 nm (3,639 miles; 5856 km) with JT9D engines or 3,220 nm (3,708 miles; 5967 km) with CF6 engines
Performance: initial cruise ceiling 39,200 ft (11950 m) with JT9D engines or 39,700 ft (12100 m) with CF6 engines; take-off field length 5,900 ft (1798 m) at maximum take-off weight

Boeing Helicopters (Boeing Vertol) CH-46 Sea Knight

Boeing Helicopters
Boeing Center, PO Box 16858,
Philadelphia, PA 19142, USA

Still the backbone of the **US Marine Corps** medium assault helicopter fleet, the **CH-46 Sea Knight** dates back to the commercial Vertol Model 107 which first flew in April 1958. The first military interest came from the US Army, which ordered three **YHC-1A**s for evaluation but in the event bought the larger Chinook. However, further interest was expressed by the USMC, which needed a turbine-powered helicopter to replace its fleet of UH-34s.

Initial USMC aircraft were designated **HRB-1** (**CH-46A** after 1962), and the first entered service with HMM-265 in June 1964. One hundred and sixty CH-46As were built, along with 14 **UH-46A**s for the **US Navy**, which used the type for vertical replenishment tasks. These were followed in production by 266 **CH-46D**s and 10 **UH-46D**s, which introduced the more powerful T58-GE-10 turboshaft and cambered rotor blades. The final production variant was the **CH-46F**, of which 174 were built and delivered between July 1968 and February 1971.

Today the principal variant is the **CH-46E**, the result of an update programme applied to both Ds and Fs to improve safety and crashworthiness. Glass-fibre rotor blades were fitted, in addition to other strengthening, while the engines were replaced with the further-uprated T58-GE-16. The 'Bullfrog' conversion has further enhanced the capability of the type, this programme adding more fuel in enlarged fuselage sponsons.

Marine Corps users

In service with the USMC, the CH-46E serves with 17 medium assault squadrons and a training unit at Tustin, CA (HMM-161, 163, 164, 166, 268 and HMT-301), New River, NC (HMM-162, 204, 261, 263, 264, 266 and 365), Kaneohe Bay, HI (HMM-165, 265, 364), Norfolk, VA (HMM-774), and El Toro, CA (HMM-764). The standard load is 17 fully-equipped troops or 15 casualty litters. Small cargo can be admitted through the rear loading ramp although in practice the aircraft are usually used for troop transport, while CH-53s undertake the heavy supply role. Typically 12 CH-46s will deploy aboard an amphibious assault ship, supported by AH-1s, CH-53s and AV-8Bs. Once they have been used to establish a beach-head, they will continue a shuttle between ship and shore, bringing in extra forces and supplies. CH-46s are also used in a Special Forces support role, and have been active on evacuation duties. Five aircraft serve with HMX-1 at MCAS Quantico in VH-46F configuration for VIP transport. A small number serve as HH-46D SAR aircraft at USMC bases at Beaufort, Cherry Point, Iwakuni and Kaneohe Bay, equipped for the role with a winch.

Navy Sea Knights serve with HC-3 and HC-11 at North Island, CA, HC-5 at Agana, Guam, and HC-6 and HC-8 at Norfolk, VA. These units fly the CH/HH/UH-46D on a variety of fleet support duties, including vertical replenishment of vessels and rescue. The latter role is performed by **HH-46D**s assigned to the base flight at NAS Point Mugu, CA.

Export orders were restricted to **Canada** and **Sweden**, although the design was licence-built, and subsequently improved, by Kawasaki in Japan as the **KV-107** (described separately). A small number of Vertol 107s was sold to Sweden as **Hkp 4A**s for use by the air force in a SAR role, although subsequent Swedish

Canada uses its aircraft in the SAR role, locally designated CH-113 Labrador. The yellow and red high-conspicuity scheme is applied fleet-wide.

Boeing Vertol CH-46D Sea Knight

Boeing Helicopters (Boeing Vertol) CH-46 Sea Knight

The CH-46E/F is the backbone of the Marine Corps assault transport fleet. The aircraft sport a variety of schemes to match different terrains.

machines were all KV-107s. Canada's **CH-113 Labradors** were procured from Boeing Vertol. Thirteen (of 18) remain in service for SAR duties, but are being replaced by Bell 412HPs.

SPECIFICATION

Boeing Vertol UH-46A Sea Knight
Rotor system: rotor diameter, each 50 ft 0 in (15.24 m); rotor disc area, total 3,926.99 sq ft (364.82 m²)

Fuselage and tail: length overall, rotors turning 83 ft 4 in (25.40 m) and fuselage 44 ft 10 in (13.66 m); height 16 ft 8.5 in (5.09 m) to top of rear rotor head; wheel track 12 ft 10.5 in (3.92 m); wheel base 24 ft 10 in (7.57 m)
Powerplant: two General Electric T58-GE-8B each rated at 1,250 shp (932 kW)
Weights: empty equipped 12,406 lb (5627 kg); maximum take-off 21,400 lb (9706 kg)
Fuel and load: internal fuel 380 US gal (1438 litres); external fuel none; maximum payload 4,000 lb (1814 kg) carried internally or 6,330 lb (2871 kg)

carried externally
Speed: never-exceed speed 138 kt (159 mph; 256 km/h); maximum cruising speed at optimum altitude 135 kt (155 mph; 249 km/h); economical cruising speed at optimum altitude 131 km/h (151 mph; 243 km/h)
Range: range 230 nm (265 miles; 426 km) with maximum internal payload or 200 nm (230 miles; 370 km) with a 6,070-lb (2753-kg) external payload
Performance: maximum rate of climb at sea level 1,440 ft (439 m) per minute; service ceiling 14,000 ft (4265 m); hovering ceiling 9,070 ft (2765 m) in ground

effect and 5,600 ft (1707 m) out of ground effect

Boeing Vertol CH-46E Sea Knight
generally similar to the UH-46A Sea Knight except in the following particulars:
Powerplant: two General Electric T58-GE-16 each rated at 1,870 shp (1394 kW)
Weights: empty 11,585 lb (5255 kg); maximum take-off 24,300 lb (11022 kg)
Fuel and load: internal fuel 350 US gal (1323 litres); maximum payload 7,000 lb (3175 kg)
Speed: maximum speed at sea level 144 kt (166 mph; 267 km/h); maximum cruising speed at sea level 143 kt (165 mph; 266 km/h)
Range: ferry range 600 nm (691 miles; 1112 km); range with 2,400-lb (1088-kg) payload 550 nm (633 miles; 1019 km)
Performance: maximum rate of climb at sea level 1,715 ft (523 m) per minute; service ceiling 9,400 ft (2865 m); hovering ceiling 9,500 ft (2895 m) in ground effect and 5,750 ft (1753 m) out of ground effect

Boeing Helicopters (Boeing Vertol) CH-47 Chinook

In widespread service with the **US Army** and other air arms around the world, the **Chinook** rivals the Sikorsky CH-53 as the world's leading medium-lift helicopter. This workhorse of the modern army won its spurs in Vietnam, and has been the subject of continual upgrading since.

Developed along Vertol's proven twin-rotor concept, the Chinook began life under the company designation **V-144**. Initially assigned the US Army designation **YHC-1B**, it was retitled **CH-47** in 1962.

First flight occurred on 21 September 1961, and the first **CH-47A** was delivered to the US Army on 16 August 1962.

By mounting the engines externally above the rear fuselage, and by placing the three-bladed rotors high above either end of the fuselage, Vertol's designers left the cabin completely clear for the carriage of troops, cargo or small vehicles. Fuselage-side sponsons provided mountings for the four-unit undercarriage and space for fuel carriage. A rear-loading ramp and slightly

tilted fuselage combine to make loading and unloading extremely easy, an important factor for combat operations under fire.

A standard crew comprises two pilots and a loadmaster/crew chief, who has a jump seat between the pilots. Guns can be mounted in the starboard entry door or the rear ramp. A normal load of up to 55 troops can be carried, or 24 litters, while the cabin has tie-down cleats for the carriage of cargo. The initial CH-47A had one cargo hook for the carriage of underslung loads,

but in modern Chinooks the number is increased to three. The rotors are counter-rotating, obviating the need for a tail rotor, and the engines are geared so that either one can drive both rotors in the event of an engine failure. As the blades are intermesh-

The Chinook is the standard workhorse of the US Army, used primarily for battlefield mobility of vehicles, artillery, supplies and large numbers of troops.

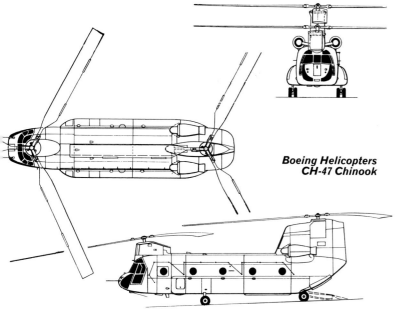

**Boeing Helicopters
CH-47 Chinook**

ing, a synchronisation unit is required to keep them at 60° to each other. The fuselage is waterproofed for emergency ditchings, although this is rarely demonstrated.

A total of 354 CH-47As was built for the US Army, and these were rapidly deployed to Vietnam where they immediately established a reputation for versatility, reliability, strength and the ability to carry out Herculean tasks of lifting. One hundred and eight **CH-47B**s followed, these having extra power and increased-diameter rotor blades. The third Chinook model, the **CH-47C**, introduced greater improvements, including further uprated engines for better lifting power and extra fuel (although not in the 'crashworthy' version ordered by some export customers). A total of 270 was built for the US Army, of which 182 were retrofitted with composite blades, integral spar inspection systems and crashworthy fuel systems.

The C model first flew on 14 October 1967, and in the early 1970s was the subject of the first export orders. **Thailand** received ex-US Army CH-47As, but **Australia** was the first foreign customer, buying 12 CH-47Cs for 'hot-and-high' operations in Papua New Guinea. **Spain**, **Canada** and the **Royal Air Force** followed, identifying their aircraft as **HT.17**, **CH-147** and **Chinook HC.Mk 1**, respectively. The British machines were the first to introduce triple-hook capability, a rotor brake, NVG-compatible cockpit, automatic fuel fire suppression system and pressure refuelling. They were retrofitted with glass-fibre blades as **Chinook HC.Mk 1B**s.In 1970, the Italian company Elicotteri Meridionali began licence-production of the CH-47C for the **Italian army** and Mediterranean customers.

Many of the improvements specified by export customers found their way to the US Army fleet, which is now to **CH-47D** standard. This version is a mix of conversions from all three former variants and some new-build machines. The first flight of a production CH-47D was on 26 February 1982, with service entry (with the 101st Airborne Division) achieved on 20 May. The full programme covers 472 aircraft (including **MH-47E**s, described separately) and entails the complete reworking of the aircraft for service into the next century. T55-L-712 turboshafts are fitted, these offering the same power as the C model's powerplant, but with a greater power reserve for emergencies and far greater battle damage resistance. Numerous other systems are improved or added, including a new NVG-

The RAF has a large force of Chinooks, currently being reworked to HC.Mk 2 standard. Some operate in a Special Forces role.

compatible flight deck, triple cargo hooks and pressure refuelling. In a similar programme, the RAF is returning its Chinooks to Boeing for rework to CH-47D standard, aircraft emerging as **Chinook HC.Mk 2**s.

In operation, the CH-47D can carry a wide variety of loads up to a maximum of 22,798 lb (10341 kg) externally or 13,907 lb (6308 kg) internally. Typical external loads include vehicles, howitzer crews and ammunition, supply containers or fuel blivets. Chinooks of both the RAF and US Army were heavily involved in the Desert Storm, several in Special Forces support roles (see following entry). Some US Army CH-47Ds, notably those of the 228th Aviation Regiment at Fort Wainwright, AK, operate on skis.

Following the US Army's CH-47D is the **CH-47D International Chinook (Model 414)**, which is tailored to the export market. The first customer was **Japan** which, after the supply of two pattern aircraft and one in kit form, is now building the aircraft under licence.

US Army re-equipment with the CH-47D is largely complete, the variant having been supplied to 17 active-duty units and several within the Army National Guard and Reserve organisations. Foreign operators, including those which fly licence-built aircraft, are as follows: **Argentina** received three CH-47Cs, of which one is believed to continue on Antarctic support duties with the air force. The Royal Australian Air Force

purchased 12 CH-47Cs for army support, and the 11 survivors were later transferred to that service but subsequently grounded. Four CH-47Ds are on order for 1995 delivery. Canada's CH-147 fleet numbered nine, but the aircraft have since been withdrawn and may be sold to the Netherlands. An order for six CH-47Ds placed by China is still embargoed by the US government. **Egypt** operates 15 Italian-built CH-47Cs from Kom Amshim, the aircraft being part of a cancelled Iranian order. The **Greek army** also received CH-47Cs from Meridionali, the nine remaining (of 10 delivered) being returned to Boeing for CH-47D conversion. Sixty-eight Meridionali CH-47Cs were delivered to **Iran**, which made heavy use of them during the war with Iraq. An unknown number remains serviceable.

Italy itself received 38 CH-47Cs from home production to serve with the 11° and 12° Gruppi Squadroni at Viterbo. Twenty-six now serve with the army, upgraded to **CH-47C Plus** standard with T55-L-412E engines and composite blades. One is in ESFC (emergency surgery flying centre) configuration as a flying hospital, while others are able to conduct firefighting and disaster relief operations. The Japanese Ground Self-Defence Force is in the process of acquiring **CH-47J**s (Kawasaki-built CH-47D), an eventual total of 42 being

All of Spain's Chinooks are to CH-47D standard. Some were built as such from new, while the remainder were modified from CH-47C standard.

expected. The JASDF wishes to acquire a total of 16. Another recipient of Italian machines was **Libya**, which split its purchase of 20 into six for the air force and 14 for the army, of which one has crashed. **Morocco** also received CH-47Cs from Meridionali, 12 serving with the Royal Moroccan air force. **Nigeria** is believed to have five CH-47s on order, to add to the two survivors of the CH-47As first supplied. Finally, the RAF's Chinook force now numbers 35 aircraft, which are in the process of becoming HC.Mk 2s, serving with Nos 7, 18, 27(R) and 78 Sqns.

South Korea has 24 International Chinooks, of which six serve with the air force and the remainder with the army. The Spanish army's BHelTra V at Colmenar Viejo operates 18 CH-47Ds, of which nine have been upgraded from C-model standard. **Taiwan** has a trio of civilian **Boeing 234MLR** models for its army's heavylift requirements, while Thailand has 12 International Chinooks on order, to add to the two survivors of the CH-47As first supplied. Finally, the RAF's Chinook force now numbers 35 aircraft, which are in the process of becoming HC.Mk 2s, serving with Nos 7, 18, 27(R) and 78 Sqns.

Boeing Helicopters (Boeing Vertol) CH-47 Chinook

Boeing Helicopters has further plans for the development of the Chinook design, including a study for the **Advanced Chinook** with 5,000 shp-class engines, redesigned rotors and additional fuel.

Boeing Vertol CH-47D Chinook
Rotor system: rotor diameter, each 60 ft 0 in (18.29m); rotor disc area, total 5,654.86 sq ft (525.34 m2)
Fuselage and tail: length overall, rotors turning 98 ft 10.75 in (30.14 m) and fuselage 51 ft 0 in (15.54 m); height 18 ft 11 in (5.77 m) to top of rear rotor head; wheel track 10 ft 6 in (3.20 m); wheel base 22 ft 6 in (6.86 m)
Powerplant: two Textron Lycoming T55-L-712 each rated at 3,750 shp (2796 kW) for take-off and 3,000 shp (2237 kW) for continuous running, or two

Textron Lycoming T55-L-712 SSB each rated at 4,378 shp (3264 kW) for take-off and 3,137 shp (2339 kW) for continuous running, in both cases driving a transmission rated at 7,500 shp (5593 kW) on two engines and 4,600 shp (3430 kW) on one engine
Weights: empty 22,379 lb (10151 kg); normal take-off 46,000 lb (20866 kg); maximum take-off 50,000 lb (22679 kg)
Fuel and load: internal fuel 1,030 US gal (3899 litres); external fuel none; maximum payload 22,798 lb (10341 kg)
Speed: maximum level speed at sea level 161 kt (185 mph; 298 km/h); maximum cruising speed at optimum altitude 138 kt (159 mph; 256 km/h)
Range: ferry range 1,093 nm (1,259 miles; 2026 km); operational radius between 100 and 30 nm (115 and 35 miles; 185 and 56 km) with maximum internal and maximum external payloads respectively
Performance: maximum rate of climb at sea level 2,195 ft (669 m) per minute; service ceiling 22,100 ft (6735 m); hovering ceiling 10,550 ft (3215 m)

Argentina bought three CH-47Cs for Antarctic support, but one was captured in the Falklands. This survivor wears a 'Malvinas' campaign badge.

Boeing Helicopters **Chinook (Special Forces)**

As part of the upgrade to the US Army's Special Operations Forces (SOF) capabilities, the service has ordered 12 (of a total requirement for 51) **MH-47E SOA**s (Special Operations Aircraft) to augment MH-60s also being procured for the role. These are based on the CH-47D airframe, but feature a full range of features to aid covert infil/exfil work.

The cockpit is fitted with a four-screen NVG-compatible EFIS, while the avionics include dual MIL-STD-1553 databases, automatic target hand-off system, jam-resistant communications, GPS receiver, APQ-174 radar for mapping and terrain-following flight down to 30 m (100 ft) in a pod on the port side of the nose, and AAQ-16 FLIR in an undernose turret. Comprehensive defences include missile-, laser- and radar-warning receivers, pulse and CW jammers and chaff/flare dispensers. Armament consists of two window-mounted M2 0.50-in machine-guns, and Stinger air-to-air missiles.

Optional equipment includes extra bolt-on fuel tanks which double fuel capacity, although this fitment requires moving the nosewheels forward to accommodate the tanks. A refuelling probe allows the **MH-47E** to refuel from HC/KC/MC-130 Hercules, and a typical deep-penetration mission lasts for 5-6 hours, to a radius of some 350 miles (565 km). Units which are due to be equipped with the MH-47E are the 2nd Battalion, 160th Special Operations Aviation Group at Fort Campbell, KY (first delivery

late 1992), to be followed by the 3rd Battalion/160th SOAG at Hunter AAF, GA, and the 1/245th Aviation Battalion (SOA), of the Oklahoma Army National Guard.

Pending delivery of the MH-47Es, the 160th SOAG made use of 32 Chinooks temporarily upgraded to **CH-47D SOA** standard with refuelling probes, thermal imaging equipment, weather radar, improved nav/comms and door-mounted 7.62-mm machine-guns. During the Gulf War, the Royal Air Force upgraded a handful of its **Chinook HC.Mk 1B** aircraft with better navigation equipment, NVG-compatible cockpits, IR searchlight and missile warning/countermeasures for Special Forces support.

Boeing Vertol MH-47E Chinook
generally similar to the Boeing Vertol CH-47D Chinook except in the following particulars:
Fuselage and tail: length overall, rotors turning 98 ft 10.75 in (30.14 m) and fuselage 52 ft 1 in (15.87 m); height 18 ft 4 in (5.59 m) to top of rear rotor head; wheel track 11 ft 11 in (3.63 m); wheel base 25 ft 10 in (7.87 m)
Powerplant: two Textron Lycoming T55-L-712 SSB each rated at 4,378 shp (3264 kW) for take-off and 3,137 shp (2339 kW) for continuous running, in both cases driving a transmission rated at 7,500 shp (5593 kW) on two engines and 4,600 shp (3430 kW) on one engine

Weights: empty 26,918 lb (12210 kg); maximum take-off 54,000 lb (24494 kg)
Fuel and load: internal fuel 15,025 lb (6815 kg); external fuel none
Speed: maximum level speed at sea level 154 kt (177 mph; 285 km/h); maximum cruising speed at sea level 140 kt (161 mph; 259 km/h)
Range: ferry range 1,200 nm (1,382 miles; 2224 km) fuel; typical range 613 nm (706 miles; 1136 km); operational radius 300 nm (345 miles; 560 km); endurance 5 hours 30 minutes
Performance: maximum rate of climb at sea level 1,840 ft (561 m) per minute; service ceiling 10,150 ft (3095 m); hovering ceiling 9,800 ft (2990 m) in ground effect and 5,500 ft (1675 m) out of ground effect

Above: The MH-47E features a full Special Ops kit, including APQ-174 radar in a nose-mounted pod and inflight-refuelling probe. Under the nose is a FLIR sensor.

Below: Known as the CH-47D SOA or MH-47D, a number of CH-47Ds was given FLIRs for the SOF role.

Boeing Helicopters/Sikorsky **RAH-66 Comanche**

The US Army announced its LHX (Light Helicopter Experimental) requirement in 1982, with an initial requirement for 5,000 helicopters to replace UH-1, AH-1, OH-6 and OH-58 scout/attack/assault aircraft. This has since been scaled down to 1,292 for the scout/attack role only. Boeing/Sikorsky's 'First Team' was awarded the contract for three dem/val aircraft on 5 April 1991.

The First Team's aircraft is known as the **RAH-66 Comanche**, and is expected to fly in August 1995. The Comanche has a five-bladed main rotor and a shrouded tail rotor. The fuselage is designed for low observability, employing some degree of faceting and sunken notch intakes for the two LHTEC T800 turboshafts. Flight control is by a triplex fly-by-wire system. The undercarriage is retractable, and missiles are housed in bays on the fuselage sides, directly attached to the bay doors which act as pylons when they are open. A chin turret houses a three-barrelled 20-mm cannon,

and in the extreme nose is a sensor turret for FLIR and laser. The RAH-66 also features a wide array of defensive equipment, including laser-, IR- and radar-warning receivers. A third of the fleet will have miniaturised Longbow radar.

Boeing/Sikorsky RAH-66 Comanche
Rotor system: main rotor diameter 39 ft 0.5 in (11.90 m); fantail rotor diameter 4 ft 6 in (1.37 m); main rotor disc area 1,197.14 sq ft (111.21 m2); fantail rotor disc area 15.90 sq ft (1.48 m2)
Fuselage and tail: length overall, rotor turning 46 ft 10.25 in (14.28 m) and fuselage 43 ft 4.5 in (13.22 m) excluding gun barrel; height overall 11 ft 1.5 in (3.39 m) over stabiliser; stabiliser span 9 ft 3 in (2.82 m)
Powerplant: two LHTEC T800-LHT-800 each rated at 1,344 shp (1002 kW)
Weights: empty equipped 9,187 lb (4,167 kg); normal

take-off 10,112 lb (4587 kg); maximum take-off 17,174 lb (7790 kg)
Fuel and load: internal fuel 260 US gal (984 litres); external fuel up to two 460-US gal (1741.5-litre) auxiliary tanks

Speed: maximum level speed 'clean' at optimum altitude 177 kt (204 mph; 328 km/h)
Range: ferry range 1,260 nm (1,451 miles; 2335 km) with external fuel; endurance 2 hours 30 minutes
Performance: maximum vertical rate of climb at sea level 1,182 ft (328 m) per minute

A mock-up of the RAH-66 reveals its futuristic lines.

Boeing/Grumman E-8 J-STARS

Making a 'star' appearance in Operation Desert Storm long before it was considered operational, the Boeing/Grumman E-8 represents a major advance in battlefield control, introducing the kind of capability for monitoring and controlling the land battle that the E-3 provides for the air battle. Like the E-3, the E-8 is based on the tried and trusted Boeing 707-320 airframe, and no new-build aircraft are envisaged.

Two **E-8A** prototypes were converted, Grumman being the prime contractor for the system. A ventral canoe fairing houses a Norden multi-mode side-looking radar, while the cabin is configured with operator consoles. A datalink provides the means to transmit gathered intelligence to the ground in near real-time. The radar can operate in synthetic aperture mode, which gives a high-resolution radar picture out to 160 miles (257 km) from the orbiting aircraft, while two pulse-Doppler modes give moving target information, allowing the controllers to monitor the positions and movements of all ground vehicles. Wide area search/moving target indicator (WAS/MTI) mode monitors a large sector of land, while sector search mode (SSM) is used on much smaller areas to follow individual vehicles. The radar can differentiate between wheeled and tracked vehicles.

Using the various modes, the J-STARS (Joint Surveillance Target Attack Radar System) can be used for general surveillance and battlefield monitoring to provide the 'big picture' to commanders, stand-off radar reconnaissance or individual targeting functions for attacking vehicles and convoys. A replay function is available so that several hours of returns can be run on fast-forward to spot overall trends in vehicle movements. A velocity threshold on the moving target modes can filter out fast-moving vehicles (i.e. private cars).

Although data can be interpreted on board, the datalink allows gathered data to be relayed immediately to mobile ground consoles. The ground systems are truck-mounted and contain similar consoles to those found on the aircraft, allowing operators on the ground to directly access the J-STARS system with their own requirements.

December 1988 saw the first J-STARS-configured E-8A take to the air for the first time, followed by a second development machine. In January 1991 both E-8As deployed to Riyadh to fly combat missions under the control of the hastily-organised 4411th Joint STARS Squadron. Forty-nine war missions were flown, for a total of 535 hours, a sizeable portion of which was spent on the search for Iraqi 'Scud' missiles. Desert Storm operations provided ground and air commanders with a wealth of material, and fully validated the concept.

In service, the system was to be have been carried on the new-build **E-8B** aircraft with F108 turbofans, but despite one **YE-8B** being procured (later sold), the carrier will now be the **E-8C** based on converted 707 airliner airframes. A total of 20 is required, the first of which flew in April 1994. Deliveries are expected from 1995, with IOC in 1997.

The two E-8As carried far more test equipment than the E-8C production aircraft. The latter also has more sensor operator stations inside the cabin.

SPECIFICATION

Boeing/Grumman E-8A

Wing: span 145 ft 9 in (44.42 m); aspect ratio 7.056; area 3,050.00 sq ft (283.35 m²)

Fuselage and tail: length 152 ft 11 in (46.61 m); height 42 ft 5 in (12.93 m); tailplane span 45 ft 9 in (13.94 m); wheel track 22 ft 1 in (6.73 m); wheel base 17.98 m (59 ft 0 in)

Powerplant: four Pratt & Whitney JT3D-7 each rated at 19,000 lb (84.52 kN) dry

Weights: maximum take-off 333,600 lb (151315 kg)

Fuel and load: internal fuel 159,560 lb (72375 kg); external fuel none; maximum theoretical payload 96,126 lb (43603 kg)

Speed: maximum cruising speed at 25,000 ft (7620 m) 525 kt (605 mph; 973 km/h); economical cruising speed at 35,000 ft (10670 m) 464 kt (534 mph; 860 km/h)

Range: range with maximum fuel 5,000 nm (5,758 miles; 9266 km)

Performance: maximum rate of climb at sea level 4,000 ft (1219 m) per minute; service ceiling 39,000 ft (11890 m)

AIRFRAME
The E-8 is based on the 707-320C airframe, the final and definitive version of the airliner. This is distinguished from earlier variants by the lack of ventral fin.

'FIDDLE'
The large teardrop fairing under the centre-section houses the antenna for the Flight Test Data Link, fitted to the E-8As only. This was used during Desert Storm for transmitting data over long distances back to central commands in Riyadh.

Boeing/Grumman E-8A

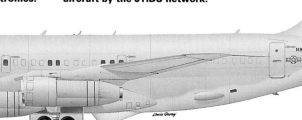

RADAR
The Norden multi-mode radar offers an imaging range in synthetic aperture radar mode of up to 175 km (100 miles). In an eight-hour sortie one million km² (386,100 sq miles) can be surveyed. The radar fitted to the E-8C features resolution three times better than that of the two E-8As.

CONSOLES
The E-8A carried 10 operator consoles and various test stations. The production E-8C has 17 operator consoles and one dedicated to defensive electronics.

'SKITTLE'
Aft of the 'Fiddle' radome is a small antenna for the Surveillance and Control Data Link, the primary means of downlinking information to Ground Station Modules. Data is linked to other aircraft by the JTIDS network.

Breguet (Dassault Aviation) Br.1150 Alizé

In December 1971 Breguet Aviation merged with Avions Marcel Dassault, resulting in Avions Marcel Dassault-Breguet Aviation

Now the most elderly combat aircraft regularly operating from aircraft-carrier decks, the **Breguet Alizé** was produced to meet a French naval requirement in the early 1950s and is expected to serve with the **Aéronavale** beyond the year 2000. Breguet proposed to use a Nene turbojet in the tail to boost performance, but after tests with this configuration in the Vultur proto-type only the turboprop was retained in the definitive Alizé, with a retractable radome for sea-search radar replacing the turbojet in the rear fuselage. After two prototypes – the first of which flew on 6 October 1956 – and three pre-production aircraft, Breguet built a total of 75 Alizés for the Aéronavale and 12 for the **Indian navy**.

Service use in France has been reduced from three to two *flottilles*, 4F and 6F, for use in the anti-submarine role from the air-craft-carriers *Foch* and *Clemenceau*. An upgrade programme initiated in 1980 intro-duced Thomson-CSF Iguane radar in the ventral radome, Omega Equinox navigation system, new communications equipment and ESM in the noses of the underwing stores panniers. This added 15 years to the expected service life, but a further modifica-tion programme for 24 surviving aircraft began in 1990 to introduce datalink, better decoy capability and other improvements to give a further service life extension. A few Alizés fly with Escadrille 59E at Hyères for training and SAR, and with 10S at St Raphael on miscellaneous test tasks along with Nord 262s and Xingus.

With the Indian navy, the original Alizés (supplemented by later purchase of about a dozen ex-Aéronavale aircraft) served with INAS 310 'Cobras' squadron from the *Vikrant*. The addition of ski-ramps to that carrier forced the remaining five Alizés ashore in 1987; a dwindling number contin-ued in service until late 1992 from Dabolin, when the last example was withdrawn from service.

The elderly Breguet Alizé continues to fly with the French Aéronavale on carrier-based ASW duties and shore-based patrols with two front-line units.

SPECIFICATION

Breguet (Dassault Aviation) Br.1150 Alizé)
Wing: span 15.60 m (51 ft 2 in); width folded 7.00 m

(22 ft 11.5 in); aspect ratio 6.76; area 36.00 m² (387.51 sq ft)
Fuselage and tail: length 13.86 m (45 ft 6 in); height 5.00 m (16 ft 4.75 in)
Powerplant: one Rolls-Royce Dart RDa.7 Mk 21 rated at 1,975 ehp (1473 ekW)
Weights: empty 5700 kg (12,566 lb); maximum take-off 8200 kg (18,078 lb)
Fuel and load: external fuel none; maximum ordnance about 1250 kg (2,756 lb)
Speed: maximum level speed 'clean' at 3000 m

(9,845 ft) 520 km/h (281 kt; 323 mph); cruising speed at optimum altitude 370 km/h (200 kt; 230 mph); patrol speed at optimum altitude 232 km/h (125 kt; 144 mph)
Range: ferry range 2870 km (1,550 nm; 1,785 miles) with auxiliary fuel; range 2500 km (1,349 nm; 1,553 miles) with standard fuel; 7 hours 40 minutes with auxiliary fuel or endurance 5 hours 5 minutes with standard fuel
Performance: maximum rate of climb at sea level 420 m (1,380 ft) per minute; service ceiling more than 6250 m (20,505 ft)

British Aerospace/Raytheon (Hawker Siddeley) 125

British Aerospace Corporate Jets Ltd 3 Bishop Square, St Albans Road West, Hatfield Hertfordshire AL10 9NE, UK

An early entrant into the executive jet field, the **de Havilland D.H.125** first flew on 13 August 1962, with the first pro-duction example flying the following Febru-ary.Its configuration is similar to that adopted for other conventional executive jets, with a mid-mounted tailplane to keep the control surfaces out of the jet efflux. The engines (originally Viper 520 turbojets each rated at 3,000 lb/13.35 kN thrust) are mounted on pylons each side of the rear fuselage, resulting in a clean wing. The roomy cabin is of constant circular cross-section over much of its length, and can be fitted out in various degrees of comfort, from standard airliner-type seating to full-scale VIP configuration. The type was also designed from the outset to be able to oper-ate from unpaved runways without special modification.

Following the maiden flight, the **RAF** ordered 20, named **Dominie** navigaton trainers (described separately). Following DH's incorporation into the Hawker Sidde-ley Group, four **H.S. 125 CC.Mk. 1** air-craft were procured by the RAF in March 1971 for communications and transport duties. These were based on the **Series 400** with 3,000-lb (13.35-kN) Rolls-Royce Viper 301 turbojets. Today they are oper-ated by No. 32 Sqn, at Northolt. The type's high speed and good payload-range capabil-ity resulted in a number of additional orders. These com-prise two **BAe 125 CC.Mk 2s** comparable to the civil **Series 600** with stretched fuse-lage and 3,750-lb (16.68-kN) static thrust Viper 601-22 turbojets, and six **BAe 125 CC.Mk 3s**, similar to the **Series 700** with Garrett TFE731 turbofans of 3,700 lb (16.46 kN) thrust. Turbofans were intro-duced to improve airfield/climb performance and to increase range and maximum speed. For commonality and economy the first six aircraft were re-engined with the TFE731, but were retired by No. 32 Sqn in May 1994. From 1988, four CC.Mk 3s received an overall grey low-visibility colour scheme and Northrop MIRTS infra-red countermea-sures fitted in an extended tail fairing. An additional aircraft (BAe 125-600B 'ZF130') is operated by BAe Dunsfold as an airborne radar testbed. Fitted with Blue Vixen radar and a full Sea Harrier FRS.Mk 2 weapons system, the aircraft has since flown with an underwing Sidewinder acquisition round.

The BAe 125 also serves in small num-bers with the air forces of **Botsawana**, **Brazil**, **Malawi**, **Malaysia** and **South Africa**. Of these, Brazil is the largest user with 12 aircraft, 10 serving on VIP duties (as the **VC-93**) and two **EC-93s** for radar cali-bration. In 1983 production moved on to the **BAe 125 Series 800**, with a new wing, uprated engines and avionics improve-ments. Six have been acquired for the Royal Flight of the **Royal Saudi air force**. Options exist for a further six aircraft under Phase Two of the Al Yamamah contract.

In 1990, the **USAF** took delivery of six 125-800s for combat flight inspection and navigation (C-FIN) duties. The aircraft were delivered 'green' by BAe and fitted with LTV Sierra Research Division equipment. Desig-nated **C-29A**, the type first flew on 11 May 1989 and replaced CT-39A and C-140As serv-ing with the 1866th FCS at Scott AFB, IL. In September 1991, control of these passed to the FAA at Oklahoma City. They are no longer designated C-29, simply 125-800.

In 1989, the **JASDF** announced the pro-curement of three aircraft similar to the C-29A. The first Sierra-equipped example made its maiden flight on 4 March 1992 and was delivered in December 1992. The JASDF has a further requirement for 27 BAe 125-800s for SAR duties. Designated **U-125A** for delivery from 1995, these will be equipped with a 360° scan radar and FLIR sensor, with provision for dropping marker flares and rescue equipment. Any further aircraft will not be sold as a British Aero-space type. In June 1993 BAe Corporate jets was acquired by the Raytheon company in the USA, which now markets the aircraft as the **Raytheon Hawker 800**. The stretched **Hawker 1000** (BAe 125-1000) long-range business jet has so far sold only to commercial customers.

SPECIFICATION

British Aerospace (de Havilland/Hawker Siddeley) 125 Series 800 (C-29A)
Wing: span 51 ft 4.5 in (15.66 m); aspect ratio 7.06; area 474.00 sq ft (34.75 m²)
Fuselage and tail: length 51 ft 2 in (15.60 m); height 17 ft 7 in (5.36 m); tailplane span 20 ft 0 in (6.10 m); wheel track 9 ft 2 in (2,79 m)
Powerplant: two Garrett TFE731-5R-1H each rated at 4,300 lb st (19.13 kN) dry
Weights: typical operating empty 15,120 lb (6858 kg); maximum take-off 27,400 lb (12429 kg)
Fuel and load: internal fuel 1,248 Imp gal (1,499 US gal; 5674 litres); maximum payload 2,400 lb (1088 kg)
Speed: never-exceed speed Mach 0.87; economical cruising speed between 39,000 and 43,000 ft (11900 and 13100 m) 400 kt (461 mph; 741 km/h)
Range: 3,000 nm (3,454 miles; 5560 km) with maximum fuel; range 2,870 nm (3,305 miles; 5318 km) with maximum payload
Performance: maximum rate of climb at sea level 3,100 ft (945 m) per minute; climb to 35,000 ft (10670 m) in 19 minutes; service ceiling 43,000 ft (13100 m); take-off balanced field length 5,620 ft (1713 m) at maximum take-off weight

For a brief period, the USAF operated its C-29As in the European One 'lizard' scheme, before their transferral to the Federal Aviation Authority as Sabre 75 replacements.

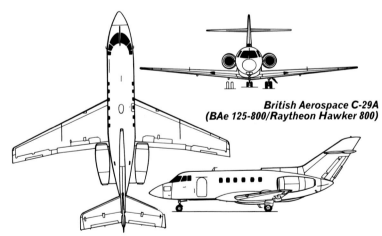

British Aerospace C-29A (BAe 125-800/Raytheon Hawker 800)

The RAF's BAe-125 CC.Mk 3s adopted this low-vis 'barley' scheme along with tail-mounted Northrop MIRTS infra-red counter measures.

British Aerospace/Avro (Hawker Siddeley) 146/RJ

Avro International Aerospace
Woodford Aerodrome, Chester Road, Stockport
Cheshire SK7 1QR, UK

In August 1973 Hawker Siddeley announced government backing for design and development of a new short-range civil transport which it identified as the HS.146. This was to be powered by four turbofan engines and would have operational noise levels considerably below announced future legislation on noise emission. This project had hardly gotten under way before nationalisation led to the shelving of the scheme. On 10 July 1978 the board of British Aerospace gave approval for a resumption of the programme. This involved not only British Aerospace, but also risk-sharing partners Avco (now Textron) Corporation in the USA and Saab-Scania in Sweden. Textron supplies the ALF502R turbofan engines (the R of the designation signifying reduced rating, which ensures that the already quiet engines have an even lower noise signature) and through its Textron Aerostructures division manufactures the wing boxes. Saab is responsible for the tailplanes and all movable control surfaces, while in the UK Short Brothers was subcontracted to fabricate pods for the ALF502 .

Production of three basic passenger versions continued until 1992. The **BAe 146-100** was designed specifically to operate from semi-prepared airstrips. Following demands for versions with less rigorous STOL capabilities and increased accommodation/payload, subsequent variants (designated **BAe 146-200** and **BAe 146-300**) featured progressively stretched fuselages and uprated engines and were optimised for operations from paved surfaces. Relaunch of the BAe 146 was announced in June 1992, with new **RJ (Regional Jet)** designations followed by numbers denoting passenger capacities (RJ 70, RJ 85 and RJ 100/RJ 115) The hallowed name of Avro was also revived to market the aircraft, the proposed joint UK/Taiwanese operation (with Taiwan Aerospace – TAC) becoming known as Avro International Aerospace. The new RJ series features more powerful Textron Lycoming LF-507-1H engines, with structural strengthening permitting increased weights. Production was to take place in Taiwan under a risk-sharing agreement, but the deal foundered in 1993, with recriminations on both sides.

In June 1983, two **BAe 146-100**s were leased as **BAe 146 CC.Mk 1**s by the **RAF**. These were evaluated at Brize Norton for suitability as replacements for the ageing Andovers of The Queen's Flight. Designated **BAe 146 CC.Mk 2**, three aircraft have been subsequently acquired for this unit. Two BAe 146-200s were delivered in mid-1986 and were followed by a further example in early 1991. All aircraft have been fitted with Loral Matador infra-red jamming systems. Four dedicated VIP/executive **Statesman** aircraft are operated by No. 1 Squadron (Royal Flight) of the **Royal Saudi Air Force** at Riyadh.

Military developments of the BAe 146 as a multi-role transport were announced in 1987. These include the **BAe 146STA** (Small Tactical Airlifter), **BAe 146MT** (Military Tanker), **BAe 146MRL** (Military Rear Loader) and **BAe 146MSL** (Military Side Loader). The BAe 146STA is based on the **BAe 146-QT** Quiet Trader freighter and features a 14-ft 7-in (4.44-m) wide rear fuselage cargo door in the port side. Loading flexibility is further enhanced by optional roller tracks which permit the movement of pallets. A sliding door set within the main cargo hold permits paradropping. This may include air-dropping of standard military pallets or up to 60 fully-equipped paratroops. Variations include options for up to 24 stretchers in the casevac role. The variant may also be fitted with an optional refuelling probe. The prototype BAe 146STA first flew in August 1988, and undertook a sales tour of Australasia and the Far East. No orders for military versions had been announced by early 1994.

SPECIFICATION

British Aerospace (Hawker Siddeley) 146 Series 100
Wing: span 86 ft 5 in (26.34 m) including 2.5-in (6.3-cm) static dischargers on each wingtip; aspect ratio 8.97; area 832.00 sq ft (77.29 m²)
Fuselage and tail: length 85 ft 11.5 in (26.20 m); height 28 ft 3 in (8.61 m); tailplane span 36 ft 5 in (11.09 m); wheel track 15 ft 6 in (4.72 m); wheel base 33 ft 1.5 in (10.09 m)
Powerplant: four Textron Lycoming ALF502R-5 each rated at 6,970 lb st (31.00 kN) dry
Weights: operating empty 49,000 lb (22226 kg); maximum take-off 84,000 lb (38102 kg)
Fuel and load: internal fuel 20,640 lb (9362 kg) standard and 22,704 lb (10298 kg) optional; external fuel none; maximum payload 19,500 lb (8845 kg)
Speed: economical cruising speed at 30,000 ft (9145 m) 382 kt (440 mph; 709 km/h)
Range: 1,672 nm (1,924 miles; 3096 km) with maximum standard fuel or 935 nm (1,077 miles; 1733 km) with maximum payload
Performance: take-off distance to 35 ft (10.7 m) 4,000 ft (1219 m) at maximum take-off weight; landing distance from 50 ft (15 m) 3,500 lb (1067 m) at normal landing weight

The British Aerospace BAe 146 CC.Mk 2 finally replaced the Andover CC.Mk 2 in RAF Queen's Flight service with the arrival of a third aircraft in December 1990. By then, the Andover had been in service for 26 years.

British Aerospace BAe 146 CC.Mk 2 (Avro Regional Jet 70)

British Aerospace (Avro/Hawker Siddeley) 748

British Aerospace plc
Warwick House, PO Box 87, Farnborough Aerospace Centre
Farnborough, Hampshire GU14 6YU, UK

Design of the Avro 748 twin-turboprop airliner was begun in January 1959. Representing the last identifiable product of the Avro (A. V. Roe) company, the aircraft was subsequently designated HS.748, following incorporation of Avro into the Hawker Siddeley Group. The Avro 748 prototype (G-APZV) was flown for the first time on 20 June 1960. Initial production models were the HS.748 Series 1, followed by the HS.748 Series 2 and HS.748 Series 2A, featuring uprated engines. Licence-production of Series 1s and 2s from 1961 was carried out by HAL in Kanpur, India, with a total of 72 aircraft delivered to the Indian Air Force. This figure includes 20 HAL-developed HAL (BAe) 748(M) dedicated military freighters with large cargo door, the final example being delivered in 1984. Persistent reports suggest that one Indian 748 has been converted to serve as an AEW testbed, with a rotodome above the rear fuselage. Eyewitnesses report seeing such an aircraft flying over Bangalore during 1990-92, presumably on test from HAL's nearby facility. Whether this aircraft is any more than an aerodynamic prototype is unknown.

From 1979, production commenced of a new basic model. Following the formation of British Aerospace, the designation became **BAe (HS) 748 Series 2B**. This featured uprated Dart turboprops for improved 'hot-and-high' performance, an extended span wing, modified tail surfaces and other refinements. The **BAe 748 Military Transport** version incorporated a reinforced floor and large rear freight door and could accommodate 58 troops, or 48 paratroops and dispatchers, or 24 stretchers and nine medical attendants.

The final production version was designated **BAe Super 748**. Based on the Series 2B, this model introduced significant new developments, including an advanced flight deck, Dart RDa.7 Mk 552 turboprops offering a 12 per cent reduction in fuel consumption and engine hush kits. British Aerospace also developed the **BAe 748 Coastguarder** dedicated maritime patrol aircraft, based on the BAe 748. This version was equipped for maritime surveillance, search and rescue and fishery protection, and had a moderate ASV/ASW capability. For these roles, it was fitted with a comprehensive avionics suite including search radar, high accuracy navigation aids (INS and Omega) with options for ECM, ESM, IFF and MAD gear. This version did not receive any orders, however.

OPERATORS

The Royal Air Force is among the armed forces which have procured the 748, operating it as the Andover (described separately). Production of the Super 748 variant ceased in 1988, by which time production of all series totalled 382, including licence-produced aircraft and Andovers. The BAe 748 is currently operated by the air forces of the following nations: Australia (10 Series 2, including two navigation trainers), the Royal Australian Navy (two operated as EW trainers),

Operating from Don Muang Airport alongside a very varied transport force are the two HS.748s of the Royal Thai Air Force.

Sanders Associates converted a single Royal Australian Navy HS.748 as an EW trainer in 1977. It now serves with HC-723 at Nowra.

British Aerospace (Avro/Hawker Siddeley) 748

Belgium (three Series 2A), Brazil (six Series 2 and six Series 2A, local designation C-91), Colombia (two Series 2A jointly operated with the airline SATENA, one example converted to Series 2B), Ecuador (five Series 2A operated jointly with TAME), Nepal (one ex-Royal Flight Series 2A), South Korea (two Series 2A), Sri Lanka (five ex-civil Series 2, including the Coastguarder demonstrator, reconfigured for the transport role), Tanzania (three Series 2A), and Thailand (five Series 2 and one Series 2A). The BAe 748 has been withdrawn in Argentina, Brunei, Venezuela and Zambia.

SPECIFICATION

British Aerospace (Avro/Hawker Siddeley) 748 Series 2B Military Transport

Wing: span 102 ft 5.5 in (31.23 m); aspect ratio 12.668; area 828.87 sq ft (77.00 m2)
Fuselage and tail: length 67 ft 0 in (20.42 m); height 24 ft 10 in (7.57 m); tailplane span 36 ft 0 in (10.97 m); wheel track 24 ft 9 in (7.54 m); wheel base 20 ft 8 in (6.30 m)
Powerplant: two Rolls-Royce Dart RDa.7 Mk 536-2

each rated at 2,280 ehp (1700 kW)
Weights: operating empty 25,730 lb (11671 kg); maximum take-off 46,500 lb (21092 kg) standard or 51,000 lb (23133 kg) optional
Fuel and load: internal fuel 1,441 Imp gal (1,730 US gal; 6550 litres); external fuel none; maximum payload 12,829 lb (5819 kg) standard or 17,270 lb (7833 kg) optional
Speed: cruising speed at optimum altitude 244 kt (281 mph; 452 km/h)
Range: 1,420 nm (1,645 miles; 2630 km) with maximum fuel and an 8,070-lb (3660-kg) payload, or

1,280 nm (1,474 miles; 2372 km) with maximum fuel and a 14,027-lb (6363-kg) payload, or 785 nm (904 miles; 1455 km) with maximum payload
Performance: maximum rate of climb at sea level 1,420 ft (433 m) per minute; service ceiling 25,000 ft (7620 m); take-off run 3,720 ft (1134 m) at maximum take-off weight; take-off distance to 50 ft (15 m) 3,800 ft (1158 m) at maximum take-off weight; landing distance from 50 ft (15 m) 2,050 ft (625 m) at normal landing weight; landing run 1,270 ft (387 m) at normal landing weight

---

British Aerospace (Avro/Hawker Siddeley) Andover

The **Andover** was the dedicated military assault transport version of the Avro 748, and was sufficiently redesigned to warrant allocation of the new type number **Avro 780**. It was designed to meet an RAF requirement for a STOL multi-role transport able to operate from rough airstrips or 300-yd (275-m) lengths of ploughed field or desert, even with obstacles on the approach. The fuselage was lengthened and the entire rear section was redesigned to incorporate a 'beaver tail' rear loading ramp, which also allowed loads to be air-dropped. Lightweight Hawker Siddeley Skydel removable roller track was provided to ease loading, and the new Dowty Rotol 'kneeling' main undercarriage allows the cabin floor 'sill' to be moved vertically or horizontally to align with the tail board of a vehicle loading freight. The main cabin could accommodate up to three Land Rovers, or a Land Rover and a Ferret armoured car, or alternatively could seat up to 58 troops, 40 paratroops or 24 stretchers.

Power was provided by a pair of 3,245-eshp (2420-kW) Rolls Royce Dart R.Da12 Mk 201C turboprops. The extra 2-ft 6-in (0.76-m) propeller diameter (by comparison with the 748) necessitated moving the engines further outboard, although overall wingspan was actually reduced by 3 in (7.6 cm). The upswept rear fuselage meant relocating the tail unit, and the tailplane gained dihedral. The Andover prototype (converted from the first Avro 748) made its maiden flight on 21 December 1963, and 31 were manufactured for the **RAF**'s Air Support Command. The aircraft proved rugged

and dependable, and was as a result extremely popular, serving with squadrons in the UK, Singapore and Aden.

The withdrawal from east of Suez reduced the Andover force to a single squadron, and the 1975 defence cuts led to the disbandment of this unit. Ten of the 29 survivors were sold to the **Royal New Zealand Air Force** (nine remain in use), five were relegated to ground training duties, and four were transferred to RAF Germany for communications use, three to the **MoD Procurement Executive** and six to No. 115 Squadron for calibration duties. A single aircraft was also used by No. 51 Squadron (the RAF's Elint unit) for trials for some years, before it too joined No. 115.

Four of No. 115 Squadron's aircraft were designated **Andover E.Mk 3**, and are fitted with a nose-mounted Milligan light (to enable engineers on the ground to calibrate ILS equipment). The E.Mk 3s received a new Litton Inertial Referenced Flight Inspection System during 1983, which cross-checks the changing sight angle of lights on the ground to work out the aircraft's glideslope, instead of relying on a ground party with theodolites. Three aircraft without Milligan lights were designated **Andover E.Mk 3A** and had a limited calibration fit, allowing them to inspect TACAN and radars, but not ILS systems. These aircraft would have had a wartime communications relay role. These three Andovers were reassigned to No. 32 Squadron for communications duties in late 1992. No.115 Sqn disbanded in October 1993 handing

over their role to a civilian contractor, a subsidiary of Hunting plc. The Andover E.Mk 3s have been retained and operate from East Midlands Airport. No. 32 Sqn's Andovers are slated for retirement during 1994.

Under Modification 207, two of No. 60 Squadron's Andovers had their forward freight doors removed and were fitted with an underfuselage camera, for an undisclosed reconnaissance role believed to be connected with flights along the Berlin corridor. They were then redesignated **Andover C.Mk 1(PR)**. One of these aircraft later passed to the A&AEE at Boscombe Down, and has been used for Open Skies arms limitation verification flights over the former USSR.

The RAF also received six Series 2 Avro 748s (XS789-XS794) under the designation Andover **CC.Mk 2** (though they had none of the features of 'real' Andovers) and these served with the Queen's Flight, at RAF Benson, and a variety of other VIP and communications units. Four survivors now fly with No. 32 Squadron at RAF Northolt, and a fifth is with the Defence Research Agency at Bedford. Another RAF 748 is also used by the DRA, this one a Series 1 previously operated by Smiths Industries.

SPECIFICATION

British Aerospace (Avro/Hawker Siddeley) Andover C.Mk 1
generally similar to the British Aerospace HS 748 Series 2B Military Transport except in the following particulars:

Wing: span 98 ft 0 in (29.87 m); aspect ratio 11.552; area 831.00 sq ft (77.20 m2)
Fuselage and tail: length 77 ft 1 in (23.75 m); height 29 ft 3 in (8.92 m); wheel base 23 ft 8 in (7.21 m)
Powerplant: two Rolls-Royce Dart RDa.12 Mk 201C each rated at 2,305 shp (1719 kW) without water/methanol injection and 2,970 shp (2214 kW) with water/methanol injection
Weights: basic empty 27,709 lb (12569 kg); operating empty 28,250 lb (12814 kg); maximum take-off 50,000 lb (22680 kg)
Fuel and load: internal fuel 1,441 Imp gal (1,730 US gal; 6550 litres) plus provision for 1,700 Imp gal (2,041 US gal; 7728 litres) of auxiliary fuel in fuselage tanks; maximum payload 14,750 lb (6691 kg)
Speed: cruising speed at 20,000 ft (6095 m) 224 kt (258 mph; 415 km/h)
Range: 1,020 nm (1,175 miles; 1891 km) with a 10,000-lb (4536-kg) payload or 325 nm (374 miles; 602 km) with maximum payload
Performance: maximum rate of climb at sea level 1,170 ft (357 m) per minute; service ceiling 24,000 ft (7315 m); take-off distance to 50 ft (15 m) 1,300 ft (369 m) at maximum take-off weight; landing distance from 50 ft (15 m) 1,300 ft (369 m) at normal landing weight

The Royal New Zealand Air Force's Andovers are split between five camouflaged tactical transports and four more distinguished looking VIP aircraft.

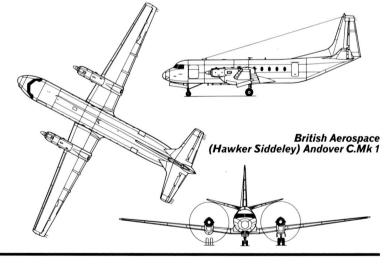

British Aerospace (Hawker Siddeley) Andover C.Mk 1

British Aerospace (Beagle/Scottish Aviation) Bulldog

Originally designed as a military trainer version of the civil Pup, the **Beagle Bulldog** was produced by Scottish Aviation (later BAe) from 1971 until 1982. An all-metal stressed-skin machine with fixed tricycle gear, the Bulldog has side-by-side dual controls, with rear space for an observer or a 220-lb (100-kg) load. The canopy slides to the rear, and other features include cockpit heating, electrically-driven slotted flaps, hydraulic wheel brakes (or optional skis), comprehensive avionics for communication and navigation, an optional glider tow hook and provision for rocket- and gun-pods.

All production Bulldogs have the same basic engine (though the AEIO-360 was offered for customers requiring 20 seconds of inverted flight at full power), driving a Hartzell constant-speed propeller. Four removable metal tanks in the wings hold 32 Imp gal (146 litres) of fuel. The Bulldog gained its popularity from a combination of low costs, robust simplicity and flawless handling in its primary training role.

The initial version was exported to **Malaysia** (15 **Bulldog Model 102**) and **Kenya** (five **Bulldog Model 103**). The chief order for this version was 78 placed by

Sweden, which designates the type as the **Sk 61**. The majority of these are operated by the Swedish army as the **Fpl 61**, as its fixed-wing training and liaison aircraft (though they were trialled with armament). Following plans to convert the army to a wholly rotary-wing force, army Bulldogs will be transferred to the Flygvapen to replace Saab Safirs. The Flygvapen already operates Bulldogs with its F5 flying school, and others are allocated to operational wings as liaison and IFR training aircraft.

In 1973 production switched to the **Bulldog Model 120**, with increased aerobatic

capability at maximum weight and a full clearance at increased weight. Orders for this comprised 130 **Bulldog Model 121** aircraft for the **RAF**, designated **Bulldog T.Mk 1**. The majority of the RAF's 118 surviving Bulldogs continue to serve with 15 University Air Squadrons (namely Aberdeen, Dundee and St Andrews; Birmingham; Bristol; Cambridge; East Lowlands; East Midlands; Glasgow and Strathclyde; Liverpool; London; Manchester; Northumbrian, Oxford; Queens; Southampton; Wales; Yorkshire), providing training to sponsored undergraduates and potential graduate entrants. Examples also fly with the College Air Squadron (Cranwell), Central Flying School (Scampton) and No.6 FTS (Finningley).

Exports include 12 **Bulldog Model 122**

aircraft for **Ghana**, 37 **Bulldog Model 123** aircraft for **Nigeria**, one **Bulldog Model 124** demonstrator and 22 **Bulldog Model 125** aircraft for **Jordan**, six **Bulldog Model 126** aircraft for **Lebanon**, nine **Bulldog Model 127** aircraft for **Kenya**, two **Bulldog Model 128** aircraft for **Hong Kong**, one **Bulldog Model 129** for a civil customer in **Venezuela**, and six **Bulldog Model 130** aircraft for **Botsawana**. In 1974 a retractable-gear **Bulldog Series 200** (**Bullfinch**) was flown, but this was not put into production. The type has since been withdrawn from service with the Royal Hong Kong Auxiliary Air Force and Botsawana. Malaysian Bulldogs have been relegated to the training of reserve pilots.

SPECIFICATION

British Aerospace (Beagle/Scottish Aviation) Bulldog T.Mk 1

Wing: span 33 ft 0 in (10.06 m); aspect ratio 8.4; area 129.40 sq ft (12.02 m²)

Fuselage and tail: length 23 ft 3 in (7.09 m); height 7 ft 5.75 in (2.28 m); tailplane span 11 ft 0 in (3.35 m); wheel track 6 ft 8 in (2.03 m); wheel base 4 ft 7 in (1.40 m)

Powerplant: one Textron Lycoming IO-360-A1B6 rated at 200 hp (149 kW)

Weights: empty 1,430 lb (649 kg); operating empty 1,475 lb (669 kg); normal take-off 2,238 lb (1015 kg) for aerobatics; maximum take-off 2,350 lb (1066 kg)

Fuel and load: internal fuel 32 Imp gal (38.4 US gal; 145.5 litres); external fuel none; provision for light armament

Speed: never exceed speed 209 kt (241 mph; 389 km/h); maximum level speed 'clean' at sea level 130 kt (150 mph; 241 km/h); maximum cruising speed at 4,000 ft (1220 m) 120 kt (138 mph; 222 km/h); economical cruising speed at 4,000 ft (1220 m) 105 kt (121 mph; 194 km/h)

Range: standard range 540 nm (622 miles; 1001 km)

Performance: maximum rate of climb at sea level 1,035 ft (315 m) per minute; service ceiling 16,000 ft (4875 m); take-off run 900 ft (274 m) at maximum take-off weight; take-off distance to 50 ft (15 m) 1,400 ft (427 m) at maximum take-off weight; landing distance from 50 ft (15 m) 1,190 ft (363 m) at normal landing weight; landing run 500 ft (152 m) at normal landing weight

g limits: -3 to +6 aerobatic and -1.8 to +4.4 utility

British Aerospace (Scottish Aviation) Bulldog T.Mk 1

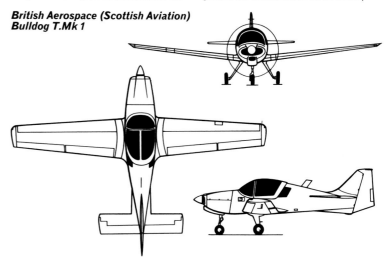

Most RAF Bulldogs serve with 16 University Air Squadrons training sponsored students and VR members, many of whom later join up.

British Aerospace (English Electric/BAC) Canberra

Britain's first jet bomber, the **Canberra**, was widely exported and was built under licence in Australia, and as the Martin B-57 in the USA. Australia, New Zealand, Ecuador, Venezuela, South Africa, Zimbabwe, France and Ethiopia have all retired their Canberras, but the type remains active in small numbers in **India**, **Peru**, **Argentina**, **Chile** and **Germany**, and in **Britain** with the RAF, Defence Research Agency and Flight Refuelling Ltd, mainly in second-line roles. The Royal Navy retired its last Canberras at the end of 1992.

The Canberra remains active in its country of birth, with several serving as testbeds and research aircraft with the Defence Research Agency now at Boscombe Down, and as target tugs/drone-launchers with Flight Refuelling Ltd at Llanbedr. Defence cuts at the end of the Cold War led to a rapid rundown in the Canberra force, which had stabilised at a full three squadrons, even though most airframes had been refurbished for service into the next century. Target facilities and ECM training is being taken over by cheaper-to-operate business jets, which will be unable to offer the Canberra's challenging handling characteristics and 'fast jet', high workload cockpit environment, which have made the type invaluable for upgrading young pilots who drop out of advanced fast jet training. Some **T.Mk 17**s and **T.Mk 17A**s are used for ECM training but are due to be retired by mid-1994, but five **PR.Mk 9**s will soldier on in the survey role into the next century, with three **T.Mk 4** dual control trainers and a pair of chaff-laying **PR.Mk 7**s.

In Peru and Argentina the Canberra remains active as a bomber, Peru having expanded its fleet to about 25 by purchasing five aircraft from South Africa. Chile and Germany both operate Canberras (two PR.Mk 9s and a single **B.Mk 2** respectively) in the survey role. The largest operator of the Canberra today is India, with about 45 aircraft still in use. A mix of **TT.Mk 4**s, **T.Mk 13**s, **B(I).Mk 12**s, **PR.Mk 57**s, **B(I).Mk 58**s, and **B(I).Mk 66**s equip No. 6 Squadron (in the anti-shipping and fleet requirements roles), No. 35 Squadron (in the ECM role) and No. 106

Squadron in the strategic reconnaissance and survey roles. No. 6 and No. 106 Squadrons each parent a target towing flight.

The prototype English Electric A1 made its maiden flight on 13 May 1949, and was followed by the production B.Mk 2 with 6,500-lb (28.9-kN) RA3 Avon Mk 101 engines. The T.Mk 4 was the training version of the B.Mk 2, lacking the latter aircraft's transparent nosecone and visual bombing system. With 7,500 lb st (33.36-kN) RA7 Avon Mk 109s and integral fuel tanks in the wings, the basic bomber became the **B.Mk 6**, and with an underfuselage gun pack, the **B(I).Mk 6**. The dedicated interdictor Canberra variant was the **B(I).Mk 8**, which was based on the B.Mk 6 but had a new nose, with the pilot sitting under a fighter-type canopy offset to port. Export versions of the Canberra B.Mk 2 included the **B.Mk 20**, **B.Mk 52**, **B.Mk 62**, and **B.Mk 82**, while the B(I).Mk 6 became the **B.Mk 56** and **B(I).Mk 66**. The B(I).Mk 8 was exported as the **B(I).Mk 12**, **B(I).Mk 58**, **B(I).Mk 68** and **B(I).Mk 88**. Export versions of the T.Mk 4 included the **T.Mk 13**, **T.Mk 21**, **T.Mk 64** and **T.Mk 84**.

The Canberra has also been used for photo reconnaissance duties, with a 14-in (35-cm) forward fuselage stretch aft of the cockpit to accommodate camera stations and with the bomb bay replaced by a separate flare bay and fuel tank. The basic RA3-engined recce aircraft was the **PR.Mk 3**, while the **PR.Mk 7** had RA7s and integral wing tanks. The PR.Mk 9 is a dedicated high-altitude version with 11,250-lb (50-kN) RA24 Avon Mk 206 engines and an extended-chord inner wing, and extended-span outer wing panels. The ailerons are hydraulically boosted and a new nose section is fitted, with an opening version of the B(I).Mk 8-style canopy for the pilot and with the navigator gaining access to his position via the hinged nose. The **PR.Mk 57** is an export version of the PR.Mk 7.

A plethora of variants was produced for other tasks, including Elint, the training of all-weather fighter crews and target facilities, while others were converted as unmanned target drones, and as test and research aircraft of every description.

With the rapid reduction in the RAF's Canberras (once thought to be ready to soldier on into the next century), only the PR.Mk 9 seems safe.

India's sizeable Canberra force has a more assured future with three units operating aircraft in the target-towing, electronic warfare and photo-reconnaissance roles. This Dayglo B(I).Mk 8 target tug (note black and yellow stripes underneath) performs a dirty, noisy cartridge start.

British Aerospace (English Electric/BAC) Canberra

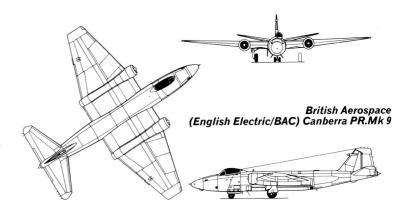

British Aerospace (English Electric/BAC) Canberra PR.Mk 9

SPECIFICATION

British Aerospace (English Electric/BAC) Canberra B(I).Mk 8

Wing: span 63 ft 11.5 in (19.50 m) without tip tanks and 65 ft 6 in (19.96 m) with tip tanks; aspect ratio 4.26; area 960.00 sq ft (89.19 m²)

Fuselage and tail: length 65 ft 6 in (19.96 m); height 15 ft 8 in (4.77 m); tailplane span 27 ft 5 in (8.36 m); wheel track 15 ft 9 in (4.80 m); wheel base 15 ft 2.75 in (5.64 m)

Powerplant: two Rolls-Royce Avon RA.7 Mk 109 each rated at 7,400 lb st (32.92 kN) dry

Weights: operating empty 27,950 lb (12678 kg); normal take-off 43,000 lb (19505 kg); maximum take-off 54,950 lb (24925 kg)

Fuel and load: internal fuel 2,457 Imp gal (2,951 US gal; 11170 litres); external fuel up to two 244-Imp gal (293-US gal; 1109-litre) wingtip tanks; maximum ordnance 8,000 lb (3629 kg)

Speed: maximum level speed 'clean' at 40,000 ft (12190 m) 470 kt (541 mph; 871 km/h) or at sea level 449 kt (517 mph; 832 km/h)

Range: ferry range 3,152 nm (3,630 miles; 5842 km); combat range 700 nm (806 miles; 1297 km) on a lo-lo-lo attack mission with maximum warload

Performance: maximum rate of climb at sea level 3,400 ft (1036 m) per minute; service ceiling 48,000 lb (14630 m); take-off distance to 50 ft (15 m) 6,000 ft (1829 m) at maximum take-off weight; landing distance from 50 ft (15 m) 3,900 ft (1189 m) at normal landing weight

---

British Aerospace (de Havilland/Hawker Siddeley) Dominie

Directly derived from one of the earliest production models of the de Havilland 125 (BAe 125), the **Dominie T.Mk 1** has been the **RAF**'s standard navigator trainer since 1966. Based on the Hawker Siddeley 125 Series 1A/B, the type was first flown on 30 December 1964. External changes included a ventral fairing extending forward of the wing, housing Doppler and Decca aerials. A revised cabin made provision for two students sitting in rearward-facing seats opposite an instructional console. The standard crew of six comprised a single pilot, two students and up to three supernumary crew members (instructors and pilot assister). The Dominie's navigation equipment included three types of communications, R/T, VOR/ILS, gyro-magnetic compass, weather radar, ground position indicator and facility for taking astro shots through a periscopic sextant.

Production of the Dominie totalled 20 aircraft, almost all of which have served with No. 6 FTS at Finningley. Initially supplementing the Vickers Varsity (withdrawn in 1976), the Dominie has accrued over 25 years' service. As the RAF has re-equipped with progressively complex aircraft, much of the equipment and techniques associated with Dominie training (originally optimised for V-Force backseaters) have

become increasingly unrepresentative, this problem being particularly acute with respect to low-level fast-jet navigator training.

To resolve this problem, the RAF initiated an update programme in 1993 involving a total of 11 aircraft. The programme is carried out by Thorn EMI in association with Marshall of Cambridge and involves installation of a Super Searcher maritime surveillance radar with associated radio, avionics and navigation mission computing systems improvements. The radar has been enhanced to provide a long/short-range ground-mapping capability at both high and low altitudes. The high-resolution radar, which is fitted with three-axis stabilisation, is unaffected by high angles of attack and rectifies a shortfall in the performance of previous Dominie equipment. The radar is integrated with tactical processing equipment and information is fed to multi-function, multi-colour displays in both cockpit and instructional installations. This enables other sensors to be incorporated, such as navaids, IFF, ESM, IRDS and acoustic devices; further extensions include facilities for datalink and surface-based command and control centres.

The update has also resulted in a rationalisation of the training programme. The normal crew complement of six or seven com-

The RAF's Dominie T.Mk 1 is derived from the HS.125 Srs 2, but with a restyled ventral fairing, originally housing Decca and Doppler.

prises two pilots, one senior instructor and three student navigators, with an additional air electronics officer when required. The updated Dominie is currently the common training vehicle for all RAF navigators, and flies an equal mix of high- and low-level training missions.

SPECIFICATIONS

British Aerospace (de Havilland/Hawker Siddeley) Dominie T.Mk 1

Wing: span 47 ft 0 in (14.33 m); aspect ratio 6.26; area 353.00 sq ft (32.79 m²)

Fuselage and tail: length 47 ft 5 in (14.45 m); height

16 ft 6 in (5.03 m); tailplane span 20 ft 0 in (6.10 m); wheel track 9 ft 2 in (2.80 m); wheel base 18 ft 8.5 in (5.70 m)

Powerplant: two Rolls-Royce (Bristol Siddeley) Viper Mk 301 each rated at 3,120 lb st (13.88 kN) dry

Weights: empty equipped 10,100 lb (4581 kg); maximum take-off 21,200 lb (9616 kg)

Fuel and load: internal fuel 1,025 Imp gal (1,231 US gal; 4660 litres); maximum ordnance none

Speed: maximum cruising speed at 25,000 ft (7620 m) 410 kt (472 mph; 760 km/h); economical cruising speed at 38,000 ft (11580 m) 365 kt (420 mph; 676 km/h)

Range: 1,162 nm (1,338 miles; 2153 km)

Performance: maximum rate of climb at sea level 2,000 ft (610 m) per minute; service ceiling 40,000 ft (12190 m)

British Aerospace Harrier GR.Mk 3/T.Mk 4

The **British Aerospace Harrier** was the world's first practical operational V/STOL strike fighter and was developed from six years of experience with the Hawker P.1127/Kestrel series of demonstrators. The first production **Harrier GR.Mk 1** made its maiden flight on 28 December 1967, entering service on 1 April 1969 with the No. 233 OCU at Wittering. Survivors were subsequently retrofitted with progressively uprated engines, resulting in the **Harrier GR.Mk 1A** (with 20,500-lb/91.2-kN thrust Pegasus Mk 102) and the **Harrier GR.Mk 3** (with 21,500-lb/95.6-kN thrust Pegasus Mk 103). A total of 118 single-seat Harriers (61 GR.Mk 1s, 17 GR.Mk 1As and 40 GR.Mk 3s) was acquired by the **RAF**.

From 1976, production GR.Mk 3s were fitted with a Marconi LRMTS (laser ranger and marked target seeker) contained in a 'thimble' nose fairing. A Marconi ARI 18223 E/J band radar warning receiver was added at the same time. A single oblique F95 70-mm camera was fitted and recce capability was further enhanced by an underfuselage camera pod. This 410-lb (186-kg) centreline pod contained a fan of four 70-mm F95 Mk 7 cameras and a single 127-mm F135 camera. No. IV Squadron had a 40 per cent commitment to recce operations.

Fourteen GR.Mk 3s were dispatched for Operation Corporate in 1982 and were fitted with radar transponders (identified by a nose bulged fairing and blade aerial). Self-

defence capability was enhanced by a Tracor AN/ALE-40 chaff/flare dispenser fitted in the rear fuselage and provision for AIM-9L AAMs on the outer two wing pylons. In 1984, Philips-MATRA Phimat chaff dispenser pods were also issued for outboard fitment. Following recapture of the Falkland Islands, a HarDet (Harrier Detachment), later renamed No. 1453 Flight, was established at Port Stanley airfield and assigned an air-defence role with AIM-9Ls, and was subsequently disbanded after the opening of Mount Pleasant airfield. The addition of four attrition replacements ordered for aircraft lost in the Falklands conflict brought total RAF single-seat Harrier procurement to 118.

Conversion of RAF units to Harrier GR.Mk 5/7s began in 1988, leaving only a few Mk 3s with No. 233 OCU (now renumbered as No. 20(R) Squadron) and No. 1417 Flight in Belize. The latter was the last front-line operator of the GR.Mk 3, bringing its aircraft home in July 1993. No. 20 (R) Sqn at Wittering maintain a handful into 1994, for instructor training and chase duties.

The first of two **Harrier T.Mk 2** prototypes was flown on 24 April 1969, and a total of 27 was delivered (23 RAF, 4 RN). To accommodate the second seat, some redesign was required, including repositioning of avionics and the port oblique camera.

The aft reaction control jet was housed in an extended fairing. The forward fuselage was extended by 3 ft 11 in (1.19 m), the ventral strake enlarged and fin moved rearwards and extended 11 in (28 cm) by a base insert. This was deemed insufficient for lateral stability at AoA exceeding 15° and the tip extension was increased to 18 in (46 cm).

These aircraft received the subsequent designations **T.Mk 2A** and **T.Mk 4** in parallel with the engine upratings fitted to the single-seaters. Lasers and RWRs were retrospectively installed on most. The LRMTS of some aircraft used exclusively for OCU training was removed, resulting in pointed noses and the designation **T.Mk 4A**. The T.Mk 4s are currently operated at Wittering by Nos 1 and 20 Squadrons. One of the latter unit's T.Mk 4s is temporarily assigned to the College of Aeronautics, Cranfield. A further two are on strength with the Strike/Attack Operational Evaluation Unit at Boscombe Down for weapons and systems testing, including the so-called 'Nightbird Harrier'. The RAF Germany Harrier squadrons (Nos 3 & IV) have no two-seaters permanently assigned.

One Harrier T.Mk 4 was converted at Cranfield to serve as a testbed for advanced control systems for VTOL aircraft, and was designated VAAC (Vectored-thrust Aircraft Advanced flight Control) Harrier. The aircraft is fitted with a Smiths Industries flight management computer based on equipment developed for the Airbus A310. Conventional controls are retained in the front seat,

No longer in front-line service, small numbers of GR.Mk 3s serve with No. 20(R) Sqn, the Harrier OCU, along with several T.Mk 4As.

with navigation controls in the rear seat linked by computer to the aircraft's control circuits, rather than being mechanically connected. The aircraft is operated by the DRA's Flight Systems Dept at Bedford.

SPECIFICATION

British Aerospace (Hawker Siddeley) Harrier GR.Mk 3

Wing: span 25 ft 3 in (7.70 m) with combat tips or 29 ft 8 in (9.04 m) with ferry tips; aspect ratio 3.175 with combat tips or 4.08 with ferry tips; area 201.10 sq ft (18.68 m²) with combat tips or 216.00 sq ft (20.07 m²)
Fuselage and tail: length 46 ft 10 in (14.27 m) with laser nose; height 11 ft 11 in (3.63 m); tailplane span 13 ft 11 in (4.24 m); outrigger track 22 ft 2 in (6.76 m); wheel base about 11 ft 4 in (3.45 m)
Powerplant: one Rolls-Royce Pegasus Mk 103 rated at 21,500 lb st (95.64 kN) dry
Weights: empty equipped 12,300 lb (5579 kg); operating empty 13,535 lb (6139 kg); normal take-off

23,500 lb (10660 kg); max take-off 25,200 lb (11431 kg)
Fuel and load: internal fuel 5,060 lb (2295 kg); external fuel up to two 330-Imp gal (396-US gal; 1500-litre) ferry tanks or two 190- or 100-Imp gal (228- or 120-US gal; 864- or 455-litre) drop tanks; maximum ordnance 5,000 lb (2268 kg) authorised or 8,000 lb (3269 kg) demonstrated
Speed: maximum level speed 'clean' at sea level 635 kt (730 mph); 1176 km/h)
Range: ferry range 1,850 nm (3,130 miles; 3428 km) with two ferry tanks; combat radius 360 nm (415 miles; 667 km) on a hi-lo-hi attack mission with a 4,400-lb (1996-kg) warload, or 200 nm (230 miles; 370 km) on a lo-lo-lo attack mission with a 4,400-lb (1996-kg) warload
Performance: maximum rate of climb at sea level 29,000 ft (8840 m) per minute; climb to 40,000 ft (12190 m) in 2 minutes 23 seconds after VTO; maximum speed in a dive, from height Mach 1.3: service ceiling 51,200 ft (15605 m); take-off run about 1,000 ft (305 m) at maximum take-off weight with a 5,000-lb (2268-kg) warload; landing run 0 ft (0 m) at normal landing weight

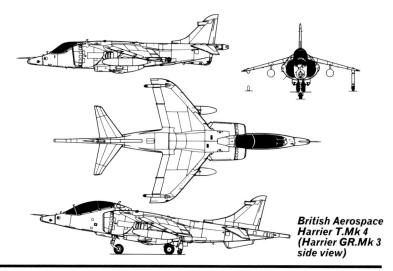

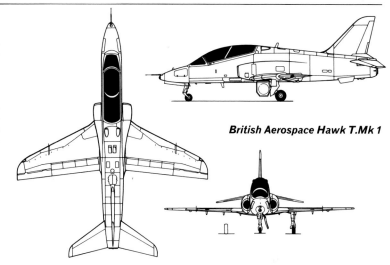

British Aerospace Harrier T.Mk 4 (Harrier GR.Mk 3 side view)

British Aerospace (Hawker Siddeley) Hawk

British Aerospace Defence
Warton Aerodrome, Preston,
Lancashire PR4 1AX, UK

When Air Staff Target (AST) 362 was issued in 1964 for a new RAF trainer to replace the Gnat, the requirement was only partially filled by a small number of two-seat Jaguars. By 1968 the shortfalll remained, and that year Hawker Siddeley Aviation initiated studies for a subsonic trainer, the original high performance criteria for such an aircraft having been waived in the interim. The company's private venture P.1182 (later HS.1182) evolved into an advanced trainer formalised as AST 397 in January 1970, HSA being awarded a production contract the following October. HSA chose a simple but robust low-wing layout for an aircraft of modest dimensions – although it was appreciably larger than the tiny Gnat – powered by a single Rolls-Royce Adour turbofan delivering 5,200 lb (23.1 kN) thrust. It was in cockpit design that the aircraft most impressed observers, this providing the instructor with forward visibility.

The name **Hawk** was chosen in 1973 and the first **Hawker Siddeley Hawk T.Mk 1** made its maiden flight on 21 August 1971. An indication of the integrity of the Hawk design was the fact that there were no prototypes or pre-production aircraft, and five of the six aircraft used for flight development were subsequently delivered to the RAF as part of the service order which totalled 175 T.Mk 1s.

Construction of the Hawk is entirely conventional. The fuselage incorporates skin, stringer and frame components. Its one-piece wing is attached by three bolts on either side, which places the associated structure under compression for integral strength. Inboard of the 'kink', the wing encloses an integral fuel tank and pick-up points for the main undercarriage. Three hardpoints were fitted as standard on RAF machines. The Hawk's RAF service began in April 1976 with delivery of the first production aircraft to No. 4 FTS at Valley. Students were given a total of 75 hours dual and solo instruction on the Hawk, about 10 hours being eliminated from the advanced stages as the new aircraft was able to undertake the weapons phase previously handled by the Hawker Hunter. Valley's initial course of Hawk pilots trained on the Hawk graduated in November 1977. BAe completed RAF deliveries by the end of 1976, other user units being No. 1 Tactical Weapons Unit at Brawdy, No. 2 TWU (Lossiemouth and later Chivenor), CFS (Valley and Scampton), ETPS (Boscombe Down) and the 'Red Arrows' aerobatic team based at Scampton.

In order to expand the Hawk's capability in the weapons training role the MoD con-

tracted for the modification of 88 aircraft in January 1983. The resulting aircraft was designated **Hawk T.Mk 1A**, the most significant difference to the earlier trainer variant being its ability to carry a pair of AIM-9L Sidewinder AAMs on underwing launchers. For close-in air combat or ground strafing, a single 30-mm gun pod could also be fitted under the fuselage. The T.Mk 1A conversion programme was completed in May 1986, and the aircraft were intended as limited-role point-defence fighters for emergency use in the UK Defence Region, and augment Phantoms and Tornados in the 'mixed fighter force'. In such a situation they would have been flown by instructors of No. 1 TWU at Brawdy as Nos 79 and 234 shadow squadrons and by No. 2 TWU at Chivenor as Nos 63 and 151 shadow squadrons. Under the Options for Change policy, No. 1 TWU was disbanded on 31 July 1992. The Hawk T.Mk 1s and 1As currently operate as advanced trainers and weapons trainers with, respectively, Nos 19 and 92 Reserve Squadrons (formerly Nos 63 and 151) of No. 7 FTS at Chivenor (to disband at the end of 1994), Nos 74 and 208 Sqn (formerly No. 234 Sqn) of No. 4 FTS at Valley, and with No. 100 Sqn at Finningley (formerly Wyton) for target towing. Hawks are also in use with the Central Flying School, the Red Arrows (RAF Scampton), and No. 6 FTS at RAF Finningley.

The Hawk's considerable development and export potential was realised in 1977

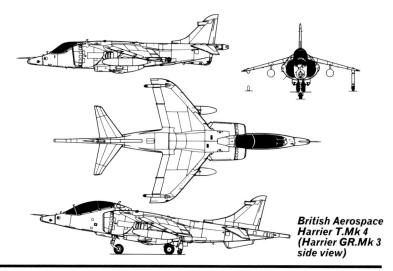

British Aerospace Hawk T.Mk 1

Several famous RAF squadron identities are allocated to Hawk units, such as 4 FTS, whose shadow identity is No. 74 ('Tiger') Sqn.

Finland's Fouga (Valmet) Magisters were replaced by BAe Hawk T.Mk 51s (also assembled largely by Valmet) as the primary jet trainer for the Suomen Ilmavoimat (Finnish air force). Aircraft are largely assigned to training units within each of the tactical wings, but some aircraft are tasked with a reconnaissance role using podded equipment, replacing early MiG-21F13s.

British Aerospace Hawk

when BAe introduced the **Series 50** upgrade for an initial sale to Finland of 50, deliveries beginning in December of that year. Forty-six were assembled by Valmet and a follow-on order for seven was placed in December 1990. In 1978, Kenya and Indonesia also purchased Hawks. The follow-on **Series 60** introduced an uprated Mk 861 Adour engine of 5,700 lb st (25.4 kN), additional wing leading-edge fences and four-position flaps to improve lift, anti-skid brakes and revised wheels and tyres. It was the subject of a series of foreign orders commencing in July 1982 to Zimbabwe, Dubai, Abu Dhabi, Kuwait, Saudi Arabia, Switzerland (19 assembled by F+W), and South Korea. ('long-nosed' version equipped with ranging radar and nosewheel steering).

OPERATORS

Abu Dhabi: Mk 60 – 16 (15 to Mk 63A)
Dubai: Mk 61 – 9
Finland: Mk 51 – 50, Mk 51A – 7
Indonesia: Mk 53 – 20
Kenya: Mk 52 – 12
Kuwait: Mk 64 – 12
Saudia Arabia: Mk 65 – 30
South Korea: Mk 67 – 20
Switzerland: Mk 66 – 20
United Kingdom: T.Mk 1 – 175 (88 to T.Mk 1A)
Zimbabwe: Mk 60 – 8, Mk 60A – 5

SPECIFICATION

British Aerospace (Hawker Siddeley) Hawk T.Mk 1
Wing: span 30 ft 9.75 in (9.39 m); aspect ratio 5.28; area 179.60 sq ft (16.69 m²)
Fuselage and tail: length 36 ft 7.75 in (11.17 m) excluding probe or 38 ft 11 in (11.86 m) including probe; height 13 ft 1.25 in (3.99 m); tailplane span 14 ft 4.75 in (4.39 m); wheel track 11 ft 5 in (3.47 m); wheel base 14 ft 9 in (4.50 m)
Powerplant: one Rolls-Royce/Turboméca Adour Mk 151-01 rated at 5,200 lb st (23.13 kN) dry
Weights: empty equipped 8,040 lb (3647 kg); normal take-off 11,100 lb (5035 kg); maximum take-off 12,566 lb (5700 kg)
Fuel and load: internal fuel 375 Imp gal (450 US gal; 1704 litres); external fuel up to two 190-, 130- or 100-Imp gal (228-, 156- or 120-US gal; 864-, 592- or 455-litre) drop tanks; maximum ordnance 1,500 lb (680 kg) in RAF service though a load of 6,800 lb (3084 kg) is possible
Speed: maximum level speed 'clean' at 11,000 ft (3355 m) 560 kt (645 mph; 1038 km/h)
Range: ferry range 1,670 nm (1,923 miles; 3094 km) with two drop tanks; standard range 1310 nm (1,509 miles; 2428 km); combat radius 300 nm (345 miles; 556 km) with a 5,600-lb (2540-kg) warload, or 560 nm (645 miles; 1038 km) with a 3,000-lb (1361-kg) warload
Performance: maximum rate of climb at sea level 9,300 ft (2835 m) per minute; climb to 30,000 ft (9145 m) in 6 minutes 6 seconds; service ceiling 50,000 ft (15240 m); take-off run 1,800 ft (549 m) at maximum take-off weight; landing run 1,600 ft (488 m) at normal landing weight
g limits: -4 to +8

Nine Hawk T.Mk 1As make up the 'Red Arrows', the RAF's display team. As AIM-9-capable aircraft, these Hawks have a wartime role as part of the RAF's mixed-fighter force.

British Aerospace **Hawk 100**

Having already developed an 'advanced' wing for the Hawk, BAe was able during the mid-1980s to offer the type as a relatively cheap dedicated dual-role weapon systems trainer and fully combat-capable ground attack aircraft based on the Hawk 60. Powerplant was an uprated RR Adour turbofan delivering 5,730 lb (25.5 kN) thrust compared to 5,700 lb (25.4 kN) thrust for the Hawk 60. Otherwise dimensionally similar, the new model had an overall wing span of 32 ft 7 in (9.93 m) as opposed to 30 ft 10 in (9.40 m) for all other Hawks. The extra 21 in (53 cm) was taken up by wingtip AIM-9 missiles and launch rails. Adapting the Hawk wing to take a full warload was aided by the modest degree of sweepback (21.5° at the leading edge), which meant that the additional pylons to accommodate heavier ordnance loads necessary for the ground attack role did not affect the aircraft's centre of gravity. With the addition of an elongated nose housing an optional FLIR and/or laser sensors, an advanced cockpit with multi-functional displays and HOTAS, plus more sophisticated avionics to exploit its enhanced combat potential, the resulting **BAe Hawk 100** (a converted development airframe) first flew in October 1987. The wing, which is stressed for six ordnance pylons enabling up to a maximum of 6,614 lb (3000 kg) of stores to be carried, incorporates combat manoeuvre flaps. As well as wingtip AAMs, a single 30-mm ADEN gun pod is an optional fitting on the fuselage centreline in place of a further stores station.

Abu Dhabi was the initial customer for the Series 100 (known as the **Series 102** with RWR, wingtip launch rails and laser designator), with 18 aircraft. **Oman** ordered four **Series 103**s in July 1990, and in December that year **Malaysia** ordered 10 Hawk **Series 108**s, the first example of which was handed over in February 1994.

South Korean aircraft are a Mk 60/100 hybrid which combines the avionics and systems improvements of the Hawk 100, with the basic airframe of the Hawk 60 trainer.

The most substantial order for the Hawk Series 100 came from **Saudi Arabia,** which under the post-Gulf War Al-Yamamah II contract signed for approximately 60 Hawks. **Brunei** has also ordered 19 aircraft, and **Indonesia** 12.

SPECIFICATION

British Aerospace Hawk Mk 100 (Enhanced Ground Attack Hawk)
Wing: span 30 ft 9.75 in (9.39 m) with normal tips or 32 ft 7.875 in (9.94 m with tip-mounted AIM-9 Sidewinder AAMs); aspect ratio 5.28; area 179.60 sq ft (16.69 m²)
Fuselage and tail: length 38 ft 4 in (11.68 m) excluding probe or 40 ft 9 in (12.42 m) including probe; height 13 ft 1.25 in (3.99 m); tailplane span 14 ft 4.75 in (4.39 m); wheel track 11 ft 5 in (3.47 m); wheel base 14 ft 9 in (4.50 m)
Powerplant: one Rolls-Royce/Turboméca Adour Mk 871 rated at 5,845 lb st (26.00 kN) dry
Weights: empty 9,700 lb (4400 kg); normal take-off about 11,350 lb (5148 kg); maximum take-off 20,061 lb (9100 kg)
Fuel and load: internal fuel 2,875 lb (1304 kg); external fuel up to 2,055 lb (932 kg) in two 190-, 130- or 100-Imp gal (228-, 156- or 120-US gal; 864-, 592- or 455-litre) drop tanks; maximum ordnance 6,614 lb (3000 kg)
Speed: never exceed speed 575 kt (661 mph; 1065 km/h) corresponding to Mach 0.87 at sea level and Mach 1.2 above 17,000 ft (5180 m); maximum level speed 'clean' at 36,000 ft (10975 m) 560 kt (645 mph; 1038 km/h)
Range: ferry range more than 1,400 nm (1,612 miles; 2594 km) with two 190-Imp gal (228-US gal; 864-litre) drop tanks; combat radius 660 nm (760 miles; 1223 km) on a hi-lo-hi attack mission with two 1,000-lb (454-kg) bombs, or 275 nm (317 miles; 510 km) on a hi-lo-hi attack mission with seven BL755 cluster bombs, or 140 nm (161 miles; 259 km) on a hi-hi-hi CAP with one 30-mm cannon and two AIM-9 Sidewinder AAMs for a loiter of 3 hours 30 minutes
Performance: maximum rate of climb at sea level 11,800 ft (3597 m) per minute; climb to 30,000 ft (9145 m) in 7 minutes 30 seconds; service ceiling 44,500 ft (13545 m); take-off run 2,100 ft (640 m) at maximum take-off weight; landing run 1,980 ft (605 m) at maximum landing weight

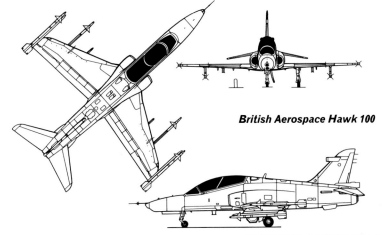

British Aerospace Hawk 100

British Aerospace Hawk 200

The international success of the two-seat Hawk models led British Aerospace to develop a single-seat variant which would attract new customers, particularly the smaller air arms requiring a relatively cheap air superiority fighter and ground attack aircraft. The BAe Hawk 200 is said to represent a far more cost-effective package in the long term, compared to the short-term option of continual refurbishment of older aircraft. A single-seater is more practical and desirable in some respects, not least because there is simply not a pool of trained navigators to occupy second seats.

By redesigning the Hawk's forward fuselage to accommodate a single cockpit, and adding a modern radar, there was still room enough to fit a pair of integral 25-mm ADEN cannon under the cockpit floor. These new guns represent a significant increase in combat capability. A seven-station wing (including wingtip AAM launchers) enables the carriage of up to 6,614 lb (3000 kg) of stores, the same as that of the Hawk 100. Constructed of conventional aluminium alloy and having about 80 per cent commonality with the two-seat models, the Hawk 200 is also powered by a single Adour Mk 871 turbofan. Even with additional equipment to tailor it for a multi-mission combat task, the aircraft has a maximum take-off weight of less than 21,000 lb (9527 kg).

The Westinghouse APG-66H radar is a multi-mode, modified version of that fitted in the F-16. With his seat set further aft than the forward seat position of the other Hawks, the pilot faces a main instrument panel which includes a comms/navigation integration panel, HUD, a multi-function CRT display, a radar display configured for the most modern symbology and a RHAW receiver. The Hawk 200 demonstrator (ZG200) made its maiden flight on 19 May 1986. Two months into the flight test programme this aircraft was destroyed in a crash, killing test pilot 'Jim' Hawkins. The probable cause of the crash was determined as pilot disorientation rather than any inherent fault, which had made 28 flights before it was lost. The second Hawk 200 (ZH200) flew on 24 April 1987. Unlike the first aircraft, ZH200 was fitted with full avionics (but no radar) and, later, a number of small but significant airframe revisions were made.

To counteract any tendency for the tailplane of the Hawk 200 to stall, a condition belatedly revealed on the trainer in 1975, the aircraft eventually received the fuselage-mounted tailplane vanes, or SMURFs (Side-Mounted Unit, horizontal tail Root Fins) developed for the US Navy's T-45 Goshawk trainer. These vanes throw a vortex over the tailplane to prevent undue travel caused by downwash from the flaps when the aircraft is in the low-speed configuration. In addition, an RWR was fitted to the fin leading edge, and the rear fuselage brake chute 'box' was deepened to house a chaff/flare dispenser and rearward-facing RWR antenna. The first APG-66-equipped Hawk 200RDA (Radar Development Aircraft) flew on 13 February 1992.

Oman became the launch customer for the Hawk 200 when 12 aircraft were ordered on 31 July 1990 as Series 203s, primarily to replace ageing Hunters. Malaysia followed suit on 10 December 1990 with an order for 18 aircraft identified as Series 208s. The Malaysian buy is for a mix of Series 100 and 200 aircraft but became embroiled in controversy after UK press speculation regarding the support of the deal with economic assistance for the controversial Pergau dam project. The first aircraft (a Series 100) was delivered in February 1994. Saudi Arabia's Al Yamamah II order may include an unconfirmed number of single-seaters within an overall buy of approximately 60 Hawks. Saudi aircraft would be APG-66H-equipped Hawk Series 205s. The Indonesian Hawk buy, of June 1993, combines both two-seat aircraft with 12 Hawk 200s reaching a confirmed total of 24 aircraft. It has been suggested that this number could rise to over 90.

Despite a slow start, hampered by the loss of this, the prototype, sales of the Hawk 200 are now building.

SPECIFICATION

British Aerospace Hawk Mk 200

Wing: span 30 ft 9.75 in (9.39 m) with normal tips or 32 ft 7.875 in (9.94 m) with tip-mounted AIM-9 Sidewinder AAMs; aspect ratio 5.28; area 179.60 sq ft (16.69 m²)

Fuselage and tail: length 37 ft 2 in (11.33 m) without probe; height 13 ft 8 in (4.16 m); tailplane span 14 ft 4.75 in (4.39 m); wheel track 11 ft 5 in (3.47 m); wheel base 11 ft 8 in (3.56 m)

Powerplant: one Rolls-Royce/Turboméca Adour Mk 871 rated at 5,845 lb st (26.00 kN) dry

Weights: basic empty 9,810 lb (4450 kg); normal take-off 16,565 lb (7514 kg); maximum take-off 20,061 lb (9100 kg)

Fuel and load: internal fuel 3,000 lb (1361 kg); external fuel up to 4,080 lb (1851 kg) in three 190-, 130- or 100-Imp gal (228-, 156- or 120-US gal; 864-, 592- or 455-litre) drop tanks; maximum ordnance 7,700 lb (3493 kg)

Speed: never exceed speed 575 kt (661 mph; 1065 km/h) corresponding to Mach 0.87 at sea level and Mach 1.2 above 17,000 ft (5180 m); maximum level speed 'clean' at sea level 549 kt (632 mph; 1017 km/h); maximum cruising speed at sea level 550 kt (633 mph; 1019 km/h); economical cruising speed at 41,000 ft (12495 m) 430 kt (495 mph; 796 km/h)

Range: ferry range 1,950 nm (2,244 miles; 3610 km) with three drop tanks, or 482 nm (554 miles; 892 km) on internal fuel; combat radius 666 nm (767 miles; 1234 km) on a hi-lo-hi anti-ship mission with one Sea Eagle missile and two drop tanks, or 862 nm (993 miles; 1598 km) on a hi-hi-hi reconnaissance mission with one reconnaissance pod and two drop tanks, or 510 nm (586 miles; 945 km) on a lo-lo-lo reconnaissance mission with one reconnaissance pod and two drop tanks, or 510 nm (587 miles; 945 km) on a hi-lo-hi battlefield interdiction mission with a 3,000-lb (1361-kg) warload, or 104 nm (120 miles; 192 km) on a lo-lo-lo close support mission with five 1,000-lb (454-kg) and four 500-lb (227-kg) bombs, or 550 nm (633 miles; 1018 km) on a hi-hi-hi airspace denial mission with two AIM-9 Sidewinder AAMs and two drop tanks for a loiter of 1 hour, or 100 nm (115 miles; 185 km) on a hi-hi-hi airspace denial mission with two AIM-9 Sidewinder AAMs and two drop tanks for a loiter of 3 hours 30 minutes, or 720 nm (828 miles; 1333 km) on a hi-hi-hi interception mission with two AIM-9 Sidewinder AAMs and two drop tanks

Performance: maximum rate of climb at sea level 11,510 ft (3508 m) per minute; service ceiling 45,000 ft (13715 m); take-off run 2,070 ft (630 m) 'clean' or 5,200 ft (1585 m) with maximum warload; take-off distance to 50 ft (15 m) 7,000 ft (2134 m) with maximum warload; landing distance from 50 ft (15 m) 2,800 ft (854 m) at 10,030 lb (4550 kg) with brake chute or 4,100 ft (1250 m) at 10,030 lb (4550 kg) without brake chute; landing run 1,960 ft (598 m) at normal landing weight

g limits: -4 to +8

British Aerospace Hawk 200

British Aerospace (Hawker/Hawker Siddeley) Hunter

British Aerospace Defence
Dunsfold Aerodrome, Godalming,
Surrey GU8 4BS, UK

The Hawker Hunter was originally designed as a day fighter replacement for the Gloster Meteor in RAF service, but was later developed to fulfil the ground attack role. The prototype first flew on 20 July 1951, giving Britain its first indigenous swept-wing fighter, and giving young RAF pilots an aircraft that was the equal to anything in the world. Production eventually reached 1,927, including some licence-production in the Low Countries. In the hands of a skilled pilot, the Hunter remained a competitive fighter well into the 1970s, with Indian, Jordanian and Iraqi pilots downing more modern fighter opponents when they took the Hunter to war.

With the Hunter F.Mk 6 (and numerous export equivalents), the Hunter received the more powerful 200 series Avon engine, an all-flying tail, and a dogtooth wing leading edge. The externally similar FGA.Mk 9 was designed from the outset as a fighter-bomber, with provision for a greater underwing weapon load, including up to four fuel tanks. The new variant (which spawned more export variants) received a strengthened landing gear and a brake chute to cope with the higher weights. A fighter reconnaissance variant, with a fan of forward- and sideways-looking oblique cameras in the nose, was closely based on the FGA.Mk 9, and designated FR.Mk 10. A handful of similar aircraft were delivered to export customers.

India's sole remaining Hunter squadron, No. 20 Sqn 'The Thunderbolts', functions as a lead-in training unit and also fields the 'Thunderbolts' aerobatic team.

British Aerospace (Hawker/Hawker Siddeley) Hunter

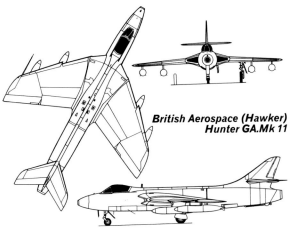

British Aerospace (Hawker) Hunter GA.Mk 11

Switzerland has long been the world's most active Hunter user, but the fighter's long career largely comes to an end in 1994. A replacement is due in the shape of the F/A-18.

Single-seat Hunters (most of them based on the FGA.Mk 9) remain in service in **Switzerland**, **Chile** and **Oman**, and as advanced trainers in **India**. In 1993 Switzerland began withdrawing Hunters in large numbers, while Oman's aircraft may have a limited service life once Hawk 200s are delivered. **Singapore** retains its Hunters, in flyable storage, while Chile is actively seeking a replacement. A handful of Hunters may also remain in service in **Zimbabwe**. The Hunter's original strengths remain important, and operators still prize its straightforward handling characteristics, easy maintenance, turn performance and powerful built-in armament of four 30-mm ADEN cannon. These are mounted in a pack, with their 540 rounds of ammunition, which can be replaced as a unit in minutes, allowing very quick turnaround times. All current front-line Hunters have been modernised with radar warning receivers and

provision for AIM-9 Sidewinder AAMs, and most also have chaff/flare dispensers and modern avionics. Swiss Hunters are compatible with a variety of modern air-to-ground weapons, including the AGM-65.

RAF two-seaters were designated **T.Mk 7** and were followed by a variety of **T.Mk 8** sub-variants for the RN. The last four RAF T.Mk 7s (used for training Buccaneer aircrew) were retired with the disbandment of No. 208 Sqn, on 31 March 1994. Seven Hunter **GA.Mk 11**s remain in use with the **Royal Navy**'s Fleet Requirements and Air Directions Unit (FRADU) in the target facilities role. These are based on the 'small-bore' Avon Mk 113-powered F.Mk 4. FRADU is also responsible for the eight surviving Hunter T.Mk 8Cs, which were shared with No. 899 Sqn until October 1993. A single Hunter FGA.9 serves with the A&AEE at Boscombe Down, largely for spray tank trials, and also to keep RNR pilots current. The

two DRA T.Mk 7s have also moved to Boscombe from Farnborough, joining T,Mk 7s used by the ETPS for inverted spinning. A single T.Mk 8M survives with BAe Dunsfold.

Most export two-seaters have the 'big bore' Avon 200 series engine, and small numbers remain in service with all users.

SPECIFICATION

British Aerospace (Hawker/Hawker Siddeley) Hunter FGA.Mk 9
Wing: span 33 ft 8 in (10.26 m); aspect ratio 3.25; area 349.00 sq ft (32.42 m2)
Fuselage and tail: length 45 ft 10.5 in (13.98 m); height 13 ft 2 in (4.01 m); tailplane span 11 ft 10 in (3.61 m); wheel track 14 ft 9 in (4.50 m); wheel base 15 ft 9 in (4.80 m)
Powerplant: one Rolls-Royce Avon RA.28 Mk 207 rated at 10,150 lb st (45.15 kN) dry
Weights: empty equipped 14,400 lb (6532 kg); normal

take-off 18,000 lb (8165 kg); maximum take-off 24,600 lb (11158 kg)
Fuel and load: internal fuel 3,144 lb (1426 kg); external fuel up to two 230 or 100-Imp gal (276- or 120-US gal; 1045- or 455-litre) drop tanks; maximum ordnance 7,400 lb (3357 kg)
Speed: maximum level speed 'clean' at 36,000 ft (10975 m) 538 kt (620 mph; 978 km/h) or at sea level 616 kt (710 mph; 1144 km/h); maximum cruising speed at 36,000 ft (10975 m) 481 kt (554 mph; 892 km/h); economical cruising speed at optimum altitude 399 kt (460 mph; 740 km/h)
Range: ferry range 1,595 nm (1,840 miles; 2961 km) with two drop tanks; combat radius 385 nm (443 miles; 713 km) on a hi-lo-hi attack mission with typical warload and two drop tanks
Performance: maximum rate of climb at sea level about 8,000 ft (2438 m) per minute; service ceiling 50,000 ft (15240 m); take-off run 2,100 ft (640 m) at normal take-off weight; take-off distance to 50 ft (15 m) 3,450 ft (1052 m) at normal take-off weight; landing run 3,150 ft (960 m) at normal landing weight

---

BAe (Hunting/BAC) Jet Provost

The **Percival** (later **Hunting Percival**) **P.84 Jet Provost** was a development of the Provost piston-engined trainer. Intended as a minimum-change private venture, the Jet Provost was in fact largely a redesigned aircraft. Its maiden flight took place on 26 June 1954 and was followed by nine production aircraft (**Jet Provost T.Mk 1**) and a single **Jet Provost T.Mk 2**. This version introduced a 1,753-lb (7.8-kN) Viper ASV.8 engine and shortened undercarriage. Provision was also made for wingtip tanks, pylons and two nose machine-guns.

From 1958 Hunting Aircraft delivered 201 **T.Mk 3** trainers with Martin-Baker ejection

seats, a clear-view canopy, tip tanks and updated avionics. BAC, which took over Hunting, continued development by fitting the much more powerful Viper 11 engine, rated at 2,500 lb (11.1 kN) thrust. One hundred and ninety-eight of the resulting **Jet Provost T.Mk 4** version were delivered to the **RAF** in 1961-64. Emphasis on high-altitude sorties had highlighted the need for cockpit pressurisation. This requirement led to the **Jet Provost T.Mk 5**, first flown on 28 February 1967, an almost completely redesigned T.Mk 4. The new front fuselage incorporated a pressurised cabin, a redesigned windscreen with sliding canopy

and a lengthened nose. A redesigned wing with a fatigue life of 5,000 hours permitted an increased internal fuel capacity. Provision was also made for wingtip tanks and underwing weapons load . These modifications led to a weight increase of more than 1,000 lb (454 kg), and a reduction in performance. BAC delivered 110 of this final version.

By the mid-1970s, the 'high performance' T.Mk 4s were phased out from the training role with exhausted airframe lives. A small number served until 1988 on ATC and FAC training. In 1973 BAC began conversion of 70 T.Mk 3s and 107 T.Mk 5s to **T.Mk 3A** and **T.Mk 5A** standard. This involved installation of VOR and DME with modifications to achieve cockpit commonality. Both are distinguished by a small 'hook' aerial at the extreme nose. Many T.Mk 5As have been further modified by the addition of lower forward fuselage strakes, in place of tip tanks. Such aircraft were loaned to units (chiefly Phantom) for spin training. The (unofficial) designation **Jet Provost T.Mk 5B** was given to aircraft equipped with tip-tanks for navigator training at No. 6 FTS. The last four RAF Jet Provosts were retired on 20 September 1993 from 6 FTS, giving way to the Shorts Tucano. One T Mk 5 remains in the hands of the ETPS at Boscombe Down.

Exports comprised 22 **Jet Provost T.Mk 51** trainers based on the T.Mk 3 but with weapons for **Sri Lanka**, **Kuwait** and the **Sudan**, 43 **Jet Provost T.Mk 52** trainers based on the T.Mk 4 for **Iraq**, **South Yemen**, the **Sudan** and **Venezuela**, and five **Jet Provost T.Mk 55**

No. 1 FTS flew its last 'JP' course in June 1993, ending their 33-year association. No. 6 FTS followed.

trainers based on the T.Mk 5 for the Sudan. The Jet Provost has been withdrawn by all foreign operators. Venezuelan Jet Provosts were replaced by a mid-1984 EMBRAER Tucano order. Three Sudanese Jet Provost T.Mk 55s are reported to remain but are believed to be non-serviceable.

SPECIFICATION

British Aerospace (Hunting/BAC) Jet Provost T.Mk 5
Wing: span 35 ft 4 in (10.77 m) without tip tanks and 36 ft 11 in (11.25 m) with tip tanks; aspect ratio 5.84; area 213.70 sq ft (19.85 m2)
Fuselage and tail: length 33 ft 7.5 in (10.25 m); height 10 ft 2 in (3.10 m); tailplane span 13 ft 6 in (4.11 m); wheel track 10 ft 8.9 in (3.27 m); wheel base 9 ft 7.4 in (2.93 m)
Powerplant: one Rolls-Royce (Bristol Siddeley) Viper Mk 202 rated at 2,500 lb st (11.12 kN) dry
Weights: empty equipped 4,888 lb (2271 kg); normal take-off 7,629 lb (3460 kg); maximum take-off 9,200 lb (4173 kg)
Fuel and load: internal fuel 262 Imp gal (315 US gal; 1191 litres) plus provision for 192 Imp gal (230.5 US gal; 873 litres) in two non-jettisonable tip tanks; external fuel none; maximum ordnance none
Speed: maximum level speed 'clean' at 25,000 ft (7620 m) 382 kt (440 mph; 708 km/h) and at sea level 355 kt (409 mph; 658 km/h)
Range: ferry range 782 nm (901 miles; 1450 km)
Performance: maximum rate of climb at sea level 4,000 ft (1219 m) per minute; service ceiling 36,750 ft (11200 m); take-off run 1,340 ft (408 m) at normal take-off weight; take-off distance to 50 ft (15 m) 2,070 ft (631 m) at normal take-off weight; landing distance from 50 ft (15 m) 2,560 ft (780 m) at normal landing weight; landing run 1,740 ft (530 m) at normal landing weight

British Aerospace (Handley Page/Scottish Aviation) Jetstream

Jetstream Aircraft
Prestwick Intl Airport
Ayrshire KA9 2RW, UK

The original prototype of the **Handley Page H.P.137 Jetstream** flew on 18 August 1967. A pressurised third-level and executive transport, it featured a circular-section fuselage offering stand-up headroom and large elliptical passenger windows. Powered by two 965-shp (720-kW) Turboméca Astazou XVI turboprops, it had a maximum weight of 12,500 lb (5670 kg) and could seat up to 18 and cruise at 241 kt (278 mph; 447 km/h). The factory was in full production when the firm went bankrupt in 1970, but many Jetstreams were completed by Scottish Aviation, among them 26 ordered by the **RAF** as **Jetstream T.Mk 1** MEPTs (multi-engined pilot trainers). The first was delivered to No. 5 FTS in June 1973. Policy then changed and the aircraft were stored during 1974.

Following their 1977 restoration to service after storage, 12 aircraft were returned to the RAF. Eleven Jetstream T.Mk 1s are currently on strength with No. 45(R) Sqn (No. 6FTS) at Finningley and are used in the multi-engine training role for pilots destined for tankers and transports. Fourteen of the remaining RAF aircraft were transferred to the **Fleet Air Arm** in 1978, and were converted to **Jetstream T.Mk 2** standard. These aircraft are similar in configuration to the T.Mk 1, but are equipped with MEL E.190 nose radar (used in weather and mapping modes) for observer training.

After Scottish Aviation was absorbed into BAe the decision was taken in 1978 to develop an improved version of the Jetstream. The resulting **BAe Jetstream Mk 31**, the first production example of which flew on 28 March 1980, introduced 900-shp (671-kW) Garrett TPE 331 turboprop engines, driving four-bladed Dowty Rotol propellers. This variant offered field performance and improved payload capability superior to the previous Astazou-powered versions. The Jetstream Mk 31 has

proved commercially successful, with 220 deliveries by late 1991. With numerous interior configurations available, the Jetstream is an ideal candidate for various paramilitary roles such as casevac, airfield calibration and patrolling of economic exclusion zones.

The Fleet Air Arm is one of two military customers which operate specialist applications versions of the Jetstream Mk 31, procuring four **Jetstream T.Mk 3** trainers for training helicopter observers in 1986. These are operated alongside the T.Mk 2 variant by No. 750 Squadron at RNAS Culdrose. A totally updated aircraft, the T.Mk 3 features eyebrow windows above the flight deck windscreen to improve all-round view. The interior is equipped with two observer training consoles with radar indicator, Doppler and TANS computer. A Racal ASR.360 multi-mode search radar is mounted in a ventral blister. The remaining customer, the **Royal Saudi Air Force**, took delivery in 1987 of two Jetstream Mk 31 navigator trainers equipped with Tornado IDS avionics. One aircraft has since been lost on approach to Dhahran in 1989.

SPECIFICATION

British Aerospace (Handley Page/Scottish Aviation) Jetstream T.Mk 1
Wing: span 52 ft 0 in (15.85 m); aspect ratio 10.0; area 270.00 sq ft (25.08 m²)
Fuselage and tail: length 47 ft 1.5 in (14.37 m); height 17 ft 5.5 in (5.32 m); tailplane span 21 ft 8 in (6.60 m); wheel track 19 ft 6 in (5.94 m); wheel base 15 ft 1 in (4.60 m)
Powerplant: two Turboméca Astazou XVID each rated at 681 kW (913 shp)
Weights: basic empty 7,683 lb (3485 kg); maximum take-off 12,566 lb (5700 kg)
Fuel and load: internal fuel 384 Imp gal (461 US gal; 1745 litres); external fuel none
Speed: never exceed speed 300 kt (345 mph; 555 km/h);

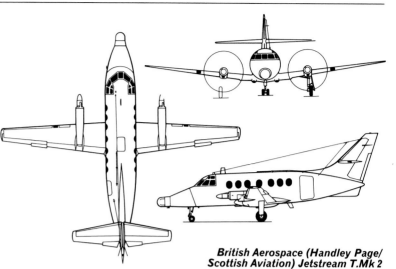

British Aerospace (Handley Page/ Scottish Aviation) Jetstream T.Mk 2

The Astazou-powered Jetstreams of No. 6 FTS (45 (Reserve) Sqn) provide multi-engined/ training for the RAF.

maximum level and maximum cruising speed 'clean' at 10,000 ft (3050 m) 245 kt (282 mph; 454 km/h); economical cruising speed at 15,000 ft (4575 m) 234 kt (269 mph; 433 km/h)
Range: 1,200 nm (1,382 miles; 2224 km)
Performance: maximum rate of climb at sea level

2,500 ft (762 m) per minute; service ceiling 25,000 ft (7620 m); take-off run 1,900 ft (579 m) at maximum take-off weight; take-off distance to 50 ft (15 m) 2,500 ft (762 m) at maximum take-off weight; landing distance from 50 ft (15 m) 2,310 ft (702 m) at normal landing weight

British Aerospace (Hawker Siddeley) Nimrod

The **Nimrod** began life as the **Hawker Siddeley 801**, a maritime reconnaissance derivative of the de Havilland Comet intended as a replacement for **RAF Coastal Command**'s ageing fleet of piston-engined Shackletons. Development began in 1964, and two unsold Comet 4Cs were converted to serve as prototypes. A MAD 'stinger' was added to the tailcone, a search radar was added in the nose, and a fin-tip radome ('football') was fitted to

While the Nimrod fleet is progressing towards retirement, it remains probably the world's most capable ASW aircraft.

accommodate ESM equipment. A new ventral weapons pannier was added beneath the cabin, giving a distinctive 'double-bubble' cross-section, these changes necessitating an increase in fin area. The first prototype was powered by the production Nimrod's intended Rolls-Royce Spey engines and made its maiden flight on 23 May 1967, serving as an aerodynamic testbed for airframe/engine integration. The second retained Avons and flew on 31 July, serving as the avionics development aircraft.

The first of 46 production **MR.Mk 1**s flew on 28 June 1968, entering service with No. 236 OCU in October 1969, eventually equipping five squadrons, one based at RAF

Luqa, Malta. The British withdrawal from Malta rendered the last batch of eight Nimrods surplus to requirements, although they could usefully have been used to spread hours more evenly across the fleet, extending the Nimrod's life. Five were delivered to the RAF, and the others were retained by BAe for trials, but their useful life was short, seven of them being selected for conversion to **AEW.Mk 3** standards, along with four earlier **MR.Mk 1**s. All of these airframes were effectively wasted, since the Nimrod AEW.Mk 3 never entered productive service, defeated by technical problems, and all but one were scrapped (the survivor becoming an instructional airframe).

From 1975 the 35 remaining MR.Mk 1s were upgraded to **MR.Mk 2** configuration, the first MR.Mk 2 being redelivered to the RAF in August 1979. The MR.Mk 2 had a completely new avionics and equipment suite, in which all major sensors and equipment items were changed. The aircraft received a new GEC central tactical system, based on a new computer and three separate processors for navigation systems, radar and acoustic sensors. The old ASV-21D radar is replaced by a Thorn EMI Searchwater, which now has a colour display. The acoustics system is compatible with BARRA, SSQ-41 and SSQ-53, TANDEM, and Ultra active and passive sonobuoys. Communications equipment is similarly upgraded.

The addition of inflight-refuelling probes (initially to 16 aircraft for participation in

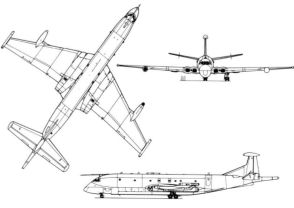

British Aerospace (Hawker Siddeley) Nimrod MR.Mk 2P

Operation Corporate) changed the aircraft designation to **MR.Mk 2P** and necessitated the addition of tiny swept finlets on the tailplanes. The Falklands War also resulted in the underwing hardpoints being used by front-line Nimrods for the first time, giving the ability to carry AIM-9 Sidewinders for self-defence, or anti-ship Harpoon missiles, Stingray torpedoes, bombs or depth charges. The planned wingtip Loral ARI.18240/1 ESM pods were added later, these requiring larger rectangular finlets. All aircraft now have both refuelling probes and ESM pods. For operations from Seeb in Oman, during Operation Desert Storm, a

number of aircraft were drawn from Nos 120 (lead), 42 and 206 Sqns to form the Nimrod MR Detachment. Several were modified to what was (unofficially) referred to as **Nimrod MR.Mk 2P(GM)** (Gulf-Mod) through the addition of an underwing FLIR turret on the starboard wing, BOZ pods and a TRD (Towed Radar Decoy).

SPECIFICATION

British Aerospace (Hawker Siddeley) Nimrod MR.Mk 2
Wing: span 114 ft 10 in (35.00 m); aspect ratio 6.2;

area 2,121.00 sq ft (197.04 m²)
Fuselage and tail: length 126 ft 9 in (38.63 m); height 29 ft 8.5 in (9.08 m); tailplane span 47 ft 7.25 in (14.51 m); wheel track 28 ft 2.5 in (8.60 m); wheel base 46 ft 8.5 in (14.24 m)
Powerplant: four Rolls-Royce RB.168-20 Spey Mk 250 each rated at 12,140 lb st (54.00 kN) dry
Weights: typical empty 86,000 lb (39010 kg); maximum normal take-off 177,500 lb (80514 kg); maximum overload take-off 192,000 lb (87091 kg)
Fuel and load: internal fuel 85,840 lb (38937 kg) plus provision for 15,100 lb (6849 kg) of auxiliary fuel in six weapon-bay tanks; external fuel none; maximum ordnance 13,500 lb (6124 kg)
Speed: maximum necessity speed at optimum

altitude 500 kt (575 mph; 926 km/h); maximum cruising speed at optimum altitude 475 kt (547 mph; 880 km/h); economical cruising speed at optimum altitude 425 kt (490 mph; 787 km/h); typical patrol speed at low level 200 kt (230 mph; 370 km/h) on two engines
Range: ferry range 5,000 nm (5,758 miles; 9266 km); endurance 12 hours 0 minutes typical, 15 hours 0 minutes maximum and 19 hours 0 minutes with one refuelling
Performance: service ceiling 42,000 ft (12800 m); take-off run 4,800 ft (1463 m) at normal maximum take-off weight; landing run 5,300 ft (1615 m) at normal landing weight

British Aerospace (Hawker Siddeley) Nimrod R.Mk 1

In addition to the 46 Nimrod MR.Mk 1s ordered as Shackleton replacements, three further aircraft (XW664-666) were ordered as replacements for No. 51 Squadron's specially modified intelligence-gathering Comets and Canberras. This role had never been formally admitted, and references to the squadron (which still shuns publicity) usually described it as a calibration unit. The three aircraft were designated **Nimrod R.Mk 1** and were delivered to RAF Wyton for fitting out in 1971. Security surrounding the aircraft was such that they were delivered as little more than empty shells, the RAF then fitting virtually all mission equipment. As a result, flight trials did not begin until late 1973, and the first operational flight took place on 3 May 1974. On 10 May 1974 the type was formally commissioned, bringing the Comet era to a close. A handful of Canberras remained on charge until mid-1976, and there are persistent rumours that the squadron 'borrowed' other Canberras for many years following.

Initially the Nimrod R.Mk 1s differed from their maritime cousins in having no MAD tailboom and no searchlight, instead having dielectric radomes in the nose of each

external wing tank and on the tail. The aircraft have been progressively modified since they were introduced, gaining more and more antennas above and below the fuselage and wing tanks, as well as Loral ARI.18240/1 wingtips ESM pods. With inflight-refuelling probes (first fitted to XW664 just before the Falklands War) the designation changed to **Nimrod R.Mk 1P**. Increased equipment has led to the deletion of several cabin windows, and in recent years the aircraft have started carrying underwing chaff/flare dispensers.

The main receivers cover the widest possible range of frequencies, with DF (direction finding) and ranging, and are thus able to record and locate the source of hostile radar and radio emissions. The aircraft almost certainly have a computerised 'threat library', allowing a detailed 'map' of potential enemy radar stations, navaids and air defence systems to be built up. Emissions from hostile fighters can also be recorded and analysed. During Cold War operations, the aircraft frequently operated in international airspace around the peripheries of the Soviet Union, necessitating extremely accurate navigation. One LORAN towel rail

antenna has thus been removed, and the aircraft has received a Delco AN/ASN-119 Carousel Mk IVA INS. The ASV21 nose radar was replaced by an EKCO 290 weather radar during the early 1980s. The Nimrod's predecessors are believed to have made 'feints' at Soviet airspace to provoke a reaction which could then be recorded.

Occasional reports of No. 51 Squadron's aircrew retiring, or reaching a landmark number of flying hours, sometimes appear in the *RAF News*, and from such reports an intriguing picture begins to emerge. The Nimrod R.Mk 1Ps seem to fly with very large crews (26-28 seems by no means extraordinary), the majority obviously being equipment operators. Most of the aircrew are extremely experienced, and are obviously hand-picked for their skill and discretion.

No. 51 Sqn gained a Battle Honour after the Falklands War in 1982 and, more recently, the squadron commander confirmed in a book that his three aircraft had operated from RAF Akrotiri in support of Operations Granby and Desert Storm, but maintained the fiction that this support took the form of radar and radio aid calibration. Daily newspapers have been more accurate, if a little sensationalist in tone, describing the aircraft as 'GCHQ's secret squadron of Nimrods', 'funded by the Foreign Office'. Other speculation has included the contention that R.Mk 1s operated from Chilean or Brazilian bases during the Falklands War. The low utilisation and lack of low-level flying has ensured that the Nimrod R.Mk 1s have not suffered the same corrosion and fatigue problems as the MR.Mk 2s, and they have a long life ahead of them.

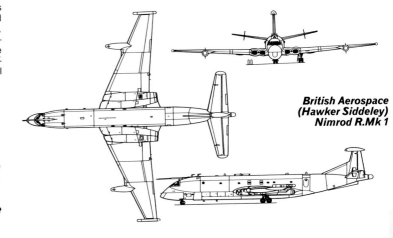

British Aerospace (Hawker Siddeley) Nimrod R.Mk 1

The three Nimrod R.Mk 1s of No. 51 Sqn will leave their Wyton home for Waddington in 1995. The RAF's EW/AEW force will be centred at that base.

British Aerospace (BAC) One-Eleven

Developed as a company-funded venture by the newly formed British Aircraft Corporation, the **BAC One-Eleven** was planned as a short-haul airliner to succeed the Vickers Viscount. Launched on the basis of an order for 10 aircraft from British United, it first flew in August 1963. The basic design was entirely conventional, with two of the newly developed Spey engines mounted on the rear of a circular-section fuselage with small elliptical passenger windows and seating for 65 to 89 passengers who board via a stairway under the tail. Features included manual ailerons but powered tail surfaces, short undercarriage, engine bleed-air de-icing of wings and tail, thrust reversers and a gas-turbine APU (auxiliary power unit) in the tailcone.

Almost all production went to commercial operators. BAC built 56 **Series 200,** nine **Series 300,** 69 **Series 400** (origi-

nally developed for the US market), nine **Series 475** specially equipped for operations from short unpaved airstrips, and 87 of the stretched **Series 500** seating up to 109. All production has now been transferred to ROMAERO SA (formerly IAv Bucuresti) in Romania, where the **Rombac One-Eleven Series 495** and stretched **Series 560** were produced until 1991 for use within Romania and for export. A corresponding programme permits licence production of Rolls-Royce Spey engines. Romanian One-Eleven versions have been equipped with engine hushkits to enable the ageing One-Eleven to meet more stringent noise requirements. One of the first Romanian-assembled aircraft (at that time, 1984, still incorporating British parts) was used as a VIP transport by the Romanian President. This aircraft has since been withdrawn from service.

There are also mixed-traffic and cargo versions, and one of the few military customers, the **Royal Air Force of Oman**, continues to operate three **Series 485s** with forward freight doors, quick-change

interiors and rough-field capability. Two early Series 217s had a long career with No. 34 (VIP) Squadron, RAAF, at Canberra. Disposal of these aircraft was arranged in January 1990. Two Series 423s were delivered to the Brazilian air force in 1969 and were subsequently sold to civilian operators. A specially modified variant of the Series 475 was offered to Japan as replacement for

RAE (now DRA) One-Elevens have been heavily used as radar testbeds and played a major part in development of the EFA's Ferranti-built ECR-90, flying from Prestwick.

the NAMC YS-11. Known as the **Series 670**, this (eventually unproduced) version featured extended wingtips and modified flaps to meet the requirement for 1,220-m (4,000-ft) field capability.

A handful of former One-Eleven airliners have been acquired for the MoD. One **Series 479** (ZE432) is on strength with the Empire Test Pilots School for training purposes, where it has replaced the Vickers Viscount for heavy type handling. The Defence Research Agency operates two One-Elevens (XX105, XX919) for a variety of

test purposes. One Series 479 (ZE433) has been fitted with Sea Harrier FRS.Mk 2 Blue Vixen radar in the nose. Similarly, a BAC One-Eleven **Series 401** (N162W) was acquired in 1989 by Westinghouse for YF-23 systems integration. Northrop and McDonnell Douglas, the prime contractors for the YF-23, built a complete prototype avionics system. The avionics systems, comprising radar, infra-red search-and-track (IRST) system and electronic warfare suite, successfully demonstrated their ability to track real targets.

SPECIFICATION

British Aerospace (BAC) One-Eleven Series 479
Wing: span 93 ft 6 in (28.50 m)
Fuselage and tail: length 93 ft 6 in (28.50 m); height 24 ft 6 in (7.47 m); tailplane span 29 ft 6 in (8.99 m); wheel base 33 ft 1 in (10.08 m)
Powerplant: two Rolls-Royce Spey Mk 512 DW each rated at 12,550 lb (55.8 kN) dry
Weights: operating empty 51,731 lb (23464 kg); maximum take-off 98,500 lb (44,678 kg)
Fuel and load: internal fuel 3,080 Imp gal (3,700 US gal;

14006 litres); external fuel none; maximum payload 21,269 lb (9647 kg)
Speed: maximum cruising speed 470 kt (541 mph; 871 km/h); economical cruising speed 400 kt (461 mph; 742 km/h); stalling speed 111 kt (128 mph; 206 km/h)
Range: still air with maximum fuel and reserves 1,985 nm (2,285 miles; 3677 km)

Northrop relied on this BAC One-Eleven for systems development on the YF-23 ATF programme, whereas the (successful) YF-22 partners used the Boeing 757 prototype.

British Aerospace Sea Harrier FRS.Mk 1

Developed from the world's first and, at that time, only V/STOL fighter for the RAF, the **BAe Sea Harrier** fortuitously filled the gap left by the phase-out of the Phantom FGR.Mk 2 and the 1979 decommissioning of HMS *Ark Royal*, the last conventional Royal Navy carrier. It coincided with the introduction of a new generation of small, 20,000-ton ASW carriers. These were intended to embark only helicopters, and the Sea Harrier was instrumental in retaining some fixed-wing strike capability when the entire Fleet Air Arm was otherwise destined to become an all-helicopter force. Concurrent with the Navy taking delivery of HMS *Invincible*, dubbed a 'through deck cruiser' rather than an aircraft-carrier to get it past UK Treasury scrutiny, the Sea Harrier became one of the most important types ever procured by the FAA. Conflict in the Falklands was to prove the prudency of the decision to adopt the Sea Harrier.

Although a Harrier, in P.1127 form, had landed aboard *Ark Royal* as early as 8 February 1963, the RN evinced little interest in the programme despite the manufacturer's assurances that the engineering changes required to produce a navalised Harrier would be minimal. Navy interest gradually increased, spurred by the knowledge that no other fixed-wing aircraft could be ordered, and by a series of successful Harrier test deployments from seagoing platforms. This culminated in May 1975 in an initial order for 24 **Sea Harrier FRS.Mk 1**s and a single **T.Mk 4A** trainer, followed by a further 10 FRS.Mk 1s in May 1978. The designation reflected the Sea Harrier's dual capability as a fleet defence fighter, reconnaissance platform and strike aircraft. On 31 March 1980, the trials unit (No. 700A Sqn), was redesignated No. 899 Sqn as the HQ unit. On the same day No. 800 Sqn formed, with four aircraft, aboard HMS *Invincible*.

The main differences between the Harrier GR.Mk 3 (described separately) and Sea Harrier were the latter's front fuselage contours, with a painted radome covering a Ferranti Blue Fox pulse-modulated radar and its associated avionics bay. The cockpit was raised 10 in (25 cm) and the canopy revised for improved pilot view. An improved Pegasus Mk 104 engine of 21,492 lb (96.3 kN) thrust was fitted. Wing pylons were stressed to take a wide variety of loads up to and including a lightweight version of the WE177 nuclear weapon. An autopilot was added, as was a revised nav-attack system and a new HUD. Magnesium was deleted from all airframe areas likely to be exposed to corrosion from salt water. Embarking aboard HMS *Hermes* in June 1981, No. 800 Sqn had by then been joined by the second Sea Harrier unit, No. 801 Sqn, which had commissioned that February. Both squadrons were subsequently deployed as

part of the RN's modest fixed-wing air assets during the Falklands conflict. The Sea Harriers served with distinction, achieving a commendable 80 per cent serviceability record in an arduous operating environment.

Expanded capability was provided for the Sea Harriers of both squadrons (and hastily reformed No. 809 Sqn) aboard *Hermes* and *Invincible* for Operation Corporate. Particularly significant was the supply of AIM-9L Sidewinders, nullifying any disadvantage the Sea Harriers suffered compared to the higher-performance equipment of the Argentinian air force. Scoring 22 confirmed victories, the Sea Harrier force lost six aircraft, all of them to causes other than aerial combat. Contributing greatly to the weapons load with which Sea Harriers were launched was the 'ski jump', a ramp fitted to carrier bows. First tested on land at an angle of 7°, it was found that a laden Harrier could use inclines of up to 13° which allowed an additional 2,500 lb (1134 kg) to be added to the MTOW. Following the South Atlantic operation, 14 Sea Harrier FRS.Mk 1s were ordered as attrition replacements and, in 1984, nine more single-seaters plus three **T.Mk 4(N)**s were added, bringing RN procurement up to 57 single-seaters and four trainers.

Combat operations had highlighted areas where the Sea Harrier could be improved, and all these have been addressed. These included the capability to carry up to four AIM-9Ls, installation of an improved radar and radar warning receiver, and stronger wing pylons to take larger- capacity drop tanks. At that time it appeared that the Soviet navy's growing carrier-building programme might require NATO-assigned forces to be capable of launching ever more powerful AAMs to block any threat posed by low-flying bombers. An important addition to the Sea Harrier's inventory in this combat scenario was a current-generation fire-and-forget missile. These coincided with a mid-life update for the Sea Harrier, and the majority of the improvements recommended for the FRS.Mk 1 were carried over to the new **FRS.Mk 2** (described separately).

In late 1978 the Indian navy became the second Sea Harrier operator, budgeting for up to 48 aircraft designated **FRS.Mk 51** (single-seater) and **FRS.Mk 60** (trainer). Six single-seaters and two trainers were ordered in December 1979. A second batch

After Operation Corporate, the retaking of the Falkland Islands in 1982, twin AIM-9 Sidewinder launch rails became the standard fit across the entire Sea Harrier FRS.Mk 1 force. This increase in combat effectiveness went hand in hand with the adoption of a toned-down grey scheme. During the Falklands fighting, differing hastily-applied grey colour schemes were worn.

POWERPLANT
The Sea Harrier FRS.Mk 1 is powered by a single Rolls-Royce Pegasus Mk 104, rated at 21,500 lb st (95.64 kN). This maritime version of the Mk 103 has sacrificial protective coatings on various ferrous components, and all the low-pressure and intermediate castings are also made of a different alloy.

TAILPLANE AND RWR
The Kestrel introduced the familiar extended tailplane associated with the first-generation Harriers, with its distinctive kinked leading edge. The one-piece variable-incidence tailplane incorporates 15° of anhedral. The prominent housing on the leading edge is for the Marconi ARI.18223 radar warning receiver (RWR), sensitive to emitters in the 2 to 20 GHz band. Receiver aerials are also located in the tailcone.

RADIO AND NAVAIDS
Apart from the Ferranti self-aligning platform and Decca Doppler, the Sea Harrier has UHF homing and a GEC Avionics AD 2770 TACAN, plus I-band transponder for navigation. Communications are handled by a Plessey PTR 377 U/VHF transceiver, with D403M transceiver for a standby VHF.

British Aerospace Sea Harrier FRS.Mk 1

On top of its overall dark sea grey finish, this Sea Harrier wears the checkerboard rudder markings and winged trident badge of No. 801 Sqn, shore-based at RNAS Yeovilton (known as HMS *Heron* in naval parlance). The aircraft's 'triple zilch' code signifies its assignment to the squadron commander.

MISSILES
As the first and (until the advent of the FRS.Mk 2) the only Harrier with a primary air-to-air role, the Sea Harrier FRS.Mk 1 is the only member of the family to be fitted with twin Sidewinder launch rails.

DECCA DOPPLER 72
Flush Doppler aerials serve the Ferranti HARS (Heading and Attitude Reference System), a twin gyro platform which provides greater accuracy than a normal INAS, and can be aligned on a moving deck.

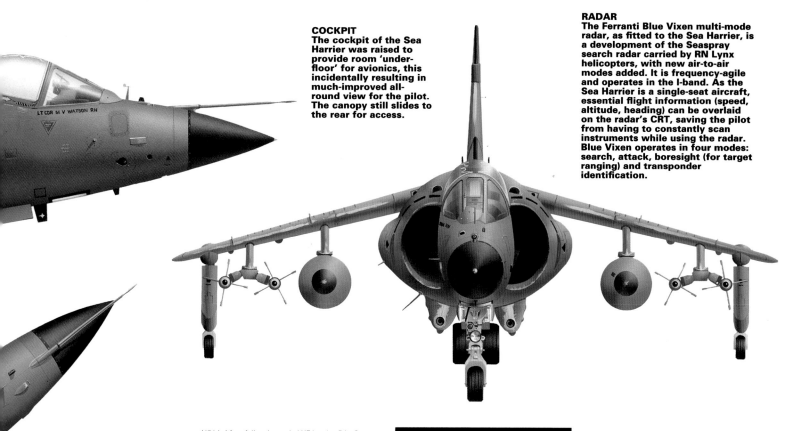

COCKPIT
The cockpit of the Sea Harrier was raised to provide room 'under-floor' for avionics, this incidentally resulting in much-improved all-round view for the pilot. The canopy still slides to the rear for access.

RADAR
The Ferranti Blue Vixen multi-mode radar, as fitted to the Sea Harrier, is a development of the Seaspray search radar carried by RN Lynx helicopters, with new air-to-air modes added. It is frequency-agile and operates in the I-band. As the Sea Harrier is a single-seat aircraft, essential flight information (speed, altitude, heading) can be overlaid on the radar's CRT, saving the pilot from having to constantly scan instruments while using the radar. Blue Vixen operates in four modes: search, attack, boresight (for target ranging) and transponder identification.

of 10 single-seaters and one trainer followed in November 1985, and a third batch, ordered in October 1986, comprised seven FRS.Mk 51s and a further FRS.Mk 60. India's carriers, *Vikrant* and *Viraat*, both currently deploy a Sea Harrier/Sea King air group.

WEAPON OPTIONS

Underfuselage mounts for two 30-mm ADEN cannon, and four underwing hardpoints stressed for up to 8,000 lb (3628 kg . Nominal carrying capabilities as follows – underfuselage and inboard wing hardpoints 2,000-lb (907 kg), outboard wing pylons 650 lb (295 kg) each. Cleared for carriage of WE177 free-fall nuclear bomb (withdrawn from inventory), standard UK 1,000-lb

(454-kg) free-fall and retarded HE bombs, BAe Sea Eagle ASM, AGM-84 Harpoon ASM, Lepus flare units, CBLS 100 practice bomb dispenser and most NATO-standard bombs, rockets and flares. Air-to-air armament can comprise four AIM-9L Sidewinders on twin-rail launcher, or MATRA Magic on Indian aircraft.

OPERATORS

Fleet Air Arm: 35 in service
No. 800 Sqn – FRS.Mk 1
No. 801 Sqn– FRS.Mk 1
No. 899 Sqn (OCU) – T.Mk 4A/4N
Indian Naval Aviation: 26 delivered
INAS 300 'White Tigers'
INAS 551 'B' Flight
– FRS.Mk 51 and T.Mk 60

SPECIFICATION

British Aerospace (Hawker Siddeley) Sea Harrier FRS.Mk 1
Wing: span 25 ft 3 in (7.70 m) with normal tips or 29 ft 8 in (9.04 m) with ferry tips; aspect ratio 3.175; area 202.10 sq ft (18.68 m2)
Fuselage and tail: length 47 ft 7 in (14.50 m) or with nose folded 41 ft 9 in (12.73 m); height 12 ft 2 in (3.71 m); tailplane span 13 ft 11 in (4.24 m); outrigger wheel track 22 ft 2 in (6.76 m); wheel base about 11 ft 4 in (3.45 m)
Powerplant: one Rolls-Royce Pegasus Mk 104 rated at 95.64 kN (21,500 lb st) dry
Weights: basic empty 13,000 lb (5897 kg); operating empty 14,052 lb (6374 kg); maximum take-off 26,200 lb (11884 kg)
Fuel and load: internal fuel 5,060 lb (2295 kg);

external fuel up to 5,300 lb (2404 kg) in two 100-Imp gal (120-US gal; 455-litre) drop tanks or two 330- or 190-Imp tanks (396- or 228-US gal; 1500- or 864-litre) ferry tanks; maximum ordnance 8,000 lb (3629 kg)
Speed: never exceed speed at high altitude 716 kt (825 mph; 1328 km/h); maximum level speed 'clean' at sea level more than 639 kt (736 mph; 1185 km/h); cruising speed at 36,000 ft (10975 m) 459 kt (528 mph; 850 km/h)
Range: combat radius 400 nm (460 miles; 750 km) on a hi-hi-hi interception mission with four AAMs, or 250 nm (288 miles; 463 km) on a hi-lo-hi attack mission
Performance: maximum rate of climb at sea level about 50,000 ft (15240 m) per minute; service ceiling 51,000 ft (15545 m); take-off run about 1,000 ft (305 m) at maximum take-off weight without 'ski jump'; landing run 0 ft (0 m) at normal landing weight
g **limits:** -4.2 to +7.8

British Aerospace Sea Harrier FRS.Mk 2

In refining the Sea Harrier as a more capable interceptor, while retaining its reconnaissance and strike capability, British Aerospace made some significant changes to the airframe. The company received a contract in January 1985 for project definition phase of the programme, which included two conversions of the Sea Harrier FRS.Mk 1 to **FRS.Mk 2** standard. Initially (in 1984) it

was reported the MoD planned to award a £200 million contract to BAe and Ferranti to cover a mid-life update of the entire Sea Harrier fleet, but these plans were substantially revised (in 1985) to cover an upgrade of some 30 airframes. The upgrade would include Blue Vixen radar, JTIDS, AIM-120 AMRAAM provision and an enhanced RWR fit. The original BAe proposal also covered

the installation of wingtip Sidewinder rails. These additions, along with several other aerodynamic refinements, were eventually cut from the project, but a kinked wing leading edge and wing fence were retained. The first of these test aircraft (ZA195) was flown on 19 September 1988, followed by the second (XZ439) on 8 March 1989. Despite the addition of an extra equipment bay and

a recontoured nose to house the Blue Vixen radar which gives it more of an elongated appearance than its predecessor, the FRS.Mk 2 is actually nearly 2 ft (0.61 m) shorter overall due to the elimination of the extended pitot head probe of the earlier variant. No increase in wingspan was found to be necessary to carry additional stores, including a pair of 190-Imp gal (864-litre) drop tanks plus Hughes AIM-120 AMRAAMs (or BAe Alarms) on each of the outer pylons, although ferry tips are available to increase span to 29 ft 8 in (9.04 m).

Two pre-production Sea Harrier FRS.Mk 2s took part in sea trials aboard HMS Ark Royal *in November 1990. This, the second aircraft (ZA195), was not fitted with Blue Vixen radar and carried an instrumentation pitot instead.*

A Sea Harrier FRS.Mk 2 Operational Evaluation Unit formed during June 1993 at Boscombe Down, as a sub-division of No.899 Sqn at RNAS Yeovilton. Some of its aircraft wear a new darker grey overall finish.

British Aerospace Sea Harrier FRS.Mk 2

The FRS.Mk 2 cockpit introduced new multi-function CRT displays and HOTAS controls to reduce pilot workload. The FRS.Mk 2 is powered by a Pegasus Mk 106 turbofan, a navalised version of the Mk 105 as fitted to the AV-8B but with no magnesium in its construction. On 7 December 1988 a contract was awarded for the conversion of 31 FRS.Mk 1s to Mk 2 standard. On 6 March 1990 an order was placed for 10 new-build FRS.Mk 2s to augment the conversions, attrition having by that time reduced the RN's Sea Harrier inventory to 39 aircraft. A further contract in January 1994 covered 18 more FRS.Mk 2s and an additional five FRS.MK 1 conversions.

Airframes undergoing conversion are stripped down at Dunsfold, before being delivered by road to Brough for the fundamental structural work. The upgraded aircraft are then returned to Dunsfold for final assembly.

Carrier qualification trials were conducted aboard HMS *Ark Royal* during November 1990 and, among other favourable factors, these proved the FRS.Mk 2 capable of operating safely from a 12° ramp. The two aircraft involved in the late 1990 trials were configured as per production aircraft, although there was only one radar between the two. In order to enhance pilot conversion training, a new two-seat trainer conversion, designated **T.Mk 8N**, is to be provided with four aircraft replacing T.Mk 4Ns in 1996. Essentially a reconfigured T.Mk 4N, this variant will duplicate FRS.Mk 2 systems, apart from radar.

The primary air-to-air missile for the Sea Harrier FRS.Mk 2 will be the Hughes AIM-120 AMRAAM. A successor to the AIM-9 for the RAF (and presumably the Navy) remains undecided. Delays, particularly in successfully marrying the aircraft to the Blue Vixen radar, have already put back the FRS.Mk 2 programme by five years and increased costs by some 20 per cent. Blue Vixen was test flown in a Sea Harrier for the first time on 24 May 1990. The Blue Vixen radar (A version) has been extensively flight tested in a BAe-operated BAC One-Eleven in a 114-hour flight programme which ended in November 1987, and again in a BAe 125 (XW930) until August 1988. Another BAe 125 (ZF130) was fitted with a complete

For its detachment to Eglin, XZ439 received this ferocious sharkmouth. An AIM-120 is mounted under the starboard wing, with a Sidewinder 'tube' converted to an instrumentation pod just visible to port.

FRS.Mk 2 cockpit in the right-hand seat and later gained a B version radar in 1989. The next hurdle to be overcome was live firing trials of the AIM-120 primary armament. Originally scheduled for mid-1991, it was not until January 1993 that the second, radar-bearing prototype (XZ439) arrived at Norfolk Virginia, aboard the new *Atlantic Conveyer*. The aircraft was flown ashore, refuelled and then carried on to Eglin AFB. The trials included 10 live firings against sub-scale MQM-107 drones and full-scale, supersonic QF-106 drones, commencing on 29 March 1993. A serious setback occurred with the loss of one of two radar-equipped aircraft (XZ495) in a crash in the Bristol Channel on 5 January 1994.

A trials unit formed at Boscombe Down in June 1993 receiving the first production FRS.Mk 2 (XZ497), on the 21st of that month. The Sea Harrier FRS.Mk 2 'OEU', currently undertaking trials at Boscombe is an off-shoot of No. 899 Sqn. and some aircraft already wear this unit's insignia.

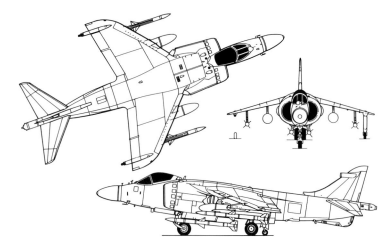

British Aerospace Sea Harrier FRS.Mk 2

SPECIFICATION

British Aerospace Sea Harrier FRS.Mk 2
generally similar to the British Aerospace Sea Harrier FRS.Mk 1 except in the following particulars:
Fuselage and tail: length 46 ft 6 in (14.17 m) or with nose folded 43 ft 2 in (13.16 m); wheel base about 12 ft 5.5 in (3.80 m)
Powerplant: one Rolls-Royce Pegasus Mk 104 rated

at 21,500 lb st (95.64 kN) dry
Fuel and load: external fuel up to 5,300 lb (2404 kg) in two 100-Imp gal (120-US gal; 455-litre) drop tanks or two 330- or 190-Imp gal (396- or 228-US gal; 1500- or 864-litre) ferry tanks; max ordnance 8,000 lb (3629 kg)
Speed: never exceed speed at high altitude 716 kt (825 mph; 1328 km/h); maximum level speed 'clean' at sea level more than 639 kt (736 mph; 1185 km/h); cruising speed at 36,000 ft (10975 m) 459 kt (528 mph; 850 km/h)

Range: combat radius 100 nm (115 miles; 185 km) on a 90-minute CAP with four AIM-120 AMRAAMs (or two AMRAAMs and two 30-mm cannon) and two 190-Imp gal (228-US gal; 864-litre) drop tanks, or 525 nm (600 miles; 970 km) on a hi-lo-hi reconnaissance mission with two 190-Imp gal (228-US gal; 864-litre) drop tanks, or 200 nm (230 miles; 370 km) on a hi-lo-hi attack mission with two Sea Eagle missiles and two 30-mm cannon, or 116 nm (133 miles; 215 km) on a hi-hi-hi interception mission with two AMRAAMs

British Aerospace (BAC) 167 Strikemaster

The obvious appeal of the Jet Provost as a highly developed and economical trainer prompted BAC to develop the type into a tactical multi-role aircraft able to fly both pilot training and weapon training sorties, in addition to performing light-attack and reconnaissance roles. The **BAC.167 Strikemaster** was developed from the **BAC.145**, virtually an armed version of the pressurised Jet Provost T.Mk 5, by fitting a more powerful engine (a Viper Mk 535 developing 3,410 lb/15.2 kN thrust) and increasing the number of stores hardpoints to eight. The airframe had been strengthened several times in the course of development of the Jet Provost and BAC.145, and in the BAC.167 it was further reinforced for operations in rigorous environments.

The Strikemaster featured side-by-side Martin-Baker Mk PB4 ejection seats, short landing gear suitable for operation from rough airstrips, fuel housed entirely in the integral and bag tanks in the wings and in fixed tip tanks, hydraulic spoiler/airbrake surfaces

above the wings, manual flight controls, a pressurised and air-conditioned cockpit, and comprehensive navigation and communications equipment (including VOR/ILS, DME and TACAN).

The first Strikemaster flew in October 1967 and the **Strikemaster Mk 80** series entered production a year later. Customers comprised Ecuador, Kenya, Kuwait, New Zealand, Oman, Saudi Arabia, Singapore, the Sudan and South Yemen. The final batch of new **Strikemaster Mk 90** aircraft was delivered to the Sudan in 1984, assembly of this batch having been relocated from Warton to Hurn. Sudan had previously been a customer for the less powerful BAC.145. Many Strikemasters have seen prolonged active service; for example, all 20 of the Sultan of Oman's **Strikemaster Mk 82** and **Mk 82A** aircraft have sustained battle damage. Surviving Omani Strikemasters have been fitted with LORAN navigation equipment and are distinguished by a large ventral 'towel-rack' aerial.

OPERATORS

Survivors continue to serve with the air arms of Kenya (five – refurbished Kuwaiti aircraft), Oman (13), Saudi Arabia (35) and Sudan (three). In 1988, the attack capability of the Botsawana air force was significantly enhanced with the delivery of nine ex-Kuwaiti Strikemaster Mk 83s, refurbished by BAe at Warton,

of which seven are still operational.

New Zealand's Strikemasters (colloquially known as 'Bluntys'), were finally retired by No. 75 Sqn in January 1993, replaced by the Aermacchi M.B.339C. Following replacement by Pilatus PC-9s (said by many to have been the RAF's preferred choice) and BAe Hawks, Saudi Strikemasters serve in refresher training and liaison duties. Ecuadorean Strikemasters, 16 of which were delivered to Taura-based Escuadrilla de Ataque 21, were finally retired in 1984 in favour of the EMB-312 Tucano. Singapore was also a major Strikemaster operator with 16 aircraft delivered during 1969, equipping No. 130 Sqn at Seletar. These were

The Strikemaster proved popular in Royal New Zealand Air Force service, but structural problems forced their premature retirement in 1992/93.

augmented by four former South Yemen aircraft and five from Oman. All have now been replaced by locally-assembled Agusta (SIAI-Marchetti) S.211s.

SPECIFICATION

British Aerospace (BAC) Strikemaster Mk 88
Wing: span 36 ft 10 in (11.23 m) over tip tanks; aspect ratio 6.35; area 213.70 sq ft (19.85 m²)
Fuselage and tail: length 34 ft 0 in (10.36 m); height 10 ft 2 in (3.10 m); tailplane span 13 ft 6 in (4.11 m); wheel track 10 ft 8.9 in (3.27 m); wheel base 9 ft 7.4 in (2.93 m)
Powerplant: one Rolls-Royce (Bristol Siddeley) Viper 20 Mk 525 rated at 3,410 lb st (15.17 kN) dry
Weights: operating empty 6,195 lb (2810 kg); normal take-off 10,500 lb (4762 kg); maximum take-off 11,500 lb (5216 kg)
Fuel and load: internal fuel 366 Imp gal (440 US gal; 1664 litres); external fuel up to two 75-Imp gal (90-US gal; 341-litre) and two 50-Imp gal (60-US gal; 227-litre) drop tanks; maximum ordnance 3,000 lb (1361 kg)
Speed: never exceed speed 450 kt (518 mph;

834 km/h); maximum level speed 'clean' at 20,000 ft (6095 m) 410 kt (472 mph; 760 km/h) and at sea level 391 kt (450 mph; 724 km/h)
Range: ferry range 1,200 nm (1,382 miles; 2224 km) with four drop tanks; combat radius 215 nm (247 miles; 397 miles) on a hi-lo-hi close support mission with a 3,000-lb (1361-kg) warload, or 355 nm (408 miles; 656 km) on a hi-lo-hi close support mission with a 2,000-lb (907-kg) warload, or 500 nm (575 miles; 925 km) on a hi-lo-hi close support mission with a 1,000-lb (454-kg) warload, or 126 nm (145 miles; 233 km) on a lo-lo-lo close support mission with a 3,000-lb (1361-kg) warload, or 175 nm (201 miles; 323 km) on a lo-lo-lo close support mission with a 2,000-lb (907-kg) warload, or 240 nm (276 miles; 444 km) on a lo-lo-lo close support mission with a 1,000-lb (454-kg) warload, or 300 nm (345 miles; 555 km) on a reconnaissance mission
Performance: maximum rate of climb at sea level 5,250 ft (1600 m) per minute; climb to 30,000 ft (9145 m) in 8 minutes 45 seconds; service ceiling 40,000 ft (12190 m); take-off distance to 50 ft (15 m) 3,500 ft (1067 m) at maximum take-off weight; landing distance from 50 ft (15 m) 2,400 ft (732 m) at normal landing weight

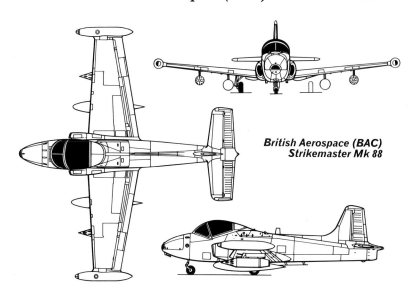

British Aerospace (BAC) Strikemaster Mk 88

British Aerospace (Vickers/BAC) **VC10**

Modification of the **Vickers (BAe) VC10** airliner into a transport gave the RAF useful passenger and cargo-carrying capacity at lower cost compared to development of a new aircraft. Meeting specification C 239 of 1960 for a strategic long-range transport for what was then Transport Command, the first military VC10s were similar to the civil Standard VC10 but had uprated Rolls-Royce Conway engines and the additional fin fuel cell of the Super VC10. Rearward-facing seats were fitted, as was a side-loading freight door and refuelling probe on the nose centreline forward of the cockpit windows. In addition, a Bristol Siddeley Artouste auxiliary power unit was located in the tailcone. As the **VC10 C.Mk 1**, the aircraft incorporated a strengthened floor and seating capacity for up to 150 passengers, or 76 stretcher cases and six medical attendants. A flight crew of four was carried.

The first RAF VC10 made its maiden flight on 26 November 1965 with initial deliveries to No. 10 Squadron at Fairford in July 1966. Subsequent procurement was five in September 1961, six in 1962 and three in July 1964. No. 10 Sqn was the sole operator of the transport version and undertook the first overseas training flight to Hong Kong in August 1966, regular route flights beginning on 4 April 1967. The squadron increased its VC10 flights to 27 a month to the Far East via the Persian Gulf, No. 10 sharing the main RAF transport base at Brize Norton with the Belfasts of No. 53 Sqn. Despite clipping 4½ hours off the flight time of the Comet and 12 hours off that of the Britannia, the VC10's Far East destinations meant a long haul of just over 19 hours to Singapore and 22 hours to Hong Kong. Carrying less than half its full payload, the VC10 had a range exceeding 5,000 miles (8047 km).

In 1978 a programme of converting VC10s to tankers to augment the Victor K.Mk 2 fleet was initiated with five ex-Gulf Air Standard VC10 Series 101s (which became **VC10 K.Mk 2**s) and four Super VC10 Series 1154s from East African Airways (**VC10 K.Mk 3**s). Carried out by BAe at Filton, the VC10 K.Mk 2/3 conversion work included the installation of extra fuel tanks in the cabin, three hose drum units (two under the wings and one in the rear fuselage) and a closed-circuit television system to enable the flight crew to monitor refuelling operations.

The first VC10 K.Mk 2s joined No. 101 Squadron at Brize Norton in May 1984, the first K.Mk 3s following in 1985. Four years later a further variant was ordered to meet Air Staff Requirements 415 and 416. These called for the conversion of five Super VC10s to short-range **VC10 K.Mk 4**s. These aircraft will be identical to the K.Mk 3 but with only the standard wing and fin fuel tankage. The first K.Mk 4 flew, after conversion at Filton, on 30 July 1993. The other current project is the upgrading of eight of No. 101 Sqn's machines to **VC10 C.Mk 1(K)** standard, retaining full passenger and freight capability but with the addition of two underwing fuel pods. BAe secured the contract and offset 40 per cent of the work to Flight Refuelling Aviation for the C.Mk 1(K)s. The K.Mk 4s will have Mk 17 and Mk 32 fuel pods, closed-circuit TV, air-to-air TACAN, avionics systems and engines of the K.Mk 3, but no cabin fuel tanks.

In 1992 it was decided to convert 13 C.Mk 1s to C.Mk 1(K) configuration under a

programme expected to last into 1995. All VC10 tankers are also to be fitted with JTIDS. Unexpectedly, No. 101 Sqn found itself preparing to go to war in August 1990, when it dispatched two aircraft to Seeb in Oman. When hostilities with Iraq began, the squadron sent further detachments to Bahrain and Saudi Arabia, all of its then-current fleet of nine VC10 K.Mks 2 and 3 eventually being committed. Primarily tasked to support RAF Desert Storm strike missions, each VC10 was able to refuel a

flight of four Tornados or Jaguars. The former required two refuellings on inbound flights and one on the return leg, and each tanker sortie usually involved the VC10 orbiting over Iraqi territory for up to one hour. Having completed 381 war sorties, No. 101 Sqn returned to the UK in March 1991 and currently remains at Brize Norton as part of No. 1 Group RAF, sharing the tanker task with No. 216's TriStar K.Mk 1s and the newly converted C.Mk 1(K)s of No. 10 Sqn. The ongoing tanker conversion programme will bring the RAF's VC10 strategic tanker force up to 27 aircraft, comprising 13 C.Mk 1(K)s, five K.Mk 2s, four K.Mk 3s and five K.Mk 4s.

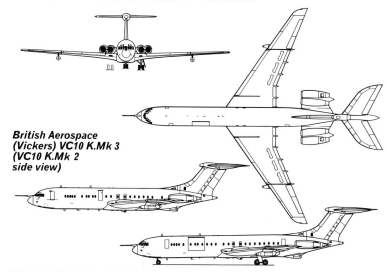

British Aerospace (Vickers) VC10 K.Mk 3 (VC10 K.Mk 2 side view)

Right: Clearly visible on the underside of this 101 Sqn VC10 K.Mk 3 are the positioning marks for the HDUs and ventral refuelling position.

Thirteen C.Mk 1s are in service with 'Shiny 10', No. 10 Squadron based at Brize Norton. They have been fitted with Loral Matador IRCM.

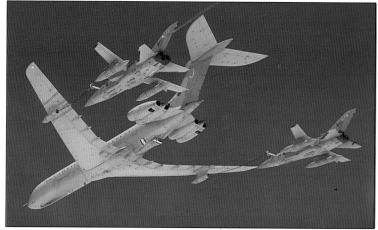

British Aerospace (Vickers/BAC) VC10

SPECIFICATION

British Aerospace (Vickers/BAC) VC10 C.Mk 1
Wing: span 146 ft 2 in (44.55 m); aspect ratio 7.29; area 2,932.00 sq ft (272.38 m²)
Fuselage and tail: length 158 ft 8 in (48.38 m) excluding probe; height 39 ft 6 in (12.04 m); tailplane span 43 ft 10 in (13.36 m); wheel track 21 ft 5 in (6.53 m); wheel base 65 ft 10.5 in (20.08 m)
Powerplant: four Rolls-Royce Conway RCo.43 Mk 301 each rated at 21,800 lb st (96.97 kN) dry
Weights: empty 146,000 lb (66224 kg); maximum take-off 323,000 lb (146510 kg)
Fuel and load: internal fuel 19,365 Imp gal (23,256 US gal; 88032 litres); external fuel none; maximum payload 57,400 lb (26037 kg)
Speed: maximum cruising speed 31,000 ft (9450 m)

The obvious addition of a Flight Refuelling Mk 32/2800 hose-drum unit beneath each wing points to the significant increase in capability provided for the RAF through the VC10 C.Mk 1(K) programme. All aircraft retain their transport role. The C.Mk 1 was delivered originally without a nose probe, but these (removable) units had been added by the mid-1980s.

505 kt (581 mph; 935 km/h); economical cruising speed at 30,000 ft (9145 m) 370 kt (426 mph; 684 km/h)
Range: 3,385 nm (3,898 miles; 6273 km) with maximum payload
Performance: maximum rate of climb at sea level 3,050 ft (930 m) per minute; service ceiling 42,000 ft

(12800 m); take-off distance to 35 ft (10.7 m) 8,300 ft (2530 m) at maximum take-off weight; balanced

landing field length 7,000 ft (2134 m) at normal landing weight

British Aerospace/McDonnell Douglas **AV-8A/C/S Harrier**

Throughout the early 1960s the US Marine Corps had an urgent requirement for an aircraft that could provide close support for amphibious landings. The choices seemed to be an armed helicopter, or ship loads of complex pre-fabricated airfield hardware, or total reliance on US Navy carriers. In 1968 the USMC evaluated the Hawker Siddeley Harrier, then still immature, and found it eminently suitable for their requirements. Plans were established to purchase 114 aircraft, designated **AV-8A**, although this was reduced to 102 and eight **TAV-8A** two-seat trainers because of the higher price of the two-seaters.

All AV-8As were built at Kingston, test-flown at Dunsfold and delivered as air freight. The first USMC production Harrier was flown on 20 November 1970 and deliveries commenced in January 1971. Allocated the Hawker Siddeley designation **Harrier Mk 50**, the aircraft initially resembled the GR.Mk 1A, with subsequent introduction of the Pegasus Mk 11 engine (which was given the US DoD designation F402-RR-402). The first 59 USMC Harriers had the FE451 nav/attack system, which was deleted and replaced by a simpler Smiths I/WAC attitude and reference heading system. In 1972 all were recycled through NAS Cherry Point to bring them to a common US standard, and without the inertial system, LRMTS laser nose or British radar warning receiver which distinguished

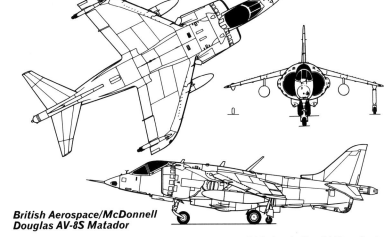

British Aerospace/McDonnell Douglas AV-8S Matador

Left: In addition to the surviving YAV-8B prototype, now serialled 704, NASA also operates this standard AV-8A, NASA 718 (N718NA). Both aircraft wear the blue and white NASA 'house colours'.

upgraded RAF aircraft. The AV-8As gained a manual fuel control (later fitted to RAF Harriers) to keep the engine running after bird-strike, and achieved clearance for US weapons including wiring and racks for AIM-9E Sidewinder AAMs (which were specified from the outset). The American Stencel SIII-S3 seat was fitted on US policy grounds, a non-toppling attitude/heading system was installed, together with tactical VHF radio using a large inclined mast aerial amidships, and the TAV-8As also received UHF for airborne command of ground forces. The Harrier equipped four USMC squadrons: VMA-513, VMA-542, VMA-231 and the conversion unit VMAT-203.

The Marines pioneered the VIFFing (vectoring in forward flight) technique, and achieved some measure of success with the relatively difficult and limited-capability AV-8A, although a large number of attrition losses occurred initially until the introduction of the trainer variant. From 1979, pending availability of a second-generation Harrier, a total of 47 aircraft (of 60 planned) was reworked to **AV-8C** standard with airframe life extension to 4,000 hours, lift-improvement devices developed for the AV-8B, Litton AN/ALR-45F radar warning receiver with wingtip and tail cone antenna, AN/ALE-39 chaff/flare dispenser, on-board oxygen generation, secure voice link and new UHF

A pair of AIM-9P-armed Armada AV-8A(S)s is here ranged on the deck of Principe de Asturias. The local designation is VA.1 Matador, but this goes largely ignored. Spanish AV-8As can carry twin Sidewinder launch rails, in the same way as FAA Sea Harrier FRS.Mk 1s, but these are rarely seen.

Spain ordered its Harriers from the US to circumvent a UK arms embargo on General Franco's regime. This is a two-seat Harrier Mk 56/TAV-8A(S).

secure radios. The F95 port oblique camera was deleted. The AV-8Cs flew alongside unconverted AV-8As until their withdrawal in February 1987, followed by the placement in storage of the last TAV-8A in November.

A Spanish naval order was placed for the AV-8A via the US government, with final assembly by McDonnell at St Louis. The purchase comprised 11 **AV-8A(S)** (Spanish designation **VA.1 Matador**) to **AV-8A Mod** standard, and two **TAV-8A(S) (VAE.1)** trainers, to **TAV-8A Mod** standard, again with tactical VHF. These aircraft were given the BAe designation **Harrier Mk 55/T.Mk 56** and were operated by Escuadrilla 008 from the wooden-decked carrier *Dédalo* (retired in 1988) and shore-based at Cádiz/Rota. In 1987 aircraft were rotated through RNAS Yeovilton to be fitted

with Sky Guardian RWR. Despite the introduction of second-generation **EAV-8B Matador II**s and the new carrier *Principe de Asturias*, the Arma Aérea de la Armada intends to operate its comparatively low-fatigued AV-8Ss until the mid-1990s.

SPECIFICATION

British Aerospace AV-8S (VA-1 Matador)
generally similar to the British Aerospace Harrier GR.Mk 3 except in the following particulars:

Fuselage and tail: length 45 ft 6 in (13.87 m)
Weights: empty equipped 12,190 lb (5529 kg); normal take-off 17,050 lb (7734 kg) for VTO; maximum take-off 22,300 lb (10115 kg) for STO
Fuel and load: maximum ordnance 5,300 lb (2404 kg)

British Aerospace/McDonnell Douglas **Harrier GR.Mk 5/5A**

BAe initiated independent development of an advanced Harrier during the late 1970s. This big-wing Harrier was known as the 'tin wing' Harrier due to the fact that its wing was of conventional alloy construction, and did not incorporate carbon-fibre. Purely a private venture, this wing might possibly have formed the basis of a new 'all-British' Harrier, although at that time the **RAF** was looking elsewhere for a Harrier successor under Air Staff Target 403. This sought a European combat aircraft to combine both Harrier and Jaguar roles while retaining a V/STOL capability. The requirement was revised as AST 409 in 1980, and a revised version of the tin-wing upgrade was designated **Harrier GR.Mk 5**. A working plan was proposed to retrofit 40 existing GR.Mk 3s with the new wing and build 60 more as GR.Mk 5s incorporating a new forward fuselage with a raised cockpit similar to that of the Sea Harrier.

At this point US government directives that the Harrier programme should proceed in co-operation with a foreign partner renewed the BAe and McDonnell Douglas partnership, with the British company becoming a sub-contractor rather than a full equal partner. Nevertheless, the work share offered to BAe under this new agreement was considerably larger than the entire British 'tin-wing' GR.Mk 5 programme, and it was instrumental in keeping the Harrier project alive and ensuring its continued RAF service. BAe consequently abandoned its own GR.Mk 5 and used the designation for

a licence-built version of the McDonnell Douglas/British Aerospace AV-8B Harrier II (described separately).

A 1982 agreement between the two companies led to the first 62 aircraft (two pre-series plus 60 production examples) of an initial RAF allocation of 100 Harrier IIs being test flown at Dunsfold on 30 April 1985. Numerous detail differences required by the GR.Mk 5 led to some delays in the programme, including the need to replace the newly specified Ferranti FIN 1057 INS with the original AV-8B Litton AN/ASN-130A system, to modify the tyres and ejection seats, and to fit extensions to the AIM-9L launch rails to accommodate Bofors chaff dispensers. That such seemingly minor changes could cause major problems was revealed in a 1988 inquiry which cited that £40 million extra funding had been needed to change just seven key systems from US to British equivalents. A two-year delay in RAF service entry was even more serious, and the delay would have been longer had aircraft not been accepted lacking major equipment items, including the new Royal Ordnance 25-mm cannon, Marconi Zeus ECM system and Plessey MAWS. Fortunately, other UK specific modifications were less troublesome, most notably the improved birdstrike resistance endowed by the RAF aircraft's thicker windscreen and reinforced leading edges.

Initial GR.Mk 5 deliveries to RAF Wittering for engineer familiarisation took place in May 1987, following establishment of the

Above right: A Harrier GR. Mk 3 of No. 233 OCU breaks from one of the unit's newly-delivered GR.Mk 5s, soon after the latter's introduction to service. The Harrier GR.Mk 5 originally wore this pale green finish, before adopting a darker finish.

Right: Not to be confused with Kingston's original (unflown) 'tin wing' Harrier GR. Mk 5, the British version of the AV-8B (also dubbed GR.Mk 5) made its maiden flight on 30 April 1985. The yellow primer-painted area approximates to the sections built by BAe.

No. 1 Sqn lost little time in taking their new GR.Mk 5s to Norway in support of regular Royal Marine exercises there. The disruptive 'snow' camouflage is a washable distemper, as also applied to Jaguars. This aircraft carries a pair of large ferry tanks in addition to a centreline baggage pod.

SPECIFICATION

British Aerospace/McDonnell Douglas Harrier GR.Mk 5

Wing: span 30 ft 4 in (9.25 m); aspect ratio 4.0; area 238.70 sq ft (22.18 m2) including 8.70 sq ft (0.81 m2) for the two LERXes

Fuselage and tail: length 47 ft 1.5 in (14.36 m); height 11 ft 7.75 in (3.55 m); tailplane span 13 ft 11 in (4.24 m); outrigger wheel track 17 ft 0 in (5.18 m)

Powerplant: one Rolls-Royce Pegasus Mk 105 rated at 21,750 lb st (96.75 kN) dry

Weights: operating empty 13,948 lb (6343 kg); normal take-off 22,950 lb (10410 kg) for STO; maximum take-off 31,000 lb (14061 kg) for STO or 18,950 lb (8595 kg) for VTO

Fuel and load: internal fuel 7,759 lb (3519 kg); external fuel up to 8,071 lb (3661 kg) in four 250-Imp gal (300-US gal; 1136-litre) drop tanks; maximum ordnance 9,200 lb (4173 kg)

Speed: maximum level speed 'clean' at 36,000 ft (10975 m) 522 kt (601 mph; 967 km/h) and 575 kt (661 mph; 1065 km/h) at sea level

Range: ferry range 2,100 nm (2,418 miles; 3891 km) with empty tanks dropped or 1,750 nm (2,015 miles; 3,243 km) with empty tanks retained; combat radius 90 nm (103 miles; 167 km) after STO on a lo-lo-lo attack mission with a 1-hour loiter carrying 12 500-lb (227-kg) bombs, or 480 nm (553 miles; 889 km) after STO on a hi-lo-hi attack mission with seven 500-lb (227-kg) bombs, or 627 nm (722 miles; 1162 km) on a hi-hi-hi interception mission with two AIM-9 Sidewinder AAMs and two drop tanks, or 100 nm (115 miles; 185 km) for a 3-hour CAP

Performance: take-off run 1,330 ft (405 m) at maximum take-off weight; landing run 0 ft (0 m) at normal landing weight

g limits: -3 to +8

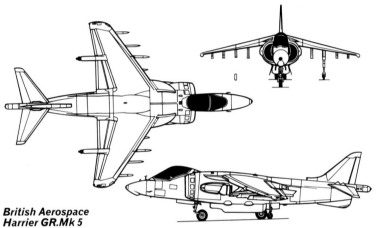

British Aerospace Harrier GR.Mk 5

Harrier Conversion Team on 1 March 1987, although delays in refining the INS and clearing the ejection seat prevented the team (later absorbed into No. 233 OCU) from beginning conversion until July 1988. No. 1 Squadron was declared operational on the GR.Mk 5 in November 1989, with No. 3 Sqn following suit in April 1990. GR.Mk 5s were also delivered to the SAOEU at Boscombe Down, for tactical and operational trials and development work.

Aircraft Nos 42-60 were completed to an interim **GR.Mk 5A** standard, with provision for GR.Mk 7 avionics, and were delivered straight into storage to await conversion to full night-attack standard. Surviving GR.Mk 5s are also being converted to the same standard. A handful of GR.Mk 5s remain with the OCU, now known as No. 20 (Reserve) Squadron at RAF Wittering (formerly 233 OCU), but are being returned to BAe for GR.Mk 7 conversion.

British Aerospace/McDonnell Douglas **Harrier GR.Mk 7**

The **Harrier GR.Mk 7** is basically the **RAF** equivalent of the night attack AV-8B, using much of the same equipment and avionics. It has the same overnose bulge housing the same GEC Sensors FLIR, but lacks the rear fuselage chaff/flare dispensers. The redundant fairing for MIRLS is also absent, and is replaced by the definitive undernose forward hemisphere antennas for the Marconi Zeus ECM system, which will replace the USMC's AN/ALR-67 when it is finally cleared for service. The Harrier GR.Mk 7 also has an NVG-compatible cockpit, allowing use of Ferranti Night-Owl NVGs instead of the GEC Cat's Eyes NVGs used by the USMC. A GEC digital colour map is fitted, in place of the old projected moving map. The first GR.Mk 7s ordered as such were the 34 aircraft requested during 1988, which took total RAF Harrier II procurement to 94 (plus two prototype/pre-series aircraft). To serve as GR.Mk 7 prototypes, both pre-series aircraft were adapted to accommodate the overnose FLIR and undernose Zeus antennas, the first flying in its new guise on 20 November 1989.

The additional capability offered by the GR.Mk 7 was such that it was soon decided

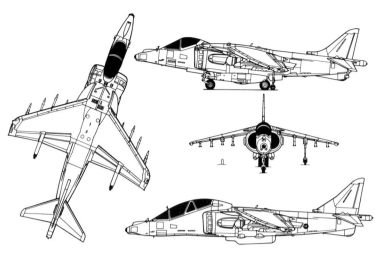

that all RAF Harriers would be retrofitted to this configuration, and to ease this process aircraft Nos 42-60 were completed as GR.Mk 5As with provision for GR.Mk 7 avionics (with an empty FLIR hump and Zeus antenna fairings) and were delivered straight to storage to await conversion. Conversions of these aircraft (and a damaged GR.Mk 5) began during December 1990, most of the former GR.Mk 5As going to No. 1 Squadron and No. 20 Squadron.

The first production GR.Mk 7 was delivered in May 1990, with service deliveries beginning in August 1990 to the Strike Attack OEU at Boscombe Down, which has used a handful of GR.Mk 7s to develop and refine operational procedures, tactics and equipment. The OEU's work has, by necessity, been largely unsung, but it has been their efforts that have enabled a much-troubled new aircraft, hampered by the non-availability of many important equipment items, to enter productive service. The unit's work with NVGs and FLIR has opened up a whole new range of possibilities for the Harrier force. Production GR.Mk 7s were delivered to No. IV Squadron (to replace first-generation GR.Mk 3s) from September 1990, and began to supplant GR.Mk 5s with No. 3 Squadron in November 1990.

From aircraft No. 77 (ZG506) all RAF Harriers have been fitted with the so-called 100 per cent LERX, which further delays the onset of wing rock and improves turn performance. These are similar to the LERXes originally designed for BAe's 'big wing' second-generation Harrier, and will replace the smaller compromise LERX on earlier aircraft by retrofit.

The failure of the MIRLS recce system designed for the Harrier GR.Mk 5 resulted in the GR.Mk 7 totally lacking any reconnaissance capability, although installation of a US Navy linescan housed in an external pod is a possible later upgrade. The Vinten Vicon 18 Srs 403 recce pod and Vicon 57 multi-sensor pod have also both been evaluated. When the RAF needed to replace Jaguars being used in Turkey to police the northern 'No-Fly Zone' over Iraq (Operation Warden), Harrier GR.Mk 7s were selected. In order to

Above: Harrier GR.Mk 7s were deployed to Incirlik, replacing Jaguars as part of Operation Warden in April 1993. They carried GR.Mk 3-vintage Vinten recce pods.

Right: Operation Warden aircraft are mix of GR.Mk 7s from Nos 3 and IV Sqns (which replaced Jaguars in April 1993). Up to 15 aircraft have been deployed from RAF Laarbrüch as No. 4 Composite Sqn.

give some recce capability, at least nine aircraft were rewired (at a cost of 600 man-hours per aircraft) to carry the old Harrier GR.Mk 3 recce pod, which contained only optical cameras, comprising a fan of four F95 cameras with 70-mm lenses and a single F135 with a 127-mm lens. No. IV Squadron had to hurriedly retrain in the recce role (which had been dropped when the GR.Mk 3 had been relinquished). Eight of the aircraft (all with the original 65 per cent LERX) were flown out to Turkey on 2 April 1993. Aircraft from No.IV Sqn have been fitted with the 100 per cent unit.

By the time some minor problems have been ironed out, the GR.Mk 7 will be an extremely versatile and effective aircraft. The twin Royal Ordnance Factory ADEN 25-mm pneumatically-cocked revolver cannon promises lower recoil, much faster initial rate of fire (important when firing short bursts) and lighter weight than the single GAU-12A fitted to US aircraft. The Plessey Missile Approach Warning System will automatically activate appropriate countermeasures and will augment Zeus, which consists of an indigenous RWR and a Northrop jammer and which will jam CW and pulse radars. Provision of a dedicated Sidewinder pylon (when cleared for use) will allow adequate defensive capability even when carrying a full offensive load. The eventual provi-

British Aerospace Harrier GR.Mk 7 (Harrier T.Mk 10 side view)

sion of an integral BOL chaff dispenser in these pylons will finally free the aircraft from having to 'loose' a pylon in order to carry a standard Phimat pod.

Some No. 1 Squadron aircraft have already had their FIN1075 INAS upgraded to FIN1075G standards, with the incorporation of a GPS receiver. The first aircraft so equipped (ZD437) flew with the new kit on 19 November 1992. The presence of GPS can be discerned by the addition of a small circular antenna on the aircraft spine. The armament of 1,000-lb (454kg) bombs, BL755s and 68-mm SNEB rocket pods is being augmented by CRV-7 rockets and CBU-87 cluster bombs, as used by RAF Jaguars during the Gulf War.

No. 1 Squadron received GR.Mk 7s during late 1992, and became the first front-line

unit to start night-attack training in earnest. Co-located No. 20 Reserve Squadron (the renumbered No. 233 OCU) also now flies GR.Mk 7s, while fully-equipped Nos 3 and IV Squadrons moved to Laarbrüch and the control of NATO's Rapid Reaction Force when RAF Gütersloh, Germany, closed in 1993.

SPECIFICATION

British Aerospace/McDonnell Douglas Harrier GR.Mk 7
generally similar to the British Aerospace/McDonnell Douglas Harrier GR.Mk 5 except in the following particulars:
Weights: operating empty 15,542 lb (7050 kg) including pilot and unused fuel

Left: A Harrier GR.Mk 7 of No. IV(AC) Squadron formates with one of its Harrier GR.Mk 3 siblings. As delivered, the RAF's GR.Mk 7s lacked the undernose fairing for the MIRLS (Miniature Infra-Red LineScan) provided for on the GR.Mk 5, and instead have two undernose Zeus ECM antennas and a FLIR housing above the nose. Note the lack of cannon.

Right: This No. 20 Sqn aircraft displays the '100 per cent LERX' which is being retrofitted to the entire fleet.

British Aerospace/McDonnell Douglas Harrier T.Mk 10

Having amply confirmed the usefulness of the two-seat **Harrier T.Mk 4** to expedite the demanding conversion from conventional fixed-wing aircraft to V/STOL's unique technique, the RAF sought to purchase a trainer fully representative of the second-generation Harrier GR.Mk 5/7's performance, equipment and capability. An interim solution of bringing existing T.Mk 4s up to **T.Mk 6** standard by fitting night-attack avionics would not have fully simulated GR.Mk 5 or GR.Mk 7 performance, and was abandoned in favour of a version based on the American TAV-8B. An additional disadvantage of the T.Mk 6 was that all existing T.Mk 4 airframes are now quite old, and are becoming structurally tired. New production of two-seat first-generation Harriers would have been possible, but offered few advantages and many disadvan-tages. A decision to proceed with what is now designated the **Harrier T.Mk 10** was taken in February 1990 and an order for 13 was confirmed early in 1992. Powered by the Pegasus Mk 105 engine, the T.Mk 10, which first flew on 7 April 1994, will be fully combat-capable with standard avionics and an ability to use a variety of weapons. In this respect it differs from its US counter-part, which carries only training armament.

SPECIFICATION

British Aerospace/McDonnell Douglas Harrier T.Mk 10
generally similar to the Harrier GR.Mk 5/7 except in the following particulars
Fuselage and tail: length 51 ft 9.5 in (15.79 m)
Fuel and load: internal fuel 7,306 lb (3314 kg)

Canadair CF-5/NF-5 Freedom Fighter

Canadair Group, Bombardier Inc., Cartierville Airport
1800 Laurentian Boulevard
St Laurent, Quebec, Canada H4R 1K2

In 1965 the Northrop F-5 was selected for what in 1968 became the NATO Canadian Forces (Air Element). Canadair Ltd at Montreal was chosen to build the aircraft under licence in two versions: the single-seat Canadair **CF-5A** and dual-control tandem-seat **CF-5D**.

Several major improvements were incorporated, the most important being uprated engines (licence-manufactured by Orenda Engines, also of Montreal) and the fitting of an inflight-refuelling probe. Soon after manufacture started, the **Royal Netherlands air force** placed an order with Canadair for 105 of the single-seater, under the local designation **NF-5A**. This had automatically-scheduled leading-edge manoeuvre flaps, Doppler navigation radar and 229-Imp gal (1041-litre) drop tanks. Manufacture involved participation of Netherlands companies but was integrated with CF-5 production, all assembly being by Canadair. In addition, four CF-5Ds, designated **VF-5**, were built for **Venezuela** in a government-to-government transaction which also included 16 ex-RCAF CF-5As.

The first CF-5A flew at Cartierville on 6 May 1968, and the type entered service with the **Canadian Armed Forces** later in the same year. The NF-5 entered Dutch service in 1969. To bring the CAF (Air Element) back up to full strength a follow-on order was placed for 20 additional CF-5Ds, and these brought the CF-5 total of all versions up to 240. The last example was delivered in 1975, the CAF designation being **CF-116**.

Replaced in the fighter-bomber role by Hornets, Canada's Freedom Fighters (14 CF-5As and 23 CF-5Ds) equip No. 419 Squadron, which functions as an advanced jet/tactical training pre-OCU unit. Detachable inflight-refuelling probes once fitted for rapid deployment/NATO reinforcement exercises now allow the aircraft to be used to teach students the rudiments of inflight refuelling.

The CF-5A can be fitted with a camera nose, containing three Vinten cameras, each with a 70-mm lens. When so fitted the aircraft are known as **CF-5A(R)s** or **CF-116A(R)s**. In Canadian service, these aircraft are retained mainly to allow a few instructors to remain recce qualified. Two-seaters cannot be fitted with the camera nose, or the inflight-refuelling probe.

After nearly 25 years' service, a comprehensive upgrade programme was authorised in 1991 by the Canadian government, with Bristol Aerospace responsible for the two-part programme. Modified aircraft serve as lead-in weapons trainers for the CF-18 Hornet force. The first stage involves airframe refurbishment and strengthening (wings, fins, control surfaces and replacement of undercarriages) to give a progressive extension of up to 2,000 flying hours. The avionics upgrade includes a GEC-Ferranti HUD/weapons aiming system featuring Hornet symbology, Litton laser INS, GEC Avionics air data computer, MIL STD 1553B digital databus, HOTAS controls, radar altimeter and new radio. Following the maiden flight of a refurbished two-seat CF-5D on 14 June 1991, a total of 11 CF-5As and all 33 CF-5Ds are scheduled to be modified.

A number of military customers have purchased the CF-5 and NF-5 following their retirement from the active inventories of the CAF and the Dutch KLu. Of these, **Turkey** is by far the largest operator, receiving at least 60 ex-Canadian CF-5s, and additional ex-Dutch NF-5As from 1992 to augment its already substantial F-5 fleet. The **Greek** F-5 fleet has also been supplemented by some 12 ex-Royal Netherlands air force NF-5s delivered in March 1991.

Venezuela's surviving 13 CF-5As and single CF-5D have not flown since May 1990, but have been augmented by a single NF-5A and five NF-5Bs, refurbished by Fokker before delivery. The CF-5D and one CF-5A were sent to Singapore for upgrade by Singapore Aerospace, and seven more are due to be upgraded and refurbished in-country in association with Singapore Aerospace. After upgrade, the aircraft will rejoin 36 Escuadrón. Three Venezuelan F-5s were reported destroyed when their Barquisimeto base was strafed during the 1992 coup.

One of No. 419 Squadron's CF-5A(R)s in flight, showing to advantage its camera nose and optional inflight-refuelling probe. The three-tone grey/blue air superiority camouflage is typical of current CAF Freedom Fighters.

SPECIFICATION

Canadair CF-5A
generally similar to the Northrop F-5A Freedom Fighter except in the following particulars:
Wing: span 25 ft 3 in (7.70 m) without tip tanks and 25 ft 9 in (7.85 m) with tip tanks; aspect ratio 3.67; area 174.00 sq ft (16.16 m²)
Powerplant: two Orenda (General Electric) J85-CAN-15 each rated at 4,300 lb st (19.13 kN) with afterburning
Weights: empty equipped 8,681 lb (3938 kg); normal take-off 14,150 lb (6418 kg); maximum take-off 20,390 lb (9249 kg)
Speed: maximum level speed 'clean' at 36,000 ft (10975 m) 848 kt (977 mph; 1572 km/h)
Performance: maximum rate of climb at sea level 33,000 ft (19958 m) per minute; take-off run 1,900 ft (579 m) at 13,400 lb (6078 kg)

Canadair CF-5A

Canadair CL-66 (CC-109) Cosmopolitan

Canadian production of the Convair 540 began in 1960 (as the **Canadair CL-66 Cosmopolitan**) using Convair-supplied jigs and tools. It was powered by 3,500-eshp (2612-kW) Napier Eland NEl 6 turboprops. Ten aircraft for the Royal Canadian Air Force were designated **CC-109**. Eight aircraft were re-engined in 1966 with 3,750-eshp (2798-kW) Allison 501D-13 turboprops (to CV-580 standard), and were being withdrawn prematurely at Ottawa during 1994.

Six surviving CL-66s serve with No. 412 Squadron at Uplands in the VIP role, having had EFIS (Electronic Flight Instrumentation System) cockpits added in the late 1980s.

SPECIFICATION

Canadair CL-66 Cosmopolitan
Wing: span 105 ft 4 in (32.11 m); aspect ratio 12.06; area 920.00 sq ft (89.54 m²)

Fuselage and tail: length 81 ft 6 in (24.85 m); height 28 ft 2 in (8.59 m)
Powerplant: two Allison 501-D13 each rated at 3,750 ehp (2796 ekW)
Weights: basic empty 32,333 lb (14666 kg); maximum take-off 53,200 lb (24130 kg)
Fuel and load: external fuel none; maximum payload

14,300 lb (6486 kg)
Speed: maximum level speed 'clean' at optimum altitude 295 kt (340 mph; 547 km/h); maximum cruising speed at 20,000 ft (6095 m) 280 kt (322 mph; 518 km/h)
Range: ferry range 1,975 nm (2,274 miles; 3660 km) with auxiliary fuel; range 1,080 nm (1,244 miles;

1996 km) with 48 passengers
Performance: climb to 20,000 ft (6095 m) in 15 minutes 36 seconds; take-off run 4,550 ft (1388 m) at maximum take-off weight; landing run 4,020 ft (1226 m) at maximum landing weight

Canadair **CL-41 (CT-114) Tutor**

One of the first generation of pure jet aircraft designed from the outset as a trainer, the **Canadair CL-41 Tutor** side-by-side two-seat basic trainer is expected to remain in the active inventory of the Air Command of the **Canadian Forces** past the year 2000. Conceived as a private venture and adopted by the then Royal Canadian Air Force after evaluation of all contemporary Western aircraft in its category, the Tutor was first flown on 13 January 1960, two prototypes being followed by delivery of the first series aircraft on 16 December 1963. A total of 190 was built for the Canadian service and, of these, about 130 currently remain – including some in storage – all having undergone progressive avionics and equipment updating.

Allocated the service designation **CT-114**, the Tutor equips No. 2 Flying Training School at Moose Jaw. Students receive 140 hours on this type to wings standard, while future combat pilots undergo a further 60 Tutor hours. Moose Jaw is also the home of the Tutor-equipped national aerobatic team, the 'Snowbirds', and, at Winnipeg, the Central Flying School utilises the Tutor for instructor training.

Production deliveries of the Tutor to the Canadian service, completed on 28 September 1966, were followed by 20 examples of an export model, the **CL-41G**, supplied to the Royal Malaysian air force between 17 May and 30 November 1967. Dubbed **Tebuan** (Wasp) in Malaysian service, the CL-41G was a dual-role aircraft, combining training and light attack tasks. Powered by a 2,950-lb st (13.12-kN) General Electric J85-J4 turbojet, it featured six wing stations for

up to 3,500 lb (1590 kg) of ordnance. It equipped No. 9 'Jebat' (Civet) Squadron for training and No. 6 'Naga' (Dragon) Squadron for light strike duties. The Tebuan was withdrawn in the mid-1980s, as a result of fatigue and corrosion problems, although six were retained in flyable storage.

The second prototype Tutor was adapted as an experimental systems trainer under the designation **CL-41R**, and possessed a standard of avionics fit similar to the F-104G Starfighter.

SPECIFICATION

Canadair CL-41A Tutor
Wing: span 36 ft 5.9 in (11.13 m); aspect ratio 6.06; area 220.00 sq ft (20.44 m²)
Fuselage and tail: length 32 ft 0 in (9.75 m); height 9 ft 3.75 in (2.84 m); tailplane span 13 ft 7 in (4.16 m); wheel track 13 ft 2.25 in (4.02 m); wheel base 11 ft 1 in (3.38 m)
Powerplant: one Orenda (General Electric) J85-CAN-J4 rated at 2,950 lb st (13.12 kN) dry
Weights: empty equipped 4,895 lb (2220 kg); normal take-off 7,397 lb (3355 kg); maximum take-off 7,788 lb (3532 kg)
Fuel and load: internal fuel 309 US gal (1170 litres); external fuel none; maximum ordnance none
Speed: maximum level speed 'clean' at 28,500 ft (8685 m) 432 kt (498 mph; 801 km/h)
Range: 541 nm (623 miles; 1002 km)
Performance: service ceiling 43,000 ft (13105 m); take-off distance to 50 ft (15 m) 2,250 ft (686 m) at maximum take-off weight; landing distance from 50 ft (15 m) 2,200 ft (671 m) at normal landing weight

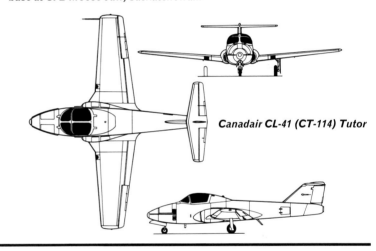

No. 2 Canadian Forces Flying Training School (CFFTS) operates the majority of Canada's surviving Tutors from its base at CFB Moose Jaw, Saskatchewan.

Canadair CL-41 (CT-114) Tutor

Canadair **CL-215/215T/415**

Intended as a dedicated fire-fighter, the **Canadair CL-215** has served in a variety of other roles. Following its maiden flight on 23 October 1967, the aircraft was initially built in four production batches totalling some 80 aircraft. The majority of orders were for the fire-fighting variant, comprising eight Canadian provinces (49), France's Sécurité Civile (15), the **Italian air force**'s 15° Stormo (five, later transferred to a nominally civilian unit) and **Venezuela** (two equipped as passenger transports). The CL-215 was also delivered to the **Greek air force**, with 19 aircraft currently serving with 355 Mira at Elefsis, and to the former **Yugoslav air force**, the current status of whose five aircraft is uncertain. In addition, a number of aircraft fully configured for the SAR role have been delivered to the **Spanish air force** (eight of a total of 26 delivered) and the **Royal Thai navy** (two).

The aircraft is a boat-type amphibian, with two piston engines mounted on an untapered high wing. The interior may be used to carry 8,000 lb (3629 kg) of cargo, 26 passengers, or, in the fire-fighting version, two 588-Imp gal (2573-litre) water tanks (this water load weighs about 13,228 lb/6000 kg). The tanks may be replenished by retractable 'pickup probes' (similar to air inlets) on each side of the hull bottom. The

aircraft can be loaded initially with water or chemical retardants at its home base, which may be on water or a land airfield. When this load has been expended, the aircraft skims across the nearest moderately smooth body of water (fresh or salt), refilling the tanks in 10 seconds. This load is then dropped and the aircraft returns for another load. Full loads have been collected in runs across 6-ft (1.8-m) waves. In 1983 a Yugoslav CL-215 made 225 drops on fires in a single day.

When the last CL-215 (of 125 built) was delivered in May 1990 to the Greek air force, plans were already underway at Canadair for the development of a turboprop variant. Two Quebec CL-215s were modified as **CL-215T** prototypes, the first

of these making its initial flight on 8 June 1989. This version utilises the well-proven airframe of the piston-engined CL-215, but replaces scarce Pratt & Whitney R-2800 radial engines with more efficient and lighter P&W Canada PW123 turboprops. These necessitate the fitment of wingtip endplates and auxiliary finlets for increased lateral stability. Other modifications include powered flying controls, a new electrical system, pressure refuelling and an upgraded flight deck. The Spanish air force has been the sole military customer for this version, receiving a total of 15 conversion kits for the aircraft of Grupo 43 at Torrejon.

Following the receipt in 1991 of a firm order from the French government for 12 new-production aircraft, the formal launch

took place of the **CL-415**. This designation has been introduced to distinguish new-build aircraft from retrofitted CL-215Ts. First deliveries, initially in firefighting configuration, are scheduled to take place during 1994 and it is envisaged that the aircraft will then be developed for utility transport, passenger and maritime reconnaissance/ASW applications. The first CL-415 flew on 8 December 1993.

A Hellenic air force CL-215 in flight, wearing the standard bright yellow and orange colour scheme applied to most examples of this versatile twin-engined amphibian. Greek CL-215s are used primarily as water bombers.

Canadair CL-215

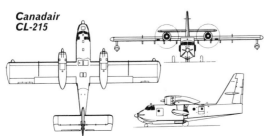

SPECIFICATION

Canadair CL-415
Wing: span 93 ft 11 in (28.63 m); aspect ratio 8.2; area 1,080.00 sq ft (100.33 m²)
Fuselage and tail: length 65 ft 0.5 in (19.82 m); height 29 ft 5.5 in (8.98 m) on land or 22 ft 7 in (6.88 m) on water; tailplane span 36 ft 0 in (10.97 m); wheel track 17 ft 4 in (5.28 m); wheel base 23 ft 9 in (7.23 m)
Powerplant: two Pratt & Whitney Canada PW123AF each rated at 2,380 shp (1775 kW)
Weights: operating empty 27,190 lb (12333 kg) as a water bomber or 26,630 lb (12079 kg) as a utility aeroplane; maximum take-off 43,850 lb (19731 kg) as a land-based water bomber or 37,850 lb (17168 kg) as a water-based water bomber or as a land/water-based utility aeroplane
Fuel and load: internal fuel 10,250 lb (4649 kg);

external fuel none; maximum payload (waterbomber) 13,500 lb (6123 kg) or 9,770 lb (4431 kg) as a utility aeroplane
Speed: maximum cruising speed at 10,000 ft (3050 m) 203 kt (234 mph; 376 km/h); economical cruising speed at 10,000 ft (3050 m) 145 kt (167 mph; 269 km/h)

Thailand's CL-215s serve with the navy's No. 2 Squadron, based at U-Tapao alongside Lake Buccaneers, GAF Nomads (Searchmasters) and Fokker F27s in the sea search, transport and surveillance roles.

Range: ferry range 1,300 nm (1,497 miles; 2409 km) with a 1,000-lb (454-kg) payload
Performance: maximum rate of climb at sea level 1,375 ft (419 m) per minute; take-off run 2,700 ft (823 m) from land and 2,670 ft (814 m) from water at maximum take-off weight; landing run 2,210 ft (674 m)

on land and 2,180 ft (665 m) on water at 37,000 lb (16783 kg)
g limits: -1 to +3.25

Canadair **CL-600/-601 Challenger 600/601**

The Challenger business jet was designed by Bill Lear, of Learjet fame. It began life as the Learstar 600 but was to be much larger than any of his previous executive jets. Intended as a 14-seat aircraft, it would be able to accommodate up to 30 in a high-density configuration. The Learstar 600 was not built and, instead, Canadair bought the rights to the aircraft in 1976. The Canadian company carried out some extensive redesign (including the addition of a T-tail) and it was another two years before the maiden flight of the revised aircraft, known as **Challenger**. Deliveries began soon after type certification in November 1978.

The initial model, the **Challenger 600**, was powered by two 7,500-lb (33.36-kN) Avco Lycoming ALF-502 turbofans. It was followed by the **Challenger 601**, externally identifiable by its distinctive winglets and powered by uprated General Electric CF34 engines. Both variants are in military service. The first military customer was **Canada**, with an order for 12 Model 600s. Seven of these airframes were extensively re-equipped to serve as **CE-144** electronic support and training aircraft to replace the Dassault Falcon 20 (CC-117) with No. 414 Squadron at Cold Lake, Alberta, and these wear a toned-down tactical grey colour scheme. The eighth aircraft is used as an avionics and electronic systems testbed, under the designation **CX-144**.

Four further Challenger 600s are operated by No. 412 Squadron at Edmonton as VIP transports under the designation **CC-144**, wearing overall gloss white with a red

lightning flash along the fuselage. All of these Challengers have since been upgraded to **Challenger 600S** standard with the addition of winglets, but there is no associated change in their Canadian Armed Forces designation. In 1985 four Model 601s (still CC-144s) were delivered to supplement the VIP fleet.

Challenger 601s also fly missions for the Luftwaffe VIP transport unit, the FBS. The first of seven aircraft was delivered 'green' to Dornier for outfitting in 1986. Five are configured as 12-16 passenger transports, one as a passenger-cargo combi aircraft and one as an air ambulance with accommodation for stretchers. A pair of Challenger 600s serves as VIP aircraft with No. 2 Squadron of the **Royal Malaysian Air Force** at Kuala Lumpur. Three Challenger 601s have also been delivered to the **People's Liberation Army Air Force in China**.

One of No. 2 Squadron, Royal Malaysian Air Force's two Canadair CL-600s, used primarily for transporting government VIPs. The aircraft thus carry a semi-military scheme, using the national flag instead of the simplified air force insignia.

SPECIFICATION

Canadair Challenger 601
Wing: span 64 ft 4 in (19.61 m) including winglets; aspect ratio 8.5; area 520.00 sq ft (48.31 m²) excluding winglets
Powerplant: two General Electric CF34-1A each rated at 8,650 lb st (38.48 kN) dry without automatic power reserve and 9,140 lb st (40.66 kN) dry with automatic power reserve
Weights: manufacturer's empty 19,950 lb (9049 kg); operating empty 24,585 lb (11151 kg); maximum take-off 43,100 lb (19950 kg)
Fuel and load: internal fuel 16,665 lb (7559 kg); external fuel none; maximum payload 4,915 lb

(2229 kg) declining to 2,000 lb (907 kg) with maximum fuel
Speed: maximum cruising speed at optimum altitude 459 kt (529 mph; 851 km/h); normal cruising speed at optimum altitude 442 kt (509 mph; 819 km/h); economical cruising speed at optimum altitude 424 kt (488 mph; 786 km/h)

Canadair Challenger 601

Range: 3,440 nm (3,961 miles; 6375 km) with five passengers
Performance: climb to initial cruising altitude in 21 minutes; maximum operating altitude 45,000 ft (12495 m); balanced take-off field length 5,400 ft (1646 m) at maximum take-off weight; landing run 3,550 ft (1082 m) at normal landing weight

Cardoen **CB 206L-III**

Industrias Cardoen LTDA, Aeropuerto Los Cerrillos
Los Conquistadores 1700, Piso 28
Santiago, Chile

Industrias Cardoen in Chile initiated development in 1988 of an adaptation of the Bell 206L-III LongRanger transport helicopter (described separately) as a multi-role military helicopter. Based on imported commercial LongRangers, two prototypes of the multi-purpose **CB 206L-III** have been produced, the first of which entered flight test on 8 December 1989.

Cardoen's CB 206L-III differs from the LongRanger primarily in having a front fuselage of narrower cross-section featuring flat-plate cockpit transparencies. Intended primarily as a gunship, the CB 206L-III is armed with gun or rocket pods, or anti-armour missiles mounted on pylons above the skid-type undercarriage, although it may be additionally configured for FLIR training, anti-drug patrol, crop spraying and police work.

A prototype was sent to the USA for FAA certification, under the auspices of Global Helicopter Technologies in Texas. Flight trials were successful but certification was witheld because of suspected Iraqi involvement in the programme.

SPECIFICATION

Cardoen CB 206L-III
Rotor system: main rotor diameter 37 ft 0 in (11.28 m); tail rotor diameter 5 ft 5 in (1.65 m); main rotor disc area 1,075.21 sq ft (99.89 m²); tail rotor disc area 23.04 sq ft (2.14 m²)
Fuselage and tail: length overall, rotors turning 42 ft 8.5 in (13.02 m); height overall 10 ft 3.75 in (3.14 m) to top of rotor head; stabiliser span 6 ft 6 in (1.98 m); skid track 7 ft 8.25 in (2.34 m)
Powerplant: one Allison 250-C30P rated at 650 shp

(485 kW) for take-off and 557 shp (415 kW) for continuous running
Weights: maximum take-off 4,250 lb (1927 kg)
Speed: never-exceed speed at sea level 130 kt (150 mph; 241 km/h); maximum cruising speed at 5,000 ft (1525 m) 110 kt (126 mph; 203 km/h)
Performance: maximum rate of climb at sea level 1,340 ft (408 m) per minute; service ceiling 20,000 ft (6,095 m); hovering ceiling 16,500 ft (5030 m) in ground effect and 5,400 ft (1645 m) out of ground effect

Cardoen CB 206L-III

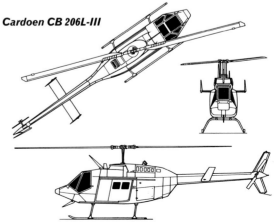

CASA/SIAT 223 Flamingo

Construcciones Aeronauticas SA
Avenida de Aragón 404 (PO Box 193)
E-28022 Madrid, Spain

Siebelwerke-ATG (SIAT) was formed in 1952, and later became part of the MBB concern. Its first design was a four-seat touring aircraft, followed by the **SIAT 223 Flamingo**, which first flew on 1 March 1967. This all-metal side-by-side two-seat trainer had a tricycle undercarriage, and was offered in two versions, the utility **SIAT 223A1** 2+2 trainer and the single/two-seat **SIAT 223K1** aerobatic version. SIAT/MBB built 50 aircraft (including 15 for the Turkish air force) before pro-

duction was transferred to Hispano (subsequently CASA) in Spain. The first Spanish Flamingo flew on 14 February 1972 and a further 49 were built. **Syria** reportedly took 48, and about 30 are believed to remain in service for primary training.

SPECIFICATION

SIAT 223A1 Flamingo
Wing: span 8.28 m (27 ft 2 in); aspect ratio 5.96; area

11.50 m² (123.79 sq ft)
Fuselage and tail: length 7.43 m (24 ft 4.5 in); height 2.70 m (8 ft 10.25 in); tailplane span 3.20 m (10 ft 6 in); wheel track 2.75 m (9 ft 0 in); wheel base 1.82 m (5 ft 11.5 in)
Powerplant: one Textron Lycoming IO-360-C1B rated at 200 hp (149 kW)
Weights: empty equipped 685 kg (1,510 lb); normal take-off 1050 kg (2,315 lb); maximum take-off 980 kg (2,160 lb)
Fuel and load: internal fuel 220 litres (58 US gal); external fuel none; ordnance none

Speed: maximum level speed 'clean' at optimum altitude 132 kt (153 mph; 245 km/h); cruising speed at optimum altitude 118 kt (136 mph; 219 km/h)
Range: 475 nm (547 miles; 880 km)
Performance: maximum rate of climb at sea level 270 m (886 ft) per minute; service ceiling 4300 m (14,110 ft); take-off run 705 ft (215 m) at maximum take-off weight

CASA 101 Aviojet

Designed by CASA with assistance from MBB and Northrop (which provided the Norcasa wing section and inlet design) the **CASA C.101 Aviojet** has been built as a trainer and light strike aircraft, winning orders from Spain, Chile, Honduras and Jordan. A development contract was signed on 16 September 1975 covering the design, development and construction of four flying prototypes of a new jet trainer for the Spanish air force. It was intended as a replacement for the Hispano HA200/HA220 Saeta, and an eventual requirement for 120 was outlined. The first prototype made its maiden flight on 27 June 1977, and the last on 17 April 1978. All four were handed over to the air force for trials at the end of 1978.

The C.101 is of modular construction, to reduce cost and complexity, and ample space was deliberately left for avionics and equipment to meet any conceivable requirement. Features include a single turbofan of high bypass ratio for good fuel economy, fed by lateral inlets above the unswept wing, stepped tandem Martin-Baker Mk 10L zero/zero ejection seats, a pressurised cockpit with separate canopies which hinge to the right, levered-suspension landing gear with a non-steerable nose-wheel, fuel contained in integral tanks in the wings and a flexible cell in the fuselage with pressure fuelling, fixed wing leading edge, slotted flaps, powered ailerons but manual elevators and rudder, and a tailplane with electric variable incidence for trimming.

The most unusual feature is that not only is there provision for underwing stores but all versions have a large fuselage bay beneath the rear cockpit in which can be housed armament (see specification) or a reconnaissance camera, ECM jammer, laser designator or other devices.

An initial contract from the **Spanish air force** covered the purchase of 60 **C.101EB-01** trainers, which were given the local designation and name **E.25 Mirlo** (Blackbird). They are powered by the 3,500-lb st (15.57-kN) Garrett TFE731-2-2J turbofan. A second contract covered another 28 aircraft, the requirement being reduced by adoption of the Chilean ENAER Pillan for basic training. Spanish C.101s are operated by the General Air Academy at San Javier and by the two squadrons of Grupo 74 at Matacan, which provide refresher flying for 'ground tour' pilots, and by trials unit Grupo 54 at Torrejon. C.101s of the Air Academy form the national 'Team Aguila' formation aerobatic display team. All aircraft received a nav/attack system modernisation between 1990 and 1992.

The **C.101EB** proved to have a better-

than-predicted performance at low level, but was disappointing at higher altitude. Thus the export **C.101BB** attack/trainer was powered by a TFE731-3-1J giving an extra 200 lb (0.89 kN) of thrust, and uses the aircraft's built-in provision for armament (Spanish C.101EBs have hardpoints, but these are not used). Six underwing pylons are provided for loads of up to 500 kg (1,100 lb), 375 kg (825 lb) and 250 kg (550 lb) going from wingroot to tip. The aircraft uses the underfuselage bay for quick-change packages of recce pack, ECM, laser designator or twin 12.7-mm machine-gun pack, as an alternative to the DEFA 30-mm cannon pod mounted on the centreline.

The **C.101BB-02** was exported to Chile, who received four CASA-built aircraft and eight built by ENAER. All are designated as **T-36** in service, and although intended for advanced training were modified with ranging radar in the nose and serve as tactical weapons trainers with 1 Grupo, Ala 4 of I Brigada. A 1984 order for five further ENAER-built aircraft, with options on 23 more, is believed to have been converted to an order for **C.101CC**s. Four very similar **C.101BB-03**s were delivered to **Honduras**.

The **C.101CC** first flew on 16 November 1983 and is a dedicated attack aircraft, powered by the 4,300-lb st (19.13-kN) TFE731-5-1J engine. The engine has a military power reserve (available for periods of up to five minutes) of 4,700 lb st (20.91 kN). There is no increase in maximum weapon load, since the pylons have not been changed, but an increase in maximum take-off weight allows more fuel to be carried with a given weapon load.

The **C.101CC-02** was ordered by **Chile** as the **A-36 Halcon** (Hawk). A first example was CASA-built, and was followed by an initial 19 ENAER-assembled aircraft, which incorporated a progressively increasing proportion of locally manufactured systems and components, which may eventually include entire forward fuselages. The aircraft serves alongside the T-36 with 1 Grupo, and with 12 Grupo, Ala 3, IV Brigada. The first A-36 briefly served as a demonstrator for the proposed **A-36M**, with dummy BAe Sea Eagle missiles underwing, but this project floundered. Sixteen examples of the **C.101CC-04** have also been delivered to **Jordan** to serve as advanced trainers with the King Hussein Air College at Mafraq.

On 25 May 1985 CASA flew the prototype **C.101DD**, powered by the TFE731-5-1J engine and with new avionics, including a GEC Doppler, inertial platform and weapon

Spanish CASA C.101s are used for training, refresher flying and to equip the national aerobatic team ('Team Aguilla').

aiming computer, and a Ferranti HUD. The aircraft also has HOTAS controls, an ALR-66 RWR and a Vinten chaff/flare dispenser, and is compatible with the AGM-65 Maverick missile. Intended as an improved trainer and light strike aircraft, the new variant has yet to attract any orders. A similar aircraft has been submitted as a contender for the **USAF/USN** JPATS requirement.

SPECIFICATION

CASA C.101CC Aviojet
Wing: span 10.60 m (34 ft 9.375 in); aspect ratio 5.6; area 20.00 m² (215.29 sq ft)
Fuselage and tail: length 12.50 m (41 ft 0 in); height 4.25 m (13 ft 11.25 in); tailplane span 4.32 m (14 ft 2 in); wheel track 3.18 m (10 ft 5.25 in); wheel base 4.77 m (15 ft 7.75 in)
Powerplant: one Garrett TFE731-5-1J rated at 4,300 lb st (19.13 kN) dry normal and 4,700 lb st (20.91 kN) dry with military power reserve
Weights: empty equipped 3500 kg (7,716 lb); normal take-off 5000 kg (11,023 lb); maximum take-off 6300 kg (13,889 lb)
Fuel and load: internal fuel 1822 kg (4,017 lb); external fuel none; maximum ordnance 2250 kg (4,960 lb)
Speed: never-exceed speed 450 kt (518 mph; 834 km/h); maximum level speed 'clean' at 20,000 ft

(6,095 m) 435 kt (501 mph; 806 km/h) and at sea level 415 kt (478 mph; 769 km/h); economical cruising speed at 30,000 ft (9145 m) 354 kt (407 mph; 656 km/h)
Range: ferry range 2,000 nm (2,303 miles; 3706 km); combat radius 280 nm (322 miles; 519 km) on a lo-lo-lo interdiction mission with one cannon pod and four 250-kg (551-lb) bombs, or 200 nm (230 miles; 370 km) on a lo-lo-lo close support mission with cannon pack and four rocket launchers, or 170 nm (196 miles; 315 km) on a lo-lo-lo close support mission with cannon pack, four rocket launchers and two 125-kg (276-lb) bombs, or 325 nm (374 miles; 602 km) on a lo-lo-lo attack mission with cannon pack and two AGM-65 Maverick ASMs, or 520 nm (599 miles; 964 km) on a hi-lo-hi photo-reconnaissance mission, or 330 nm (380 miles; 611 km) on an ECM mission with a loiter of 3 hours 15 minutes, or 200 nm (230 miles; 370 km) on an armed patrol with gun pack and a loiter of 3 hours 30 minutes
Performance: maximum rate of climb at sea level 4,900 ft (1494 m) per minute at normal power and 6,100 ft (1859 m) per minute with MPR; climb to 25,000 ft (7620 m) in 6 minutes 30 seconds; service ceiling 42,000 ft (12800 m); take-off run 1,835 ft (559 m) at 4500 kg (9,921 lb); take-off distance to 50 ft (15 m) 2,460 ft (750 m) at 4500 kg (9,921 lb); landing distance from 50 ft (15 m) 2,625 ft (800 m) at 4700 kg (10,361 lb); landing run 1,575 ft (480 m) at 4700 kg (10,361 lb)
g limits: -3.9 to +7.5 at 4800 kg (10,582 lb) or -1 to +5.5 at 6300 kg (13,889 lb)

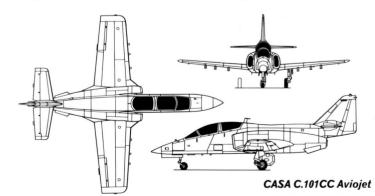

CASA C.101CC Aviojet

CASA 212 Aviocar

The dumpy **Aviocar** has developed into more than the useful light STOL transport conceived in Spain during the late 1960s. Intended to carry 16 equipped troops or 19 passengers, and able to load

cargo rapidly via its rear ramp, the prototype flew on 26 March 1971. Production began in the following year of the **Series 100**, powered by two Garrett TPE331-5 turboprops of 533 kW (715 shp) each. The Span-

ish air force was, naturally, an early customer and eventually received 79 of this variant, mainly the **T.12B (C.212A)** transport, but also a few **T.12C (C.212AV)** VIP aircraft, **TE.12B (C.212E1)** dual control

trainers and **TR.12A (C.212B1)** survey machines. Exports ranged between **Chile**, **Indonesia** and **Portugal**, where IPTN launched licensed production for Far East customers. Portugal has two **EC.212**s for

109

CASA 212 Aviocar

electronic intelligence gathering and ECM duties, these readily identifiable by their blunt noses and fin-tip pods containing antennas.

Installation from 1979 onwards of TPE331-10s rated at 679 kW (900 shp) resulted in the **C.212 Series 200**, which increases the earlier aircraft's 6500-kg (14,330-lb) maximum take-off weight to 7700 kg (16,975 lb) for normal operations or 8000 kg (17,637 lb) in military overload conditions. Spain bought three Series 200s for ECM training as the **TR.12D** and seven for SAR as the **D.3B**, The **D.3A** designation covered two T.12Bs converted for medevac. The SAR version, fitted with a prominent nose radome for an AN/APS-128 search radar (270° scan), is similar to the maritime patrol model used by **Mexico**, **Sweden** (designated **Tp 89**), **Sudan** and **Venezuela**.

Operational equipment is installed to meet individual requirements, but typically includes ESM equipment, MAD, sonobuoy launcher, sonobuoy data processing equipment, searchlight, FLIR and an underfuselage radome for 360° scanning radar. Homing torpedoes can be dropped, although no customer is confirmed as having taken up the option of Sea Skua or AS 15TT anti-ship missiles. Fisheries protection variants have less offensive equipment such as SLAR and pollution-detecting IR/UV sensors, such operators including **Sweden** and **Spain**. Transport Series 200 operators include **Abu Dhabi**, **Chad**, **Colombia**, **Djibouti**, **Equatorial Guinea**, **Ghana**, **Indonesia**, **Jordan**, **Myanmar**, **Nicaragua**, **Panama**, **Paraguay**, **Transkei**, **Uruguay**, **Venda**, **Venezuela** (navy) and **Zimbabwe**.

In **Series 300** form, flown in September 1984, the Aviocar has winglets but retains the -10 engines. The military **Series 300M**

has been bought in small numbers by **Angola**, **Bolivia**, **Bophuthatswana**, **Colombia**, **France** (**C.212C** civil version), **Lesotho**, **Panama, Venda** and the **US Coast Guard**, complemented by sales of the maritime patrol **300MP** to **Angola**, **Argentina** (coast guard), and the **Spanish** government. One standard transport Series 300 was modified for the **US Army** with undisclosed sensors as the prototype 'Grisly Hunter' drug interdiction aircraft; production conversions are based on the de Havilland Canada Dash 7 transport. At least four further Series 300s are used by the USAF for undisclosed missions, two operating in 1992 from Incirlik, Turkey, possibly into northern Iraq. **Chile** is also an operator but the sub-variant is not known. Sales of all C.212s had reached about 450 by 1993, including 155 Series 100s and 209 Series 200s. **Indonesia** contributed 126 to this total. Almost half have gone to civil customers.

SPECIFICATION

CASA C.212 Series 300 Aviocar
Wing: span 20.28 m (66 ft 6.5 in); aspect ratio 10.0; area 41.00 m² (441.33 sq ft)
Fuselage and tail: length 16.15 m (52 ft 11.75 in); height 6.60 m (21 ft 7.75 in); tailplane span 8.40 m (27 ft 6.75 in); wheel track 3.10 m (10 ft 2 in); wheel base 5.55 m (18 ft 2.5 in)
Powerplant: two Garrett TPE331-10R-513C each flat-rated at 900 shp (671 kW) without automatic power reserve and 925 shp (690 kW) with auto reserve
Weights: manufacturer's empty 3780 kg (8,333 lb); empty equipped 4400 kg (9,700 lb) in freight configuration; normal take-off 7700 kg (16,975 lb); maximum take-off 8000 kg (17,637 lb)
Fuel and load: internal fuel 1600 kg (3,527 lb) plus provision for one 1000-litre (264-US gal) or two 750-litre (198-US gal) ferry tanks in the cabin; external fuel

up to 800 kg (1,764 lb) in two 500-litre (132-US gal) underwing tanks; maximum payload 2820 kg (6,217 lb)
Speed: maximum operating speed 'clean' at optimum altitude 200 kt (230 mph; 370 km/h); maximum cruising speed at 10,000 ft (3050 m) 191 kt (220 mph; 354 km/h); economical cruising speed at 10,000 ft (3050 m) 162 kt (186 mph; 300 km/h)
Range: range 1,446 nm (1,665 miles; 2680 km) with maximum standard and auxiliary fuel and a 1192-kg (2,628-lb) payload, or 907 nm (1,045 miles; 1682 km)

with maximum standard fuel and a 2120-kg (4,674-lb) payload, or 450 nm (519 miles; 1433 km) with maximum payload
Performance: maximum rate of climb at sea level 1,630 ft (497 m) per minute; service ceiling 26,000 ft (7925 m); take-off distance to 50 ft (15 m) 2,000 ft (610 m) at maximum take-off weight; landing distance from 50 ft (15 m) 1,516 ft (462 m) at normal landing weight; landing run 935 ft (285 m) at normal landing weight

This CASA C.212-300 serves with the tiny air arm of Bophuthutswana. Other customers for this extraordinarily versatile light transport include the US Army National Guard and US Coast Guard.

CASA C.212 Series 300 Aviocar

CATIC J-9

China National Aero-Technology Import and Export Corporation
5 Liangguochang Road (PO Box 647)
Beijing 100010, People's Republic of China

The **CATIC J-9**, seen only in model form, and probably unbuilt, is an advanced tactical fighter aircraft apparently loosely based on **Mikoyan MiG-23** technology. MiG-23s were reportedly acquired from Egypt for evaluation in return for Chengdu F-7s and MiG-21/F-7 spare parts and support. The J-9 project is probably waiting for foreign orders or funding prior to prototype construction. Two slightly different J-9 configurations have been observed, each with a revised wing and with quite different intakes. The J-9 seems to combine a standard MiG-23 type fuselage with a new low-set fixed delta wing and with canard foreplanes on the engine intakes. This gives the aircraft a configuration reminiscent of the Saab 37 Viggen. Compared to the standard MiG-23, the J-9 has a slightly recon-

toured fin, with a square top, reduced leading-edge sweep and an abbreviated dorsal fin fillet. The folding ventral fin is unchanged. One configuration (possibly the first) had a simple delta wing and retained MiG-23-type intakes with variable intake ramps, while the second introduced leading-edge root extensions of greater sweep and intakes with variable shock-cone centrebodies. Both configurations appeared to retain the MiG-23's ventral cannon pod, and carried outboard underwing fuel tanks and inboard PL-10 air-to-air missiles. Because the aircraft is as yet unbuilt, it probably has not been assigned to a particular factory (eg. Harbin, Xian or Chengdu) and is thus listed under the broad CATIC (China National Aero-Technology Import and Export Corporation).

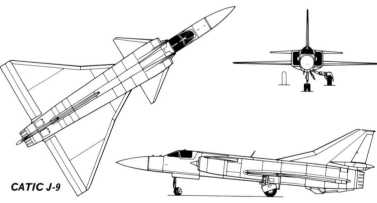

CATIC J-9

Cerva CE.43 Guépard

Cerva no longer exist

The **Cerva CE.43 Guépard** was an all-metal version of the **Wassmer 4/21 Prestige** lightplane, a four/five-seater powered by a 186-kW (250-hp) Lycoming IO-540 engine. The prototype flew on 18 May 1971, production ending in 1976 at 43 aircraft. Wassmer and Société Siren combined to form CERVA (the Consortium Européen de Realisation et de Ventes d'Avions). The French military was a customer, and 19 are still in service, most with the Centre d'Essais en Vol and one with the Aéronavale.

Cessna Model 150/152

Cessna Aircraft Company (Subsidiary of Textron Inc.)
PO Box 7706, Wichita, Kansas
67277-7706, USA

The **Model 150** was flown as a prototype on 15 September 1957, and entered production in the following August, marking Cessna's re-entry in the side-by-side two-seat lightplane market. Powered by a 100-hp (74.6-kW) Continental O-200-A, the Model 150 was built in sub-types A to

N, each embodying progressive improvements (eg. the **Models 150D** and **150F** respectively introduced a cut-down rear fuselage and a swept vertical tail). Reims licence-built Models 150F to M in France (as the **F150F** to **F150M**), and a fully aerobatic version of the standard Model 150 with a

strengthened airframe, the **Aerobat**. The **Model 152** was the Model 150M with a 110-hp (82-kW) Textron Lycoming O-235 engine. This, too, was licence-built by Reims and produced in an Aerobat version.

Both Models 150 and 152 were adopted by a number of air arms for primary tuition

and liaison tasks. Examples of the former (both built by the parent company and Reims) are currently serving with the **Burundi** army aviation (one), the **Haitian air corps** (three), the air component of the **Iranian army** (two), the **Ivory Coast** Air Transport and Liaison Group (two), the

Paraguayan navy (four), the **Somali aeronautical corps** (four, probably grounded), the **Peruvian air force** (two) and navy (one), and the air forces of **Sri Lanka** (two of five delivered) and **Zaïre** (15).

The Model 152 at present serves with the air components of the **Botswana defence force** (two), the **Gabonese air force** (one) and the **Mexican navy** (seven). In Aerobat form it is operated by the air forces of **Bolivia** (12) and **Ecuador** (four).

SPECIFICATION

Cessna Model 150
Wing: span 32 ft 8.5 in (9.97 m); aspect ratio 6.7; area 157.00 sq ft (14.59 m²)
Fuselage and tail: length 23 ft 11 in (7.29 m); height 8 ft 6 in (2.59 m); tailplane span 10 ft 0 in (3.05 m);

wheel track 7 ft 7.75 in (2.32 m); wheel base 4 ft 10 in (1.47 m)
Powerplant: one Teledyne Continental O-200-A rated at 100 hp (74.5 kW)
Weights: empty equipped 1,000 lb (454 kg); maximum take-off 1,600 lb (726 kg)
Fuel and load: internal fuel 26 US gal (98 litres) plus provision for 12 US gal (45.8 litres) of auxiliary fuel; external fuel none; maximum ordnance none
Speed: never-exceed speed 141 kt (162 mph; 261 km/h); maximum level speed 'clean' at sea level 109 kt (125 mph; 201 km/h); maximum cruising speed at 7,000 ft (2135 m) 106 kt (122 mph; 196 km/h); economical cruising speed at 10,000 ft (3050 m) 82.5 kt (95 mph; 153 km/h)
Range: ferry range 735 nm (846 miles; 1361 km); range 420 nm (484 miles; 779 km)
Performance: maximum rate of climb at sea level 670 ft (204 m) per minute; service ceiling 14,000 ft (4265 m); take-off run 735 ft (224 m) at maximum take-off weight; take-off distance to 50 ft (15 m) 1,385 ft (422 m) at maximum take-off weight; landing distance

from 50 ft (15 m) 1,075 ft (328 m) at normal landing weight; landing run 445 ft (136 m) at normal landing weight

Cessna Model 152
generally similar to the Cessna Model 150 except in the following particulars:

Surprisingly few air forces use the Cessna 150, the most popular civilian flying club trainer, in the basic training role. These Sri Lankan 150s are used for liaison.

Powerplant: one Textron Lycoming O-235-L2C rated at 110 hp (82 kW)
Weights: maximum take-off 1,670 lb (757 kg)
Speed: maximum cruising speed at 7,000 ft (2135 m) 107 kt (123 mph; 198 km/h)
Performance: maximum rate of climb at sea level 715 ft (218 m) per minute; take-off run 725 ft (221 m)

Cessna **Model 172/T-41 Mescalero**

Cessna introduced the 150-hp (112-kW) Lycoming O-320-E2D-powered **Model 172** four-seat commercial lightplane in November 1955. A military version was procured off the shelf in July 1964 by the USAF for initial flight screening. Two hundred and four aircraft were purchased and were designated **T-41A Mescalero**. Subsequent versions based on the 210-hp (157-kW) Continental IO-360-D-powered **Model R172** were the US Army's **T-41B** (255 procured), the USAF's **T-41C** (52 procured) and the **T-41D** (238 procured) for supply under the Military Assistance Program. More than 250 T-41s remain in service with the USAF and US Army; T-41Ds, together with similar Model 172s or Reims-built **FR172s** obtained in off-the-shelf purchases, were delivered to the armed services of some 30 countries.

Current operators include **Angola**, **Bolivia**, **Chile**, **Colombia**, **Dominican Republic**, **Ecuador**, **El Salvador**, **Greece**, **Guatemala**, **Honduras**, **Indonesia**, **Ireland**, **South Korea**, **Liberia**, **Nicaragua**, **Pakistan**, **Panama**, **Peru**, the **Philippines**, **Saudi Arabia**, **Thailand**, **Trinidad and Tobago** and **Turkey**. In Ireland the Cessnas, actually Reims-built **FR172H** and **FR172K Rocket**, are used in a front-line role, flying army co-operation, security

escort and border patrol duties with the Gormanstown-based Army Co-operation Squadron.

SPECIFICATION

Cessna Model 172F (T-41A Mescalero)
Wing: span 35 ft 7.5 in (10.86 m); aspect ratio 7.3; area 174.0 sq ft (16.16 m²)
Fuselage and tail: length 26 ft 11 in (8.20 m); height 8 ft 9.5 in (2.68 m); tailplane span 11 ft 4 in (3.45 m); wheel track 8 ft 3.5 in (2.53 m); wheel base 5 ft 4 in (1.63 m)
Powerplant: one Teledyne Continental O-300-C rated at 145 hp (108 kW)
Weights: operating empty 1,245 lb (565 kg); maximum take-off 2,300 lb (1043 kg)
Fuel and load: internal fuel 42 US gal (159 litres); maximum payload 980 lb (445 kg)
Speed: maximum level speed at sea level 121 kt (139 mph; 224 km/h); maximum cruising speed at 9,000 ft (2745 m) 114 kt (131 mph; 211 km/h)
Range: ferry range 556 nm (640 miles; 1030 km); range 534 nm (615 miles; 990 km)
Performance: maximum rate of climb at sea level 645 ft (196 m) per minute; service ceiling 13,100 ft (3995 m); take-off run 865 ft (264 m) at maximum take-off weight; landing run 520 ft (158 m) at maximum landing weight

Military Cessna 172s are designated T-41. This one serves with the Pakistani air force for liaison duties, though the type is also used for primary training by the air force academy.

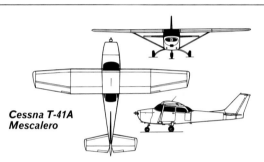

Cessna T-41A Mescalero

Cessna **Model 180/182/U-17**

Utilising the same wing as the Model 172, the Cessna **Model 180** four-seat light cabin monoplane flew as a prototype on 26 May 1952 with a 225-hp (168-kW) Continental O-470-A engine, production deliveries commencing in the following February. Manufactured in progressively improved versions (**Models 180A** to **180G**), it was also modified for the utility role (**Models 180H** to **180K**), in which form it was named **Skywagon**, seven of the **Model 130H** version being ordered under the US MAP as **U-17Cs**.

The Model 180 was procured in small quantities for liaison and utility tasks by a number of armed forces. It remains in service with the **Philippine air force** (six), **Guatemala** (two), **Honduras** (one), **Nicaragua** (four), **Mexico** (three), **El Salvador** (three) and **Venezuela** (two).

The **Model 182** was introduced in 1956 and was fundamentally a Model 180 with a fixed tricycle undercarriage and a 230-hp (172-kW) Continental O-470-R engine. The

aircraft, along with the **Model 182A** production version, was named **Skylane**. In line with parent company practice, it was manufactured in progressively refined versions through **Model 182R**. This version offered a turbocharged 230-hp (172-kW) Textron Lycoming O-540-L3C5D engine in place of the Continental O-470; the Model R182 differed only by having a retractable undercarriage. The **Models 182J-L** and **Model 182N** were licence-built in Argentina by DINFIA, and the **Model 182P**, **Model 182Q** and **R182** in France by Reims Aviation as the **F182P**, **F182Q**, and **FR182**, respectively.

More than 30 Model 182s remain in the inventory of the **Argentine air force**; six are operated by the **Guatemalan air force**; the **Venezuelan** air force and army operate nine and three, respectively; and individual examples are flown by the **Royal Lesotho defence force**, the **Peruvian army**, and the air forces of **El Salvador** and **Uruguay**.

SPECIFICATION

Cessna Model 180 Skywagon
Wing: span 35 ft 10 in (10.92 m); aspect ratio 7.52; area 174.00 sq ft (16.16 m²)
Fuselage and tail: length 25 ft 9 in (7.85 m); height 7 ft 9 in (2.36 m); tailplane span 10 ft 10 in (3.30 m); wheel track 7 ft 8 in (2.33 m)
Powerplant: one Teledyne Continental O-470-R rated at 230 hp (171.5 kW)
Weights: empty equipped 1,560 lb (707 kg); maximum take-off 2,800 lb (1270 kg)
Fuel and load: internal fuel 65 US gal (246 litres) plus provision for 84 US gal (318 litres) of ferry fuel; external fuel none
Speed: maximum level speed 'clean' at sea level 148 kt (170 mph; 274 km/h); maximum cruising speed at 6,500 ft (1980 m) 141 kt (162 mph; 261 km/h); economical cruising speed at 10,000 ft (3050 m) 105 kt (121 mph; 195 km/h)
Range: ferry range 803 nm (925 miles; 1489 km); range 604 nm (695 miles;

1118 km)
Performance: maximum rate of climb at sea level 1,090 ft (332 m) per minute; service ceiling 19,600 ft (5975 m); take-off run 625 ft (190 m) at maximum take-off weight; take-off distance to 50 ft (15 m) 1,205 ft (367 m) at maximum take-off weight; landing distance from 50 ft (15 m) 1,365 ft (416 m) at normal landing weight; landing run 480 ft (146 m) at normal landing weight

Cessna Model 182 Skylane

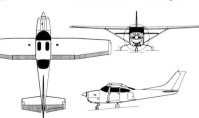

Cessna Model 185/U-17A Skywagon

Basically a strengthened **Model 180C** airframe and intended for the multi-purpose role, the **Model 185 Skywagon** light utility aircraft was first flown in July 1960. Accommodation was provided for up to six persons, and the passenger seats were removable to permit the entire cabin to be utilised for freight transportation. A glass-fibre belly cargo pod was optional, and provision was made for the attachment of skis or floats.

A total of 262 of the **Models 185B, C, D** and **E** (each of which introduced minor changes) was ordered as **U-17A**s for supply to recipients of the Military Assistance Program. These were followed by 205 **Model A185E** and **F** Skywagons with 285-hp (212-kW) Continental IO-520-D engine as **U-17B**s.

Substantial numbers of U-17As and Bs remain in military service, together with small numbers of the essentially similar Model 185 Skywagon. The largest operator is **Turkish army aviation**, with almost 100 U-17s in its inventory. These are used primarily for basic fixed-wing training, but can also be called on for FAC duties. Other army air components utilising the U-17A and/or Model 185 Skywagon are those of **Greece** and **Iran**, both of which have some 20 U-17s on strength, **Peru** with three and **Thailand** with 14. Four serve with the **Panamanian** national air service. Additional users of these Cessna utility aircraft include the air forces of **Bolivia** (12), **Nicaragua**, **Paraguay** (three), **Peru** (three), **Philippines** (15) and **Uruguay** (eight).

SPECIFICATION

Cessna Model 185 Skywagon
generally similar to the Cessna Model 180 Skywagon except in the following particulars:
Powerplant: one Teledyne Continental IO-520-D rated at 300 hp (224 kW)
Weights: empty equipped 1,600 lb (726 kg); maximum take-off 3,350 lb (1519 kg)
Fuel and load: internal fuel 65 US gal (246 litres) plus provision for 19 US gal (72 litres) of auxiliary fuel; external fuel none
Speed: maximum level speed 'clean' at sea level 155 kt (178 mph; 286 km/h); maximum cruising speed at 7,500 ft (2285 m) 147 kt (169 mph; 272 km/h); economical cruising speed at 10,000 ft (3050 m) 112 kt (129 mph; 208 km/h)
Range: ferry range 899 nm (1,035 miles; 1665 km); range 573 nm (660 miles; 1062 km)
Performance: maximum rate of climb at sea level 1,010 ft (308 m) per minute; service ceiling 17,150 ft (5230 m); take-off run 770 ft (235 m) at maximum take-off weight; take-off distance to 50 ft (15 m) 1,365 ft (416 m) at maximum take-off weight; landing distance from 50 ft (15 m) 1,400 ft (427 m) at normal landing weight; landing run 480 ft (146 m) at normal landing weight

The Turkish army's Cessna 185s wear a businesslike olive drab colour scheme, with small patches of red to improve conspicuity. The powerful little taildragger is an excellent training aircraft, especially for pilots destined for similarly configured aircraft like the Cessna Bird Dog. The 185 can also be used in the forward air control role itself, and in the FAC training role.

Cessna Models 206/207/210 Super Skywagon/Centurion

The Cessna **Models 206, 207** and **210** were the principal representatives of a family of light cabin monoplanes confusingly assigned non-sequential type numbers. The first of these was, in fact, the Model 210, which, flown as a prototype on 25 February 1957, was developed from the **Model 182B** with a 260-hp (194-kW) Continental IO-470-E engine and a retractable undercarriage. Progressively improved versions (**Models 210A** to **210R**) were developed, these being known as the **Centurion** from the **Model 210D**, which introduced the 285-hp (212-kW) Continental IO-520-D engine. With an optional TSIO-520 engine with turbo-supercharger, this is known as the **Turbo Centurion**, and, with cabin pressurisation, as the **Pressurised Centurion** (**P210N** and **P210R**). A few Model 210s remain in military service and are operated by the air forces of **Bolivia** (three), **Dominica** (one) and the **Philippines** (three used for weather reconnaissance).

The **Model 206 Super Skywagon**, introduced in 1964, was evolved from the **Model 205**, which, in turn, was a fixed-undercarriage version of the **Model 210C**. Like the Model 205, the 206 had internal capacity raised from four to up to six seats, power being provided by a 285-hp (212-kW) Continental IO-520-A in place of the preceding model's 260-hp (194-kW) IO-470-S.

TOGW was increased by 300 lb (136 kg) and a double cargo door was provided in the starboard side. Versions of the Super Skywagon with progressively minor changes were the **U206** to **U206E**, while the **U206F** introduced a camber-lift wing and the **U206G** was dubbed **Stationair** when fitted with a turbocharged engine.

Various versions of the Model 206 serve in liaison and utility roles with several military services, the largest operator being the air force of the **Israeli defence force** with more than 20. The **Bolivian air force** and navy possess about 10, the **Paraguayan air force** has three, **Costa Rica**'s public security air section has four, and the **Peruvian** and **Venezuelan** armies have two and four, respectively.

The **Model 207 Skywagon** was a stretched development of the **Model 206D** with an 18-in (46-cm) baggage section ahead of the windshield and a 27-in (68.5-cm) plug aft of the wing to provide for seven seats in four rows. It was initially fitted with a 300-hp (224-kW) IO-520-F engine or turbocharged TSIO-520-G, but in the **Model 207A** the optional turbocharged engine was changed to a 310-hp (231-kW) TSIO-520-M. From 1980, the Model 207A was fitted with eight seats and became the **Stationair 8**. The Model 207 is operated by the **Argentine army** (five), the **Indonesian air force** (four) and army (two), and the **Paraguayan air force** (five).

One of six Cessna U206Fs used by the French Gendarmerie in the surveillance role. They augment helicopters.

SPECIFICATION

Cessna Model 206 Stationair
Wing: span 36 ft 7 in (11.15 m); aspect ratio 7.63; area 175.50 sq ft (16.30 m²)
Fuselage and tail: length 28 ft 0 in (8.53 m); height 9 ft 6.75 in (2.92 m); tailplane span 13 ft 0 in (3.96 m); wheel track 8 ft 1.75 in (2.48 m)
Powerplant: one Teledyne Continental IO-520-F rated at 300 hp (224 kW)
Weights: empty 1,710 lb (776 kg); maximum take-off 3,600 lb (1633 kg)
Fuel and load: internal fuel 65 US gal (246 litres) plus provision for 19 US gal (72 litres) of auxiliary fuel; external fuel none
Speed: maximum level speed 'clean' at sea level 151 kt (174 mph; 280 km/h); maximum cruising speed at 6,500 ft (1980 m) 142 kt (164 mph; 264 km/h); economical cruising speed at 10,000 ft (3050 m) 114 kt (131 mph; 211 km/h)
Range: ferry range 886 nm (1,020 miles; 1641 km) with auxiliary fuel; range 695 nm (800 miles; 1287 km) with standard fuel
Performance: maximum rate of climb at sea level 920 ft (280 m) per minute; service ceiling 14,800 ft (4510 m); take-off run 900 ft (274 m) at maximum take-off weight; take-off distance to 50 ft (15 m) 1,780 ft (543 m) at maximum take-off weight; landing distance from 50 ft (15 m) 1,395 ft (425 m) at normal landing weight; landing run 735 ft (224 m) at normal landing weight

Cessna Models 208/U-27 Caravan I

The largest single-engined aircraft built by Cessna and of wholly new design, albeit retaining the classic high wing and fixed tricycle-gear configuration, the Cessna **Model 208** was the first all-new single-engined general aviation aircraft designed from the outset to be powered by a turboprop. Initially flown in engineering prototype form on 9 December 1982, the Model 208 was conceived for both civil and military roles, the military version, designated **U-27A Caravan I**, appearing in 1986. The U-27A can accommodate a pilot and up to nine passengers, and is powered by a 600-hp (448-kW) Pratt & Whitney Canada PT6A-114 turboprop.

Intended for a range of missions that include freight delivery, logistic support, paratroop and supply dropping, medevac, electronic surveillance, forward air control, troop transportation, maritime patrol and SAR, the U-27A possesses one centreline and six wing hardpoints. It has been proposed with a 360° FLIR turret and Stinger AAM self-defence armament to meet a USAF Special Operations Command gunship requirement. Military customers have included the **Liberian army** (one example), the **Brazilian air force** (seven) and the **Thai army** (10).

SPECIFICATION

Cessna Model 208A Caravan I
Wing: span 52 ft 1 in (15.88 m); aspect ratio 9.6; area 279.40 sq ft (25.96 m²)
Fuselage and tail: length 37 ft 7 in (11.46 m); height 14 ft 2 in (4.32 m); tailplane span 20 ft 6 in (6.25 m); wheel track 11 ft 8 in (3.56 m); wheel base 11 ft 7.5 in (3.54 m)
Powerplant: one Pratt & Whitney Canada PT6A-114 flat-rated at 600 shp (447 kW)
Weights: empty 3,800 lb (1724 kg); maximum take-off 7,300 lb (3311 kg)
Fuel and load: internal fuel 2,224 lb (1009 kg); no external fuel; maximum payload 3,000 lb (1361 kg)
Speed: maximum operating speed 175 kt (202 mph;

325 km/h); maximum cruising speed at 10,000 ft (3050 m) 184 kt (212 mph; 341 km/h)
Range: 1,370 nm (1,578 miles; 2539 km)

Performance: maximum rate of climb at sea level 1,050 ft (320 m) per minute; maximum operating altitude 27,600 ft (8410 m); take-off run 970 ft (296 m)

at maximum take-off weight; take-off distance to 50 ft (15 m) 1,665 ft (507 m) at maximum take-off weight; landing distance from 50 ft (15 m) 1,550 ft (472 m) at

normal landing weight; landing run 645 ft (197 m) at normal landing weight
g limits:: -1.52 to +3.8

Cessna **Model 305/L-19/O-1 Bird Dog**

Built as a private venture and first flown in December 1949, the Model 305 was winning contender in an April 1950 US Army competition for a tandem two-seat liaison and observation monoplane. Ordered in June 1950 as the **L-19** and named **Bird Dog**, the aircraft was redesignated **O-1** in 1962. The first production Bird Dog was rolled out in November 1950. Subsequently, a total of 2,499 of the **O-1A** version was built, a further 66 being completed as **O-1B**s for the US Marine Corps, 307 having dual controls as **TO-1D**s and the definitive series model being the **O-1E**, of which 494 were delivered. The last-mentioned variant, introduced in 1957, featured uprated equipment, and served with distinction with the USAF in Vietnam. Fuji in Japan built 14 **L-19E-1**s and eight **L-19E-2** instrument trainers after delivery of 107 ex-US Army

L-19As to the JGSDF in 1954/55, with the local name of **Soyokaze** (Breeze). Despite their age, more than 200 Bird Dogs remain in active military inventories worldwide, the principal operators being the **South Korean air force** (20), and the army air components of **Pakistan** (40), **Thailand** (28) and **Turkey** (50); other operators include **Austria** (five), **France** (two), **Indonesia** (two), **Italy** (three) and **Malta** (five).

SPECIFICATION

Cessna Model 305C (O-1E Bird Dog)
Wing: span 36 ft 0 in (10.97 m); aspect ratio 7.45; area 174.00 sq ft (16.16 m²)
Fuselage and tail: length 25 ft 9 in (7.85 m); height 7 ft 3.5 in (2.22 m)

Austrian Cessna O-1 Bird Dogs continue in the FAC role with Flieger-regiment III, operating in conjunction with Saab 105s.

Powerplant: one Continental O-470-11 rated at 213 hp (159 kW)
Weights: empty 1,614 lb (732 kg); maximum take-off 2,400 lb (1087 kg)
Speed: maximum level speed 'clean' at sea level 131 kt (151 mph; 243 km/h); maximum cruising speed

at 5,000 ft (1525 m) 90 kt (104 mph; 167 km/h)
Range: range 460 nm (530 miles; 853 km)
Performance: maximum rate of climb at sea level 1,150 ft (351 m) per minute; service ceiling 18,500 ft (5640 m)

Cessna **Model 310/320/L-27/U-3 Skyknight**

The first of the post-World War II Cessna light twins, the Cessna **Model 310** five-seater powered by 240-hp (179-kW) Continental O-470-B engines was flown as a prototype on 3 January 1953. It was to remain in production in successive versions (**Models 310** to **310R**) until 1981, a number being acquired by military services for communications and liaison tasks. The **Model 310D** introduced a swept vertical tail and the **Model 310G** featured a six-seat cabin, the latter becoming the **Model 320 Skyknight** with turbocharged TSIO-470-3 engines. Later variants such as the **Model 310P**, **310Q** and **310R** varied in detail changes and introduced more powerful engines.

The USAF contracted for 80 **Model 310A**s off the shelf for communications as the **L-27A** (later **U-3A**), these being followed by 36 **Model 310E**s as **L-27B**s (later **U-3B**s). Many of these were passed to the Army National Guard and Army Reserve, being finally withdrawn in the late 1980s. A few Model 310s remain in military

service, including **France**'s Armée de l'Air (12), the air wing of the **Tanzanian People's Defence Force** (six 310Qs), the **Colombian air force** (two), **Indonesian army** (two 310Ps), **Iranian army** (six 310Ps) and the **Venezuelan navy** (two). Individual examples serve with the air forces of **Madagascar**, **Mexico**, **Paraguay**, the **Philippines**, **Trinidad and Tobago**, and **Uruguay**. The **Ecuadorean navy** and the **Peruvian air force** each possess a single Model 320. The largest operator is the **Zaïrean air force**, with over 10 310Rs.

SPECIFICATION

Cessna Model 310L (U-3A)
Wing: span 36 ft 11 in (11.25 m); aspect ratio 7.61; area 179.0 sq ft (16.63 m²)
Fuselage and tail: length 29 ft 6 in (8.99 m); height 9 ft 11 in (3.02 m); tailplane span 17 ft 0 in (5.18 m); wheel track 12 ft 0 in (3.66 m); wheel base 9 ft 6 in (2.90 m)

Five Cessna 310s are used by Colombia's Escuadron Avanzada 613 for navigation and multi-engine pilot training.

Powerplant: two Teledyne Continental IO-470-VO each rated at 260 hp (194 kW)
Weights: empty 3.125 lb (1418 kg); maximum take-off 5,200 lb (2360 kg)
Fuel and load: internal fuel 51 US gal (193 litres) plus provision for 41 US gal (155 litres) of auxiliary fuel in two wing tanks
Speed: maximum level speed at sea level 206 kt (237 mph; 381 km/h); maximum cruising speed at 6,500 ft (1980 m) 190 kt (219 mph; 352 km/h); economical cruising speed at 10,000 ft (3050 m) 155 kt

(170 mph; 288 km/h)
Range: ferry range 1,680 nm (1,935 miles; 3114 km) with 41 US gal (155 litres) of auxiliary fuel; range 675 nm (777 miles; 1248 km)
Performance: maximum rate of climb at sea level 1.540 ft (470 m) per minute; service ceiling 19,900 ft (6065 m); take-off run ft m) at maximumtake-off weight; take-off distance to 50 ft (15 m) 1,726 ft (523 m) at maximum take-off weight; landing distance from 50 ft (15 m) 1,582 ft (482 m) at max landing weight

Cessna **Model 318B/T-37 Tweet**

The T-37 was developed to meet a 1952 USAF requirement for a jet-powered primary trainer. Two **XT-37** prototypes were ordered, and the first flew on 12 October 1954, powered by 920-lb st (4.1-kN) YJ69-T-9 turbojets (licence-built versions of the French Turboméca Marboré) in the wingroots. The aircraft had side-by-side seating for the crew under a one-piece canopy and behind a one-piece windscreen, with a central strengthening strip. Overall configuration was conventional, although the horizontal tailplane was located midway up the fin to remain clear of the jet exhaust. The manual controls had electric trimmers, while flaps and wide-track undercarriage were hydraulically actuated.

Cessna T-37Bs and T-37Cs are operated by 361 Mira in the training role. This aircraft is one of the T-37Bs acquired secondhand from the Royal Jordanian Air Force.

An initial batch of 10 **T-37A**s was followed by 524 more basic A models. The first one flew on 27 September 1955 but service entry was delayed until 1957 by the need for modifications. During 1959 production switched to the 1,025-lb st (4.56-kN) J69-T-25-engined **T-37B**, which also introduced improved navigation and communications equipment and provision for wingtip fuel tanks. A total of 466 was built, some being exported. Forty-seven were funded by the Luftwaffe but remained in the USA, in USAF markings, for training Luftwaffe pilots. All surviving T-37As were also brought up to T-37B standard through modification. From April 1961, the USAF switched to 'straight-through' jet training on the T-37, as had been planned, but high costs forced the reintroduction of a 30-hour primary phase on the T-41A in 1965. All-through jet training was briefly reintroduced, but today pilots are 'screened' on the T-41.

The T-37 was to have been replaced by the Fairchild T-46A, but this aircraft was cancelled in 1986. A proposed T-37 derivative, the **T-48**, attracted little support, and from 1989 the Sabreliner Corp. began supplying modification kits to the USAF to allow its surviving T-37s to be structurally rebuilt for extended service. Current plans call for the T-37 to be replaced by the winning JPATS contender, which may be a turboprop-powered aircraft.

The ultimate Tweet was never used by the USAF, instead being built for export and for Military Assistance Program and Foreign Military Sales. A total of 269 **T-37C**s were built, all incorporating provision for a limited light strike capability with a K14C gunsight, and underwing pylons (one on each wing) which could carry stores of up to 250 lb (113 kg), including a General Electric 0.5-in machine-gun pod. A survey or reconnaissance camera can be carried in the fuselage.

SPECIFICATION

Cessna Model 318B (T-37B Tweet)
Wing: span 33 ft 9.3 in (10.30 m); aspect ratio 6.2; area 183.9 sq ft (17.09 m²)
Fuselage and tail: length 29 ft 3 in (8.92 m); height 9 ft 2.3 in (2.80 m); tailplane span 13 ft 11.25 in (4.25 m); wheel track 14 ft 0.5 in (4.28 m); wheel base 7 ft 9 in (2.36 m)
Powerplant: two Teledyne Continental J69-T-25 each rated at 1,025 lb (4.56 kN) dry
Weights: empty 3,870 lb (1755 kg); maximum take-off 6,600 lb (2993 kg)
Fuel and load: internal fuel 309 US gal (1170 litres); external fuel none
Speed: maximum level speed at 25,000 ft (7620 m) 369 kt (425 mph; 684 km/h); normal cruising speed at 25,000 ft (7620 m) 330 kt (380 mph; 612 km/h)
Range: range 809 nm (932 miles; 1500 km)
Performance: maximum rate of climb at sea level 3,370 ft (1037 m) per minute; service ceiling 39,200 ft (11950 m); take-off distance to 50 ft (15 m) 2,000 ft (610 m); landing distance from 50 ft (15 m) 2,545 ft (776 m) at normal landing weight

OPERATORS

T-37Cs were supplied to Burma (12), Chile (12 plus 22 T-37Bs), Colombia (10), Greece (24 plus eight T-37Bs), Jordan (18 T-37Bs), Pakistan (24 plus 28 T-37Bs), Peru (12 plus 20 T-37Bs), Portugal (30), Thailand (six plus 16 T-37Bs), and Turkey (47). T-37As and T-37Bs serve with the USAF

These T-37s wear the markings of Pakistan's 'Sherdils' aerobatic team, flown by pilots from the air academy at Risalpur. Pakistani T-37s will be replaced by a turboprop trainer and by the CNAMC K-8.

Cessna Model 318B (T-37B Tweet)

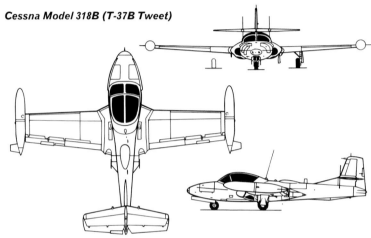

Cessna **Model 318E/A-37 Dragonfly**

A light attack derivative of the T-37 basic trainer, the side-by-side two-seat **A-37 Dragonfly** flew as a prototype (**YAT-37D**) on 22 October 1963, powered by two 2,400-lb st (10.67-kN) General Electric J85-GE-5 turbojets. Thirty-nine T-37Bs were similarly converted (with J85-GE-17A engines derated to 2,400 lb st/10.67 kN) on the assembly line to become **A-37A**s. These aircraft, like the two YAT-37Ds, featured armour protection, an internally-housed 7.62-mm Minigun, eight wing stores stations for ordnance and fuel, wingtip fuel tanks, ground-attack avionics and larger wheels and tyres.

Stressed to 6*g* rather than 5*g*, a full-production version was ordered by the USAF as the **A-37**; this version introduced inflight refuelling capability and J85-GE-17A engines rated at 2,850 lb st (12.67 kN). Deliveries began in May 1968, with a total of 577 examples manufactured, production being completed in 1975. The A-37B could carry up to 5,680 lb (2576 kg) of bombs, rockets and stores dispensers, and at least 130 were retrospectively fitted with avionics optimised for the forward air control role as **OA-37B**s. The last USAF A-37s retired in 1992.

Both A-37B and OA-37B serve extensively with Latin American air arms. **Chile** has operated the A-37B since 1974, and has some 20 serving in operational training and light attack roles with Grupo 12 at Punta Arenas. **Colombia** has a similar number of A-37Bs and OA-37Bs with Grupo III at Barranquilla, having flown Dragonflies since 1980. **Ecuador** has operated A-37Bs since 1976, some 10 remaining with Escuadrón 2311 'Dragones' at Manta. **Guatemala**, the earliest Latin American Dragonfly operator, received its first A-37Bs in 1971, and seven remain with its

Recent deliveries of ex-USAF A-37Bs to the Fuerza Aérea Colombiana have included at least four FAC-configured OA-37Bs. All aircraft wear an effective camouflage scheme with toned-down national markings, except for a tiny national tricolour in full colour on the trailing edge of the rudder.

Escuadrón de Caza-Bombardeo at La Aurora. **Honduras** has had A-37Bs since 1975 and OA-37Bs since 1984, and has a dozen of these at La Ceiba with its Escuadrilla de Ataque. **Peru** has 16 A-37Bs remaining from 36 supplied 1975-77, these equipping Escuadrones 711 and 712 of Grupo Aéreo 7 at Piura. **Salvador** has six A-37Bs and OA-37Bs remaining from 19 A-37Bs and three OA-37Bs delivered since 1982. **Uruguay** has 15 A-37Bs with Grupo de Aviación 2 at Durazno, these remaining from some 20 received through the 1970s and 1980s.

Other current operators of the A-37B are **South Korea** and **Thailand**. The former has some two dozen ex-South Vietnamese aircraft with its 12th Fighter Wing, these having been received in September-October 1976, and the latter has a dozen A-37Bs (and ex-T-37s converted to a generally similar standard) at Ubon Ratchathani with

Squadron 211 of Wing 21. **Vietnam** holds some A-37Bs in storage, these being ex-South Vietnamese aircraft captured at the end of the Vietnamese conflict (and including some actually used operationally at the end of the war) and since unsuccessfully offered for sale on several occasions.

Thailand gained its A-37Bs in 1975, on the fall of South Vietnam, flown by fleeing pilots. This one wears a new grey scheme.

SPECIFICATION

Cessna Model 318E (OA-37B Dragonfly)
Wing: span 35 ft 10.5 in (10.93 m) with tip tanks; aspect ratio 6.2; area 183.9 sq ft (17.09 m²)
Fuselage and tail: length excluding probe 29 ft 3.5 in (8.93 m); height 8 ft 10.5 in (2.70 m); tailplane

span 13 ft 11.25 in (4.25 m); wheel track 14 ft 0.5 in (4.28 m); wheel base 7 ft 10 in (2.39 m)
Powerplant: two General Electric J85-GE-17A each rated at 2,850 lb st (12.68 kN) dry
Weights: basic empty 6,211lb (2817 kg); empty equipped 5,843 lb (2650 kg); maximum take-off 14,000 lb (6350 kg)
Fuel and load: internal fuel 3,307 lb (1500 kg); external fuel up to four 100-US gal (378-litre) drop tanks; maximum ordnance 4,100 lb (1860 kg)
Speed: never-exceed speed 455 kt (524 mph; 843 km/h); maximum level speed at 16,000 ft (4875 m) 440 kt (507 mph; 816 km/h); maximum cruising speed at 25,000 ft (7620 m) 425 kt (489 mph; 787 km/h)

Range: range with maximum internal and external fuel at 25,000 ft (7620 m) 878 nm (1,012 miles; 1628 km); range with maximum warload 399 nm (460 miles; 740 km)
Performance: maximum rate of climb at sea level 6,990 ft (2130 m) per minute; service ceiling 41,765 ft (12730 m); take-off run 1,740 ft (531 m) at maximum take-off weight; take-off distance to 50 ft (15 m) 2,595 ft (791 m) at maximum take-off weight; landing distance from 50 ft (15 m) 6,600 ft (2012 m) at normal landing weight; landing run 4,150 ft (1265 m) at maximum landing weight or 1,710 ft (521 m) at normal landing weight

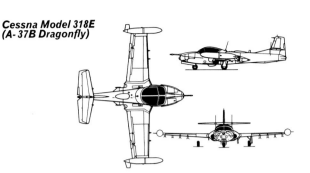

Cessna Model 318E
(A-37B Dragonfly)

Cessna **Model 337/O-2 Super Skymaster**

A development of the distinctive centre-line-thrust **Model 336 Skymaster** six-seat light twin, the **Model 337 Super Skymaster**, flown as a prototype on 30 March 1964, differed in having a retractable undercarriage and uprated 210-hp (157-kW) Continental IO-360-C engines. In December 1966, the Model 337 was ordered by the USAF for forward air control duties as the **O-2A**, with wing hardpoints for marker flares, rockets or gun pods; a total of 501 O-2As was delivered from April 1967. Thirty-one commercial Model 337s ordered off the shelf were adapted for psycho-warfare as **O-2Bs**, these each having three loudspeakers and provision for leaflet dispensers.

Turbocharged Skymasters

The **Model 337B** introduced the turbocharged TSIO-360-A engine (**T337B**) as an option, and cabin pressurisation was first made available with the **Model 337G** (**P337G**). A military version developed in France by Reims Aviation (which licence-manufactured successive commercial versions as the **F337E** to **F337H**) was known as the **FTB337G Milirole**. This had four wing hardpoints and the new high-lift flaps (as part of Robertson STOL modifications) introduced with the commercial Model 337G (**F337G**). A further military version,

similarly fitted with four wing hardpoints, was marketed by Summit Aviation as the **Sentry O2-337**, this being an adaptation of the turbocharged T337.

SPECIFICATION

Cessna Model 337M (O-2A)
Wing: span 38 ft 0 in (11.58 m); aspect ratio 7.13; area 202.5 sq ft (18.81 m²)
Fuselage and tail: length 29 ft 9 in (9.07 m); height 9 ft 4 in (2.84 m); tailplane span 10 ft 0.625 in (3.06 m); wheel track 8 ft 2 in (2.49 m); wheel base 7 ft 10 in (2.39 m)
Powerplant: two Teledyne Continental IO-360C/D each rated at 210 hp (157 kW)
Weights: empty 2,848 lb (1292 kg); maximum take-off 5,400 lb (2449 kg)
Fuel and load: internal fuel 82 US gal (348 litres) plus provision for 56 US gal (212 litres) of auxiliary fuel in two wing tanks; external fuel none
Speed: maximum level speed at sea level 173 kt (199 mph; 320 km/h; cruising speed at 10,000 ft (3050 m 125 kt (144 mph; 232 km/h)
Range: typical range 920 nm (1,060 miles; 1706 km)
Performance: maximum rate of climb at sea level 1,180 ft (360 m) per minute; service ceiling 19,800 ft (5885 m); take-off distance to 50 ft (15 m) 1,545 ft (471 m) at maximum take-off weight; landing distance from 50 ft (15 m) 1,650 ft (503 m) at maximum landing weight

Six Cessna 337s, four of which wear this colourful red and white scheme, are flown by the Sri Lankan air force maritime squadron.

OPERATORS

Zimbabwe operates the 16 survivors of 18 Reims-built FTB 337Gs obtained clandestinely in February 1976 by the Rhodesian air force. Named **'Lynx'**, these were fitted with turbocharged engines and were armed with two 7.62-mm (0.303-in) machine-guns above the cabin and 37-mm SNEB rockets, Frantans (frangible plastic-shelled napalm tanks), small bombs and flare dispensers. They undertook light strike, COIN and FAC duties during Rhodesia's long bush war and were fitted with redesigned heat-shielded exhausts as a counter to SA-7 SAMs. Commercial versions are in service with the **Burkina Faso** and **Togo** air forces, each having one Model

337D; the **Sri Lanka** air force (four Model 337FBs and two Skymasters of unidentified sub-type); the navies of **Ecuador** (two T337Fs and one Model 337G); **Mexico** (two Model 337Fs) and **Peru** (one P337G); the **Chilean army** (three Model 337Gs); and the **Jamaica Defence Force**'s Air Wing (one Model 337G). The Reims-built Super Skymaster serves with the **Burkina Faso** and **Togo** air forces, each operating a single F337E. The Summit Sentry O2-337 derivative version is operated by the **Haitian air corps** (four) and **Thai air force** (five). Ex-USAF O-2As remain with the **Costa Rican Public Security air section** (two), the **Dominican air force** (four), the **South Korean air force** (seven) and the **Salvadorean air force** (seven); the last-mentioned service also operates one O-2B.

Cessna **Model 400 Series, Titan and Golden Eagle**

The models in the 400 series are the largest of the propeller-driven Cessna light transport aircraft, examples of most of which have been procured in small numbers by military services. First to appear was the **Model 411**, an eight-seat aircraft powered by two 375-hp (280-kW) Continental GTSIO-520-M engines and flown as a prototype on 18 July 1962. The **Model 411A** was similar apart from a lengthened baggage nose and optional extra engine nacelle fuel tanks. Several remain in service with **France**'s Armée de l'Air from 12 originally acquired for communications tasks, and one Model 411 serves with both the **Mexican navy** and **Thai air force**.

Progressive development led to the **Model 401**, which, flown on 26 August 1965, was a lower-priced alternative to the Model 411. This variant had substantially the same airframe but was powered by 300-hp (224-kW) TSIO-520-E engines set further outboard on the wings and had a six-seat interior. The parallel **Model 402**, similar apart from a reinforced cabin floor and an optional cargo door, was the recipient of several small military orders. The **Models 402A** and **B** introduced minor changes, but the **Model 402C** was characterised by a longer-span wing, bonded wet wing with tip tanks and 325-hp (242-kW) TSIO-520-VB engines.

The Model 402 is operated by the air

forces of **Bolivia** (one for photo survey), Colombia (two in concert with two **Model 404s**), **Malaysia** (10) and **Paraguay** (one). In addition, the aircraft is in the inventory of the **Bolivian navy** (one), **Mexican navy** (two) and the air detachment of the **Venezuelan National Guard** (which operates at least one example).

A stretched version of the Model 402B with a larger vertical tail and 375-hp (280-kW) Continental GTSIO-520-M engines was first flown on 26 February 1975 as the **Model 404 Titan**. The Model 404 has been delivered to several military air arms, including the US Navy (one example operated as the **C-28A**), **Royal Bahamas Defence Force** (one example together with single examples of the **Model 414** and **Model 421**), **Bolivian air force** (one), **Dominican air force** (one Model 404 alongside a single Model 401), **Mexican navy** (one) and the air wing of the **Tanzanian People's Defence Force** (two).

Pressurised versions

The **Model 414** is a pressurised version of the Model 401B with two 310-hp (231-kW) Continental TSIO-520-N engines, a single example being operated by the **Royal Bahamas Defence Force**. The **Model 421** is essentially a pressurised version of the Model 411A with 375-hp (280-kW) Continental GTSIO-520-D engines. Successive

The RNZAF's three Cessna 421s were sold during late 1990 as an economy measure, but the type is in widespread military use elsewhere. The Cessna 421 is distinguished by its long nose and round windows.

production versions of the latter were the **Model 421A** with detail changes, the **Model 421B** with repositioned GTSIO-520-E engines on longer-span wings, a longer nose and strengthened undercarriage, and the **Model 421C** with a wet wing and GTSIO-520-L engines. Four Model

421s are used by **Turkish army aviation**, and single examples are included in the inventories of the air transport and liaison group of the **Ivory Coast**, the **Pakistan army**, and the air forces of **Paraguay** and **Sri Lanka**.

A Cessna 402 of No. 2 Squadron, Royal Malaysian air force, based at Simpang for liaison and staff transport duties. Cessna's versatile twins are popular light transport and liaison aircraft, especially with the world's smaller air forces. More than 1,600 Cessna 402s were built.

SPECIFICATION

Cessna Model 421A
Wing: span 39 ft 10.25 in (12.15 m) with tip tanks; aspect ratio 7.95; area 200.00 sq ft (18.58 m²)
Fuselage and tail: length 33 ft 9 in (10.29 m); height 11 ft 8 in (3.56 m); tailplane span 17 ft 0 in (5.18 m);

wheel track 14 ft 8 in (4.47 m); wheel base 10 ft 5.75 in (3.20 m)
Powerplant: two Teledyne Continental GTSIO-520-D each rated at 375 hp (280 kW)
Weights: empty 4,252 lb (1928 kg); maximum take-off 6,840 lb (3102 kg)
Fuel and load: internal fuel 175 US gal (662 litres) standard or 202 US gal (765 litres) optional; external fuel none

Speed: maximum level speed 'clean' at 16,000 ft (4875 m) 240 kt (276 mph; 444 km/h) and at sea level 207 kt (238 mph; 383 km/h); maximum cruising speed at 22,500 ft (6860 m) 227 kt (261 mph; 420 km/h); economical cruising speed at 25,000 ft (7620 m) 196 kt (226 mph; 364 km/h)
Range: ferry range 1,488 nm (1,713 miles; 2756 km) with optional fuel; range 1,020 nm (1,174 miles; 1889 km) with standard fuel

Performance: maximum rate of climb at sea level 1,680 ft (512 m) per minute; service ceiling 27,000 ft (8230 m); take-off run 2,040 ft (622 m) at maximum take-off weight; take-off distance to 50 ft (15 m) 2,563 ft (781 m) at maximum take-off weight; landing distance from 50 ft (15 m) 2,110 ft (643 m) at normal landing weight; landing run 1,045 ft (319 m) at normal landing weight

Cessna Model 500/550/560 Citation Series

Small numbers of several derivative versions of the **Cessna Model 500**, all possessing the generic appellation of **Citation**, have been procured by various military services. An eight-seat business jet powered by two 2,200-lb st (9.78-kN) Pratt & Whitney JT15D-1 turbofans, the Model 500 Citation flew as a prototype on 15 September 1969. From late 1976, the **Model 500 Citation I** superseded the original series version, featuring a higher aspect ratio wing and JT15D-1A engines. One example currently serves in the photo survey role with the **Argentine army**. Operators of this Citation version for liaison and communication tasks are the **Chinese People's Liberation Army Air Force** (three), and the air forces of **Mexico** and **Venezuela** (one each) and the **Ecuadorean navy** (one).

The **Model 550 Citation II** was first flown on 31 January 1977 and introduced a fuselage lengthened by 3 ft 9 in (1.14 m) to raise capacity to 12 seats, increased fuel capacity and 2,500-lb st (11.12-kN) JT15D-4 engines. This variant serves with the **Spanish navy** (three) and the air forces of **Myanmar** (one), **Turkey** (four) and **Venezuela** (two).

The **Model S550 Citation S/II** was first flown on 14 February 1984 and introduced a new aerofoil, wing leading-edge cuffs and JT15D-4B turbofans. A variant of this sub-type was adopted by the US Navy as a radar trainer. With a shorter wing span and 2,900-lb st (12.89-kN) JT15D-5 engines, this became the **Model 552/T-47A**. Fifteen were acquired by the service and were operated from Pensacola, FL, by VT-86 until

replaced by the Rockwell T-39 Sabreliner. The normal crew of the T-47A included a civilian pilot, a US Navy instructor and three students. A further development of the S/II flew as an engineering prototype on 18 August 1987. Designated **Model 560 Citation V**, the type featured JT15D-5A engines and incorporated a 2-ft (0.61-m) fuselage stretch. Deliveries commenced in April 1989. The Citation V is currently operated by the **Moroccan air force** (two), the **Seychelles** defence force (one) and the **Venda Defence Force**.

SPECIFICATION

Cessna Model 552 (T-47A Citation)
Wing: span 46 ft 6 in (14.18 m)
Fuselage and tail: length 47 ft 10.75 in (14.60 m); height 14 ft 9.75 in (4.51 m); tailplane span 19 ft 0 in (5.79 m); wheel track 17 ft 7 in (5.36 m); wheel base

Left: Pilots seconded from the Seychelles Coast Guard Air Wing fly the Presidential/VIP Cessna Citation V. Small numbers of these bizjets are used by air forces and government flights.

Below: This Spanish Cessna 550 Citation II is designated TR.20 locally, and is fitted with a survey camera in a wingroot fairing. It serves with Esc. 403 at Cuatro Vientos.

18 ft 2.5 in (5.55 m)
Powerplant: two Pratt & Whitney Canada JT15D-5 each rated at 2,900 lb st (12.89 kN) dry
Weights: empty equipped 9,035 lb (4098 kg); maximum take-off 15,000 lb (6804 kg)
Fuel and load: internal fuel 5,820 lb (2640 kg); external fuel none

Speed: maximum level speed at 40,000 ft (12190 m) 420 kt (484 mph; 779 km/h); maximum cruising speed 402 kt (463 mph; 745 km/h)
Range: typical range 1,700 nm (1,958 miles; 3151 km) Performance: maximum rate of climb at sea level about 4,000 ft (1219 m) per minute; service ceiling 43,000 ft (13100 m)

Cessna Model 526 CitationJet JPATS

First flown on 21 December 1993, the **Model 525 CitationJet JPATS** was closely based upon the CitationJet business jet, retaining the same Williams International F129 turbofans buried in a new fuselage with a new blown canopy covering tandem-set cockpits and with a new low-set tailplane. The engines are 'fed' by plain D-section intakes above and ahead of each wingroot. The only twin-engined contender for the USAF/USN JPATS requirement, the aircraft is also the only completely indigenous design in the competition. If successful, the aircraft would be built at the com-

pany's Mid-Continent facility. A second prototype joined the flight test programme during early 1994 for certification and demonstration, prior to the expected award of a contract in December 1994, for the first 151 of an anticipated 766-aircraft order.

The CitationJet JPATS trainer made its maiden flight in primer finish, such was the perceived urgency of getting airborne before the end of 1993. The aircraft is the only all-new, all-American trainer being submitted to meet the JPATS.

Changhe Aircraft Factory Z-8

*Changhe Aircraft Factory
PO Box 109, Jingdezhen
Jiangxi 333002, PRC*

At the same time that China's Aviation of the **People's Liberation Navy** placed orders for 16 Aérospatiale SA 321Ja Super Frelon helicopters, arrangements were begun to establish production of versions of the Super Frelon in China. Design work was begun in 1976 but was suspended from 1979 to mid-1984. Development work at the Changhe Aircraft Factory at Jingdezhen (Jiangxi province) resulted in a prototype first flight on 11 December

1985, with a second flown in October 1987. Domestic type approval was awarded on 8 April 1989. With the designation **Zhishengji-8** (for the eighth vertical take-off aircraft type), the Super Frelon entered production against an initial contract for 10 for the Naval Air Force. The first of these was handed over on 5 August 1989 to the PLA Naval Air Force for service trials.

Although based on the SA 321Ja utility/transport version of the Super Frelon,

the Z-8 is expected to undertake a variety of duties including troop transport, SAR, ASW/ASV, minelaying/sweeping, aerial survey and fire-fighting.

The Z-8 is of wholly indigenous manufacture, although some components are of French origin. The Changzhou (CLXMW) WZ6 turboshafts are derived from the Super Frelon's Turboméca Turmo IIIC engines. Work commenced in 1975, followed by testing in 1980-82 and first flight

on a Z-8 in 1985. Although not quite as powerful as the Turmo IIIC, the WZ6 nevertheless has a power reserve of 20 per cent at sea level.

In addition to the crew of two or three, the Z-8 can accommodate 27 fully armed troops in the cabin, or 39 without equipment; up to 15 stretchers and a medical attendant; or a BL-212 jeep and its crew. Loading is carried out via a hydraulically actuated rear door and a starboard-mounted sliding door at the front of the cabin. SAR equipment can include a 275-kg (606-lb) capacity hydraulic rescue hoist and two five-person liferafts. The Z-8 may also be equipped with sonar, search radar, sonobuoys or other equipment for fire-fighting and geological survey. It may be fitted additionally with depth charges, torpedoes, anti-shipping missiles or mine-laying/mine-sweeping gear.

SPECIFICATION

Changhe Z-8
Rotor system: main rotor diameter 18.90 m (62 ft 0 in); tail rotor diameter 4.00 m (13 ft 1.5 in); main rotor disc area 280.47 m² (3,019 sq ft); tail rotor disc area 12.57 m² (135.27 sq ft)

Fuselage and tail: length overall, rotors turning 23.035 m (75 ft 7 in); height overall 6.66 m (21 ft 10.25 in) with rotors turning
Powerplant: three Changzhou (CLXMW) Wozhou-6 each rated at 1156 kW (1,550 shp)
Weights: empty equipped 7550 kg (16,645 lb); normal take-off 10592 kg (23,351 lb); maximum take-off 12074 kg (26,618 lb)
Fuel and load: internal fuel 3900 litres (1,030 US gal) plus provision for 1900 litres (502 US gal) of auxiliary fuel in cabin tanks; external fuel none; maximum payload 5000 kg (11,023 lb)
Speed: never-exceed speed 315 km/h (170 kt; 195 mph); maximum cruising speed at optimum altitude 266 km/h (143 kt; 165 mph); economical cruising speed at optimum altitude 255 km/h (137 kt; 158 mph)
Range: ferry range 1400 km (755 nm; 870 miles) with auxiliary fuel; range 820 km (442 nm; 509 miles) with standard fuel on two engines; endurance 4 hours

The Changhe Z-8 serves with the Chinese navy. This aircraft, still in primer finish, has ASW radar radomes in the fronts of the undercarriage sponsons.

43 minutes with standard fuel
Performance: maximum rate of climb at sea level 690 m (2,263 ft) per minute; service ceiling 6000 m (19,685 ft); hovering ceiling 5500 m (18,045 ft) in ground effect and 4400 m (14,435 ft) out of ground effect

---

Chengdu JJ-5/FT-5

Chengdu Aircraft Industrial Corporation
PO Box 800, Chengdu
Sichuan 610092, PRC

The basic Chinese-built MiG-17F was produced by the Shenyang Aircraft Factory, but later derivatives were developed and constructed by Chengdu. The first such development was the **J-5A**, which was basically a Chinese-built MiG-17PF with AI radar in a larger, longer, forward fuselage. Relatively small numbers were produced, and none are known to have been exported. The prototype made its maiden flight on 11 November 1964.

More successful was the **JJ-5**, a two-seat trainer derivative of the J-5. This had a slightly lengthened fuselage, and the nose intake and jetpipe were refined. Development began in 1965, when it was becoming clear that the MiG-15UTIs then in use lacked performance and had some unacceptable handling characteristics. The cres-

cent wing of the MiG-17, with its reduced sweep on the outer wings, solved many of these problems, including a tendency to pitch up at high angles of attack and unpredictable handling at transonic speeds.

The JJ-5 first flew on 8 May 1966, and 1,061 had been built by 1986, when production ceased. It was powered by a Wopen WP-5D turbojet which remained an obvious copy of the Rolls-Royce Nene. The JJ-5 has been exported (as the **FT-5**) to a number of customers, most notably **Pakistan**, which uses the aircraft as the standard advanced jet trainer. Others have been procured by **Albania**, **Bangladesh**, **Sri Lanka**, **Sudan** and **Zimbabwe**, and perhaps by **North Korea** and **Tanzania**. Interestingly, Mikoyan itself never designed a two-seat MiG-17 variant, since the Soviet air

forces regarded the MiG-15UTI as being adequate for the training of MiG-17 and MiG-19 aircrew.

SPECIFICATION

Chengdu JJ-5
Wing: span 9.628 m (31 ft 7 in); aspect ratio 4.10; area 22.60 m² (243.27 sq ft)
Fuselage and tail: length 11.50 m (37 ft 9 in); height 3.80 m (12 ft 5.75 in); wheel track 3.85 m (12 ft 7.5 in)
Powerplant: one Xian (XAE) Wopen WP-5D rated at 26.48 kN (5,952 lb st) dry
Weights: empty equipped 4080 kg (8,995 lb); normal take-off 5400 kg (11,905 lb); maximum take-off 6215 kg (13,701 lb)

Fuel and load: internal fuel 1500 litres (396 US gal); external fuel up to two 400-litre (106-US gal) drop tanks
Speed: never-exceed speed at 5000 m (16,405 m) 1048 km/h (565 kt; 651 mph); normal operating speed 'clean' at optimum altitude 775 km/h (418 kt; 482 mph)
Range: ferry range 1230 km (664 nm; 764 miles) with drop tanks; endurance 2 hours 38 minutes with drop tanks
Performance: maximum rate of climb at sea level 1620 m (5,315 ft) per minute; service ceiling 14300 m (46,915 ft); take-off run 760 m (2,493 ft) at maximum take-off weight; landing run 830 m (2,723 ft) at maximum landing weight

Two FT-5s serve with Sri Lanka's only fast-jet unit, No. 5 Squadron, for jet conversion training onto the Chengdu F-7BS.

Today in Pakistani service, the FT-5 serves with No. 1 Fighter Conversion Unit at Mianwali in the advanced tactical training role.

Chengdu J-7/F-7 'Fishbed'

China was granted a licence to manufacture the MiG-21F-13 and its Tumanskii R-11F-300 engine in 1961, and a handful of Mikoyan-built aircraft were delivered to serve as patterns. Not all the necessary technical documents had been delivered by the time the two countries severed ties, however, and J-6 (MiG-19) production was accordingly given a higher priority. A MiG-21-based prototype was constructed at Shenyang and first flew on 17 January 1966, powered by the Wopen WP-7, which was claimed to be an improved R-11F-300. Certificated for production in June 1967, despite the enormous upheavals of the Cultural Revolution and January Storm, the initial batch of aircraft was manufactured by the Shenyang Aircraft Factory. Some of these were later delivered to **Albania** and **Tanzania** as **F-7A**s.

Production transferred to Chengdu, where the basic aircraft received the new designation **J-7I**, retaining the F-7A tag for export. Broadly equivalent to the late-series MiG-21F-13, the aircraft had the later medium-chord tailfin but retained two 30-

Early versions of the F-7 had an undernose pitot probe, and were broadly equivalent to the early MiG-21F-13, with a 30-mm cannon in each wingroot but with the later broad-chord tailfin. This PL-5-armed aircraft is a J-7II, identifiable by its separate canopy and windscreen. The J-7II also introduced a more powerful and reliable engine.

Sri Lanka operates four aircraft which it designates F-7BS. These combine Chinese avionics in a J-7II fuselage with the four-pylon wing of the F-7M. They are Sri Lanka's only front-line fast jets.

Right: Full-standard F-7Ms equip Nos 5 and 35 Squadrons of the Bangladesh air force at Dhaka and Chittagong. The aircraft are pooled and wear the markings of both units.

mm cannon under the wingroots, like the earliest 'Fishbed-Cs'.

Early J-7s were not popular with their pilots, not least because of their unusual and failure-prone linked canopy and ejection seat, whereby the canopy worked as a blast shield on ejection. Development of the **J-7II** began in 1975, and the new variant incorporated a new Type II ejection seat under a conventional jettisonable upward/rearward-hinging canopy and separate windscreen. The new seat had a powerful rocket motor for smoother acceleration and a higher trajectory, and gave ground-level ejection capability for the first time (at speeds in excess of 140 kt). The J-7II also had provision for a 720-litre (158.4-Imp gal) centreline fuel tank and a relocated brake chute in a tubular fairing at the base of the fin; the aircraft made its maiden flight on 30 December 1978. To give improved performance the more powerful (13,448-lb st/ 59.8-kN) Wopen WP-7B engine was fitted,

A patch on the nose shows where the short-lived Skybolt name has been overpainted on this AIM-9P Sidewinder-armed F-7P of No. 20 Squadron, one of four Pakistani squadrons operating the type in the air defence role.

which also gave longer time between overhaul figures (these were doubled to 200 hours), better heat shielding and longer life. The later WP-7B(M) was fitted to later aircraft, and featured an APU fuelled by kerosene, rather than petrol.

There are reports that an improved version of the J-7II, with an air data computer, modern HUD and redesigned wing, first flew in April 1990 under the designation **J-7E**. This has a cranked arrow wing, with new outer panels of increased span and area. Powered by an uprated WP-7F engine, the J-7E has four underwing pylons and is reportedly compatible with the PL-8 AAM. The basic J-7II has been widely exported, in several sub-variants. The **F-7B** is a minimum-change variant, apparently with R.550 Magic compatibility. The F-7B has been exported to **Egypt** and **Iraq**, and some Chinese sources have stated that a delivery to **Jordan** took place in 1982.

Four F-7Bs with F-7M wings, designated **F-7BS**, have also been delivered to **Sri Lanka** for service with No. 5 Squadron. These aircraft retain Chinese avionics, and have never been photographed with more than two underwing pylons, although pre-

sumably four can be fitted.

The J-7II is also available in an upgraded form, under the designation **F-7M Airguard**. This has an extra pair of underwing pylons and a strengthened undercarriage, and the pitot probe is relocated above the nose. Internally the F-7M features a GEC Avionics 956 HUDWAC, a new longer-range ranging radar with improved ECCM characteristics, a new air data computer, radar altimeter, IFF and secure communications, all served by an improved electrical system, and an improved Wopen WP-7B(BM) powerplant. The aircraft also has a strengthened windscreen and is compatible with the Chinese PL-7 AAM. The F-7M has been exported to **Bangladesh**, **Iran** and reportedly **Jordan**. **Zimbabwe**'s aircraft may be F-7Bs or later F-7Ms.

A similar version, the **F-7P Skybolt**, was exported to **Pakistan**. The 'Skybolt' name was quickly dropped, and was overpainted on the noses of Pakistan's first batch of aircraft soon after delivery. The F-7P incorporated 24 modifications to meet Pakistani requirements, but differs little in external appearance. The Mk IV ejection seat is considerably improved with a drogue

gun and enhanced auto-separation, and can be used at ground level at speeds in excess of 75 kt. Only nine pins need to be removed before flight, instead of 11 on the original F-7M seat. The Chinese ejection seat is to be replaced by a Martin-Baker Mk 10L. All four underwing weapons pylons are wired for the carriage of air-to-air missiles, including the R.550 Magic and AIM-9 Sidewinder. Twenty were delivered before production switched to the further improved **F-7MP**, 60 of which were delivered. In Pakistani service the F-7MP retains the simple F-7P designation but can be recognised by pairs of tiny forward and rear hemisphere RWR antennas on each side of the fin tip. The F-7P and F-7MP equip four PAF squadrons.

Chengdu has also produced a longer-range all-weather version of the J-7, in association with the Guizhou factory which builds two-seat JJ-7/FT-7 trainers. Designated **J-7III**, the aircraft is externally similar to the Soviet MiG-21M, with the same SPS blown flaps, underfuselage 23-mm gun pod, broad-chord tailfin, bulged spine, and blast fences below the auxiliary intakes. Design began in 1981 and yielded a flying prototype on 26 April 1984. The J-7III has a new all-

ARMAMENT
The F-7P can be fitted with up to four underwing pylons (though two is more usual) and these can be used to carry a variety of stores. In Pakistani service, the aircraft can carry AIM-9P Sidewinders (shown here), or MATRA R.550 Magics. The centreline hardpoint is usually used for the carriage of a supersonic fuel tank. Air-to-air missiles are augmented by a pair of NORINCO Type 30-1 belt-fed cannon, with 60 rounds per gun, mounted in the wingroots.

INTAKE
The F-7P uses a simple pitot intake in the nose, with a variable conical centrebody sliding in and out to match intake area to flight conditions and thrust demanded. The centrebody is computer controlled and is fully variable, whereas on the original MiG-21F-13 it had only three positions. It houses the aircraft's primitive ranging radar.

COCKPIT
Whereas the original MiG-21F-13 and J-7I had single-piece forward-hinging canopies with a built-in windscreen, the F-7P has a more conventional canopy with a separate, fixed three-piece windscreen.

weather radar in an enlarged radome, and uses the F-7P's Type IV ejection seat. The aircraft is powered by the 14,550-lb st (64.72-kN) Wopen WP-13, which was developed from the WP-7 but features an improved compressor and bearings, and a host of measures to enhance reliability.

Unbuilt versions of the J-7 include the **Chengdu/Grumman Sabre** or **Super 7**. This was to have been built for Pakistan and was to have featured a Westinghouse APG-66 radar in a solid nosecone, a new wide-angle HUD, and lateral air intakes in the wingroots. The aircraft was to have been re-engined, with either a General Electric F404/RM-12 or a Turbo Union RB.199. Enlarged wings featured computer-controlled leading-edge manoeuvre slats, and an enlarged spine housed extra fuel. Other improvements included provision of an arrester hook, single point pressure refuelling and strengthened undercarriage. The Super 7 pilot surveyed the world from a new F-20-style canopy and frameless wrap-around windscreen, and sat on a new ejection seat. Development was suspended by the US government after the Tienanmen Square massacre, but seems to have been restarted using a mix of Russian and non-US Western technology. One hundred RD-33 engines (which power the MiG-29) have been purchased for the programme, for example.

SPECIFICATION

Chengdu F-7M Airguard
Wing: span 7.154 m (23 ft 5.625 in); aspect ratio 2.2;

area 23.00 m² (247.58 sq ft)
Fuselage and tail: length 13.945 m (45 ft 9 in) excluding probe and 14.885 m (48 ft 10 in) including probe; height 4.103 m (13 ft 5.5 in); tailplane span 3.74 m (12 ft 3.25 in); wheel track 2.692 m (8 ft 10 in); wheel base 4.807 m (15 ft 9.25 in)
Powerplant: one Liyang (LMC) Wopen WP-7B(BM) rated at 43.15 kN (9,700 lb st) dry and 59.82 kN (13,448 lb st) with afterburning. This is derived from the Tumanskii R-11F-300
Weights: empty 5275 kg (11,629 lb); normal take-off 7531 kg (16,603 lb)
Fuel and load: internal fuel 2385 litres (630 US gal); external fuel up to 1680 litres (444 US gal) in one 720-litre (190.2-US gal) drop tank and two 500-litre (132-US gal) drop tanks or three 500-litre (132-US gal) drop tanks; maximum ordnance 1000 kg (2,205 lb), usually comprising underwing AAMs (up to four AIM-9 or similar) with a single centreline fuel tank
Speed: maximum level speed 'clean' between 41,000 and 60,700 ft (12500 and 18500 m) 2175 km/h (1,175 kt; 1,350 mph)
Range: ferry range 2230 km (1,203 nm; 1,386 miles) with drop tanks; combat radius 600 km (324 nm; 373 miles) on a hi-lo-hi interdiction mission with two 150-kg (331-lb) bombs and three 500-litre (132-US gal) drop tanks, or 370 km (200 nm; 230 miles) on a lo-lo-lo close air support mission with four rocket launchers, or 650 km (351 nm; 404 miles) on a long-range interception mission with two AAMs and three 500-litre (132-US gal) drop tanks; endurance 45 minutes on a CAP at 36,000 ft (10975 m) with two AAMs and three 500-litre (132-US gal) drop tanks
Performance: maximum rate of climb at sea level 10800 m (35,433 ft) per minute; service ceiling 59,700 ft (18200 m); take-off run 700 to 950 m (2,297 to 3,117 ft) at normal take-off weight; landing run 600 to 900 m (1,969 to 2,953 ft)
g limits: +8

Chengdu Aircraft Corporation F-7P

This Chengdu F-7P serves with No. 20 Squadron at Rafiqi, and was one of the initial batch of 20. Later Pakistani aircraft were officially F-7PMs with a new cockpit layout and some avionics improvements. All Pakistani F-7s use the simple F-7P designation in service, and wear a two-tone air superiority grey colour scheme, sometimes with toned-down national insignia, as seen here.

COLOUR SCHEMES
Chinese and Sri Lankan J-7s and F-7s mostly wear an off-white, pearl grey colour scheme, but other operators have chosen darker greys or desert camouflage.

POWERPLANT
The original J-7I and J-7II were powered by the 12,676-lb (56.4 kN) Wopen WP-7 (Tumanskii R11F-300) turbojet, whereas the F-7M and F-7P use the 13,448-lb (59.82 kN) Wopen WP-7B, and the heavyweight all-weather J-7III uses the 14,550-lb (64.72 kN) Wopen WP-13.

UPGRADED DERIVATIVES
The proposed Super 7, being continued despite the ending of US participation, will incorporate advanced avionics and a real air-intercept radar. Potential powerplants include the Klimov RD-33 used by the MiG-29.

EJECTION SEAT
Many export F-7s, including those operated by Pakistan, are fitted with the Martin-Baker Mk 10 zero-zero rocket-powered ejection seat.

AVIONICS
The F-7P uses predominantly Western avionics and systems, including a GEC Avionics 956 HUDWAC (Head-Up Display and Weapons Aiming Computer).

Christen **Pitts S-2**

Aviat Inc.
Airport Box 1149, Afton
Wyoming 83110

First flown in September 1944, the Pitts **S-1 Special** was a highly successful single-seat aerobatic biplane that gave rise in 1967 to a two-seat derivative, the **S-2A Special**. More than 1,500 Pitts Specials have been built, mostly by amateur constructors. The original Pitts Enterprises was acquired by Christen Industries Inc. in 1981, production of both single- and two-seaters continuing at the Aerotek factory in Afton, WY. Pitts biplanes have been chosen by several air force aerobatic teams, notably the Venezuelan 'Falcons' and Chilean 'Halcones', but neither of these teams currently flies its Pitts. Closely associated with the Royal Jordanian air force, the 'Royal Jordanian Falcons' team flew three S-2As.

Chile's 'Halcones' display team has now transitioned to the Extra 300, which has also replaced those of the 'Royal Jordanian Falcons'. Individual aircraft serve with a variety of military unit's flying clubs.

CNAMC/PAC **K-8 Karakorum**

Nanchang Aircraft Manufacturing Company
PO Box 5001-506, Nanchang
Jiangxi 330024, PRC

Subject of a jointly-financed programme shared between **China** and **Pakistan**, the **K-8 Karakorum** was designed by China Nanchang Aircraft Manufacturing Company (CNAMC), which is also primarily responsible for construction and flight development. Pakistan Aeronautical Complex (PAC) contributes manpower at the Nanchang complex as well as some funding, to give a 25 per cent market share. Responsibility for marketing is undertaken by China National Aero-Technology Import & Export.

The K-8 is a basic jet trainer of conventional straight-wing tandem-seat configuration. PAC is responsible for manufacture of the fin, tailplane and some other components to give a total share of approximately 25 per cent of the airframe. First identified as the **Nanchang L-8**, it is named for the mountain range on the China/Pakistan border. For the benefit of international marketing it features a considerable proportion of Western equipment, including a Garrett TFE731 turbofan, Collins EFIS and Martin-Baker CN10LW lightweight ejection seats. Provision is made for light armament on four wing pylons plus a centreline 23-mm gun pack with self-computing optical gunsight, giving the K-8 a light strike capability

in addition to a weapons training role. Each station can carry up to 250 kg (551 lb) of stores.

Full-scale development was launched in 1987 with construction of three flying and one static trials aircraft. The first of these flew on 21 November 1990; two more prototypes were flown in 1991, with another in 1992. The test programme was set for completion by the first quarter of 1993. A pre-production batch of 15 aircraft was launched, the first of which flew in 1993, and plans were made for evaluation of aircraft from this batch by the air forces of China and Pakistan. The PAF is reported to have a requirement for 75 K-8s; total Chinese procurement is uncertain.

SPECIFICATION

CNAMC/PAC K-8 Karakorum
Wing: span 9.63 m (31 ft 7.25 in); aspect ratio 5.45; area 17.02 m² (183.2 sq ft)
Fuselage and tail: length (including nose probe) 11.60 m (38 ft 0.75 in); height 4.21 m (13 ft 9.75 in); wheel track 2.43 m (7 ft 11.75 in); wheel base 4.38 m (14 ft 4.5 in)
Powerplant: one 16.01-kN (3,600-lb st) Garrett TFE731-2A-2A turbofan

The K-8 Karakorum is a single-engined advanced jet trainer being jointly developed by China and Pakistan.

Weights: empty equipped 2687 kg (5,924 lb); maximum take-off (clean) 3630 kg (8,003 lb); maximum take-off (with external stores) 4330 kg (9,546 lb)
Fuel and load: internal fuel 780 kg (1,720 lb); external fuel (two drop tanks) 390 kg (860 lb); maximum external stores 950 kg (2,094 lb)
Speed: never-exceed speed 950 km/h (512 kt; 590 mph); maximum level speed at sea level 800 km/h (432 kt; 497 mph); approach speed 200 km/h (108 kt; 124 mph)

Range: with maximum internal fuel 1400 km (755 nm; 870 miles); with maximum internal/external fuel 2250 km (1,214 nm; 1,398 miles); endurance (maximum internal fuel) 3 hours; endurance (maximum internal/external fuel) 4 hours 25 minutes
Performance: maximum climb rate at sea level 1620 m (5,315 ft) per minute; service ceiling 13000 m (42,650 ft); take-off run 410 m (1,345ft); landing run 512 m (1,680 m)
g limits: -3 to +7.33

Convair **240/C-131/440**

Convair (itself a product of the 1943 merger of Consolidated and Vultee) was absorbed by General Dynamics in 1954, as the Convair Division, losing its separate identity during the early 1960s

By the end of 1993 no more than two examples of the family of Convair twin-engined transports remained in military service. This duo comprised a single, elderly, ex-civilian **Convair 240**, operated by the Grupo Aéreo de Transporte Especiales (GATE) in Paraguay, and one surviving **Convair 440** in service with Transporte Aéreo Militar (TAM), a component of the Bolivian air force. A handful of piston-engined **C-131A Samaritan** and turboprop **VC-131Hs** were used through the 1980s by US Air Force and Air National Guard and US Navy Reserve, respectively. The C-131

has since been replaced by the C-9, C-12 and C-26 in USAF/ANG service. VR-48 of the USNR transferred its last C-131H to the US Department of State on 30 August 1990 and relinquished the type in favour of the C-20. Several C-131s remained active with the Department of State in 1994.

Bolivia is the only remaining military user of the Convair 440, while Paraguay still uses the 240. Other Convairs serve with paramilitary agencies, including the US Department of State.

Convair **880**

The **Convair 880** first flew on 27 January 1959, but proved to be too expensive for any major sales success. A number survived for some years with small operators after their initial first-line service was over.

A single aircraft (BuNo. 161572) was acquired in the early 1980s by the US Navy for trials work, under the non-standard designation **UC-880**. Based at Patuxent River, it flew with the Naval Air Test Center (now

the Naval Air Warfare Center/Aircraft Division). A single hose-drum unit was incorporated in the lower rear fuselage for refuelling work, and the aircraft sported a large ventral radome and numerous antennas for equipment test work. It retired in 1994.

The last flying Convair 880 was operated by the US Navy from the NAWC at Patuxent River, fulfilling a variety of test and support roles.

Convair QF-106 **Delta Dart**

In 1991, the Convair QF-106 began to replace the North American QF-100 as the USAF's principal FSAT (Full-Scale Aerial Target) and is now in full use with the 475th Weapons Evaluation Group at Tyndall AFB, FL, and at Holloman AFB, NM.

The F-106 first flew on 26 December 1956, and occupied an important place in the air defence network of the United States for many years. The Delta Dart retired from service with the New Jersey ANG in 1989. It was chosen as the next-generation FSAT because its speed and manoeuvrability better represented high-performance targets for air-to-air missile engagements. One hundred and ninety-four **QF-106** conversions by Honeywell are planned for the US Air Force, the conversion involving removal of some systems, installation of remote-piloting equipment (although the QF-106 remains 'man-rated'), and fitment of propane burners under wing pylons to provide infra-red sources for heat-seeking missiles. The last fully manned F-106, NASA's vortex flap research F-106B, has now been withdrawn from use.

Convair QF-106s are operated as unmanned target drones, remaining capable of manned flight. They are operated by the 475th Weapons Evaluation Group's 82nd TATS (Tactical Aerial Target Squadron) at Tyndall AFB, Florida. The aircraft are regularly expended in missile trials and missile/gunnery competitions. Underwing pylons carry propane burners to give a stronger IR signature.

SPECIFICATION

Convair F-106A Delta Dart
Wing: span 38 ft 3.5 in (11.67 m): aspect ratio 2.32: area 631.3 sq ft (58.65 m²)
Fuselage and tail: length (including nose probe) 70 ft 8.75 in (21.56 m); height 20 ft 3.3 in (6.18 m); wheel track 15 ft 5.67 in (4.71 m): wheel base 24 ft 1.5 in (7.35 m)
Powerplant: one Pratt & Whitney J75-P-17 turbojet rated at 17,200 lb st (76.51 kN) dry and 24,500 lb st (108.98 kN) with afterburning
Weights: empty 24,155 lb (10957 kg); maximum take-off 41,831 lb (18974 kg)
Fuel and load: internal fuel 9,841 lb (4464 kg); external fuel (two drop tanks) 4,654 lb (2111 kg)
Speed: maximum speed at 40,000 ft (12192 m) 2413 km/h (1302 kt; 1,500 mph); combat speed at 52,000 ft (15850 m) 1090 km/h (588 kt; 676 mph)
Range: on internal fuel 1150 miles (1850 km); combat radius 490 miles (790 km)
Performance: initial climb rate 39,800 ft (12131 m) per minute: service ceiling 58,000 ft (17678 m)

Curtiss **C-46 Commando**

Curtiss ceased to exist in 1954, the aeroplane division of Curtiss Wright having closed earlier, during 1947

Like the famed Douglas C-47, the nearly contemporary **Curtiss C-46 Commando** demonstrated extraordinary longevity of service, albeit in much smaller quantities. In the two decades following the end of World War II, air arms of a dozen or more nations used ex-USAAF **C-46A**s and, as a consequence of such service in **China**, a quantity of these twin-engined transports passed eventually into the inventory of the Chinese People's Liberation Army Air Force. A modification programme introduced the locally-produced 1380-kW (1,850 hp) HS8 radial 14-cylinder engine based on the Shvetsov ASh-82V in the surviving Chinese C-46s, and it is believed that a handful may remain airworthy in China's remoter areas. Elsewhere, the last surviving military C-46A was thought to be in service with the **Haitian air corps**.

Dassault (Breguet/Dassault-Breguet) **Atlantic**

Dassault Aviation
9 Rond-Point Champs-Elyseés
75008 Paris

The **Atlantic 1** originated in a 1957 NATO requirement (NBMR-2) for a long-range maritime reconnaissance aircraft. The winner was the **Breguet Br.1150** (this company being absorbed by Dassault in 1971), fabricated by the SECBAT (Société d'Etudes et de Construction de Breguet Atlantic) consortium, which then included SABCA and SONACA in Belgium, Fokker in Holland, Dornier and MBB in West Germany, Aérospatiale in France and Aeritalia in Italy. Assembled by Breguet, the first of four prototypes was flown at Toulouse on 21 October 1961.

Carrying 12 crew, the Atlantic is equipped with Thomson-CSF search radar in a retractable bin and American ASW avionics similar to those of the Lockheed Neptune. Standard NATO stores can be carried in the 30 ft (9.15 m) unpressurised weapons bay in the lower section of the 'double bubble' fuselage, most of the external skin being light alloy sandwich. The first of 20 for the **West German navy** and 40 for France's **Aéronavale** entered service in December 1965. French aircraft serve with 21F and 22F at Nîmes-Garons and 23F and 24F at Lann-Bihoué. The Aéronavale began retirement of first-generation Atlantics in 1992, although some aircraft will be retained for surveillance tasks, perpetuating the detachments already established at Djibouti, Dakar (Senegambia), Réunion and in the Antilles.

German Atlantics of MFG 5, Kiel-Holtenau (except for five equipped for Elint missions under the Peace Peek programme) have completed an update programme involving new Texas Instruments radar, Emerson Electric sonar and Loral ESM equipment in wingtip pods. In parallel, airframe improvements have doubled flying life to 10,000 hours. By contrast, the six survivors of nine delivered to No. 321 Squadron of the Royal Netherlands navy at Valkenburg in 1969-72 began phasing out in January 1984, replaced by P-3Cs. **Italy**'s 18 Atlantics were supplied between June 1972 and July 1974 to complete production, and are operated by 30° Stormo at Cagliari/Elmas and 41° Stormo at Catania/Sigonella on patrols of the Mediterranean. **Pakistan** obtained three from the French navy in 1975-76; wearing 'navy' titles, these are flown by No. 29 Squadron of the Pakistan air force from Sharea Faisal (Drigh Road).

SPECIFICATION

Dassault Aviation (Breguet/Dassault-Breguet) Atlantic 1
Wing: span 36.30 m (119 ft 1 in); aspect ratio 10.95; area 120.34 m² (1,295.37 sq ft)
Fuselage and tail: length 31.75 m (104 ft 2 in); height 11.33 m (37 ft 2 in); tailplane span 12.31 m (40 ft 4.5 in); wheel track 9.00 m (29 ft 6.25 in); wheel base 9.44 m (31 ft 0 in)
Powerplant: two Rolls-Royce Tyne RTy.20 Mk 21 each rated at 6,100 ehp (4549 ekW)
Weights: empty equipped 25000 kg (55,115 lb); maximum take-off 44500 kg (98,104 lb)
Fuel and load: internal fuel 18500 kg (40,785 lb); external fuel none; maximum ordnance 3500 kg (7,716 lb)
Speed: maximum level speed 'clean' at optimum altitude 658 km/h (355 kt; 409 mph); maximum cruising speed at 7200 m (23,620 ft) 556 km/h (300 kt; 345 mph); normal patrol speed at optimum altitude 315 km/h (170 kt; 196 mph)
Range: ferry range 9000 km (4,856 nm; 5,592 miles); endurance 18 hours 0 minutes
Performance: service ceiling 10000 m (32,810 ft); take-off distance to 10.5 m (35 ft) 1500 m (4,921 ft) at maximum take-off weight

Six German Atlantics were modified to serve as Elint platforms under the codename Peace Peek. One has since been lost.

Most of the Aéronavale's basic Atlantics have been replaced by the newer Atlantique, and some have been scrapped.

Left: Italian Atlantics are due to remain in service for some time and are being upgraded with Atlantique systems, and will also receive a Nimrod acoustics processor.

Right: Pakistan operates three ex-French navy Atlantics. These serve with No. 29 Squadron, at Sharea Faisal.

Dassault Atlantique 2 (ATL 2)

Originally called the **ANG (Atlantic Nouvelle Génération)**, the **Dassault Atlantique 2** was intended as a multi-national programme to replace the Atlantic (now called Atlantic 1) with its various users. **France** is currently the sole customer, though that country's requirement for 30 aircraft (originally 42) makes the project viable even if the rate of manufacture is too low for competitive costings.

After very prolonged studies, the Atlantique 2 was designed as a 'minimum-change' aircraft, totally new in avionics, systems and equipment but with these packaged into an airframe differing only in ways to increase service life, reduce costs and minimise maintenance. Structural changes include detail redesign to give a 30,000-hour fatigue life, improved bonding and anti-corrosion protection, and better inter-panel sealing. An Astadyne gas-turbine auxiliary power unit is fitted, and production machines are fitted with Ratier-BAe propellers with larger composite blades.

The Atlantique 2's sensors include the Thomson-CSF Iguane frequency-agile radar with a new interrogator and decoder, an SAT/TRT Tango FLIR in a chin turret, over 100 sonobuoys in the rear fuselage, a new Crouzet MAD in the tailboom, and the Thomson-CSF ARAR 13 ESM installation with frequency analysis at the top of the fin and D/F in the new wingtip nacelles. All processors, data buses and sensor links are of standard digital form, navaids include an inertial system and Navstar satellite receiver, and every part of the avionics and communications has been upgraded. This avionics fit represents a substantial improvement over the first-generation Atlantic 1, and is cost-effective due to the minimal airframe changes incurred. The main weapons bay, housed in the unpressurised lower fuselage, can accommodate all NATO standard bombs, depth charges, two ASMs, up to eight Mk 46 torpedoes or

seven French Murène advanced torpedoes. A typical load consists of one AS37 Martel or one AM39 Exocet ASM and three torpedoes. Additional stores up to 3500 kg (7,716 lb) may be carried on four underwing pylons, including future ASMs, AAMs and equipment pods. The Atlantique has a rarely used secondary transport function, and could also be used in a limited overland electronic reconnaissance role.

The first Atlantique 2 flew in May 1981 and production deliveries began in 1989. Flottille 23F was the first unit to convert, the process being completed in 1991. Flottille 24F, also at Lann-Bihoué, took delivery of its Atlantique 2s in 1992. Flottilles 21F and 22F, based at Nîmes-Garons, began conversion in 1994.

Proposed variants of the Atlantique 2 include a Nimrod replacement for the RAF, with additional turbofans (possibly Garrett TFE731s) in pods under the wing and with either Allison T406s or General Electric T407s replacing the Tynes; an **Atlantique 3** with further improvements; and the **Europatrol**, a derivative aimed at the replacement of NATO's P-3 Orions. A Tyne upgrade has also been proposed for the Atlantique.

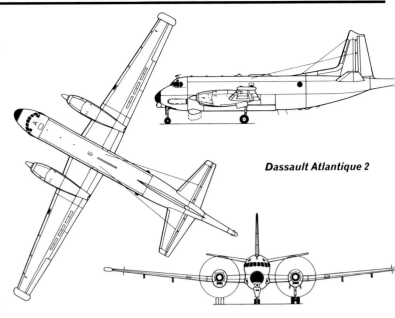

Dassault Atlantique 2

WEAPON OPTIONS

The Atlantique 2 has an internal weapons bay for the carriage of various bombs, up to eight depth charges and torpedoes. The latter can either be a maximum of eight Mk 46 or seven Murène weapons. The bay can also accommodate two anti-ship missiles, currently either AM39 Exocet or AS37 Martel. A typical load comprises one Exocet and three torpedoes. Additional missile armament can be carried on four underwing pylons, comprising ARMAT anti-radiation missiles or Magic 2 self-defence air-to-air missiles. Aft of the weapons bay is a sonobuoy launcher with over 100 buoys. Up to 160 smoke markers and flares are also carried, launched through the lower rear fuselage.

SPECIFICATION

Dassault Aviation Atlantique 2

Wing: span 37.42 m (122 ft 9.25 in) including wingtip ESM pods; aspect ratio 10.9; area 120.34 m² (1,295.37 sq ft)

Fuselage and tail: length 31.62 m (103 ft 9 in); height 10.89 m (35 ft 8.75 in); tailplane span 12.31 m (40 ft 4.5 in); wheel track 9.00 m (29 ft 6.25 in); wheel base 9.40 m (30 ft 10 in)

Powerplant: two Rolls-Royce Tyne RTy.20 Mk 21 each rated at 6,100 ehp (4549 ekW)

Weights: empty equipped 25600 kg (56,437 lb); normal take-off 44200 kg (97,443 lb) for the ASW or ASV roles, or 45000 kg (99,206 lb) for the combined ASW and ASV roles; maximum take-off 46200 kg (101,852 lb)

Fuel and load: internal fuel 18500 kg (40,785 lb); external fuel none; maximum external ordnance

3500 kg (7,716 lb); maximum internal ordnance 2500 kg (5,511 lb)

Speed: never-exceed speed Mach 0.73; maximum level speed 'clean' at optimum altitude 648 km/h (349 kt; 402 mph); maximum cruising speed at 7200 m (23,620 ft) 555 km/h (300 kt; 345 mph); normal patrol speed between sea level and 1525 m (5,000 ft) 315 km/h (170 kt; 196 mph)

Range: ferry range 9075 km (4,897 nm; 5,639 miles); operational radius 3333 km (1,799 nm; 2,071 miles) for a 2-hour patrol in the ASV role with one AM9 Exocet missile, or 1850 km (999 nm; 1,150 miles) for a 5-hour patrol in the ASW role at 1000 m (3,280 ft), or 1110 km (599 nm; 690 miles) for an 8-hour patrol in the ASW role at low altitude; endurance 18 hours

Performance: maximum rate of climb at sea level 884 m (2,900 ft) per minute; service ceiling 9145 m (30,000 ft); take-off distance to 10.5 m (35 ft) 1840 m (6,037 ft) at maximum take-off weight; landing distance from 10.5 m (35 ft) 1500 m (4,921 ft) at normal landing weight

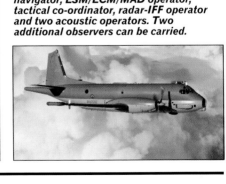

Although superficially externally similar to the Atlantic 1, the Atlantique 2 has a completely revised equipment fit which makes it a far more capable maritime patroller. The most notable differences are the Tango FLIR sensor in a chin-mounted turret, and the revised wingtip/fintip antenna installations for the ESM equipment. The airframe is essentially similar to the earlier variant but has far greater corrosion protection, highly necessary for prolonged flight in the demanding overwater regime. The standard crew comprises two pilots, flight engineer, observer in glazed nose, radio navigator, ESM/ECM/MAD operator, tactical co-ordinator, radar-IFF operator and two acoustic operators. Two additional observers can be carried.

Dassault (Dassault-Breguet) Etendard IVM/P

The original **Dassault Etendard** (standard, or national flag) was the company's entry in a 1955 NATO competition for a light strike fighter able to operate from unpaved strips. Dassault developed subsequent versions, which were deemed to be underpowered. As a private venture, Dassault installed the much more powerful SNECMA Atar 08 turbojet and this version, which first flew on 24 July 1956, was designated **Etendard IV**. After rejection by the NATO nations in favour of the Fiat G91, the Etendard underwent a protracted modification programme to meet an **Aéronavale** requirement for a carrier-based attack and reconnaissance aircraft.

Two versions were developed to fulfil these maritime roles. Compared with the original land-based aircraft, both maritime variants are equipped with such standard naval features as long-stroke undercarriage,

arrester hook, catapult attachments and associated strengthening, folding wingtips and a high-lift system which combined leading-edge and trailing-edge flaps, as well as two perforated belly airbrakes.

Initial deployment

The first version was designated **Etendard IVM** and deployed aboard the carriers *Foch* and *Clemenceau* (Flottilles 11F and 17F) along with the training unit 15F.

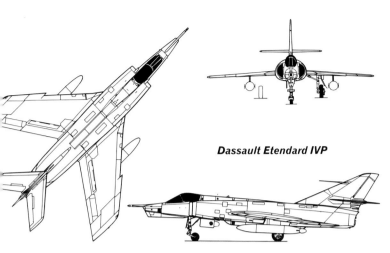

Dassault Etendard IVP

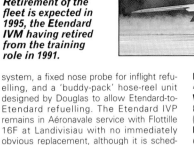

The elderly Etendard IVPs of 16 Flottille are maintained at Landivisiau to provide carrierborne detachments for reconnaissance and buddy tanking. Retirement of the fleet is expected in 1995, the Etendard IVM having retired from the training role in 1991.

The prototype of this variant flew for the first time on 21 May 1958, and was followed by six pre-production aircraft. The first of 69 production Etendard IVMs for the French navy was delivered on 18 January 1962, and production was completed in 1964. The Etendard IVM was equipped with Aïda all-weather fire-control radar and Saab toss-bombing computer. A unique nose-mounted underfin blade fairing contained the guidance aerial for the AS20 radio-command missile (now obsolete). The Etendard IVM was withdrawn from service in July 1991 and has been replaced by the Super Etendard (described separately).

The seventh Etendard was the prototype of the **Etendard IVP**, a reconnaissance/tanker version, of which 21 were ordered. The first flight was made on 19 November 1960. The primary design changes include nose and ventral stations for three and two OMERA reconnaissance cameras (replacing attack avionics and guns respectively), an independent navigation system, a fixed nose probe for inflight refuelling, and a 'buddy-pack' hose-reel unit designed by Douglas to allow Etendard-to-Etendard refuelling. The Etendard IVP remains in Aéronavale service with Flottille 16F at Landivisiau with no immediately obvious replacement, although it is scheduled to be retired in 1995. The 10 to 12 survivors are used for carrierborne reconnaissance and as buddy tankers for the Super Etendard, having seen action over Bosnia.

SPECIFICATION

Dassault-Breguet Etendard IVP
Wing: span 9.60 m (31 ft 6 in); aspect ratio 3; area 29 m² (312 sq ft)
Fuselage and tail: length 14.40 m (47 ft 3 in); height 4.30 m (14 ft 1 in)

Powerplant: one SNECMA Atar 8B turbojet rated at 43.16 kN (9,700 lb) thrust
Weights: empty 5900 kg (13,000 lb); normal take-off 8165 kg (18,000 lb); maximum take-off 10200 kg (22,485 lb)
Fuel and load: internal fuel 3300 litres (726 Imp gal); external fuel two 600-litre (132-Imp gal) underwing tanks; maximum external ordnance 1360 kg (3,000 lb);
Speed: maximum level speed 'clean' at optimum altitude Mach 1.08; maximum level speed 'clean' at sea level 1099 km/h (683 mph); landing speed 220 km/h (138 mph)
Range: low-level sortie at sea level 600 km (370 miles); medium-altitude sortie 1600 km (1,000 miles); ferry range 3000 km (1,860 miles)
Performance: maximum rate of climb at sea level 6000 m (19,685 ft) per minute; service ceiling 15500 m (50,850 ft); take-off distance 700 m (2,295 ft); landing distance without tailchute 800 m (2,625 ft); landing distance with tailchute 500 m (1,640 ft)

Dassault (Dassault-Breguet) **Falcon/Mystère 10**

At the 1969 Paris air show, Dassault-Breguet announced the go-ahead of its **Mystère 10** (later **Falcon 10**), a smaller yet faster cousin to its successful Mystère/Falcon 20. The prototype flew on 1 December 1970 with General Electric CJ610 turbojets, but these were soon changed for Garrett geared turbofans. A very neat machine similar in layout to the Falcon 20 family, it differed in having wings of higher aspect ratio for improved cruise efficiency, with full-span slats and double-slotted flaps, the latter being worked hydraulically like the primary flight controls. By the time production ended in 1990, 226 examples had been delivered, the later production machines having minor changes and being designated **Mystère-Falcon 100**. Components were made by diverse companies in France, Spain and Italy, Dassault-Breguet handling assembly and test.

Small numbers of Falcon 10s were sold to governments as VIP transports and to foreign military customers. In addition, the French **Aéronavale** took delivery of seven specially-equipped **Mystère-Falcon 10MER** aircraft. These fulfil a range of important tasks which include acting as 'silent' (non-emitting) targets to test air-defence systems and interceptors, as conventional night and instrument pilot trainers, for calibration of radars and approach systems (especially on ships), and for transport, casevac and VIP communications. At least one has been fitted with four wing pylons on which have been seen ESM and RWR receivers, ECM jammer pods, chaff/dispenser pods and various forms of armament. The aircraft fly with Escadrille de Servitude 57S at Landivisiau, at least four aircraft being configured for radar training.

SPECIFICATION

Dassault Aviation Falcon/Mystère 10
Wing: span 13.08 m (42 ft 11 in); aspect ratio 7.1; area 24.10 m² (259.42 sq ft)
Fuselage and tail: length 13.86 m (45 ft 5.75 in); height 4.61 m (15 ft 1.5 in); tailplane 5.82 m (19 ft 1 in); wheel track 2.86 m (9 ft 5 in); wheel base 5.30 m (17 ft 4.75 in)
Powerplant: two Garrett TFE731-2 each rated at 3,230 lb st (14.37 kN) dry
Weights: empty equipped 4880 kg (10,760 lb); maximum take-off 8500 kg (18,740 lb)
Fuel and load: internal fuel 2680 kg (5,908 lb); external fuel none; maximum payload 1090 kg (2,400 lb) declining to 840 kg (1,852 lb) with maximum fuel
Speed: maximum cruising speed at 7620 m (25,000 ft) 912 km/h (492 kt; 566 mph)
Range: 3560 km (1,920 nm; 2,210 miles) with four passengers
Performance: operational ceiling 13715 m (45,000 ft) with four passengers; balanced take-off field length 960 m (3,150 ft) with four passengers and fuel for a 1850-km (999-nm; 1,150-mile) stage, or 1325 m (4,347 ft) with four passengers and maximum fuel; landing field length 1065 m (3,494 ft) with four passengers

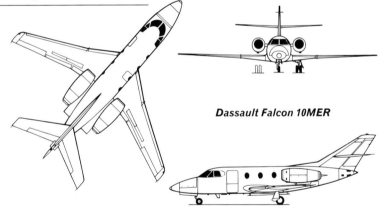

Dassault Falcon 10MER

The Mystère 10MER fulfils a variety of roles for the Aéronavale. Seven aircraft are assigned to Escadrille 57S at Landivisiau, used for transport and liaison, radar systems training and target facilities.

Dassault (Dassault-Breguet) **Falcon/Mystère 20/200/HU-25**

Originally called the **Mystère 20**, the **Dassault-Breguet Falcon 20** twin-engined business jet first flew on 7 May 1963. From the outset it was developed as a 'top of the range' aircraft, with extensive integral tankage, fully powered controls and General Electric CF700 aft-fan engines flat-rated at 4,200 lb (18.58 kN) thrust each, with target-type reversers. The 69-in (1.75- m) diameter cabin could be furnished for up to 12 passengers, though corporate versions seated nine or fewer passengers. Initial US sales resulted from a link with PanAm (today's Falcon Jet Corporation is a Dassault subsidiary), and this helped sales of many specially-equipped versions for military purposes. All versions described have conventional metal fail-safe structures, manufacture of which is shared with other companies in France and Spain. The leading-edge slats, slotted flaps, wing-mounted air-brakes, flight controls and twin-wheel landing gear units are all actuated hydraulically. Engine bleed air is used for wing and engine inlet de-icing.

In January 1977 the sale of 41 **Falcon 20G** aircraft to the US Coast Guard (designated **HU-25A Guardian**) introduced the unique three-spool ATF3 turbofan, which was fitted as standard from 1983 in production **Falcon 200**s. The fuselage has been modified to incorporate two observation windows and a drop hatch for rescue supplies, which typically weigh up to 3,200 lb (1450 kg). The normal crew consists of two pilots, two observers and a sensor systems

Dassault (Dassault-Breguet) Falcon/Mystère 20/200/HU-25

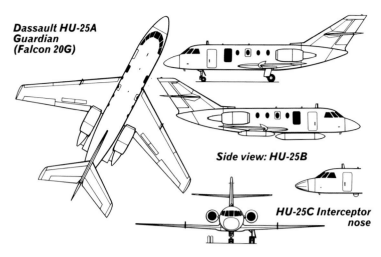

Dassault HU-25A Guardian (Falcon 20G)

Side view: HU-25B

HU-25C Interceptor nose

Pollution monitoring is a role of the seven HU-25Bs serving with the USCG, equipped with SLAR pod and linescan. The HU-25B was deployed to the Gulf region after the 1991 conflict to monitor oil slicks, operating from Bahrain.

operator. The HU-25A was obtained for medium-range, all-weather SAR, maritime surveillance and environmental protection duties. In original configuration, the machines were given a sophisticated array of equipment including an AN/APS-127 radar. Communications equipment includes dual HF, VHF-AM, IFF, single VHF-FM and UHF radios. Navaids include an inertial platform, Omega, dual VOR/ILS/MB, DME, ADF, radio altimeters, R-nav system and TACAN. The HU-25A has four fuselage hardpoints to carry rescue packs and four underwing hardpoints for sensor pods.

Today just over half of the Guardians delivered remain in their original configuration. Seven aircraft have been further modified as **HU-25B**s. These differ by having a Motorola AN/APS-131 SLAR in a fuselage pod offset slightly to starboard, a Texas Instruments RS-18C linescan unit in another pod under the starboard wing and a laser-illuminated TV under the port wing. The Coast Guard operates these Guardians on surveillance duties with responsibility for detection of maritime pollution. A further nine aircraft have been modified for drug interdiction duties under the designation **HU-25C Interceptor**. Fitted with West-inghouse AN/APG-66 search radar in the

nose, turret-mounted WF-360 FLIR sensor and new secure communications gear, the HU-25C is tasked with the pursuit and ident-ification of suspicious sea and air traffic, and entered service in May 1988.

The **Falcon 20H Gardian** maritime surveillance version is operated by the French Aéronavale in the Pacific by 9 Escadrille de Servitude at Tontouta, New Caledonia, and 12S at Faaa, Tahiti. Two air-craft are tasked with patrol and SAR duties within French territorial economic zones in the Pacific. The Gardian has extremely com-prehensive avionics including Thomson-CSF Varan radar and VLF Omega navigation, and is characterised by a an extra-large observa-tion window in the port side of the fuselage.

The **Falcon 200 Gardian 2** was a sim-plified export version marketed for Exocet attack, ESM/ECM, target designation and target towing, but is now cancelled. The basic Falcon 200 is offered with equipment for every kind of specialised role. Libya and France's Armée de l'Air use the **Falcon 20 SNA** version with Mirage radar and elec-tronics for training in low-level attack, while the UK (Royal Navy) and Norway are among seven users of EW/ECM versions.

Further French Falcons have radar installed for training of Mirage 2000, Mirage IVP and Mirage F1CR crews. Dassault has modified a Falcon 20 to test the Rafale's RBE2 radar. The majority of users, however, fly small numbers of the Falcon 20/200 on VIP and staff transport duties. Dassault ended production in 1988 of all Falcon 20/200 variants, although there are several ongoing update programmes.

OPERATORS

France and the US Coast Guard are the major operators of the Falcon/Mystère 20. Other operators are Belgium, Central African Republic, Chile, Djibouti, Egypt, Guinea-Bissau, Iran, Libya, Morocco, Norway, Pakistan, Peru, Portugal, Spain, Sudan, Syria and Venezuela. Virtually all fly the aircraft in a staff/VIP transport function, although Norway uses the type for ECM training. The same role is performed by Falcon 20s of Flight Refuelling Aviation, a UK-based civilian contractor supporting NATO activities.

SPECIFICATION

Dassault Aviation Falcon/Mystère 200

Wing: span 16.32 m (53 ft 6.5 in); aspect ratio 6.5; area 41.00 m² (441.33 sq ft)

France operates many special variants of Falcon 20. The Aéronavale flies the Gardian on maritime patrol duties, characterised by the large observation window. They serve in New Caledonia and Tahiti.

Fuselage and tail: length 17.15 m (56 ft 3 in); height 5.32 m (17 ft 5 in); tailplane span 6.74 m (22 ft 1 in); wheel track 3.34 m (10 ft 11.5 in); wheel base 5.74 m (18 ft 10 in)
Powerplant: two Garrett ATF3-6A-4C each rated at 5,200 lb st (23.13 kN) dry
Weights: empty equipped 8250 kg (18,188 lb); maximum take-off 14515 kg (32,000 lb)
Fuel and load: internal fuel 4845 kg (10,681 lb); external fuel none; maximum payload 1265 kg (2,789 lb) with maximum fuel
Speed: maximum cruising speed at 9150 m (30,020 ft) 870 km/h (470 kt; 541 mph); economical cruising speed at 12500 m (41,010 ft) 780 km/h (421 kt; 485 mph)
Range: range 4650 km (2,509 nm; 2,889 miles) with eight passengers and maximum fuel
Performance: service ceiling 13715 m (45,000 ft); balanced take-off field length 1420 m (4,659 ft) with eight passengers and maximum fuel; landing distance with eight passengers 1130 m (3,707 ft)

Dassault **Falcon/Mystère 50**

Dassault's first new business jet to com-plement the Falcon 20 was the small Falcon 10. In the mid-1970s the decision was taken to produce an aircraft which, while offering the same cabin cross-section as the Falcon 20, would have much greater range. The immediate objective was a trans-USA capability with a typical corporate pay-load of two crew and nine passengers, and this requirement was met by the Dassault design. The original prototype **Falcon/**

Mystère 50 was first flown on 7 Novem-ber 1976 and was followed by the first pro-duction aircraft on 2 March 1979.

The Falcon 50 has the same external fuselage cross-section as the Mystère-Falcon 20, but has been extensively redesigned, introducing area ruling (a sharply waisted rear fuselage and engine pod designed by computational fluid dynam-ics) and an advanced new wing with com-pound leading-edge sweep and optimised

supercritical section. The innovative deci-sion was taken to fit three engines, the choice falling on an uprated version of the Garrett TFE731 geared turbofan engine used in the Falcon 10 and 100. The third engine duct extends well forward above the rear fuselage, the inlet being faired into a vertical tail less acutely swept than that of previous Falcons. The tailplane has increased span and slight anhedral and is fit-ted with normal and high-rate emergency incidence controls. The wing is fitted with full-span slats and double-slotted flaps, giv-ing a maximum lift coefficient greater than that of previous Falcons and enabling a simi-lar field length to the Falcon 20/Gardian. The cabin can be furnished for similar groups of passengers; a typical arrangement seats eight or nine, with aft toilet, and forward crew toilet, galley and wardrobe.

A total of 225 Falcon 50s had been sold by 1992. VIP versions, usually for four/five passengers, have been bought by the gov-ernments of **Djibouti, France, Iraq, Italy**

(three convertible to air ambulance configu-ration), **Jordan, Morocco, Portugal, Rwanda, Spain** (operated under the des-ignation **T.16**) , **Sudan** and **Yugoslavia.**

SPECIFICATION

Dassault Aviation Falcon/Mystère 50

Wing: span 18.86 m (61 ft 10.5 in); aspect ratio 7.6; area 46.83 m² (504.09 sq ft)
Fuselage and tail: length 18.52 m (60 ft 9.25 in); height 6.97 m (22 ft 10.5 in); tailplane span 7.74 m (25 ft 4.75 in); wheel track 3.98 m (13 ft 0.25 in); wheel base 7.24 m (23 ft 9 in)
Powerplant: three Garrett TFE731-3 each rated at 3,700 lb st (16.46 kN) dry
Weights: empty equipped 9150 kg (20,172 lb); maximum take-off 17600 kg (38,801 lb) standard or 18500 kg (40,785 lb) optional
Fuel and load: internal fuel 7040 kg (15,520 lb); external fuel none; maximum payload 1570 kg (3,461 lb) standard or 2170 kg (4,784 lb) optional
Speed: maximum cruising speed at optimum altitude 880 km/h (432 kt; 497 mph)
Range: range 6480 km (3,497 nm; 4,027 miles) with eight passengers
Performance: service ceiling 14935 m (49,000 ft); balanced take-off field length 1365 m (4,478 ft) with eight passengers and maximum fuel; landing run 1080 m (3,543 ft) with eight passengers

Military use of the Falcon 50 is restricted to staff/VIP transport. Portugal is one such user, this aircraft operating with Esquadra 504. The unit is based at Montijo, and also flies the Falcon 20.

Dassault Falcon/Mystère 900

Superficially similar to the Falcon 50, this stretched version of the Falcon tri-jet – known as **Mystère 900** in French service – has a fuselage of greater cross-section, providing an additional 8 cm (3 in) of passenger headroom, uprated engines and slightly modified wings. Intended primarily for civilian use, it first flew on 21 September 1984. The first of two VVIP Mystère 900s was delivered to the **French air force**'s Groupe de Liaisons Aériennes Ministérielles at Villacoublay in November 1987. Similarly-tasked machines have been bought by **Algeria**, **Australia**, **Gabon**, **Malaysia**, **Nigeria** and **Spain**, the latter assigning the local designation **T.18**. Two **Falcon 900**s were delivered to the **Japan ASDF** for long-range maritime surveillance duties.

These aircraft are fitted with US search radar, operations control station, special communications radio, HU-25A Guardian-style observation windows and a drop hatch for sonobuoys, flares and markers.

SPECIFICATION

Dassault Aviation Falcon/Mystère 900
Wing: span 19.33 m (63 ft 5 in); aspect ratio 7.6; area 49.03 m² (527.75 sq ft)
Fuselage and tail: length 20.21 m (66 ft 3.75 in); height 7.55 m (24 ft 9.25 in); tailplane span 7.74 m (25 ft 4.75 in); wheel track 4.45 m (14 ft 7.25 in); wheel base 7.93 m (26 ft 0.25 in)
Powerplant: three Garrett TFE731-5AR-1C each rated at 4,500 lb st (20.02 kN) dry

Weights: empty equipped 10170 kg (22,421 lb); operating empty 10545 kg (23,348 lb); maximum take-off 20640 kg (45,503 lb)
Fuel and load: internal fuel 8690 kg (19,158 lb); external fuel none; maximum payload 1885 kg (4,156 lb)
Speed: maximum cruising speed at 11000 m (36,090 ft) 893 km/h (492 kt; 555 mph)
Range: 7227 km (3,900 nm; 4,491 miles) with eight passengers or 6412 km (3,460 nm; 3,984 miles) with maximum payload
Performance: maximum cruising height 15550 m (51,015 ft); balanced take-off field length 1515 m (4,970 ft) with eight passengers and maximum fuel; balanced landing field length 700 m (2,297 ft) at 12250 lb (27,006 lb)

Two Mystère 900s serve with France's Groupe de Liaison Aériennes Ministérielles (GLAM). As its name implies, the unit provides transport for high-ranking government officials.

Dassault Mirage III

One aircraft established the reputation of France as a manufacturer of world-class jet fighters: the **Mirage III**. With just the right blend of speed, sophistication and simplicity, this Mach 2 delta provided the core of French air defence and attack forces during the 1960s and well into the 1970s, while gaining significant overseas sales which were to lead to follow-up orders for later Mirages and other French defence equipment. The prototype flew on 17 December 1956, but the last of 1,422 Mirage IIIs, 5s and 50s (the two last-mentioned described separately) was not completed until 1992. Even then, several air forces had just completed or were in the process of upgrading their Mirage IIIs for further service.

Discounting some designation anomalies, 'Mirage III' covers aircraft equipped with nose radar, the first of which for the Armée de l'Air were 10 **IIIA** pre-series machines and – entering service in July 1961 – 95 interceptor **IIICs**. These had rocket motors in the rear fuselage to assist the 58.84-kN (13,227-lb st) afterburning SNECMA Atar 9B-3 turbojet when undertaking high-altitude missions, although the facility was little used. The IIIC has been withdrawn, as have most of the **IIIB** two-seat trainers, although a few **IIIB-1** test-beds and **IIIB-RV** refuelling trainers may remain. Single-seat **IIICZs** exported to South Africa were withdrawn in October 1990, and 19 **IIICJ** veterans of Middle East wars were transferred from Israel to Argentina in 1982 and remain in service.

The second phase of Mirage III development was the **IIIE**, flown on 5 April 1961 and optimised for strike/attack as well as interception. Retaining Thomson-CSF Cyrano II radar and with engine modestly uprated to Atar 09C standard at 60.81 kN

(13,669 lb), the IIIE series has a 30-cm (12-in) avionics bay added behind the cockpit, Doppler navigation and slight undercarriage changes to accommodate an AN52 nuclear bomb or large drop-tank on the fuselage centreline. France received 183, plus 20 equivalent **IIIBE** trainers. The IIIE's nuclear tasking was lost to Mirage 2000Ns in 1988 and by 1994 only one French squadron remained in the defence-suppression and conventional attack roles. This will retire in mid-1994. With a camera nose, the IIIE became the Mirage **IIIR**, 70 of which were delivered to the FAF, the last 20 as **IIIRDs** with Doppler. All of these have been supplanted by Mirage F1CRs.

Abroad, Argentina received 17 **IIIEAs** for interception, armed with MATRA R.530 radar-homing and R.550 Magic heat-seeking AAMs. Brazil acquired 16 **IIIEBRs** and, from 1988, six ex-French aircraft upgraded with foreplanes and new avionics, to which standard 10 older aircraft are being raised. In Lebanon, the 10 Mirage **IIIELs** have long been in storage, while Pakistan is expanding its fleet by rebuilding many of the 50 **IIIOs** bought in 1990 after Australia withdrew its fleet. These will join the survivors of 18 **IIIEPs** and 13 reconnaissance **IIIRPs** bought new by the PAF.

Four more countries have chosen extensive Mirage update programmes, but that for Spain's **Mirage IIIEEs** (locally designated **C.11**) fell victim to funding cuts in 1992 and the aircraft have been withdrawn. South Africa bought 17 **IIIEZs**, four **RZs** and four **R2Zs**, the last-mentioned fitted with 70.61-kN (15,873-lb st) Atar 09K50s. Upgrading of the IIIEZs is under way to Atlas Cheetah (described separately) standard, following similar conversion of **IIIDZ** and **IIID2Z** two-seat trainers. Switzerland received 36 Mirage **IIIS** and 18 **IIIRS** aircraft, which are now fitted with new avionics and canards. Since new, the IIIS has been a non-standard Mirage, equipped with a Hughes TARAN 18 radar and navigation

Argentina's Mirage IIIEAs carry the basic interceptor armament of one MATRA R.530 and two R.550 Magics.

Dassault Mirage IIIE

suite for compatibility with Hughes Falcon AAMs. Venezuela bought seven Mirage **IIIEVs**, followed by Mirage 5s, all of which are being uprated to **Mirage 50EV** configuration. All Mirage IIIE operators have small numbers of two-seat **IIID** conversion trainers.

WEAPON OPTIONS

Cannon armament of 30-mm DEFA 552 cannon with 125 rounds per gun. Basic IIIC interceptor version with centreline pylon for one radar-guided missile, initially Nord 5103 or MATRA R.511, subsequently MATRA R.530 (Hughes AIM-26 Falcon on Swiss aircraft). Two wing pylons for infra-red guided missile, either AIM-9B/P Sidewinder or MATRA R.550 Magic (V3 Kukri on South African aircraft). Attack capability in form of JL-100 fuel tank/rocket pod.
Mirage IIIE multi-role aircraft introduced a maximum of five pylons with a maximum weapon load of 4000 kg (8,818 lb) including most free-fall bombs and

Brazil's fleet of Mirage IIIEBRs (illustrated) and IIIDBRs has been reworked by Dassault, complete with the obligatory canard foreplanes.

rocket pods. Attack missiles include Aérospatiale AS30 and MATRA AS37 Martel. French aircraft wired for AN52 15-kT yield tactical nuclear free-fall bomb.

SPECIFICATION

Dassault Aviation Mirage IIIE
Wing: span 8.22 m (26 ft 11.6 in); aspect ratio 1.94; area 35.00 m² (376.75 sq ft)
Fuselage and tail: length 15.03 m (49 ft 3.5 in); height 4.50 m (14 ft 9 in); wheel track 3.15 m (10 ft 4 in); wheel base 4.87 m (15 ft 11.75 in)
Powerplant: one SNECMA Atar 9C-3 rated at 41.97 kN (9,436 lb st) dry and 60.80 kN (13,668 lb st) with afterburning, and provision for one jettisonable SEPR 844 rocket booster rated at 14.71 kN (3,307 lb st)
Weights: empty 7050 kg (15,542 lb); normal take-off 9600 kg (21,164 lb); maximum take-off 13700 kg (30,203 lb)
Fuel and load: internal fuel 2390 litres (631.4 US gal) increasable by 550 litres (145 US gal) if the rocket pack is not fitted; external fuel up to two 1700-, 1300-, 1100- or 625-litre (449-, 343-, 291- or 165-US gal) drop tanks, or two 500-litre (132-US gal) non-jettisonable supersonic tanks, or two 250-litre (66-US gal) JL-100 combined drop tanks/rocket launchers, or two 1100-litre (291-US gal) fuel/electronic equipment tanks; maximum ordnance 4000 kg (8,818 lb)

Dassault Mirage III

There were two basic styles of two-seater, the IIIB with a standard radome (although without radar), and the IIIBE/D with a solid nose. Illustrating the former is a IIIB-2(RV), with dummy refuelling probe for training Mirage IV pilots.

Speed: maximum level speed 'clean' at 12000 m (39,370 ft) 2350 km/h (1,268 kt; 1,460 mph); cruising speed at 11000 m (36,090 ft) 956 km/h (516 kt; 594 mph)
Range: ferry range 4000 km (2,152 nm; 2,486 miles) with three drop tanks; combat radius 1200 km (647 nm; 746 miles) on a hi-hi-hi mission with very small warload
Performance: maximum rate of climb at sea level more than 5000 m (16,405 ft) per minute; climb to 11000 m (36,090 ft) in 3 minutes 0 seconds; service ceiling 17000 m (55,775 ft) or 23000 m (75,460 ft) with rocket pack; take-off run between 700 and 1600 m (2,297 and 5,249 ft) depending on mission-related

maximum weight; landing run 700 m (2,297 ft) with brake chute
g limits: +4.83 in a sustained turn at Mach 0.9 at 5000 m (16,405 ft)

OPERATORS

There is much confusion surrounding the Mirage III/5/50 family, some members being designated as Mirage 5s but bearing all the characteristics (i.e. Cyrano air-to-air radar) of the Mirage IIIE. For simplicity, the operators are presented according to designation. The numbers relate to actual deliveries rather than surviving aircraft:
Argentina: IIIBJ (3), IIICJ (19), IIIDA (4), IIIEA (17) – a large proportion remain in active service
Australia: IIID (16), IIIO(F) (49), IIIO(A) (51) – final flight of Australian Mirage in 1989. Survivors stored pending sale to Pakistan
Brazil: IIIDBR (6), IIIDBR-2 (2), IIIEBR (16), IIIEBR-2 (4) – local designation of F-103D for two-seater and

F-103E for single-seater. 18 believed left in service following upgrade
France: IIIB (27), IIIB-1 (5), IIIB-2(RV) (10), IIIBE (17), IIIC (95), IIIE (183), IIIR (50), IIIRD (20) – Mirage IIIC withdrawn from service, and Mirage IIIE due for retirement in 1995, ending front-line service. A handful of aircraft used by the Centre d'Essais en Vol
Israel: IIIBJ (5), IIICJ (72) – survivors sold to Argentina
Lebanon: IIIBL (2), IIIEL (10) – survivors unserviceable
Pakistan: IIIDP (5), IIIEP (18), IIIRP (13), IIIO (43), IIID (7) – original purchases mostly still in service and being augmented by upgraded ex-RAAF aircraft
South Africa: IIIBZ (3), IIICZ (16), IIIDZ (3), IIID2Z (11), IIIEZ (17), IIIRZ (4), IIIR2Z (4) – early aircraft withdrawn from service, while EZs and D2Zs undergoing Cheetah

The reconnaissance variants of Mirage III feature a revised nose with a fan of cameras underneath the nose, and a forward-facing unit in the chisel-shaped extreme nose. The Swiss Mirage IIIRS fleet has been updated with canards and Dalmo Victor RWR antennas.

upgrade
Spain: IIIDE (6), IIIEE (24) – retired
Switzerland: IIIBS (4), IIICS (1), IIIDS (2), IIIRS (18), IIIS (36) – survivors active after canard upgrade
Venezuela: IIIDV (3), IIIEV (7) – in process of update to 50EV standard

Dassault **Mirage IV**

In 1954 the French government decided to create a national Force de Frappe (nuclear deterrent), one element of which would be a manned bomber. Originally planned as a bigger aircraft with large Pratt & Whitney engines, the **Dassault Mirage IV** was finally scaled down as the **Mirage IVA** with two Atar turbojets, which meant that it could not fly two-way missions to Soviet targets. The prototype flew on 17 June 1959, and following considerable further development a production run of 50 was authorised, later followed by a further 12. The force was completed in March 1968, but since then upgrading of aircraft still in

service has been a continuous process.
Aerodynamically, the Mirage IVA is broadly similar to a scaled-up Mirage III, with side-by-side engines, pilot and navigator in tandem cockpits with upward-hinged canopies, four-wheel bogie main landing gears, tall steerable twin-wheel nose gear and a slender nose terminating in an inflight-refuelling probe. This probe is vital to any mission, because virtually all combat sorties are planned on the basis of one or more refuellings from a Boeing C-135FR tanker or via a buddy pack from an accompanying Mirage IVA. Navigation is by a CSF surveillance radar under the belly, Marconi

Doppler, Dassault computer and SFENA autopilot, more recently upgraded by adding dual inertial systems. OMERA Robot strike cameras are fitted, and the original weapon load comprised a 60-kT nuclear bomb recessed into the rear fuselage, though by removing the large drop tanks it is possible to carry six conventional bombs or four AS37 Martel anti-radar missiles. For many years the force at readiness comprised 36 aircraft (of 51 bomber versions available) assigned to EB 91 and EB 94 and dispersed in small groups around seven bases. In emergency, further dispersal is possible, using chemicals to harden tracts of farmland and six rockets under each wing to blast the aircraft off after a short run. Some were configured for reconnaissance with a semi-recessed camera/SLAR package.

In the late 1980s 19 Mirage IVAs (18 and an attrition replacement) were converted to **Mirage IVP** standard, and this is the only version left in service. Together with updated avionics including a twin inertial platform and Thomson-CSF Serval RWRs, the IVP introduced the ability to carry the Aérospatiale ASMP stand-off nuclear missile on a pylon under the belly. ASMP offers a 300-kT TN81 warhead, and variable delivery profiles dependent on altitude with a maximum range of 155 miles (250 km) at high level, increasing survivability.

A Mirage IVP blasts off from Mont-de-Marsan, using all 12 RATOG bottles. The latter allowed the Mirage IV to react quickly, and to launch from semi-prepared strips.

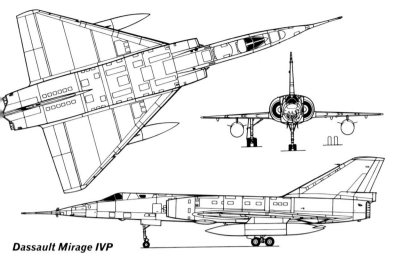

Dassault Mirage IVP

A reduction in the Mirage IV force means that only 14 are operational, serving with two squadrons of Escadre de Bombardement 91, Force Aériennes Stratégiques. Each squadron maintains a detachment, so Mirage IVs are deployed to four bases for security reasons. EB 1/91 'Gascogne' is headquartered at BA118 Mont-de-Marsan, and has its detachment at BA115 Orange/Caritat, while EB 2/91 'Brétagne' is based at Cazaux and detaches to BA125 Istres/Le Tubé. EB 91 has also completely absorbed the Mirage IV training task previously undertaken by CIFAS 328 at Bordeaux.

SPECIFICATION

Dassault Aviation Mirage IVP
Wing: span 11.85 m (38 ft 10.5 in); aspect ratio 1.8; area 78.00 m² (839.61 sq ft)
Fuselage and tail: length 23.50 m (77 ft 1.2 in); height 5.65 m (18 ft 6.4 in)

Powerplant: two SNECMA Atar 9K-50 each rated at 49.03 kN (11,023 lb st) dry and 70.61 kN (15,873 lb st) with afterburning
Weights: empty equipped 14500 kg (31,966 lb); maximum take-off 31600 kg (69,666 lb)
Fuel and load: internal fuel 14000 litres (3,698 US gal); external fuel up to two 2500-litre (660-US gal) drop tanks; maximum ordnance 900 kg (1,984 lb) in missile role or 7200 kg (15,873 lb) in bomber role
Speed: maximum level speed 'clean' at 11000 m (36,090 ft) 2338 km/h (1,262 kt; 1,453 mph) or at sea level about 1349 km/h (728 kt; 838 mph); normal penetration speed at 11000 m (36,090 ft) 1913 km/h (1,172 kt; 1,189 mph)
Range: ferry range 4000 km (2,158 nm; 2,486 miles) with drop tanks; typical combat radius 1240 km

This aircraft was one of two involved in ASMP trials, and shows the position of the missile pylon and the bombing radar. The ASMP is available with either TN80 150-kT yield warhead or TN81 of 30-kT yield. Using terrain avoidance profiles at low level, the ASMP has a range of about 80 km (50 miles). At high altitude this is extended to 250 km (155 miles).

(668 nm; 771 miles)
Performance: climb to 11000 m (36,090 ft) in 4 minutes 15 seconds; service ceiling 20000 m (65,615 ft)

Dassault **Mirage 5/50**

In 1966 the Israeli air force asked Dassault to build a simplified version of the Mirage IIIE optimised for the daytime VFR ground-attack mission. The basic changes in developing this **Mirage 5** were to move the avionics racking from behind the cockpit to the nose, deletion of radar being the main feature. Extra fuel was added in the fuselage, and the nose reprofiled to be much slimmer. Two extra fuselage weapons pylons were added, splayed outwards, so that a maximum of 4000 kg (8,818 lb) of stores could be carried in addition to 1000 litres (220 Imp gal) of fuel, although such a configuration would demand a long runway for take-off. Alternatively the Mirage 5 could be used in the daytime fighter role with infra-red air-to-air missiles, cannon and up to 4700 litres (1,034 Imp gal) of external fuel. The prototype first flew on 19 May 1967.

Using the designation **Mirage 5J**, the Israeli order for 50 was embargoed by President de Gaulle and the stored aircraft were then delivered to the Armée de l'Air as the **Mirage 5F**. The survivors flew with EC 2/13 and EC 3/13, with the former disbanding and the latter receiving Mirage F1CTs.

Following the initial order, the Mirage 5 proved popular with many customers around the world, who wanted a cheap but potent fighter-bomber. Dassault produced a two-seat **Mirage 5D** and reconnaissance-configured **Mirage 5R** to complement the basic model. As the production run of 525 aircraft progressed, the original no-frills aircraft became available with an ever-greater range of avionics options, including reintroduction of the radar. Lightweight radars such as the Cyrano IV, Agave or Aïda II were fitted, or laser rangefinders. Indeed, Dassault could mix and match a wide range of avionics to suit any nation's requirements, and many aircraft have been upgraded during their service lives. Identifying variants of the Mirage deltas is a highly confusing topic, made all the worse by radical upgrade programmes led by both Dassault and IAI, and IAI's own construction/upgrading programme which encompasses the Nesher, Dagger, Kfir and Nammer variants (described under IAI).

Greater thrust

A major programme was the **Mirage 50**, which introduced the Atar 9K-50 engine, as developed for the Mirage F1. The greater thrust endows the aircraft with better runway performance, faster acceleration, larger weapon load and improved manoeuvrability. The prototype Mirage 50 first flew on 15 April 1979, and Chile was the first customer with an order for 16,

Egypt's Mirage 5E2s were equipped to a high standard with fin-mounted radar warning receivers and an undernose laser rangefinder.

although four South African IIIR2Zs had already been delivered with 9K-50 engines. The Mirage 50 package is available as a conversion of both Mirage IIIs and 5s, and the complete range of Mirage III/5 avionics/weapons is available on the Mirage 50, thereby bringing together the two separate development strands of the Dassault deltas, but at the same time creating further confusion concerning designations.

Over half of the Mirage III/5/50 operators have opted for update programmes, pursued either with indigenous systems integrators or with help from Dassault or IAI. Important modifications applied to many of the aircraft concerned include the addition of refuelling probes, improved nav/attack avionics and the fitment of canard foreplanes to improve manoeuvrability and runway performance. Brief details of these are given with the current Mirage 5/50 user list which follows: Abu Dhabi has **Mirage 5AD** fighters, **5RAD**s for reconnaissance and **5DAD** trainers. No upgrade programme has been announced. Argentina has **Mirage 5P**s in addition to IAI Daggers. These have been updated with laser rangefinder, HUD and refuelling probe. Belgium recently operated **5BA** ground attack

The Mirage 5 stemmed from an Israeli order for a low-cost day fighter, but the order was embargoed. The Mirage 5Js subsequently became 5Fs, and were delivered to the Armée de l'Air. They mainly served with EC 13, which operated the survivors until June 1994 when EC 2/13 disbanded.

Dassault Mirage 5B

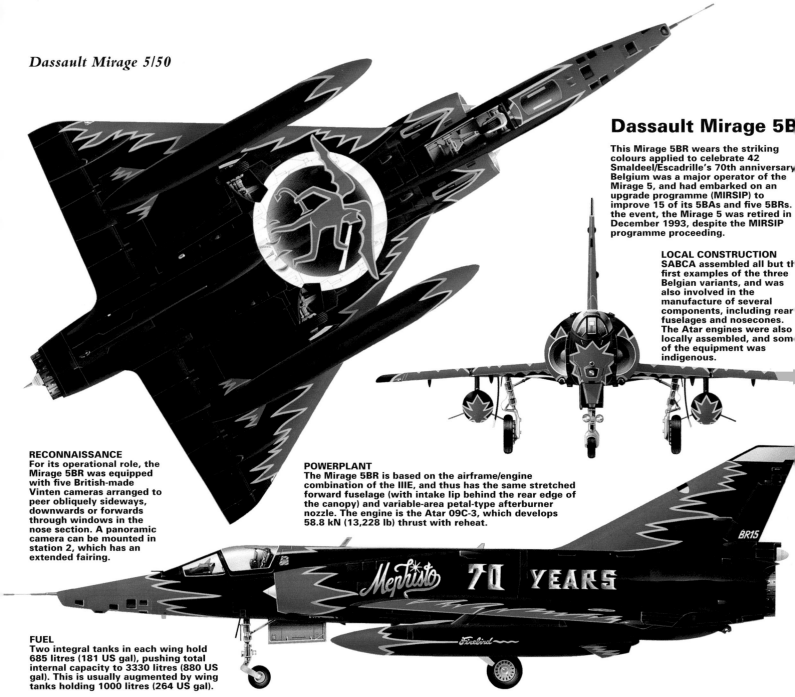

This Mirage 5BR wears the striking colours applied to celebrate 42 Smaldeel/Escadrille's 70th anniversary. Belgium was a major operator of the Mirage 5, and had embarked on an upgrade programme (MIRSIP) to improve 15 of its 5BAs and five 5BRs. [..] the event, the Mirage 5 was retired in December 1993, despite the MIRSIP programme proceeding.

LOCAL CONSTRUCTION
SABCA assembled all but th[..] first examples of the three Belgian variants, and was also involved in the manufacture of several components, including rear fuselages and nosecones. The Atar engines were also locally assembled, and som[..] of the equipment was indigenous.

RECONNAISSANCE
For its operational role, the Mirage 5BR was equipped with five British-made Vinten cameras arranged to peer obliquely sideways, downwards or forwards through windows in the nose section. A panoramic camera can be mounted in station 2, which has an extended fairing.

POWERPLANT
The Mirage 5BR is based on the airframe/engine combination of the IIIE, and thus has the same stretched forward fuselage (with intake lip behind the rear edge of the canopy) and variable-area petal-type afterburner nozzle. The engine is the Atar 09C-3, which develops 58.8 kN (13,228 lb) thrust with reheat.

FUEL
Two integral tanks in each wing hold 685 litres (181 US gal), pushing total internal capacity to 3330 litres (880 US gal). This is usually augmented by wing tanks holding 1000 litres (264 US gal).

aircraft, **5BD** two-seaters and **5BR**s with reconnaissance nose. Of these, 15 **BA**s and five **BD**s were being upgraded with HUD, laser rangefinder and canards to serve with 42 Smaldeel/Escadrille, although all were retired in December 1993 as the MIRSIP programme neared completion. Interest in the aircraft has come from Chile and the Philippines.

Chile operates **Mirage 50C**s and a **50DC** with Grupo 4 of 4 Brigada Aérea at

Although designated Mirage 5DE, this is one of Libya's radar- and Doppler-equipped aircraft – to all intents and purposes a Mirage IIIE.

Punta Arenas. With IAI assistance, ENAER is upgrading them to **50CN Pantera** standard, which involved the fitment of canard foreplanes and Israeli avionics. Colombia operates **5COA**s in the fighter role, **5COR**s for reconnaissance and **5COD** two-seaters with Escuadrón de Combate 212. IAI, which also supplied Kfirs, completed the conversion of the 5CODs with some Kfir avionics and 50 per cent Kfir canards. The remainder of the fleet is being converted with 75 per cent canards in Colombia, being designated **Mirage 50M**.

Egypt has completed a minor update programme on some of its Mirages. These comprise **5SDE/SSE** interceptors, **5SDR**

reconnaissance platforms, **5SDD** trainers and **5E2** attack aircraft. Gabon operates **5G** interceptors, **5G-II** attack aircraft and **5DG** two-seaters. Libya has Mirage **5D**s in the attack role, **5E**s for fighter duties, **5DR**s for reconnaissance and **5DD**s for training. Pakistan has updated its Mirage fleet with new avionics. Aircraft in service include various Mirage III models and **5PA**s and Cyrano- or Agave-equipped **5PA2**s and **5PA3**s for fighter-bomber and anti-shipping work, plus **5DPA** and **5DPA2** for conversion. Peru has upgraded its fleet with refuelling probes and laser rangefinder. The fleet comprises Mirage **5P4**s and **5DP4**s. Venezuela has re-engined both single- and two-seat aircraft with Atar 9K-50s, raising their designation to Mirage **50EV** and **50DV,** respectively.

New 50EVs and a 50DV are in service, augmented by secondhand aircraft upgraded to 50EV standards. Venezuelan aircraft feature canards, refuelling probe, Cyrano IVM3 radar and Exocet capability. Zaïre has not upgraded its aircraft, and operates Mirage **5M**s and a **5DM** trainer.

Information on relevant numbers is presented within the 'Operators' section.

Fully upgraded, the Mirage III/5 is still a highly capable warplane. Representing the pinnacle of Dassault upgrades is this Venezuelan 50EV, with Atar 09K-50 engine, refuelling probe, Serval RWR, canard foreplanes, ULISS 81 INS and Cyrano IV-M3 radar.

Pakistan's 5PA2 and 5PA3 aircraft feature a more rounded nose housing a multi-mode radar. The 5PA2 has the Cyrano IV for air-to-air work and the 5PA3 (illustrated) an Agave unit for anti-ship duties with the Exocet missile.

WEAPON OPTIONS

Similar to those of Mirage III family, although not nuclear-capable. Some aircraft designated Mirage 5 have Cyrano fire-control radar and are in effect Mirage IIIs. These can launch radar-guided air-to-air missiles, but other Mirage 5 family members cannot. Egypt's Mirage 5s employ US weapons, including the Rockeye cluster bomb. Venezuelan and some Pakistani aircraft (5PA3) have Cyrano IVM3 or Agave radar and the ability to launch the AM39 Exocet anti-ship missile.

OPERATORS

Abu Dhabi: 5AD (12), 5DAD (3), 5EAD (14), 5 RAD (3) – 23 single-seat fighters, three reconnaissance aircraft and the three trainers remain in service
Argentina: 5P (10) – nine remain in service
Belgium: 5BA (63), 5BR (27), 5BD (16) – remaining Mirages retired in December 1993
Chile: 50C (6), 50DC (3), 50FC (8) – all single-seaters and one trainer serve with Grupo 4. Aircraft being converted to 50CN Pantera standard
Colombia: 5COA (14), 5COD (2), 5COR (2) – 10 fighters and all reconnaissance/trainers still in

service. In the process of update to 50M standard
Egypt: 5SDE (54), 5SDD (6), 5SDR (6), 5E2 (16) – most remain in service
Gabon: 5DG (4), 5G (3), 5G-II (4) – two 5G, three 5G-II and three 5DG remain in service
Libya: 5D (53), 5DD (15), 5DE (32), 5DR (10) – around 35 5Ds, 30 5DEs, eight 5DRs and 10 5DEs are thought to survive, but serviceability is low
Pakistan: 5DPA2 (2), 5PA (28), 5PA2 (28), 5PA3 (12) – most still in service
Peru: 5P (22), 5P3 (10), 5P4 (2), 5DP (4), 5DP3 (2) – current fleet comprises 12 single-seaters upgraded to 5P4 standard and three 5DP4 two-seaters
Venezuela: 5V (6), 5DV (1), 50EV (9) – fleet undergoing upgrade to 50DV/EV standard, including Mirage IIIs
Zaïre: 5M (8), 5DM (3) – serviceability of fleet is low

SPECIFICATION

Dassault Aviation Mirage 5A (Mirage 5F)
Wing: span 8.22 m (26 ft 11.6 in); aspect ratio 1.94; area 35.00 m2 (376.75 sq ft)
Fuselage and tail: length 15.55 m (51 ft 0.2 in); height 4.50 m (14 ft 9 in); wheel track 3.15 m (10 ft 4 in); wheel base 4.87 m (15 ft 11.75 in)
Powerplant: one SNECMA Atar 9C rated at 41.97 kN (9,436 lb st) dry and 60.80 kN (13,668 lb st) with afterburning
Weights: empty equipped 7150 kg (15,763 lb); normal take-off 9900 kg (21,825 lb); maximum take-off 13700 kg (30,203 lb)
Fuel and load: internal fuel 2860 litres (755.5 US gal); external fuel up to two 1700-, 1300-, 1100- or 625-litre (449-, 343-, 291- or 165-US gal) drop tanks, or two 500-litre (132-US gal) non-jettisonable

supersonic tanks, or two 250-litre (66-US gal) JL-100 combined drop tanks/rocket launchers, or two 1100-litre (291-US gal) non-jettisonable fuel/electronic equipment tanks; maximum ordnance 4000 kg (8,818 lb)
Speed: maximum level speed 'clean' at 12000 m (39,370 ft) 2350 km/h (1,268 kt; 1,460 mph); cruising speed at 11000 m (36090 ft) 956 km/h (516 kt; 594 mph)
Range: combat radius 1250 km (675 nm; 777 miles) on a hi-lo-hi attack mission at Mach 0.85 with two 400-kg (882-lb) bombs and maximum external fuel, or 685 km (370 nm; 426 miles) on a lo-lo-lo attack mission at Mach 0.6 with two 400-kg (882-lb) bombs and maximum external fuel
Performance: maximum rate of climb at sea level 11160 m (36,614 ft) per minute; service ceiling 18000 m (59,055 ft) or 23000 m (75,460 ft) with rocket pack; take-off run between 915 m (3,002 ft) at normal take-off weight and 1830 m (6,004 ft) at maximum take-off weight; landing run 1830 m (6,004 ft) at maximum landing weight

Dassault Aviation Mirage 50M
Wing: span 8.22 m (26 ft 11.6 in); aspect ratio 1.94; area 35.00 m2 (376.75 sq ft); optional canard foreplane area 1.00 m2 (10.76 sq ft)
Fuselage and tail: length 15.56 m (51 ft 0.6 in); height 4.50 m (14 ft 9 in); wheel track 3.15 m (10 ft 4 in); wheel base 4.87 m (15 ft 11.75 in)
Powerplant: one SNECMA Atar 9K-50 rated at 49.03 kN (11,023 lb st) dry and 70.82 kN (15,873 lb st) with afterburning
Weights: empty equipped 7150 kg (15,763 lb); normal take-off 10000 kg (22,046 lb); maximum take-off 14700 kg (32,407 lb)
Fuel and load: internal fuel 2288 kg (5,044 lb) for

One of many dramatic upgrade programmes, the ENAER Pantera 50CN is based on the Mirage 50 with uprated engine, but also features a Kfir-style nose with Elta EL/M-2001B ranging radar, fin-mounted Caiquen III radar warning receivers, IAI-designed canards and numerous avionics upgrades.

Mirage III conversions or 2710 kg (5,974 lb) for Mirage 5 conversions; external fuel up to two 1700-, 1300-, 1100- or 625-litre (449-, 343-, 291- or 165-US gal) drop tanks, or two 500-litre (132-US gal) non-jettisonable supersonic tanks, or two 250-litre (66-US gal) JL-100 combined drop tanks/rocket launchers, or two 1100-litre (291-US gal) non-jettisonable Bidon Cyclope fuel/electronic equipment tanks; maximum ordnance 4000 kg (8,818 lb)
Speed: maximum level speed 'clean' at 12000 m (39,370 ft) 2338 km/h (1,262 kt; 1,453 mph); cruising speed at 11000 m (36,090 ft) 956 km/h (516 kt; 594 mph)
Range: combat radius 1315 km (710 nm; 817 miles) of a hi-hi-hi interception mission with two AAMs and three drop tanks, or 1260 km (680 nm; 783 miles) on a hi-lo-hi attack mission with two 400-kg (882-lb) bombs and three drop tanks, or 630 km (340 nm; 391 miles) on a lo-lo-lo attack mission with two 400-kg (882-lb) bombs and three drop tanks
Performance: maximum rate of climb at sea level 11160 m (36,614 ft) per minute; climb to 13715 m (45,000 ft) in 4 minutes 42 seconds; service ceiling 18000 m (59,055 ft); take-off run 800 m (2,625 ft) with two Magic AAMs or 1830 m (6,004 ft) at maximum take-off weight; landing run 1830 m (6,004 ft) at normal landing weight

Dassault **Mirage F1A/D/E**

While most export customers for the Mirage F1 interceptor series were content to specify aircraft based on the original Armée de l'Air F1C (described separately), the South African Air Force recognised the advantages of a simplified version for day visual attack missions. This exactly parallels the Mirage 5, which is a similar simplified version of the Mirage III. Like the Mirage 5, the resulting **Dassault-Breguet Mirage F1A** is visually distinguished by having a slender conical nose, resulting from removal of the large Cyrano IVM radar. In its place is the ESD Aïda II ranging radar as fitted to some Mirage 5s. Again like the Mirage 5s, the large instrument boom housing the pitot/static heads is attached on the underside of the nose, out of the way of the Aïda II radar set.

The main advantages of the Mirage F1A are its relatively low cost and extra range/payload capability. The main avionics racking is moved from behind the cockpit to the nose, making room for an extra fuselage tank. Other additions are a Doppler radar, and a retractable refuelling probe. The Mirage F1A was bought by Libya (16) and South Africa, which received 32 aircraft designated **Mirage F1AZ** for service with No. 1 Sqn. In addition to Aïda radar, South African F1AZs are fitted with a laser-ranger. A licence to build the Mirage and its Atar engine is held by Armscor, though Atlas Aircraft, the main South African aircraft manufacturer, has never announced more than the manufacture of parts. South African F1AZs were involved in offensives into Angola and anti-guerrilla operations in

south-west Africa, utilising MATRA F4 rocket pods in addition to indigenous CFD-200 chaff/flare dispensers and bombs.

On 22 December 1974 Dassault flew a prototype designated **Mirage F1E**, powered by the then-new M53 engine. This aircraft failed to win large orders from four European NATO countries, and the M53-powered version was abandoned. Instead, and repeating the practice established with the Mirage III, the designation was then applied to an upgraded multi-role fighter/attack version for export customers. Outwardly resembling the F1C, the F1E has a SAGEM inertial system, EMD.182 central digital computer, VE.120C head-up display, Crouzet air-data computer and digital arma-

Iraq's first batch of F1EQs were principally fighters, armed with Super 530F and Magic 1 missiles.

ment/navigation controls. Like all F1 versions, the F1E can be fitted with comprehensive radar-warning receivers, chaff/flare dispensers and active ECM jammer pods, the most important of the latter being the Thomson-CSF Remora and Caiman. The **Mirage F1D** is essentially similar to the F1B (described separately) trainer procured by the Armée de l'Air, differing only by being based on the F1E export variant, although they are fitted with SEMMB Mk 10 zero-zero ejection seats with command ejection. These trainers are fully combat capable and have been acquired in small numbers by some F1E operators.

Most export F1D/Es have been fitted

Only South Africa and Libya purchased the F1A, this example carrying a squadron badge.

Dassault Mirage F1A/D/E

The F1D (and essentially similar F1B) is a two-seater conversion/continuation trainer. Qatar operates a pair of F1DDAs.

with bullet antennas for Thomson-CSF BF radar warning receiver and VOR aerials located in the fin. In addition, some aircraft received an HF fillet aerial at the forward joint of the fin. Iraqi F1Es were used extensively in the eight-year war with Iran, and more recently during the Gulf War in 1991. Basic multi-role aircraft (**F1EQ**, **F1EQ-2**) were followed by the **F1EQ-4** with refuelling probe and reconnaissance pod capability, and **F1EQ-5** and **F1EQ-6** with Thomson-CSF Agave radar and Exocet capability.

The F1EQ-6 had SHERLOC RWR from the outset, also retrofitted to the F1EQ-5s.

WEAPON OPTIONS

The attack-optimised F1A features two 30-mm DEFA 553 cannon with 125 rounds per gun. One centreline and two underwing pylons can mount a wide variety of unguided stores up to 4000 kg (8,820 lb), with MATRA Magic air-to-air missiles on the wingtip rails. South African F1AZs carry a variety of Israeli and indigenous weapons, including Armscor 250-kg (550-lb) fragmentation bombs and rocket pods.
The multi-role F1E can carry similar weapons, but is also equipped to fire radar-guided missiles. Iraqi F1EQ-5s and F1EQ-6s carry Exocet anti-ship missiles.

OPERATORS

Mirage F1As were sold to South Africa (32 F1AZs) and Libya (16 **F1AD**s accompanied by six **F1BD** trainers).

The Mirage F1E has achieved some degree of export success and has been acquired by Ecuador (16 **Mirage F1JA**s based on the F1E and two **Mirage F1JE** trainers), Iraq (110 **F1EQ**s ordered, although only 93 have been delivered), Jordan (17 **F1EJ**s), Libya (16 **F1ED**s), Morocco (14 **F1EH**s and six **F1EH-200**s), Qatar (12 **F1EDA**s and two **F1DDA** trainers) and Spain (22 **F1EE-200**s operated under the local designation **C.14B**).

RADAR WARNING
The fin mounts forward- and rearward-facing antennas for the Thomson-CSF BF radar warning receiver. Sideways cover is provided by disc antennas flush with the fin sides.

Iraq's later Mirages are fitted with Agave radar and wear a slate-blue colour scheme for the anti-ship role.

SPECIFICATION

Dassault Aviation Mirage F1A/E
generally similar to Mirage F1C (described separately) except in the following particulars:
Fuselage and tail: length 15.30 m (50 ft 2.5 in)
Weights: empty 7600 kg (16,755 lb)
Speed: maximum level speed 'clean' at 11000 m (36,090 ft) 2125 km/h (1,146 kt; 1.320 mph)
Performance: maximum rate of climb at sea level 12000 m (39,370 ft) per minute with afterburning

Dassault Mirage F1AZ

Surviving South African Mirages wear this distinctive camouflage scheme. National and squadron insignia are often oversprayed. The aircraft serves with No. 1 Sqn, based at Hoedspruit, the last SAAF Mirage F1 user following the retirement of the F1CZs.

FUEL
Total internal capacity is 4300 litres (1,136 US gal) in 14 bag tanks located in the fuselage and inner wing. This is augmented by 1200 litres (317 US gal) in each of two underwing drop tanks.

RANGING RADAR
The F1A fighter-bomber carries a small EMD Aïda 2 ranging radar in the extreme nose. The radar has a fixed antenna and provides automatic search, acquisition, ranging and tracking for targets within its 16° field of view. Data is presented to the pilot in his gyro gunsight.

UNDERNOSE FAIRING
The undernose bulge houses a Thomson-CSF TMV-360 laser rangefinder, which provides accurate distance-measuring for the ground attack role.

ARMAMENT
The basic armament consists of two internal cannon, with most stores carried on multiple dispensers on the centreline. Although not carried here, the F1AZ can be fitted with wingtip launch rails for the V3B Kukri or V3C Darter indigenous air-to-air missile.

PROBE
South Africa's F1AZs have retractable refuelling probes on the starboard side for inflight refuelling.

Dassault **Mirage F1B/C**

Despite its suffix, the **Mirage F1C** was the initial production version of Dassault's successor to the Mirage III/5. Forsaking the delta for a high-mounted wing and conventional tail surfaces, the private venture prototype flew on 23 December 1966 and was officially adopted in May 1967, when three prototypes were ordered. With more power provided by a 70.61-kN (15,873-lb st) SNECMA Atar 09K50 reheated turbojet, the F1 easily out-performs the Mirage III, offering 43 per cent more internal fuel capacity, 2.5 tonnes more on gross weight despite a smaller wing area, 30 per cent shorter take-off run, 25 per cent slower approach speed and improved manoeuvrability at all speeds. Much of this derives from the fact that the F1 is fitted with flaps and leading-edge slats, neither of which is compatible with the Mirage III's delta wing.

To meet the prime requirement for an all-weather interceptor, the F1C is equipped with a Thomson-CSF Cyrano IV monopulse radar operating in I/J band. A later modification to IV-1 standards added limited lookdown capability, but as ground attack is only a secondary role for the F1C there are no ground mapping or continuous target ranging options. Single targets only can be tracked, but radar performance is noticeably degraded by poor weather. F1C production deliveries began in May 1973 and were followed in December of the same year by re-equipment of the first squadron, a component of 30 Wing at Reims, east of Paris. F1Cs were initially restricted in armament to their two internal 30-mm cannon. In 1976, the MATRA R.530 was issued to F1C units, followed a year later by the new heat-seeking MATRA R.550 Magic attached to wingtip rails. One or two R.530FEs were carried, options being between radar-homing and IR versions of the missile. In December 1979, the differently-shaped Super 530F-1 entered service with the F1C force, aircraft carrying one under each wing.

The Armée de l'Air acquired 83 basic F1Cs, of which the final 13 were fitted with Thomson-CSF BF radar warning receiver 'bullet' antennas on the fin. The first series of F1Cs equipped two squadrons of 30 Wing, followed by two in 5 Wing at Orange and two of 12 Wing at Cambrai. A further 79 machines, delivered between March 1977 and December 1983, have fixed refuelling probes and are designated **F1C-200**. Probe installation requires a minute plug in the forward fuselage, increasing the aircraft's length by 7 cm (3 in). All three wings operated a mixture of F1Cs and F1C-200s, allowing 10 Wing at Creil to equip one squadron and 12 Wing to gain a third component. In 1985, Creil's aircraft became the third squadron of 30 Wing.

The structure of three wings of three squadrons each was completed by the

Above: EC 1/30 was due to relinquish its F1C-200s in 1994. This example carries a Super 530F under the wing, the standard medium-range weapon.

Right: EC 4/30 maintains a 10-12 aircraft deployment in support of the French garrison in Djibouti. The sand and chocolate scheme reflects the arid terrain.

OCU, which was based at Orange. The AA ordered 20 **F1B** tandem-seat trainers, delivered between October 1980 and March 1983 for pilot conversion. Incorporation of a second cockpit adds only 30 cm (12 in) to the standard F1C's length, as remaining space is made by deleting the fuselage fuel tank and both internal cannon. Empty weight increases by 200 kg (441 lb), due partly to the installation of two French-built Martin-Baker Mk 10 zero-zero ejection seats (the F1C having Mk 4 seats with a forward speed limitation). Otherwise, the F1B is combat capable and can compensate for its internal deficiencies by carrying cannon pods and external fuel tanks. Refuelling probes occasionally fitted to the aircraft are, in fact, dummies for training with C-135FR tankers.

Availability of the Mirage 2000C reduced French Mirage F1B/F1C/-200 squadrons to six by 1993, comprising two in 12 Wing and four in 30 Wing, one of which is detached to Djibouti, its aircraft wearing sand and chocolate camouflage in place of blue-grey and regularly carrying ground attack ordnance. Mirage F1Cs displaced by the 2000C are being converted to **F1CT** standard (described separately).

Exports of the F1C have been made to six countries, four of which went on to adopt the multi-role F1E (described separately). South Africa received the first of 16 **F1CZ**s in 1975 for No. 3 Squadron at

Waterkloof. They saw action in the confrontation with Angola until the coming of relative peace resulted in the squadron disbanding in September 1992 and putting its Mirages into storage. Likewise active in African skies, Morocco's 30 **F1CH**s, supplied from 1978, flew from Sidi Slimane and advanced bases in support of missions against guerrilla forces in Western Sahara. Jordan began receiving 17 **F1CJ**s in 1981 for 25 Squadron at Shaheed Mwaffaq as-Salti AB, Azraq, and Kuwait took 18 **F1CK**s (from 1976) and nine **F1CK2**s (from 1984) for 18 and 61 Squadrons at Ali al Salem AB. The CK2 standard, to which all survivors have been upgraded, includes air-to-surface capability, as evidenced by delivery of MATRA ARMAT anti-radar missiles. Kuwaiti F1s fought in defence of their country in August 1990 and during the Operation Desert Storm liberation of January-February 1991. Kuwait was ahead of France in ordering the two-seat version, its first **F1BK** flying on 26 May 1976.

Greece is the sole F1 operator not to obtain a trainer, all its 40 aircraft being **F1CG**s delivered from August 1975. Based at Tanagra, near Athens, they were dispersed on arrival of Mirage 2000s: 342 Squadron to Heraklion and 334 Squadron to

Agrinion. A further NATO country, Spain, bought 45 Mirage **F1CE**s with the local designation **C.14A**, equipping 141 and 142 Squadrons at Los Llanos from 1975. The C.14A's radars have since been upgraded to Cyrano IVM standard, adding air-to-surface modes, and they also have the option of carrying AIM-9P Sidewinder AAMs.

WEAPON OPTIONS

Standard air-to-air configuration of two AIM-9 or Magic IR missiles on wingtip rails, and either one MATRA R.530 on centreline or two Super 530F on wing pylons. DEFA 553 30-mm cannon with 125 rounds per gun standard. Basic ground attack capability available. Other missile alternatives include ARMAT anti-radiation missiles (France and Kuwait) and V3B Kukri/V3C Darter (South Africa).

SPECIFICATION

Dassault Aviation Mirage F1C

Wing: span 8.40 m (27 ft 6.75 in) without tip stores and about 9.32 m (30 ft 6.75 in) with tip-mounted Magic AAMs; aspect ratio 2.82; area 25.00 m² (269.11 sq ft)

Fuselage and tail: length 15.30 m (50 ft 2.5 in); height 4.50 m (14 ft 9 in); wheel track 2.50 m (8 ft 2.5 in); wheel base 5.00 m (16 ft 4.75 in)

Powerplant: one SNECMA Atar 9K-50 rated at 49.03 kN (11,023 lb st) dry and 70.21 kN (15,785 lb st) with afterburning

Weights: empty 7400 kg (16,314 lb); normal take-off 10900 kg (24,030 lb); maximum take-off 16200 kg (35,715 lb)

Fuel and load: internal fuel 4300 litres (1,136 US gal); external fuel up to one 2200-litre (581-US gal) and two 1130-litre (298-US gal) drop tanks; maximum ordnance 6300 kg (13,889 lb)

Speed: maximum level speed 'clean' at 11000 m (36,090 ft) 2338 km/h (1,262 kt; 1,453 mph)

Range: combat radius 425 km (229 nm; 264 miles) on a hi-lo-hi attack mission with 14 250-kg (551-lb) bombs, or 600 km (324 nm; 373 miles) on a lo-lo-lo attack mission with six 250-kg (551lb) bombs and two

Jordan operates both the air defence F1CJ (illustrated), which wears a light grey camouflage, and the multi-role F1EJ which wears tactical three-tone camouflage.

(36,090 ft) 2338 km/h (1,262 kt; 1,453 mph)
Range: normal mission endurance 2 hours 0 minutes for training
Performance: maximum rate of climb at sea level 4200 m (13,780 ft) per minute without afterburning; stabilised supersonic ceiling 16000 m (52,495 ft)

OPERATORS

EC 3/30 conducts all Mirage F1 training for the Armée de l'Air, and consequently has a high proportion of F1B two-seaters.

drop tanks, or 1390 km (749 nm; 863 miles) on a hi-lo-hi attack mission with two 250-kg (551-lb) bombs and three drop tanks; endurance 2 hours 15 minutes on a CAP with two Super 530 AAMs and one drop tank

Performance: maximum rate of climb at sea level 12780 m (41,930 ft) per minute with afterburning; service ceiling 20000 m (65,615 ft); take-off run 600 m (1,969 ft) at 11500 kg (25,353 kg); landing run 670 m (2,198 ft) at 8500 kg (18,739 lb)

Dassault Aviation Mirage F1B
generally similar to the Dassault Aviation Mirage F1C except in the following particulars:
Wing: span 8.44 m (27 ft 8.3 in) without tip stores
Fuselage and tail: length 15.55 m (51 ft 0.2 in); height 4.49 m (14 ft 8.8 in)
Weights: operating empty 8200 kg (18,078 lb) including pilots; normal take-off 11200 kg (24,691 lb)
Fuel and load: internal fuel 3850 litres (1,017 US gal); external fuel up to one 2200-litre (581-US gal) and two 1130-litre (298-US gal) drop tanks; maximum ordnance 6300 kg (13,889 lb)
Speed: maximum level speed 'clean' at 11000 m

The F1CK-2 was similar to the F1E, and had a ground attack role. This example carries retarded bombs.

Delivery totals given:
France: F1B (20), F1C (166) – remaining aircraft serve with EC 3/12, EC 1/30, EC 3/30 and EC 4/30, the latter based in Djibouti
Greece: F1CG (40) – serve with 334 and 342 Mira
Iraq: F1BQ (15) – augment F1EQ single-seat force
Jordan: F1BJ (2), F1CJ (17) – service with No. 25 Sqn in air defence role
Kuwait: F1BK (2), F1BK-2 (4), F1CK (18), F1CK-2 (9) – all single-seaters upgraded to F1CK-2 standard which is multi-role version similar to F1E with ARMAT capability. Fifteen escaped Iraqi invasion to fly 128 combat missions in the Gulf War. All withdrawn from use in 1993 following delivery of Hornets
Morocco: F1CH (30) – used in air defence role
South Africa: F1CZ (16) – used for air defence by No. 3 Sqn, scoring several kills over Angolan MiGs. Unit disbanded September 1993 with remaining aircraft being stored. Two aircraft used by Atlas and one by Leningrad (Klimov) to test re-engining with RD-33 engine. Re-engining of remaining aircraft may follow
Spain: F1BE (6), F1CE (45) – serve on multi-role squadrons alongside F1EEs

Dassault Mirage F1CE

Spain's mixed F1 force is now all concentrated in Ala 14. This unit maintains a detachment on the Canaries to provide air defence for the island group. All Spanish Mirages have an important secondary ground attack tasking.

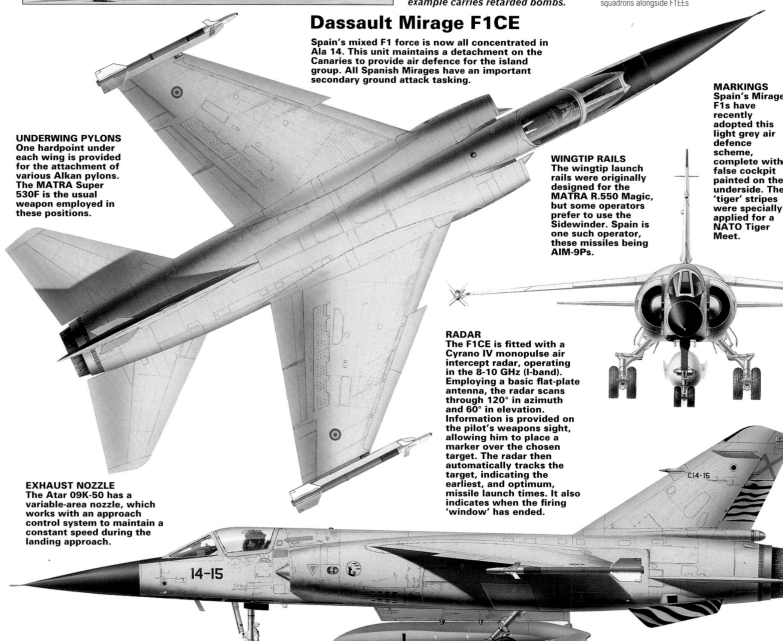

UNDERWING PYLONS
One hardpoint under each wing is provided for the attachment of various Alkan pylons. The MATRA Super 530F is the usual weapon employed in these positions.

WINGTIP RAILS
The wingtip launch rails were originally designed for the MATRA R.550 Magic, but some operators prefer to use the Sidewinder. Spain is one such operator, these missiles being AIM-9Ps.

MARKINGS
Spain's Mirage F1s have recently adopted this light grey air defence scheme, complete with false cockpit painted on the underside. The 'tiger' stripes were specially applied for a NATO Tiger Meet.

RADAR
The F1CE is fitted with a Cyrano IV monopulse air intercept radar, operating in the 8-10 GHz (I-band). Employing a basic flat-plate antenna, the radar scans through 120° in azimuth and 60° in elevation. Information is provided on the pilot's weapons sight, allowing him to place a marker over the chosen target. The radar then automatically tracks the target, indicating the earliest, and optimum, missile launch times. It also indicates when the firing 'window' has ended.

EXHAUST NOZZLE
The Atar 09K-50 has a variable-area nozzle, which works with an approach control system to maintain a constant speed during the landing approach.

Dassault Mirage F1CR

As soon as it was clear that the Mirage F1 would support a major production run, Dassault studied a dedicated reconnaissance version, the major potential customer being the **Armée de l'Air** which would need to replace its Mirage IIIRs. With the escalating price of combat aircraft, a strong case existed for the development of pods that could be carried by non-dedicated aircraft. In fact, some Armée de l'Air Mirage F1s, and those of some export customers, notably Iraq's F1EQs, have been seen with various centreline reconnaissance pods.

Development did continue of a dedicated tactical reconnaissance platform for the Armée de l'Air, designated **Mirage F1CR-200**, the first of which flew on 20 November 1981. For its intended role, the Mirage F1CR carries a wealth of reconnaissance equipment both internally and externally. An SAT SCM2400 Super Cyclope infra-red linescan unit is installed in place of the cannon, and an undernose fairing houses either a 75-mm Thomson-TRT 40 panoramic camera or 150-mm Thomson-TRT 33 vertical camera. Other internal equipment includes a Cyrano IVMR radar with extra ground-mapping, blind let-down, ranging and contour-mapping modes compared to the fighter's radar, and provision of a navigation computer and ULISS 47 INS.

Additional sensors are carried in various centreline pods, these including Thomson-CSF Raphaël TH side-looking airborne radar, HAROLD long-range oblique camera or Thomson-CSF ASTAC electronic intelligence pod. Various combinations of cameras can

During the latter part of the Gulf War ER 33's Mirages flew alongside Jaguars on bombing missions.

also be mounted in a pod. A refuelling probe is on the starboard side of the nose.

Sixty-four F1CRs were ordered, of which 52 remain in service. The first production aircraft flew on 10 November 1982, and the first squadron, Escadron de Reconnaissance 2/33 'Savoie', became operational at BA124 Strasbourg/Entzheim in July 1983. ER 1/33 'Belfort' and ER 3/33 'Moselle' followed, conversion from Mirage IIIRs being completed in 1988. F1CRs were dispatched to Saudi Arabia for participation in Desert Shield/Storm, where they were used for reconnaissance missions before being

grounded due to confusion with Iraqi Mirage F1EQs. When allowed to resume flying, they displayed their little-known secondary ground attack role by being used to drop bombs on Iraqi positions, their radar making them more effective than Jaguars. In 1994, ER 33 will move to Reims.

SPECIFICATION

Dassault Aviation Mirage F1CR-200
generally similar to the Dassault Aviation Mirage F1C except in the following particulars:

Weights: empty about 7900 kg (17,416 lb)
Speed: maximum level speed with a centreline mission pod at 11000 m (36,090 ft) 1915 km/h (1,033 kt; 1,190 mph)
Range: operational radius 1390 km (749 nm; 863 miles) on a hi-lo-hi mission with one mission pod and two drop tanks

An F1CR-200 on patrol over northern Iraq, during the UN effort to protect Kurdish populations. The aircraft carries Raphaël SLAR on the centreline, ECM pod and chaff dispenser and wingtip Magic 2s.

Dassault Mirage F1CT

A logical product of the shortfall in French ground attack capability and a surplus of air defence fighters following Mirage 2000C deliveries, the **Mirage F1CT** derives its designation from being a tactical (*tactique*) air-to-ground version of the F1C interceptor – specifically, the probe-equipped F1C-200. Two prototypes were converted by Dassault at Biarritz (the first flying on 3 May 1991) and 55 more are fol-

lowing from the air force workshops at Clermont-Ferrand/Aulnat by 1995. Deliveries began on 13 February 1992, allowing one squadron of 13 Wing at Colmar to achieve IOC in November of that year.

The F1CT programme upgrades intercep-

Dassault Mirage F1CT

The F1CT conversion gives ageing interceptors a new lease of life. The wraparound camouflage is unique to this variant, as is the undernose laser rangefinder. Interception capability is retained.

tors to a similar standard to the tactical recce F1CR. Radar changes from Cyrano IV to IVMR, with additional air-to-ground modes, and is backed by a SAGEM ULISS 47 inertial platform, Dassault Electronique M182XR central computer, Thomson VE120 HUD, Thomson-TRT TMV630A laser rangefinder beneath the nose, Martin-Baker Mk 10 zero-zero ejection seat, improved radar warning receiver, chaff/flare dispensers and secure radio.

Structurally, the cockpit is rebuilt and the wing strengthened and modified for activation of the outboard hardpoints, while the port cannon is removed to make space for the additional equipment and the whole airframe is rewired and fitted with new dielectric panels. Strengthening of the centreline pylon permits carriage of the large, 2200-litre (484-Imp gal) tank originally developed for the Iraqi Mirage F1EQ. Externally, the blue-grey air defence camouflage is exchanged for wrap-around green and grey.

The F1CT carries bombs and rocket pods for its new mission, but retains the ability to launch Super 530 and Magic 2 AAMs as a pure interceptor.

SPECIFICATION

Dassault Aviation Mirage F1CT
generally similar to the Dassault Aviation Mirage F1C

Dassault **Mirage 2000B/C/E/R**

For the third Mirage generation, Dassault returned to the delta configuration, using a negative longitudinal stability and a fly-by-wire flight control system to eliminate many of the shortcomings of a conventionally-controlled delta such as the Mirage III. As such, the Mirage 2000 has its predecessor's big high-lift wing, large internal volume (for fuel and avionics) and low wave drag, but the improved agility, slow speed handling and more docile landing speed available from a computer-controlled, naturally unstable aircraft: the best of all worlds. Conceived in 1972 and originally known as **Delta 1000**, the aircraft remained a low-key project until December 1975, when cancellation of the

Abu Dhabi's Mirage 2000 order included eight 2000RAD reconnaissance aircraft with provision for carrying various centreline pods. These include the COR-2 optical sensor pod shown here.

projected, twin-engined Dassault ACF left the Armée de l'Air without a new interceptor programme. An official specification was written round the aircraft in March 1976 and priority given to development in time for a 1982 service debut.

Now standard equipment of the French fighter arm, the Mirage 2000 has a large

wing – and thus low loading – fitted with leading-edge slats which deploy automatically during combat manoeuvring. Two-piece elevons occupy the trailing edge. Whereas a Mirage III raising elevons to

rotate for take-off would be forcing itself back onto the runway, an unstable delta has the centre of gravity behind the aerodynamic centre and so lowers elevons (creating lift) to achieve rotation. The take-off run is shorter and greater weapon loads can be carried in comparison to an aerodynamically-stable delta. Engine air intakes of the 2000 are the traditional Mirage type with movable half-cone centrebodies and are fitted with small strakes which create vortices at high angles of attack and so help to minimise yaw. Construction is of traditional metals, but with sparing use of carbon-fibre for some doors and panels.

New-generation engine

SNECMA's M53 reheated turbofan – perhaps more accurately described as a 'leaky turbojet' because of its low bypass ratio of 0.32 – was transferred to the Mirage 2000 after the ACF's demise. On the 83.36 kN (18,839 lb st) of a single M53-2, the first of five prototype Mirage 2000s was airborne at Istres on 10 March 1978 and gave a convincing display of slow-speed manoeuvrability at Farnborough a mere six months later.

India's Mirage 2000Hs were purchased for the air defence role, and can fire the Super 530D missile.

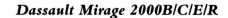

The first 15 Mirage 2000s had black radomes covering the RDM radar. This did not have a target illuminator for the Super 530 missile, despite the weapon being carried by this aircraft.

AIR-TO-AIR WEAPONS
Peru's Mirages are equipped with the standard export RDM radar, and are therefore restricted to the Super 530F missile (as opposed to the RDI/530D combination used by the French which is not approved for export). MATRA Magic 2 infrared missiles are the short-range armament, augmented by the internal 30-mm DEFA 554 cannon.

ATTACK WEAPONS
Peru's Mirage 2000s have a true multiple tasking. They regularly carry the TLIS laser designator pod for use with Aérospatiale AS30L laser-guided missiles, and GL 1000 LGBs. Alternatively a variety of unguided bombs can be carried, and reconnaissance pods.

DEFENCES
The Mirage 2000 is well-protected against missile threats, all equipment being integrally mounted. The Thomson-CSF Serval radar warning receiver has antennas in the fin fairing and outer wings, and provides a threat display in the cockpit. ECM jammers are mounted in the tailcone bullet fairing and fin.

Dassault Mirage 2000P

The only South American purchaser of the Mirage 2000, Peru initially ordered 24 2000P single-seaters and two 2000DP two-seaters, but was forced by budgetary considerations to cut the single-seat buy to just 10. These aircraft equip Escuadrón 412, Grupo de Caza 4, based at La Joya.

RADAR
The Thomson-CSF RDM radar is a low PRF Doppler multi-purpose system. It offers four basic modes: air-to-air search and interception, air-to-ground attack, strikemapping and terrain avoidance, and maritime search. In the air-to-air mode the radar offers a 60° cone of coverage with antenna drive rates of 50° or 100° per second.

GUNS
The DEFA 554 cannon weighs 80 kg (176 lb) and is 2.01 m (6 ft 7in) long. The weapon is a single-barrel revolving-chamber gas-operated weapon, with two rates of fire available: 1,800 rpm for air-to-air and 1,100 rpm for air-to-ground. The RDM radar provides a 3.5° beamwidth for automatic tracking within the HUD sight.

MAGIC MISSILE
Weighing 90 kg (198 lb) at launch, of which 13 kg (28.6 lb) is the high explosive warhead, the Magic 2 has an effective range of 5 km (3.1 miles). The weapon is detonated by RF fuse.

SUPER 530F MISSILE
The Super 530F has a length of 3.54 m (11 ft 7 in) and a launch weight of 245 kg (540 lb). The effective range is 25 km (15.5 miles).

A fin of broader chord with less complex leading-edge shape and trailing-edge root fairings were introduced during the test programme and fitted to the first production **Mirage 2000C** for its initial flight at Bordeaux on 20 November 1982. As with the 36 machines which followed, power was increased to 88.26 kN (19,842 lb st) through installation of an M53-5. In line with Dassault variant suffix policy, there was no Mirage 2000A, as this would have been a non-radar aircraft.

Mirage 2000C deliveries began in April 1983, allowing the first squadron to achieve IOC in July 1984. Eventually, three squadrons of the 2nd Fighter Wing at Dijon were equipped with early production aircraft having -5 engines and the multi-role Thomson-CSF RDM (Radar Doppler à Modulations). These early aircraft are to be upgraded to 2000-5 standard from 1994-97. From the 38th 2000C onwards, these changed to 64.3-kN (14,462-lb st) M53-P2 powerplants and Thomson-CSF/Dassault Electronique RDI (Radar Doppler à Impulsions) nose radar. RDI, development of which was delayed, has a new slotted flat-plate antenna and is optimised for look-

down/shoot-down intercepts with the MATRA Super 530D semi-active radar-homing AAM. Two Super 530s are normally carried on inboard wing pylons, accompanied by a pair of short-range IR-guided MATRA 550 Magic 2s outboard – plus, of course, the pair of DEFA 554 30-mm cannon. With RDM radar, Mirage 2000Cs carried Super 530F and Magic 1 missiles. RDI/M53-P2 aircraft serve with the 5th Wing at Orange and 12th at Cambrai. Both series can be fitted with a detachable refuelling probe.

A two-seat trainer, the Mirage **2000B** flew in production form on 7 August 1983.

Increased in length by only 19 cm (7½ in), it loses 110 litres (24 Imp gal) of internal fuel and both cannon in order to accommodate the second Martin-Baker Mk 10 zero-zero ejection seat. From the 15th aircraft radar is RDI, although all trainers have M53-5 engines. French 2000Bs and Cs are sometimes, and confusingly, referred to jointly as **Mirage 2000DA**s, for Défense Aérienne (Air Defence). Orders were prematurely terminated in 1991 as an economy measure when 136 Mirages 2000Cs and 32 2000Bs were under contract. French attack versions are discussed separately.

Dassault Mirage 2000B/C/E/R

Seen on a delivery flight, this is one of Egypt's four 2000BMs.

ARMAT anti-radiation missiles or two AM39 Exocet anti-ship missiles are options.

The Mirage 2000B two-seater sacrifices no combat capability, but has a reduced fuel capacity.

For export, the RDM-equipped, M53-P2-powered variant is designated **Mirage 2000E** (or **2000ED** in trainer guise) and equipped to carry up to 6300 kg (13,890 lb) of ground attack ordnance as an alternative to AAMs. In addition to free-fall weaponry, Mirage 2000Es have been cleared to launch MATRA ARMAT anti-radar missiles and Aérospatiale AS30L laser-guided missiles (accompanied by Thomson-CSF ATLIS designator pods). Egyptian aircraft, delivered in 1986-88, comprise 16 Mirage **2000EM**s and four **2000DM**s. India ordered a total of 42 M53-5-engined **2000H**s and seven **2000TH** trainers which were received between 1985 and 1988 by Nos 1 and 7

Squadrons at Gwalior, wearing air defence camouflage. These have since been re-engined with M53-P2 turbofans and are compatible with Super 530D missiles, perhaps confirming reports that Antilope 5 or RDI radar is fitted. Plans were abandoned for Hindustan Aeronautics to assemble a further 45 kits and build 65 from indigenous parts when alternative MiG-29 'Fulcrums' were bought from the USSR in 1984.

Peru obtained 10 Mirage **2000P**s and two **2000DP**s in 1986-87, employing them mainly on attack duties with 412 Squadron at La Joya. Like their French counterparts, Abu Dhabi's aircraft had their combat debut in the 1991 Gulf War, operating from their peacetime base at Maqatra, but saw no action. ADAF Mirages comprise 22 **2000EAD**s, six **2000DAD** trainers and eight **2000RAD** reconnaissance variants

supplied between 1989 and 1990. The **2000R** has a radar nose and carries its sensors in the form of centreline pods: COR2 multi-camera; SLAR 2000 side-looking airborne radar; or HAROLD long-range optical. All the ADAF Mirages have the MATRA Spirale chaff/flare system and provision for AIM-9P Sidewinder AAMs in addition to Super 530 and Magic. Half also feature improved ECM bought from Elettronica of Italy. Greece took delivery of 36 **2000EG**s and four **2000BG**s in 1988-92. The aircraft are shared by 331 and 332 Squadrons of 114 Wing at Tanagra where they provide the primary air defence for Athens. They have an enhanced version of the Thomson-CSF Serval radar warning receiver fitted to all Mirage 2000B/C/Es. In 1992, Pakistan agreed to buy 44 aircraft – either new Mirage 2000Es or secondhand 2000Cs (RDM/M53-5) from French stocks – but Jordan was forced by financial problems to cancel an order for 12 aircraft in 1991.

WEAPON OPTIONS

Two internal DEFA 554-30-mm cannon with 125 rounds per gun. Five underfuselage and four underwing hardpoints. Maximum weapon load 6300 kg (13,890 lb). Standard air defence load-out is two MATRA Magic 2 infra-red missiles and two Super 530D radar-guided missiles. Early aircraft only equipped to fire Super 530F. In ground attack role up to 18 250-kg bombs or BAP 100 anti-runway bombs, two 900-kg BGL 1000 laser-guided bombs, six Belouga cluster bombs, two AS30L laser-guided missiles, two

SPECIFICATION

Dassault Aviation Mirage 2000C
Wing: span 9.13 m (29 ft 11.5 in); aspect ratio 2.03; area 41.00 m² (441.33 sq ft)
Fuselage and tail: length 14.36 m (47 ft 1.25 in); height 5.20 m (17 ft 0.75 in); wheel track 3.40 m (11 ft 1.75 in); wheel base 5.00 m (16 ft 4.75 in)
Powerplant: one SNECMA M53-P2 rated at 64.33 kN (14,462 lb st) dry and 95.12 kN (21,384 lb st) with afterburning
Weights: empty 7500 kg (16,534 lb); normal take-off 10680 kg (23,545 lb); maximum take-off 17000 kg (37,478 lb)
Fuel and load: internal fuel 3160 kg (6,966 lb); external fuel up to 3720 kg (8,201 lb) in one 1300-litre (343-US gal) and two 1700-litre (449-US gal) drop tanks; maximum ordnance 6300 kg (13,889 lb)
Speed: maximum level speed 'clean' at 11000 m (36,090 ft) more than 2338 km/h (1,262 kt; 1,453 mph)
Range: ferry range 3335 km (1,800 nm; 2,072 miles) with drop tanks; combat range more than 1480 km (800 nm; 920 miles) with four 250-kg (551-lb) bombs, or more than 1850 km (1,000 nm; 1,150 miles) with two drop tanks
Performance: maximum rate of climb at sea level 17060 m (55,971 ft) per minute; service ceiling 18000 m (59,055 ft); climb to 15000 m (49,215 ft) 4 minutes; time to intercept a Mach 3 target at 24400 m (80,050 ft) from brakes-off less than 5 minutes; take-off run about 450 m (1,476 ft) at normal take-off weight
g limits: +9 normal and +13.5 ultimate

OPERATORS

Delivery totals:
Abu Dhabi: 2000EAD (22), 2000DAD (6), 2000RAD (8)
Egypt: 2000EM (16), 2000BM (4)
France: 2000B (32), 2000C (136)
Greece: 2000EG (36), 2000BG (4)
India: 2000H (42), 2000TH (7)
Peru: 2000P (10), 2000DP (2)

The Mirage 2000C is best-known for its fighter role, but it does have a considerable ground attack capability. Shown here is the ARMAT anti-radiation missile, carried by an early production EC 2 aircraft.

Dassault **Mirage 2000-5**

Significant enhancement of the Mirage 2000C/E series was launched in 1986 with a view to improving export prospects. Two trials aircraft tested elements of the new programme: Mirage 2000-3 with a five-screen pilot's display from the Rafale programme replacing the original instrumentation, and Mirage 2000-4 integrating the new MATRA MICA AAM, four of which can be carried in a rectangular pattern beneath the inner wings, augmented by a pair of MATRA Magic 2s outboard. These features, when added to a Thomson-CSF RDY multi-mode radar, a new central processing unit, a holographic HUD, an ICMS Mk 2 counter-measures suite and an additional electrical generator, produced the **2000-5**. A trainer prototype flew on 24 October 1990 and was followed by a single-seat equivalent on 27 April 1991. Options available include MATRA Super 530 or BAe Sky Flash AAMs in place of MICA and (from 1995) an M53-P20 powerplant with an increased thrust rating of 98.06 kN (22,046 lb st).

RDY radar is optimised for air interception and is capable of tracking eight targets while scanning. However, its other modes include land and sea options similar to the RDM of Mirage 2000Es, so that the 2000-5 is also able to launch a pair of Aérospatiale AM39 Exocet anti-ship missiles as well as MATRA ARMAT, Aérospatiale AS30L and laser-guided bombs. The MATRA APACHE stand-off weapons dispenser is to be integrated when it enters service. In 1992, Dassault failed to interest Finland in 67 Mirage 2000-5s but received a commitment from **Taiwan** for 60. This order was confirmed in late 1992 and includes 1,000 Magic 2 and MICA AAMs. The first aircraft is scheduled

Above right: Mirage 2000-04 was the testbed for the Dash 5's MATRA MICA missiles. Under the port wing is the MICA EM active-radar version, while under the starboard is the MICA IR infra-red version, distinguished by its blunt nose. Both versions employ inertial guidance for most of their flight, with mid-course update from the launch aircraft's radar. They then switch to autonomous guidance for the terminal phase. The missile is believed to have a range in the order of 50 km (31 miles).

Right: The first true 2000-5 was this two-seater, demonstrating the carriage of four MICA missiles and two Magics. The Dash 5 has additional RWR aerials on the fin.

for delivery in 1995. The first 17 **Armée de l'Air** Mirage 2000Cs are to be upgraded to this standard from 1994-97, having their RDM radars replaced by RDY, and receiving a new cockpit and new upgraded M53 turbofans.

SPECIFICATION

Dassault Aviation Mirage 2000-5
generally similar to the Dassault Aviation Mirage

2000C except in the following particulars:
Powerplant: one SNECMA M53-P20 rated at 98.07 kN (22,046 lb st) with afterburning
Weights: empty 7500 kg (16,534 lb); normal take-off 9500 kg (20,944 lb); maximum take-off 15000 kg (33,069 lb)

Dassault **Mirage 2000D/N/S**

French requirements for an interdictor to replace the Mirage IVP in carrying an Aérospatiale ASMP stand-off nuclear bomb resulted in Dassault receiving a contract in 1979 for two prototypes of what was then designated **Mirage 2000P (Pénétration)** but soon became the **2000N (Nucléaire)**. Based on the 2000B two-seat trainer, the strike Mirage has a strengthened airframe for low-level flight and con-

siderable differences in avionics. Most significant is a Dassault Electronique/Thomson-CSF Antilope 5 nose radar optimised for terrain following, ground mapping and navigation, but with additional air-to-air and air-to-sea modes. The radar displays information in the pilot's HUD and on a three-colour head-down display with moving-map overlay, and provides automatic terrain following down to 91 m (300 ft) at speeds up

to 600 kt (1112 km/h; 691 mph). In the rear seat, the WSO has twin inertial navigation systems, two altimeters and an additional moving map.

ASMP, carried on the centreline pylon, delivers a 150- or 300-kT warhead up to 80 km (50 miles) from a low-altitude launch point. Outboard the Mirage 2000N carries a pair of large, 2000-litre (528-US gal) drop-tanks and two self-defence MATRA Magic AAMs. Further protection is provided by the Serval radar warning receiver (as 2000C), Dassault Electronique Sabre electronic jammers and a MATRA Spirale chaff/flare sys-

tem. From the 32nd French 2000N onwards, Mirage 2000Ns are equipped to carry alternative loads of conventional ordnance up to a maximum of 6300 kg (13,890 lb). This can include Aérospatiale

The primary role of the 2000N is launch platform for the ASMP nuclear missile. This is the standard configuration, with self-defence Magic 2s and large wing tanks. The initial 2000N batch is tasked only with ASMP carriage, and is designated 2000N-K1.

Left: The second 2000N was used in the development effort for the 2000D. Here it carries a pair of BGL 1000 laser-guided bombs but without the associated ATLIS designator.

Right: The 2000S is the export version of the 2000D, and has similar weapons. Shown are AS30Ls, with Rubis FLIR pod and ATLIS designator.

AS30L and MATRA BGL bombs (both guided by a Thomson-CSF ATLIS laser designation pod), MATRA APACHE stand-off munitions dispensers, Aérospatiale AM39 Exocet anti-ship missiles, MATRA ARMAT for anti-radar attacks, MATRA Durandal anti-runway bombs and other rockets, cluster bombs and area-denial weapons. In service the ASMP-only aircraft are known as **2000N-K1** while the dual-role aircraft are **2000N-K2**s.

Initially flown on 3 February 1983, the 2000N achieved IOC in July 1988 when the first of an eventual three squadrons in 4 Wing at Luxeuil was reformed. Orders for 2000Ns were reduced as a result of lessening tensions in Europe, but delays with the

Rafale programme generated a requirement for more aircraft with only conventional weapons capability. The latter became the **Mirage 2000N' (N Prime)**, a confusing

designation which was amended to **2000D**. When further orders were curtailed in 1991, **France** had ordered 75 Mirage 2000Ns (31 ASMP/K1, 44 ASMP/conventional/K2) and 75 Mirage 2000Ds. The first 2000D flew on 19 February 1991, its differences from earlier standard comprising deletion of the interface between ASMP and the aircraft's navigation equipment, addition of a global positioning system and a redesign of cockpit instrumentation. All versions have provision for a refuelling probe immediately ahead of the windscreen, offset to starboard. Mirage 2000Ds are being delivered from 1993 onwards to 3 Wing at Nancy, although the unit's No. 2 Squadron became operational with interim equipment of 2000N-K2s in September 1991.

Dassault announced in 1989 that an export version of the 2000D would be avail-

able from 1994, known as the **Mirage 2000S (Strike)**. It also has Antilope 5 radar and terrain-following capability. No orders have been received.

WEAPON OPTIONS

Mirage 2000D/N has nine hardpoints: one centreline and two inboard wing hardpoints stressed for 1800 kg (3,970 lb) each, four fuselage hardpoints stressed for 400 kg (880 lb) each and two outer wing hardpoints stressed for 300 kg (660 lb) each; maximum external load 6300 kg (13,890 lb); outer wing pylons usually carry MATRA Magic 2 infra-red air-to-air missiles in all configurations.
Nuclear strike: single 850-kg (1,874-lb) Aérospatiale ASMP stand-off nuclear missile (150-kT or 300-kT yield) on LM-770 centreline pylon, and two underwing fuel tanks.
Precision attack: MATRA BGL laser-guided bombs (250 kg/550 lb, 400 kg/880 lb or 1000 kg/2,200 lb) or

ECM
The 2000N has the Serval RWR system with VCM-65 cockpit display. A Caméléon jammer is carried at the base of the fin. The suite is to be updated to ICMS Mk 1 standard, an integrated system combining Serval, Spirale and new Sabre jammers.

Dassault Mirage 2000N-K1

Augmenting the Mirage IVP in the nuclear role, the Mirage 2000Ns of 4 Escadre de Chasse are assigned to the Forces Aériennes Stratégiques. The wing operates approximately 45 aircraft in three squadrons, this aircraft wearing the markings of Escadron de Chasse 1/4 'Dauphiné'.

ASMP MISSILE
Designed to provide a more credible penetration capability than Mirage IVs armed with free-fall weapons, the ASMP (Air-Sol Moyenne Portée) missile has a reported range of 80 km (50 miles) from low-altitude launch and 250 km (155 miles) from high altitude. A solid propellant booster accelerates the missile to Mach 2, when a ramjet takes over. Intakes for this motor are mounted on the sides. Guidance is inertial with terrain mapping.

RADAR
The Dassault Electronique/Thomson-CSF Antilope V is a J-band attack radar, providing ground mapping and terrain-following functions with additional air-to-air capability. The data is presented on a head-up display and on a colour head-down multi-function display.

POWERPLANT
The 2000N is powered by the M53-P2, rated at 64.3 kN (14,462 lb) thrust dry and 95.kN (21,385 lb) with afterburning. The engine is 5.07 m (16 ft 7.5 in) long and has a diameter of 1.055 m (3 ft 5.5 in). The dry weight is only 150 kg (3,307 lb).

SPIRALE
The 2000N-K1s were not originally fitted with Spirale countermeasures, but these have been retrofitted. The system consists of integral infra-red warning receivers, and an interface with the radar warning receivers. These trigger the launch of chaff (starboard) or flare (port) cartridges from boxes in the wing/fuselage fairings. A missile plume detector is located in each Magic launcher.

NAVIGATION
For accurate navigation the 2000N has a twin ULISS 52P inertial navigation system. The 2000D also has Navstar GPS equipment for INS updates.

The 2000D was declared operational on 29 July 1993, when six aircraft of EC 5/330 (part of the CEAM trials unit) were announced ready for combat. The aircraft are destined for service with EC 3 at Nancy.

two 520-kg (1,145 lb) Aérospatiale AS30L laser-guided missiles on inboard wing pylons, with ATLIS designator pod on starboard forward fuselage station and centreline fuel tank.

Airfield attack: two MATRA APACHE stand-off dispensers with Samanta anti-runway sub-munitions, 12 MATRA Durandal runway-penetrating weapons or 18 Brandt BAP100 runway-cratering munitions.

Defence suppression: two MATRA ARMAT anti-radiation missiles on underwing pylons.

Maritime attack: two Aérospatiale AM39 Exocet anti-ship missiles on underwing pylons.

General attack: two MATRA APACHE stand-off dispensers armed with either Arcadie anti-armour or Mimosa general purpose sub-munitions on underwing pylons, 18 Brandt BAT120 anti-armour munitions, six MATRA Belouga cluster bombs, six Brandt BM 250 or BM 400 modular bombs, four MATRA F4 rocket pods with 18 68-mm rockets each, or two Dassault CC630 gun pods with two 30-mm cannon each.

Reconnaissance/jamming: COR2 multi-sensor reconnaissance, AA-3-38 HAROLD LOROP, NOR real-time reconnaissance, TMV-018 Syrel Elint or TMV-004 Caiman ECM systems pod-mounted on centreline station.

Inflight refuelling: Intertechnique 231-300 'buddy' refuelling pod on centreline pylon.

Additional equipment: Rubis FLIR pod on forward port fuselage station; TMV-002 Remora jammer.

SPECIFICATION

Dassault Aviation Mirage 2000D
generally similar to the Dassault Aviation Mirage

Right: Mixing nuclear with conventional capabilities is the 2000N-K2. This desert scheme can be applied over the standard green and grey camouflage for contingency out-of-area operations or deployments to Red Flag exercises.

2000C except in the following particulars:
Wing: span 9.26 m (3 ft 4.5 in)
Fuselage and tail: length 14.55 m (47 ft 9 in); height 5.15 m (16 ft 10.75 in)
Speed: maximum level speed 'clean' at 11000 m (36,090 ft) 2338 km/h (1,262 kt; 1,453 mph); penetration speed at 60 m (197 ft) 1112 km/h (600 kt; 691 mph)

Dassault **Rafale A**

Dassault's **Avion de Combat Experimentale**, or **ACX**, evolved as an early 1980s technology demonstrator for a national combat aircraft programme even before France's withdrawal from the European Fighter Aircraft project in August 1985.

The withdrawal was prompted ostensibly because the French forces, and especially the navy, wanted a lighter and smaller design weighing just over 8 tonnes (17,637 lb). While emerging with a 9.5-tonne (20,945-lb) basic mass empty, similar to the

The one-off Rafale A was considerably larger than the service aircraft developed from it. Now grounded, it was instrumental in the development of the combat aircraft and its new technology M88 engines.

EAP, the ACX demonstrator, first flown on 4 July 1986, established and proved the basic aerodynamic design, configuration and performance of the planned **Rafale**, or ACT, as well as its fly-by-wire control system and mainly composite structure, although using two 68.6-kN (15,422-lb) GE F404-400 as interim powerplants.

After 460 initial test sorties, including touch-and-go deck-landings on the French carrier *Clemenceau*, Rafale A's port F404 was replaced by one of 15 flight development examples of the ACT's definitive SNECMA M88-2 turbofans, then reheat-rated at 73.5 kN (16,523 lb). With these engines the aircraft resumed flight trials on 27 February 1990, reaching Mach 1.4 in dry thrust and 40,000 ft (12192 m). Continuing ACX development, comprising 197 more flights by 1 July 1992 and many since, allowed cancellation in 1991 of the originally planned second Armée de l'Air prototype, C02, as part of major French defence economies. The Rafale A made its 865th and last flight on 24 January 1994.

SPECIFICATION

Dassault Aviation Rafale A
Wing: span 11.20 m (36 ft 9 in); wing aspect ratio 2.67; wing area 47.00 m2 (505.92 sq ft)
Fuselage and tail: length 15.80 m (51 ft 10 in); wheel track 2.675 m (8 ft 9.25 in); wheel base 5.185 m (17 ft 0.25 in)
Powerplant: two SNECMA M88-2 each rated at 48.69 kN (10,946 lb st) dry and 72.96 kN (16,402 lb st) with afterburning
Weights: basic empty 9500 kg (20,944 lb); normal take-off 14000 kg (30,864 lb); maximum take-off 20000 kg (44,092 lb)
Fuel and load: internal fuel more than 4250 kg (9,369 lb); external fuel up to two 2000-litre (528-US gal) drop tanks
Speed: maximum level speed 'clean' at 11000 m (36,090 ft) 2125 km/h (1,147 kt; 1,321 mph)
Performance: take-off run 400 m (1,313 ft) at 14000 kg (30,864 lb) or about 700 m (2,297 ft) at 20000 kg (44,092 lb)
g limits: -3.6 to +9

Dassault **Rafale B/C/D**

Originally known as the **ACT (Avion de Combat Tactique)**, the multi-role Rafale will replace up to half a dozen French air force strike/interceptor and recce types, including the Mirage III and 5, Mirage F1 and Jaguar, and probably the strategic Mirage IVP. While retaining the ACX's main design features, the Armée de l'Air's generic **Rafale D** family (D=*discret*, or stealth) is fractionally smaller and lighter than the demonstrator, with an empty weight below 9 tonnes (19,841 lb). Changes to reduce the radar cross-section include more rounded wingroot fairings, internally gold-coated canopy, radar-absorbing dark grey paint and a reprofiled rear-fuselage/fin

junction. The fin itself is lower and is topped by an ECM fairing to house Rafale's Spectra automated and integrated defensive subsystems' RWR and lateral IR missile-launch detector windows.

Rafale D's canard mounting fairings have small forward extensions to house Spectra antennas, the all-moving canards themselves – linked with undercarriage extension to tilt 20° upwards to provide extra lift for

The sole Rafale C prototype displays its carefully blended wing/fuselage surfaces and the wingtip carriage for MATRA Magic 2 missiles.

Dassault Rafale B/C/D

Both Armée de l'Air versions in flight: the service has decided to procure the two-seat Rafale B as the predominant combat version, considering the workload to be too high for a single pilot on many key missions. Service entry is now expected in the year 2002, as the navy's need is considered greater than that of the air force.

landing – being bigger than the ACX's, and of superplastic-formed titanium instead of carbon composites. Composites and other new materials comprise over 50 per cent of the definitive Rafale's airframe weight instead of about 30 per cent in the ACX. An aerodynamic addition from the ACX is a small curved strake from the wingroot leading edge to the outer intake wall, above the muzzle port for the 30-mm (1.18-in) GIAT-built DEFA M791B cannon in the starboard fuselage. Rafale armament also comprises 14 (less one fuselage pylon in the navalised ACM) underwing and ventral fuselage weapons stations with an 8-tonne (17,637-lb) total capacity.

Stores options

Five of the stores stations have fuel tank pick-ups, or all may be used for such weapons as up to eight MATRA MICA semi-active radar-guided or IR-homing AAMs, Aérospatiale AS30L laser-guided stand-off ASMs, MATRA Defence Apache stand-off munitions dispenser, the nuclear medium-range ASMP or projected long-range ASLP, and Aérospatiale AM39 Exocet anti-ship missiles. These operate in conjunction with Rafale's Thomson-CSF/Dassault Electronique RBE2 fire-control radar, the first in Europe with two-plane electronic scanning. Based on Thomson-CSF's Radant phased-array beam-steering system, the RBE2 incorporates terrain-following, navigation, ground-attack and interception functions, with instant mode-transfer capability, automatic multi-target tracking and simultaneous targeting with up to eight AAMs.

The first batch of Rafales for the **Armée de l'Air** will not have ASMP capability, and will lack certain other systems of the definitive aircraft such as Spectra, helmet-mounted sight and automatic terrain-following. They will be known as S01 aircraft, this measure having been taken to expedite the programme (first-batch naval aircraft will also be similarly downgraded). Second-batch S02 Rafales will have a high-discretion jam-resistant passive optronic surveillance and imaging system with a laser rangefinder, or Optronique Secteur Frontale (IRST), mounted forward of the cockpit and supplementing the radar for the passive multi-target identification and angular tracking at ranges up to 70-80 km (44-49 miles).

Following operational experience with its Jaguars and Mirage 2000Cs during the Gulf War, which demonstrated the demanding workload involved in current single-pilot combat operations, the French air force reviewed its Rafale D procurement plans to increase the proportion of two-seat operational versions, despite their higher cost. This inevitably resulted in smaller overall totals within specified budget allocations, although such contractions, in any case, accord with French post-Soviet long-term planning economies. These will see the planned turn-of-the-century 450 combat aircraft establishment cut back to around 390, and Rafale D procurement reduced from the original 250, including 25 two-seat operational trainers, to 235. In late 1992, Defence Minister Joxe said these would be split between only 95 single-seaters and 140 two-seat versions, for service from 2002. From 1996, production Rafales are scheduled to be fitted with uprated M88-3 turbofans developing 93 kN (20,907 lb) of thrust for take-off.

The single-seat **Rafale C** prototype made its first flight on 19 May 1991, and remains the only such prototype of the air force single-seater. A single two-seat **Rafale B** first flew on 30 April 1993, fitted with RBE2 and Spectra system. Originally envisaged as a combat-capable conversion trainer for the single-seater, this is now being developed as the principal Armée de l'Air operational variant.

SPECIFICATION

Dassault Aviation Rafale C
Wing: span 10.90 m (35 ft 9.125 in) with tip-mounted AAMs; wing area 46.00 m2 (495.16 sq ft)

Fuselage and tail: length 15.30 m (50 ft 2.375 in)
Powerplant: two SNECMA M88-3 each rated at 86.98 kN (19,555 lb st) with afterburning
Weights: maximum take-off 21500 kg (47,399 lb)
Fuel and load: internal fuel more than 5325 litres (1,407 US gal); external fuel up to one 1700-litre (449-US gal), two 2000-litre (528-US gal) and/or two 1300-litre (343-US gal) drop tanks; maximum ordnance 6000 kg (13,228 lb)
Speed: maximum level speed 'clean' at 11000 m (36,090 ft) 2125 km/h (1,147 kt; 1,321 mph)
Range: combat radius 1093 km (590 nm; 679 miles) on a low-level penetration mission with 12 250-kg (551-lb) bombs, four MICA AAMs and 4300 litres (1,136 US gal) of fuel in three drop tanks, or 1853 km (1,000 nm; 1,152 miles) on a long-range air-to-air mission with eight MICA AAMs and 6600 litres (1,742 US gal) of fuel in four drop tanks
Performance: take-off run 400 m (1,312 ft) at normal take-off weight for an air defense mission or 600 m (1,969 ft) at maximum take-off weight for an attack mission
g limits: -3.6 to +9

Dassault **Rafale M**

Originally known as the **Avion de Combat Marine (ACM)**, the prototype Rafale M01 first flew on 12 December 1991, being followed by M02 on 8 November 1993. Main ACM changes weighing some 1,653 lb (750 kg) concern major reinforcement of the Messier-Bugatti undercarriage, the long-stroke mainwheel legs of which must absorb no-flare landing impacts of up to 21 ft/sec (6.5 m/sec), with decelerations of -4.5g, against only 10 ft/sec (3 m/sec) for land-based Rafales. ACM nose-leg design was also the first in France to require attachment of a take-off catapult bar, plus provision of a 'jump-strut' for automatic unstick rotation, which will work in conjunction with a small 'ski-jump' bow-ramp. For accelerated take-offs, the **Rafale M** nose gear stores catapult loads of about 90 tonnes (198,416 lb) from initial compression following application of full engine power. Off the catapult, after automatic severance of the deck hold-back link, the released shock-strut immediately restores its accumulated energy, its abrupt extension raising the aircraft's nose to shorten its take-off run. It then automatically reconfigures by reactivation of its metering holes, for optimum shock absorption for landing.

After initial tests on a modified Mirage 2000 at the CEAT aeronautical test centre in Toulouse, the M01 undercarriage underwent its first full-scale trials in mid-1992. Phase 1 of the trials at NAS Lakehurst, NJ, comprised 39 clean aircraft catapult launches at up to 135 kt (155 mph; 250 km/h) which, apart from demonstrating the required jump-strut performance, also confirmed operation of the 360° electro-hydraulic swivelling twin nosewheels. In Phase 2, at the USN Air Test Center, Patuxent River, MD, 68 arrested landings were made on a simulated carrier deck, as well as six inflight arrester-wire engagements. Further simulated deck trials were conducted in January 1993, before Rafale M01 first went to sea, on the carrier *Foch*, from 1 April of that year. Carrier trials with both maritime prototypes are continuing, although the carrier requirements of the Bosnian situation caused severe disruptions. A removable bow ramp is fitted to *Foch* when required for tests, but in the future a permanent installation will employ a hinged ramp, which can be lowered for the launching of other aircraft types.

Dassault Rafale M

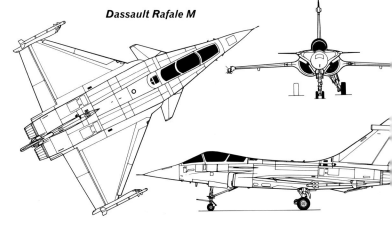

Aéronavale's Rafale M requirement remains unchanged at 86 navalised single-seat interceptor/strike versions, the French navy being the first Rafale recipient from planned deliveries of 14 ACMs to reform Flottille 14F in 1998. These will equip the nuclear-powered carrier *Charles de Gaulle*, now due to commission the same year. Funding for a long-planned sister vessel, *Le Richelieu*, was promised in late 1992 by Defence Minister Pierre Joxe in the 1995-97 budget period, for commissioning in 2006, to allow for periodic refits of *Charles de Gaulle*. Like the air force, the navy will receive its first batch of 20 Rafales in reduced-capability S01 form to bring forward operational service. Subsequent aircraft will be to the definitive S02 form with ASMP, OSF, Spectra, helmet-mounted sight and voice command controls.

*Rafale M underwent its dummy deck trials at Lakehurst and Patuxent River. The carrier trials were undertaken aboard **Foch**.*

Dassault **Super Etendard**

After much political in-fighting, a mid-1970s French naval requirement for 100 new carrier-based strike-fighters, for which procurement of navalised Jaguar Ms was originally proposed, eventually resulted in a 1973 contract to Dassault-Breguet for 60 developments of the Etendard IV. Dassault had already produced 69 Etendard IVM strike-fighters and 21 tactical-recce IVPs for the **Aéronavale**'s new carriers since mid-1962. The upgraded **Super Etendard** was planned with an 11,025-lb st (49-kN) SNECMA Atar 8K-50 instead of the original 9,923-lb (44-kN) Atar 8C, and some 90 per cent airframe commonality. A new wing leading-edge profile and redesigned flaps ensured a mainly unchanged carrier deck performance, despite heavier operating weights.

To widen its anti-ship strike and air-to-air capabilities, the Super Etendard also featured a new SAGEM/Kearfott ETNA nav/attack system, and a Thomson-CSF/Electronique Serge Dassault Agave

I-band monopulse radar in place of the Etendard IVM's basic GAMD Aïda 7, a SAGEM-Kearfott SKN602 INS, Crouzet 66 air data computer and associated 97 nav display and armament systems, Thomson-CSF VE-120 HUD, LMT TACAN, and TRT radio altimeter. A retractable air-refuelling probe is fitted forward of the cockpit.

Three Etendard IVM airframes were converted as Super Etendard prototypes, flying from 29 October 1974. Seventy-one production Super Etendards then began replacing Etendard IVs and F-8E(FN) Crusader interceptors in Aéronavale's Flottilles 11F, 14F and 17F from June 1978, the first having initially flown on 24 November 1977.

By the time the Falklands War started in April 1982, the **Argentine navy** (sole Super Etendard export customer) had received the first five of 14 aircraft on order to equip CANA's 2° Escuadrilla at Cdte Espora NAB when not carrier-based, together with five AM39 Exocets. Operating from Rio Gallegos, these made their

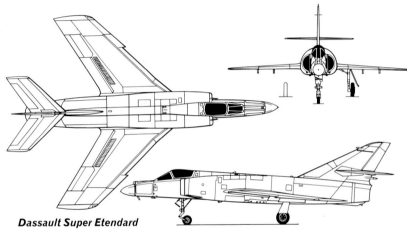

Dassault Super Etendard

operational debut sinking HMS *Sheffield* off the Falklands on 4 May 1982, followed by the destruction of the supply ship *Atlantic Conveyor* on 25 May, for no Super Etendard losses. At least three have since been lost

by 2° Escuadrilla of 3° Escuadra, which still operates the rest from Cdte Espora. In October 1983 five Aéronavale Super Etendards were leased to the **Iraqi air force** and a substantial number of AM39s were sold for use against Iranian tankers in the Iran/Iraq war, scoring many successes. The four surviving aircraft were returned to France in early 1985 following replacement by Agave-equipped Mirage F1EQs.

A mid-1980s upgrade programme costing some FF2 billion ($400 million) was planned to extend the long-range attack and anti-ship strike capabilities of the Aéronavale's nearly 60 surviving Super Etendards. Some 53 had already been modified at Cuers to launch the 300-kT Aérospatiale ASMP stand-off nuclear weapon. Main changes were avionics modernisation, including new cockpit instrumentation, HOTAS, and a new Electronique Dassault Anemone radar which incorporated track-while-scan, air-to-surface ranging, ground mapping and search functions. New systems include a Thomson-CSF wide-angle (22°) HUD with TV or IR imaging, SHERLOC RWR and a VCN65 ECM display, SAGEM INS and a UAT90 weapons and air data computer with more processing capacity. Provision is also made for night-vision goggles, while airframe changes to ensure a 6,500-hour fatigue life will help extend Super Etendard service to about 2008.

Argentina's first five Super Etendards in formation: these were the aircraft which had been delivered by the start of the Falklands War, and which were responsible for two sinkings during the conflict.

Dassault Super Etendard

Left: The nuclear strike role for the Aéronavale is undertaken by the Super Etendard armed with a single ASMP missile. This is balanced by a fuel tank on the opposite wing.

Right: Super Etendards form the bulk of the carrier air wing. Combat deployments included service over Lebanon and Bosnia.

The prototype upgraded Super Etendard first flew from Istres on 5 October 1990, Dassault modifying two more for operational development. Following disbandment of Flottille 14F in July 1991, prior to its eventual re-equipment as Aéronavale's first Rafale M fighter unit, its Super Etendards replaced the last 11 Etendard IVPs equipping Escadrille de Servitude 59S at Hyères for operational conversion of French naval pilots after deck-landing training in Fouga Zéphyrs at the same base. Flottilles 11F and 17F at Landivisiau and Hyères comprise the Aéronavale's remaining front-line Super Etendard squadrons and will operate the aircraft being upgraded by the Cuers naval workshops from 1993 to 1998.

SPECIFICATION

Dassault Aviation Super Etendard
Wing: span 9.60 m (31 ft 6 in); width folded 7.80 m (25 ft 7 in); aspect ratio 3.23; area 28.40 m² (305.71 sq ft)
Fuselage and tail: length 14.31 m (46 ft 11.5 in); height 3.86 m (12 ft 8 in); wheel track 3.50 m (11 ft 6 in); wheel base 4.80 m (15 ft 9 in)
Powerplant: one SNECMA Atar 8K-50 rated at 49.03 kN (11,023 lb st) dry
Weights: empty equipped 6500 kg (14,330 lb); normal take-off 9450 kg (20,833 lb); maximum take-off 12000 kg (26,455 lb)
Fuel and load: internal fuel 3270 litres (864 US gal); external fuel up to one 600-litre (158-US gal) and two 1100-litre (290-US gal) drop tanks; maximum ordnance 2100 kg (4,630 lb)
Speed: maximum level speed 'clean' at 11000 m (36,090 ft) 1380 km/h (744 kt; 857 mph) and at sea level 1180 km/h (637 kt; 733 mph)
Range: combat radius 850 km (459 nm; 528 miles) on a hi-lo-hi anti-ship mission with one AM39 Exocet missile and two drop tanks
Performance: maximum rate of climb at sea level 6000 m (19,685 ft) per minute; service ceiling more than 13700 m (44,950 ft)

WEAPON OPTIONS

For anti-ship roles, the Super Etendard carries two Aérospatiale AM39 Exocets, or up to 2100 kg (4,630 lb) of other stores on two fuselage and four underwing pylons. In addition to AN52 tactical nuclear bombs or the ASMP stand-off missile, these can also accommodate four 68-mm (2.68-in) rocket pods, laser-guided weapons, up to 27 BAP 100 or 120 concrete-piercing bombs, drop tanks or ECM pods, or MATRA Magic short-range AAMs, supplementing two internal 30-mm (1.18-in) DEFA cannon, with 125 rpg.

Dassault/Dornier **Alpha Jet**

Following 1960's Franco-German studies into future advanced training requirements, national specifications were merged in 1968 and a joint development and production programme agreed in July 1969. This involved 200 aircraft for each country, from national assembly lines, for which the TA501 project submitted by Dassault, Breguet and Dornier was selected in July 1970, after comparative studies of the SNIAS/MBB E.650 Eurotrainer and VFW-Fokker VFT-291. All three projects proposed using two 10.98-kN (2,470-lb) thrust SNECMA/Turboméca Larzac 02 turbofans, the Luftwaffe having rejected further single-engine high-performance aircraft purchases following heavy F-104 losses.

The resultant **Alpha Jet**, derived from the Breguet 126 and Dornier P.375 projects, had shoulder-mounted swept wings and stepped tandem cockpits, Martin-Baker AJRM4 (French) or Stencel S-III-S3 (FRG) ejection seats, and lateral engine nacelle stowage of the short low-pressure mainwheel units. French and German equipment fits vary considerably, the Luftwaffe having then decided to continue military pilot training in the US, changing its requirements to a light ground-attack replacement for its Fiat G91R/3s. This necessitated advanced nav/attack systems, including a Lear-Siegler twin-gyro INS, Litton Doppler navigation radar, Kaiser/VDO HUD, and a belly-mounted 27-mm (1.06-in) Mauser MK 27 cannon pod. French Alphas can carry a ventral 30-mm (1.18-in) DEFA 553 cannon pod with 150 rounds, both variants having four underwing pylons for up to 2500 kg (5,511 lb) of stores, including bombs, rockets, missiles or drop tanks.

Programme go-ahead

Alpha Jet development was finally approved in February 1972, two prototypes being ordered in each country from newly-combined Dassault-Breguet and Dornier. The first, F-ZJTS, flew at Istres on 26 October 1973, the second (D-9594/F-ZWRU) following at Oberpfaffenhofen on 9 January 1974, and the remaining two by the year's end. During development, Larzac 04-C1 engine output increased to 13.19 kN

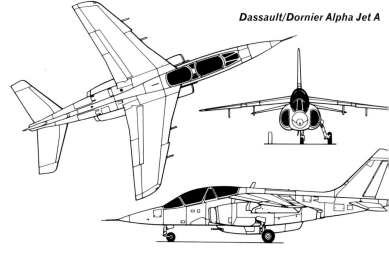

Dassault/Dornier Alpha Jet A

(2,965 lb) in the C6 version, and outer wing leading-edge extensions, plus a change to single-slotted Fowler flaps and hydraulic servo-powered control surfaces, allowed transonic performance to be combined with approach speeds of only 110 kt (127 mph; 204 km/h). Later the Luftwaffe Alpha Jets were re-engined with the Larzac 04-C20 of 14.12 kN (3,175 lb) thrust.

French production **Alpha Jet E**s (Ecole) began flying from Istres on 4 November 1977, six arriving at CEAM for service trials in 1978. Replacement of Lockheed/Canadair T-33s in Armée de l'Air training units started in May 1979 with GE 314 at Tours, 12 Alphas then equipping the 'Patrouille de France' national aerobatic team in the same year. Other French training units re-equipped by 1985 included the 8ᵉ Escadre at Cazaux, replacing the last 30 Mystère IVAs for weapons training from April 1982.

Left: Luftwaffe Alpha Jets were intended for the light attack role, and usually carried an underfuselage cannon pod.

Below: French Alphas are employed on advanced training duties.

German production started with the first **Alpha Jet A** (Appui Tactique) flying on 12 April 1978 at Oberpfaffenhofen. Each country eventually ordered only 175 aircraft.

The last German Alpha Jet delivery, in January 1983, completed re-equipment of JBG 41 at Husum, JBG 43 at Oldenburg and JBG 49 at Furstenfeldbruck, plus 18 for JBG 44 shadow training unit at Beja, in Portugal. These were being withdrawn from late 1992 for planned disposal to France, Portugal and Turkey, apart from 45 to be retained by JBG 49 for lead-in fighter training. By early 1994 only 50 had been delivered to Portugal, the future of the others remaining uncertain. Egypt assembled 26 **Alpha Jet MS1** trainers at Helwan from September 1982 onwards, following receipt of four completed by Dassault.

In 1980 work began on an alternative close support version, which first flew on 9 April 1982. In addition to light attack and anti-helicopter roles, the new version had great potential for the fighter lead-in training role. New avionics included a SAGEM ULISS 81 INS, Thomson-CSF VE 110 CRT HUD and TMV 630 laser rangefinder in a modified nose and TRT AHV 9 radio altimeter, linked through a digital databus. Customers for this variant were Egypt (with designation **MS2**) and Cameroon. As with the MS1, Egypt received the first four MS2s from Dassault, and co-produced the remainder.

The **Alpha Jet NGEA** (Nouvelle Génération Appui/Ecole, later known as **Alpha Jet 2**) programme was launched to further the previous work on the MS2. In addition to the new avionics, the Alpha Jet 2 featured provision for MATRA Magic 2 air-to-air missiles, and uprated Larzac 04-C20 engines.

Dassault has also proposed an MS2-derived **Alpha Jet 3 Advanced Training System**, or **Lancier**, with twin multi-function cockpit displays for mission training with such sensors as AGAVE or Anemone radar, FLIR, laser, video and ECM systems, plus advanced weapons. This has yet to proceed beyond the flying testbed stage. Dassault later proposed a naval trainer version, with strengthened landing gear, to replace the Aéronavale's Zéphyr trainers.

OPERATORS

Delivery numbers given:
Belgium: Alpha Jet E (33)
Cameroon: close support Alpha Jet (7)
Egypt: MS1 (30), MS2 (15)
France: Alpha Jet E (175)
Germany: Alpha Jet A (175)
Ivory Coast: Alpha Jet E (12)

Above: Qatar's Alpha Jets serve with No. 11 Close Support Squadron, and in peacetime undertake weapons training. In wartime they would form a light attack unit, crewed by instructors.

Morocco: Alpha Jet E (24)
Nigeria: Alpha Jet E (24)
Portugal: Alpha Jet A (50)
Qatar: Alpha Jet E (6)
Togo: Alpha Jet E (5)

SPECIFICATION

Dassault Aviation (Dassault-Breguet)/Dornier Alpha Jet E (Alpha Jet Advanced Trainer/Light Attack Version)
Wing: span 9.11 m (29 ft 10.75 in); aspect ratio 4.8; area 17.50 m² (188.37 sq ft)
Fuselage and tail: length 11.75 m (38 ft 6.5 in); height 4.19 m (13 ft 9 in); tailplane span 4.33 m (14 ft 2.5 in); wheel track 2.71 m (8 ft 10.75 in); wheel base 4.72 m (15 ft 5.75 in)
Powerplant: two SNECMA/Turboméca Larzac 04-C6 each rated at 13.24 kN (2,976 lb st) dry
Weights: empty equipped 3345 kg (7,374 lb); normal take-off 5000 kg (11,023 lb); maximum take-off 8000 kg (17,637 lb)
Fuel and load: internal fuel 1520 or 1630 kg (3,351 or 3,595 lb); external fuel up to 720 kg (1,587 lb) in two 450- or 310-litre (119- or 82-US gal) drop tanks; maximum ordnance more than 2500 kg (5,511 lb)
Speed: maximum level speed 'clean' at 10000 m (32,810 ft) 916 km/h (494 kt; 569 mph) and at sea level 1000 km/h (539 kt; 621 mph)
Range: ferry range more than 4000 km (2,159 nm; 2,486 miles) with four drop tanks; operational radius 670 km (361 nm; 416 miles) on a lo-lo-lo training mission with two drop tanks, or 540 km (291 nm; 335 miles) on a lo-lo-lo training mission on internal fuel, or 1450 km (782 nm; 901 miles) on a hi-hi-hi training mission with two drop tanks, or 1230 km

Egypt has 15 Alpha Jet MS2s, with nose-mounted laser rangefinder.

(664 nm; 764 miles) on a hi-hi-hi training mission on internal fuel; endurance more than 3 hours 30 minutes at high altitude on internal fuel or more than 2 hours 30 minutes at low altitude on internal fuel
Performance: maximum rate of climb at sea level 3660 m (12,008 ft) per minute; climb to 9150 m (30,020 ft) in less than 7 minutes; service ceiling 14630 m (48,000 ft); take-off run 370 m (1,215 ft) at normal take-off weight; landing run about 500 m (1,640 ft) at normal landing weight

The Alpha Jet is primarily used as an advanced trainer, and several nations have put its agility and performance to good use for aerobatic displays. Belgium uses the aircraft (left) for solo displays, while the 'Patrouille de France' uses the type (right) for formation displays.

de Havilland **D.H.104 Devon/Dove**

First flown on 25 September 1945 in civil guise, the eight- to 11-seat **de Havilland D.H.104 Dove** proved to be one of the most successful small transports of the immediate post-war era. Production of 544 aircraft included military versions, at first developed for the **RAF** to Specification C.13/47 as the **Devon C.Mk 1** with 330-hp (246-kW) DH Gipsy Queen 71 or **Devon C.Mk 2** with 400-hp (298.5-kW) Gipsy Queen 175 engines. The **Sea Devon C.Mk 20** variant was operated by the **RN**.

Few Doves remain in service. Sri Lanka has just retired its aircraft to storage after having used them for maritime patrols.

Almost all Devons and Doves have now been retired, although a small number remains in service as a navigation/radio ship and crew ferry with the RAF's Battle of Britain Memorial Flight, and with the MoD(PE) in the UK. Other examples are in **Jordan** and **Sri Lanka** (the latter in flyable storage). Jordan's single surviving Dove was returned to the UK for overhaul at Staverton in early 1993, to allow it to serve into the next century.

SPECIFICATION

de Havilland Dove 7 and 8

Wing: span 57 ft 0 in (17.37 m): aspect ratio 9.70: area 335.0 sq ft (31.12 m²)

Fuselage and tail: length 39 ft 4.0 in (11.99 m); height 13 ft 4.0 in (4.06 m); wheel track 13 ft 9.0 in (4.19 m): wheel base 13 ft 0 in (3.96 m)
Powerplant: two 400-hp (298-kW) de Havilland Gipsy Queen 70-3 inline piston engines
Weights: empty 6,580 lb (2985 kg); maximum take-off 8,950 lb (4060 kg)
Fuel and load: internal fuel capacity 130 Imp gal (591.5 litres); external fuel none; payload 1,868 lb (847 kg)

Speed: maximum level speed at 8,000 ft (2440 m) 210 mph (182 kt; 338 km/h); maximum cruising speed 200 mph (174 kt; 288 km/h)
Range: 500 miles (805 km) with 1,700-lb (771-kg) payload
Performance: climb rate at sea level 750 ft (229 m) per minute; service ceiling 20,000 ft (6100 m); take-off distance to 50 ft (15 m) 2,366 ft (721 m); landing distance from 50 ft (15 m) 2250 ft (686 m)

de Havilland **D.H.106 Comet**

The **de Havilland D.H.106 Comet** was the world's first jet airliner to enter regular service and first flew on 27 July 1949. **Comet C.Mk 2**s and **C.Mk 4**s served RAF Transport Command until 1967 and 1975, respectively, three other **Mk 2R**s having a specialised Elint role in the RAF. The only other military user was the RCAF, with two **Series 1A** transports. Several ex-civil Comets became important testbeds for systems and equipment in the hands of MoD(PE) at DRA (formerly RAE) Farnborough and Bedford. Of these, one **Comet 4**, XV814 (ex-BOAC G-APDF) was retired from on radio and avionics trials at Farnborough in early 1993 to provide spares for a **Comet 4C** (XS235 'Canopus') which was still serving with the A & AEE in 1994.

The last flying Comet is XS235, operating as a testbed with the A&AEE at Boscombe Down.

de Havilland **D.H.114 Heron**

Evolved as a complementary larger version of the D.H.104 Dove, the **D.H.114 Heron** featured a longer fuselage of similar cross-section, and an enlarged wing for four 250-hp (186.5-kW) DH Gipsy Queen 30 Mk 2 engines. Military use included four for the Queen's Flight in Britain (one **C.Mk 3**, three **C.Mk 4**) and five for the RN, all now out of service. At least nine other nations acquired the Heron in small numbers for military service. **Sri Lanka**'s Herons remain in flyable storage. These include examples with the original Gipsy engines and those which had undergone the **Riley Heron** conversion with flat-six Lycoming engines.

Sri Lanka's Herons are in open storage, but remain flyable. This example is a Riley Heron with flat-six engines.

de Havilland Canada **DHC-1 Chipmunk**

de Havilland Inc.
Garrett Boulevard, Downsview,
Ontario, M3K 1Y5, Canada

First aircraft designed by DHC, the **de Havilland Canada DHC-1 Chipmunk** was a primary trainer developed immediately after World War II and first flown on 22 May 1946. Powered initially by a 145-hp (108-kW) DH Gipsy Major 1C, this low-wing monoplane seated the student pilot and instructor in tandem under a single-piece sliding canopy and featured fixed tailwheel landing gear. Of all-metal stressed-skin construction, the Chipmunk was originally only partially aerobatic but was ordered into production in Canada for the RCAF.

After evaluation in the UK, Specification 8/48 was issued by the British Air Ministry and production was undertaken by the parent company in the UK. Designated **Chipmunk T.Mk 10**, 735 examples were delivered to the RAF, equipping almost every primary flying training unit in the service. The fully-aerobatic Chipmunk T.Mk 10 differed from the Canadian-built **Chipmunk T.Mk 1** for the RCAF in having a multipanel sliding canopy and being powered by the Gipsy Major 8. Some of the RAF Chipmunks later had their flying controls removed from the rear cockpit when, in the 1950s, they joined RAF light communications flights in Germany.

Canadian production amounted to 218 aircraft, later versions (from the **DHC-1B-1** onwards) being fully aerobatic, and military exports were undertaken to Chile (**DHC-1B-S4**), Egypt (**DHC-1B-S1**) and Thailand (**DHC-1B-S2**); these were all powered by Gipsy Major 10s. With this engine the aircraft served with the RCAF as the **Chipmunk T.Mk 2**.

Two hundred and seventeen export Chipmunks were produced in the UK during the 1950s and supplied, as the **Chipmunk T.Mk 20** powered by the Gipsy Major 10 Series 2, to 10 foreign air forces, while civilianised **Chipmunk T.Mk 21** aircraft were sold to the air forces of Portugal and Ceylon. Licence-production was also undertaken by OGMA in Portugal, which produced 60 aircraft. Canadian export **Chipmunk T.Mk 30** trainers were sold to Colombia, Uruguay and Lebanon.

In the early 1990s military Chipmunks still served as trainers in **Portugal** and **Sri Lanka** (in storage), while 10 surviving **Thai** aircraft had been re-engined with Rolls-Royce Continental IO-360s. In the **RAF** a total of about 70 Chipmunk T.Mk 10s was still flying in the training role in 1993, equipping the Elementary Flying Training School at RAF Swinderby and 12 of the 13 Air Experience Flights. A single example serves with the Battle of Britain Memorial Flight for tailwheel training, and two with the RAF's Berlin Station Flight at RAF Gatow (until mid-1994). The Swinderby Chipmunks were replaced by Slingsby T-67s during 1993. The British Army possessed about 16 Chipmunk T.Mk 20s in its Advanced and Intermediate Fixed-Wing Flights for training purposes.

de Havilland Canada DHC-1 Chipmunk T.Mk 10

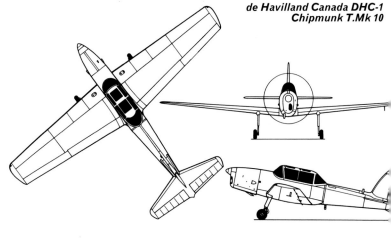

SPECIFICATION

de Havilland Canada DHC-1 Chipmunk T.Mk 10

Wing: span 34 ft 4 in (10.45 m): aspect ratio 6.81; area 172.50 sq ft (16.03 m²)
Fuselage and tail: length 25 ft 5 in (7.75 m); height 7 ft 0 in (2.13 m)

Powerplant: one de Havilland Gipsy Major 8 rated at 145 hp (108 kW)
Weights: empty equipped 1,425 lb (646 kg); maximum take-off 2,014 lb (914 kg)
Fuel and load: external fuel none; maximum ordnance none
Speed: maximum level speed 'clean' at sea level 120 kt (138 mph; 222 km/h); cruising speed at optimum altitude 101 kt (116 mph; 187 km/h)

Range: 243 nm (280 miles; 451 km)
Performance: maximum rate of climb at sea level 800 ft (244 m) per minute; climb to 5,000 ft (1525 m) in 7 minutes 18 seconds; service ceiling 15,800 ft (4815 m)

The main use of the RAF Chipmunks is to provide flight experience to air cadets.

Initial training for UK Army Air Corps pilots is provided on Chipmunk T.Mk 10s at Middle Wallop.

de Havilland Canada **DHC-2 Beaver**

Having first flown in August 1947, the seven-passenger Pratt & Whitney R-985-AN-1-engined **DHC-2 Beaver** STOL utility transport won a 1951 joint US Army/Air Force design contest for a new liaison aircraft. Two Army and four Air Force evaluation **YL-20** Beavers preceded major joint-service contracts in 1952, totalling by late 1960 959 **L-20A**s, including six slightly-modified **L-20B**s. Most went to the US Army, comprising its main fixed-wing inventory, and became popular during the Korean War. As **U-6A**s in the 1962 'utility' redesignations, US Army Beavers were also used on skis in Alaska and elsewhere. Three remain active with the **USN Test Pilot's School**.

Military operators included Argentina (six), Australia (two), Austria (six), Cambodia, Chile (15), Colombia (18), Cuba (three), Dominica (four), Finland (one), Ghana (14), Haiti (two), Indonesia (one), Iran (five), Kenya (10), South Korea, Laos (six), Netherlands (nine), Oman (four), Peru (four), Philippines (six), Thailand (four), Turkey (eight), United Kingdom (42), Uruguay (one), Yugoslavia and Zambia (nine). Few Beavers

now remain in military use, probably limited to nine in **Colombia**, two in **Haiti** and one in **Turkey**.

Having built 1,691 Beavers by the early 1960s, DHC switched production to a turbo-prop version, the **DHC-2 Mk III**, powered by a 550-shp (410.30-kW) Pratt & Whitney Canada PT6A-6A. This first flew on 30 December 1963 with a 30-in (76-cm) longer forward fuselage and two more passenger seats, plus a taller square-cut fin and ventral strake. DHC-2 Mk III orders totalled 59 by early 1968, known military customers in the early 1990s including the **Uganda Police Air Wing**.

SPECIFICATION

de Havilland Canada DHC-2 Beaver
Wing: span 48 ft 0 in (14.63 m); aspect ratio 9.22; area 250.00 sq ft (23.225 m2)
Fuselage and tail: length 30 ft 4 in (9.25 m); height 9 ft 0 in (2.74 m); tailplane span 15 ft 10 in (4.83 m); wheel track 10 ft 2 in (3.10 m); wheel base 22 ft 9 in (6.94 m)
Powerplant: one Pratt & Whitney R-985 Wasp Junior

rated at 450 hp (336 kW)
Weights: empty 2,850 lb (1293 kg); operating empty 3,000 lb (1361 kg); maximum take-off 5,100 lb (2313 kg)
Fuel and load: internal fuel 95 US gal (359 litres) plus provision for 43.25 US gal (164 litres) of auxiliary fuel in two wing tanks; external fuel none; maximum payload 1,350 lb (613 kg)
Speed: maximum level speed 'clean' at 5,000 ft (1525 m) 139 kt (160 mph; 257 km/h) and at sea level 122 kt (140 mph; 225 km/h); maximum cruising speed at 5,000 ft (1525 m) 124 kt (143 mph; 230 km/h) and at sea level 117 kt (135 mph; 217 km/h); economical cruising speed at 5,000 ft (1525 m) 113 kt (130 mph; 209 km/h) and at sea level 109 kt (125 mph; 201 km/h)
Range: 676 nm (778 miles; 1252 km) with maximum fuel or 419 nm (483 miles; 777 km) with maximum payload

Colombia operates a few Beavers on light transport duties. Original deliveries totalled 18.

Performance: maximum rate of climb at sea level 1,020 ft (311 m) per minute; service ceiling 18,000 ft (5485 m); take-off run 560 ft (170 m) at maximum take-off weight; take-off distance to 50 ft (15 m) 1,015 ft (310 m) at maximum take-off weight; landing distance from 50 ft (15 m) 1,000 ft (305 m) at normal landing weight; landing run 500 ft (152 m) at normal landing weight

---

de Havilland Canada **DHC-3 Otter**

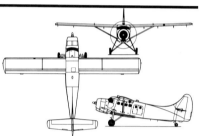

Scaled up from the successful Beaver, with a bigger (600-hp/447.6-kW) Pratt & Whitney R-1340-S1H1-G radial engine, the 11-passenger STOL **DHC-3 Otter** first flew on 12 December 1951. It was also designed for use on wheels, floats, amphibious floats or skis. Launch orders included 39 for the Royal Canadian Air Force (later increased to 69) and, following demonstrations in 1953, the US Army received its first six **YU-1** versions in March 1955. These preceded further batches of 84, 70 and 29, or 189 **U-1A**s in all, plus 13 US Navy **UC-1**s (later **U-1B**s). Otter production eventually totalled over 460 by 1966.

The RAF acquired a single ski-equipped Otter (XL710) for the 1956 British Trans-Antarctic Expedition. Other military customers included Argentina (three), Australia

(two), Bangladesh (four), Burma (nine), Cambodia (one), Chile (seven), Colombia (four), Costa Rica (three), Ethiopia (four), Ghana (12), India (33), Indonesia (10), Nicaragua (four), Nigeria (three), Norway (eight), Panama (five), Paraguay (one) and the Philippines (two), most now being retired. The **US Navy Test Pilot's School** uses a single U-1B, another remains active in **Nicaragua**, and two are in use in **Panama**.

SPECIFICATION

de Havilland Canada DHC-3 Otter
Wing: span 58 ft 0 in (17.68 m); aspect ratio 8.97; area 375.00 sq ft (34.84 m2)
Fuselage and tail: length 41 ft 10 in (12.75 m);

height 12 ft 7 in (3.84 m); tailplane span 21 ft 2 in (6.46 m); wheel track 11 ft 2 in (3.42 m); wheel base 27 ft 10 in (8.49 m)
Powerplant: one Pratt & Whitney R-1340-S1H1-G/S3H1-G Wasp rated at 600 hp (447 kW)
Weights: empty 4,431 lb (2010 kg); operating empty 5,287 lb (2398 kg); maximum take-off 8,000 lb (3629 kg)
Fuel and load: internal fuel 213.75 US gal (809 litres); external fuel none; maximum payload 3,150 lb (1429 kg)
Speed: maximum level speed 'clean' at 5,000 ft (1525 m) 139 kt (160 mph; 257 km/h) and at sea level 133 kt (153 mph; 246 km/h); maximum cruising speed at 5,000 ft (1525 m) 120 kt (138 mph; 222 km/h) and at sea level 115 kt (132 mph; 212 km/h); economical cruising speed at optimum altitude 105 kt (121 mph; 195 km/h) and at sea level 105 kt (121 mph; 195 km/h)
Range: 1,320 nm (1,520 miles; 2446 km) with

de Havilland Canada DHC-3 Otter

maximum fuel or 760 nm (875 miles; 1408 km) with a 2,100-lb (953-kg) payload; endurance 8 hours 36 minutes
Performance: maximum rate of climb at sea level 850 ft (259 m) per minute; service ceiling 18,800 ft (5730 m) with S1H1-G engine or 17,400 ft (5305 m) with S3H1-G engine; take-off run 630 ft (192 m) at maximum take-off weight; landing distance from 50 ft (15 m) 880 ft (268 m) at normal landing weight; landing run 440 ft (134 m) at normal landing weight

---

de Havilland Canada **DHC-4 Caribou**

Conceived in an attempt to combine the payload of the Douglas DC-3 with the STOL performance of the DHC-2 and DHC-3, the **de Havilland Canada DHC-4 Caribou** is a shoulder-wing twin-engined aircraft powered by two 1,450-bhp (1081-kW) Pratt & Whitney R-2000-7M2 14-cylinder radials. Accommodation was initially for up to 32 troops or, in an ambulance version, up to 22 litter patients. The high-aspect-ratio wing with full-span double-slotted flaps (the outboard components acting as independent ailerons) incorporates anhedral on the inboard sections to reduce the length of the main landing gear units and allow the cabin floor to be no higher than truck-bed height to facilitate rear loading. The rear ramp can be lowered for inflight paradropping.

The DHC-4 was first flown on 30 July 1958, but already the US Army had ordered five evaluation **YAC-1** aircraft in the previous year. Preliminary US type approval was gained in December 1960 at a gross weight of 26,000 lb (11794 kg), this being applicable to the basic DHC-4 and the **AC-1** (later **CV-2A**) in US Army service. Later the **DHC-4A** obtained type approval at 28,500 lb (12928 kg) gross weight, this version entering US service as the **CV-2B**. Operational use by the US Army encompassed delivery of infantry troops and their light wheeled vehicles (the CV-2B could carry two fully loaded jeeps and their crews) from

major airports to forward landing strips from where they could be taken into combat by helicopters. CV-2s saw considerable action in Vietnam but, being the largest aircraft ever operated by the US Army, were transferred to the USAF early in 1967, and the surviving 134 aircraft were redesignated **C-7A**.

Only limited use of the DHC-4A was made by the Canadian Armed Forces and by 1979 all had been retired, most of them being supplied to the air forces of Colombia, Oman and Tanzania. The Caribou, on account of its good STOL qualities, proved very popular among air forces obliged to operate over mountainous and jungle terrain and about 30 continue to provide military transport service in **Australia**, **Cameroon**, **Liberia** and **Malaysia**. Total DHC-4 production was 307 aircraft, with manufacture ending in 1973.

SPECIFICATION

de Havilland Canada DHC-4A Caribou
Wing: span 95 ft 7.5 in (29.15 m); aspect ratio 10.0; area 912.00 sq ft (84.72 m2)
Fuselage and tail: length 72 ft 7 in (22.13 m); height 31 ft 9 in (9.70 m); tailplane span 36 ft 0 in (10.97 m); wheel track 23 ft 1.5 in (7.05 m); wheel base 25 ft 8 in (7.82 m)
Powerplant: two Pratt & Whitney R-2000-7M2 Twin

Wasp each rated at 1,450 hp (1081 kW)
Weights: operating empty 18,260 lb (8283 kg) including two crew; normal take-off 28,500 lb (12928 kg); maximum take-off 31,300 lb (14197 kg)
Fuel and load: internal fuel 820 US gal (3137 litres); external fuel none; maximum payload 8,740 lb (3965 kg)
Speed: maximum level speed 'clean' at 6,500 ft (1980 m) 188 kt (216 mph; 347 km/h); maximum cruising speed at 7,500 ft (2285 m) 158 kt (182 mph; 293 km/h); economical cruising speed at 7,500 ft

(2285 m) 158 kt (182 mph; 293 km/h)
Range: range 1,135 nm (1,307 miles; 2103 km) with maximum fuel or 210 nm (242 miles; 390 km) with maximum payload
Performance: maximum rate of climb at sea level 1,355 ft (413 m) per minute; service ceiling 24,800 ft (7560 m); take-off run 725 ft (221 m) at maximum take-off weight; take-off distance to 50 ft (15 m) 1,185 ft (361 m) at maximum take-off weight; landing distance from 50 ft (15 m) 1,235 ft (376 m) at normal landing weight; landing run 670 ft (204 m) at normal landing weight

The Royal Malaysian air force flies the DHC-4 on assault transport duties.

de Havilland Canada DHC-5 Buffalo

Despite being evolved largely in concert with (and to meet the requirements of) the US Army, the **de Havilland Canada DHC-5 Buffalo** failed to secure a production contract from that service because of the transfer of the US Army's large fixed-wing aircraft to the USAF in 1967, the latter being adequately equipped with military transports. Designed to accommodate up to 41 combat troops, a Pershing missile, a 105-mm (4.13-in) howitzer or a 3/4-ton truck, the DHC-5 (first flown on 9 April 1964) is a twin-turboprop shoulder-wing monoplane of similar configuration to, but larger than, the Caribou (it was originally termed the **Caribou II**), but without anhedral on the wing centre-section. With maximum STOL payload of 12,000 lb (5443 kg), the current **DHC-5D** requires no more than a 984-ft (300-m) take-off ground run.

The first four aircraft produced in 1964-65 were delivered to the US Army under the designation **YAC-2** (later changed to **CV-7A** and subsequently **C-8A**) but, as already stated, no American production order followed. Instead, 15 **DHC-5As** were delivered to the **Canadian Armed Forces** in 1968 with the designation **CC-115**, and of these six serve today in the SAR role. **Brazil** was the first overseas mili-

tary customer in 1969, eventually receiving 18 aircraft designated **C-115B** locally, most of which were to serve as transports at Campo Grande. **Peru**'s air force received 16 DHC-5As and these equip a transport squadron at Jorge Chavez.

Without the intended American orders, this level of sale was inadequate to support further production, and manufacture of the DHC-5A ended in 1972. Development was confined to proposed re-engined versions (**DHC-5B** with CT64-P4C and **DHC-5C** with CT64-P4C or Rolls-Royce Dart RDa.12 turboprops), neither of which was built. Instead, the **DHC-5D** with General Electric CT64-820-4 engines attracted sufficient interest overseas and in 1974 this version re-entered production. Ten DHC-5Ds sold to **Egypt** featured LAPES for the paradropping of supplies; in 1985 four of these were converted as navigation trainers by the Swedish company Swedair. The Buffalo is currently operated by the air forces of **Abu Dhabi** (defence force), **Cameroon**, **Ecuador**, **Kenya**, **Mauritania**, **Mexico** (and Mexican navy), **Sudan**, **Tanzania**, **Togo**, **Zaïre** and **Zambia**. Total production of all versions of the DHC-5 reached 123 aircraft, with production ending in December 1986.

SPECIFICATION

de Havilland Canada DHC-5 Buffalo
Wing: span 96 ft 0 in (29.26 m); aspect ratio 9.75; area 945.00 sq ft (87.79 m²)
Fuselage and tail: length 79 ft 0 in (24.08 m); height 28 ft 8 in (8.73 m); tailplane span 32 ft 0 in (9.75 m); wheel track 30 ft 6 in (9.29 m); wheel base 27 ft 11 in (8.50 m)
Powerplant: two General Electric CT64-820-1 each rated at 3,055 ehp (2278 ekW)
Weights: operating empty 23,157 lb (10505 kg) including three crew; maximum take-off 41,000 lb (18598 kg)
Fuel and load: internal fuel 2,087 US gal (7900 litres); external fuel none; maximum payload 13,843 lb (6279 kg)
Speed: maximum level speed 'clean' and maximum cruising speed 'clean' at 10,000 ft (3050 m)
235 kt (271 mph; 435 km/h); economical cruising speed at 10,000 ft (3050 m) 181 kt (208 mph; 335 km/h)
Range: 1,885 nm (2,171 miles; 3493 km) with maximum fuel and a 4,000-lb (1814-kg) payload, or 440 nm (507 miles; 815 km) with maximum payload
Performance: maximum rate of climb at sea level 1,890 ft (576 m) per minute; service ceiling 30,000 ft (9145 m); take-off run 1,040 ft (317 m) at maximum take-off weight on grass; take-off distance to 50 ft (15 m) 1,540 ft (470 m) at maximum take-off weight from grass; landing distance from 50 ft (15 m) 1,020 ft (342 m) at normal landing weight on grass; landing run 610 ft (186 m) at normal landing weight on grass

Canada uses a few Buffalos for rescue tasks in the mountains.

de Havilland Canada DHC-6 Twin Otter

Originally developed in the 1960s and first flown on 20 May 1965, the **de Havilland DHC-6 Twin Otter** was first powered by two 579-ehp (432-kW) PT6A-6 turboprop engines and was intended to extend the transport potential of the popular single-engined DHC-3 Otter while retaining the efficient high-lift wing for STOL performance. The new 13/18-seat transport retained no more than the original basic wing structure with its full-span double-slotted flaps and ailerons, and from the fourth aircraft onwards the **DHC-6 Series 100** adopted PT6A-20 engines. Optional conversion from fixed tricycle-wheel landing gear to floats or skis was available.

FAA type approval was gained in 1966 and quickly led to commercial orders, but military interest was slow to materialise.

Nevertheless, eight aircraft were delivered to the **Canadian Armed Forces** as **CC-138** search and rescue aircraft, and after 115 Series 100 aircraft had been completed production switched to the **DHC-6 Series 200** with lengthened nose and increased baggage capacity; 115 examples of this version were produced (few of them for military customers) before DHC embarked on the current **DHC-6 Series 300**. In this version, the more powerful PT6A-27 engines allow capacity to be increased to 20 passengers, and an increase in maximum take-off weight of 1,000 lb (454 kg).

Current military Twin Otter operators are **Argentina**, **Benin**, **Chile**, **Ecuador**, **Ethiopia**, **France**, **Haiti**, **Nepal**, **Norway**, **Panama**, **Paraguay**, **Peru**, **Sudan**

and **Uganda**. A total of 10 DHC-6s was supplied to the **USA** as the **V-18 Twin Otter**. Eight survivors are currently operated, comprising two **UV-18Bs** by the USAF Academy and six **UV-18A** aircraft by the Alaska ArNG's 1-207th Aviation Group.

In 1982 DHC offered three dedicated military Twin Otter variants: the **DHC-6-300M** was a 15-troop transport convertible to 20 seats, or with paratroop or ambulance layout; the **DHC-6-300M(COIN)** was a counter-insurgency variant with provision for armour protection, a cabin-mounted machine-gun and underwing ordnance; and the **DHC-6-300MR** was a maritime reconnaissance model with search radar under the nose and underwing searchlight pod. A single DHC-6-300MR has been purchased by the Senegal Department of Fisheries.

SPECIFICATION

de Havilland Canada DHC-6 Twin Otter Series 300
Wing: span 65 ft 0 in (19.81 m); aspect ratio 10.1; area 420.00 sq ft (39.02 m²)
Fuselage and tail: length 51 ft 9 in (15.77 m); height 19 ft 6 in (5.94 m); tailplane span 20 ft 8 in (6.30 m); wheel track 12ft 2 in (3.71 m); wheel base 14 ft 10.5 in (4.53 m)
Powerplant: two Pratt & Whitney Canada PT6A-27 each rated at 620 shp (462 kW)
Weights: operating empty 7,415 lb (3363 kg) including two crew; maximum take-off 12,500 lb (5670 kg)
Fuel and load: internal fuel 2,583 lb (1171 kg); external fuel none; maximum payload 4,280 lb (1941 kg) for 100 nm (115 miles; 185 km)
Speed: maximum cruising speed at 10,000 ft (3050 m) 182 kt (210 mph; 338 km/h)
Range: 700 nm (806 miles; 1297 km) with a 2,500-lb (1134-kg) payload
Performance: maximum rate of climb at sea level 1,600 ft (488 m) per minute; service ceiling 26,700 ft (8140 m); take-off run 700 ft (213 m) at maximum take-off weight for STOL or 860 ft (262 m) at maximum take-off weight for normal operation; take-off distance to 50 ft (15 m) 1,200 ft (366 m) at maximum take-off weight for STOL or 1,500 ft (457 m) at maximum take-off weight for normal operation; landing distance from 50 ft (15 m) 1,050 ft (320 m) at normal landing weight for STOL or 1,940 ft (591 m) at normal landing weight for normal operation; landing run 515 ft (157 m) at normal landing weight for STOL or 950 ft (290 m) at normal landing weight for normal operation

The Twin Otter's 'go-anywhere' ability makes it highly attractive to air arms with difficult terrain to cover. Chile uses its aircraft on airline-style operations in regions with few roads.

de Havilland Canada DHC-7 Dash 7

Representing a courageous attempt to exploit the demand by 'third-level' airlines for medium-capacity accommodation in STOL transports, the **de Havilland Canada DHC-7 Dash 7** was first flown on 27 March 1975, gaining its type approval certificate 25 months later. Four PT6A-50

turboprops drive large-diameter propellers at low speed to achieve low noise-level blade-tip speeds. The high-mounted, high-aspect-ratio wing is equipped with large-area double-slotted flaps and includes a pair of inboard spoilers acting as lift-dumpers on landing and an outboard pair acting differentially in flight to assist aileron control.

Accommodation in the **DHC-7 Series 100** is for up to 50 passengers in a circular-section pressurised fuselage, or mixed freight/seats in the **DHC-7 Series 101**.

The Dash 7 has been sold in small quantities to military users. Two aircraft, designated **CC-132**, were supplied to the Canadian Armed Forces, comprising a VIP

32-seater and a Series 101 with mixed cargo and passenger layout. Both aircraft flown by No. 412 Squadron of the CAF, based at Lahr in West Germany, were replaced by DHC-8s. One DHC-7 is operated by the **Venezuelan navy** on maritime patrol duties, and three serve with the **US Army** under the 'Grizzly Hunter' programme, using advanced sensors in drug interdiction and battlefield surveillance roles.

SPECIFICATION

de Havilland Canada DHC-7 Dash 7 Series 100
Wing: span 93 ft 0 in (28.35 m); aspect ratio 10.00; area 860.0 sq ft (79.90 m²)
Fuselage and tail: length 80 ft 7.7 in (24.58 m); height 26 ft 2.0 in (7.98 m); wheel track 23 ft 6.0 in (7.16 m); wheel base 27 ft 6 in (8.38 m)
Powerplant: four Pratt & Whitney Aircraft of Canada PT6A-50 turboprop engines, each flat rated at 1,120 shp (835 kW)
Weights: basic empty weight 27,000 lb (12247 kg); maximum take-off weight 44,000 lb (19958 kg)
Fuel and load: maximum useable fuel (standard tanks) 9,925 lb (4502 kg); external fuel none; payload (50 passengers or cargo) 11,310 lb (5130 kg)

Speed: maximum cruising speed at 8,000 ft (2440 m) at all-up weight of 41,000 lb (18597 kg) 231 kt (266 mph; 428 km/h)
Range: at 15,000 ft (4,575 m) with 50 passengers and baggage, at long-range cruising speed 690 nm (795 miles; 1279 km); with standard fuel and 6,500-lb (2948-kg) load, long-range cruising speed 1,170 nm (1,347 miles; 2168 km)
Performance: climb rate at sea level 1,220 ft (372 m) per minute: service ceiling 21,000 ft (6400 m); FAR Pt 25 take-off field length at all-up weight of 41,000 lb (18597 kg) and 25° flap 2,260 ft (689 m); FAR Pt 25 STOL landing field length at maximum landing weight and 45° flap 1,950 ft (594 m)

The 'Grizzly Hunter' aircraft of the US Army are used in the large drug interdiction campaign.

de Havilland (Bombardier) DHC-8 Dash 8/E-9

In the same way that companies worldwide have targeted niche areas, market research in the late 1970s by de Havilland Canada brought the conclusion that a 30/40-seat short-haul transport (slotting between the company's 19-seat DHC-6 Twin Otter and 50-seat DHC-7 Dash 7) could prove a profitable venture. Thus, design of the **de Havilland Canada DHC-8** was initiated, followed by the construction of four flying prototypes. The first machine (C-GDNK) recorded the type's maiden flight on 20 June 1983. These four prototypes saw extensive flying in a test programme that led to certification by Canada and the United States before the end of 1984.

The DHC-8, named **Dash 8**, is in many respects a twin-engined reduced-scale version of the DHC-7, but with less emphasis on STOL performance. Its configuration includes a high-set wing (to optimise cabin space) and a T-tail well clear of the slipstream from the four-bladed constant-speed/reversible propellers, driven in production aircraft by two Pratt & Whitney Canada PW120A turboprops. The landing gear is of retractable tricycle type with twin wheels on each unit, the main units being

housed in the engine nacelles when raised. As configured for commuter use the cabin seats 36, but other options include layouts for up to 40 passengers, or mixed pasenger/cargo traffic, or a 17-seat corporate interior. The production **Dash 8 Series 100** is available in **Commuter** and **Corporate** versions, the latter typically carrying 17 passengers over a range of 1,520 miles (2446 km) with full IFR reserves. Operated by a flight crew of two, plus a cabin attendant, the Dash 8 has a flight deck and cabin which are both air-conditioned and pressurised. The **Series 200** introduced uprated PW123C engines among other improvements, while the **Series 300** is a stretched variant which first flew on 15 May 1987. The **Series 400** programme relates to a further stretch yet to be launched.

The Dash 8 is currently operated in small numbers by three air forces. **Canada** acquired two **CC-142** (**DHC-8M-100**) transports for No. 412 Squadron and four **CT-142** navigation trainers with mapping radar in an extended nose. Three standard DHC-8-100s serve with the **Kenyan air force** on transport duties. Two aircraft are operated by the **US Air Force** by the

475th WEG at Tyndall AFB, FL. Designated **E-9A**, the pair is used for range support, and the aircraft are equipped with phased array radar in a large fuselage fairing and telemetry/communications relay equipment.

SPECIFICATION

de Havilland DHC-8 Dash 8M Series 100
Wing: span 85 ft 0 in (25.91 m); aspect ratio 12.4; area 585.00 sq ft (54.35 m²)
Fuselage and tail: length 73 ft 0 in (22.25 m); height 24 ft 7 in (7.49 m); elevator span 26 ft 0 in (7.92 m); wheel track 25 ft 10 in (7.87 m); wheel base 26 ft 1 in (7.95 m)
Powerplant: two Pratt & Whitney Canada PW120A each rated at 2,000 shp (1491 kW)
Weights: operating empty 22,000 lb (9979 kg); maximum take-off 34,500 lb (15649 kg)

Fuel and load: internal fuel 5,678 lb (2576 kg) with option for a maximum of 10,244 lb (4646 kg); external fuel none; maximum payload 9,000 lb (4082 kg) in passenger configuration or 9,849 lb (4467 kg) in freight configuration
Speed: maximum cruising speed at 15,000 ft (4570 m) 267 kt (308 mph; 497 km/h) and at 20,000 ft (6095 m) 265 kt (305 mph; 492 km/h)
Range: 1,190 nm (1,370 miles; 2205 km) with maximum passenger payload or 550 nm (633 miles; 1019 km) with maximum freight payload
Performance: maximum rate of climb at sea level 1,560 ft (475 m) per minute; certificated ceiling 25,000 ft (7620 m); balanced take-off field length 3,150 ft (960 m) at maximum take-off weight; balanced landing field length 2,980 ft (908 m) at normal landing weight

The enlarged nose radar identifies this as a CT-142 navigation trainer.

Dornier Do 27

*Dornier Luftfahrt GmbH
Dornier Airfield, D-8031 Wessling, Germany*

Marking the post-war re-emergence of the famed Dornier name, the **Do 25** was developed under the direction of Dr Claudius Dornier working in the Oficinas Tecnicas Dornier set up in Madrid. The first of two Do 25 prototypes was flown on 25 June 1954, the aircraft being an all-metal high-wing monoplane with fixed undercarriage and STOL performance. Powered by a 150-hp (112-kW) ENMA Tigre G-4-B piston engine, the four-seat Do 25 evolved into the **Do 27** with a 275-hp (205-kW) Lycoming GO-480-B1A6 engine, production of which was initiated by CASA in Spain (as the **C-127**) to meet a Spanish air force requirement for 50 of these general-purpose light transport and communications aircraft.

The Do 27 prototype was in fact completed by the reconstituted Dornier Werke in Germany, and production was initiated there also, with the first production aircraft flying on 17 October 1956. Production of the Do 27 in Germany totalled 571 examples and was completed in 1966. A large

proportion of this total was for military use, including 177 **Do 27A-1**s with gross weight of 1570 kg (3,460 lb); 88 **Do 27A-3**s with increased gross weight of 1750 kg (3,858 lb); 65 **Do 27A-4**s with wide track undercarriage and gross weight of 1850 kg (4,080 lb); 86 dual-control **Do 27B-1**s and 16 **Do 27B-2**s at the higher gross weight. All of these were for the Luftwaffe, which eventually took 428 into its inventory, including some ex-civil models.

Production of the Do 27 also included 14 of the **H-2** model for the Swiss air force with 340-hp (253-kW) GSO-480-B1B6 engine, three-bladed propeller and enlarged tail unit. Twelve **Do 27J-1**s were delivered to the Belgian army, and the Portuguese air force received 16 **Do 27K-1**s and 24 **K-2**s, slightly differing versions of the Do 27A-4. When the Luftwaffe began to dispose of its Do 27As, Portugal acquired at least a further 76, and others went to Nigeria (20), Israel (20), Sudan (three), Turkey (three) and the Congo (two). Some of the Portuguese air-

craft eventually found their way into the Angolan air force. The Do 27 has been additionally used by the air arms of Burundi, Guinea-Bissau, Belize, Rwanda and Sweden. Small numbers remain in service.

Israel maintains a handful of single-engined Do 27s for light transport and training. These serve alongside the Do 28A/B twin-engined development.

Dornier Do 28

Building on its experience gained with the Do 27, Dornier developed in 1959 a twin-engined derivative as the **Do 28**. First

flown on 29 April 1959, the Do 28 used essentially the same fuselage as the Do 27, with a nose fairing replacing the latter's

engine and a transverse beam through the lower fuselage to carry a pair of 180-hp (134-kW) Lycoming O-360-A1A engines. The wing span was extended while the chord remained unchanged. Production totalled 60 each of the **Do 28A-1** and **B-1** versions, the latter with 290-hp (216-kW)

IO-360s and other modifications, and was primarily for civilian use. Several Do 28s were used by the Nigerian and Katangan forces during the conflicts in those African countries. Other military users are the **Turkish army** (three) and the **Israel Defence Force/Air Force**.

Dornier Do 28D/Model 128 Skyservant

Although retaining the same configuration as the Do 28 and displaying an obvious family resemblance, the **Do 28D Skyservant** was almost totally a new design. First flown on 23 February 1966, the Do 28D was a further step in Dornier's evolution of rugged light transports with STOL performance and combined military and civil applications. Powered by 380-hp (284-kW) Lycoming IGSO-540-A1E engines, the Do 28D had a larger, flat-sided fuselage that was readily adaptable for specialised roles, a new tail unit, all-new systems and equipment, and a wing similar to that of the original Do 28.

After Dornier had built the prototype and six production Do 28Ds, the wing span was increased by 50 cm (1 ft 7 in) and gross weight by 150 kg (330 lb). This established the **Do 28D-1** production standard, 54 being built including four as VIP transports for the **Luftwaffe**. The improved **Do 28D-2** version was then selected by the Luftwaffe as its standard light transport/communications aircraft, with an order for 101 supplemented by 20 for the **Bundesmarine**. Numerous detail refinements were made in the Do 28D-2, which

had an internal redesign to lengthen the cabin by 15 cm (6 in), increased fuel capacity and gross weight increased first to 3800 kg (8,370 lb) and eventually to 4015 kg (8,844 lb).

Production of the Do 28D-2 totalled 172 and was almost wholly for military or quasi-military users. Other than the German air force and navy, these included **Cameroon** (two), **Ethiopian police** (two), **Israel** (15), **Kenya** (six), **Malawi** (six), **Morocco** (two, for maritime patrol), **Nigeria** (20), **Somalia** police air wing (two), **Thailand**'s border police (three), **Turkey** (nine) and **Zambia** (10). At least six more went to the Turkish army from ex-Luftwaffe stocks, which also provided 12 for **Greece**. One of the Luftwaffe Skyservants was fitted with turbo supercharged TIGO-540 engines and flown by Dornier in March 1980 as the **Do 28D-2T**, and conversion of the entire fleet followed. Two of the Bundesmarine aircraft were fitted with LM Ericsson SLAR, IR/UV scanners and cameras for pollution control duty starting in January 1986, under the designation **Do 28D-2OU**.

During 1980, Dornier replaced the Do 28D-2 in production with the generally simi-

lar but updated **Model 128-2** (the 'Do' prefix being dropped at this time). Only a handful of Dornier 128-2s was built, including two for the Transportes Aériens de **Benin** and two for the **Nigerian air force**.

Dornier had also adapted the Skyservant for turboprop power, at first fitting a pair of 400-shp (298-kW) Lycoming LTP101-600 engines in the **Do 28D-5X**, flown on 9 April 1978. This same prototype was then fitted with similarly derated Pratt & Whitney Canada PT6A-110 turboprops and, as the **Do 28D-6X**, flew on 4 March 1980. With the latter engines, the **Turbo-Skyservant** entered limited production as the **Dornier 128-6**, the principal order being for 16 for the Nigerian air force. Three others went to the Cameroon air force for the maritime surveillance role, with MEL Marec radar in a chin installation.

SPECIFICATION

Dornier Do 28D-1 Skyservant
Wing: span 15.50 m (50 ft 10.25 in); aspect ratio 8.4; area 28.60 m2 (307.86 sq ft)
Fuselage and tail: length 12.00 m (39 ft 4.5 in);

Turkey operates a considerable number of Do 28D-2s, several featuring unidentified radomes.

height 3.90 m (12 ft 10 in); tailplane span 6.20 m (20 ft 4 in); wheel track 3.52 m (11 ft 6 in); wheel base 8.50 m (27 ft 10.75 in)
Powerplant: two Textron Lycoming IGSO-540 each rated at 380 hp (283 kW)
Weights: empty 2166 kg (4,775 lb); maximum take-off 3650 kg (8,047 lb)
Fuel and load: internal fuel 822 litres (217 US gal); external fuel none
Speed: maximum level speed 'clean' at 10,500 ft (3200 m) 173 kt (199 mph; 320 km/h); maximum cruising speed at 10,000 ft (3050 m) 155 kt (178 mph; 286 km/h); economical cruising speed at 10,000 ft (3050 m) 124 kt (143 mph; 230 km/h)
Range: 976 nm (1,124 miles; 1810 km)
Performance: maximum rate of climb at sea level 1,180 ft (360 m) per minute; service ceiling 24,280 ft (7400 m); take-off distance to 50 ft (15 m) 1,140 ft (347 m) at maximum take-off weight for STOL or 1,700 ft (518 m) at maximum take-off weight for conventional operation; landing distance from 50 ft (15 m) 1,220 ft (372 m) at normal landing weight for STOL or 1,960 ft (597 m) at normal landing weight for conventional operation

Dornier Do 228

When Dornier adopted the designation 128-2 and 128-6 for the Skyservant variants previously known as the Do 28D-2 and Do 28D-6, two further derivatives of the basic twin-engined transport were in the project phase as the **Do 28E-1** and **Do 28E-2**. Given a go-ahead in November 1979, these then became the **Dornier 228-100** and **228-200** respectively, differing essentially only in fuselage length and operational weights.

Using the same fuselage cross-section as the Skyservant, the Dornier 228-100 was

sized to seat 15 passengers, while the longer 228-200 would seat 19. Prototypes flew, respectively, on 28 March and 9 May 1981, and deliveries began (for airline use) in 1982.

Of just over 200 Dornier 228s built (by 1994), the majority are for commercial use, the major exception being the **Indian Air Force** and the **Indian Coast Guard**. The latter began to operate the first of 36 **Dornier 228-201**s in July 1986, these having MEL Marec II radar, a Swedish IR/UV linescan sensor and other special fea-

tures. At least 43 Dornier 228-201s are being acquired by the Indian Air Force, and the **Indian Navy** has a requirement for 27, depending upon the Coast Guard upon the assembly/licence-production line set up by HAL at Bangalore. After Dornier had delivered three 228-201s to the Indian CG (and five for airline use), HAL flew the first Indian-assembled aircraft on 31 January 1986.

One 228-201 was evaluated by both the **Bundesmarine** and **Luftwaffe**, this later becoming a 'hack' for use by the latter, while the former acquired another fully equipped for maritime pollution control which is now operated by MFG 5. Other military users are **Finland** (multi-sensor aircraft for para-military Frontier Guard), **Malawi** (three 228-201s and a single **228-202**), **Niger** (one -201 delivered in April 1986), **Nigeria** (one -100 transport and two VIP -200s), the Royal **Oman** police air wing (two -100s), and the **Royal Thai navy** (three equipped for maritime reconnaissance with Bendix 1500 radar).

SPECIFICATION

Dornier Do 228 Maritime Patrol Version A
Wing: span 16.97 m (55 ft 8 in); aspect ratio 9.0; area

India is the largest military operator of the Do 228, aircraft serving with the Air Force, Navy (illustrated) and Coast Guard. The latter service has aircraft equipped with search radar in a fairing under the forward cabin.

32.00 m2 (344.46 sq ft)
Fuselage and tail: length 15.04 m (49 ft 4.125 in); height 4.86 m (15 ft 11.5 in); tailplane span 6.45 m (21 ft 2 in); wheel track 3.30 m (10 ft 10 in); wheel base 5.53 m (18 ft 1.25 in)
Powerplant: two Garrett TPE331-5-252D each rated at 715 shp (533 kW)
Weights: empty, standard 2960 kg (6,526 lb); operating empty 3935 kg (8,675 lb); maximum take-off 5980 kg (13,183 lb)
Fuel and load: internal fuel 1885 kg (4,155 lb) plus provision for 395 kg (871 lb) of auxiliary fuel; external fuel none; maximum payload 2117 kg (4,667 lb)
Speed: average cruising speed at optimum altitude for maximum range 165 kt (190 mph; 305 km/h), or for maximum endurance 100 kt (115 mph; 185 km/h)
Range: 940 nm (1,982 miles; 1740 km) with standard fuel; search time at maximum-range cruising speed at 2,000 ft (610 m) close to base 7 hours 45 minutes, or at maximum range cruising speed at 2,000 ft (610 m) 400 nm (460 miles; 740 km) from base 3 hours 45 minutes, or at maximum-endurance cruising speed at 2,000 ft (610 m) close to base 9 hours 45 minutes, or at maximum-endurance cruising speed at 2,000 ft (610 m) 400 nm (460 miles; 750 km) from base 4 hours 45 minutes
Performance: maximum rate of climb at sea level 1,910 ft (582 m) per minute; service ceiling 28,000 ft (8535 m); take-off run 1,450 ft (442 m) at maximum take-off weight; take-off distance to 50 ft (15 m) 1,945 ft (592 m) at maximum take-off weight

Douglas DC-3/C-47 Dakota/Turbo Dakota

Of all the types of aircraft serving with military forces worldwide, the **Douglas C-47/DC-3** is perhaps the best-known and probably the longest serving. As the commercial Douglas DST transport, the prototype of this ubiquitous family first flew on 17 December 1935. Production Model DC-3s were in airline service before World War II, and the first military examples entered US Army Air Corps service in October 1938. The definitive military **C-47 Skytrain** began deliveries in February 1942 and by the time production ended in 1946 a total of 10,655 aircraft of basic DC-3 type had been built, all but a few hundred in military guise. Numerous designations were applied to different versions used by the US Army Air Force and Navy, of which the **C-47**, **C-53** and **C-117** variants were the most significant. The name **Dakota** was adopted in Britain and became widely used. The type was also built in the Soviet Union as the **Lisunov Li-2**.

The basic **C-47A Skytrain** was pow-

ered by two 1,200-hp (896-kW) Pratt & Whitney R-1830-90D or -92 radials. It had a normal take-off weight of 29,300 lb (13320 kg) and accommodated up to 28 troops or four tons of cargo. Retired from US service from 1945 onwards, thousands of C-47As became available for sale or donation to other air forces (or for adaptation for commercial service). In 1994, relatively small numbers remained operational with the air arms of about three dozen nations, of which the most important, numerically, were the **Republic of China** (Taiwan), **Colombia**, **Greece**, **Israel**, **Salvador**, **South Africa**, **Thailand**, **Turkey** and **Vietnam**. In Colombia, Salvador and Thailand, examples of the **AC-47** gunship are also being used, with three side-firing 7.62-mm machine-guns mounted in the cabin.

Many efforts have been made to

Some of Israel's C-47s are used in an electronic warfare role, and are festooned with antennas.

enhance the performance of the C-47/DC-3, as well as to prolong its service life and to extend its utility. In particular, a number of turboprop installations have been made, of which the latest and apparently most successful, in military applications, is that developed by Basler Turbo Conversions Inc. The **Basler Turbo-67** introduces two Pratt & Whitney Canada PT6A-67R turboprops with five-bladed Hartzell propellers, and a lengthening of the forward fuselage by 3 ft 4 in (1.02 m) to bring the pilots forward of the plane of the propellers and preserve CG within acceptable limits. Revisions

in the cabin layout increase the seating capacity to a maximum of 34 troops or five LD3 cargo containers.

Deliveries of the Turbo-67 began in 1990, recipients including the air forces of Colombia, **Bolivia**, **Guatemala** and Salvador (with an AC-47 gunship conversion as well as a transport). Early in 1992, the South African Air Force began to accept the **C-47TP Super Dakota** conversion by Professional Aviation, similar in almost all respects to the Basler Turbo-67. Production conversion lines set up by the SAAF at the Swartkops and Ysterplaat bases were to convert the entire fleet of over 40 Dakotas to this standard, with the first assigned to No. 35 Squadron at Cape Town in 1992 for SAR duty.

Speed: never-exceed speed 206 kt (237 mph; 381 km/h); maximum level speed 'clean' at optimum altitude 187 kt (215 mph; 346 km/h); maximum cruising speed at 5,000 ft (1525 m) 168 kt (194 mph; 312 km/h); economical cruising speed at 6,000 ft (1830 m) 143 kt (165 mph; 266 km/h)
Range: 1,311 nm (1,510 miles; 2430 km) with maximum fuel or 304 nm (350 miles; 563 km) with maximum payload
Performance: maximum rate of climb at sea level 1,070 ft (326 m) per minute; service ceiling 21,900 ft (6675 m)

Colombia operates two AC-47 gunships, distinguished by the blast deflector around the door and blanked-off rear windows.

Douglas **DC-4/C-54 Skymaster**

The **Douglas DC-4** was conceived as the fourth in the Douglas Commercial series of transport aircraft, and first flew on 26 March 1942 (after an earlier **DC-4E** prototype, in June 1938, proved to be unsuitable for development). Early production of the DC-4 was absorbed by the USAAF under the **C-54** designation, leaving commercial exploitation to follow post-war. Like the DC-3, the DC-4/C-54 found its way into the inventories of many air forces around the world but few currently remain. The final users of the type were the air forces of **Mexico** (two, now grounded), **Niger** (one), the **Republic of Korea** (two remaining from 17 received from US stocks in 1966-67) and **South Africa** (two equipped for

Elint duties, all believed grounded). The **Skymaster** was designed to be flown with a crew of five and normally accommodated up to 50 equipped troops or a freight load of 32,000 lb (14515 kg).

SPECIFICATION

Douglas DC-4
Wing: span 117 ft 6 in (35.82 m); aspect ratio 9.44; area 1,462.00 sq ft (135.82 m²)
Fuselage and tail: length 93 ft 10 in (28.60 m); height 27 ft 7 in (8.41 m)
Powerplant: four Pratt & Whitney R-2000-2SD-13G Twin Wasp each rated at 1,450 hp (1081 kW)
Weights: empty equipped 43,300 lb (19641 kg);

normal take-off 63,500 lb (28804 kg); maximum take-off 73,000 lb (33113 kg)
Fuel and load: internal fuel 9,500 lb (4309 kg); external fuel none; maximum payload 14,200 lb (6441 kg)

Speed: maximum speed 'clean' at optimum altitude 230 kt (265 mph; 426 km/h); maximum cruising speed at 10,000 ft (3050 m) 180 kt (207 mph; 333 km/h)
Range: 1,893 nm (2,180 miles; 3510 km) with maximum fuel or 999 nm (1,150 miles; 1851 km) with maximum payload

Two of South Africa's DC-4s were used for Elint and EW work.

Douglas **DC-6/C-118 Liftmaster**

Development of the **Douglas DC-6** represented a logical evolution from the DC-4, with which it shared the same configuration, but featured enlarged dimensions, increased power and greater load capacity. First flown on 15 February 1946, the 76-seat DC-6 was produced principally for commercial use, but 167 were built for the USAF and USN with the **C-118A** and **R6D-1** designations. Several foreign air forces acquired ex-commercial **DC-6A**s, **DC-6B**s or, in a few cases, C-118As, and of these about a dozen were still flying in 1994. The final users of the type include the air forces of **Colombia**, **Guatemala**, **Honduras**, **Mexico**, **El Salvador**, **South Korea** and **Taiwan**.

SPECIFICATION

Douglas DC-6B
Wing: span 117 ft 6 in (35.81 m); aspect ratio 9.17; area 1,463.00 sq ft (139.91 m²)
Fuselage and tail: length 105 ft 7 in (32.18 m); height 29 ft 3in (8.92 m)
Powerplant: four Pratt & Whitney R-2800-CB17 Double Wasp each rated at 2,500 hp (1864 kW)
Weights: operating empty about 62,000 lb (28123 kg); maximum take-off 107,000 lb (48534 kg)
Fuel and load: internal fuel 32,950 lb (14946 kg); external fuel none; maximum payload 24,565 lb (11143 kg)
Speed: never-exceed speed 312 kt (359 mph; 578

km/h); maximum cruising speed at optimum altitude 274 kt (316 mph; 509 km/h); typical cruising speed at 20,000 ft (6095 m) 234 kt (270 mph; 435 km/h)

Taiwan was one of the last military users of the DC-6, this aircraft flying on services to Quemoy. It has recently been replaced by Boeing 727s.

Range: 2,320 nm (2,672 miles; 4300 km) with maximum fuel or 1,650 nm (1,900 miles; 3058 km) with maximum payload
Performance: maximum rate of climb at sea level 1,120 ft (341 m) per minute; balanced take-off field length 6,150 ft (1875 m) at maximum take-off weight; balanced landing field length 5,000 ft (1525 m)

Douglas **DC-8/EC-24A**

First of the Douglas jetliners and launched to compete with the Boeing 707, the **Douglas DC-8** first flew on 30 May 1958. Production ended in May 1972 with 556 built in six major series and numerous sub-variants. Of these, the **Series 10** to **Series 50** were dimensionally similar, with a fuselage length of 150 ft 6 in (45.87 m) and typically about 120 seats;

differences concerned engine choice, fuel capacity and operating weights. Two different longer fuselages were offered in the **Series 60** versions, to seat up to 259 or 189 passengers, and the **Series 70** designation identified a retrofit programme for the Series 60 to introduce 22,000-lb (97.86-kN) thrust CFM56 turbofans in place of Pratt & Whitney JT3D turbojets.

The French **Armée de l'Air** was the first of the small number of military users of the DC-8, acquiring one **Series 55CF** new and several others ex-airline. The constitution of the French fleet has varied from time to time, the final disposition comprising a single Series 55 and three **Series 72**s (converted from **Series 62**s) that equip ET 3/60 'Esterel' in the 60ᵉ Groupe de Transport for long-range strategic transport and in the VIP role from Charles de Gaulle, Paris. A fifth DC-8, a **Series 53**, also serves in the ECM/Elint role, flown by the 51 Escadron

Electronique 'Aubrac' in CTAA at Evreux.

Two ex-Swissair DC-8 **Series 62CF**s equipping the Escuadrilla Presidencial of the **Fuerza Aérea Peruana** are the only other aircraft of this type remaining in military service in the transport role. More specialised is the single **Series 54F** freighter, ex-United Airlines, flown by the **US Navy** as the **EC-24A** since 1987. This unique aircraft, with an extensive electronic suite, serves with the Fleet Electronic Warfare Support Group (FEWSG) to simulate the C³ threat in fleet exercises.

Two one-off specials are the DC-8 SARIGUE (left) used by the French for electronic reconnaissance, and the EC-24A (right), used by the US Navy for fleet ECM exercises. The latter is operated by Chrysler from Waco.

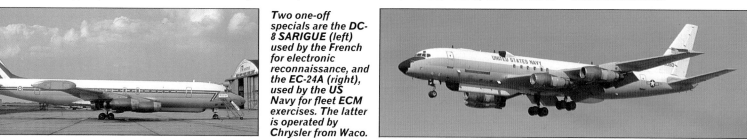

EH Industries **EH.101 Merlin**

EH Industries Ltd
500 Chiswick High Road
London W4 5RG, UK

The **EH.101** has its roots in the Westland WG 34 design that was adopted in late 1978 to meet Britain's Naval Staff Requirement 6646 for a Sea King Replacement (SKR). Work on the WG 34 was cancelled before a prototype had been completed, however, opening the way for revision of the design to meet both Royal Navy and Italian navy requirements. Negotiations between Westland and Agusta began in November 1979. This led to the setting up of European Helicopter Industries Ltd, which was given a formal go-ahead in February 1984, when the two governments agreed to fund nine prototypes, and subsequent development.

Although replacing the Sea King was the primary objective, determining the size and weight of the EH.101 design, several other potential roles were planned from the outset, including military and civil transport and utility duties. Some roles can be performed using the same basic fuselage as the naval helicopter but, alternatively, the EH.101 can be fitted with a modified rear fuselage incorporating a ramp. The nine prototypes ordered were assigned specific tasks concerned with the basic dynamics, specific RN and Italian Marina ASW equipment fits, the military tactical/logistic transport, the civil utility version and the commercial **Heliliner**.

The EH.101 is a three-engined helicopter with a single five-bladed composite main rotor, and BERP-derived high-speed tips. Much use is made of composites throughout, although the fuselage itself is mainly of aluminium alloy. Systems and equipment vary with role and customer. For the Royal Navy, which calls the EH.101 the **Merlin HAS.Mk 1**, IBM is the prime contractor in association with Westland and provides equipment as well as overall management and integration; other avionics include GEC

Ferranti Blue Kestrel 360° search radar, GEC Avionics AQS-903 processing and display system, Racal Orange Reaper ESM and Ferranti/Thomson-CSF dipping sonar. Armament on the Merlin comprises four Marconi Sting Ray torpedoes, with two sonobuoy dispensers. Options include the Exocet, Harpoon, Sea Eagle and Marte Mk 2 missiles.

The initial RN requirement for 50 Merlins to operate from Type 23-frigates, 'Invincible'-class aircraft-carriers, RFAs and other ships or land bases has been reduced to 44 for delivery starting in 1996 costing £1.5 billion. These are to be powered by the 2,312-shp (1724-kW) Rolls-Royce Turboméca RTM 322 turboshafts, whereas the Italian navy, which is expected to acquire up to 24 EH.101s (16 orders with eight on option), has specified 1,714-shp (1278-kW) General Electric T700-GE-T6A engines, assembled in Italy. Earlier variants of the GE engine, (the commercial CT7), were used to power the prototypes, the first of which (PP1, ZF641: a non-specific, basic test vehicle) flew at Yeovil on 9 October 1987. A similar Agusta-built basic model (PP2), flew in Italy on 26 November 1987. Next to fly in Italy, on 26 April 1989, was a prototype of the Italian ASW version (PP6), followed in the UK by a basic ASW version (PP4, ZF644) on 15 June and the Merlin prototype (PP5, ZF649) on 24 October in the same year. PP3 and PP8 were both finished to civilian Heliliner standard.

The Italian PP2 was lost in an accident on 21 January 1993, resulting in a suspension of all flight testing until 24 June that year. The RTM 322 engines were first flown (in PP4) in July 1993, and subsequently fitted to PP5.

A prototype with the ramp (Agusta-built PP7) flew on 18 December 1989, representing the military utility variant, which is expected to be ordered by the RAF as its

next medium-lift helicopter. The first customer for the utility variant was to have been Canada, which ordered 15 EH.101s, for SAR duties. Replacing 13 existing CH-113A Labradors (Boeing-Vertol CH-46s), these aircraft were to have been designated **CH-149 Chimo**. Canada also ordered 35 naval versions to meet its New Shipborne Aircraft requirement for a Sea King Replacement, designated **CH-148 Petrel**. Assembled and fitted out by IMP Group Ltd in Canada, these EH.101s were to be powered by 1,920-shp (1432-kW) CT7-6A1 turboshafts. The deal was a hard-fought one, subject to constant scrutiny and not unimportant to the success of the EH.101. Deliveries were scheduled to begin in late 1997 (CH-148)/early 1998 (CH-149). However, an increasingly bitter argument over the costs versus acquisition of less complex aircraft saw the EH.101 become a campaign issue in the Canadian elections of 1993. The pro-EH.101 Conservative government was ousted by Jean Chrétien's Liberal party who, true to their pledge, cancelled the entire programme. This will allegedly cost Canada more in punitive cancellation costs then if the buy had gone ahead, to say nothing for the jobs and industrial offsets lost.

Right: **HMS Iron Duke**, *a Type 23 frigate, is typical of the vessels from which the RN's Merlins will operate.*

Below: The military utility EH.101 is designed to lift six tons or 30 equipped troops. This is PP9, the final, Italian-built (civil) utility version.

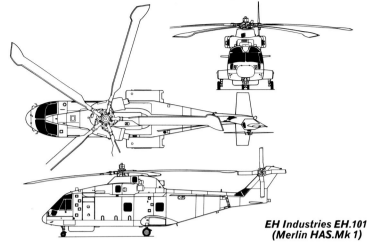

EH Industries EH.101 (Merlin HAS.Mk 1)

SPECIFICATION

European Helicopter Industries EH.101 Merlin (naval model)

Rotor system: main rotor diameter 61 ft 0 in (18.59 m); tail rotor diameter 13 ft 2 in (4.01 m); main rotor disc area 2,922.60 sq ft (271.51 m²); tail rotor disc area 136.17 sq ft (12.65 m²)

Fuselage and tail: length overall, rotors turning 74 ft 10 in (22.81 m) and fuselage 74 ft 9.6 in (22.80 m); length with main rotor blades and tail pylon folded 52 ft 6 in (16.00 m); height overall 21 ft 10 in (6.65 m) with rotors turning and with main rotor blades and tail pylon folded 17 ft 1 in (5.21 m)

Powerplant: (British helicopters) three Rolls-Royce/Turboméca RTM322-01 each rated at 2,312 shp (1724 kW) and 2,100 shp (1566 kW) for maximum and intermediate contingencies respectively, or (Italian helicopters) three General Electric T700-GE-T6A each rated at 1,714 shp (1279 kW), 1,682 shp (1254 kW) and 1,437 shp (1071 kW) for maximum contingency, intermediate contingency and continuous running respectively

Weights: (estimated) basic empty 15,700 lb (7121 kg); operating empty 20,500 lb (9298 kg); maximum take-off 29,830 lb (13530 kg)

Fuel and load: internal fuel 7,580 lb (3438 kg) plus provision for 1,896 lb (860 kg) of auxiliary fuel; external fuel none; maximum ordnance 2,116 lb (960 kg)

Speed: never-exceed speed 167 kt (192 mph; 309 km/h); average cruising speed 160 kt (184 mph; 296 km/h); economical cruising speed 140 kt (161 mph; 259 km/h)

Range: ferry range 1,000 nm (1,152 miles; 1853 km) with auxiliary fuel; endurance 5 hours on station with maximum weapon load

EMBRAER (Neiva) **T-25 Universal**

Empresa Brasileira de Aeronáutica SA
Caixa Postal 343
12227-901 São José dos Campos, SP, Brazil

The **T-25 Universal** was developed by the Neiva company (acquired by EMBRAER in 1980) to meet a **Brazilian air force** requirement for a basic trainer to replace the T-6 Texan and S-11/S-12 Instructor. The specification called for side-by-side

seating with provision for a third occupant behind the two pilots. Prototype testing began on 29 April 1966 and production deliveries started in the late summer of 1971, against Brazilian air force requirements that eventually totalled 140. About

100 remain in service, for primary and specialised training roles and for general duties. Brazilian student pilots in their second and third years at the Air Force Academy fly 25 and 50 hours respectively on the T-25 before moving on to the Tucano. The sole

export order was for 10 aircraft from the **Chilean army**, five of which were transferred to the air force in 1979. These were subsequently phased out of service in 1983 when five were transferred to the **Fuerza Aérea Paraguaya**, where they still serve.

EMBRAER EMB-110/111 Bandeirante

The aircraft which launched EMBRAER as a force among aerospace manufacturers was first flown on 19 August 1972, in response to a light transport requirement by the **Brazilian air force** and the country's airlines. A nine-seat predecessor powered by the same Pratt & Whitney Canada PT6A engines had been tested in prototype form (as the **YC-95** or **EMB-100**), but the **EMBRAER EMB-110 Bandeirante** (Pioneer) featured a much larger cabin which found favour with civil operators overseas, as well as with the Brazilian military.

The first three of 80 Bandeirantes ordered by the **Brazilian air force** were delivered in February 1973. The type is now the mainstay of the transport force, serving in one squadron of the Rio-based 2° Grupo, seven others allocated to the regional air commands, and also in a transport conversion unit. The 60 **C-95** models were 12-seat versions, and were supplemented by 20 **C-95A** (**EMB-110K1**) freighters with a 0.85-m (2 ft 9½ in) stretch ahead of the wing, uprated PT6A-34 turboprops (replacing -27s) and a 1.80 x 1.42 m (71 x 56 in) freight door. This door incorporates a 1.30 x 0.80-m (51 x35-in) opening to facilitate air dropping or for use as an emergency exit.These were followed by 31 examples of the **C-95B**, a military version of the improved **EMB-110P** civil model, two of which were also bought by **Gabon**.

None of the Brazilian air force Bandeirante units is exclusively equipped with the C-95. In 2o Grupo de Transporte at Galeao they are augmented by a handful of older, larger BAe 748s, while the regional air command units operate their Bandeirantes alongside Piper Senecas. The regional units are 1 ETA at Belem, 2 ETA at Recife, 3 ETA at Galeao, 4 ETA at Cumbica, 5 ETA at Brasilia and 6 ETA at Porto Alegre. The **Uruguayan air force** took delivery of five 15-seat **EMB-110C**s in 1975, and the **Chilean navy** bought three navalised **EMB-110CN**s in the following year.

Four specialised versions have also entered Brazilian military service. The first of these to join the Brazilian air force was the eight-seat **EC-95** for checking and calibration of navigation aids. Four of these (designated **EMB-110A** by the manufacturer) are in service. These aircraft serve with the Grupo Especial de Inspeção e Vigilancia (GEIV – Special Inspection and Checking Group) at Rio de Janeiro, alongside a

handful of ageing EC-47 Dakotas.

The EC-95 was followed by six seven-seat **R-95** (**EMB-110B**) photographic survey versions. These have apertures in the cabin floor to accommodate a Zeiss camera and associated equipment. Doppler and inertial navigation systems are also fitted. The R-95s serve with 6° Grupo of the Coastal Command (COMCAS) at Recife and supplement three RC-130E Hercules. One example of the EMB-110B has been acquired by Uruguay. Two previously undelivered EMB-110P1A civilian transports were bought by the **Colombian air force** along with three for the **Peruvian government** the following year

COMCAS also operates the **P-95** maritime surveillance version which the company designates **EMB-111A**. Twenty-one of these joined the two squadrons of 7° Grupo, which had been inactive since its last Lockheed P-2 Neptunes were retired in 1976. An Eaton-AIL AN/APS-128 Sea Patrol search radar is housed in a large nose radome, and is fully integrated with the aircraft's inertial navigation system. A high-power searchlight, signal cartridge launcher and an ESM system are also carried, and rockets can be launched from four underwing pylons. Wingtip fuel tanks increase the aircraft's endurance to nine hours.

Brazilian P-95s are locally known as the **'Bandeirulha'**, a contraction of 'Bandeirante Patrulha'. Brazil later bought a second batch of improved **P-95B** aircraft with upgraded avionics and strengthened airframes. All P-95s have been brought up to this standard. 1 Esquadrao of 7° Grupo de Aviacao is based at Salvador, while 2 Esquadrao flies from Florianopolis. Six **EMB-111AN** aircraft were delivered to the Chilean navy, and a single example to the **Gabonese air force**.The Chilean navy EMB-111ANs were delivered in lieu of four surplus SP-2E Neptunes embargoed by the US government, and are used by VP-3 in the maritime patrol role. The two EMB-111As are also operated by the air forces of **Angola**.

A SAR version is designated **SC-95B**, or **EMB-110P1(K)**. Deliveries began in late

The armed maritime reconnaissance P-95 Bandeirante (EMB-111) has been bought in two batches by the Brazilian navy; 12 P-95s and 10 improved P-95Bs.

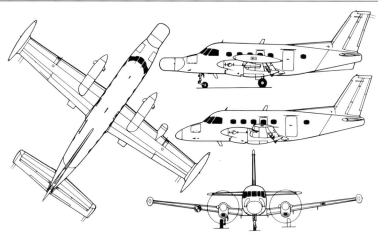

EMBRAER EMB-111A Bandeirante/P-95 (EMB-110/C-95 side view)

1981 of eight to 10° Grupo of COMCAS at Campo Grande. Six stretchers can be accommodated alongside observation and rescue personnel. Two 'bubble' windows are fitted on each side of the fuselage. One was also delivered to **Senegambia**.

SPECIFICATION

EMBRAER EMB-111 (P-95A)
Wing: span 15.95 m (52 ft 4 in) with tip tanks; aspect ratio 8.07; area 29.10 m² (313.23 sq ft)
Fuselage and tail: length 14.91 m (48 ft 11 in); height 4.91 m (16 ft 1.25 in); tailplane span 7.54 m (24 ft 9 in); wheel track 4.94 m (16 ft 2.5 in); wheel base 4.26 m (13 ft 11.75 in)

Powerplant: two Pratt & Whitney Canada PT6A-34 each rated at 750 shp (559 kW)
Weights: empty equipped 3760 kg (8,289 lb); maximum take-off 7000 kg (15,432 lb)
Fuel and load: internal fuel 2550 litres (674 US gal)
Speed: maximum cruising speed at 10,000 ft (3050 m) 194 kt (223 mph; 360 km/h); economical cruising speed at 1,000 ft (3050 m) 187 kt (2154 mph; 347 km/h)
Range: 1,590 nm (1,830 miles; 2945 km)
Performance: maximum rate of climb at sea level 1,190 ft (362 m) per minute; service ceiling 25,500 ft (7770 m); take-off run 2,135 ft (650 m) at maximum take-off weight; take-off distance to 50 ft (15 m) 3,445 ft (1050 m) at maximum take-off weight; landing distance from 50 ft (15 m) 2,100 ft (640 m) at normal landing weight; landing run 1,475 ft (450 m) at normal landing weight

EMBRAER EMB-120 Brasilia

From the success of the Bandeirante, which established EMBRAER as a major force in the commuter airliner market, the Brazilian firm decided to step up to a much improved, stretched development. From its inception in 1979, the EMB-120 Brasilia progressed towards its maiden flight on 27 July 1983, becoming one of the first of the 1980s 'new generation' of commuter aircraft. The Brasilia was designed for two-crew operations with a load of 30 passengers, and utilised a semi-monocoque fuselage with a low wing and cantilever T-tail. It was certified by the Brazilian CTA in May 1985, powered by a pair of 1,590-shp (1185-kW) Pratt & Whitney Canada PW115 turboprops. The first civilian delivery was made to Atlantic Southeast Airways in the United States on June 1985 and since then over 330 Brasilias have been ordered. The type achieved its 2,000,000th flying hour in January 1993, having carried over 41,000,000 passengers by that time.

The **Brazilian air force** has so far been the only military customer for the EMB-120. Five VIP transport versions designated **VC-97** were delivered between 1987 and 1988, but one was written off in a training acci-

EMBRAER's EMB-120 Brasilia has thus far failed to emulate the military sales of the EMB-110/111 Bandeirante family. The sole customer has been the home air force, taking delivery of five aircraft.

dent in July 1988. The remaining aircraft are operated by 6° ETA of the Comando Aéreo Regional based at the capital, Brasilia. The VC-97 is equivalent to the **EMB-120RT** (Reduced Take-off), the standard production version introduced from the fourth aircraft. This saw a change in powerplant from the original PW115 to the 1,800-shp (1,342-kW) PW118 turboprop, driving four-bladed Hamilton Standard propellers. A hot-and-high version, powered by PW118As, is also available. The next version was the extended-range **EMB-120ER** which offers an increased maximum take-off weight. This entails no major structural changes and so earlier aircraft can be easily brought up to this standard. The longer-legged EMB-120ER formed the baseline for the next version to be offered, the 1992 **EMB-120X** (provisional) **Improved Brasilia**, launched in 1994 as the **EMB-120ER Advanced**,

this aircraft incorporates many detail and style changes along with new avionics and an improved cabin. The EMB-120ER benefits from the work EMBRAER has completed on its new advanced turboprop, the CBA-123, and is available for delivery from August 1994.

Of more interest to military customers are the **EMB-120 Cargo**, an all-cargo version stressed for loads of up to 4,000 kg (8,818 lb), the **EMB-120 Combi**, capable of carrying 19 passengers and 1100-kg (2,425-lb) of freight, and the **EMB-120QC** (Quick Change) which can be transformed from its standard 30-seat layout to a 3500-kg (7,716-lb) capacity freighter in 50 minutes. First commercial deliveries of the EMB-120QC were made in May 1993.

EMBRAER EMB-121 Xingu

Between 1976 and 1987 EMBRAER built 105 examples of the **EMB-121 Xingu**, half of this total being delivered for military use in **Brazil** and **France**. Conceived as a corporate transport derived from the **EMB-120 Bandeirante** commuter, the Xingu offered comfortable seating for six passengers in a pressurised fuselage, combined with a T-tail and a wing/powerplant installation based on that of the Bandeirante. Powered by two PT6A-28 turboprops and with a gross weight of 5200 kg (11,466 lb), the Xingu prototype entered flight test on 10 October 1976, followed by a pre-production aircraft on 20 May 1977 with increased gross weight of 5670 kg (12,500 lb). The last Xingu was delivered on 19 August 1987.

The first six production **Xingu I**s were delivered to the Forca Aérea Brasileira as **VU-9**s to be operated as VIP transports by the 6° Esquadrão de Transporte Aérea; six more were acquired later, as well as two ex-civil examples, with the new designation **EC-9**.

In September 1980 the French defence ministry selected the Xingu to serve in both the Armée de l'Air and Aéronavale as a multi-engine trainer and fast communications aircraft. An order was placed for 41 Xingus: 25 **EMB-121AA** for the Armée de l'Air and 16 **EMB-121AN** for the Aéronavale. Deliveries began in March 1982 and were completed by the end of 1983. In the Armée de l'Air, the Xingu serves primarily with GE 319 at Avord in the training role, with a few detached to the communications squadrons. Naval use is centred on 52S, the training squadron at Lahn-Bihoué, with several Xingus attached to 10S.

SPECIFICATION

EMBRAER EMB-121 Xingu
Wing: span 14.45 m (47 ft 5 in); aspect ratio 7.18; area 27.50 m² (296.00 sq ft)
Fuselage and tail: length 12.25 m (40 ft 2.25 in); height 4.74 m (15 ft 6.5 in); tailplane span 5.58 m (18 ft 3.75 in); wheel track 5.24 m (17 ft 2.25 in); wheel base 2.88 m (9 ft 5.5 in)
Powerplant: two Pratt & Whitney Canada PT6A-28 each rated at 680 shp (507 kW)
Weights: empty equipped 3620 kg (7,984 lb); maximum take-off 5670 kg (12,500 lb)
Fuel and load: internal fuel 1666 litres (440 US gal); external fuel none; maximum payload 860 kg (1,896 lb)
Speed: maximum cruising speed at 11,000 ft (3355 m) 243 kt (280 mph; 450 km/h); economical cruising speed at 20,000 ft (6095 m) 197 kt (227 mph; 365 km/h)
Range: 1,270 nm (1,462 miles; 2353 km) with maximum fuel and a 610-kg (1,345-lb) payload, or 1,225 nm (1,411 miles; 2270 km) with a 780-kg (1,720-lb) payload
Performance: maximum rate of climb at sea level 1,400 ft (426 m) per minute; service ceiling 26,000 ft

(7925 m); take-off distance to 50 ft (15 m) 2,840 ft (866 m) at maximum take-off weight; landing distance

from 50 ft (15 m) 2,790 ft (850 m) at maximum landing weight

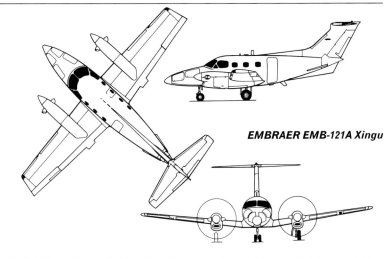

EMBRAER EMB-121A Xingu

The chief operators of the EMB-121 are the Armée de l'Air (left) and the Aéronavale (right), which between them accounted for a substantial part of the Xingu's production run. They are used on navigation training exercises and liaison flights.

EMBRAER EMB-312/312H Tucano

Development of the turboprop, high-performance **EMBRAER EMB-312 Tucano** (Toucan) trainer started in 1978 in response to a **Brazilian air force** specification for a Cessna T-37 replacement. First flown on 16 August 1980, the initial **T-27 Tucano** was delivered to the Air Force Academy near São Paulo in September 1983. Most of the 133 aircraft ordered by the FAB (including 10 in 1990 and five in 1993) are operated by

this unit, although some will also serve in a conversion unit. An option for 40 more T-27s is held. The Brazilian air force formation aerobatic team, the 'Escuadron de Fumaca' ('Smoke Squadron'), received T-27 Tucanos to replace its ageing North American Harvards, and has displayed extensively throughout the American continent.

Designed from the outset to provide a 'jet-like' flying experience, the Tucano has a

single power lever governing both propeller pitch and engine rpm, ejector seats, and a staggered tandem-place cockpit. Four underwing hardpoints can carry up to 1000 kg (2,205 lb) of ordnance for weapons training.

An export order for 134 Tucanos was concluded with **Egypt** in September 1983. All except the first 10 of these were licence-assembled at Helwan. The Egyptian air force operates only 54 locally-assembled Tucanos, about 80 aircraft having been supplied to the **Iraqi** air force. These were followed by deliveries (including current firm orders) to the air forces of **Argentina** (30) **Honduras** (12), **Iran** (25), **Paraguay** (five), **Peru** (30) and **Venezuela** (31). Another major order came into effect in October 1991 (though it was placed in July 1990) when **France** announced its intention to purchase 80 EMBRAER-built **EMB-312F** aircraft for delivery from July 1993. This French version boasts an increased fatigue life, ventral airbrake and French avionics. The first two aircraft had

been delivered to the CEV test establishment at Mont-de-Marsan by July 1993. Twenty will be delivered between July 1994 and July 1995, the second batch of 28 between July 1995 and July 1996, and the final 30 in two even batches finishing in May 1998. A further South American customer was the **Colombian** air force, which had received 14 by the end of 1992.

The Tucano's most notable export success came in March 1985, when it won a hotly-contested British order for 131 aircraft to replace the **RAF**'s BAe (Hunting) Jet Provosts. In order to secure the contract, the aircraft's engine was replaced with the considerably more powerful 820-kW (1,100-shp) Garrett TPE331-12B turboprop, and extensive redesign and replacement of systems was undertaken to meet more rigorous RAF criteria, on life span and bird-strike resistance. The Tucano is produced under licence by Shorts in Belfast, which is manufacturing 130 for the RAF and additionally produced aircraft to the same standard for the air forces of **Kenya** (12) and **Kuwait** (16). Total firm orders, including Shorts-built versions, stood at 654 aircraft by early 1994, of which almost 600 exam-

Above: This FAB T-27 wears the badge of 2ª ELO (liaison and observation squadron), Coastal Command, a former T-25 operator.

Below: FAB T-27s are now adopting this two-tone grey scheme, in addition to base codes. Here, 'PV' stands for Porto Velho.

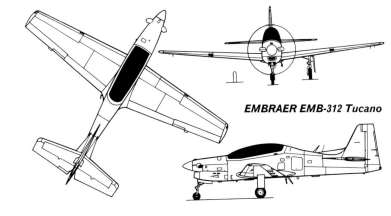

EMBRAER EMB-312 Tucano

ples had been delivered. The Shorts-built **S312** (referred to by the RAF as the **Tucano T.Mk 1**) is described in more detail in a separate entry.

In June 1991, EMBRAER announced the **EMB-312H Super Tucano**, featuring an uprated P&WC PT6A-68/1 engine. Fuselage plugs fore and aft totalling 1.37 m (4 ft 6 in) have been inserted to accommodate the 1193-kW (1,600-shp) turboprop and to maintain stability and CoG. This version is offered in the USAF/USN JPATS competition, in association with Northrop. A converted Tucano (PP-ZTW) toured bases in the US during August 1992, before the first production standard aircraft (PP-ZTV) flew on 15 May 1993. During 1994 it is expected that the Brazilian government will order 50 new, armed aircraft under the designation **EMBRAER ALX** (essentially single-seat Super Tucanos). These will be operated by the air force, but purchased by the planning ministry as part of its anti-narcotics and smuggling operations. By 1996 up to 120 ALXs may be obtained, though this total may comprise a number of standard two-seat Tucanos as well.

This Tucano is an EMBRAER-owned development ship which served as a Garrett-powered testbed for the RAF's Tucano development, before being converted to EMB-321H standard by September 1991. The Super Tucano has been further developed, becoming the armed, single-seat ALX.

SPECIFICATION

EMBRAER EMB-312 Tucano
Wing: span 11.14 m (36 ft 6.5 in); aspect ratio 6.4; area 19.40 m² (208.82 sq ft)
Fuselage and tail: length 9.86 m (32 ft 4.25 in); height 3.40 m (11 ft 1.75 in); tailplane span 4.66 m (15 ft 3.5 in); wheel track 3.76 m (12 ft 4 in); wheel base 3.16 m (10 ft 4.5 in)
Powerplant: one Pratt & Whitney Canada PT6A-25C rated at 750 shp (559 kW)
Weights: basic empty 1810 kg (3,991 lb); normal take-off 2550 kg (5,622 lb); maximum take-off 3175 kg (7,000 lb)
Fuel and load: internal fuel 529 kg (1,166 lb); external fuel up to two 330 litre (81.2-US gal) ferry tanks; maximum ordnance 1000 kg (2,205 lb)

Speed: never-exceed speed 280 kt (322 mph; 519 km/h); maximum level speed 'clean' at 10,000 ft (3050 m) 242 kt (278 mph; 448 km/h); maximum cruising speed at 10,000 ft (3050 m) 222 kt (255 mph; 411 km/h); economical cruising speed at 10,000 ft (3050 m) 172 kt (198 mph; 319 km/h)
Range: ferry range 1,797 nm (2,069 miles; 3330 km) with two ferry tanks; typical range 995 nm (1,145 miles; 1844 km) with internal fuel; endurance about 5 hours 0 minutes with internal fuel

Performance: maximum rate of climb at sea level 680 m (2,231 ft) per minute; service ceiling 30,000 ft (9145 m); take-off run 1,250 ft (381 m) at normal take-off weight; take-off distance to 50 ft (15 m) 2,330 ft (710 m) at normal take-off weight; landing distance from 50 ft (15 m) 1,985 ft (605 m) at normal landing weight; landing run 1,215 ft (370 m) at normal landing weight
g limits: -3 to + 6 at normal take-off weight or -2.2 to +4.4 at maximum take-off weight

EMBRAER **EMB-326 Xavante**

Under licence from Aermacchi, EMBRAER assembled 166 **MB-326GB** basic jet trainer/ground attack aircraft for the **Força Aérea Brasiliera**, operated under the local designation **T-26**. Armed aircraft are designated **AT-26,** all carry the name **Xavante**, a Brazilian Indian tribe.

About 100 Xavantes have remained in Brazilian service, shared between the light attack and training roles. Operating in the former capacity are 1ª Esq in the 4° Grupo de Aviacao de Caca at Fortaleza and 1° Esq and 3° Esq in 10° GAvCa at St Maria. Among the aircraft at the latter base are a number equipped with cameras and flight-refuelling probes, with the designation **RT-26** to indicate the reconnaissance role. Before

joining the AT-26 squadrons, pilots convert on the same type at the training centre at Natal.

Additional aircraft were assembled for export to **Paraguay** (10) and **Togo** (six). Brazil has transferred 11 of its AT-26s to **Argentina**, where Italian-built MB 326s were already in service. The Brazilian-assembled **EMB-326GB**s also remain in service in the light attack/weapons training roles.

SPECIFICATION

EMBRAER EMB-326 Xavante
generally similar to the Aermacchi M.B.326

Deliveries of 166 EMB-326GB Xavantes to the Força Aérea Brasiliera took place between 1971 and 1981. The Xavante has six underwing hardpoints, and for reconnaissance duties the inner station on the port wing can be fitted with a pod housing four 70-mm Vinten cameras.

ENAER **T-35 Pillán**

Empresa Nacional de Aeronáutica de Chile
Avienda José Miguel Carrera 11087
P.36 ½, Santiago, Chile

Beginning in 1980, ENAER assembled 27 Piper PA-28 Dakotas for flying clubs and the **Chilean air force**, the latter sought a similar two-seat fully-aerobatic trainer. Piper responded by developing the PA-28R-300, based on the Saratoga with a new centre-section, an aerobatic wing, and a 300-hp (224-kW) Lycoming engine. Two Piper-built prototypes first flew on 6 March and 31 August 1981, followed by three assembled by ENAER.

Known in Chile as the **T-35 Pillán** (Devil), the aircraft entered production for the Chilean air force as a basic, intermediate and instrument flying trainer. Deliveries began to the Air Academy in August 1985, comprising a total of 60 **T-35A** primary and 20 **T-35B** instrument trainers, both types

serving in the Escuela de Aviación 'Capitan Avalos' at El Bosque, Santiago. A few also serve at Los Cerillos, where Grupo 11 provides support for II Brigada, Ala 2.

ENAER has also produced 41 **T-35C** Pilláns for **Spain**, assembled by CASA, to serve with the air force as the **E.26 Tamiz**. These are used for primary training at the General Air Academy, San Javier; several are also operated by Ala 54 in Mando de Materiel (Personnel Command). The **T-35D** instrument trainer has been procured by the **Panamanian** national air service (10 delivered in 1988-89) and **Paraguay** (15). On 5 March 1988, ENAER flew the prototype **T-35S**, powered by an Allison 250-B17 turboprop for use as an aerobatic trainer and display aircraft.

SPECIFICATION

ENAER T-35A Pillán
Wing: span 29 ft 0 in (8.84 m); aspect ratio 5.7; area 147.34 sq ft (13.69 m²)
Fuselage and tail: length 26 ft 3 in (8.00 m); height 8 ft 8 in (2.64 m); tailplane span 10 ft 0 in (3.05 m); wheel track 9 ft 11 in (3.02 m);
Powerplant: one Textron Lycoming IO-540-K1K5 rated at 300 hp (224 kW)
Weights: empty equipped 2,050 lb (930 kg); normal take-off 2,900 lb (1315 kg) for aerobatics; maximum take-off 2,950 lb (1338 kg)
Fuel and load: internal fuel 462 lb (210 kg); external

fuel none; maximum ordnance 1,100 lb (499 kg)
Speed: never-exceed speed 241 kt (277 mph; 446 km/h); maximum level speed 'clean' at sea level 168 kt (193 mph; 311 km/h); maximum cruising speed at 8,800 ft (2680 m) 144 kt (166 mph; 266 km/h
Range: 650 nm (748 miles; 1204 km) at 55 per cent power or 590 nm (679 miles; 1093 km) at 75 per cent power; endurance 5 hours 36 minutes at 55 per cent power or 4 hours 24 minutes at 75 per cent power
Performance: maximum rate of climb at sea level 1,525 ft (465 m) per minute; climb to 10,000 ft (3050 m) in 8 minutes 48 seconds; service ceiling 19,160 ft (5840 m); take-off run 940 ft (287 m) at maximum take-off weight; take-off distance to 50 ft (15 m) 1,620 ft (494 m) at maximum take-off weight

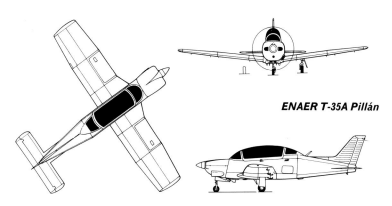

The Pillán is now the Fuerza Aérea de Chile's primary trainer, serving in both T-35A form and the IFR-equipped T-35B. In Spanish hands, as the Tamiz (T-35C), it is also an integral part of the training syllabus.

ENAER T-35A Pillán

ENAER T-35DT Aucán (Turbo Pillán)

Design studies for a **Turbo Pillán** began in 1985, and in 1986 ENAER fitted a Pillán (CC-PZH) with a 420-shp (313-kW) Allison 250-B17D turboprop to produce the **T-35TX Aucán** (Blithe Spirit). After its maiden flight in February of that year, and the first public showing at FIDAE, the Aucán chalked up some 500 flying hours until 1987, when it was returned to ENAER for further modification. It subsequently took to the air, in a revised form, having been modified with a sideways-opening, one-piece canopy. In 1990 ENAER awarded the US Soloy Corporation, of Olympia, Washington, a contract to further develop the Allison 250 installation and produce a modification kit for existing piston-engined T-35 Pilláns. Soloy has forged the market in such piston-to-turbine conversions, having started out

by modifying helicopters such as the Bell Model 47 and Hiller H-12. The first Pillán to receive the Soloy treatment (CC-PZG) flew in March 1991 and ENAER are marketing this version as the **T-35DT Turbo Pillán**.

SPECIFICATION

ENAER T-35DT Turbo Pillán
generally similar to the ENAER T-35A Pillán except in the following particulars:
Fuselage and tail: length 28 ft 2.5 in (8.60 m); wheel base 6 ft 6.75 in (2.00 m)
Powerplant: one Allison 250-B17D rated at 420 shp (313 kW)
Weights: empty equipped 2,080 lb (943 kg)
Fuel and load: internal fuel 73.4 US gal (277.8 litres)
Speed: maximum level speed 'clean' at sea level 176 kt

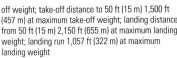

Bearing the legend 'Allison Turbine Power' on the nose, this is the original Allison 250-powered ENAER T-35TX, Aucán, first flown in February 1986. ENAER have now moved on to the T-35DT.

(203 mph; 326 km/h); maximum cruising speed at 7,600 ft (2315 m) 182 kt (209 mph; 337 km/h)
Range: 300 nm (345 miles; 556 km)
Performance: maximum rate of climb at sea level 1,750 ft (533 m) per minute; service ceiling 24,300 ft (7405 m); take-off run 880 ft (268 m) at maximum take-

off weight; take-off distance to 50 ft (15 m) 1,500 ft (457 m) at maximum take-off weight; landing distance from 50 ft (15 m) 2,150 ft (655 m) at maximum landing weight; landing run 1,057 ft (322 m) at maximum landing weight

---

Enstrom F-28/Model 280/480 (TH-28)

*The Enstrom Helicopter Corp.
PO Box 490, 2209 North 22nd St, Twin County Airport
Menominee, San Antonio, TX 78217, USA*

The first **Enstrom F-28** light helicopter flew in May 1962, and some 900 examples have been built in successive models. The **F-28F Falcon** is the current basic utility model, certificated in 1981 and fitted with a 225-hp (168-kW) Textron Lycoming HIO-360-FIAD flat-four engine with turbo-supercharger.

Similarly powered, the **Model 280FX** appeared in 1985 featuring a number of refinements such as a redesigned air inlet system, fully-faired skid landing gear, covered tail rotor shaft, tail rotor guard and a new tailplane with endplate fins. Both versions are fitted with a three-bladed main rotor.

The first military sale was not made until 1989 when 15 of the three-seat **Model 280FX** helicopters were supplied to the **Chilean** army for primary training. Subsequently, the **Peruvian** army acquired 10 **F-28Fs**. In 1994 **Columbia** will receive 12 F-28Fs under the FMS programme.

Below: The Chilean army operates 15 Enstrom 280FXs as primary trainers. This version differs from the Model 280 by having a faired-over rear-rotor drive shaft, and other aerodynamic refinements.

The Model 280FX served as the basis for Enstrom's four-seat **Model 480**, which became its entrant for the US Army's NTH (New Training Helicopter) competition, as the **TH-28**. After a modified Allison 250-powered 280FX was flown in December 1988, the first true 'wide-body' (three-seats) Model 480 took to the air in October 1989. The TH-28 was certified in September 1992 and four aircraft embarked on a 1,500-hour test programme. Intended as a basic trainer and light patrol helicopter, the TH-28 featured military spec systems such as crash-worthy fuel tanks and crew seating, and the cockpit could be configured for VFR or IFR operations. In the event, the TH-28 lost out to the the Bell TH-67 in the NTH competition.

SPECIFICATION

Enstrom Model F-28F Falcon
Rotor system: main rotor diameter 32 ft 0 in (9.75 m); tail rotor diameter 4 ft 8 in (1.42 m); main rotor disc area 804.25 sq ft (74.71 m2); tail rotor disc area 17.10 sq ft (1.59 m2)
Fuselage and tail: length overall, rotors stationary 29 ft 3 in (8.92 m); height overall 9 ft 2 in (2.79 m) to

top of rotor head; skid track 7 ft 3 in (2.21 m)
Powerplant: one Textron Lycoming HIO-360-F1AD rated at 225 hp (168 kW)
Weights: empty equipped 1,570 lb (712 kg); maximum take-off 2,600 lb (1179 kg)
Fuel and load: internal fuel 42 US gal (159 litres) plus provision for 13 US gal (49 litres) of auxiliary fuel in a baggage compartment tank; external fuel none
Speed: never-exceed speed, maximum level speed 'clean' between sea level and 3,000 ft (915 m) and

maximum cruising speed 97 kt (112 mph; 180 km/h); economical cruising speed at optimum altitude 89 kt (102 mph; 165 km/h)
Range: 228 nm (263 miles; 423 km); endurance 3 hours 30 minutes
Performance: maximum rate of climb at sea level 1,450 ft (442 m) per minute; certificated operating ceiling 12,000 ft (3660 m); hovering ceiling 7,700 ft (2345 m) in ground effect at 2,600 lb (1179 kg) and 8,700 ft (2650 m) out of ground effect at 2,050 lb

Above: Peru purchased 10 Enstrom F28Fs, the baseline Enstrom helicopter, to replace the Bell 47 as the Army's basic trainer.

Below: The latest development of the F-28 for the military market is the four-seat TH-28 (480). This is the essentially civilian-spec prototype.

Eurocopter (Aérospatiale) SA 330 Puma

*Eurocopter France
PO Box 13
F-13725 Marignane, France*

Standard transport helicopter of the French army, to whose specification it was designed, the Puma is in service with many air arms around the globe. The Puma represents the first successful venture in medium helicopter design by France, the earlier products of Sud Aviation – Sikorsky S-58 and SA 321 Super Frelon – relying wholly or partly on US technology. The official requirement called for day or night operation in all weathers and all climates,

although power reserves and a radar installation to meet those demands were not available until the design had been developed over several years. Royal Air Force needs for a Whirlwind and Belvedere replacement resulted in the Puma being included in the 1967 Anglo-French helicopter agreement. As a result, Westland built 292 Gazelles and 48 Pumas, in return for which France bought the grand total of 40 Westland Lynxes.

Eight prototypes of the **SA 330** were ordered in June 1963, the first taking to the air at Marignane on 15 April 1965 and the last going to the UK for evaluation. On 25 November 1970, just over two years after that delivery, the first of an initial batch of 40 **Puma HC.Mk 1s** for the RAF flew at Yeovil. Two Turboméca Turmo turboshafts of 984 kW (1,320 shp) each gave a maximum take-off weight of 6400 kg (14,109 lb) and limiting speed of 151 kt (280 km/h; 174

mph) to the initial production versions. These were **SA 330B** for ALAT (Aviation Légère de l'Armée de Terre), **SA 330C** for military export, **SA 330E** as the RAF's Puma HC.Mk 1, and the civilian **SA 330F**. In 1974, availability of the 1174-kW (1,575-shp) Turmo IVC powerplant better equipped the Puma for hot-and-high operations, increasing its take-off weight to 7400 kg (16,314 lb) and maximum speed to 158 kt (294 km/h; 182 mph). Production in this guise con-

The Puma HC.Mk 1s of No. 1563 Flight are the last RAF aircraft left in Belize, following the departure of the Harriers of No. 1417 Flight. They are based at Belize Intl.

For their deployment to Kuwait and Iraq during the Gulf War, French army Pumas adopted identification stripes, along with a desert paint scheme.

cerned the civilian **SA 330G** and military **SA 330H**, although the French air force, which bought 37, used the misleading designation **SA 330Ba**.

Glass-fibre rotors became available in 1977, uprating the G and H to **SA 330J** and **SA 330L** respectively. The new blades were retrofitted to some early aircraft, including those of the RAF and 40 per cent of ALAT's 132 SA 330Bs. In addition, the French army bought 15 SA 330Ba versions and a few replacements from the Romanian line after Aérospatiale ended production with the 686th Puma. ICA (now IAR) at Brasov, Romania, obtained a licence for the SA 330L in 1977 and had built about 200 by mid-1994, (this version is described separately). While Pumas normally carry 15 fully-equipped troops or 2 tonnes of internal cargo (2.5 tonnes underslung), the Romanian variant has a powerful armament option, typically comprising four underslung rocket pods and four AT-3 'Sagger' ATMs above the outrigger pylons, plus two machine-gun pods scabbed to the forward fuselage. British Army and ALAT Pumas can carry a pintle-mounted machine-gun in the cabin door, some of the latter's machines additionally receiving a prominent nose-mounted OMERA ORB 37 radar. Five of Portugal's 10 Pumas have ORB 31 radar and flotation gear for their SAR task and all were converted locally by OGMA during the late 1980s to **SA 330S** standard with SA 330L systems and rotors, plus Makila powerplants as in the Super Puma. In Indonesia, PTN assembled 11 SA 330Js (**NSA-330**) from French kits, the last in 1983.

Some Portuguese Pumas, such as this SAR aircraft based in the Azores, carry OMERA ORB-31 Hercules radar and flotation gear.

South Africa, isolated by the UN arms embargo, pursued its own line of Puma development which culminated in the Atlas XH-2/CSH-2 Rooivalk attack helicopter. More recognisable as Pumas were the two **Atlas XTP-1** testbeds (described separately) of the SA 330, which undertook development work for the Rooivalk and led to a possible 'gunship Puma' which underwent SAAF evaluation as a potential alternative to the Rooivalk, when the latter was facing cancellation. Using Rooivalk systems and weapons pylons, the gunship Puma (which has been fitted with a variety of weapons options) has carried Atlas Swift laser-guided ATGMs and Atlas Darter or Viper AAMs. South Africa has undertaken its own Makila re-engining programme, turning Pumas into **Gemsboks**, now **Oryx** (described separately), with the additional power necessary to replace Super Frelons.

RAF Pumas are particularly advanced in terms of operational equipment, having acquired 'polyvalent' air intake filters, an ARI.18228 radar warning receiver, cockpit lighting compatible with night vision goggles and, for the 1991 Gulf War, M.130 chaff/flare dispensers and AN/AAR-47 missile approach warning systems. RAF Pumas in Northern Ireland additionally have an AN/ALQ-144 IR jammer to deflect heat-seeking missiles. Some of these RAF Pumas are believed to be equipped with the Ferranti/Barr and Stroud Type 221 thermal imager for surveillance duties, under the codename Pleasant 3.

One ALAT Puma is testbed for the Orchidée/HORIZON surveillance radar (described in the AS 532 entry). Romania is offering a 'glass cockpit' version called **Puma 2000** (described seperately), with a night vision system and pilot's helmet-mounted display.

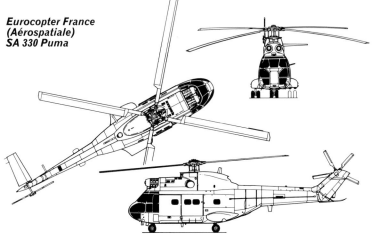

Eurocopter France (Aérospatiale) SA 330 Puma

The French Orchidée battlefield surveillance radar programme was shelved in 1990, to be reactivated in the Gulf war. The success there of the development aircraft lead to a new programme, HORIZON.

Eurocopter (Aérospatiale) *SA 330 Puma*

Royal Air Force Puma HC.Mk 1s (and Wessexes also), such as this No. 230 Sqn aircraft, are adopting a two-tone green wrap-around camouflage scheme in favour of their original green and black finish.

The standard Aviation Légère de l'Armée de Terre (ALAT) camouflage for its SA 330Bs is this smart three-tone green and brown one.

OPERATORS

Abu Dhabi (UAE): SA 330C/F (9)
Argentina: SA 330L (1) – coast guard
Cameroon: SA 330C (2)
Chile: SA 330F/L (15) – army
Ecuador: SA 330L (1) – army
Ethiopia: IAR.330 (1)
France: SA 330B/H (30), SA 330B/H (125) – army
Gabon: SA 330C/H: 2/2
Guinea Republic: IAR.330 (1)
Indonesia: SA 330J/L (14)
Iraq: SA 330 (22)
Ivory Coast: SA 330C (3)
Kuwait: SA 330H (6)
Lebanon: SA 330L (9)
Malawi: SA 330J (1)
Morocco: SA 330C (30)
Nepal: SA 330C/G (1/1)
Nigeria: SA 330L (2)
Pakistan: SA 330J (35) – army
Portugal: SA 330C (10)
Romania: IAR-330 (90)
Senegambia: SA 330F (2)
South Africa: SA 330F/J/L (65), Oryx (25)
Spain: SA 330C/H/J (HT.19) (5)
Togo: SA 330 (1)
United Kingdom: HC.Mk 1 (41)
Zaïre: SA 330C/IAR-330 (9)

SPECIFICATION

Eurocopter France (Aérospatiale) SA 330L Puma
Rotor system: main rotor diameter 15.00 m (49 ft 2.5 in); tail rotor diameter 3.04 m (9 ft 11.5 in); main rotor disc area 176.71 m² (1,902.20 sq ft); tail rotor disc area 7.26 m² (78.13 sq ft)
Fuselage and tail: length overall, rotors turning 18.15 m (59 ft 6.5 in) and fuselage 14.06 m (46 ft 1.5 in); height overall 5.14 m (16 ft 10.5 in) and to top of rotor head 4.38 m (14 ft 4.5 in); wheel track 2.38 m (7 ft 10.75 in); wheel base 4.045 m (13 ft 3 in)
Powerplant: two Turboméca Turmo IVC each rated at 1175 kW (1,575 shp)
Weights: empty 3615 kg (7,970 lb); maximum take-off 7500 kg (16,534 lb)
Fuel and load: internal fuel 1544 litres (408 US gal) plus provision for 1900 litres (502 US gal) of auxiliary fuel in four cabin tanks; external fuel up to two 350-litre (92.5-US gal) auxiliary tanks; maximum payload 3200 kg (7,055 lb)
Speed: never exceed speed 204 km/h (158 kt; 182 mph); maximum cruising speed 'clean' at optimum altitude 271 km/h (146 kt; 168 mph)
Range: 572 km (308 nm; 355 miles)
Performance: maximum rate of climb at sea level 552 m (1,810 ft) per minute; service ceiling 6000 m (19,685 ft); hovering ceiling 4400 m (14,435 ft) in ground effect and 4250 m (13,940 ft) out of ground effect

Eurocopter (Aérospatiale) **SA 341/342 Gazelle**

Successor to the Sud Alouette II, the **Gazelle** originated in a mid-1960s project by Sud Aviation. Despite using many of its predecessor's dynamic systems, the **X.300**, soon renamed **SA 341**, achieved increased speed and manoeuvrability through adoption of a more powerful turboshaft, re-styled cabin, covered tailboom, and advanced rotor technology. Part of the last-mentioned came from a 1964 agreement with MBB for joint development of a rigid main rotor head and glass-fibre blades – normal today, but both advanced concepts for their time. Simplicity, strength and reduced maintenance demands are achieved by a rigid head, but a compromise was made at the prototype stage, by which the Gazelle's main rotors have flap hinges without drag hinges. Additionally, the revolutionary 'fenestron', or fan-in-fin tail rotor, was designed to be shielded from forward airflow. Plans were for it to be disengaged to save power during cruising, at which time vertical tail surfaces would be able to take over the task of offsetting torque. Airflow problems around the freewheeling fan resulted in the fenestron being rotated at all times, although it does still allow a power saving of five per cent.

UK requirements to expand its rotary-wing industry resulted in the Anglo-French helicopter agreement of 22 February 1967, by which the Gazelle, Puma and British-designed Lynx came under joint Westland-Sud (Aérospatiale after 1 January 1970) parentage. The **SA 340** prototype flew on 12 April 1968 with conventional rotors and the Alouette II's 268-kW (360-shp) Astazou powerplant, following abandonment by Turboméca of the proposed 336-kW (450-shp) Oredon. A machine with more representative rotors followed on 12 April 1968 demonstrating control difficulties which resulted in the above-mentioned compromises in the design. Revised as the SA 341 and named Gazelle in July 1969, the pre-production version had a longer cabin with

The Qatar Emiri Air Force's HOT missile-armed SA 342Ls operate in support of the army's French-built AMX-30S main battle tanks.

wo rear access doors, larger tail surfaces and a 440-kW (590-shp) Astazou III. Series manufacture began with a civil-registered demonstrator flying on 6 August 1971.

Six versions were launched initially: **SA 341B**, the British Army Gazelle **AH.Mk 1**; **SA 341C**, Royal Navy **HT.Mk 2** trainer; **SA 341D**, Royal Air Force **HT.Mk 3** trainer; **SA 341E**, RAF **HCC.Mk 4** VIP transport (all with Astazou IIIN); **SA 341F**, French army (ALAT) with Astazou IIIC; **SA 341G**, civilian; and **SA 341H**, military export. When the Westland line closed in 1984, it had built 294 Gazelles, including 282 for the UK forces, 212 of which were AH.Mk 1s. No HCC.Mk 4s were constructed as such. Generally unarmed, the AH.Mk 1 carried rockets during the 1982 Falklands War, while nearly 70 were fitted during the late 1980s with roof-mounted GEC-Ferranti AF532 magnifying sights for target finding. Of 170 SA 341Fs, ALAT converted 40 to carry four Euromissile HOT anti-tank missiles as **SA 341Ms** and 62 with a GIAT M621 20-mm cannon to starboard and a SFOM 80 sight as the **SA 341F/Canon**. Others have acquired a SFIM M334 Athos scouting sight similar to that of the AS 532.

Powered by a 640-kW (858-shp) Astazou XIVH, the **SA 342** flew in prototype form on 11 May 1973, replacing the SA 341 after 928 had been built in France and the UK. Foreign exports began with the civil **SA 342J** and military **SA 342K**, the latter soon replaced by **SA 342L**s with an improved fenestron. The ALAT equivalent is designated **SA 342M** and over 200 have been delivered since 1 February 1980, armed with four HOTs and an M397 sight, the latter to be replaced by the night-capable Viviane during the early 1990s. For the 1991 Gulf War, 30 were converted to **SA 342M/Celtic** with a pair of MATRA Mistral SAMs on the port side and a SFOM 80 sight. The definitive anti-helicopter model, with four Mistrals and a T2000 sight, will be designated **SA 342M/ATAM** on 30 conversions. SA 342Ms have an Astazou XIVM turboshaft with automatic start-up and a maximum take-off weight of 1900 kg (4,188 lb), increased to 2000 kg (4,409 lb) in wartime. Avionics include an autopilot and a Sextant Nadir self-contained navigation system, including Doppler. Upward-facing exhaust diffusers are optional for combat.

Egypt, Iraq, Morocco and Syria, among others, have equivalents to the HOT- and cannon-armed Gazelles, but versions built in Yugoslavia by SOKO at Mostar (Bosnia-Herzegovina) have Russian armament options. Following 132 **SA 341H Partizans**,

French Army Light Aviation (ALAT) fields some 710 helicopters including the survivors of 170 S 341Fs, 200 SA 342Ms and a further 18 SA 342Ls, originally built for China. A mix of HOT-armed SA 342Ms is seen here backed up by unarmed Gazelle/Athos scouts. A Mistral AAM fit is under development.

SOKO was well advanced with 170 SA 342Ls before civil war intervened in 1991. Versions comprise the **SA 341L HERA** scout and **SA 342L GAMA**, the latter armed with four AT-3 'Sagger' ATMs and two SA-7 'Grail' SAMs, plus an M334 sight. The Arab-British Helicopter Company in Egypt assembled 48 SA 342Ls from French kits, deliveries beginning in December 1983. Twelve Egyptian Gazelles have SFIM Osloh I laser designation systems for artillery direction.

OPERATORS

Abu Dhabi (UAE): SA 342 (11)
Angola: SA 342 (13)
Burundi: SA 342L (2)
Cameroon: SA 342L (4)
Cyprus: SA 342L-1 (3) – national guard
Ecuador: SA 342K/L (13) – army
Egypt: SA 342K/L (84), SA 342L (12) – army
France: SA 342M (185), SA 341M/F (100/55)
Gabon: SA 342L (5)
Guinea Republic: SA 342M (1)
Iraq: SA 342L (40)
Ireland: SA 342L (2)
Jordan: SA 342 (2)
Kenya: SA 342K (1)
Kuwait: SA 342K (20)
Lebanon: SA 342L (7)
Libya: SA 342 (40)

Morocco: SA 342L (24)
Qatar: SA 342L (14), SA 341G (2) – police
Rwanda: SA 342L (6)
Senegambia: SA 341H (1)
Serbia (Yugoslavia): SA 341/342L 119
        SA 341 (1) – navy
Slovenia: SA.341 (1)
Syria: SA 342 (55)
Trinidad and Tobago: SA 341G (2)
Tunisia: SA 342 (2)
United Kingdom: HT.Mk 3/HCC Mk 4 (27/3) – RAF
        HT.Mk 2/HT.Mk 3 (26) – navy
        AH.Mk 1 (160) – army

Eurocopter France (Aérospatiale) SA 342 Gazelle

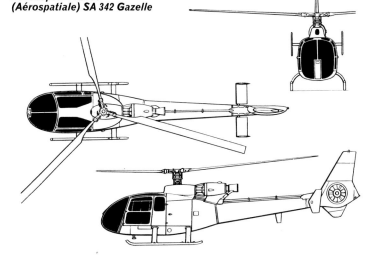

Former Yugoslavian Gazelles are now largely in the hands of the Serbian JRV. These have been active in the Balkan fighting since the invasion of Slovenia in June 1991 and can carry an effective armament of four AT-3 'Sagger' ATGMs or two SA-7 'Grail' AAMs on removable pylons.

SPECIFICATION

Eurocopter France (Aérospatiale) SA 341F Gazelle
Rotor system: main rotor diameter 10.50 m (34 ft 5.5 in); fenestron diameter 0.695 m (2 ft 3.375 in); main rotor disc area 86.59 m² (932.08 sq ft); fenestron disc area 0.38 m² (4.08 sq ft)
Fuselage and tail: length overall, rotor turning 11.97 m (39 ft 3.2 in) and fuselage 9.53 m (31 ft 3.2 in); height overall 3.18 m (10 ft 5 ¼ in) and to top of rotor head 2.72 m (8 ft 11 in); skid track 2.015 m (6 ft 7.3125 in)
Powerplant: one Turboméca Astazou IIIA rated at 440 kW (590 shp)
Weights: empty 920 kg (2,028 lb); maximum take-off 1800 kg (3,968 lb)
Fuel and load: internal fuel 445 litres (117.5 US gal) plus provision for 290 litres (76.5 US gal) of auxiliary fuel in two tanks; external fuel none; maximum payload 700 kg (1,540 lb)
Speed: never-exceed speed at sea level 310 km/h (168 kt; 193 mph); maximum cruising speed at sea level 264 km/h (142 kt; 164 mph); economical cruising speed at sea level 233 km/h (125 kt; 144 mph)
Range: 670 km (361 nm; 416 miles) with standard fuel
Performance: maximum rate of climb at sea level 540 m (1,770 ft) per minute; service ceiling 5000 m (16,405 ft); hovering ceiling 2850 m (9,350 ft) in ground effect and 2000 m (6,560 ft) out of ground effect

Prospective RAF rotary wing pilots win their spurs on the Gazelle HT.Mk 3s at No. 2 FTS, Shawbury. The unit's second squadron flies the Wessex.

The two Gazelles operated by No. 1 Wing, Irish Air Corps, were advertised for sale in 1993 but have now been firmly retained for basic training.

Eurocopter (Aérospatiale) SA 365 Dauphin

In the early 1970s Aérospatiale (now known as Eurocopter France) began development of a helicopter to supersede the Alouette III. The initial version, known as the **SA 360 Dauphin**, featured a four-bladed main rotor, a 13-bladed fenestron, tailwheel landing gear and standard accommodation for a pilot and up to nine passengers. A 980-shp (731-kW) Turboméca Astazou XVI powered the first prototype, which first flew on 2 June 1972. The 1,050-shp (783-kW) Astazou XVIIIA powered production aircraft and, despite development of a dedicated **SA 361H** military helicopter, it was obvious that the Dauphin's military potential lay with a twin-engined helicopter. One SA 361 was taken on charge by the French army for trials, and is still in use.

Designated **SA 365C Dauphin 2**, the twin-engined version is powered by a pair of 650-shp (485-kW) Turboméca Arriel turboshafts, and flew for the first time on 24 January 1975. Greater success was achieved by the **SA 365N**, which introduced a retractable tricycle undercarriage, greater use of composites in the construction and other improvements. This model first flew on 31 March 1979, and was followed by the **SA 365N1**, which introduced an 11-bladed fenestron and uprated Arriel 1C1 engines. Further improvements resulted in the **SA 365N2** with Arriel 1C2 engines and the option for an EFIS cockpit. In January 1990 the Aérospatiale helicopters were redesignated, the Dauphin 2 becoming the **AS 365N**. Aérospatiale developed three dedicated military variants, the **AS 365F**, **AS 365M** (both described under the **AS 565 Panther** entry) and **SA 366G** (described separately).

In 1980 China's CATIC (Chinese national aero technology import-export corporation) signed a licence-production deal with Aérospatiale, to develop a version of the AS 365N destined for use with the People's Liberation Army. An initial batch of 50 **Harbin (HAMC) Z-9 Haitun**s (Dolphin) was built, the first (French-built, Chinese-assembled) example flying in 1982. Gradually, more indigenous components were assimilated in the run until the last example was delivered in January 1992. Under the provisions of a further agreement signed in 1988, Harbin is currently building the **Z-9A-100** which is almost wholly Chinese in origin. This version made its maiden flight on 16 January 1992. Chinese type approval was obtained on 30 December 1992. Z-9s were adopted by CAAC, the national airline, and several army units. An anti-tank version armed with the Norinco Red Arrow ATGM flew in late 1988/early 1989, and the navy is also seeking an anti-submarine warfare version.

OPERATORS

Bophuthatswana: SA 365N1 (1)
Burkina Faso: SA 365N (2)
Cameroon: SA 365N (1)
Congo: SA 365C (1)
Dominican Republic: SA 365C (1)
Fiji: SA 365N (1)
France: SA 365N (3) – air force, SA 361 (1) – army
India: SA 365N (6)
Ivory Coast: SA 365C (3)
Malawi: SA 365N (1)
Rwanda: SA 365N (1)
Sri Lanka: SA 365C (2)

SPECIFICATION

Eurocopter (Aérospatiale) AS 365N1 Dauphin 2
Rotor system: main rotor diameter 11.94 m (39 ft 2 in); fenestron diameter 1.10 m (3 ft 7.4375 in); main rotor disc area 111.97 m² (1,205.26 sq ft); fenestron disc area 0.95 m² (10.23 sq ft)
Fuselage and tail: length overall, rotor turning 13.88 m (45 ft 6.5 in) and fuselage 11.63 m (38 ft 1.875 in); height overall 3.98 m (13 ft 0.75 in) and to top of rotor head 3.52 m (11 ft 6.5 in); wheel track 1.90 m (6 ft 2.75 in); wheel base 3.61 m (11 ft 10.25 in)
Powerplant: two Turboméca Arriel 1C1 each rated at 540 kW (724 shp) for take-off and 437 kW (586 shp) for continuous running
Weights: empty equipped 2161 kg (4,764 lb); maximum take-off 4100 kg (9,039 lb)
Fuel and load: internal fuel 1135 litres (300 US gal) plus provision for 180 litres (47.5 US gal) of auxiliary fuel in a baggage compartment tank
Speed: never-exceed speed at sea level 296 km/h (160 kt; 184 mph); maximum cruising speed at sea level 283 km/h (153 kt; 176 mph); economical cruising speed at sea level 260 km/h (140 kt; 161 mph)
Range: 852 km (460 nm; 530 miles) on standard fuel
Performance: maximum rate of climb at sea level 396 m (1,300 ft) per minute; service ceiling 3600 m (11,810 ft); hovering ceiling 2100 m (6,890 ft) in ground effect and 1100 m (3,610 ft) out of ground effect

Usually a lucrative market for Aérospatiale types, comparatively few Dauphins have found their way into French military service. This single SA 365 is operated by the GLAM (Groupe de Liaison Aériennes Ministérielles), the air force's Villacoublay-based ministerial transport unit. Small numbers also fly with the ALAT (army aviation).

The Z-9 (AS 365N) is in production in China, along with a licensed version of the Super Frelon. Z-9 and Z-9As serve with the AFPLA and navy.

Eurocopter France (Aérospatiale) AS 365N2 Dauphin II

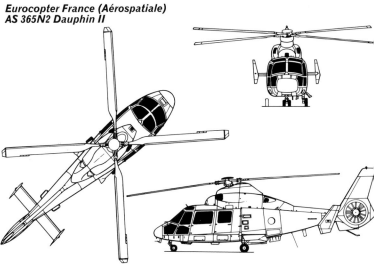

One of the few military operators of the SA 365C is Sri Lanka. Obtained in 1977, its two VIP-configured examples are currently withdrawn from use.

Eurocopter (Aérospatiale) SA 366/HH-65 Dolphin

Under the designation **SA 366G1**, Aérospatiale developed a variant of the Dauphin to answer a **US Coast Guard** requirement to replace its elderly Sikorsky HH-52s. In order to satisfy political requirements, the **Dolphin** featured many US-built components, including a pair of Textron Lycoming LTS101-750A-1 engines, each rated at 680 shp (507 kW). The Dolphin has been criticised for being underpowered, especially in recent times as ever more equipment has been added. A programme to re-engine with Allison/Garrett LHTEC T800s reached prototype trials stage but has progressed no further.

The **HH-65A** is intended to operate the SRR (short-range recovery) mission from both shore bases and Coast Guard vessels. Several design features contribute to improving safety of operations, including the passive failure characteristics of the automatic flight control system, and omnidirectional airspeed system which provides informational airspeed system which provides information while the aircraft is hovering. Inflatable flotation bags are provided for waterborne operations up to sea state 5. The communications and navigation equipment was the responsibility of prime contractor Rockwell Collins, and includes comprehensive radio systems and a datalink for transmission of parameters such as aircraft position to ship or shore base. A nose-mounted Northrop See Hawk FLIR sensor aids poor weather rescue operations. The HH-65's all-weather rescue equipment includes a starboard-side rescue hoist and searchlight. The standard crew of three comprises pilot, co-pilot and hoist operator.

The first HH-65A flew in France on 23 July 1980, and was later shipped to an Aérospatiale division in Texas for fitment of US equipment and certification. The first aircraft was delivered to the Coast Guard on 1 February 1987, procurement totalling 96.

Eurocopter France (Aérospatiale) HH-65A Dolphin (AS 366G1)

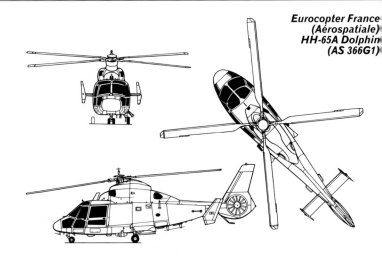

Two of these are loaned to the United States Navy Test Pilots' School at Patuxent River, while the others are distributed to Coast Guard Air Stations at Astoria, Borenquin, Brooklyn, Cape Cod, Cape May, Chicago, Corpus Christi, Detroit, Elizabeth City, Houston, Los Angeles, Miami, Mobile, New Orleans, North Bend, Port Angeles, Sacramento, San Diego and Savannah.

Two United States Coast Guard trials aircraft were purchased by **Israel**, which at one time intended to buy a further 20 for service from its naval patrol boats.

SPECIFICATIONS

Eurocopter (Aérospatiale) HH-65A Dolphin
Rotor system: main rotor diameter 11.94 m (39 ft 2 in); fenestron diameter 1.10 m (3 ft 7¼ in); main rotor disc 111.90 m² (1,204.5 sq ft); fenestron disc area 0.95 m² (10.23 sq ft)
Fuselage and tail: length overall, rotors turning 13.88 m (45 ft 6.5 in) and fuselage 11.63 m (38 ft

1¾in); height overall 3.98 m (13 ft ¾ in) and to top of rotor head 3.52 m (11 ft 6.5 in); wheel track 1.90 m (6 ft 2.75 in); wheel base 3.61 m (11 ft 10.25 in)
Powerplant: two Textron Lycoming LTS101-750A-1 each rated at 680 shp (507 kW)
Weights: empty equipped 2718 kg (5,992 lb); maximum take-off 4050 kg (8,928 lb)
Fuel and load: internal fuel 1135 litres (300 US gal) plus provision for up to 180 litres (47.5 US gal) of auxiliary fuel in one optional baggage compartment tank or 475 litres (125.5 US gal) of ferry fuel in an optional tank replacing the rear seats; external fuel none
Speed: never-exceed speed 175 kt (324 km/h; 201 mph); maximum cruising speed at optimum altitude 139 kt (257 km/h; 160 mph)
Range: 410 nm (472 miles; 760 km) with maximum fuel or 216 nm (400 km; 248 miles) with maximum passenger payload; rescue range 166 nm (307 km; 191 miles); endurance 4 hours 0 minutes
Performance: hovering ceiling 2290 m (7,510 ft) in ground effect and 1627 m (5,340 ft) out of ground effect

The USCG's HH-65A Dolphin fleet has been the subject of controversy regarding its Arriel-derived LTS 101-750B-2 powerplant. Re-engining options with the promise of improved performance have, so far, been discounted.

Eurocopter (Aérospatiale) AS 532 Cougar (AS 332)

Logically, if unimaginatively, known as the AS 332 Super Puma when first proposed in 1974, the **Cougar** was devised as a successor to the SA 330. Retaining the Puma appearance, including retractable undercarriage, and profiting from glass-fibre rotor technology, the Super Puma is most readily identifiable by its prominent ventral fin and nose radome for optional Bendix/King RDR 1400 or Honeywell Primus 500 weather radar. Primarily aimed at the civil market, the helicopter nevertheless incorporates features of value to military operators, including a gearbox operable for one hour without lubricant and rotors which remain safe for 40 hours after hits by 12.7-mm (0.5-in) small-arms fire. The Puma's Turmo powerplants gave way to a pair of Makila 1As delivering 1327 kW (1,780 shp) and able to wind up from idle to full power in just 1.5 seconds. Certain Super Puma components (including gearbox engines and elements of the tail unit) have been incorporated into South Africa's extensive Puma upgrade programme (described under the **Atlas Gemsbok** entry).

First flown on 13 September 1978, the Super Puma entered service in 1981 as the **AS 332B** and civilian **AS 332C**. Both these initial variants retained the Puma's 11.4-m³ (402.6-cu ft) cabin volume, with seating for 21 passengers or 12-15 equipped troops. The following year, deliveries began of the 'stretched' **AS 332M** and civilian **AS 332L**, lengthened by 76 cm (30 in) and with 13.3 m³ (469.7 cu ft) of volume to permit carriage of four extra passengers. In January 1990, military variants were renamed Cougar and renumbered **AS 532** and

adopted new variant suffixes: **AS 532AC** and **UC** for short fuselage, military armed/unarmed; **AS 532AL** and **UL** for long fuselage, military armed/unarmed; **AS 532MC**, naval SAR and surveillance; and **AS 532SC**, naval, armed anti-submarine/anti-ship. Both maritime models were previously **AS 332F**, there being no long-fuselage maritime model. Civil production has concentrated on the **AS 332L Super Puma**, of which over 70 are in service, mainly in oil exploration support. The current production version is the **AS 332L1** and a further improved version, the **AS332L Tiger**, has been developed for North Sea oil support operator Bristow Helicopters. Later examples of **Cougar Mk I** have Makila 1A1s of 1400 kW (1,877 shp).

A development prototype first flew on 6 February 1987 of the **Cougar Mk II** (**AS 332L2 Super Puma II**), featuring 1569-kW (2,104-shp) Makila 1A2s and a further fuselage stretch to accommodate 28 passengers. Mk IIs entered service in 1992 and will be used as the platform for French army aviation's (ALAT) HORIZON battlefield surveillance radar in the late 1990s. The French army originally requested 20 aircraft equipped with the Orchidée system, trialled on an AS 330B. This proved prohibitively expensive and was cancelled in 1990, only to be resurrected for Operation Desert Storm (Operation Daguet). The experience gained from its 24 operational missions led to the HORIZON (Hélicoptère d'Observation Radar et d'Investigation sur ZONe) system. Eurocopter received a development contract in October 1992 for two aircraft, combining the capabilities of Orchidée with the

endurance of the larger AS 532UL, and the first (fully-equipped) flight took place on 8 December 1992. Delivery of the first aircraft to the ALAT occurred in April 1994 and the army has six **AS 532UL HORIZON**s on order. The French army is also replacing its original AS 330s with AS 532 Cougars, the first 22 aircraft being delivered to the Force d'Action Rapide by the end of 1991.

While armament options for the army Cougar are restricted to gun and rocket pods, the AS 532SC has provision for a pair of Aérospatiale AM39 Exocet anti-ship missiles or homing torpedoes. Operation from ship platforms is also possible, using haul-down gear to permit flying in rough seas.

Large sponsons with inflatable floats are standard naval equipment, and are optional on other models. Having produced standard AS 330 Pumas under licence during the early 1980s, **IPTN (Eurocopter)** in Indonesia moved on to AS 332C and AS 332L Super Puma production (described seperately), rolling out their first aircraft for a civilian customer in April 1983. Four have so far been delivered to the Indonesian navy as transports, along with a VIP version for the ministry of finance, and three AS 332L-1s for the Presidential flight in 1992. Indonesian aircraft are designated **NAS 332**. Other foreign service designations include Brazil (**CH-34**), Spain (**HD.21** – SAR, **HT.21** – VIP) and Sweden (**Hkp 10** – SAR). By early 1994 over 400 Super Pumas/Cougars had been ordered, with half the production dedicated to military orders.

Sweden's long-range SAR capability increased with the delivery of 12 Hkp 10s (AS 332M-1s), replacing older Vertol V-107s. Hkp 10s fly with F15 and F21.

A confirmed Aérospatiale operator, the Swiss air force took a major step forward in 1987 with the acquisition of its first AS 332s in preference to the Sikorsky UH-60.

The AS 532s of the Royal Saudi Naval Force are Exocet-capable. During the Gulf war they flew from their base at Al Jubail on maritime patrol missions.

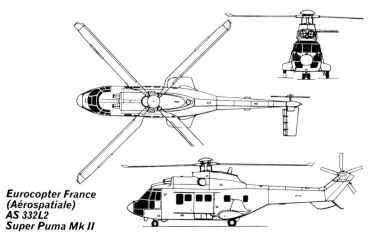

Eurocopter France (Aérospatiale) AS 332L2 Super Puma Mk II

Eurocopter AS 532 Cougar (AS 332)

Abu Dhabi (UAE): AS 332B/M/M1 (6/2/2)
Argentina: AS 532UC (24) – army
Brazil: AS 332M (10); AS 332F (6) – navy
Cameroon: AS 332L (11)
Chile: AS 532SC (6) – navy; AS 332B (2) – army
China: AS 332 (6)
Ecuador: AS 332B (6) – army
France: AS 332C/L 3/2; AS 332M (30) – army
Gabon: AS 332L (1) – Presidential guard
Indonesia: AS 332 (7); AS 332L (7) – navy
Japan: AS 332L (3) – army
Jordan: AS 332M-1 (12)
Kuwait: AS 532SC (4) – navy
Malaysia: NAS 332M (5)
Mexico: AS 332L (4)
Nepal: AS 332L (1)
Nigeria: AS 332L-1 (2)
Oman: AS 332 (2)
Panama: AS 332L (2)
Qatar: AS 332F (12)
Saudi Arabia: AS 532UC/SC (6/6) – navy
Singapore: AS 332M (28)
South Korea: AS 332L (4)
Spain: AS 332B (11); AS 332 (18) – army
Sweden: AS 332M-1 (12)
Switzerland: AS 332M-1 (15)
Togo: AS 332L (1)
Turkey: AS 532UL (20) – army
Venezuela: AS 332M-1 (8)
Zaïre: AS 332 (1)

SPECIFICATION

Eurocopter (Aérospatiale) AS 532UC Cougar
Rotor system: main rotor diameter 15.60 m
(51 ft 2.25 in); tail rotor diameter 3.05 m (10 ft 0 in);
main rotor disc area 191.13 m² (2,057.43 sq ft); tail
rotor disc area 7.31 m² (78.64 sq ft)
Fuselage and tail: length overall, rotors turning
18.70 m (61 ft 4.25 in) and fuselage 15.53 m
(50 ft 11.5 in) including tail rotor; height overall 4.92 m
(16 ft 1.75 in), with blades and tail pylon folded 4.80 m
(15 ft 9 in) and to top of rotor head 4.60 m (15 ft 1 in);
wheel track 3.00 m (9 ft 10.25 in)
Powerplant: two Turboméca Makila 1A1 each rated
at 1400 kW (1,877 shp)
Weights: empty 4330 kg (9,546 lb); normal take-off
9000 kg (19,841 lb) with an internal load; maximum
take-off 9350 kg (20,615 lb) with an external load
Fuel and load: internal fuel 1497 litres (395 US gal)
plus provision for 1900 litres (502 US gal) of auxiliary
fuel in four cabin tanks; external fuel up to two
325-litre (86-US gal) auxiliary tanks; maximum payload
4500 kg (9,921 lb)
Speed: never-exceed speed 278 km/h (150 kt;
172 mph); maximum cruising speed at sea level
262 km/h (141 kt; 163 mph)
Range: 618 km (334 nm; 384 miles) with standard
fuel; endurance 3 hours 20 minutes
Performance: maximum rate of climb at sea level
420 m (1,378 ft) per minute; service ceiling 4100 m
(13,450 ft); hovering ceiling 2700 m (8,860 ft) in ground
effect and 1600 m (5,250 ft) out of effect

Eurocopter (Aérospatiale) AS 532MC/SC Cougar
generally similar to the Eurocopter (Aérospatiale)
AS 532UC Cougar except in the following particulars:
Fuselage and tail: height overall 4.92 m (16 ft
1.75 in) and with main rotor blades and tail rotor
folded 4.80 m (15 ft 9 in)
Weights: empty 4500 kg (9,921 lb)
Speed: maximum cruising speed at sea level
240 km/h (130 kt; 149 mph)
Range: 870 km (470 nm; 540 miles) with standard fuel
Performance: maximum rate of climb at sea level
372 m (1,220 ft) per minute

Eurocopter (Aérospatiale) AS 532UL Cougar
generally similar to the Eurocopter (Aérospatiale)
AS 532UC Cougar except in the following particulars:
Fuselage and tail: length, fuselage 16.29 m (53 ft 5
in) including tail rotor; wheel base 5.28 m
(17 ft 4 in)
Weights: empty 4460 kg (9,832 lb)
Fuel and load: internal fuel 2020 litres (533 US gal)
plus provision for 1900 litres (502 US gal) of auxiliary
fuel in four cabin tanks
Range: 842 km (455 nm; 523 miles) with standard fuel
ferry range 1245 km (671 nm; 773 miles) with
auxiliary fuel

Eurocopter (Aérospatiale) AS 532U2 Cougar Mk II
Rotor system: main rotor diameter 16.20 m (53 ft
1.75 in); tail rotor diameter 3.15 m (10 ft 4 in); main
rotor disc area 206.12 m² (2,218.73 sq ft); tail rotor
disc area 7.79 m² (83.88 sq ft)
Fuselage and tail: length overall, rotors turning

19.50 m (63 ft 11 in) and fuselage 16.74 m (54 ft
11 in); height overall 4.97 m (16 ft 4 in) with tail rotor
turning and to top of rotor head 4.60 m (15 ft 1 in);
stabiliser span 2.17 m (7 ft 1.5 in); wheel track 3.00 m
(9 ft 10 in); wheel base 5.28 m (17 ft 4 in)
Powerplant: two 1569-kW (2,014-shp) Turboméca
Makila 1A2 each rated at 1373 kW (1,841 shp) for
take-off and 1236 kW (1,657 shp) for continuous
running
Weights: manufacturer's empty 4760 kg (10,493 lb);
normal take-off 9500 kg (20,943 lb); maximum take-off
10000 kg (22,046 lb)
Fuel and load: internal fuel 1596 kg (3,519 lb) in
standard tanks or 1516 kg (3,342 lb) in crashworthy
tanks plus provision for up to 3949 litres
(1,043 US gal) of auxiliary fuel; external fuel none;
maximum payload 4500 kg (9,921 lb)
Speed: never exceed speed 327 km/h (177 kt;
203 mph); maximum cruising speed at optimum
altitude 273 km/h (147 kt; 170 mph); economical
cruising speed at optimum altitude 242 km/h (131 kt;
150 mph)
Range: 796 km (430 nm; 496 miles) with standard
fuel; ferry range 1176 km (635 nm; 730 miles) with
auxiliary fuel; endurance 4 hours 20 minutes with
standard fuel
Performance: maximum rate of climb at sea level
384 m (1.260 ft) per minute; service ceiling 4100 m
(13,450 ft); hovering ceiling 2540 m (8,335 ft) in ground
effect and 1900 m (6,235 ft) out of ground effect

Eurocopter (Aérospatiale) **AS 350 (AS 550) Ecureuil/Fennec**

First flown on 27 June 1974, the four/five-
seat **AS 350 Ecureuil** (squirrel) was
developed as a successor for the Alouette
as a light multi-purpose helicopter. Featuring
a Starflex main rotor hub, the prototype
was powered by a Textron Lycoming LTS
101 turboshaft, but the second AS 350,
flown on 14 February 1975, used a Túr-
boméca Arriel. Intended for commercial
use, the **AS 350B** and **AS 350C** entered
production with Arriel 1B and LTS 101
engines respectively, the latter being aimed
at the US market, and known as the **AStar**.
A fully-armed version of the Ecureuil was
developed as the **AS 350L**, with a wide
range of weapon options including a 20-mm
M621 cannon, twin 7.62-mm gun pods, various rocket pods and the Saab/Emerson
Electric Heli-TOW anti-tank system with
four Hughes TOW ATGMs. Twelve of the
latter ordered by Denmark were redesignated **AS 550C2 Fennec** in 1990 before
delivery. Other military versions offered
became **AS 550U2** (unarmed, utility),
AS 550A2 (armed, cannon or rockets),
AS 550C2 (armed, anti-tank missiles),
AS 550M2 (unarmed naval utility) and
AS 550S2 (armed naval anti-shipping).
The Ecureuil has been assembled under
licence in Brazil by Helibras and is similar to
AS 350B standard. Versions are identified as

HB 350B/B1 (unarmed) or **HB 350L1**
(armed), with the name **Esquilo**. Deliveries
comprised HB 350B/B1s for the Brazilian air
force, under the local designations **CH-50**
and **TH-50** for communications and training, respectively, and nine for the Brazilian
navy's HU-1 general-purpose helicopter
squadron (1° Esquadrão de Helicopteros de
Emprego Gerel), with optional machine-gun
and rocket pod armament. The Brazilian
army has 16 fully-armed HB 350L1s for its
1st Aviation Battalion at Taubate, São Paulo,
using the designation **HA-1** (with 20 more
ordered in 1992).

OPERATORS

Abu Dhabi (UAE): AS 350 (1)
Australia: AS 350B (6) – navy; AS 550U (18) – army
Benin: AS 350B (1)
Botswana: AS 350L (2)
Brazil: HB 350B (30); HB 350B (9) – navy
AS 350 (20) – army
Central African Republic: AS 350B (1)
Denmark: AS 550C2 (12) – army
Ecuador: AS 350B (4) – army

*Danish AS 550C2s are referred to as
Fennecs and equipped with ESCO
Heli-TOW systems.*

France: AS 350B (22) – navy; AS 350 (1) – army
Gabon: AS 350B (2)
Guinea Republic: AS 350 (1)
Mali: AS 350B (1)
Paraguay: HB 350B (3)
Peru: AS 350B-1 (3)
Singapore: AS 350E (6), AS 550C2/U2 (10/10)
Tunisia: AS 350B (6)

SPECIFICATION

Eurocopter (Aérospatiale) AS 550 Fennec
Rotor system: main rotor diameter 10.69 m (35 ft
0.75 in); tail rotor diameter 1.86 m (6 ft 1.25 in); main
rotor disc area 89.75 m² (966.09 sq ft); tail rotor disc
area 2.72 m² (29.25 sq ft)

*In May 1984
HC-723 of
the Royal
Australian
Navy
received six
AS 350Bs.
They have
been fitted
with a
lightweight
Doppler nav
system.*

Fuselage and tail: length overall, rotors turning
12.94 m (42 ft 5.5 in) and fuselage 10.93 m
(35 ft 10.5 in) including tail rotor; height overall 3.34 m
(10 ft 11.5 in); skid track 2.28 m (7 ft 5.75 in)
Powerplant: one Turboméca Arriel 1D1 rated at
546 kW (732 shp)
Weights: empty 1220 kg (2,689 lb); maximum take-off
2250 kg (4,960 lb)
Fuel and load: internal fuel 540 litres (142.6 US gal)
Speed: never-exceed speed at sea level 287 km/h
(155 kt; 178 mph); maximum cruising speed at sea
level 246 km/h (133 kt; 153 mph)
Range: 666 km (360 nm; 414 miles)
Performance: maximum rate of climb at sea level
534 m (1,750 ft) per minute; service ceiling 4800 m
(15,750 ft); hovering ceiling 2550 m (8,350 ft) out of
ground effect

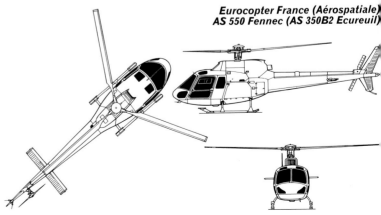

*Eurocopter France (Aérospatiale)
AS 550 Fennec (AS 350B2 Ecureuil)*

Eurocopter (Aérospatiale) AS 355 Ecureuil 2/AS 555 Fennec

A twin-engined version of the AS 350 Ecureuil was launched by Aérospatiale in mid-1978 and the first of two prototypes flew on 28 September 1979. Many components of the original single-engined design were retained, the major changes being concerned with the powerplant, transmission, fuel system and fuselage structure. The first production version was the **AS 355E** with 313-kW (420-shp) Allison 250-C20F turboshafts, followed by the **AS 355F** with wide-chord rotor blades and other improvements. Known as the **Ecureuil 2** or, in North America, the **Twin Star**, the twin-engined version was designated **AS 355M** for military use, this changing to **AS 555 Fennec** in January 1990.

Principal user of the military version is the French air force, which has ordered a total of 52. Eight **AS 355F1**s serve with the 67e Escadre d'Hélicoptères at Villacoublay and with EHOM 68 in French Guyana, the latter armed with an M621 20-mm cannon on the starboard fuselage side. Delivered from 19 January 1990, the remaining 44 are **AS 555AN** Fennecs, with 340-kW (456-shp) Turboméca Arrius-1M turboshafts, of which 24 are for training use and others used in anti-helicopter role with a centrally-mounted 20-mm cannon and T-100 sight. The French army (ALAT) began to take delivery in February 1992 of 10 **AS 555UN** Fennecs for IFR training. In Brazil, the **AS 355F2** has been assembled by Helibras as the **HB 355F2 Esquilo**, with the Brazilian air force taking 13 for service as armed **CH-55**s (11) with 1° Esq of 8° Grupo de Aviacão at Manaus and as VIP transport **VH-55**s (two) in the Grupo de Transporte Especial at Brasilia. Nine more serve the Brazilian navy as **UH-12B**s, with the Helibras designation **HB 355F2**. Aérospatiale has demonstrated an **AS 555SR** naval version of the Fennec carrying a Bendix 1500

radar under the nose, a Crouzet MAD and armament of two homing torpedoes as alternative to the cannon or rocket armament of the **AS 555AR**. Other Fennec variants are the **AS 555UR** utility model and **AS 555MR** naval utility model.

OPERATORS

Benin: AS 355M-2 (2)
Brazil: AS 355F (13); AS 355F-2 (11) – navy
Djibouti: AS 355F/M (2/1)
Fiji: AS 355F-1 (1)
France: AS 355F-1/N (52); AS 555UN (4) – army
Malawi: AS 355 (2)
Sierra Leone: AS 355 (2)

SPECIFICATION

Eurocopter (Aérospatiale) AS 555N Fennec
Rotor system: main rotor diameter 10.69 m (35 ft 0.75 in); tail rotor diameter 1.86 m (6 ft 1.25 in); main rotor disc area 89.75 m² (966.09 sq ft); tail rotor disc area 2.72 m² (29.25 sq ft)
Fuselage and tail: length overall, rotors turning 12.94 m (42 ft 5.5 in) and fuselage 10.93 m (35 ft 10.5 in) including tail rotor; height overall 3.34 m (10 ft 11.5 in); skid track 2.28 m (7 ft 5.75 in)
Powerplant: two Turboméca TM 319 Arrius -1M each rated at 340 kW (456 shp) for take-off and 295 kW (395 shp) for continuous running
Weights: empty 1382 kg (3,046 lb); normal take-off 2540 kg (5,600 lb); maximum take-off 2600 kg (5,732 lb)
Fuel and load: internal fuel 730 litres (193 US gal); external fuel none
Speed: never exceed speed at sea level 278 km/h (150 kt; 172 mph); maximum cruising speed at sea level 225 km/h (121 kt; 140 mph)
Range: 722 km (389 nm; 448 miles); operational radius 129 km (70 nm; 80.5 miles) on SAR mission with two survivors; endurance 1 hour with two torpedoes, or 2 hours 20 minutes with one torpedo or one cannon or two rocket launchers, or 1 hour 50 minutes with one cannon and two rocket launchers
Performance: maximum rate of climb at sea level 408 m (1,340 ft) per minute; service ceiling 4000 m (13,125 ft); hovering ceiling 2600 m (8,530 ft) in ground effect and 1550 m (5,085 ft) out of ground effect

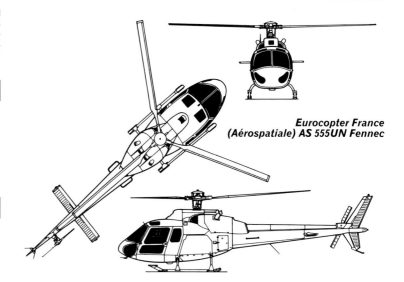

Eurocopter France (Aérospatiale) AS 555UN Fennec

Of 52 AS 555 Fennecs delivered to the Armée de l'Air, 44 are TM 319-powered AS 555ANs, but the first eight were AS 555Fs fitted with Allison 250 turboshafts.

Eurocopter (Aérospatiale) AS 365 Dauphin II/AS 565 Panther

A multi-role military prototype of the twin-engined **Dauphin** was flown on 29 February 1984 as the **AS 365M**, after earlier development of the single-engined **SA 361H** to investigate and demonstrate the potential military application for light assault and anti-tank duties. The AS 365M could carry 10-12 soldiers, or an armament of eight HOT ATGMs or 44 SNEB rockets. A further developed prototype appeared in April 1986 as the **AS 365K**, for which the name **Panther** was adopted. Variants of the Panther now marketed are the basic armed **AS 565AA**, the anti-tank **AS 565CA**, the utility **AS 565UA**, the armed naval **AS 565SA** and the unarmed **AS 565MA** for SAR and other naval tasks. Helibras assembles the AS 565 in Brazil as the **BH 565**, designated **HM-1** by the Brazilian army, which has purchased 36.

One AS 565 was fitted with a pair of LHTEC T800-LHT-800 turboshafts in a joint Aérospatiale/LTV programme to offer the US Army a UH-1H replacement. This prototype first flew as the **Panther 800** in the US on 12 June 1992.

Prior to redesignation of the AS 365 in the Panther series, Saudi Arabia ordered 24 of the navalised **AS 365F**, comprising four in **AS 565SC** configuration for SAR duties with ORB 32 radar and the remainder as **AS 565SA**s with Agrion 15 radar and an armament of four Aérospatiale AS15TT anti-shipping missiles. Three AS 365Fs acquired by the French navy are used for plane guard

duties aboard the *Jeanne d'Arc* by Flottille 35S, with a potential requirement for a further 15 AS 565MAs and perhaps an additional 25. Five **AS 365N2**s ordered by the Republic of China police in 1992 are used for SAR and patrol duties in Taiwan.

Other purchasers of AS 365Fs include Ireland, with two for fishery patrol from the corvette *L. E. Eithne* and three for SAR and transport duties. All Irish aircraft are fitted with Bendix RDR-1500 radar, SFIM 155 autopilot, Sextant ONS 200A and Nadir Mk

The Irish Air Corps operates five AS 365Fs from its main base at Casement Aerodrome, Baldonnel, with a west-coast SAR detachment at Finner Camp, Co. Donegal.

The Brazilian army operates 36 Panthers, under the local designation HM-1. Its final 10 aircraft were assembled by Helibras.

Eurocopter (Aérospatiale) AS 365 Dauphin II/AS 565 Panther

II navigation, Cina B Doppler and auto-stab with a five-screen EFIS cockpit. The two dedicated naval aircraft are fitted with Harpoon deck landing gear. Angola has six cannon-armed **AS 565AA**s for patrol and reconnaissance and 10 **AS 565UA** transports. Chile has ordered four armed AS 565MAs to be equipped with Murène torpedoes or Exocet missiles.

Chinese production of the AS 365 Dauphin began in 1982 at Harbin, with 50 completed by 1992 and work started on second batch of 30. Production includes **Z-9** and **Z-9A** versions (named **Haitun** in Chinese service) equivalent to **AS 365N** and **N1** respectively, with Chinese-built

Arriel 1C and 1C1 engines designated WZ8 and WZ8A. Nine Z-9As have been acquired by the Royal Thai navy.

OPERATORS

Angola: SA 365M (12)
Brazil: SA 565UA (36)
China: Z-9/Z-9A (80)
France: SA 365F (4) – navy
India: SA 365F (5)
Ireland: SA 365F (5)
Saudi Arabia: AS 565MA (4), AS 565SA (20) – navy
Taiwan: SA 365N-2 (5)
Thailand: Z-9A (9) – navy

SPECIFICATION

Eurocopter (Aérospatiale) AS 565UA Panther
Rotor system: main rotor diameter 11.94 m (39 ft 2 in); fenestron diameter 1.10 m (3 ft 7 in); main rotor disc area 111.97 m² (1,205.26 sq ft); fenestron disc area 0.95 m² (10.23 sq ft)
Fuselage and tail: length overall, rotor turning 13.68 m (44 ft 10.6 in) and fuselage 12.11 m (39 ft 8.75 in); height overall 3.99 m (13 ft 1 in) and to top of rotor head 3.52 m (11 ft 6.5 in); wheel track 1.90 m (6 ft 2.75 in); wheel base 3.61 m (11 ft 10.25 in)
Powerplant: two 584-kW (783-shp) Turboméca Arriel 1M1 each rated at 558 kW (749 shp) for take-off and 487 kW (560 kW) for continuous running

Weights: empty 2193 kg (4,835 lb); normal take-off 4100 kg (9,039 lb); maximum take-off 4250 kg (9,369 lb)
Fuel and load: internal fuel 1135 litres (300 US gal) plus provision for 180 litres (47.5 US gal) of auxiliary fuel in a baggage compartment tank; external fuel none; maximum payload 1600 kg (3,527 lb)
Speed: never exceed speed 296 km/h (160 kt; 184 mph); maximum cruising speed at sea level 278 km/h (150 kt; 173 mph)
Range: 875 km (472 nm; 544 miles) with standard fuel
Performance: maximum rate of climb at sea level 420 m (1,378 ft) per minute; hovering ceiling 2600 m (8,530 ft) in ground effect and 1850 m (6,070 ft) out of ground effect

---

Eurocopter (MBB) **BO 105**

Eurocopter Deutschland
PO Box 9801140, D-8000 Munich 80
Germany

Work on the agile **BO 105** started in 1964, and the first prototype flew on 16 February 1967 under the power of two Allison 250-C18 turboshafts, followed by two more prototypes, one of which featured the MAN-Turbo 6022 engine. For production aircraft the Allison 250-C20 was chosen. The basic **BO 105C** and **BO 105CB** (introduced in 1975) can carry five and one pilot, although the **BO 105CBS** is a slightly stretched version carrying six. Their most important feature is the rigid GRP main rotor with a hingeless (except for the feathering hinge) forged titanium hub. This makes the BO 105 fully aerobatic and agile in its anti-tank/scout roles. In addition to manufacture at Eurocopter Deutschland at Donauwörth, the BO 105 is assembled by CASA in Spain, IPTN in Indonesia and Eurocopter Canada, the latter being wholly responsible for the **BO 105LS** hot-and-high version, which is powered by uprated Allison 250-C28C engines.

By far the most important customer was the German army (Heeresflieger), buying 100 **BO 105M**s for the scout role under the designation **VBH** (Verbindungs und Beobachtungs Hubschrauber), and 212 **BO 105P**s for the anti-armour role under the designation **PAH-1** (Panzerabwehr-Hubschrauber-1). The latter are armed with six Euromissile HOT anti-tank missiles in horizontal, side-by-side tubes, aimed through a roof-mounted stabilised sight. The PAH-1 is the subject of three updating programmes, the first of which is the **PAH-1A1 Phase 1**, which fits new rotor blades, improved cooling and intakes, entering service in 1991. Under consideration is the **PAH-1 Phase 2**, to provide night-fighting capability with infra-red roof-mounted sight and digital HOT 2 missiles on lightweight 'diagonally' staggered pylons. This shelved programme may be revived if the planned buy of PAH-2 Tigers is reduced. Finally, consideration was given to the conversion of 54 PAH-1s to **BSH** (Begleitschutz Hubschrauber) standard for use as escorts, adding four Stinger air-to-air missiles. The **BO 105/Ophelia** was a trials aircraft for evaluation of mast- and helmet-mounted sighting systems.

BO 105s also achieved substantial export sales, proving able to fulfil a number of role requirements, including short-range SAR, utility and VIP transport, light attack, scouting and anti-armour work. Of the current operators, Iraq is the most important numerically with about 75, followed by Spain which operates over 70 locally-assembled aircraft. The Spanish army operates three variants, comprising 28 anti-armour **BO 105ATH**s (designated **HA.15**) with HOT missiles, 18 armed reconnaissance **BO 105GSH**s (designated **HR.15**) with 20-mm Rheinmetall cannon, and 14 unarmed **BO 105LOH**s (also **HR.15**) for observation duties. The LOHs were subsequently modified with two 7.62-mm

machine-guns to become GSHs.

Since 1977 IPTN in Indonesia manufactured the BO 105 under licence as the **NBO-105**, with rotors and transmission supplied from Germany. Current production version, from aircraft No. 101 onwards, is the stretched **NBO-105S**. Aircraft are currently being completed at a rate of 2½ per month, with deliveries approaching 130, largely for the Indonesian armed forces and government departments. Sweden operates ESCO Helitow-equipped BO 105CBSs, and unarmed SAR aircraft as the **Hkp 9B**.

OPERATORS

Bahrain: BO 105C (3)
Brunei: BO 105CB/CBS (5/1)
Chile: BO 105CB (6)
Ciskei: BO 105 (1)
Colombia: BO 105CB (2) – army
Dubai (UAE): BO 105S (6)
Germany: BO 105P/M (208/96) – army
Indonesia: NBO 105C/CB (12); NBO 105SC (4) – navy; NBO 105C/CB (18) – army
Iraq: BO 105C (75)
Jordan: NBO 105C (3)
Kenya: BO 105S (1)
Lesotho: BO 105CBS (2)
Mexico: BO 105C/CB (6/5) – navy
Netherlands: BO 105C (28)
Peru: BO 105C/L (18/6)
Philippines: BO 105C/SC (4/10) – navy
Sierra Leone: BO 105C (1)
Spain: BO 105 (68)
Sweden: BO 105CB (20)
Trinidad and Tobago: BO 105CBS (1)

SPECIFICATION

Eurocopter (MBB) BO 105CB
Rotor system: main rotor diameter 9.84 m (32 ft 3.5 in); tail rotor diameter 1.90 m (6 ft 2.75 in); main rotor disc area 76.05 m² (818.62 sq ft); tail rotor disc area 2.835 m² (30.52 sq ft)
Fuselage and tail: length overall, rotors turning 11.86 m (38 ft 11 in) and fuselage 8.56 m (28 ft 1 in); height overall 3.00 m (9 ft 10.25 in)
Powerplant: two Allison 250-C20B each rated at 420 shp (313 kW) for take-off and 400 shp (298 kW) for continuous running
Weights: empty 1276 kg (2,813 lb); normal take-off 2400 kg (5,291 lb); maximum take-off 2500 kg (5,511 lb)
Fuel and load: internal fuel 456 kg (1,005 lb) plus provision for 320 kg (705 lb) of auxiliary fuel in a cabin tank; external fuel none
Speed: never-exceed speed at sea level 145 kt (167 mph; 270 km/h); maximum cruising speed 'clean' at sea level 130 kt (150 mph; 242 km/h)
Range: ferry range 600 nm (691 miles; 1112 km) with auxiliary fuel; range 355 nm (409 miles; 658 km) with maximum payload
Performance: maximum rate of climb at sea level 1,575 ft (480 m) per minute; maximum operating altitude 17,000 ft (5180 m); hovering ceiling 8,400 ft (2560 m) in ground effect and 5,300 ft (1615 m) out of ground effect

To the German army the armed BO 105 is the PAH-1 (now upgraded to PAH-1A1 standard). Unarmed scout aircraft are designated VBH.

Sweden's BO 105s (Hkp 9Bs) serve in both armed and unarmed versions. This is one of the latter, a SAR Hkp 9B with emergency flotation gear.

In 1982 the Mexican navy received six BO 105Cs, followed by six Bo 105CBs in 1986. The BO 105s can operate from the navy's 'Halcon'-class corvettes.

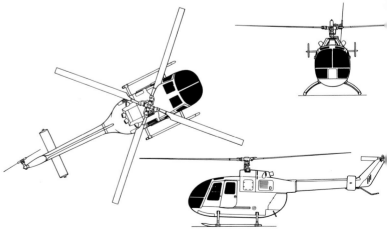

Eurocopter Germany (MBB/Deutsche Aerospace) BO 105

Eurocopter (MBB)/Kawasaki BK 117

Primarily of commercial interest, the **BK 117** emerged as a joint venture between Germany and Japan, with first prototype flight on 13 June 1979 and first production examples flown in Japan on 24 December 1981 and Germany on 23 April 1982. At the 1985 Paris air show, MBB exhibited the **BK 117A-3M**, a dedicated military version with eight HOT-2 missiles, roof-mounted sight, trainable machine-gun turret under the cockpit, ECM and Racal Prophet RWR systems and a CRT cockpit. Utilising the capacious airframe to the full, MBB trialled several weapons fits including pylon-mounted rocket pods and four TOW missiles. A mast-mounted sight was also fitted. By 1988, however, no customers had been found and the BK 117A-3M was abandoned, leaving the military market solely to 'civilian' aircraft.

About two dozen BK 117s have entered military service, from a total production of some 360. They include a batch of 16 **BK 117B-1**s delivered from September 1988 to March 1989 to the **Iraqi** air force for SAR duty. This variant is powered by two 442-kW (592-shp) Textron Lycoming LTS-101-750B-1 turboshafts and accommodates a pilot and up to 10 passengers (more usually seven). A straight-in cargo loading facility is offered through clamshell doors at

the rear of the cabin. IPTN in Indonesia once again signed a licence-production deal with Eurocopter to build **NBK-117**s, but completed only four.

Other military users include the defence forces of all four of the homelands granted nominal independence by the South African government, comprising **Ciskei** (three **BK 117A-1**), **Bophuthatswana** (two **BK 117A-3**), **Transkei** (two A-3) and **Venda** (two A-3). Two are also in use with **Sharjah**, as part of the United Arab Emirates armed forces. Quasi-military users include the **US Customs Service** (flown by the Puerto Rico-based **FURA** organisation) which has three equipped for mission support with FLIR, searchlight and cockpit lighting, and the **Peruvian** ministry of the interior with two for anti-drug surveillance. The Technical Research and Development Institute (formerly Command) of the **Japan Air Self-Defence Force** operates a single aircraft from Gifu as part of its Air Proving Wing.

This BK 117 wears the (English) legend of the JASDF's Technical Research and Development Institute. The BK 117 is in auspicious company as part of this, the JASDF's air proving wing, flying alongside various examples of the F-15, F-4, T-33, T-2 and C-1.

SPECIFICATION

Eurocopter (MBB)/Kawasaki BK 117B-2
Rotor system: main rotor diameter 11.00 m (36 ft 1 in); tail rotor diameter 1.956 m (6 ft 5 in); main rotor disc

area 95.03 m² (1,022.9 sq ft); tail rotor disc area 3.00 m² (32.34 sq ft)
Fuselage and tail: length overall, rotors turning 13.00 m (42 ft 8 in) and fuselage 9.91 m (32 ft 6¼ in)
Powerplant: two Textron Lycoming LTS 101-750B-1 each rated at 528 kW (708 shp) for take-off and 516 kW (692 shp) for maximum continuous
Weights: basic empty 1727 kg (3,807 lb); maximum take-off, with internal and external load 3350 kg (7,385 lb)
Fuel and load: total internal 697 litres (184 US gal)

plus provision for 200 litre (53 US gal) in auxiliary tank
Speed: never-exceed speed 150 kts (278 km/h; 172 mph); maximum cruising speed 135 kts (250 km/h; 155 mph)
Range: at sea level with standard fuel, no reserves 292 nm (541 km/335 miles)
Performance: maximum forward rate of climb , at sea level 660 m (2,165 ft) per minute; maximum operating altitude 4575 m (15,000 ft); hovering ceiling 3565 m (11,700) in ground effect and 2955 m (9700 ft) out of ground effect.

Eurocopter HAC Tigre/PAH-2 Tiger/HAP Gerfaut

The **Eurocopter Tiger** has its origins in Germany's requirement for a second-generation Panzerabwehr-Hubschrauber (**PAH-2**). With the French army seeking an anti-tank helicopter (Hélicoptère Anti-Char, or **HAC**) in a similar category, a Memorandum of Undertaking was signed in 1984 for the joint development of a new aircraft. The programme was halted in mid-1986 to allow a complete reappraisal of requirements and costs, to be resumed in March 1987 in a modified form to cover a common anti-tank version, and an armed escort version (Hélicoptère d'Appui Protection, or **HAP**) for the French army.

To handle the programme, Aérospatiale in France and MBB in Germany set up the jointly-owned Eurocopter GmbH; subsequently, all helicopter activities of the two companies have been merged under the Eurocopter name. A development contract awarded to Eurocopter on 30 November 1989 provided for five aircraft, of which three are unarmed aerodynamic prototypes, one is in full anti-tank configuration representing the **Tiger** (Germany)/**Tigre** (France) and one is the escort **Gerfaut**. As finally configured, the Tiger (the generic name for the helicopter) has a slender low-drag fuselage with two seats in tandem,

stepped and offset to each side of the centreline. The structure makes extensive use of composites, and an advanced four-bladed composite semi-rigid main rotor is fitted. The three-bladed tail rotor is of Aérospatiale's Spheriflex type and a fixed tricycle undercarriage is used, with single wheels. Weapons carriage is on anhedral stub wings with provision for a cannon turret undernose.

Redundant hydraulic, electrical and fuel systems contribute to the Tiger's survivability, and a MIL-STD-1553B databus provides the basis for the avionics system and integration of weapons system with crew-controlled sensors. End-plate fins fitted on the

tailplane for early prototype flights were discarded for a time, and later re-introduced in a more forward position.

In its German **PAH-2 Tiger** configuration, the helicopter was to have carried up to eight HOT 2 or Trigat missiles, or four of these weapons plus four Stinger 2 AAMs for self-defence. Sighting would have been by means of a mast-mounted FLIR for the

The prototype French Gerfaut escort/scout (foreground) formates on the first Tigre anti-tank helicopter. Both are now involved in the flight test programme.

Eurocopter HAC Tigre/PAH-2 Tiger/HAP Gerfaut

pilot, who has a helmet sight. This variant has been abandoned in favour of a utility (or, more accurately, multi-role) version, since the upgraded MBB BO105 is now felt to be adequate to meet the anti-armour threat, but not the intervention and crisis reaction needs, of the 1990s.

Germany has therefore decided on a new variant, known as **UHU** (Unterstützungshubschrauber), of as yet unknown configuration but optimised for multi-role duties, including escort work. This might infer greater air-to-air capability (not least for self-defence), perhaps using the DAV millimetre-wave radar being developed by Dassault Electronique for the Tiger/Tigre.

The French **HAC Tigre** uses similar armament and equipment to the PAH-2 but will use MATRA Mistral AAMs for defence. The **HAP Gerfaut** will have a 30-mm GIAT cannon in an undernose turret and will carry two 22-round 68-mm unguided SNEB 68-mm rocket pods, plus either four Mistral AAMs or two 12-round rocket pods. Roof-mounted TV, FLIR, laser rangefinder and direct optics will be used on the Gerfaut.

As part of the Tiger development programme, an Aérospatiale Panther was used as a testbed for the MTR 390 engines, flying for the first time on 14 February 1991. Three other testbeds – two Pumas and a Dauphin – were used to test the mast-mounted sight, the night-vision sight and the fire control system. On schedule, the first of the Tiger prototypes (PT1) flew at Marignane on 29 April 1991, at first with a mast-mounted sight, but reconfigured a year later with a canopy sight in the Gerfaut configuration. PT2 (a Gerfaut with all essential avionics and systems) was rolled out at

Ottobrunn on on 9 November 1991 and first flew on 22 April 1993. PT3 followed it into the air on 19 November 1993. While both these aircraft will serve, at first, as avionics testbeds, they will be converted to full Gerfaut and Tiger standard respectively, by 1997. The fully-equipped Gerfaut (PT4) and Tiger/Tigre (PT5) are to fly in October 1994 and March 1995. It is likely that the (German) PT5 will be completed to UHU standard.

Estimated requirements, subject to final confirmation, are for 75 HAP and 140 HAC for France and 212 PAH-2/UHU for Germany. The German order has been subject to serious revision and the 1995 budget submission included funds for only 75 aircraft. It now looks as if this will be returned to its original level, which will have beneficial cost implications for a third potential European operator. The British army is also looking for an 'off-the-shelf' battlefield helicopter to be chosen in late 1994. British Aerospace is leading the Eurocopter bid for the 90-helicopter order, and contacts have been made with French and German authorities. The UK has been offered full membership of the Tiger project should the aircraft be selected for the British armed forces, which would improve the terms of its purchase appreciably. Despite the army's original preference for an existing, uncomplicated helicopter, this deal may prove persuasive.

In March 1994 Eurocopter and MTU were forced to make changes to the MTR 390 engine, having suffered three turbine-blade failures. Vibration, due to air flow through the turbine, caused the loss of sections of blade after its shroud failed. The modified engine now has fewer stator

vanes ahead of the the turbine, and a lighter containment shroud. By mid-1994 all 15 engines involved in the test programme, including those flying on a Panther testbed, had been so modified

Early schedules for deliveries have slipped. The French 1995-2000 arms procurement Bill has set back the first Gerfaut delivery to 2001, with the Tigre following within a year. Originally planned deliveries were scheduled to commence to the army in 1997 and 1998 respectively. The UHU/Tiger should start to reach the German Bundeswehr in 1999.

SPECIFICATION

Eurocopter HAC Tigre and PAH-2 Tiger
Rotor system: main rotor diameter 13.00 m (42 ft 7.75 in); tail rotor diameter 2.70 m (8 ft 10.25 in); main rotor disc area 132.73 m2 (1,428.76 sq ft); tail rotor disc area 5.73 m2 (61.63 sq ft)
Fuselage and tail: fuselage 14.00 m (45 ft 11.25 in);

height overall 4.32 m (14 ft 2 in) to top of turning tail rotor and 3.81 m (12 ft 6 in) to top of rotor head; wheel track 2.40 m (7 ft 10.5 in); wheel base 7.65 m (25 ft 1 in)
Powerplant: two MTU/Turboméca/Rolls-Royce MTR 390 each rated at 958 kW (1,285 shp) for take-off and 873 kW (1,171 shp) for continuous running
Weights: basic empty 3300 kg (7,275 lb); normal take-off 5800 kg (12,787 lb); maximum overload take-off 6000 kg (13,227 lb)
Fuel and load: internal fuel 1360 litres (359 US gal); external fuel none
Speed: maximum cruising speed at optimum altitude 280 km/h (151 kt; 174 mph); economical cruising speed at optimum altitude 250 km/h (135 kt; 155 mph)
Range: endurance 3 hours 10 minutes
Performance: maximum rate of climb at sea level more than 600 m (1,969 ft) per minute; hovering ceiling over 2000 m (6,560 ft) out of ground effect

French aircraft PT1 in HAP Gerfaut configuration displays its 30-mm Giat AM-30781 cannon, 22-round SNEB pods, Mistral AAMs and mast-mounted STRIX sight.

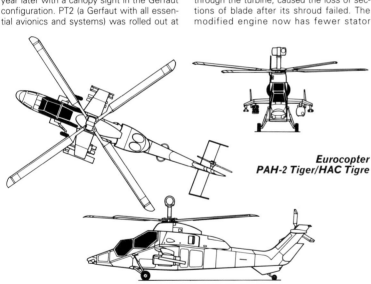

Eurocopter PAH-2 Tiger/HAC Tigre

Eurofighter European Fighter Aircraft 2000

Eurofighter Jagdflugzeug GmbH
Arabellastrasse 16 (PO Box 860366)
D-8000 Munich 81, Germany

As a follow-on to the tri-national Tornado programme, the Eurofighter consortium was formed in June 1986 by the same three countries – Britain, Germany and Italy (soon joined by Spain) – to produce an air superiority fighter by the late 1990s. Other European countries, notably France, had been involved in earlier **EFA** discussions, but shunned the final consortium to pursue independent programmes.

Much experience was gained with main EFA concepts, including an unstable aerodynamic configuration with canard foreplanes, active digital fly-by-wire control system, complex avionics, multi-function cockpit displays, carbon-fibre composites and extensive use of aluminium-lithium alloys and titanium and even direct voice input, from BAe's **Experimental Aircraft Programme** (**EAP**). This was funded (after German withdrawal) jointly by the UK MoD

and industry, with some Italian participation from 1982. First flying on 8 August 1986, the twin-RB.199 EAP amassed invaluable data in 259 test sorties totalling over 195 hours before retirement on 1 May 1991.

Finalised in September 1987, the EFA European Staff Requirement for Development specified a relatively light and sophisticated twin-turbofan single-seat fighter optimised for BVR and close air combat, but capable of secondary air-to-surface roles and operation from short, austere air strips, with a low radar cross-section and high

The EAP demonstrator had excellent high-alpha capability. At high angles of attack the lower lip of the sophisticated vari-cowl chin intake hinged down to ensure a clean, uninterrupted supply of air to the engine in all flight regimes.

supersonic performance, agility and carefree handling. Germany and Italy sought only air-to-air roles, but accepted the common specification of a 9.75-tonne (21,495-lb) basic mass empty, 50 m² (538.2 sq ft) gross wing area, and 90-kN (20,233-lb) reheat thrust per engine. These were new EJ200 twin-spool turbofans from the Eurojet consortium (comprising Rolls-Royce, MTU, Fiat Avio and SENER (now ITP) in Spain) with some 30 per cent fewer parts than the Tornado's RB.199, and with 60 kN (13,488 lb) maximum dry thrust.

A £5.5 billion contract signed on 23 November 1988 covered building and testing until 1999 of eight prototypes, including two two-seat versions, in Britain (three), Germany (two), Italy (two) and Spain (one), funded in proportion to national industrial participation: 33 per cent each by BAe and MBB (now Deutsche Aerospace), 21 per cent by Aeritalia (now Alenia), and 13 per cent by CASA. Eventual purchase was envisaged from 1996 of 765 EFAs; 250 each for the RAF and the Luftwaffe, 165 for the AMI and 100 for the Ejercito del Aire.

After major contention, in May 1990 the new ECR-90 multi-mode pulse-Doppler look-up/look-down fire-control radar with multiple target search and detection was chosen for EFA (over an uprated Hughes APG-65), to be developed and produced by GEC Ferranti, with FIAR in Italy and INISEL in Spain. While optimised for Hughes AIM-120 use, ECR-90 also provides continuous wave illumination for semi-active radar-guided air-to-air missiles. Four AAMs may be carried in semi-recessed low-drag fuselage stations, with nine other stores pylons (three also plumbed for drop tanks), having a 14,330-lb (6500-kg) total capacity. Cannon armament comprises a 27-mm (1.06-in) Mauser Mk 27 in the starboard fuselage.

EFA's radar is supplemented by an infra-red search and tracking system (IRST), with passive multi-target tracking and imaging, for which the Eurofirst group of FIAR (Italy), Thorn-EMI Electronics (UK) plus Eurotronica (Spain) received a development contract in mid-1992. This followed orders for integrated defensive aids sub-systems placed with a Marconi Defence Systems/Elettronica consortium to cover missile approach, laser and radar warning systems, wingtip ESM/ECM pods, chaff/flare dispensers and towed decoys, although Germany and Spain may seek cheaper off-the-shelf equipment.

A production investment decision was originally due by early 1993, but EFA cost studies by incoming German Defence Minister Volker Rühe in April 1992, which challenged the system unit price estimates of DM133.9 million (then $83.7 million) as unaffordable, resulted in major project reviews against threats of a German withdrawal. After considering seven possible EFA revisions, mostly single-engined, the four nations agreed on a slightly simplified and less capable New EFA or Eurofighter 2000 variant in late 1992, with options for cheaper individual equipment fits, reducing system unit costs to a minimum DM90 million. The German aircraft seem likely now to incorporate 'off-the-shelf' avionics (such as the APG-65 radar), lower levels of self protection equipment and other reductions, leading to a 30 per cent cut in overall cost.

While Britain is still nominally committed to its original 250-full standard EFA requirement, with initial deliveries in about 2000, Germany now plans to have only eight squadrons with 12-15 aircraft each, reducing Luftwaffe purchases with reserves to about 138 (potentially as few as 120). Germany is also deferring its EFA production decision until 1995, for service from 2002 or later.

Within days of DA.1's first flight, the British-assembled DA.2 flew from Warton, piloted by BAe's director of flight operations, Chris Yeo.

This would see Germany's workshare fall to 22 per cent, and the UK's rise to 42 per cent. Italy now requires only 130 EFAs to re-equip five squadrons from 2005 (having leased 24 ex-RAF Tornado F.Mk 3s in the interim) and an OCU, while Spain will fund no more than 72 Eurofighters (and has been offered 40 ex-USAF F-16A/Bs, by Lockheed, in the meantime), cutting overall EFA programme totals to less than 600 aircraft.

The first two EFA prototypes, DA.1 (98+29) and DA.2 (ZH588) flew on 27 March and 6 April 1994 from Manching and Warton, for 45 and 50 minutes respectively. Both are fitted with interim RB.199-22 turbofans, and Alenia's DA.3 will be the first with definitive EJ200 engines. DA.3 is due to fly before the end of 1994, but problems in integrating the EJ200's digital engine-control unit (developed by DASA and MTU), may delay this. The British-assembled aircraft was flight ready in advance of DA.1, but BAe was committed to waiting for the 'rival' to fly first. Prior to DA.1's flight DASA introduced revised software to permit high-speed taxiing runs before the March date. This came after the aircraft burst a tyre in similar trials in late January 1994, and was no doubt influenced by the troubled JAS 39 project, in which BAe is also involved.

BAe's DA.4 is the first two-seat EFA and also the ECR-90 development prototype, while MBB will use DA.5 for avionics and weapons integration. CASA will assemble and fly the second two-seat prototype (DA.6) with Alenia building DA.7, now the last development aircraft following the economies, which cut two prototypes.

Having passed the hurdle of its first flight, Eurofighter 2000 now faces a wrangle over workshare, specifically any diminution in German involvement. DA.1 was scheduled for transferral to BAe at Warton after 10 flying hours, but this period has been extended in deference to German objections. BAe and GEC-Marconi are also interested in increasing their managerial input in the flight control system (FCS), which previously has been the sole preserve of DASA. FCS development was central to Eurofighter 2000's three-year delay. Furthermore, DASA is now proposing utilising FCS software developed for the X-31 demonstrator aircraft, flying in the USA for the German MoD/DARPA/US Navy. DASA is keen to incorporate its X-31 experience in the European aircraft, to the extent that it has already proposed a thrust-vectoring mid-life update, for Eurofighter. This 'Kampfwertsteigerung', or combat improvement programme, could see the addition of 'paddles' to the EJ200 powerplant, as X-31 itself is progressing towards tailless flight in late 1995 with just such a system.

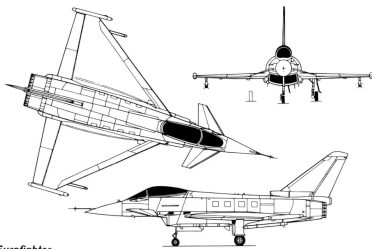

Eurofighter
European Fighter Aircraft 2000

SPECIFICATION

Eurofighter European Fighter Aircraft 2000
Wing: span 10.50 m (34 ft 5.5 in); wing aspect ratio 2.205; wing area 50.00 m² (538.21 sq ft); canard foreplane area 2.40 m² (25.83 sq ft)
Fuselage and tail: length 14.50 m (47 ft 7 in); height about 4.00 m (13 ft 1.5 in)
Powerplant: two Eurojet EJ200 each rated at about 60.0 kN (13,490 lb st) dry and 90.0 kN (20,250 lb st) with afterburning
Weights: empty 9750 kg (21,495 lb); maximum take-off 21000 kg (46,297 lb)
Fuel and load: internal fuel 4000 kg (8,818 lb); external fuel up to one 1500-litre (396-US gal) and two 1000-litre (264-US gal) drop tanks; maximum ordnance

Seen during its public unveiling, this aircraft is BAe-assembled DA.4, the first two-seater. DA.1 and 2 are primarily concerned with flight system testing, while DA.3 is the first with EJ200 engines. DA.4 is the primary ECR-90 radar testbed.

6500 kg (14,330 lb)
Speed: maximum level speed 'clean' at 11000 m (36,090 ft) 2125 km/h (1,147 kt; 1,321 mph)
Range: combat radius between 463 and 556 km (250 and 300 nm; 288 and 345 miles)
Performance: take-off run 500 m (1,640 ft) at normal take-off weight; landing run 500 m (1,640 ft) at normal landing weight
g limits: -3 to +9

Excalibur **Queenaire 800 (U-8F)**

*Excalibur Aviation Company
8337 Mission Road, San Antonio
Texas 78714, USA*

San Antonio-based Excalibur Aviation Co. specialised for many years in the conversion of Beechcraft Twin Bonanzas and Queen Airs to improve their performance. The Excalibur **Queenaire 800** modification of the Queen Air 65, A65 and 80 has been sold to the **US Army**, and more than 50 Beech U-8Fs (described separately) have been modified to enhance their service life with the Army National Guard. The Queenaire 800 introduces 400-hp (298-kW) Textron Lycoming IO-720-A1B flat-eight

engines with Hartzell three-bladed, constant-speed, fully-feathering propellers, new engine mountings, exhaust system and low-drag nacelles, and fully-enclosed wheel well doors. Similar modifications to Queen Air A80 and B80 are referred to as Excalibur **Queenaire 8800**s. By 1994 approximately 170 had been undertaken, most notably for the US Army but also for a small number of other military customers, such as **Argentina**, **Colombia** and the **Dominican Republic**.

SPECIFICATION

Excalibur Queenaire 800 and 8800
generally similar to the Beech Queen Air Model 65, A65 and 80 except in the following particulars:
Powerplant: two Textron Lycoming IO-720-A1B each rated at 400 hp (298 kW)
Weights: empty equipped (Queenaire 800) 5,400 lb (2,449 kg), (Queenaire 8800) 5,800 lb (2631 kg); maximum take-off, (Queenaire 8000) 8,000 lb (23268 kg), (Queenaire 8800) 8800 lb (3991 kg)

Range: with maximum fuel and reserves, (Queenaire 800) 1,322 nm (2451 km/1,523 miles), (Queenaire 8800) 1,547 nm (2867 km/1,782 miles)
Performance: maximum cruising speed at 8,300 ft (2530 m) 201 kt (372 km/h; 231 mph); maximum rate of climb at sea level, (Queenaire 800) 1,5235 ft (468 m) per minute, (Queenaire 8800) 1,490 ft (454 m) per minute; stalling speed, gear and flaps down, (Queenaire 800), 68 kts (126km/h;78 mph), (Queenaire 8800), 70 kt (129 km/h; 80 mph); service ceiling, (Queenaire 800) 19,700 ft (6005 m), (Queenaire 8800) 18,700 ft (5700 m)

Extra **300**

Under the direction of Walter Extra, the German company produced the **Extra 300** tandem two-seat unlimited aerobatic aircraft powered by a Textron Lycoming AEIO-540-L1B5 flat-six engine. The earlier **Extra 230** had a wooden wing, but the Extra 300 uses a composite unit. Only two military customers have purchased the type, these being the **French** and **Chilean** air forces. Six were delivered in 1989-90 to Grupo de Aviación No. 11 at Santiago-Los Cerillos for use by the Escuadrilla de Alta Acróbacia, better known as the Chilean air force's display team 'Los Halcones', which formerly flew the Pitts S-2A/S. The French air force's 'Equipe de Voltige' has purchased an **Extra 300** and an **Extra 300S** for aerobatic use at Salon de Provence. The quasi-military Royal Jordanian 'Falcons' team has also re-equipped with the Extra 300.

SPECIFICATION

Extra 300
Wing: span 8.00 m (26 ft 3 in); aspect ratio 5.98; area 10.70 m2 (115.17 sq ft)
Fuselage and tail: length 7.12 m (23 ft 4.25 in); height 2.62 m (8 ft 7.25 in); tailplane span 3.20 m (10 ft 6 in); wheel base 1.80 m (5 ft 11 in)
Powerplant: one Textron Lycoming AEIO-540-L1B5 rated at 300 hp (224 kW)
Weights: empty 630 kg (1,389 lb); normal take-off 820 kg (1,808 lb) for single-seat aerobatics or 870 kg (1,918 lb) for two seat aerobatics; maximum take-off 950 kg (2,094 lb)
Fuel and load: internal fuel 38 litres (10 US gal); external fuel none; maximum ordnance none
Speed: never-exceed speed 220 kt (253 mph; 407 km/h); maximum level speed 'clean' at optimum altitude 185 kt (213 mph; 343 km/h); maximum manoeuvring speed 158 kt (182 mph; 293 km/h)
Range: 526 nm (605 miles; 974 km)
Performance: maximum rate of climb at sea level 3,300 ft (1006 m) per minute; take-off distance to 50 ft

(15 m) about 248 m (814 ft) at maximum take-off weight; landing distance from 50 ft (15 m) about 548 m (1,798 ft) at normal landing weight
g limits: -10 to +10 single-seat aerobatic, or -8 to +8 two-seat aerobatic, or -3 to +6 at max take-off weight

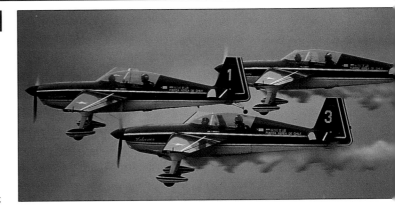

'Los Halcones' are the Chilean air force aerobatic display teams, and one of several such groups which have traded in their Pitts Specials for the new German-built mounts.

Fairchild **A-10/OA-10 Thunderbolt II**

*Fairchild Aircraft Incorporated
PO Box 790490, San Antonio
Texas 78279-0490, USA*

Originally conceived as a counter-insurgency aircraft to help the war effort in South East Asia, the **Fairchild A-10A Thunderbolt II** emerged as a dedicated close air support aircraft, with the primary role of destroying enemy armour. In this role it is in the process of being replaced by the Lockheed F-16, but the 'Warthog' has adopted a new role of forward air control.

Two **YA-10A**s were built in answer to the USAF's AX competition. These were judged the winner on 18 January 1973 after evaluation against the Northrop A-9, and were followed by six pre-production aircraft.

The first of these was subsequently converted into the sole two-seat **YA-10B**, or **N/AW A-10**, intended for night/adverse weather work, with the addition of a weapons system officer. This programme was cancelled, but 707 A-10As followed the eight development machines.

'Warthog' is a name that has stuck with the A-10, largely on account of its awkward looks. The design, however, is central to the ability of the A-10 to operate effectively in a lethal battlefield environment. Until the recent innovation of an autopilot, the A-10 had to be constantly flown hands-on by the

pilot. This has obvious disadvantages for long flights, but bestows outstanding agility on the aircraft, enabling it to jink and weave at very low level. Survivability is the key to the shape of the A-10, the engines being mounted high on the rear fuselage where they are shrouded from ground fire from most angles by either the wings or tailplane. A strong structure and system redundancy ensures the A-10 can stay aloft with large amounts of battle damage, including an engine or fin shot away. Titanium armour 'bathtubs' protect both the pilot and the ammunition tank.

Furthermore, the aircraft was designed for rapid and easy maintenance. In a combat scenario the A-10 would fly a large number of short sorties, spending the minimum amount of time on the ground while refuelling and re-arming. Rapid maintenance and repair can also be accomplished at this time, by virtue of simple systems and ready-access panels.

Gulf veteran 'Hogs' from the New Orleans-based 706th TFS 'Cajuns' break for the camera on their return from Operation Desert Storm.

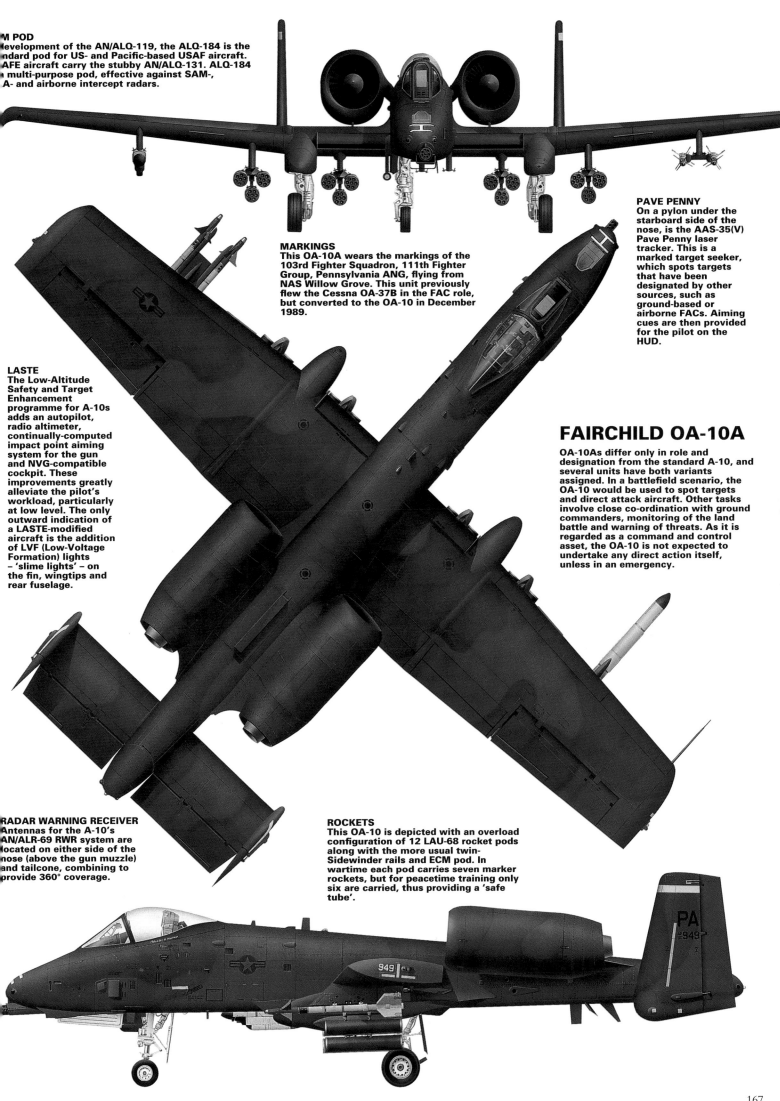

M POD
evelopment of the AN/ALQ-119, the ALQ-184 is the
ndard pod for US- and Pacific-based USAF aircraft.
AFE aircraft carry the stubby AN/ALQ-131. ALQ-184
multi-purpose pod, effective against SAM-,
A- and airborne intercept radars.

MARKINGS
This OA-10A wears the markings of the
103rd Fighter Squadron, 111th Fighter
Group, Pennsylvania ANG, flying from
NAS Willow Grove. This unit previously
flew the Cessna OA-37B in the FAC role,
but converted to the OA-10 in December
1989.

PAVE PENNY
On a pylon under the
starboard side of the
nose, is the AAS-35(V)
Pave Penny laser
tracker. This is a
marked target seeker,
which spots targets
that have been
designated by other
sources, such as
ground-based or
airborne FACs. Aiming
cues are then provided
for the pilot on the
HUD.

LASTE
The Low-Altitude
Safety and Target
Enhancement
programme for A-10s
adds an autopilot,
radio altimeter,
continually-computed
impact point aiming
system for the gun
and NVG-compatible
cockpit. These
improvements greatly
alleviate the pilot's
workload, particularly
at low level. The only
outward indication of
a LASTE-modified
aircraft is the addition
of LVF (Low-Voltage
Formation) lights
– 'slime lights' – on
the fin, wingtips and
rear fuselage.

FAIRCHILD OA-10A

OA-10As differ only in role and
designation from the standard A-10, and
several units have both variants
assigned. In a battlefield scenario, the
OA-10 would be used to spot targets
and direct attack aircraft. Other tasks
involve close co-ordination with ground
commanders, monitoring of the land
battle and warning of threats. As it is
regarded as a command and control
asset, the OA-10 is not expected to
undertake any direct action itself,
unless in an emergency.

RADAR WARNING RECEIVER
Antennas for the A-10's
AN/ALR-69 RWR system are
ocated on either side of the
nose (above the gun muzzle)
and tailcone, combining to
provide 360° coverage.

ROCKETS
This OA-10 is depicted with an overload
configuration of 12 LAU-68 rocket pods
along with the more usual twin-
Sidewinder rails and ECM pod. In
wartime each pod carries seven marker
rockets, but for peacetime training only
six are carried, thus providing a 'safe
tube'.

Fairchild A-10/OA-10 Thunderbolt II

When fired, the GAU-8/A emits an unmistakable noise, like ripping canvas, which is audible for several miles. Several attempts at fitting gas deflector shields on the muzzle have been made but none proved ideal, and the plain barrel end has become standard.

total worn by any aircraft was 86, by 'The Fortune Teller' (78-0593/MB) from the 353rd TFS/354th TFW which operated along with all deployed A-10s, from King Fahd Airport, Saudi Arabia.

WEAPON OPTIONS

In terms of ordnance, the A-10 is designed around the enormous GAU-8/A 30-mm seven-barrelled rotary cannon, which is the world's most powerful airborne gun. However, the principal weapon of the A-10 is the AGM-65 Maverick missile, which has either TV- or IR-guidance. This provides good stand-off range for the anti-armour role or against other 'hard' targets. Various cluster and free-fall bombs can also be carried, although use of these would force an overflight of the target, which is likely to be in the thick of a heavily-gunned battlefield, and so are rarely employed.

Avionics of the A-10 remained very basic for most of the aircraft's career. A HUD was provided, and a screen for displaying images from Mavericks. A Pave Penny seeker on a pylon under the forward fuselage spotted targets designated by laser. No laser designator or rangefinder is fitted. Most current aircraft have received the LASTE modification, which finally adds an autopilot to relieve the arduous task of keeping the A-10 straight and level throughout the flight. LASTE also improves gun accuracy considerably, while the most visible feature is the addition of formation lights.

Entering service at Davis-Monthan AFB, AZ, the A-10 was first flown by the 355th TFTW, and was later issued to the 23rd TFW, 354th TFW and various Reserve/ANG units in the CONUS, and units in Korea and Alaska. By far its most important theatre was Europe, where the 81st TFW flew six squadrons from the twin bases at Woodbridge and Bentwaters in England.

Debates raged as to the vulnerability of the A-10, and it was finally decided to gradually withdraw the type in favour of the F-16. At the same time, redundant A-10s became available to replace the ancient OV-10 in the forward air control role. Without any change to the aircraft, these were redesignated **OA-10A** and distributed to tactical air support squadrons. For the FAC role the A-10s are armed with AIM-9s for self-defence and rocket pods for marking targets.

While the A-10 force was put into decline, both as a result of USAF policy and of more general force cutbacks resulting from the 'peace dividend', the 'Warthog' suddenly found itself at war. Under the auspices of the 354th TFW (Provisional), 144 A-10s from the US and UK flew many Desert Storm missions, involving anti-armour work, air defence suppression and 'Scud' hunting. Throughout the conflict, the A-10 performed admirably, resulting in the destruction of huge numbers of tanks, artillery pieces and vehicles. A pilot from the 10th TFW at Alconbury and another from the 706th TFS at New Orleans were both credited with shooting down Iraqi helicopters. On 25 February 1991 two aircraft from the 76th TSFS/23rd TFW claimed 23 tanks destroyed in one day, under the direction of an OA-10 FAC. The highest mission

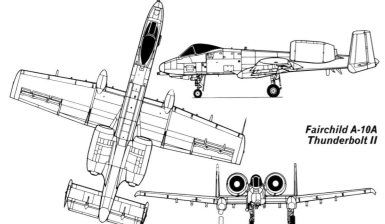

Fairchild A-10A Thunderbolt II

The A-10 is built around the General Electric GAU-8/A Avenger 30-mm, seven-barrelled cannon. It is spun up to its full firing rate of 4,200 rounds per minute in 0.55 seconds. and has a maximum capacity of 1,350 30-mm rounds in a linkless feed system. The rounds are fed from the drum onto a continuous belt to the gun, while spent cartridges and unfired rounds are returned via the belt to the drum.The ammunition is held in a drum that is 6 ft 1 in (1.85 m) long and 2 ft 9 in (0.85 m) in diameter. The gun and feed system is over 13 ft (4 m) long, of which 7 ft 6 in (2.30 m) is barrel. Three types of ammunition are provided for the GAU-8/A. The PGU-13/B is an HEI (High Explosive, Incendiary) round, suitable for use against soft targets, or lightly armoured vehicles. It has a fragmenting jacket filled with standard explosives. The PGU-14/B is the API (Armour-Piercing, Incendiary) round and is of greatest use against armour. A lightweight, aluminium body surrounds a depleted uranium core, which is of very substantial mass, and penetrates armour through kinetic effect alone. While the round is (supposedly) minimally radioactive, uranium is highly flammable and combusts with the heat of the impact once inside a tank. Finally, the PGU-15/B is a TP (Training Practice) round, with no explosive filling. It matches the ballistics of the HEI round for aerial marksmanship. For normal combat sortie, the HEI and API are carried in a ratio of 1:5 (Combat Mix). Despite the manifest ability of the gun, the AGM-65 Maverick is the weapon of choice for the A-10's primary anti-armour mission. Two versions of the 8-ft 2-in (2.49-m) missile are in general use: the AGM-65B with TV scene magnification guidance, and the AGM-65D with an imaging infra-red (IIR) seeker. Both versions have a 125-lb (57-kg) shaped-charge, high explosive warhead, though the AGM-65D is heavier than the AGM-65B. A third version can also be found in use with the A-10, the AGM-65G. This is an IIR weapon with an improved seeker enabling the pilot to designate a specific point within a larger heat source. For use against larger, fixed targets (such as SAM or radar sites), it carries a 300-lb (136-kg) blast penetration warhead. On the port outboard pylon a twin-rail AIM-9L Sidewinder launcher is now a standard fitting, while an ECM pod balances it on the opposite wing. Four pylons are located under each wing (two inboard of undercarriage) along with three under the fuselage. The centreline pylon and its two flanking hardpoints cannot be used simultaneously. Maximum external load is 16,000 lb (7257 kg). The A-10 can carry a potential maximum load of 10 AGM-65 or 28 Mk 82 500-lb LDGP bombs, or 16 Mk 84 1,000-lb bombs, or eight CBU-87 cluster munitions, or 16 CBU-52/71 cluster munitions, two SUU-23/25/30/65 dispensers, practice bombs, assorted ECM pods, travel pods and up to three drop tanks (one centreline). The A-10 has been cleared for, but seldom carries, GBU-10/12 LGBs, BLU-52 tear-gas canisters, M117 LDGP bombs, and the UK's BL755 cluster bomb. A typical general-purpose load for the A-10 during Desert Storm comprised single Mavericks on each main wing pylon, and six SUU-30/64/65 cluster bombs on the unoccupied pylon. Standard ordnance for the OA-10, along with the GAU-8A, is the LAU-68 rocket pod, with a maximum of seven rounds carried. The rockets are Mk 66 motors, usually with white phosphorus warheads.

Defence against ground fire was the primary motivation behind the grey scheme now adopted by many A-10s. The false cockpit painted undernose is very much an 'anti-aircraft' measure.

Capt. Bob Swain piloted 'Chopper Popper', which gained the A-10's first air-to-air kill (type unsure, but probably an MBB BO 105), on 6 February 1991, using its GAU-8. A second A-10 gun kill was chalked up against an Mi-8 nine days later.

OPERATORS

Despite the outstanding results gained by the A-10 in the war with Iraq, the draw-down process continued. In 1994 the A/OA-10 was serving with the 23rd Fighter Wing at Pope AFB, NC, 57th Wing at Nellis AFB (A-10 Weapons School and 422nd TES), the 355th FW at Davis-Monthan AFB and the 20th FW at Shaw AFB within Air Combat Command. One squadron (354th FS) of the 355th Wing is based at McChord AFB, Washington, to support local Army ground units. In other CONUS commands, the A-10 still serves with the 442nd FW (Richards-Gebaur AFB, MO), 917th FW (Barksdale AFB, LA) and 930th Fighter Group (Grissom AFB, Indiana) of the Air Force Reserve, the 103rd FG (Bradley IAP, CT), 104th FG at Barnes Airfield, Massachusetts, the 110th FG (A-10 and OA-10 at Battle Creek, MI), 111th FG (OA-10 at Willow Grove, PA), and 175th FG (A-10 and OA-10 at Baltimore, MD) within the Air National Guard structure and a handful of test/evaluation units.

Outside the CONUS structure two squadrons of OA-10s fly with the 51st Wing at Osan AB, Korea (19th TASS) and the 354th Wing at Eielson AFB, AK (11th TASS). Once the bastion of A-10 power, USAF Europe is left with only the 510th Fighter Squadron (renumbering as the 81st FS) at Spangdahlem, Germany. The parent unit is the 52nd FW.

No export sales were made of the A-10, although in 1994 50 aircraft were being readied at Davis-Monthan AFB for delivery to the Turkish air force (announced in June 1993), and potentially to be based at Eskisehir. Subsequently, this deal has been suspended owing to US reluctance to fund a Turkish buy, which effectively costs the US Government $2 million per aircraft. More deliveries of surplus US aircraft may be made in the future. Greece was also touted as a prospective recipient of surplus aircraft, but this now looks unlikely.

This ALQ-184-equipped OA-10A is based at Eielson AFB, Alaska, with the 354th Wing (formerly the 343rd).

SPECIFICATION

Fairchild Republic A-10A Thunderbolt II
Wing: span 57 ft 6 in (17.53 m); aspect ratio 6.54; area 506.00 sq ft (47.01 m²)
Fuselage and tail: length 53 ft 4 in (16.26 m); height 14 ft 8 in (4.47 m); tailplane span 18 ft 10 in (5.74 m); wheel track 17 ft 2.5 in (5.25 m)
Powerplant: two General Electric TF34-GE-100 each rated at 9,065 lb st (40.32 kN) dry
Weights: basic empty 21,541 lb (9771 kg); operating empty 24,959 lb (11321 kg); forward airstrip armed 32,771 lb (14865 kg); max take-off 50,000 lb (22680 kg)
Fuel and load: internal fuel 10,700 lb (4853 kg); external fuel up to three 600-US gal (2271-litre) drop tanks; maximum ordnance 16,000 lb (7,258 kg) or, with full internal fuel, 14,341 lb (6505 kg)

Speed: never-exceed speed 450 kt (518 mph; 834 km/h); maximum level speed 'clean' at sea level 381 kt (439 mph; 706 km/h)
Range: ferry range 2,131 nm (2,454 miles; 3949 km) with drop tanks; combat radius 540 nm (620 miles; 1000 km) on a deep strike mission or 250 nm (288 miles; 463 km) on a close air support mission with

a 1.7-hour loiter
Performance: maximum rate of climb at sea level 6,000 ft (1828 m) per minute; take-off run 4,000 ft (1220 m) at maximum take-off weight or 442 m (1,450 ft) at forward strip weight; landing run 2,000 ft (610 m) at max weight or 1,300 ft (396 m) at forward strip weight

Fairchild **AU-23A Peacemaker**

After acquiring, in 1966, a licence to produce the Pilatus PC-6 Turbo Porter light transport, Fairchild developed an armed version for the USAF-managed Credible Chase programme. This was intended to produce a 'mini-gunship' for the South Vietnamese air force, armed with a side-firing 20-mm cannon and a range of other weapons and sensors. Fifteen **Fairchild AU-23A Peacemaker**s were purchased by the USAF for evaluation (against the Helio AU-24A) but procurement for the VNAF did not proceed. All the AU-23As

were allocated to the Royal Thai air force in 1973 through the Pave Coin programme, and the RTAF ordered 20 more two years later after transferring five to the air police.

Based at Lop Buri under the control of No. 2 Wing, the AU-23A Peacemakers serve with No. 202 Squadron in the COIN and armed utility role. The primary armament of one XM-197 cannon, firing 700 rpm, is supplemented by two side-firing or underwing pod-mounted 7.62-mm SUU-11A/A Miniguns firing at 2,000 or 4,000 rpm. Four wing hardpoints supplement a 500-lb (227-kg)

fuselage centreline position to give a maximum external load of 2,000 lb (908 kg), which can include SUU-40 flare launchers, 0.50-in (12.7-mm) machine-gun pods, 2.75-in and 5-in Zuni unguided rocket pods, fragmentation, napalm or general-purpose high-explosive bombs, assorted smoke or chemical dispensers, camera pods, loud hailers or leaflet dispensers.

SPECIFICATION

Fairchild AU-23A Peacemaker
Wing: span 49 ft 8 in (15.14 m); aspect ratio 7.96; area 310.01 sq ft (28.80 m²)
Fuselage and tail: length 36 ft 10 in (11.23 m);

height 12 ft 3 in (3.73 m); elevator span 16 ft 9.5 in (5.12 m); wheel track 9 ft 10 in (3.00 m); wheel base 25 ft 10 in (7.87 m)
Powerplant: one Garrett TPE331-1-101F rated at 650 shp (485 kW)
Weights: maximum take-off 6,100 lb (2767 kg)
Fuel and load: internal fuel 127 US gal (480 litres); external fuel none; maximum ordnance 700 lb (318 kg)
Speed: maximum level speed 'clean' at optimum altitude 151 kt (174 mph; 280 km/h); cruising speed at optimum altitude 142 kt (163 mph; 262 km/h)
Range: typical range 485 nm (558 miles; 898 km)
Performance: maximum rate of climb at sea level 1,500 ft (457 m) per minute; service ceiling 22,800 ft (6950 m); take-off run 510 ft (155 m) at maximum take-off weight; landing run 295 ft (90 m) at normal landing weight

Fairchild **C-119 Flying Boxcar**

More than 1,000 C-119s were built after its first flight in November 1947. Derived from the wartime C-82 Packet, the **Fairchild C-119 Flying Boxcar** became the tactical transport workhorse of the USAF, replacing both the C-82 and C-47, and was built also for the USN, USMC, India, Italy and Belgium. Other air forces acquired fleets of C-119s retired from USAF service, among them the **Republic of China** air force, which received 120 of the **C-119G** model in 1969. About half of these remain in service with Nos 102 and 103 Squadrons in the 6th Troop Carrier and Anti-Submarine Combined Wing at Pingtung and are expected to continue into the 21st century as the only surviving military C-119s.

The C-119G was Fairchild's final production variant, featuring an increased gross weight and first introducing Aeroproducts propellers. Typically, 62 fully-equipped troops can be carried, and there are paradrop doors in each side of the split clamshell-type rear cargo-loading doors to permit simultaneous departures from each side of the aircraft.

SPECIFICATION

Fairchild Hiller C-119G Flying Boxcar
Wing: span 109 ft 3 in (33.30 m); aspect ratio 8.53; area 1,400.00 sq ft (130.06 m²)
Fuselage and tail: length 86 ft 6 in (26.36 m);

The Fairchild C-119 is still largely the backbone of the Republic of China Air Force transport effort, equipping two units. A small number of C-130s are in use also.

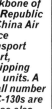

height 26 ft 4 in (8.03 m)
Powerplant: two Wright R-3350-89W Cyclone each rated at 3,400 hp (2535 kW)
Weights: empty 39,982 lb (18136 kg); maximum take-off 74,400 lb (33748 kg)
Speed: maximum level speed 'clean' at 17,000 ft

(5180 m) 257 kt (296 mph; 476 km/h); maximum cruising speed at optimum altitude 174 kt (200 mph; 322 km/h)
Range: 1,890 nm (2,280 miles; 3669 km)
Performance: maximum rate of climb at sea level 750 ft (229 m) per minute

Fairchild C-123 Provider

No military transport had a more unusual origin than the **Fairchild C-123 Provider**, the evolution of which can be traced back to design of an all-metal troop and cargo glider, the Chase XG-20. After a prototype XG-20 had been fitted with two R-2800 Double Wasp piston engines, the USAF bought 302 production examples of the **C-123B** from Fairchild, including 24 intended from the start for Venezuela and Saudi Arabia. In the transport role, the Provider can carry 60 equipped troops or 50 stretchers. A post-production modification programme added a pair of underwing jet pods to boost performance in the **C-123K** version.

As well as serving as tactical transports and in several specialised roles in Vietnam, C-123Bs and C-123Ks were added to the inventories of several Asian air forces comprising the Philippines, South Korea, South Vietnam, Taiwan and **Thailand**, which remains the largest user, with 10 Providers serving in No. 602 Squadron of Wing 6 at Don Muang. They are soon due to be retired in favour of G222s, along with a similar number of long-in-the-tooth C-123s flying with the Air Transport Wing of the **Republic of Korea** air force at Pusan. A pair of C-123Ks is believed to be still in service with the **Fuerza Aérea El Salvador**.

Amazingly, a large share of the Royal Thai Air Force's transport taskings fall on the old but broad shoulders of the Fairchild C-123K Provider. These veterans still serve with 602 Sqn, as part of No. 6 Wing at Bangkok (Don Muang). This is a C-123K with a single podded J85 turbojet under each wing for extra thrust.

SPECIFICATION

Fairchild Hiller C-123K Provider
Wing: span 110 ft 0 in (33.53 m); aspect ratio 9.89; area 1,223.00 sq ft (113.62 m²)
Fuselage and tail: length 76 ft 3 in (23.92 m); height 34 ft 1 in (10.39 m)
Powerplant: two Pratt & Whitney R-2800-99W Double Wasp each rated at 2,500 hp (1865 kW) and two General Electric J85-GE-17 each rated 2,850 lb st (12.69 kN) dry
Weights: empty 35,366 lb (16042 kg); operating empty 36,576 lb (16591 kg); maximum take-off 60,000 lb (18288 kg)
Fuel and load: maximum payload 15,000 lb (6804 kg)
Speed: maximum level speed 'clean' at 10,000 ft (3050 m) 198 kt (228 mph; 367 km/h); max cruising speed at 10,000 ft (3050 m) 150 kt (173 mph; 278 km/h)
Range: ferry range 2,848 nm (3,280 miles; 5279 km); range 899 nm (1,035 miles; 1666 km) with maximum payload
Performance: take-off run 1,167 ft (356 m) at maximum take-off weight; take-off distance to 50 ft (15 m) 1,809 ft (551 m) at maximum take-off weight; landing distance from 50 ft (15 m) 1,800 ft (549 m) at normal landing weight

Fairchild (Swearingen) C-26/Metro III/Merlin IV/MMSA (SMA)

In March 1988, the USAF selected the **Fairchild Metro III** transport to replace the Convair C-131s used by the **ANG**, and commenced deliveries in March 1989 of 13 under the designation **C-26A**. These serve in the Air National Guard Operational Support Aircraft (ANGOSA) role, with quick-change interiors for passengers, stretchers or cargo. A further contract awarded in January 1991 provided for up to 53 **C-26B**s with delivery starting January 1992; these are fitted with TCAS II, GPS and microwave landing systems, the first US military aircraft to be so equipped. A single **UC-26C** serves with the Texas ANG on anti-drug missions, fitted with APG-66 radar and a FLIR to intercept low-flying aircraft.

Fairchild has also marketed the Metro as a **Special Mission Aircraft (SMA)**, with various configurations for maritime patrol, submarine detection, flight inspection, photo reconnaissance, AEW and Elint roles. The **Swedish air force** acquired a **Merlin IVC** (Metro III equivalent) for use as a VIP transport, designated **Tp 88**, and took delivery in 1987 of a second splinter-camouflaged Tp 88 for development of an AEW version. This aircraft has been fitted with a large dorsal planar radar antenna housing for Ericsson PS-890 Erieye E/F band radar, with which it first flew (with operational radar) in May 1991. The Swedish air force has a requirement for about a dozen similar AEW aircraft but has elected to use the Saab 340 as its AEW platform.

Fairchild has now flown and exhibited its Metro 23-derived **Multi-Mission Surveillance Aircraft (MMSA)**. This is a rapidly configurable airframe, capable of undertaking survey, surveillance, Elint and conventional reconnaissance duties while retaining its transport/VIP/air ambulance capability. Along with Lockheed Fort Worth (formerly General Dynamics), Fairchild has developed a centreline systems pod for the MMSA, along with C³I consoles in the cabin, a dedicated surveillance radar fit and accompanying cockpit systems. The pod can house a Loral FLIR and infra-red line scan, electro-optical cameras, LOROP (LOng Range OPtical) gear, air-to-air and sea surveillance radar. Fitting of the GEC-Marconi Seaspray 2000 radar is under investigation. Aircraft will be built, and fitted out, on demand. A Mitsubishi FLIR can also be provided for the pilot.

Fairchild have delivered small numbers of VIP transport Metro III/Merlin IVs to other military customers including **Argentina** (Merlin IVA – three), and **Thailand** (Merlin IVA – two). The MMSA was under evaluation by Turkey, Poland and Hungary in 1993/94 but Turkey, at least, opted for the Britten-Norman Islander-based MSSA.

SPECIFICATION

Fairchild C-26A/B
Wing: span 57 ft 0 in (17.37 m); aspect ratio 10.5; area 309.0 sq ft (28.71 m²)
Fuselage and tail: length 59 ft 4.25 in (18.09 m); height 16 ft 8 in (5.08 m); tailplane span 15 ft 11.5 in (4.86 m); wheel track 15 ft 0 in (4.57 m); wheel base 19 ft 1.5 in (5.83 m)
Powerplant: two Garrett TPE331-121UAR each rated at 1,119 shp (834 kW)
Weights: operating empty 9,180 lb (4164 kg); maximum take-off 14,500 lb (6577 kg) standard or 16,000 lb (7257 kg) optional
Fuel and load: internal fuel 4,342 lb (1969 kg); external fuel none; maximum payload 5,000 lb (2268 kg)
Speed: maximum cruising speed at 15,000 ft (4570 m) at 12,500 lb (5670 kg) 279 kt (321 mph; 517 km/h); economical cruising speed at 25,000 ft (7620 m) 252 kt (290 mph; 467 km/h)
Range: at optional maximum take-off weight 1,063 nm (1,224 miles; 1,970 km) or at standard maximum take-off weight 384 nm (442 miles; 711 km)
Performance: maximum rate of climb at sea level 2,370 ft (722 m) per minute; service ceiling 27,500 ft (8380 m); take-off distance to 50 ft (15 m) 3,340 ft (1018 m) at standard maximum take-off weight; landing distance from 50 ft (15 m) 2,450 ft (747 m) at normal landing weight

Right: Sweden flies the Metro III/Tp 88 as a VIP transport, along with Beech 200s.

Below: the MMSA is the current 'special mission' Metro.

FAMA/FMA IA-50 Guaraní II

Developed from the Huanquero and Guaraní I, the **IA-50 Guaraní II** was developed for the **Argentine air force** as a transport and utility aircraft. The first Guaraní II flew on 23 April 1963. The type features a low-set wing with two Turboméca Bastan VI turboprops, a cabin for up to 15, and a large, sharply-swept tail. One was fitted with ski undercarriage for Antarc-tic operations. Forty-one were built, including prototypes, and all served in Argentina.

A handful remains in service with II Brigada Aérea at Base Aérea General Urquiza at Paraná. Four were configured for photo-survey, and three fly navaid and landing system calibration flights. All survivors are to be replaced by surplus US C-12 Hurons during 1994.

SPECIFICATION

FAMA/FMA IA-50 Guaraní II
Wing: span 19.59 m (64 ft 3.25 in) without tip tanks; aspect ratio 9.18; area 41.81 m² (450.05 sq ft)
Fuselage and tail: length 15.30 m (50 ft 2.5 in); height 5.61 m (18 ft 5 in); tailplane span 6.50 m (21 ft 4 in)
Powerplant: two Turboméca Bastan VIA each rated at 930 shp (693 kW)
Weights: empty equipped 3924 kg (8,650 lb); maximum take-off 7200 kg (15,873 lb) without tip tanks and 7750 kg (17,085 lb) with tip tanks
Fuel and load: internal fuel 1910 litres (505 US gal) plus 144 litres (38 US gal) in two non-jettisonable tip tanks; maximum payload 1500 kg (3,307 lb)
Speed: maximum level speed 'clean' at optimum altitude 270 kt (311 mph; 500 km/h); maximum cruising speed 265 kt (305 mph; 491 km/h)
Range: 2575 km (1,389 nm; 1,600 miles) with maximum fuel or 1995 km (1,077 nm; 1,240 mile) with maximum payload
Performance: maximum rate of climb at sea level 805 m (2,640 ft) per minute; service ceiling 41,000 m (12500 m); take-off run 420 m (1,380 ft) at maximum take-off weight

FAMA/FMA IA-58 Pucará

Fábrica Militar de Aviones SA
Avienda Fuerza Aérea Argentina Km 5½
5103 Guarnición Aérea Córdoba, Argentina

Meeting a **Fuerza Aérea Argentina (FAA)** requirement for a close air support, reconnaissance and counter-insurgency aircraft, the **Pucará** was an indifferent performer in the 1982 Falklands War with the United Kingdom and consequently suffered a loss of support for its *modus operandi*. The Pucará concept originated in the early 1960s, when anti-guerrilla and counter-insurgency were the types of warfare anticipated by Argentina. Fabrica Militar de Aviones (FMA) was then a component of the FAA's Support Command and produced the **IA-58** design with twin turboprops and all-metal construction. The prototype flew on 20 August 1969, powered by a pair of 674-kW (904-ehp) Garrett TPE331-U-303 powerplants, but the production version utilised 671-kW (1,022-ehp) Turboméca Astazou XVIGs, which powered the second aircraft for its maiden flight on 6 September 1970.

Named for the stone forts built by the indigenous South American people, the Pucará is a manoeuvrable and rugged aircraft able to operate from short, rough airstrips – 80 m (262 ft) is enough when helped by three JATO bottles. A tall, retractable tricycle undercarriage provides ample space for weapons and the generous propeller ground clearance necessary for flights from uneven land. Crew are provided with Martin-Baker Mk 6 zero/zero ejection seats, the rear occupant having full dual controls and a cockpit floor raised 25 cm (10 in). The forward windscreen is armoured, as is the cabin floor. In practice, a second crew member is rarely necessary for COIN missions and the aircraft is usually flown with the rear seat empty.

Weapons, which are aimed with a SFOM 83A-3 sight, include fixed armament of two 20-mm Hispano cannon under the nose and four 7.62-mm Browning machine-guns abreast of the cockpit. With these and full fuel load, an additional 1500 kg (3,307 lb) of external stores can be carried in the form of bombs, rockets, cannon pods, napalm drop tanks or reconnaissance pods.

The first production **IA-58A** flew on 8 November 1974 and deliveries began to the FAA in 1976 for three squadrons of Grupo 3 at Reconquista and one squadron of 9 Grupo at Comodoro Rivadavia. Early action was seen late in 1976 against rebel forces in north-west Argentina. An initial order for 60 was augmented by a follow-on batch of 48, but the last 22 of these were not accepted by the FAA and offered for sale. Furthermore, a total of 40 surplus aircraft were made available for export in 1986, as soon as production had ended. All 24 aircraft deployed to the Falkland Islands in 1982 were lost to sabotage, ground fire and bombing, or were captured by British forces, one of these latter later flying in British military markings for evaluation. Another was lost operating from Comodoro Rivadavia, although a Pucará shot down a Westland Scout helicopter. Prior to the conflict, in October 1981, the first of six aircraft diverted from FAA orders had been delivered to **Uruguay** for Grupo de Aviación 2 of Brigada Aérea II at Durazno. **Colombia** was presented with three for drugs interdiction operations in late 1989, these flown by Escuadrón 212 of Grupo II at Apiay. Argentina now has only 40 aircraft with two remaining squadrons of Grupo 3. Some have the rear cockpit deleted in favour of additional fuel. Work on installation of a new navigation and attack system (SINT) began in the late 1980s, but was soon terminated due to financial problems.

More ambitious upgrades also failed to gain acceptance. **IA-58B** was the designation for a single prototype, flown 15 May 1979, with cannon uprated to two 30-mm DEFA 553s, deeper forward fuselage and improved avionics. The planned 40 aircraft emerged as IA-58As. Taking aboard lessons of the Falklands War, the **IA-58C** 'Pucará Charlie' was a proposed rebuild of IA-58As with two DEFA 553s in addition to the six 20-mm and 7.62-mm weapons, the front cockpit faired over, rear cockpit enlarged and protected by further armour, and weapon options expanded with Martin Pescador (Kingfisher) ASMs and MATRA Magic self-defence AAMs. Additional avionics were added in the form of a radar warning receiver, Omega/VLF navigation and radar altimeter, while the engines gained self-start capability and modified exhausts to reduce infra-red emissions. Only one prototype was produced, and flew on 30 December 1985. It has been suggested that the FAA is considering retrofitting its surviving Pucarás to IA-58C standard, but no progress has been made.

IA-66 was the designation of a sixth prototype Pucará which flew in 1980, powered by 746-kW (1,000-ehp) Garrett TPE331-11-601W engines driving Dowty Rotol propellers. The latter were replaced by McCauley units in 1983, but no production aircraft were ordered. Several reported contracts for IA-58As have failed to materialise, such as 50 for **Egypt** and 12 for the **Central African Republic**, although one of six aircraft for **Mauritania** was actually painted before the 1978 order was cancelled. **Iraq** requested 20 in 1985, but was turned down by the Argentine government. In 1992 four IA-58As were supplied to **Sri Lanka**.

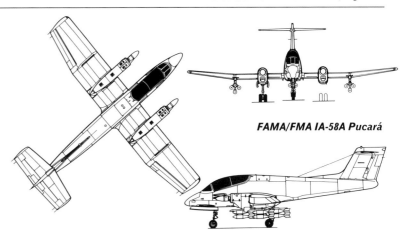

FAMA/FMA IA-58A Pucará

SPECIFICATION

FAMA/FMA IA-58A Pucará
Wing: span 14.50 m (47 ft 6.8 in); aspect ratio 6.94; area 30.30 m² (326.16 sq ft)
Fuselage and tail: length 14.253 m (46 ft 9 in); height 5.362 m (17 ft 7 in); tailplane span 4.70 m (15 ft 5 in); wheel track 4.20 m (13 ft 9.25 in); wheel base 3.885 m (12 ft 9 in)
Powerplant: two Turboméca Astazou XVIG each rated at 729 kW (978 shp)
Weights: empty equipped 4020 kg (8,862 lb); normal take-off 5300 kg (11,684 lb); maximum take-off 6800 kg (14,991 lb)
Fuel and load: internal fuel 1000 kg (2,205 lb); external fuel up to 1359 kg (2,997 lb) in one 1100- or 318-litre (290- or 84-US gal) and two 318-litre (84-US gal) drop tanks; maximum ordnance 1500 kg (3,307 lb)
Speed: never exceed speed 405 kt (466 mph; 750 km/h); maximum level speed 'clean' at 9,845 ft (3000 m) 270 kt (311 mph; 500 km/h); maximum cruising speed at 19,685 ft (6000 m) 259 kt (298 mph; 480 km/h); economical cruising speed at optimum altitude 232 kt (267 mph; 430 km/h)
Range: ferry range 3710 km (2,002 nm; 2,305 miles) with three drop tanks; combat radius 225 km (121 nm; 140 miles) on a lo-lo-lo attack mission with a 1500-kg (3,307-lb) warload, or 325 km (175 nm; 202 miles) on a lo-lo-hi attack mission with a 1500-kg (3,307-lb) warload, or 350 km (189 nm; 217 miles) on a hi-lo-hi attack mission with a 1500-kg (3,307-lb) warload, or 400 km (216 nm; 248 miles) on a lo-lo-lo attack mission with a 1000-kg (2,205-lb) warload, or 575 km (310 nm; 357 miles) on a lo-lo-hi attack mission with a 1000-kg (2,205-lb) warload, or 650 km (350 nm; 404 miles, on a hi-lo-hi attack mission with a 1000-kg (2,205-lb) warload
Performance: maximum rate of climb at sea level 1080 m (3,543 ft) per minute; service ceiling 32,800 ft (10000 m); take-off run 300 m (984 ft) at 5500 kg (12,125 lb); take-off distance to 50 ft (15 m) 705 m (2,313 ft) at 5500 kg (12,125 lb); landing distance from 50 ft (15 m) 603 m (1,978 ft) at 5100 kg (11,243 lb); landing run 200 m (656 ft) at 5100 kg (11,243 lb)
g limits: +3 to -6

In December 1989 Colombia received three IA-58As for 'anti-narcotics' operations, alongside AC-47s.

FAMA/FMA IA-63 Pampa

Argentina's Fabrica Militar de Aviones SA (FMA, or Military Aircraft Factory), which is operated by the Argentine air force, started **IA-63** development in 1979 to replace the FAA's ageing licence-built four-seat FMA Morane-Saulnier MS.760 Paris II light jets used since 1958 as armed trainers, from 48 originally procured. FMA received technical assistance with design of the Pampa from Dornier, based on its Alpha Jet advanced trainer experience, and the Pampa was selected after the evaluation of seven joint project studies. It retained an Alpha Jet-type configuration, although with unswept wings and tailplane in a lighter airframe powered by a single 3,500-lb (15.57-kN) Garrett TFE731-2-2N turbofan. Other design features include dual-system hydraulic servo primary controls with three-axis electro-mechanical trim and an emergency ram-air turbine. Hydraulic power is also used for operation of the tricycle landing gear, single-slotted Fowler-type flaps, and the twin air brakes above the rear fuselage.

Student and instructor are accommodated in stepped tandem UPC (Stencil) S-III-S31A63 lightweight zero-zero ejection seats in the pressurised cockpit. Dornier also built the wings and tailplanes of the three flying and two static test prototypes, the first of which (EX-01) made its initial flight on 6 October 1984, and is continuing to assist FMA with Pampa marketing. Plans did not materialise for a fourth prototype, powered by a 2,900-lb (12.9-kN) Pratt & Whitney JT15D-5 turbofan.

The first of 18 IA-63s, comprising three pre-series and 15 initial production Pampas from a planned batch of 64, were delivered to II Squadron of the 4 Brigada Aerea, also

FAMA/FMA IA 63 Pampa

known as the Escuela de Caza (Fighter School), at El Plumerillo from March 1988 to provide advanced training and weapons instruction. In the latter role and for light attack duties, for which most FAA Pampas are being upgraded, the IA-63 has four underwing and one fuselage weapons pylons, with a maximum capacity of 3,417 lb (1550 kg). This could include a ventral 30-mm DEFA cannon pod with 145 rounds, and up to six Mk 81 250-lb (114-kg) bombs or two each of Mk 81s and 500-lb Mk 82 (227-kg) bombs.

FAA plans for Pampa procurement included a requirement for 36 more aircraft for front-line units, increasing total purchases to 100 aircraft, but severe funding problems have delayed further production deliveries. Similar problems have been encountered with a deck-training version in which the Argentine navy was interested for its carrier 25 de Mayo.

A version of the IA-63, known as the **Pampa 2000**, is being offered for the US JPATS programme by FMA in conjunction with the Vought Aircraft Company, plus Loral for ground-based training, UNC for aircraft logistics support and Allied Signal as suppliers of the engine, avionics and environmental control system. The second prototype (EX-02) and two production aircraft were sent to the US for modification to Pampa 2000 standard. If selected, **Vought** would build the aircraft in Dallas using 90 per cent US components. The programme suffered a blow with the loss of EX-02 in the UK on 31 August 1992, prior to its debut at that year's Farnborough show. In September 1993 the Pampa 200 began a two-month tour of USAF and USN bases, beginning at Andrews AFB, Maryland.

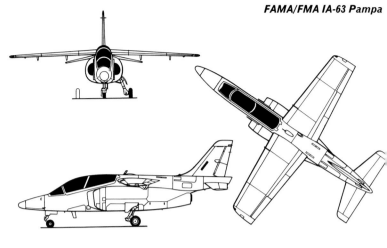

SPECIFICATION

FAMA/FMA IA-63 Pampa
Wing: span 9.686 m (31 ft 9.25 in); aspect ratio 6.0; area 15.633 m2 (168.27 sq ft)
Fuselage and tail: length 10.93 m (35 ft 10.25 in) excluding probe; height 4.29 m (14 ft 1 in); tailplane span 4.576 m (15 ft 0.33 in); wheel track 2.663 m (8 ft 8.75 in); wheel base 4.418 m (14 ft 6 in)
Powerplant: one Garrett TFE731-2-2N rated at 3,500 lb st (15.57 kN) dry
Weights: empty equipped 2821 kg (6,219 lb); normal take-off 3800 kg (8,377 lb); maximum take-off 5000 kg (11,023 lb)
Fuel and load: internal fuel 1118 kg (2,465 lb) including 415 litres (109 US gal) of auxiliary fuel in outer-wing tanks; external fuel none; maximum ordnance 1160 kg (2,557 lb)
Speed: maximum level speed 'clean' at 7000 m (22,965 ft) 442 kt (509 mph; 819 km/h) or at sea level 405 kt (466 mph; 750 km/h); cruising speed at 4000 m (13,125 ft) 403 kt (464 mph; 747 km/h)
Range: ferry range 1853 km (1,000 nm; 1,151 miles) with auxiliary fuel; range 1500 km (809 nm; 932 miles); mission radius 440 km (237 nm; 273 miles) on a hi-hi-hi air-to-air gunnery mission with a 250-kg (551-lb) warload, or 360 km (194 nm; 223 miles) on a hi-lo-hi air-to-ground mission with a 1000-kg (2,205-lb) warload; endurance 3 hours 48 minutes
Performance: maximum rate of climb at sea level 1560 m (5,118 ft) per minute; service ceiling 12900 m (42,325 ft); take-off run 424 m (1,390 ft) at 3700 kg (8,157 lb); take-off distance to 15 m (50 ft) 700 m (2,297 ft) at 3700 kg (8,157 lb); landing distance from 15 m (50 ft) 850 m (2,789 ft) at 3500 kg (7,716 lb); landing run 461 m (1,512 ft) at 3500 kg (7,716 lb)
g limits: -3 to +6 (+4.5 sustained)

Below: The Pampa is now operational with the Fuerza Aérea Argentina. Aircraft serials are carried only inside the nosewheel door.

Right: The second IA 63 served as the prototype for the Pampa 2000, but crashed during a display practice at Bournemouth in 1992.

FFA AS 202 Bravo

FFA Flugzeugwerke Altenrhein AG
CH-9423 Altenrhein
Switzerland

Designed as the **S.202** by SIAI-Marchetti in Italy, the **Bravo** two/three-seat trainer was launched as a joint project between that company and Flug und Fahrzeugwerke AG in Switzerland. Prototypes were flown on 7 March and 7 May 1969, respectively in Switzerland and Italy. FFA took full control in 1973, with subsidiary Repair AG responsible for marketing. Production was primarily for military flying schools, and was concentrated on the 180-hp (134-kW) **AS 202/18A** variant, although it included 34 of the 115-hp (86-kW) **AS 202/15** variant. FFA also built prototypes with a 260-hp (194-kW) Lycoming (**AS 202/26A**) and with a 320-shp (239-kW) Allison 250-B17 turboprop (**AS 202/32**).

Production of the AS 202/18A has included four sub-variants. The **A1** has an aerobatic gross weight of 950 kg (2,094 lb) and was supplied to **Morocco** (18, used at the flying school at Menara-Marrakesh) and to **Uganda** (eight for the central flying school). The **A2** has a gross weight of 980 kg (2,160 lb), electric trim and an extended canopy. **Iraq** received 48 of this model for its IrAF College at Tihret; between 10 and 12 were reported to have been transferred to the **Royal Jordan Air Force**. The **A3** had mechanical trim and a 24-volt electrical system. **Indonesia** acquired 40, to serve in No. 101 Squadron (Skwadron Latih Mulah) at the flying school (Sekolah Penerbang) at Adisutjipto. Finally, the **Royal Flight of Oman** acquired four **A4**s, with weight increased to 1,010 kg (2,226 lb) and CAA-approved special instrumentation. Production halted in 1989, with 180 delivered, though the line remains open for orders.

SPECIFICATION

FFA AS 202/18A Bravo
Wing: span 9.75 m (31 ft 11.75 in); aspect ratio 6.5; area 13.86 m2 (149.19 sq ft)
Fuselage and tail: length 7.50 m (24 ft 7.25 in); height 2.81 m (9 ft 2.75 in); tailplane span 3.67 m (12 ft 0.5 in); wheel track 2.25 m (7 ft 4.5 in); wheel base 1.78 m (5 ft 10 in)
Powerplant: one Textron Lycoming AEIO-360-B1F rated at 180 hp (134 kW)
Weights: empty equipped 710 kg (1.565 lb); normal take-off 980 kg (2,160 lb) for aerobatics; maximum take-off 1080 kg (2,381 lb)
Fuel and load: internal fuel 170 litres (44.9 US gal); external fuel none; maximum ordnance none
Speed: never exceed speed 173 kt (199 mph; 320 km/h); maximum level speed 'clean' at sea level 130 kt (150 mph; 241 km/h); maximum cruising speed at 8,000 ft (2440 m) 122 kt (141 mph; 226 km/h); economical cruising speed at 10,000 ft (3050 m) 109 kt (126 mph; 203 km/h)
Range: with maximum fuel and no reserves 615 nm (1140 km; 707 miles)
Performance: maximum rate of climb at sea level 800 ft (244 m) per minute; service ceiling 17,000 ft (5180 m); take-off run 215 m (705 ft) at maximum take-off weight; take-off distance to 50 ft (15 m) 415 m (1,360 ft) at maximum take-off weight; landing distance from 50 ft (15 m) 465 m (1,525 ft) at normal landing weight
g limits: -3 to +6

Indonesia is the major user of the Bravo, having received 40 AS 202A3s as primary trainers.

FLS (Lovaux) **Optica/Scoutmaster**

FLS Aerospace (Lovaux) Ltd
Bournemouth International Airport
Christchurch, Dorset BH23 6NW, UK

Designed primarily for use as a specialised observation aircraft by civil and quasi-military agencies, the **OA7-300 Optica** has applications for coastal patrol, visual reconnaissance and liaison duty. An electronic surveillance version has also been proposed as the **Scoutmaster**, equipped with search radar and FLIR. The private-venture Optica, designed by Edgley, was first flown on 14 December 1979. Subsequent small-scale production by Brooklands Aerospace ended after a factory fire destroyed nine aircraft before delivery, and the Lovaux subsidiary of FLS Aerospace acquired the design in 1990, transferring production to its Bournemouth factory. Production resumed in 1992 after UK certification in December 1991. Small numbers of Opticas have been delivered to civilian and police customers, but no military orders have yet been received.

SPECIFICATION

FLS Aerospace (Lovaux) Optica OA7-300
Wing: span 39 ft 4 in (11.99 m); aspect ratio 9.1; area 170.50 sq ft (15.84 m²)
Fuselage and tail: length 26 ft 9 in (8.15 m); height 7 ft 7 in (2.31 m) over tailplane and 6 ft 6 in (1.98 m) over shroud excluding antenna; tail unit span 11 ft 2 in (3.40 m) to centreline of booms; wheel track 11 ft 2 in (3.40 m); wheel base 9 ft 0 in (2.73 m)
Powerplant: one Textron Lycoming IO-540-V4A5D rated at 260 hp (194 kW)
Weights: empty equipped 2,090 lb (948 kg); maximum take-off 2,900 lb (1315 kg)
Fuel and load: internal fuel 250 litres (66 US gal); external fuel none
Speed: never-exceed speed 140 kt (161 mph; 259 km/h); maximum level speed 'clean' at optimum altitude 115 kt (132 mph; 213 km/h); maximum cruising speed at optimum altitude 103 kt (109 mph; 191 km/h);

FLS was concerned solely with civil airliner maintenance until it acquired the assets of Brooklands Aerospace in 1990. Part of this deal included rights to the Brooklands (formerly Edgley) Optica.

economical cruising speed at optimum altitude 86 kt (99 mph; 159 km/h)
Range: 570 nm (656 miles; 1056 km) at 70 kt (81 mph; 130 km/h) or 370 nm (426 miles; 685 km) at 110 kt (127 mph; 204 km/h); endurance 8 hours at 70 kt (81 mph; 130 km/h) or 2 hours 45 minutes at 110 kt (127 mph; 204 km/h)

Performance: maximum rate of climb at sea level 810 ft (247 m) per minute; service ceiling 14,000 ft (4275 m); take-off run 1,082 ft (330 m) at maximum take-off weight; take-off distance to 50 ft (15 m) 1,548 ft (472 m) at maximum take-off weight; landing distance from 50 ft (15 m) 1,820 ft (555 m) at normal landing weight

FLS (Trago Mills) **SAH-1 Sprint**

The **SAH-1** has the potential to be an excellent military basic and primary trainer. It has impeccable handling characteristics, sensible, robust, no-frills engineering, a roomy side-by-side cockpit and superb all-round vision. The brainchild of a Cornish supermarket magnate (the Trago Mills chain of shops), the prototype was constructed under the Trago Mills name and bore as its designation the initials of its designer, Sidney Arthur Holloway. The aircraft first flew on 23 August 1983 and received rave reviews, and was borrowed by the ETPS at Boscombe Down, whose commandant, Air Vice Marshal Geoff Cairns, later became test pilot.

The prototype was powered by a 120-hp (89.52-kW) Textron Lycoming O-235-L2A engine driving a fixed-pitch propeller, but production aircraft will be fitted with a 160-hp (119.36-kW) AEIO-320-DB. Plans for a line in Hungary fell through, but the com-

In the hands of FLS, the Sprint finally gained its UK CofA on 17 July 1994. The fully aerobatic production aircraft is now a serious contender in the military market.

pany was bought out by Orca Aircraft in 1988, which collapsed one year later. The **SAH-1** itself was too good to be lost, how-

ever, and all rights were sold to FLS (Lovaux) in October 1991. The first production example flew on 16 December 1993.

Fokker **F27 Friendship**

Apart from the Antonov An-24/26 family, the **Fokker F27 Friendship** is the world's best-selling airliner in the 50-seat class. Originally planned as a 32-seat passenger aircraft, its efficiency led to stretching into the 50- and even 60-seat class and, as the **F-27J** and **FH-227**, 205 were made under licence by **Fairchild** in the USA. All versions have a high-mounted high-aspect wing with slotted flaps and integral tanks, a pressurised fuselage with a 2.49-m (98-in) wide cabin and 1.93-m (76-in) high, pneumatically-operated undercarriage and pneumatic de-icers on all leading edges.

By 1960 Fokker was offering the **F27 Mk 300 Combiplane**, with large forward cargo doors, strong floor and quick-change passenger/cargo interior. With further minor modifications this became the **F27 Mk 300M Troopship**, nine of which were sold to the **KLu** (Royal Netherlands air force) to follow three Series 100s. The name Troopship was subsequently dropped, and for many years the standard military model was the **F27 Mk 400M**, first flown in 1965. This was fitted with

1700-ekW (2,280-ehp) Dart Mk 536 turboprops, replaced from 1984 by the more efficient Mk 552 model. Normal accommodation is 46 paratroops in folding canvas seats, dispatched through doors on each side at the rear. Alternatively, 6025 kg (13,283 lb) of cargo or 24 USAF-type stretchers and nine seats may be carried. A cartographic version is also available with inertial navigation system, two super-wide-angle cameras and a navigation sight and optional target-tow gear. Fokker also built the **F27 Mk 500**, with a fuselage lengthened to 25.06 m (82 ft 2.5 in) for up to 60 seats.

In addition to the Netherlands, the F27 is currently operated in the transport role by **Algeria** (three), **Argentina** (13), **Bolivia** (five), **Côte d'Ivoire** (one), **Finland** (three), **Ghana** (four), **Guatemala** (three), **Iceland** (coast guard), **India** (two for the coast guard), **Indonesia** (seven), **Iran** (18), **Mexico** (seven), **Myanmar** (four), **New Zealand** (three, stored), **Pakistan** (three) **Peru** (one), **Philippines** (nine), **Senegambia** (six), **Sudan** (one), **Thailand** (two) and **Uruguay** (three) and the **US**

Army (two, designated **C-31A**). The C-31As were used by the US Army's 'Golden Knights' display team.

In 1975 Fokker completed definition of a specialised maritime patrol version of the F27 as the **Fokker F27 Maritime**. Intended for all forms of coastal surveillance, SAR and environmental control missions, the Maritime has a crew of up to six and can mount 12-hour patrols. It is equipped with Litton APS-504 search radar in a belly blister, nose-mounted Bendix weather radar, and a fully comprehensive navigation systems, as well as a fully equipped tactical compartment, crew rest areas and bulged observation windows to the flight deck and rear of the cabin. This version was subsequently sold to **Angola** and **Peru** (where it is no longer operated) and is currently in use in the **Netherlands** (two), **Nigeria** (two), **Pakistan** (four), **Philippines** (three), **Spain** (three) and **Thailand** (three).

Thailand's aircraft are armed, but otherwise not to **Maritime Enforcer** standard. This variant is tasked for armed surveillance, ASW, anti-ship attack and other combat roles, and is equipped with a LAPADS processor system for active and passive sonobuoys, MAD and comprehensive ESM and IR detection systems, plus optional underwing searchlight. The **Maritime Enforcer 2** is based on the next-generation **Fokker 50** (described separately),

with PW 124 engines, six-bladed propellers and completely new systems.

SPECIFICATION

Fokker F27 Mk 400M Troopship
Wing: span 29.00 m (95 ft 2 in); aspect ratio 12.0; area 70.00 m² (753.50 sq ft)
Fuselage and tail: length 23.56 m (77 ft 3.5 in); height 8.50 m (27 ft 11 in); tailplane span 9.75 m (32 ft 0 in); wheel track 7.20 m (23 ft 7.5 in); wheel base 8.74 m (28 ft 8 in)
Powerplant: two Rolls-Royce Dart RDa.7 Mk 532-7 each rated at 2,050 shp (1528.5 kW) plus 525 lb st (2.34 kN) dry
Weights: manufacturer's empty 24,720 lb (11213 kg); operating empty 25,307 lb (11479 kg) in freight configuration, or 26,240 lb (11902 kg) in medevac configuration, or 26,696 lb (11655 kg) in paratroop configuration; maximum take-off 45,000 lb (20412 kg)
Fuel and load: internal fuel 5140 litres (1,358 US gal); external fuel none; maximum payload 12,863 lb (5834 kg) in freight configuration, or 11,991 lb (5439 kg) in medevac configuration, or 12,425 lb (5635 kg) in paratroop configuration
Speed: normal cruising speed at 20,000 ft (6095 m) 259 kt (298 mph; 480 km/h)
Range: 670 nm (771 miles; 1241 km) with maximum space-limited payload, or 540 nm (622 miles; 1001 km) with maximum payload, or 975 nm (1,123 miles; 1807 km) with maximum fuel and an 8,842-lb (3961-kg) payload
Performance: maximum rate of climb at sea level 1,620 ft (494 m) per minute; service ceiling 30,000 ft (9145 m); take-off run 3,900 ft (1189 m) at 42,000 lb (19051 kg)

Left: The Philippines air force operates eight F27s as transports and one as a Presidential aircraft.

Right: The Pakistan navy obtained four F27s, and both were then converted by Fokker to full F27MPA standard from 1985, supplanting Breguet Atlantics.

Fokker F28 Fellowship

NV Koninklijke Nederlandse Vliegtuigfabreik Fokker
PO Box 12222, NL-1100 AE, Amsterdam-Zuidoost
The Netherlands

Prototype development of the **Fokker F28 Fellowship** twin-jet airliner began with a first flight on 9 May 1967. Production of 241 F28s between 1968 and 1986 included about 20 for military or quasi-military use, the type being particularly successful as a Presidential transport in several smaller nations, most notably in South America and Africa, where its rough-field capability is most appreciated. The most widely used versions were the original 65-seater **Mk 1000** (with fewer seats in VIP configuration), and the **Mk 1000-C** with side-loading freight door and mixed passenger/cargo interior. With the same fuselage, the **Mk 3000** featured increased wing span and uprated engines, while the **Mk 4000** had a longer fuselage accommodating 79 seats.

Examples of the Mk 1000 are flown for Presidential and VIP transportation by **Argentina** (two, air force), **Colombia** (one, air force), **Gabon** (one, operated in civilian marks for the government), **Netherlands** (Dutch Royal Flight, civil registered), **Indonesia** (one, air force), **Ivory Coast** (one, operated in civilian marks for the government), **Peru** (one, air force) and **Togo** (one, operated in civilian marks for the government), while a similar role is performed

by a Mk 3000 in **Ghana** (one, air force) and **Tanzania** (one, operated in civil marks for the government). The **Argentine navy** also operates three F28 Mk 3000s, and one was deployed to Saudia Arabia in support of coalition operations during Desert Storm. A Mk 4000 can be found in service with the **Ivory Coast** (one, operated in civilian marks for the government). Also, in Colombia, is a single Mk 3000C used by the military airline **SATENA** (based at Bogota), while a similar role is performed by one Mk 4000 of Esc 1111 in **Ecuador**, this being the designation of the military airline **TAME** (based at Quito). This aircraft is civil registered but has been allocated a military serial. In Argentina, the airline **LADE** has the use of four Mk 1000-Cs, in its military role as II Escuadron de Transporte in I Transport Wing. While these aircraft undertake scheduled services to remote (uneconomic) destinations, they wear military colours. **Malaysia** – another early operator of the F28 Mk 1000 – has retired the last of two.

SPECIFICATION

Fokker F28 Mk 3000 Fellowship
Wing: span 25.07 m (82 ft 3 in); aspect ratio 7.96;

Fokker's F28 has proved a popular choice for VIP units in South America. Since 1971 the FAC (Colombian air force) has flown this one example as part of its Presidential flight.

area 79.00 m² (850.38 sq ft)
Fuselage and tail: length 27.40 m (89 ft 10.75 in); height 8.47 m (27 ft 9.5 in); tailplane span 8.64 m (28 ft 4.25 in); wheel track 5.04 m (16 ft 6.5 in); wheel base 8.90 m (29 ft 2.5 in)
Powerplant: two Rolls-Royce Spey RB.183-2 Mk 555-15P each rated at 9,900 lb st (44.04 kN) dry
Weights: operating empty 36,997 lb (16781 kg); maximum take-off 73,000 lb (33113 kg)
Fuel and load: internal fuel 17,240 lb (7820 kg) standard or 23,080 lb (10469 kg) optional with centre section tankage; external fuel none; maximum payload

19,000 lb (8618 kg)
Speed: maximum cruising speed at 22,965 ft (7000 m) 454 kt (523 mph; 843 km/h); economical cruising speed at 30,000 ft (9145 m) 466 kt (421 mph; 678 km/h)
Range: 1,710 nm (1,969 miles; 3169 km) with maximum fuel and 65 passengers
Performance: maximum cruising altitude 35,000 ft (10670 m); balanced take-off field length 5,200 ft (1585 m) at maximum take-off weight; balanced landing field length 3,495 ft (1065 m) at normal landing weight

Fokker 50/Enforcer 2/Kingbird/60 Utility

The **Republic of China** air force is the first customer for the **Fokker 50** in its basic transport configuration, with three acquired in 1992. The F50 is a lengthened, re-engined derivative of the F27, first flown on 28 December 1985 and intended primarily for the airline market. In this guise, it can carry 46 to 68 passengers, with combi and all-cargo versions also available.

A range of special-purpose variants is available, based for the most part on equipment fits originally proposed with the F27. These variants include the **Black Crow 2** comm/Elint version, fitted with an ARCO Systems AR-7000 Sigint system; the unarmed **Maritime Mk 2**, fitted with Texas Instruments AN/APS-134 search radar; the armed **Maritime Enforcer Mk 2**

The Enforcer Mk 2 has provision for four torpedoes (Mk 44, 46, Stingray or similar), or depth charges, along with Exocet, Harpoon, Sea Eagle or Sea Skua anti-ship missiles.

for maritime patrol; the **Kingbird Mk 2** for AEW with phased array radar; the **Sentinel Mk 2** with AN/APS-134(V)7 synthetic aperture radar, AN/APS-135(V) SLAR, and podded EO imaging system for surveillance and reconnaissance; and the **Troopship Mk 3** stretched to incorporate a forward cargo door to starboard and capable of carrying 50 troops with paradrop facility. The prototype Enforcer made its maiden flight on 27 January 1993, the only version yet to fly.

In early 1994 deliveries began of four F50s for the **Singapore** air force, as Skyvan replacements with No. 121 Sqn, at Changi. Singapore has options on three further transport versions and is the launch customer for the Maritime Enforcer with five aircraft on order. The latter will be fitted with a 360° radar (Texas Instruments APS-134), a GEC VOO-1069 FLIR, a CAE ASQ-504(V) internal MAD and a CDC UYS-503 sonobuoy processing suite.

An order in 1994 from the **Royal Netherlands Air Force** launched

Fokker's latest military turboprop development, the **Fokker 60 Utility**. Based on the Fokker 50 Utility/Troopship, the F60 is stretched by a further 1.62 m (5 ft 4 in) to accommodate a cargo door measuring 3.05 x 1.78 m (10 ft x 5 ft 10 in), which enables the aircraft to carry an F100 engine for an F-16. Fokker is also developing and integrating a dedicated infra-red suppression and RWR fit for the Dutch air force. The cost of this will be covered through a royalty agreement between Fokker and the air force for the first 12 export aircraft fitted with similar equipment.

SPECIFICATION

Fokker 50 Maritime Enforcer Mk 2
Wing: span 29.00 m (95 ft 1.75 in); aspect ratio 12.0; area 70.00 m² (753.50 sq ft)
Fuselage and tail: length 25.247 m (82 ft 10 in); height 8.317 m (27 ft 3.5 in); tailplane span 9.746 m (31 ft 11.75 in); wheel track 7.20 m (23 ft 7.5 in);

wheel base 9.70 m (31 ft 10 in)
Powerplant: two Pratt & Whitney Canada PW125B each flat-rated at 2,500 shp (1864 kW)
Weights: operating empty 29,352 lb (13314 kg); normal take-off 45,900 lb (20820 kg); maximum take-off 47,500 lb (21545 kg); maximum emergency take-off 50,000 lb (22680 kg)
Fuel and load: maximum fuel 16,000 lb (7257 kg) including two 938-litre (248US gal) underwing auxiliary tanks
Speed: normal cruising speed at optimum altitude 259 kt (298 mph; 480 km/h); typical patrol speed at 2,000 ft (610 m) 149 kt (172 mph; 277 km/h)
Range: ferry range 3,680 nm (4,237 miles; 6820 km); operational radius 1,200 nm (1,382 miles; 2224 km) with a 4,000-lb (1814-kg) mission load
Performance: service ceiling 25,000 ft (7620 m); take-off run 5,000 ft (1524 m) at 47,000 lb (21320 kg); landing run 2,500 ft (762 m) at normal landing weight

The second Fokker 50 served as the the Enforcer 2 prototype, and performed the initial systems and avionics integration.

Fokker 100

First flown on 30 November 1986, the **Fokker 100** is an extensively modernised, upgraded and lengthened derivative of the F28, offering airlines a 107-seat twin-turbofan short/medium-range airliner. Some 250 have been ordered, with more than 100 on option, and production proceeds at a rate exceeding five a month. Among customers to date only one is of quasi-military nature, involving a single air-

craft leased as a Presidential transport in the **Ivory Coast**. A VIP version with an appropriate cabin layout and optional belly fuel tanks is designated **Fokker Executive Jet 100**. There is also a quick-change cargo version, the **Fokker 100QC**.

SPECIFICATION

Fokker 100
Wing: span 28.08 m (92 ft 1.5 in); aspect ratio 8.4; area 93.50 m² (1,006.46 sq ft)
Fuselage and tail: length 35.53 m (116 ft 6.75 in);

height 8.50 m (27 ft 10.5 in); tailplane span 10.04 m (32 ft 11.25 in); wheel track 5.04 m (16 ft 6.5 in); wheel base 14.01 m (45 ft 11.5 in)
Powerplant: two Rolls-Royce Tay Mk 620-15 each rated at 13,850 lb st (61.61 kN) dry, or two Rolls-Royce Tay Mk 650-15 each rated at 15,100 lb st (67.17 kN) dry
Weights: typical operating empty 24355 kg (53,693 lb); maximum take-off 43090 kg (94,996 lb) standard or 44450 kg (97,993 lb) optional
Fuel and load: internal fuel 13040 litres (3,445 US gal) standard or 14590 litres (3,854 US gal) optional; external fuel none; maximum payload 12385 kg (27,304 lb)

Speed: maximum operating speed 'clean' at 24,200 ft (7375 m) 452 kt (520 mph; 837 km/h)
Range: 1,340 nm (1,543 miles; 2,483 km) at standard maximum take-off weight with 107 passengers and Tay Mk 650-15 engines, or 1,525 nm (1,756 miles; 2826 km) at optional maximum take-off weight with 107 passengers and Tay Mk 650-15 engines
Performance: service ceiling 35,000 ft (10670 m); balanced take-off field length 6,070 ft (1850 m) at maximum take-off weight with Tay Mk 620-15 engines or 5,512 ft (1680 m) at maximum take-off weight with Tay Mk 650-15 engines; balanced landing field length 4,594 ft (1400 m) at maximum landing weight

Fuji-Bell HU-1H and Advanced 205B

Fuji Heavy Industries Ltd
Subaru Building, 7-2, 1-chome
Nishi-shinjuku Shinjuku-ku, Tokyo 160, Japan

The sole production source of the Bell Model 205 helicopter is now Fuji in Japan, which manufactures the Bell UH-1H under sub-licence from Bell's Japanese licensee, Mitsui and Co. An earlier production programme involved the construction of 34 Bell 204Bs and 22 Bell 204B-2s. The standard production model for the **JGSDF** is designated **HU-1H** and utilises the same airframe as the Bell UH-1H, but introduces composite rotor blades and a two-bladed tractor tail rotor. The first Fuji-built example flew in July 1973. Over 130 Fuji-built Bell UH-1B/Hs have been delivered to the JGSDF, 40 of which have been converted

for mine-laying duties. A total of 149 HU-1Hs had been ordered by the end of 1993.

A joint Fuji-Bell upgrade of the Model 205 first flew in Texas on 23 April 1988. Initially designated the **Advanced Model 205A-1**, this version introduces UH-1N-type tapered rotor blades, a Textron Lycoming T53-L-703 engine, and Model 212-type transmission rated at 962 kW (1,290 shp) with LIVE (Liquid Inertial Vibration Eliminator). It has now been redesignated the **Advanced 205B**. The upgraded variant was demonstrated to the US Army and undertook a sales tour of the Far East in 1989, but has so far failed to secure any orders.

SPECIFICATION

Fuji-Bell UH-1H

Rotor system: main rotor diameter 48 ft 0 in (14.63 m); tail rotor diameter 8 ft 6 in (2.59 m); main rotor disc area 1,809.56 sq ft (168.11 m2); tail rotor disc area 56.74 sq ft (5.27 m2)
Fuselage and tail: length overall, tail rotor turning 44 ft 10 in (13.67 m) and fuselage 40 ft 7 in (12.37 m); height overall 14 ft 6 in (4.42 m) with tail rotor turning and 13 ft 0.75 in (3.98 m) to top of rotor head; stabiliser span 9 ft 4 in (2.84 m); skid track 8 ft 6.5 in (2.60 m)
Powerplant: one Kawasaki (Textron Lycoming)

T53-K-13B rated at 1,400 shp (1044 kW)
Weights: empty 5,270 lb (2390 kg); maximum take-off 9,500 lb (4309 kg)
Fuel and load: internal fuel 223 US gal (844 litres) plus provision for 300 US gal (1136 litres) of auxiliary fuel in two tanks; external fuel none; maximum payload 3,880 lb (1759 kg)
Speed: maximum level and cruising speed at optimum altitude 110 kt (127 mph; 204 km/h)
Range: at sea level 252 nm (290 miles); 467 km)
Performance: maximum rate of climb at sea level 1,600 ft (488 m) per minute; service ceiling 12,600 ft (3840 m); hovering ceiling 13,600 ft (4145 m) in ground effect and 1,100 ft (335 m) out of ground effect

---

Fuji KM-2/T-3

After building 124 examples of the Beech T-34A under licence, Fuji developed an improved **KM-2** version to serve the **JMSDF** as a primary trainer. The first flew in July 1962 and was delivered in late September. Sixty-two were procured with the name **Kornadori** (robin), although this name is no longer used. The KM-2 was powered by a 340-hp (254-kW) Lycoming IGSO-480-A1C6 engine and supplied primarily to the 201st Kyoiku Kokutai (air training squadron) at Ozuki, where about 20 remained in 1994. Two **TL-1**s delivered to JGSDF in 1981 are army equivalents of the KM-2 and remain in service as trainers at the Koku Gakko (air training school). Equivalent to the KM-2 for the J**ASDF**, the **T-3** first flew on 17 January 1978, production of 50 being spread over the next 14 years for service with the 11th and 12th Hiko Kyoiku-dans (flying training wings). Based at Shizuhama and Hofu respectively, the T-3s provide the first 75 hours of primary pilot training in the JASDF.

SPECIFICATION

Fuji KM-2B

Wing: span 10.04 m (32 ft 11.25 in); aspect ratio 6.11; area 16.50 m2 (177.61 sq ft)

Fuselage and tail: length 8.036 m (26 ft 4.25 in); height 3.023 m (9 ft 11 in); elevator span 3.712 m (12 ft 2.25 in); wheel track 2.924 m (9 ft 7 in); wheel base 2.266 m (7 ft 5.25 in)
Powerplant: one Textron Lycoming IGSO-480-A1A6 rated at 340 hp (254 kW)
Weights: empty 1120 kg (2,469 lb); maximum take-off 1510 kg (3,329 lb)
Fuel and load: internal fuel 70 US gal (265 litres); external fuel none; maximum ordnance none
Speed: never-exceed speed 223 kt (257 mph; 413 km/h);

Though it bears the hallmarks of the Beech design, Fuji's T-3 is intended as a successor to the T-34 Mentor. JASDF pilots who have completed their 75-hour course in the T-3 graduate to the newly-arrived Kawasaki T-4.

maximum level speed 'clean' at 16,000 ft (4875 m) 203 kt (234 mph; 377 km/h); maximum cruising speed at 8,000 ft (2440 m) 177 kt (204 mph; 328 km/h); economical cruising speed at 8,000 ft (2440 m) 137 kt (158 mph; 254 km/h)
Range: 521 nm (600 miles); 965 km)
Performance: maximum rate of climb at sea level

1,520 ft (463 m) per minute; service ceiling 26,800 ft (8170 m); take-off run 870 ft (265 m) at maximum take-off weight; take-off distance to 50 ft (15 m) 1,650 ft (503 m); landing distance from 50 ft (15 m) 1,430 ft (436 m) at normal landing weight; landing run 780 ft (238 m) at normal landing weight

---

Fuji T-1

Japan's first indigenous jet aircraft design to enter production, the **Fuji T-1** evolved as a basic trainer for the JASDF. It featured modestly swept wings and tandem seating beneath a long canopy. The definitive version was to be powered by the 2,645-lb st (11.8-kN) Ishikawajima-Harima J3-IHI-3 engine, and was designated Fuji **T1F1**. However, a Bristol Orpheus 805 engine was used in the initial production batch of 44 **T-1A**s (Fuji **T1F2**s) ordered by the JASDF after testing two prototypes, the first of which flew on 19 January 1958. These were followed by 20 **T-1B**s with the J3 engine, initially flown in the converted first prototype on 17 May 1960. The designation **T-1C** (**T1F3**) referred to aircraft retrofitted with an uprated 3,085-lb st (13.8-kN) J3-IHI-7 engine, first flown in April 1965. The T-1 was named **Hatsutaka** (Young Hawk) in 1964 but the name is no longer used.

Delivery of T-1As began in 1959, deliveries of the T-1B ending in 1963. Most aircraft went into service with the 13th Hiko Kyoiku-dan (Air Training Wing) at Ashiya, for the second phase of pilot training. The type remains in service, but from 1988 has been phased out in favour of the Kawasaki T-4.

Few Fuji T-1s remain in service. Those that do are largely in the hands of the APW and 13th ATW.

SPECIFICATION

Fuji T-1A

Wing: span 10.49 m (34 ft 5 in); aspect ratio 4.95; area 22.22 m2 (239.18 sq ft)
Fuselage and tail: length 12.12 m (39 ft 9.2 in); height 4.08 m (13 ft 4.6 in); tailplane span 4.40 m (14 ft 5 in); wheel track 3.20 m (10 ft 6 in); wheel base 3.86 m (12 ft 8 in)

Powerplant: one Rolls-Royce (Bristol Siddeley) Orpheus Mk 805 rated at 4,000 lb st (17.79 kN) dry
Weights: empty equipped 2420 kg (5,335 lb); normal take-off 4150 kg (9,149 lb); maximum take-off 5000 kg (11,023 lb)
Fuel and load: internal fuel 370 US gal (1401 litres); external fuel up to two 120-US gal (454-litre) drop tanks; maximum ordnance 680 kg (1,500 lb)
Speed: maximum level speed 'clean' at 36,000 ft (10975 m) 499 kt (575 mph; 925 km/h) but limited in

practice to 464 kt (534 mph; 859 km/h); cruising speed at 30,000 ft (9145 m) 334 kt (385 mph; 620 km/h)
Range: ferry range 1,004 nm (1,156 miles; 1860 km) with drop tanks; range 702 nm (808 miles; 1300 km) with standard fuel
Performance: maximum rate of climb at sea level 6,500 ft (1981 m) per minute; service ceiling 47,245 ft (14400 m); take-off run 1,300 ft (396 m) at normal take-off weight; take-off distance to 50 ft (15 m) 2,000 ft (610 m) at normal take-off weight

Fuji **T-5**

uji developed a turboprop version of the KM-2 in 1984 as the **KM-2D**, the prototype making its first flight on 28 June that year. Certification in Japanese aerobatic and utility categories was obtained on 14 February 1985. With an emerging requirement to update its fleet of KM-2 trainers, the **JMSDF** contracted Fuji in March 1987 for the development of a further improved turboprop variant, the **KM-2Kai**, featuring a modernised cockpit with side-by-side seating and a sliding canopy in place of the original KM-2's side doors and the KM-2B's tandem seats. There is room in the cockpit for a further two seats. Designated **T-5** in Japan's joint services system, the first production KM-2Kai flew on 27 April 1988, and orders have been placed to date for 29 T-5 conversions of KM-2s. Service use is concentrated in 201 Kokutai of the Ozuki Kyoiku Kokuyun, alongside the remaining KM-2Bs.

This is the first production Fuji T-5 (KM-2Kai) delivered to the JASDF. Procurement is proceeding at a modest pace whenever yearly funding is released.

SPECIFICATION

Fuji KM-2Kai (T-5)
Wing: span 10.04 m (32 ft 11.25 in); aspect ratio 6.11; area 16.50 m2 (177.61 sq ft)
Fuselage and tail: length 8.44 m (27 ft 8.25 in); height 2.96 m (9 ft 8.5 in); elevator span 3.712 m (12 ft 2.25 in); wheel track 2.924 m (9 ft 7 in); wheel base 2.266 m (7 ft 5.25 in)
Powerplant: one Allison 250-B17D flat-rated at 350 shp (261 kW)
Weights: empty 1082 kg (2,385 lb); normal take-off 1585 kg (3,494 lb); maximum take-off 1805 kg (3,979 lb)
Fuel and load: internal fuel 644 kg (1,420 lb)

Speed: never exceed speed 223 kt (256 mph; 413 km/h); maximum level speed 'clean' at 8,000 ft (2440 m) 193 kt (222 mph; 357 km/h); economical cruising speed at 8,000 ft (2440 m) 155 kt (178 mph; 287 km/h)
Range: 510 nm (587 miles; 945 km)
Performance: maximum rate of climb at sea level

1,700 ft (518 m) per minute; service ceiling 25,000 ft (7620 m); take-off run 990 ft (302 m) at maximum take-off weight; take-off distance to 50 ft (15 m) 1,410 ft (430 m); landing distance from 50 ft (15 m) 1,690 ft (515 m) at normal landing weight; landing run 570 ft (174 m) at normal landing weight

General Dynamics **F-111A/D/E/G, R/F-111C and FB-111A**

eveloped to meet a **US** joint service requirement for a long-range interceptor (Navy) and deep-strike interdictor (Air Force), the **General Dynamics F-111** had a long and troubled development, and it was not until late in its career that it achieved its true potential. The **F-111B** Navy fighter was cancelled in 1968 after having proved considerably overweight, creating a vacuum which was eventually filled by the F-14 Tomcat. The Air Force variants were more successful, but the 'Aardvark' suffered many setbacks before emerging as arguably the world's best long-range interdictor platform.

Among the many innovations introduced by the F-111, the most notable was the variable-geometry wing – the first on a combat aircraft. The wing sweeps from 16° to 72.5°, conferring the ability to take off with a heavy load of fuel and weapons yet achieve supersonic speed at low level and up to Mach 2.5 at altitude. A 'clean' F-111 has the ability to 'supercruise' (fly supersonicaly without afterburner), a feature made much of with the ATF requirement of the 1990s. Power is provided by a pair of fuel-efficient TF30s, but in the early versions the thrust was considered insufficient. Although there is a weapons bay, most ordnance is carried on the wing pylons. The side-by-side crew occupy a cockpit escape capsule, which ejects in one piece – another novelty of the type.

The F-111 first flew on 21 December 1964, and the first of 141 **F-111A**s entered service in 1967. This variant saw service in South East Asia in 1968 and 1972-75. The second production variant was the **F-111E**, which differed from the A model by having slightly upgraded avionics. These aircraft served for most of their career at Upper Heyford in England. Following was the **F-111D**, which had more powerful engines and radically updated avionics system. When it worked, the system was by far the most capable fitted to any 'Aardvark', but it was maintenance-intensive and ultimately proved over-ambitious. The F-111D served with the 27th TFW at Cannon AFB, NM, until final retirement in late 1992.

Strategic Air Command purchased the **FB-111A** model, which was equipped for strategic nuclear missions. This featured longer-span wings for additional range. When these were retired, some were reworked for the 27th TFW as **F-111G**s, and these served in a training role until 1993. Currently the only early-generation aircraft left in USAF service are 25 F-111Es which were transferred to Cannon in 1993 to fulfil a type conversion role with the 428th Fighter Squadron, 27th Fighter Wing. All these aircraft have received the AMP avionics upgrade.

Export sales were limited to **Australia**, although the Royal Air Force ordered (and subsequently cancelled) the type. Australia's aircraft were delivered in 1973 after a prolonged wrangle over technical difficulties. Featuring the long-span wings of the FB-111A but the low-powered engines and avionics of the F-111A, the **F-111C** was purchased for service with No. 82 Wing at RAAF Amberley, Queensland, which received 24. Four ex-USAF F-111As were purchased as attrition replacements and modified to F-111C standard, and in the early 1990s the RAAF purchased 15 F-111Gs (FB-111As). Originally these were to be held in storage for when the current F-111C fleet reached the end of its fatigue life, but the first examples have already entered service. All RAAF F-111C/Gs have entered an Avionics Upgrade Program.

No. 82 Wing has two squadrons. No. 1 Squadron is the main strike unit, flying 12 aircraft. These can be equipped with the Pave Tack acquisition/designation pod, laser-guided bombs and GBU-15 EO-guided bombs (although the associated datalink pod was not supplied, limiting GBU-15 attacks to line-of-sight only) and a complete range of free-fall weapons, including the indigenous Karinga cluster bomb. A maritime attack capability is conferred by the ability to launch up to four AGM-84 Harpoon anti-ship missiles; AGM-88 HARM is also integrated with the F-111C.

In addition to strike duties, No. 6 Squadron is tasked with type conversion and with reconnaissance. For the latter role it operates four **RF-111C** aircraft. These were modified from F-111Cs with a multi-sensor reconnaissance pallet mounted in the former bomb bay. The pallet mounts panoramic and vertical cameras, TV monitors and infra-red linescan. A single F-111 is assigned for test duties to the ARDU (Aircraft Research and Development Unit) at RAAF Edinburgh, New South Wales.

Above: No. 6 Sqn, with its blue lightning flash, is the RAAF's de facto F-111 OCU, but is also tasked with a reconnaissance role. This is undertaken by four RF-111Cs, one of which is seen here.

Below: Operating outside the dedicated F-111 world of No. 82 Wing is the Aircraft Research and Development Unit (ARDU), based at RAAF Edinburgh. It is assigned this F-111C, largely for weapons trials.

SPECIFICATION

General Dynamics F-111A and F-111E
generally similar to the General Dynamics F-111F except in the following particulars:
Powerplant: two Pratt & Whitney TF30-P-3 each rated at 18,500 lb st (82.29 kN) with afterburning
Weights: operating empty 46,172 lb (20943 kg); maximum take-off 91,300 lb (41414 kg)
Fuel and load: internal fuel 5,033 US gal (19052 litres)

SPECIAL FEATURES
Australian F-111Cs have been heavily modified since their introduction, becoming almost as capable as USAF F-111Fs. All are compatible with the AVQ-26 Pave Tack laser designator and can carry the GBU-15 electro-optical, glide bomb. Unique among the F-111 community is their AGM-84 Harpoon, and AGM-88 HARM capability.

WING STRUCTURE
The F-111C has inherited the long-span wings of the FB-111, which span 70 ft (21.34 m) at minimum angle, compared to 63 ft (19.20 m) for USAF F-111s. At maximum sweep this decreases to 33 ft 11 in (10.34 m) for the F-111C as opposed to 31 ft 11½ in (9.74 m) for USAF aircraft. The wings move between 16° and 72.5°, feature a NACA 63 aerofoil section throughout and are built around five spars. The skin is made from sculpted panels, each machined in one piece running from root to tip.

AUP
Rockwell has developed an Avionics Update Program (AUP) similar to the Pacer Strike modification for F-111Fs. The most important element of this is the substitution for 256K weapons computers of the 64K units now carried. Other USAF improvements, such as the very high-speed integrated-circuit computer complex (VCC), will most likely be added in time.

ARMAMENT
In the precision strike role, RAAF F-111s are equipped with 2,000-lb GBU-10 (illustrated) and 500-lb GBU-12 Paveway II LGBs. Ten Pave Tack laser designators are available to provide guidance for these weapons. A self-defence fit of two AIM-9P Sidewinders can be carried on shoulder pylons. An important new addition to the F-111's armoury is the AGM-84 Harpoon anti-ship missile, which significantly increases Australia's ability to protect its sea lanes.

MARKINGS
The Australian 'Aardvarks' were delivered in the standard three-tone 'South East Asia' scheme of the USAF, with black undersides, and thus most have remained. However, the first AUP aircraft was repainted in the US in an overall grey scheme and this is likely to be adopted fleetwide. The fin is adorned with the squadron marking, in this case No. 6 Sqn's blue lightning bolt. No. 1 Sqn once wore a similar yellow flash, but this has now given way to a swept numeral '1' (still in yellow) with a kookaburra superimposed. All aircraft retain the national flag on the fintip, in front of the rudder.

General Dynamics F-111C

Finally acquired in 1973 after a 10-year procurement nightmare, the F-111Cs have provided the RAAF with its prime strike aircraft ever since. They have also been developed into a long-range reconnaissance platform, and adapted for increasingly important maritime strike duties. Currently undergoing the AUP upgrade in the USA, F-111s will remain in RAAF service for many years yet. To this end, 15 ex-USAF F-111Gs (converted FB-111As) have been acquired to augment the F-111Cs.

General Dynamics **F-111F**

Last of the F-111's production variants, the **F-111F** is also the last in operational service with the **US Air Force**, flying with the 522nd, 523rd and 524th Fighter Squadrons of the 27th Fighter Wing at Cannon AFB, NM.

Production of the F-111F totalled 106, initial deliveries going to Mountain Home AFB, ID, from 1972. In 1977 the force was deployed to Lakenheath in England with the 48th TFW. In 1992, the force returned to the United States after replacement by the F-15E Eagle.

Although not as capable in avionics terms as the F-111D, the F-111F nevertheless proved much easier to maintain. Mk IIB avionics, as developed for the FB-111A, were combined with the Weapons Control Panel from the F-111E. The main attack radar is the AN/APQ-161, allied to the AN/APQ-171 terrain-following radar.

By far the most important improvement introduced by the F-111F was the uprated powerplant, the TF30-P-100, which raised thrust:weight ratio from 0.39 in the early variants to 0.53. Thus, the F was the only version not considered to be underpowered.

F-111Fs were built (like all 'Aardvarks' except for the FB-111A/F-111G) with provision for a 20-mm Vulcan cannon in the weapons bay, but in practice this has never been used. For self-defence the F-111F routinely carries the AIM-9P-3 Sidewinder – later versions of this missile have larger fins and there is insufficient clearance for their use. On the F model, the weapons bay is now used primarily for the carriage of the AN/AVQ-26 Pave Tack pod, which incorporates a FLIR sensor and bore-sighted laser rangefinder/designator. This allows the aircraft to autonomously deliver laser-guided bombs.

Primary weapons of the F-111F are the 500-lb GBU-12 Paveway II, 2,000-lb GBU-10 Paveway II and 2,000-lb GBU-24 Paveway III laser-guided bombs. The latter allows a low-level delivery profile with great accuracy, or delivery at medium altitude from a greater stand-off range. Both 2,000-lb weapons are available with either a standard Mk 84 warhead or a BLU-109 penetration warhead for use against hardened targets such as bunkers or aircraft shelters. The GBU-28 'Deep Throat' is a 4,800-lb Paveway III weapon hastily developed during Desert Storm to penetrate and destroy very deep bunkers. Only two were delivered, on the last night of the conflict.

Additionally, the F-111F routinely carries a wide range of 'dumb' ordnance, including iron bombs, cluster weapons and BLU-107 Durandal runway-cratering munitions. The capability remains for the carriage of free-fall nuclear weapons, principally the B61 tactical weapon. An F-111F speciality is the GBU-15 2,000-lb EO-guided bomb. This has either a Mk 84 or BLU-109 warhead, and has either a TV- or IR-seeker adapted from those fitted to Maverick missiles. For stand-off launch, the AXQ-14 or ZWS-1 datalink pod is fitted to guide the GBU-15s.

F-111Fs have seen considerably more action than other variants. Aircraft from the 48th TFW at Lakenheath were chosen to attack targets around Tripoli during the April 1986 Operation El Dorado Canyon raid. In August 1990 the wing began to deploy 'Aardvarks' to Taif in Saudi Arabia, and during the ensuing Gulf War 66 F-111Fs were in-theatre. Using a wide range of weapons, but specialising in LGB attacks, the F-111Fs proved to be the real workhorses of the air war, accounting for the greatest proportion of targets destroyed in Iraq and Kuwait. Apart from the 'bunker-busting' GBU-28 attacks, notable exploits were the GBU-15 attack on an oil pumping station to halt an environmentally disastrous flow of oil into the Gulf, 'tank-plinking' anti-armour missions with GBU-12s, the leading role in the

Left: A fully armed F-111F of the 492nd TFS 'Bowlers'/48th TFW (Provisional) displays its warload of GBU-24 Paveway III LGBs and AIM-9P-3 Sidewinders for defence.

Left: This is the 2,000-lb GBU-28 'Deep Throat' penetration bomb dropped on the Al Taji command bunker on the last night of the Gulf War. The GBU-28 was specially developed using spare naval gun barrels as strong casings.

Below: The USAF's F-111 (and EF-111) fleet is now centralised at Cannon AFB. They are scheduled to remain in service until 2015 at the earliest.

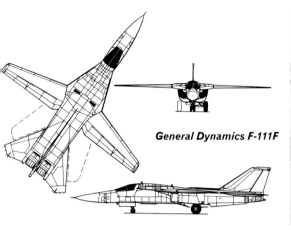

General Dynamics F-111F

shelter and bridge take-down campaign, and a direct hit on an ammunition store which caused the largest man-made non-nuclear explosion ever recorded by seismologists.

Since the end of the Gulf War, a detachment of F-111Fs (with a number of F-15Es) remains in Turkey as part of Operation Provide Comfort. The 84 surviving F-111Fs are undergoing the Pacer Strike update, managed by Rockwell. This replaces analog systems with digital avionics, and will keep the F-111Fs current up to their planned retirement date in 2010. Despite the considerable capabilities of the F-111F in the low-

level, night/adverse weather precision attack regime (unmatched by any other current type), the force is a prime candidate for early retirement. All USAF F-111 airframes, including EF-111s (described separately), are now concentrated in a six-squadron wing at Cannon AFB.

SPECIFICATION

General Dynamics F-111F
Wing: span 63 ft 0 in (19.20 m) spread and 31 ft 11.4 in (9.74 m) swept; aspect ratio 7.56 spread and 1.55

swept; area 525.00 sq ft (48.77 m²) spread and 657.07 sq ft (61.07 m²) spread
Fuselage and tail: length 73 ft 6 in (22.40 m); height 17 ft 1.4 in (5.22 m)
Powerplant: two Pratt & Whitney TF30-P-100 each rated at 25,100 lb st (111.65 kN) with afterburning
Weights: operating empty 47,481 lb (21537 kg); maximum take-off 100,000 lb (45360 kg)
Fuel and load: internal fuel 5,025 US gal (19021 litres); external fuel up to four 600-US gal (2271-litre) drop tanks; maximum ordnance 31,500 lb (14228 kg)
Speed: maximum level speed 'clean' at 36,000 ft (10975 m) 1,433 kt (1,650 mph; 2655 km/h); cruising speed at high altitude 496 kt (571 mph; 919 km/h)

Four F-111F loaded with GBU-24A/Bs prepare to taxi out from their shelters at Taif, Saudi Arabia, during Operation Desert Storm. The first F-111s arrived in Saudi on 25 August 1990, but had to wait until the night of 16 January 1991 for action.

Range: more than 2,540 nm (2,925 miles; 4707 km) with internal fuel
Performance: service ceiling 60,000 ft (18290 m); take-off distance to 50 ft (15 m) 3,120 ft (951 m); landing run less than 3,000 ft (915 m) at normal landing weight

Gloster **Meteor**

Britain's first jet fighter to achieve production, the Meteor has now all but disappeared after lengthy service in several ver-

sions. In the UK, one **D.Mk 16** target drone continues to serve at DRA Llanbedr (with one in storage); this version is a derivative of the original **F.Mk 8** single-seat fighter. For trials of its ejection seats, Mar-

tin-Baker has long made use of specially-modified **T.Mk 7 (Mod)** two-seaters (often referred to as **T.Mk 7½**), and has four airframes at Chalgrove, of which two are used to provide spares for the airworthy pair.

The last Meteors can be found with ejection-seat manufacturer Martin-Baker (above, named 'Asterix') and the DRA, with a Meteor D.Mk 16 drone.

Grob **G 103 Viking and G 109 Vigilant**

Burkhart Grob Luft- und Raumfahrtb GMBH & Co KG Am Flugplatz, D-8939 Mattsies Germany

The German sailplane producer Grob has specialised in the development of glass-fibre airframes. To replace a long-serving fleet of wooden gliders used by the Volunteer Gliding Schools of the ATC, the British Defence Ministry selected in 1984 the **Grob G 103 Twin II Acro** tandem two-seat sailplane. An order for 100 was placed and the designation **Viking T.Mk 1** assigned to these aircraft, delivery of which began in September 1984. The Viking T.Mk 1 now equips those Air Cadet Volunteer Gliding Schools that provide winch-launched training, with the **Vigilant T.Mk 1** (**Grob G 109**) at the self-launching schools.

The **G 109B** powered sailplane was first flown in March 1983 as a version of the G 109 with increased wing span. Production ended in 1986 but was resumed in 1990 to meet an RAF order for 53. As the **Vigilant**

T.Mk 1, the G 109B entered service in March 1990 and serves at the Volunteer Gliding Schools of the ATC and CCF, and at the Air Cadets Central Gliding School. The Vigilant is powered by a Limbach engine, while the G 109B is usually fitted with a 90-hp (67-kW) Grob 2500 engine. This variant is used by the quasi-military **Royal Thai Aero Club** at Don Muang.

SPECIFICATION

Grob G 109
Wing: span 16.60 m (54 ft 5.5 in); aspect ratio 13.5; area 20.40 m² (219.59 sq ft)
Fuselage and tail: length 7.80 m (25 ft 7 in); height 1.80 m (5 ft 10.75 in)
Powerplant: one Limbach L 2000 EB 1A rated at 80 hp (59 kW)

Weights: empty 580 kg (1,278 lb); maximum take-off 825 kg (1,818 lb)
Fuel and load: internal fuel 80 litres (21.1 US gal); external fuel none
Speed: maximum level speed 'clean' at optimum

altitude 129 kt (149 mph; 240 km/h) in smooth air or 100 kt (115 mph; 185 km/h) in rough air
Performance: best glide ratio 30 at 65 kt (75 mph; 120 km/h); minimum sinking speed 3.77 ft (1.15 m) per second at 51 kt (59 mph; 95 km/h)

To the RAF's Volunteer Gliding Schools the Grob G 109 is known as the Vigilant T.Mk 1. The type has replaced Slingsby Ventures at the 12 VGS sites.

Grob/E-Systems/Garrett **Egrett/Strato 1**

A 'poor-man's U-2R', the Egrett originated to meet a **Luftwaffe** requirement for a long-duration high-altitude surveillance aircraft, after plans to acquire a squadron of Lockheed TR-1s had been abandoned. A three-company group collaborated to initiate the project, comprising Grob in Germany, and E-Systems and Garrett in the US, from which the name **Egrett** was derived. Grob was primarily responsible for design of the essentially glass-fibre airframe, Garrett contributed the powerplant, and E-Systems, as programme leader, was responsible for systems integration.

The Egrett concept makes use of a single-seat fuselage providing adequate space for a variety of interchangeable mission packages (including electronics, electro-optical or IR surveillance, long-range radar). Long-span wings of very high aspect ratio demonstrate sailplane design influence and underline the Egrett's high-altitude role and, combined with the efficient TPE331 turboprop, allow the aircraft to fly for long periods at high altitude.

A proof-of-concept vehicle, the **D-450 Egrett I**, flew on 24 June 1987 in Germany, and in September 1988 this set a class-altitude record of 53,787 ft (16394 m). The D-450 had a span of 28.00 m (91 ft 10 in) and, unlike the definitive version, was fitted with a fixed main landing gear. It was followed on 20 April 1989 by the first **D-500 Egrett II**, with a second similar D-500 flying on 9 September 1990 and two more completed in 1991. Egrett II has a 33.00-m (108-ft 3-in) wingspan and retractable main gear, stowage for which is provided in wing fairings. The fourth aircraft (**Prisma**) introduced detachable winglets while the fifth, equipped especially for civilian communications relay, was named **Strato 1**.

Funded by the Luftwaffe since 1987, the Egrett-2 met the so-called 'EASysluft' requirement for a data-gathering and evaluation system, which it is the Luftwaffe's responsibility to provide on behalf of all three services. Late in 1992 official approval was given for production of 10 more D-500s, of which one was to be a two-seater, with deliveries from 1997 to 2001. Despite plans being drawn up to base 16 operational Egretts at Pferdsfeld, the Luftwaffe programme was subsequently cancelled in February 1993 in the light of the lack of threat posed by eastern Europe. Construction of the **G-520T** two-seater continued, however, and this aircraft flew on 21 April 1993. This has obtained German

and US certification, but a launch customer has yet to be found.

SPECIFICATION

Grob/E-Systems/Garrett Egrett II
Wing: span 31.40 m (103 ft 0.25 in)
Fuselage and tail: length 12.20 m (40 ft 0.25 in); height 5.80 m (19 ft 0.25 in); wheel track about 4.80 m (15 ft 9 in); wheel base about 3.66 m (12 ft 0 in)
Powerplant: one Garrett TPE331-14F rated at about 800 shp (596.5 kW)
Weights: maximum take-off 4700 kg (10,362 lb)
Fuel and load: internal fuel 1075 kg (2,370 kg); external fuel none; maximum payload 1000 kg (2,205 lb)
Speed: maximum level speed 'clean' at optimum

The model in which the Luftwaffe wa interested was the D-500 Egrett II. Various sensors could be housed in the lower fuselage, a direction-findin antenna being shown here.

altitude 240 kt (276 mph; 445 km/h); maximum cruising speed at optimum altitude 190 kt (219 mph; 352 km/h)
Range: endurance limited to between 10 and 12 hours by pilot fatigue
Performance: maximum rate of climb at sea level more than 1,500 ft (457 m) per minute; climb to 40,000 ft (12190 m) in 35 minutes 0 seconds; service ceiling more than 45,000 ft (13715 m); take-off run 2,000 ft (656 m) at maximum take-off weight
g limits: -3 to +5 in gust conditions

Grob **Strato 2C**

Designed for stratospheric and climatic research, the **Grob Strato 2C** also has potential for development in the military

surveillance role. Construction of a prototype is financed by the German Ministry for Research and Development, with first flight

set for November 1994. Using experience gained with the Egrett-1 programme, Grob adopted all-composite construction and two 400-hp (300-kW) Teledyne Continental GT-550 piston engines driving five-bladed propellers. The crew of two will have a pres-

surised cockpit with galley and toilet, as the Strato 2C has a planned endurance of 48 hours and a maximum range of 25,300 nm (29,130 miles/18100 km) at altitudes up to 85,300 ft (26000 m).

Grumman **A-6/KA-6 Intruder**

*Grumman Corporatior
1111 Stewart Avenue, Bethpage
NY 11714, US/*

During the Korean War the US services flew more attack missions than any other, in the case of the **US Navy** and **US Marine Corps** primarily with elderly piston-engined aircraft. What they learned during this conflict convinced them of the need for a specially-designed jet attack aircraft that could operate effectively in the worst weather. In 1957 eight companies submitted 11 designs in a US Navy competition for a new long-range, low-level tactical strike aircraft. Grumman's **G-128** design,

selected on the last day of the year, was to fulfil that requirement admirably, becoming a major combat type in the later war in South East Asia, and leading to a family of later versions.

Eight development **A-6A**s (originally designated **A2F-1**) were ordered in March 1959, a full-scale mock-up was completed and accepted some six months later, and the first flight was made on 19 April 1960. The jet pipes of its two 8,500-lb (37.81-kN) static thrust Pratt & Whitney J52-P-6

engines were designed to swivel downwards, to provide an additional component of lift during take-off. This feature was omitted from production aircraft, which instead have jet pipes with a permanent slight downward deflection. The first production A-6As were delivered to US Navy Attack Squadron VA-42 in February 1963, and by the end of the following year deliveries had reached 83, to VA-65, VA-75 and VA-85 of the US Navy and VMA(AW)-242 of the US Marine Corps.

The first unit to fly on combat duties in Vietnam was VA-75, whose A-6As began operating from USS *Independence* in March 1965, and from then Intruders of various models became heavily involved in fighting in South East Asia. Their DIANE (Digital Integrated Attack Navigation Equipment) gave them a first-class operating ability and efficiency in the worst of the humid, stormy weather offered by the local climate, and with a maximum ordnance load of more than 17,000 lb (7711 kg) they were a potent addition to the US arsenal in South East Asia.

An A-6E practises dive attacks with dummy Mk 83 bombs. The Intruder forms the backbone of the US Navy's heavy attack capability, capable of launching most of the stores in the inventory.

Production of the basic A-6A ran until December 1969 and totalled 482 aircraft, plus another 21 built as **EA-6A**s (described separately), retaining a partial strike capability but developed primarily to provide ECM support for the A-6As in Vietnam and to act as Elint gatherers. The first EA-6A was flown in 1963, and six A-6As were also converted to EA-6A configuration. A more sophisticated electronic warfare version, the EA-6B, is described separately.

A-6A conversions

The following variants of the Intruder were also produced by the conversion of existing A-6As. First of these (19 converted) was the **A-6B**, issued to one USN squadron and differing from the initial model primarily in its ability to carry the US Navy's AGM-78 Standard ARM instead of the AGM-12B Bullpup. For identifying and acquiring targets not discernible by the aircraft's standard radar, Grumman then modified 12 other A-6As to **A-6C** standard, giving them an improved capability for night attack by installing FLIR and low-light-level TV equipment in a turret under the fuselage. A prototype conversion of an A-6A to **KA-6D** inflight-refuelling tanker was flown on 23 May 1966, and production contracts for the tanker version were placed. These were subsequently cancelled, but 78 A-6As were instead converted to KA-6D configuration

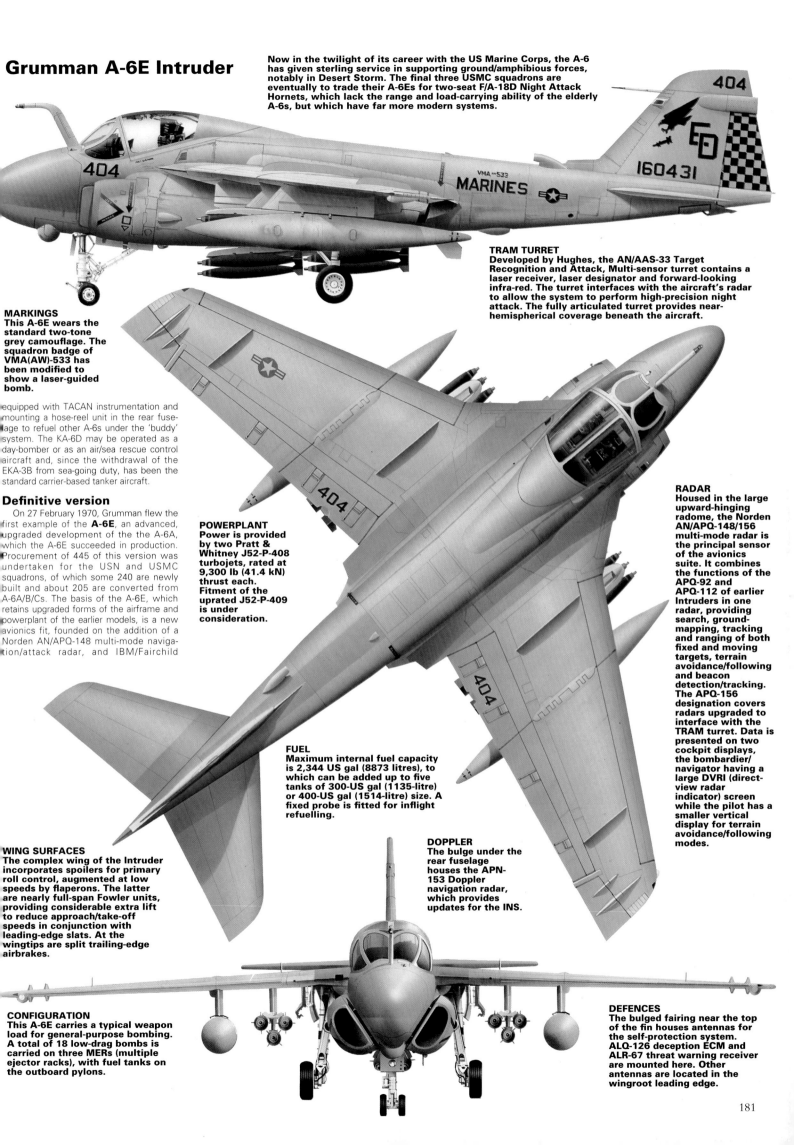

Grumman A-6E Intruder

Now in the twilight of its career with the US Marine Corps, the A-6 has given sterling service in supporting ground/amphibious forces, notably in Desert Storm. The final three USMC squadrons are eventually to trade their A-6Es for two-seat F/A-18D Night Attack Hornets, which lack the range and load-carrying ability of the elderly A-6s, but which have far more modern systems.

MARKINGS
This A-6E wears the standard two-tone grey camouflage. The squadron badge of VMA(AW)-533 has been modified to show a laser-guided bomb.

equipped with TACAN instrumentation and mounting a hose-reel unit in the rear fuse-lage to refuel other A-6s under the 'buddy' system. The KA-6D may be operated as a day-bomber or as an air/sea rescue control aircraft and, since the withdrawal of the EKA-3B from sea-going duty, has been the standard carrier-based tanker aircraft.

Definitive version

On 27 February 1970, Grumman flew the first example of the **A-6E**, an advanced, upgraded development of the the A-6A, which the A-6E succeeded in production. Procurement of 445 of this version was undertaken for the USN and USMC squadrons, of which some 240 are newly built and about 205 are converted from A-6A/B/Cs. The basis of the A-6E, which retains upgraded forms of the airframe and powerplant of the earlier models, is a new avionics fit, founded on the addition of a Norden AN/APQ-148 multi-mode naviga-tion/attack radar, and IBM/Fairchild

TRAM TURRET
Developed by Hughes, the AN/AAS-33 Target Recognition and Attack, Multi-sensor turret contains a laser receiver, laser designator and forward-looking infra-red. The turret interfaces with the aircraft's radar to allow the system to perform high-precision night attack. The fully articulated turret provides near-hemispherical coverage beneath the aircraft.

POWERPLANT
Power is provided by two Pratt & Whitney J52-P-408 turbojets, rated at 9,300 lb (41.4 kN) thrust each. Fitment of the uprated J52-P-409 is under consideration.

RADAR
Housed in the large upward-hinging radome, the Norden AN/APQ-148/156 multi-mode radar is the principal sensor of the avionics suite. It combines the functions of the APQ-92 and APQ-112 of earlier Intruders in one radar, providing search, ground-mapping, tracking and ranging of both fixed and moving targets, terrain avoidance/following and beacon detection/tracking. The APQ-156 designation covers radars upgraded to interface with the TRAM turret. Data is presented on two cockpit displays, the bombardier/navigator having a large DVRI (direct-view radar indicator) screen while the pilot has a smaller vertical display for terrain avoidance/following modes.

FUEL
Maximum internal fuel capacity is 2,344 US gal (8873 litres), to which can be added up to five tanks of 300-US gal (1135-litre) or 400-US gal (1514-litre) size. A fixed probe is fitted for inflight refuelling.

DOPPLER
The bulge under the rear fuselage houses the APN-153 Doppler navigation radar, which provides updates for the INS.

WING SURFACES
The complex wing of the Intruder incorporates spoilers for primary roll control, augmented at low speeds by flaperons. The latter are nearly full-span Fowler units, providing considerable extra lift to reduce approach/take-off speeds in conjunction with leading-edge slats. At the wingtips are split trailing-edge airbrakes.

CONFIGURATION
This A-6E carries a typical weapon load for general-purpose bombing. A total of 18 low-drag bombs is carried on three MERs (multiple ejector racks), with fuel tanks on the outboard pylons.

DEFENCES
The bulged fairing near the top of the fin houses antennas for the self-protection system. ALQ-126 deception ECM and ALR-67 threat warning receiver are mounted here. Other antennas are located in the wingroot leading edge.

The A-6 was heavily committed to Desert Storm with both the Navy and Marine Corps. These aircraft are from Saratoga's VA-35, each armed with 12 Mk 82 retarded iron bombs. The double yellow band on the bombs signifies the Navy's version, which has a special fire-protective coating.

AN/ASQ-133 computerised navigation/attack system, Conrac armament control unit, and an RCA video-tape recorder for assessing damage caused during a strike mission. The Norden APQ-148/156 radar, which replaces the two older radars of the A-6A, provides ground mapping, terrain avoidance/clearance, and target identification/tracking/ rangefinding modes, with cockpit displays for both the pilot and navigator/bombardier, who sit side-by-side in the well-forward cockpit. Nine A-6Es were additionally converted to tanker configuration.

Following the first flight of a test aircraft on 22 March 1974, all US Navy and US Marine Corps Intruders were progressively updated still further under a programme known as **TRAM** (Target Recognition Attack, Multisensor). To the A-6E-standard Intruder, this adds a Hughes turreted electro-optical package of FLIR and laser detection equipment integrated with the Norden radar; adds CAINS (carrier airborne inertial navigation system); provides the capability for automatic carrier landings; and incorporates provision for the carriage and delivery of automatic-homing and laser-guided air-to-surface weapons. The first US Navy squadron to be equipped with the **A-6E TRAM** version was VA-165, which was deployed aboard USS *Constellation* in 1977.

Grumman developments

Further development of the design resulted in the **A-6F**, a revised A-6E airframe with new radar, digitised avionics and F404 turbofans. Three prototypes were flown, the first on 26 August 1987, but the variant was cancelled when the Navy began the pursuit of the 'stealthy' A-12. Grumman for a time continued development of the **A-6G**, basically the F model but retaining the ageing J52 engines. When the A-12 itself was cancelled, the US Navy was left without a major tactical aircraft programme, and the A-6 was faced with continued fleet service with no immediate replacement.

Consequently, the A-6E has been the subject of continuing upgrades. Rewinging with composite units was considered a necessity to keep the fleet airworthy, while

in 1990/91 the US Navy began receiving its first **SWIP** aircraft, which introduced various stand-off weapons capability including AGM-65 Maverick, AGM-84 Harpoon Block 1C, AGM-84E SLAM and AGM-88 HARM. Already the A-6E TRAM had 'smart' weapon capability in the form of laser-guided bombs and AGM-123 Skipper laser-guided missile. Further updating was implemented in late 1992 with the first flight of the Block 1-A upgrade machine, this standard introducing a HUD for the pilot, revised wing fillets and extra fuel.

In service, the A-6 has proved to be a durable and highly versatile warplane. After its baptism of fire in Vietnam, the type has seen action in Lebanon, Libya and the Gulf. As its career has progressed, the weapons repertoire has blossomed, and the latest standard of upgrade can carry virtually every item of ordnance in the US Navy inventory.

Currently the A-6E serves with 13 active-duty US Navy squadrons (VA-34, 35, 36, 52, 65, 75, 85, 95, 115, 145, 155, 165 and 196), two fleet replenishment squadrons (VA-42 and 128), two Reserve units (VA-205 and 304), various trials organisations, and three remaining US Marine Corps units (VMA(AW)-224, 332 and 533). The latter are due to relinquish their aircraft in favour of the two-seat F/A-18D Hornet in the mid-1990s. Two US Navy A-6 units are to disband during each fiscal year, bringing forward the retirement date and ending the rewinging and update programmes.

WEAPON OPTIONS

The A-6 carries its stores on one centreline and four wing pylons, each stressed for a maximum of 3,600 lb (1633 kg). Total weapon load is 18,000 lb (8165 kg). Virtually all of the US Navy/Marine Corps inventory of stores can be carried.

General purpose: up to 22 500-lb (227-kg) Mk 82s or 10 1,000-lb (454-kg) Mk 83s can be carried, although lesser numbers are more common. Bombs available in both low-drag and air-inflatable retard configuration. Alternatively Mk 77 fire bombs or Mk 7/20 cluster bombs (with varying sub-munitions) can be carried

Anti-ship: two AGM-84 Harpoon missiles can be carried on wing pylons, often backed up with iron bombs

Defence suppression: four AGM-88 HARMs carried on wing pylons or up to 26 ADM-141 decoy drones (for saturating air defences with spurious signals)

Precision attack: two AGM-84E SLAM (Stand-off Land Attack Missile) on wing pylons, up to four GBU-10, 12 or 16 laser-guided bombs, two AGM-62 Walleye TV-guided bombs, or two AGM-123 Skipper laser-guided missiles (GBU-16 1,000-lb (454-kg) LGB with rocket motor attached)

Nuclear attack: up to three B57 or B61 free-fall weapons on centreline and two inboard wing pylons

Refuelling: one D-704 buddy-buddy refuelling pod on centreline

Miscellaneous: various naval mines and destructors, ECM jamming pods, AIM-9 Sidewinders (for self-defence) can be carried

SPECIFICATION

Grumman A-6E Intruder

Wing: span 53 ft 0 in (16.15 m); width folded 25 ft 4 in (7.72 m); aspect ratio 5.31; area 528.90 sq ft (49.13 m²)

Fuselage and tail: length 54 ft 9 in (16.69 m); height 16 ft 2 in (4.93 m); tailplane span 20 ft 4.5 in (6.21 m); wheel track 10 ft 10.5 in (3.32 m); wheel base 17 ft 2.25 in (5.24 m)

Powerplant: two Pratt & Whitney J52-P-8B each rated at 9,300 lb st (41.37 kN) dry

Weights: empty 27,613 lb (12525 kg); maximum take-off 58,600 lb (26580 kg) for catapult launch or 60,400 lb (27397 kg) for field take-off

Fuel and load: internal fuel 15,939 lb (7230 kg); external fuel up to 10,050 lb (4558 kg) in five 400-US gal (1514-litre) drop tanks; maximum ordnance 18,000 lb (8165 kg)

Speed: never-exceed speed 700 kt (806 mph; 1297

The hose-drogue unit projecting from under the rear fuselage identifies the dedicated KA-6D tanker. The aircraft lacks TRAM turret and bombing radar, and the right-hand seat is devoid of all offensive equipment. Three or four KA-6Ds are usually assigned to an Intruder squadron.

km/h); maximum level speed 'clean' at sea level 560 kt (644 mph; 1037 km/h); cruising speed at optimum altitude 412 kt (474 mph; 763 km/h)

Range: ferry range 2,818 nm (3,245 miles; 5222 km) with empty tanks dropped or 2,380 nm (2,740 miles; 4410 km) with empty tanks retained; range with maximum military load 878 nm (1,011 miles; 1627 km)

Performance: maximum rate of climb at sea level 7,620 ft (2323 m) per minute; service ceiling 42,400 ft (12925 m); minimum take-off run 3,890 ft (1186 m); take-off distance to 50 ft (15 m) 4,560 ft (1390 m) at maximum take-off weight; landing distance from 50 ft (15 m) 2,540 ft (774 m) at normal landing weight; minimum landing run 1,710 ft (521 m)

Augmenting the KA-6D in the tanker role, the standard A-6E can carry a D-704 refuelling pod on the centreline pylon.

Grumman EA-6A Intruder

Based on the original A-6A variant of the Intruder, the **Grumman EA-6A** was conceived in response to a Marine Corps requirement for an EF-10B Skyknight replacement and entered service with three composite reconnaissance/electronic warfare squadrons in the mid-1960s. Production totalled just 27 airframes, of which a dozen were essentially conversions of existing A-6As, and most were retired from front-line service in the late 1970s when the Marines received EA-6B Prowlers.

Externally, the most visible difference between the EA-6A and its attack-dedicated A-6A counterpart was the bulbous fin-top fairing which housed antennas associated

with the electronic warfare equipment. This included a Bunker-Ramo AN/ALQ-86 signals surveillance system and AN/ALH-6 signals recording system as well as AN/ALQ-31 and AN/ALQ-76 noise jammers, with the latter being housed in distinctive slab-sided under-wing pods. Although mainly employed for electronic warfare, the EA-6A evidently retained a limited attack capability, although it appears this was seldom used, especially in Vietnam, where it saw extensive service in support of strike aircraft and as a gatherer of intelligence relating to the North's electronic order of battle.

By late 1993, a handful of EA-6As were still in service, operating with VAQ-33 from

The EA-6A was used by the USMC in the EW role. Following replacement by the EA-6B, a few continued in Navy service as EW aggressors.

Key West, FL, under the overall direction of the Fleet Electronic Warfare Support Group. Their principal task was to act as electronic

aggressors in the training of **US Navy** air- and sea-borne forces but are now believed to have been withdrawn.

Grumman EA-6B Prowler

Production of the US Navy's standard carrierborne electronic warfare aircraft terminated in July 1991 with 170 aircraft built, but efforts at improving the already impressive potential of the **Grumman EA-6B Prowler** are continuing and should lead to the ADVCAP (Advanced Capability) or Block 91 derivative. Development of upgraded receiver and processor equipment associated with the AN/ALQ-99 TJS (Tactical Jamming System) was launched by Litton Industries in 1983, with flight trials getting under way in 1990. Assuming that test objectives are satisfactorily met, deployment of Block 91-configured Prowlers is expected to occur in the second half of the 1990s, with current planning anticipating that these will result from a CILOP remanufacture programme.

Fundamentally a four-seater variation on the well-proven Intruder, the EA-6B entered service during 1971 as a replacement for the EKA-3B Skywarrior. Key equipment includes the TJS, which is capable of operation in fully-automatic, semi-automatic and manual modes and which employs 'noise' jamming originating from a maximum of five external transmitter pods.

Progressive update initiatives have resulted in the appearance of ever more capable versions. Excluding three prototype conversions of A-6As and five development airframes, the first 23 production aircraft were to 'Basic' standard, using ALQ-99 TJS and ALQ-92 with an EW potential that was limited to four specific frequency bands. They were followed in 1973 by the first of 25 **EXCAP** (Expanded Capability) airframes with improved equipment and the ability to cover threats across eight bands using ALQ-99A TJS.

The next version to appear was **ICAP** (Improved Capability), which made its debut in 1976 and which incorporated new display and reduced reaction times, along with AN/ALQ-126 multiple-band defensive breakers, updated radar deception gear and the automatic carrier landing system. In addition to 45 new-build machines, 17 surviving Basic and EXCAP airframes were brought to

the full Improved Capability standard.

Software and display improvements were among the changes made on the **ICAP-II** version, which flew for the first time in June 1980, with all 55 surviving ICAPs being upgraded. ICAP-II is the current service model and is able to handle groups of weapons systems, embodying such refinements as power management and improved identification of hostile emitters, while simultaneously being more reliable and more easily maintained than its predecessors. The external jammer pods were upgraded to be able to generate signals within seven bands (instead of one) and to jam in two bands simultaneously. As with the original ICAP, it has a crew of four and it has also recently acquired the ability to use more direct methods in countering the threat posed by enemy SAM sites, for it is now able to function as a 'shooter' with the AGM-88A HARM defence suppression missile. The **ICAP-II/Block 86** can be distinguished by three new sweptback antennas on the spine and under the nose, associated with HARM capability.

New-build and conversions

Procurement of ICAP-II also followed a twin-track approach, the Navy and Marine Corps receiving a mixture of remanufactured and new-build aircraft to this standard. These presently equip about a dozen deployable Navy squadrons which are mostly concentrated at NAS Whidbey Island, WA, from where they routinely embark aboard aircraft-carriers of both major fleet organisations. Non-deployable and second-line elements comprise a permanently shore-based training unit, a Reserve Force squadron and a specialist EW-dedicated aggressor training squadron at Whidbey Island, plus a second Reserve squadron at NAF Washington/Andrews AFB, MD.

Most recently, EA-6Bs have been upgraded to two **ADVCAP** configurations. The basic ADVCAP has new jammer transmission and passive detection capabilities and an expanded AN/ALE-39 chaff dis-

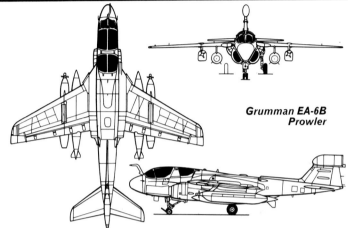

Grumman EA-6B Prowler

penser fit. The aircraft is also fitted with GPS, and has provision for AN/ALQ-165 ASPJ and a new disk-based recorder/programme loader. The prototype first flew on 29 October 1990.

An Avionics Improvement Program will lead to a remanufactured ADVCAP/Block 91 EA-6B with new displays, radar improvements, an improved tactical support jamming suite, AN/ALQ-149 communications jamming system and a digital autopilot. Aerodynamic improvements were developed under the **VEP** (Vehicle Enhancement Program) project and comprise the addition

After rationalisation of their EA-6B assets, the USMC now has four active-duty squadrons.

of fuselage strakes, modified flaps, slats, speed brakes and a fin extension. The VEP prototype first flew on 15 June 1992 and featured uprated powerplants and two additional dedicated HARM pylons.

Marine Corps usage of the Prowler is more limited, comprising four front-line squadrons at MCAS Cherry Point, NC, which operate detachments to the Far East on rotation.

Left: Block 86 EA-6Bs made extensive use of their HARM firing capability during Desert Storm.

Above: This VAQ-137 EA-6B carries a standard load of three ALQ-99 jamming pods and two AGM-88 HARMs.

Grumman EA-6B Prowler

HARM MISSILE
With a range of approximately 15 miles (25 km), the AGM-88 has a length of 13 ft 8 in (4.17 m) and launch weight of 796 lb (361 kg), of which 145 lb (66 kg) is a high-explosive fragmentation warhead. The seeker is a passive radar head which can be pre-programmed or launched in an opportunist manner. Fusing is by active laser.

TAIL FAIRING
Known as the 'football', the large fin-tip fairing houses the principal array of System Integration Receivers (SIRs). These detect hostile transmissions and relay data to the central computer. The fin-top SIRs cover bands 4-9, while the bulged fairings lower down the fin cover bands 1-3.

CREW STATIONS
The four-man crew consists of pilot (front port) and three ECM Officers. ECMO 1 occupies the front starboard seat, operating the navigation, radar and communications jamming systems. ECMO 2 and 3 sit in the rear cabin, operating the tactical jamming system.

ALQ-99 SYSTEM
The AIL Systems Inc. ALQ-99F is the EA-6B's jamming system, consisting of the SIR receivers, central processing computer and up to five (normally three) pods. These can operate in full auto (detection and automatic assignment of jamming power), semi-auto (ECM operators assign power) and manual (ECM operators manually search spectrum and assign jamming) modes.

FUSELAGE
In order to accommodate the two extra crew stations, the basic A-6 fuselage was lengthened by 4 ft 6 in (1.37 m).

RADAR
The search and navigation radar is the Norden APS-130. This is a downgraded version of the A-6E's APQ-156, with attack functions deleted. The radar provides accurate ground mapping.

SPECIFICATION

Grumman EA-6B Prowler
Wing: span 53 ft 0 in (16.15 m); width folded 25 ft 10 in (7.87 m); aspect ratio 5.31; area 528.90 sq ft (49.13 m²)
Fuselage and tail: length 59 ft 10 in (18.24 m); height 16 ft 3 in (4.95 m); tailplane span 20 ft 4.5 in (6.21 m); wheel track 10 ft 10.5 in (3.32 m); wheel base 17 ft 2 in (5.23 m)
Powerplant: two Pratt & Whitney J52-P-408 each rated at 11,200 lb st (49.8 kN) dry
Weights: empty 31,572 lb (14321 kg); normal take-off from a carrier in stand-off jamming configuration with five jammer pods 54,461 lb (24703 kg) or from

land with maximum internal and external fuel 60,610 lb (27493 kg); maximum take-off 65,000 lb (29484 kg)
Fuel and load: internal fuel 15,422 lb (6995 kg); external fuel up to 10,025 lb (4547 kg) in five 400-US gal (1514-litre) drop tanks
Speed: never-exceed speed 710 kt (817 mph; 1315 km/h); maximum level speed 'clean' at sea level 566 kt (651 mph; 1048 km/h) or with five jammer pods 530 kt (610 mph; 982 km/h); cruising speed at optimum altitude 418 kt (481 mph; 774 km/h)
Range: ferry range 2,085 nm (2,399 miles; 3861 km) with empty tanks dropped or 1,756 nm (2,022 miles; 3254 km) with empty tanks retained; range 955 nm (1,099 miles; 1769 km) with maximum external load
Performance: maximum rate of climb 'clean' at sea level 12,900 ft (3932 m) per minute or with five jammer pods 10,030 ft (3057 m) per minute; service ceiling 'clean' 41,200 ft (12550 m) or with five jammer pods 38,000 ft (11580 m); take-off run 2,670 ft (814 m) with five jammer pods; take-off distance to 50 ft (15 m) 2,850 ft (869 m) 'clean' or 3,495 ft (1065 m) with five jammer pods; landing distance from 50 ft (15 m) 2,700ft (823 m) at maximum landing weight; landing run 1,900 ft (579 m) 'clean' or 2,150 ft (655 m) with five jammer pods

Grumman EA-6B ICAP-II Prowler

The ICAP-II is the current service standard of EA-6B, in its Block 86 version capable of launching the HARM missile. This adds a considerable lethal SEAD capability to the basic jamming function. The ICAP-II vastly increased jamming capability. Previously, each ALQ-99 pod could jam in only one frequency band, but with ICAP-II this increased to any one of seven bands. The pod can also jam in two different bands simultaneously. Improved software and a new AYK-14 central computer further enhanced capability.

DECM
Self-protection for the EA-6B is provided by a deception jamming suite. The forward antenna is at the base of the refuelling probe.

BEERCAN FAIRING
On the trailing edge of the 'football' is the 'beercan' fairing for the aft-facing ALQ-126 DECM system.

TJS POD
In the ALQ-99F system each Tactical Jamming System pod contains two high-powered noise jammers and a tracking receiver. Electrical power for the pod is provided by an external turbine generator on the front, which spins in the slipstream.

Grumman **C-2 Greyhound**

As had happened earlier with the S-2 Tracker, the turbine-engined E-2 Hawkeye provided the basis for a COD transport for service with the **US Navy** in the vital role of transferring urgently required personnel and material from shore bases to aircraft-carriers operating at sea, and *vice versa*.

Although its origins in the E-2 Hawkeye are readily apparent, the resulting **Grumman C-2 Greyhound** is significantly different. Perhaps the most notable change related to the fuselage, which is of much greater cross-section, incorporating an upswept aft fuselage section complete with cargo door and an integral loading ramp permitting bulky items such as turbojet engines to be manhandled with relative ease.

Less apparent, but no less important, is the fact that the horizontal and vertical tail surfaces were redesigned, the absence of the Hawkeye's distinctive 'pancake' radome smoothing out airflow patterns in this area and eliminating the requirement for dihedral and inwardly-canted fins and rudders. Of the other changes, perhaps the most notable involved strengthening the nose wheel unit to permit operation at higher gross weights. Fuel capacity was also increased.

As far as payload is concerned, the Greyhound can accommodate up to 39 passengers or 20 stretchers and four attendants or, alternatively, approximately 18,000 lb (8165 kg) of palletised cargo.

Flying for the first time as the **YC-2A** on 18 November 1964, the Greyhound was initially built in only modest numbers, just 19 aircraft being accepted for service with the Navy between 1965 and 1968. Plans to acquire 12 more at this time fell victim to cancellation and, by the early 1970s, attrition had reduced the quantity in service to just a dozen, these operating alongside

even older C-1A Traders from Navy installations both in the Pacific and Mediterranean theatres.

Faced with the question of replacing the vintage C-1A, and in view of the attrition of the Greyhound fleet, the Navy opted to reinstate the C-2A in production during 1982. The first examples of 39 additional Greyhounds were delivered to VR-24 at Sigonella, Sicily, shortly before the end of 1985. Under the terms of the $678 million multi-year contract, procurement continued until 1989. Today the C-2A serves with VRC-30 at North Island, VRC-40 at Norfolk and VRC-50 at NAS Cubi Point, Philippines, VR-24 at Sigonella having disbanded in 1993. Additionally, the two Hawkeye training units, VAW-110 at Miramar and VAW-120 at Norfolk, operate small numbers of Greyhounds to train crews for the COD units.

SPECIFICATION

Grumman C-2A Greyhound
Wing: span 80 ft 7 in (24.56 m); width folded 29 ft 4 in (8.94 m); aspect ratio 9.28; area 700.00 sq ft (65.03 m2)
Fuselage and tail: length 56 ft 10 in (17.32 m); height 15 ft 10.5 in (4.84 m); tailplane span 26 ft 2.5 in (7.99 m); wheel track 19 ft 5.75 in (5.93 m); wheel base 23 ft 2 in (7.06 m)
Powerplant: two Allison T56-A-425 each rated at 4,912 ehp (3663 ekW)
Weights: empty 36,346 lb (16486 kg); maximum take-off 57,500 lb (26081 kg)
Fuel and load: internal fuel 12,400 lb (5625 kg); external fuel none; maximum payload 10,000 lb (4536 kg) for carrier operation or 15,000 lb (6804 kg) for land operation
Speed: maximum level speed at optimum altitude 310 kt (357 mph; 574 km/h); maximum cruising speed at optimum altitude 260 kt (299 mph; 482 km/h)

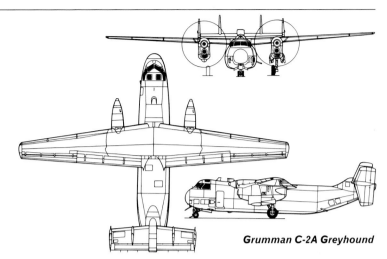

Grumman C-2A Greyhound

Range: ferry range 1,560 nm (1,796 miles; 2891 km); range with a 10,000-lb (4536-kg) payload more than 1,040 nm (1,200 miles; 1930 km)
Performance: maximum rate of climb at sea level 2,610 ft (796 m) per minute; service ceiling 33,500 ft (10210 m) on a ferry mission or 28,800 ft (8780 m) with maximum payload; minimum take-off run 2,180 ft (664 m); take-off distance to 50 ft (15 m) 3,060 ft

The Greyhound is dedicated to supporting carriers at sea, transporting supplies and personnel.

(932 m) at maximum take-off weight; landing distance from 50 ft (15 m) 2,666 ft (691 m) at maximum landing weight or 1,735 ft (529 m) at maximum arrested landing weight; minimum landing run 1,428 ft (435 m)

Grumman **E-2 Hawkeye**

Initially designated **W2F**, the **E-2 Hawkeye** has been the **US Navy**'s airborne early warning platform since entering service in 1964, in time to perform with distinction during the Vietnam War. The early **E-2A** and **E-2B** versions are no longer in

service, today's Hawkeyes being to **E-2C** standard, the first example of which flew on 20 January 1971. Identified by a cooling intake behind the cockpit, the E-2C introduced a new APS-125 radar and far better signal processing compared to its predeces-

sors. The basic E-2C has been the subject of continual updating over the years.

Radar units have changed to APS-138, and from 1989 the APS-139. Now the APS-145 is being fitted to new aircraft and is being retrofitted to earlier aircraft. This radar offers better resistance to jamming and is more capable in an overland role. Other upgrades in the offing concern the IFF (identification, friend or foe) system and the

installation of JTIDS (Joint Tactical Information Distribution System). Low-rate production is almost at an end with the delivery of the 139th aircraft for the US Navy, plus export examples.

Great care has to be taken during the approach, as the E-2's large wing span leaves little room for manoeuvre on a crowded deck.

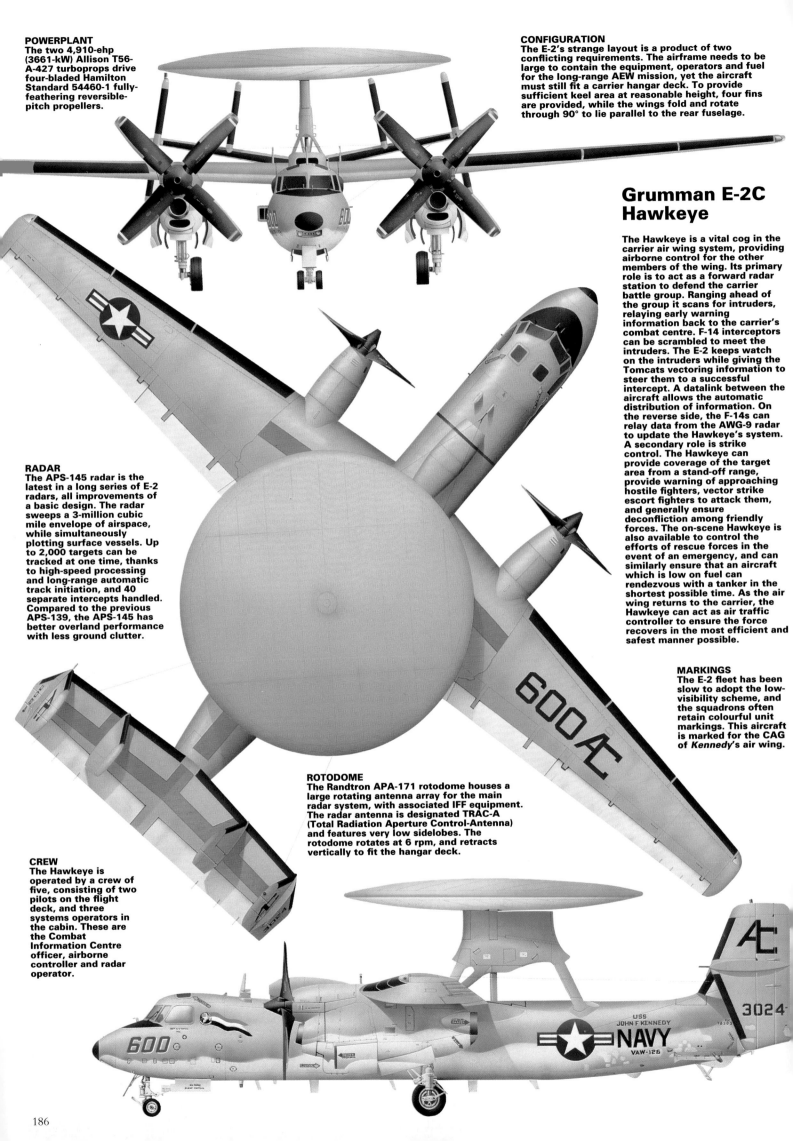

POWERPLANT
The two 4,910-ehp (3661-kW) Allison T56-A-427 turboprops drive four-bladed Hamilton Standard 54460-1 fully-feathering reversible-pitch propellers.

CONFIGURATION
The E-2's strange layout is a product of two conflicting requirements. The airframe needs to be large to contain the equipment, operators and fuel for the long-range AEW mission, yet the aircraft must still fit a carrier hangar deck. To provide sufficient keel area at reasonable height, four fins are provided, while the wings fold and rotate through 90° to lie parallel to the rear fuselage.

Grumman E-2C Hawkeye

The Hawkeye is a vital cog in the carrier air wing system, providing airborne control for the other members of the wing. Its primary role is to act as a forward radar station to defend the carrier battle group. Ranging ahead of the group it scans for intruders, relaying early warning information back to the carrier's combat centre. F-14 interceptors can be scrambled to meet the intruders. The E-2 keeps watch on the intruders while giving the Tomcats vectoring information to steer them to a successful intercept. A datalink between the aircraft allows the automatic distribution of information. On the reverse side, the F-14s can relay data from the AWG-9 radar to update the Hawkeye's system. A secondary role is strike control. The Hawkeye can provide coverage of the target area from a stand-off range, provide warning of approaching hostile fighters, vector strike escort fighters to attack them, and generally ensure deconfliction among friendly forces. The on-scene Hawkeye is also available to control the efforts of rescue forces in the event of an emergency, and can similarly ensure that an aircraft which is low on fuel can rendezvous with a tanker in the shortest possible time. As the air wing returns to the carrier, the Hawkeye can act as air traffic controller to ensure the force recovers in the most efficient and safest manner possible.

RADAR
The APS-145 radar is the latest in a long series of E-2 radars, all improvements of a basic design. The radar sweeps a 3-million cubic mile envelope of airspace, while simultaneously plotting surface vessels. Up to 2,000 targets can be tracked at one time, thanks to high-speed processing and long-range automatic track initiation, and 40 separate intercepts handled. Compared to the previous APS-139, the APS-145 has better overland performance with less ground clutter.

MARKINGS
The E-2 fleet has been slow to adopt the low-visibility scheme, and the squadrons often retain colourful unit markings. This aircraft is marked for the CAG of *Kennedy*'s air wing.

ROTODOME
The Randtron APA-171 rotodome houses a large rotating antenna array for the main radar system, with associated IFF equipment. The radar antenna is designated TRAC-A (Total Radiation Aperture Control-Antenna) and features very low sidelobes. The rotodome rotates at 6 rpm, and retracts vertically to fit the hangar deck.

CREW
The Hawkeye is operated by a crew of five, consisting of two pilots on the flight deck, and three systems operators in the cabin. These are the Combat Information Centre officer, airborne controller and radar operator.

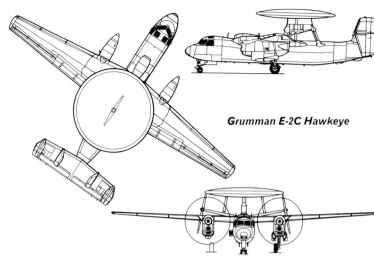

Grumman E-2 Hawkeye

Grumman E-2C Hawkeye

Although best-known as a carrierborne aircraft, the Hawkeye is flown in a land-based role by the export customers. Japan has a large force based at Misawa with 601 Hikotai.

Designed for maximum endurance in a unique role, the Hawkeye has several unusual design features, the most obvious of which is the rotodome, which houses antennas for the main radar and IFF systems. This is raised on jacks before flight, but lowered on deck to fit the hangar. The two T56 turboprops provide sufficient power for carrier operations, yet, combined with the high aspect ratio wing and good internal fuel capacity, provide long patrol endurance. The strange tail arrangement is a compromise between providing enough keel area for aerodynamic purposes and restricting the height to that of the carrier's hangar deck. The wings fold backwards after swivelling through 90°. The large wing span causes some difficulties when landing, requiring a precise approach on the part of the pilots as wingtip clearance on the deck is minimal.

The Hawkeye carries a crew of five, consisting of pilot, co-pilot, CIC (combat information centre) officer, air control officer and radar operator. E-2s usually launch ahead of other carrier aircraft so as to be on station from the beginning of operations. The 'double-cycle' method is often used so that the 'Hummer', as the E-2 is colloquially known,

is airborne throughout two sets of launches and recoveries of tactical aircraft. Flying at an altitude of about 30,000 ft (9145 m), the Hawkeye in the AEW role extends the detection range of the battle group by about 300 miles (480 km) for aircraft and 160 miles (258 km) for cruise missiles. Surface vessels can also be located. Constant communication is maintained with the carrier's CIC by means of a secure datalink.

Datalinks can also be maintained with F-14 Tomcats in the fighter control tasking. The Tomcats themselves can also supply data to the Hawkeye's system. During attacks by tactical aircraft, the Hawkeye can act as an airborne control and command post, supplying directions to attack aircraft and escorting fighters to deconflict them, in addition to providing warnings of hostile aircraft. Air traffic control uses include vectoring aircraft on to tankers, diverting them to alternative landing sites should the carrier be unable to recover them or controlling a traffic stacking pattern in the event of a large-scale recovery process.

In US Navy service, the E-2C flies with active-duty units at NAS Miramar, CA (VAW-112, 113, 114, 116 and 117), NAS Atsugi, Japan (VAW-115), and NAS Norfolk, VA (VAW-121, 122, 123, 124, 125 and 126). Two training units fly the type as fleet replenishment squadrons (VAW-110 at Miramar and VAW-120 at Norfolk), while two USN Reserve squadrons also fly the type (VAW-78 at Norfolk and VAW-88 at Miramar). Until recently the US Coast Guard

operated the type on anti-drug patrols, but these are back with the Navy following the delivery of the Coast Guard's EC-130V radar platform. The **TE-2C** specialist trainer version used by the Navy is no longer believed to be in service.

Foreign interest in the Hawkeye has brought several orders. **Israel** received four in 1978, these aircraft being put to good use in the 1982 war over the Bekaa valley, when IDF/AF fighters destroyed over 80 Syrian MiGs. The **Japanese Air Self-Defence Force** took a batch of four in 1982 and a similar number in 1984, these flying from Misawa with 601 Hikotai and upgraded with APS-145 radar in 1991. Five more were ordered for 1993 delivery. **Egypt** took five from October 1987, and ordered a sixth in 1989. **Singapore** acquired four in 1987, with a further requirement for two. **Taiwan** has bought four aircraft, originally built as E-2Bs but reworked to modern standards as the **E-2T**. The first conversion was completed by Grumman for a 1993 delivery: the remainder are being updated in Taiwan. **Thailand** has a requirement for four aircraft and, finally, **France** is also to acquire four, having a requirement for AEW aircraft to operate from its new nuclear-powered carrier, the *Charles de Gaulle*.

SPECIFICATION

Grumman E-2C Hawkeye
Wing: span 80 ft 7 in (24.56 m); folded width 29 ft 4 in (8.94 m); aspect ratio 9.3; area 700.00 sq ft (65.03 m²)
Fuselage and tail: length 57 ft 6.75 in (17.54 m); height 18 ft 3.75 in (5.58 m); tailplane span 26 ft 2.5 in (7.99 m); wheel track 19 ft 5.75 in (5.93 m); wheel base 23 ft 2 in (7.06 m)
Powerplant: two Allison T56-A-425 each rated at 4,910 ehp (3661 kW)
Weights: empty 38,063 lb (17265 kg); maximum take-off 51,933 lb (23556 kg)
Fuel and load: internal fuel 12,400 lb (5624 kg); external fuel none; maximum ordnance none
Speed: maximum level speed 323 kt (372 mph; 598 km/h); maximum cruising speed at optimum altitude 311 kt (358 mph; 576 km/h); ferry cruising speed at optimum altitude 268 kt (308 mph; 496 km/h)
Range: ferry range 1,394 nm (1,605 miles; 2583 km); operational radius 175 nm (200 miles; 320 km) for a patrol of 3 to 4 hours; endurance with maximum fuel 6 hours 6 minutes
Performance: maximum rate of climb at sea level 2,515 ft (767 m) per minute; service ceiling 30,800 ft (9390 m); minimum take-off run 2,000 ft (610 m); take-off distance to 50 ft (15 m) 2,600 ft (793 m) at maximum take-off weight; landing run 1,440 ft (439 m)

Grumman **F-14A** **Tomcat**

Designed as a successor to the F-4 in the fleet air defence role for the **US Navy**, the Tomcat was originally conceived to engage and destroy targets at extreme range, before they could pose a threat to the carrier battle group. The **Grumman**

For the tactical reconnaissance role, the F-14A carries the multi-sensor TARPS pod between the engine fairings.

F-14A Tomcat remains a formidable warplane, even though the original F-14A has been in service for more than 20 years. Production of the F-14A for the Navy eventually totalled 556 examples, while 80 broadly similar machines were purchased by **Iran** before the downfall of the Shah. Of the latter, only 79 were actually delivered (one being diverted to the US Navy). The F-14A continues to be the Navy's primary air defence aircraft despite the introduction of

the improved **F-14B** and **F-14D** (described separately) which have been built and deployed in modest numbers.

The key to the F-14's effectiveness lies in its advanced avionics suite, the Hughes AWG-9 fire control system representing the most capable long-range interceptor radar in service, with the ability to detect, track and engage targets at ranges in excess of 100 miles (160 km). Early aircraft also had an IRST system, replacing this during production (and by retrofit) with a long-range video camera known as TCS. The armament options allow the aircraft to engage targets over a huge range from close up to extreme

BVR (beyond visual range).

Although never tested in combat, the Hughes AIM-54 Phoenix remains the longest-ranged air-to-air missile in service today and has demonstrated the ability to detect and kill targets at unparalleled distances. In the medium-range arena, Tomcat has the option of either the AIM-7 Sparrow or the AIM-120 AMRAAM, while for short-range, close-in engagements, the F-14 car-

The Sparrow is the Tomcat's medium-range weapon, filling the gap between the Phoenix and Sidewinder.

Grumman F-14A Tomcat

RADAR
The Hughes AWG-9 radar system is immensely powerful. It can track 24 targets simultaneously, and attack six, while still continuing in the search mode.

NAV/COMM EQUIPMENT
The two blade aerials on the spine serve the UHF/TACAN (front) and datalink/IFF (rear). Radio and navigation equipment includes APX-72 IFF transponder, APX-76 IFF interrogator, ARC-51 and ARC-159 UHF radios, ARR-69 auxiliary receiver, KY-28 cryptographic system, ASN-92 INS, APN-154 beacon augmentor, APN-194 radar altimeter, ARN-84 TACAN and ARA-50 automatic direction-finder.

Grumman F-14A Tomcat

Typical of the 500-plus aircraft delivered to the US Navy before the introduction of the F-14B and F-14D models, this 'Turkey' wears the smart and historic markings of VF-31 'Tomcatters', during the time the squadron was assigned to USS *Forrestal*'s Air Wing Six. The aircraft is configured with a TARPS pod, with Sparrows and Sidewinders for self-defence.

TARPS POD
The Tactical Air Reconnaissance Pod System is carried on the starboard side of the underfuselage. In the nose of the pod is a CAI KS-87B frame camera peering obliquely forwards through a slanted flat-pane window. Further back is a bar window for a Fairchild KA-99 panoramic camera, which gives almost horizon-to-horizon coverage. Finally there is a Honeywell AAD-5 infra-red linescan for night-time and bad weather reconnaissance.

SPARROW MISSILE
The standard medium-range missile is the AIM-7M/P Sparrow. The M introduced an inverse monopulse seeker, improved ECCM, new warhead and many other features, while the P has further improvements, including a command link to the missile to improve its capabilities against sea-skimming cruise missiles. The missile is 12 ft (3.66 m) long with a body diameter of 8 in (20.3 cm). The central wings have a span of 3 ft 4 in (1.02 m). Launch weight is 507 lb (230 kg), of which 86 lb (39 kg) is a high-explosive blast fragmentation warhead (replacing the continuous rod warhead of earlier variants). This is fused by active radar. The solid propellant motor gives a range of about 28 miles (45 km).

FUEL
The Tomcat is blessed with considerable internal tankage. Integral tanks in the outer wing sections hold 295 US gal (1117 litres) each. Two fuselage fuel tanks either side of the wing carry-through hold 648 US gal (2453 litres) and 691 US gal (2616 litres). Two further feeder tanks raise total internal capacity to 2,385 US gal (9029 litres). Under-intake tanks as fitted here, each hold 267 US gal (1011 litres).

CONTROL SURFACES
The main control surfaces are grouped at the rear. The twin fins each have powerful rudders for yaw control, while the tailplanes are all-moving control surfaces, providing both roll and pitch control. Roll control at low speeds is augmented by overwing spoilers. To keep approach speeds down, the Tomcat has powerful high-lift flaps and slats on the moving portion of the wing, both running nearly full span.

UNDERCARRIAGE
The landing gear is immensely strong to absorb the high sink rate and deceleration on landing. The mainwheels retract forwards, rotating through 90° to lie flat in the wing gloves. The nosewheel has excellent steerability for tight manoeuvring on deck.

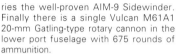

ries the well-proven AIM-9 Sidewinder. Finally there is a single Vulcan M61A1 20-mm Gatling-type rotary cannon in the lower port fuselage with 675 rounds of ammunition.

Development was initiated in the late 1960s, following on the cancellation of the ill-fated F-111B, leaving the Navy in the unenviable position of having no new fighter in prospect. Grumman had already invested a considerable amount of effort in the navalised F-111B, and used this experience in designing a new variable-geometry fighter (the Model G-303) which was duly selected by the Navy in January 1969. Grumman's use of a variable-geometry wing allowed excellent high-speed performance to be combined with docile low-speed handling characteristics and a high degree of agility. Even today, the F-14A is a superb dogfighter, except when compared with the latest optimised air superiority fighters. A dozen development aircraft were ordered, with the first making its maiden flight on 21 December 1970.

Tomcat into service

The programme made reasonably swift progress, culminating in deliveries to the Navy from October 1972, with the first operational cruise in 1974. Production continued into the 1980s and a total of 26 front-line and four second-line squadrons was eventually equipped with the F-14A.

The introduction of updated F-14B and F-14D versions has reduced the number of

Above: Two Tomcats from VF-2 in the landing pattern, with arrester hooks deployed. The pair shows the differences between the old-style colours and the new low-visibility markings.

Right: The F-14A has always had a limited air-to-ground capability, but until recently this was not exercised. The use of the 'Bombcat' is now more prevalent as the US Navy looks for more multi-role flexibility.

squadrons equipped with the original production model. The total number of squadrons has been further reduced, to 17, including four Reserve squadrons, by the reconfiguration of the carrier air wing to include a larger number of multi-role F/A-18 Hornets, several air wings having already transitioned to a one F-14/three F/A-18 squadron mix. Since plans to rework a substantial number of F-14As to F-14B or F-14D standard have been abandoned, it is nevertheless likely to continue in use for some considerable time, albeit in reducing numbers.

The F-14 has suffered many difficulties since entering fleet service. Many were engine-related, the Pratt & Whitney TF30 turbofan proving something of an Achilles heel. Fan blade losses caused several crashes before improved quality control and steel containment cases alleviated the

worst consequences of engine failure. In addition, the engine was prone to compressor stall, especially during air combat manoeuvring training, and the aircraft's vicious departure characteristics (especially with one engine out) resulted in many further losses. Many problems were solved when the revised TF30-P-414A version of the powerplant was adopted as standard.

In addition to fleet air defence tasks, F-14As are also used for reconnaissance missions, using the Tactical Air Reconnais-

sance Pod System (TARPS), and it is usual for three TARPS-capable aircraft to be assigned to one of each carrier air wing's F-14 units. More recently, the F-14A has also acquired a secondary air-to-ground role, capitalising on a modest attack capability that was built in from the outset, but never utilised. Today the training syllabus includes some emphasis on strike missions, although these would only normally be undertaken in a permissive combat environment. The 'Bombcat' carries only con-

WING
At the heart of the Tomcat's structure is the 22-ft (6.7-m) span wing carry-through, which has dihedral to reduce the cross-sectional area of the fuselage. At each end is the pivot point for the moving wing panel. The wings sweep from 20° to 68° in flight, controlled automatically by a computer which takes air and attitude data and then programmes the wings for optimum performance. In order to reduce the amount of room the Tomcat takes up on the carrier deck, the wings can be swept to a 75° ground oversweep position for parking.

The Tomcat works closely with the E-2C Hawkeye. The two aircraft systems exchange information by datalink.

Standard armament consists of an internal M61A1 Vulcan 20-mm six-barrelled cannon, and an AIM-9M Sidewinder on the shoulder launch rail of each pylon under the wing glove. Lower launch rail of each glove pylon can accommodate either an AIM-7M Sparrow or an AIM-54C Phoenix. Four further AIM-7M or AIM-54C can be carried under the fuselage between the engine trunks. AIM-7Ms carried in semi-recessed bays, while AIM-54C mounted on pallets which fit into Sparrow bays. Normal load-out comprises two or four Phoenix under fuselage and two Sparrows on the pylon which, combined with the AIM-9M and cannon, gives a superb all-round mix for the fighter mission. Fuel tanks are often carried on hardpoints under the intakes. In the tactical reconnaissance role the TARPS multi-sensor pod is carried under the rear fuselage, with an ALQ-167 jamming pod on the front starboard Phoenix pallet a common option. Phoenix pallets can also mount bomb racks for 1,000-lb Mk 83 or 2,000-lb Mk 84 GP bombs or other free-fall weaponry.

ventional 'iron' bombs, and has no PGM (precision-guided munition) capability except when operating in conjunction with a separate designator aircraft.

Grumman F-14A Tomcat

Wing: span 64 ft 1.5 in (19.54 m) spread, 38 ft 2.5 in (11.65 m) swept and 33 ft 3.5 in (10.15 m) overswept; aspect ratio 7.28; area 565.00 sq ft (52.49 m²)

Fuselage and tail: length 62 ft 8 in (19.10 m); height 16 ft 0 in (4.88 m); tailplane span 32 ft 8.5 in (9.97 m); wheel track 16 ft 5 in (5.00 m); wheel base 23 ft 0.5 in (7.02 m)

Powerplant: two Pratt & Whitney TF30-P-412A/414A turbofans each rated at 20,900 lb st (92.97 kN) with afterburning

Weights: empty 40,104 lb (18191 kg) with -414A engines; normal take-off 'clean' 58,715 lb (26632 kg); maximum take-off 59,714 lb (27086 kg) with four Sparrows or 70,764 lb (32098 kg) with six Phoenix; overload take-off 74,349 lb (33724 kg)

Fuel and load: internal fuel 16,200 lb (7348 kg); external fuel up to 3,800 lb (1724 kg) in two 267-US gal (1011-litre) drop tanks; maximum ordnance 14,500 lb (6577 kg)

Speed: maximum level speed 'clean' at high altitude 1,342 kt (1,544 mph; 2485 km/h) and at low altitude 792 kt (912 mph; 1468 km/h); cruising speed at optimum altitude between 400 and 550 kt (460 and 633 mph; 741 and 1019 km/h)

Range: maximum range with internal and external fuel about 1,735 nm (2,000 miles; 3220 km); radius on a combat air patrol with six AIM-7 Sparrows and four AIM-9 Sidewinders 665 nm (766 miles; 1,233 km)

Performance: maximum rate of climb at sea level more than 30,000 ft (9145 m) per minute; service ceiling more than 50,000 ft (15240 m); minimum take-off run 1,400 ft (427 m); minimum landing run 2,900 ft (884 m)

Only a handful of F-14s from the 79 delivered are believed to remain operational with the Islamic Republic of Iran Air Force. These are considered high-value assets, and are used as mini-AWACS aircraft, directing other less capable fighters. At least one was shot down by an Iraqi Mirage F1.

Grumman **F-14B/D Tomcat**

Problems with the Pratt & Whitney TF-30 turbofan engine of the F-14A were a key factor in the development of re-engined and upgraded variants of the Tomcat. One of the original prototype airframes was fitted with two F401-PW-400s and employed for an abbreviated test programme as the **F-14B** as early as 1973-74. Technical problems and financial difficulties forced the abandonment of the programme, and the aircraft was placed into storage, re-emerging as the F-14B Super Tomcat with F101DFE engines. This engine was developed into the General Electric F100-GE-400 turbofan, which was selected to power production improved Tomcat variants. It was decided to produce two distinct new Tomcats, one designated **F-14A(Plus)** (primarily by conversion of existing F-14As) with the new engine, and another, designated **F-14D**, with the new engine and improved digital avionics. The F-14A(Plus) was originally regarded as an interim type, all examples of which would eventually be converted to full F-14D standards.

Subsequently, the F-14A(Plus) was formally redesignated as the F-14B, 38 new-build examples being joined by 32 F-14A rebuilds in equipping half-a-dozen deployable squadrons starting in 1988. These incorporated some avionics changes, including a modernised fire control system, new radios, upgraded RWRs, and various cockpit changes. F-14Bs were the first re-engined Tomcats to enter fleet service. F-14Bs have equipped six squadrons, VF-24, VF-74, VF-103, VF-142, VF-143 and VF-211, of which VF-24 and VF-211 subsequently transitioned back to the F-14A to leave the F-14B as an Atlantic Fleet-only aeroplane.

Two modified F-14As flew as F-14D prototypes and the first F-14D to be built as

The F-14B and D (illustrated) are quickly distinguished by the revised jetpipes for the new engines. The D model has a twin sensor installation under the nose.

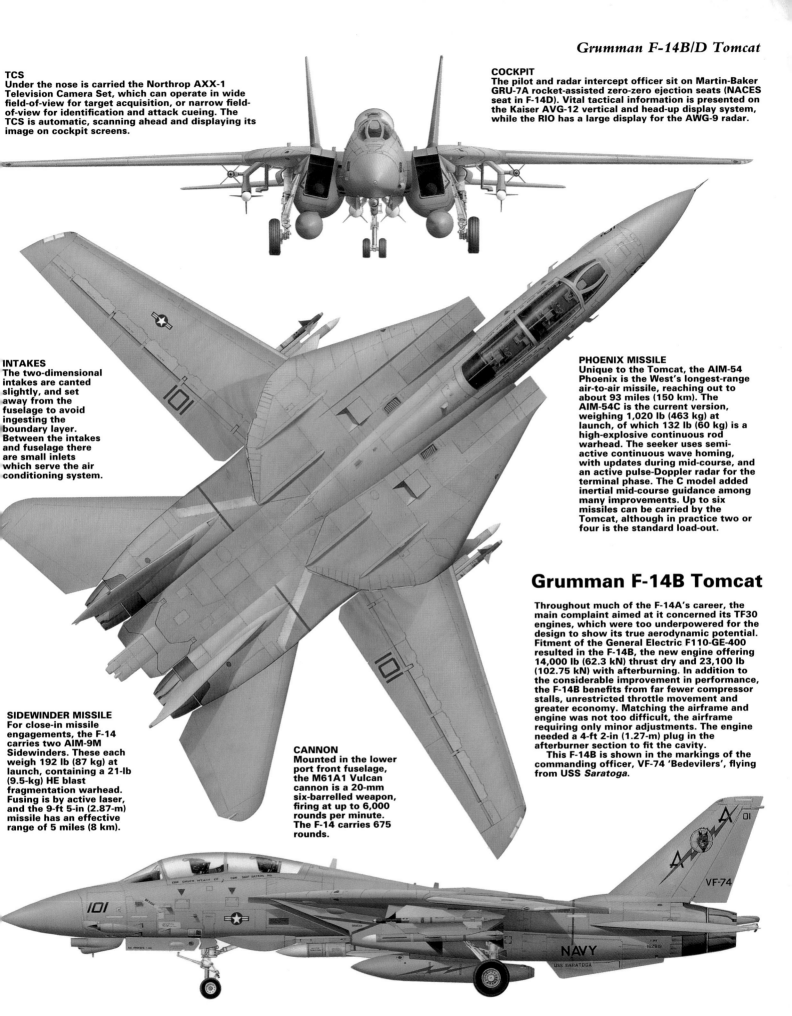

TCS
Under the nose is carried the Northrop AXX-1 Television Camera Set, which can operate in wide field-of-view for target acquisition, or narrow field-of-view for identification and attack cueing. The TCS is automatic, scanning ahead and displaying its image on cockpit screens.

COCKPIT
The pilot and radar intercept officer sit on Martin-Baker GRU-7A rocket-assisted zero-zero ejection seats (NACES seat in F-14D). Vital tactical information is presented on the Kaiser AVG-12 vertical and head-up display system, while the RIO has a large display for the AWG-9 radar.

INTAKES
The two-dimensional intakes are canted slightly, and set away from the fuselage to avoid ingesting the boundary layer. Between the intakes and fuselage there are small inlets which serve the air conditioning system.

PHOENIX MISSILE
Unique to the Tomcat, the AIM-54 Phoenix is the West's longest-range air-to-air missile, reaching out to about 93 miles (150 km). The AIM-54C is the current version, weighing 1,020 lb (463 kg) at launch, of which 132 lb (60 kg) is a high-explosive continuous rod warhead. The seeker uses semi-active continuous wave homing, with updates during mid-course, and an active pulse-Doppler radar for the terminal phase. The C model added inertial mid-course guidance among many improvements. Up to six missiles can be carried by the Tomcat, although in practice two or four is the standard load-out.

Grumman F-14B Tomcat

Throughout much of the F-14A's career, the main complaint aimed at it concerned its TF30 engines, which were too underpowered for the design to show its true aerodynamic potential. Fitment of the General Electric F110-GE-400 resulted in the F-14B, the new engine offering 14,000 lb (62.3 kN) thrust dry and 23,100 lb (102.75 kN) with afterburning. In addition to the considerable improvement in performance, the F-14B benefits from far fewer compressor stalls, unrestricted throttle movement and greater economy. Matching the airframe and engine was not too difficult, the airframe requiring only minor adjustments. The engine needed a 4-ft 2-in (1.27-m) plug in the afterburner section to fit the cavity.

This F-14B is shown in the markings of the commanding officer, VF-74 'Bedevilers', flying from USS *Saratoga*.

SIDEWINDER MISSILE
For close-in missile engagements, the F-14 carries two AIM-9M Sidewinders. These each weigh 192 lb (87 kg) at launch, containing a 21-lb (9.5-kg) HE blast fragmentation warhead. Fusing is by active laser, and the 9-ft 5-in (2.87-m) missile has an effective range of 5 miles (8 km).

CANNON
Mounted in the lower port front fuselage, the M61A1 Vulcan cannon is a 20-mm six-barrelled weapon, firing at up to 6,000 rounds per minute. The F-14 carries 675 rounds.

such made its maiden flight on 9 February 1990. The F-14D added digital avionics, with digital radar processing and displays (adding these to standard AWG-9 hardware under the redesignation APG-71), and a side-by-side undernose TCS/IRST sensor pod. Other improvements introduced by the F-14D include OBOGS (on-board oxygen-generating system), NACES ejection seats, and AN/ALR-67 radar warning receiver equipment. Like the F-14A, the F-14D has a limited ground attack capability. The US Department of Defense's decision to cease funding the **F-14D** has effectively halted the Navy's drive to upgrade its force of Tomcats. In consequence, the service has received only 37 new-build examples of the F-14D, while plans to upgrade approximately 400 existing F-14As to a similar standard have also been severely curtailed and only 18 have been updated, ending in March 1993.

Deliveries to the Navy began in November 1990, when training squadron VF-124

Left: An underview of an F-14B shows the Tomcat's hardpoints to advantage. The recesses under the fuselage house Sparrows or mount pallets for Phoenix missiles, bombs, ECM pods or the TARPS pod. Under the forward portion of each intake trunk is an attachment for fuel tanks, while the wing glove section has a pylon for further missiles, including a shoulder rail for a Sidewinder.

Above: The F-14D model was first assigned to VF-124 at NAS Miramar, California. This unit acts as the training unit for the West Coast/Pacific Fleet Tomcat community. The East Coast equivalent, VF-101 at NAS Oceana, received the F-14B model. The Navy has recently announced that all Tomcat training is to be consolidated at Oceana, where VF-101 will operate all three Tomcat variants.

accepted its first F-14D at Miramar. Initially, it appeared that VF-51 and VF-111 would be the first deployable units to convert. However, a subsequent realignment of fleet fighter resources saw VF-11 and VF-31 move from Oceana to Miramar and receive the F-14Ds previously earmarked for VF-51 and VF-111. Since then VF-2 and VF-14 have re-equipped with the F-14D.

SPECIFICATION

Grumman F-14D Tomcat
generally similar to the Grumman F-14A Tomcat except in the following particulars:
Powerplant: two General Electric F110-GE-400 turbofans each rated at 14,000 lb st (62.27 kN) dry and

23,100 lb st (102.75 kN) with afterburning
Range: combat radius on a combat air patrol with six AIM-7 Sparrows and four AIM-9 Sidewinders 1,075 nm (1,239 miles; 1994 km)
Weights: empty 41,780 lb (18951 kg); normal take-off 64,093 lb (29072 kg) for a fighter/escort mission or 73,098 lb (33157 kg) on a fleet air defence mission; maximum take-off 74,349 lb (33724 kg) lb
Speed: maximum level speed 'clean' at high altitude

1,078 kt (1,241 mph; 1997 km/h); cruising speed at optimum altitude 413 kt (475 mph; 764 km/h)
Range: maximum range with internal and external fuel about 1,600 nm (1,842 miles; 2965 km)
Performance: maximum rate of climb at sea level more than 30,000 ft (9145 m) per minute; service ceiling more than 53,000 ft (16150 m); take-off run 2,500 ft (762 m) from land at maximum take-off weight; landing run 2,400 ft (732 m) on land

Grumman **F-14 Super Tomcat 21**

In recent times, Grumman has devoted a considerable amount of effort to designing advanced Tomcat variants in the hope of securing orders for continued work in either new or rebuild form, partly to fill the gap left by cancellation of the A-12 Avenger and partly as an alternative to the proposed NATF (Navy Advanced Tactical Fighter) project. Most of these projects aimed to enhance the air-to-ground capability of the Tomcat.

The **Quickstrike F-14** was a minimum

change aircraft, with FLIR and expanded radar modes, an NVG-compatible cockpit and extra hardpoints. The Super Tomcat 21 was a more ambitious aircraft, taking the Quickstrike as a starting point and intended as a multi-role alternative to NATF, offering 90 per cent capability at 60 per cent cost.

Two basic versions were envisaged, with the **Super Tomcat 21** being optimised for air-to-air tasks but also being capable of undertaking air-to-ground strike missions. Revamping of aerodynamic aspects centred

around adoption of an enlarged wing glove area as well as a bigger tailplane assembly and revised slat and flap surfaces. Between them, these would bestow extra fuel capacity, giving greatly increased duration, while handling qualities would be improved with a reduced approach speed and the ability to undertake zero-wind launch. Weapons system improvement would include helmet-mounted sighting devices, radar and FLIR pods for attack tasks.

The second version was the **Attack**

Super Tomcat 21. This would be a dedicated strike/attack model, with superior air-to-ground potential. Improvements listed for the baseline Super Tomcat 21 would be augmented by adoption of a new radar, and Grumman's proposal did specifically mention the unit that was under development for the A-12 before it was abandoned. At the present time, it seems unlikely that either proposal will reach fruition, nor will the **ASF-14**, a proposed version using ATF systems and powerplants.

Grumman **G-164 Ag-Cat**

Since 1968, the **Greek air force** has had responsibility for crop-spraying on behalf of the ministry of works, forming for this purpose Mira 359 Aerporikis Exipiretisis Dimosion Ypresion (MAEDY, or Air Force Squadron No. 359 for crop-spraying for ministry of works). This led to the unusual appearance of a fleet of Grumman Ag-Cat biplanes in full air force insignia. The **G-164 Ag-Cat** had first flown on 22 May 1957 as Grumman's only venture into agricultural air-

craft, production being handled from the outset by the Schweizer company, which acquired full rights to the design in 1981. Greece acquired 23 Ag-Cats with 450-hp (336-kW) Pratt & Whitney R-985 engines and enclosed cockpits.

A pair of Greek air force Ag-Cats rests between crop-spraying duties. The air force undertakes such work for the government.

Grumman **OV-1/RV-1 Mohawk**

The **Grumman OV-1/RV-1 Mohawk** is nearing the end of a 35-year service life as the **US Army**'s principal fixed-wing battlefield surveillance and intelligence-gathering aircraft. Though not fast enough to operate at the front in a high-density con-

flict, the Mohawk enjoys unique capabilities for combat support from rough forward airstrips in Third World conflicts.

The crew of two, pilot and observer, sit side-by-side on Martin-Baker J5 ejection seats beneath a bubble-like braced canopy

which offers excellent visibility. All Mohawk variants are equipped with cameras and upward-firing flares for the nocturnal photo-reconnaissance mission. The current OV-1D is dual-role capable, being convertible to either IR or SLAR monitoring missions.

The prototype **YOV-1A** (originally, **YAO-1A**) first flew on 14 April 1959, the only version with dual flight controls and the first turbine-powered aircraft accepted for US Army-wide use. Thirteen service-test and 64 production models were built. The **OV-1B (AO-1B)**, delivered in April 1961, carried AN/APS-94 SLAR in a long pod beneath the right side of the fuselage and introduced a 6-ft (1.83-m) increase in span.

The **OV-1C (AO-1C)**, first delivered in October 1961, introduced the UAS-4 infra-red mapping sensor mounted in the central fuselage and was retrofitted with T53-L-15s used on all subsequent variants. **Israel** received four OV-1Cs (the only overseas purchaser, although the Mohawk was evaluated by France, Germany, Pakistan and the Philippines), subsequently upgraded to OV-1D standard and retrofitted with indigenous sensors.

The definitive Mohawk for battlefield surveillance and target-acquisition duties was the **OV-1D/RV-1D**. Thirty-seven were built new, and 111 earlier Mohawks were upgraded to this standard. The OV-1D's sensors include AN/APD-7 radar surveillance system, AN/AAS-24 infra-red scanners, and KS-60 cameras. Most are now in Army National Guard service. Two GOV-1D ground trainers are based at Fort Eustis, VA.

Some 36 RV-1Ds were converted from earlier airframes under the Quick Look II programme for Elint duties, apparently equipped with AN/ALQ-33 tactical Elint system, AN/ASN-86 inertial navigation system, and real-time data processing and transmission equipment. One example is reported to have been shot down over Central America in 1984.

The US Army does not acknowledge the existence of the **EV-1E Quick Look III** tactical Elint variant used to collect and relay hostile emissions while patrolling a border. Israel reportedly modified one of its airframes as the testbed for this US Army version, which served in Korea and Germany.

One Mohawk was used by NASA for engine-noise monitoring tests with a wing-mounted 2,200-lb (9.78-kN) thrust Pratt & Whitney Canada JT15D-1 turbofan engine. Total production was 380 Mohawks, with production ending in December 1970 and

upgrade work completed in July 1987. OV-1/RV-1 Mohawks are approaching fatigue life limits and have become expensive to operate. By 1996, all will be replaced by RC-12K/N aircraft employing the Guardrail Common Sensor system. Twenty OV-1s were transferred to **Argentina** from US Army stocks, while some US OV-1Ds previously deployed to **South Korea** were handed over to the host nation.

SPECIFICATION

Grumman OV-1D Mohawk

Wing: span 48 ft 0 in (14.63 m); aspect ratio 6.4; area 360.00 sq ft (33.45 m2)

Fuselage and tail: length 41 ft 0 in (12.50 m); height 12 ft 8 in (3.86 m); tailplane span 15 ft 11 in (4.85 m); wheel track 9 ft 2 in (2.79 m); wheel base 11 ft 8.25 in (3.56 m)

Powerplant: two Textron Lycoming T53-L-15 each rated at 1,100 shp (820 kW)

Weights: empty equipped 11,067 lb (5020 kg); normal take-off 13,650 lb (6197 kg); maximum take-off 19,230 lb (8722 kg)

Fuel and load: internal fuel 297 US gal (1125 litres); external fuel up to two 150-US gal (567-litre) drop tanks; maximum ordnance 2,700 lb (1225 kg)

Speed: maximum level speed 'clean' at 5,000 ft (1525 m) 258 kt (297 mph; 478 km/h); maximum cruising speed at optimum altitude 239 kt (275 mph; 443 km/h)

Range: ferry range 1,068 nm (1,250 miles; 1980 km) with drop tanks

The Mohawk is slowly being retired from US Army service, its role having passed to the Beech RC-12, but some surplus aircraft have been supplied to Argentina. The OV-1D can be reconfigured for either infra-red or radar reconnaissance, with interchangeable sensors and cockpit displays.

Performance: maximum rate of climb at sea level 2,350 ft (716 m) per minute; service ceiling 30,300 ft (9235 m); minimum take-off run 580 ft (177 m); take-off distance to 50 ft (15 m) 880 ft (268 m) at maximum take-off weight; landing distance from 50 ft (15 m) 866 ft (264 m) at maximum landing weight; typical landing run 540 ft (165 m)

Grumman **S-2 Tracker**

The **Grumman S-2 Tracker** is still used by several nations, some of which have only recently updated their fleets through acquisition of surplus USN S-2s taken from storage at Davis-Monthan AFB, near Tucson in Arizona.

One of the most successful ASW aircraft yet conceived, the Tracker first flew in December 1952 and entered service with the US Navy in 1954. It was continuously updated, while many of the earlier machines found work as utility and training aircraft, as the **US-2A/B** and **TS-2A**, respectively. Some TS-2As remained active as multi-engine pilot trainers until replaced by the Beech T-44A in 1980. Most Trackers currently active are late-production **S-2E**s and **S-2G**s, the latter being an S-2E with updated electronics.

Some operators have opted to convert their aircraft to **Turbo-Tracker** standard, fitting Garrett TPE331-15AW or Pratt & Whitney Canada PT6A-67CF turboprops in conversions offered by IMP (Canada), Bedek (Israel), and Grumman and Marsh in the US.

Remaining Trackers are still active with **Argentina** (six **S-2E(UP) Turbo**s converted by Bedek and three S-2As), **Brazil** (eight S-2As and five S-2Es being converted with IMP kits), **Peru** (seven S-2E and four S-2G), **South Korea** (nine S-2As and 15 S-2Es), **Taiwan** (32 S-2E and **S-2F**s in the

process of conversion to Turbo standard), **Thailand** (six S-2F/US-2Cs, likely to have been withdrawn), **Turkey** (33 S-2A/Es) and **Uruguay** (three S-2As and three S-2Gs).

SPECIFICATION

Grumman S-2E Tracker

Wing: span 72 ft 7 in (22.13 m); width folded 27 ft 4 in (8.33 m); aspect ratio 10.63; area 496.00 sq ft (46.08 m2)

Fuselage and tail: length 43 ft 6 in (13.26 m); height 16 ft 7 in (5.06 m); wheel track 18 ft 6 in (5.64 m)

Powerplant: two Wright R-1820-82WA Cyclone each rated at 1,525 hp (1137 kW)

Weights: empty 18,750 lb (8505 kg); normal take-off 24,413 lb (11074 kg); maximum take-off 29,150 lb (13222 kg)

Grumman S-2E Tracker

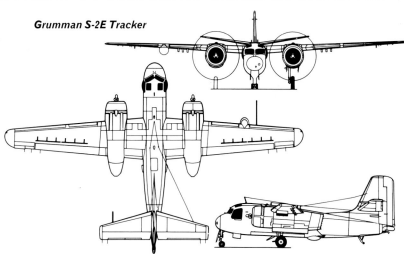

Taiwan retains the Tracker for anti-submarine work. It is one of the nations updating its aircraft with turboprop engines to increase the performance, economy and mission capability. The aircraft fly with the 439th Wing at Pingtung, operated by 33 and 34 Squadrons.

Grumman S-2 Tracker

Fuel and load: internal fuel 4,368 lb (1981 kg); external fuel none; maximum ordnance 4,810 lb (2182 kg)
Speed: maximum level speed 'clean' at sea level more than 230 kt (265 mph; 426 km/h); cruising speed at optimum altitude 180 kt (207 mph; 333 km/h); patrol speed at 1,500 ft (457 m) 130 kt (150 mph; 241 km/h)
Range: ferry range 1,130 nm (1,301 miles; 2094 km); range 1,000 nm (1,152 miles; 1853 km); endurance 9 hours
Performance: maximum rate of climb at sea level 1,390 ft (425 m) per minute; service ceiling 21,000 ft (6400 m); take-off run 1,300 ft (396 m) at maximum take-off weight; take-off distance to 50 ft (15 m) 1,875 ft (572 m) at maximum take-off weight

Several companies offer turbine conversions of Tracker aircraft. IAI has won a contract to re-engine Argentina's six aircraft with the Garrett TPE331-15 turboprop (installed by Marsh Aviation) and hopes to gain more orders, despite other competitors in the S-2 re-engining market. IAI also offers avionics upgrading for the S-2, greatly enhancing its effectiveness.

Grumman **U-16 Albatross**

The air force of **Greece** is the last of more than a dozen military air arms that have operated the **Grumman HU-16 Albatross** SAR and maritime reconnaissance amphibian. Since the first flight of the Albatross on 24 October 1947, Grumman built 418, primarily for US Navy and Air Force, as well as export to foreign countries through MAP. Powered by two 1,425-hp (1063-kW) Wright R-1820-76A piston radial engines, the Albatross was built in two principal versions, initially (**HU-16A**) with a wing span of 80 ft 0 in (24.38 m) and later (**HU-16B**) with a span of 96 ft 8 in (29.46 m).

For anti-submarine warfare, a version with nose-mounted search radar was supplied to Norway. Twelve of these aircraft were later transferred to Greece, where the survivors continue in service with 353 Mira in the 112a Pterix Mahis (Combat Wing) at Elefsis. In Indonesia four HU-16s were flown until recently as part of the equipment of No. 5 Skwadron at Semarang alongside helicopters, flying in the SAR/transport role.

Now reaching the end of its long military career, the Albatross remains in service only with the Greek air force's 353 Mira at Elefsina. The unit is appropriately nicknamed 'Albatros'. The HU-16Bs provide SAR and coastal patrol cover.

SPECIFICATION

Grumman HU-16B Albatross
Wing: span 96 ft 8 in (29.46 m); aspect ratio 9.03; area 1,035.00 sq ft (96.15 m2)
Fuselage and tail: length 62 ft 10 in (19.15 m); height 25 ft 10 in (7.87 m); tailplane span 31 ft 0 in (9.45 m)
Powerplant: two Wright R-1820-76A Cyclone each rated at 1,425 hp (1062 kW)
Weights: empty 22,883 lb (10380 kg); normal take-off 30,353 lb (13768 kg); maximum take-off 34,000 lb (15422 kg) on water and 37,500 lb (17010 kg) on land
Fuel and load: internal fuel 1,088 US gal (4119 litres); external fuel up to two 295-US gal (1117-litre) drop tanks; maximum ordnance none
Speed: maximum level speed 'clean' at sea level 205 kt (236 mph; 380 km/h); cruising speed at optimum altitude 149 kt (172 mph; 277 km/h)
Range: ferry range 3,010 nm (3,466 miles; 5578 km); range 1,490 nm (1,716 miles; 2761 km)
Performance: maximum rate of climb at sea level 1,170 ft (357 m) per minute; ceiling 23,500 ft (7165 m)

Grumman/General Dynamics **EF-111 Raven**

Based on the original F-111A production variant of the General Dynamics swing-wing strike fighter, the **EF-111A Raven** evolved as a specialised electronic warfare platform capable of undertaking stand-off and penetration escort missions. Responsibility for development was entrusted to Grumman, which already had considerable expertise in the EW field, having produced the EA-6A version of the Intruder for the Marine Corps and the even more capable EA-6B Prowler for both the USN and USMC.

All EF-111As now serve with the 27th FW. The two operating units are the 429th and 430th (illustrated) Electronic Combat Squadrons.

Indeed, the TJS that forms the core of the EF-111A's impressive capability is fundamentally a variation of the AN/ALQ-99 TJS as fitted to the EA-6B. The Raven introduces a much improved equipment package, however, with certain key items being housed internally rather than in underwing pods as on the EA-6B. It also embodies a greater degree of automation so as to allow it to be fully and effectively managed by just

one EWO, rather than three as in the Prowler. As in all versions of the F-111 family, the Raven pilot and EWO occupy side-by-side seating in an escape capsule.

Receiving antennas associated with the TJS are located in the distinctive bulbous fin-cap fairing, while the jamming transmitters are contained in space previously occupied by the F-111A's internal weapons bay.

CONVERSION PROGRAMME

Grumman was awarded the contract to develop the EF-111 on 26 December 1974. An aerodynamic prototype flew on 15 December 1975, and the first 'full-up' aircraft on 10 March 1977. A total of 42 F-111As was modified, retaining the bomber's TF30-P-3 engines and Triple Plow I intakes. The conversion involved reworking the weapons bay to accommodate the jammers, adding the fin antennas and removing all offensive equipment. The right side of the cockpit was revised to incorporate EW displays and controls, with some navigation equipment being relocated to the pilot's position.

MISSION

The EF-111 operates in three principal roles: stand-off, strike escort and close air support. In the stand-off role the EF-111 supplies jamming from safe airspace. It can either blanket a hostile air defence or, with the aid of lethal SEAD assets, punch a hole through a heavily defended border to provide a corridor through which strike aircraft can flow. In the strike escort role it accompanies the strike force throughout the penetration mission, while in the close support role it neutralises radars in the battlefield while attack aircraft take on armour formations. The EF-111 operates closely with the F-4G Wild Weasel (lethal SEAD) and EC-130H Compass Call (command, control and communications jamming) to present a powerful counter to any air defence system.

JAMMERS

The main jamming equipment is housed in the former weapons bay, with the transmitters housed in the 16-ft (4.9-m) ventral canoe fairing. There are 10 transmitters, five exciters and six digitally-tuned receivers. The equipment covers seven frequency bands. At the rear of the bay are two air-water heat exchangers which cool the system.

SELF-DEFENCE MISSILES

One set of wing pylons is retained to allow the EF-111 to carry AIM-9 Sidewinders for self-defence. The aircraft's performance and onboard jammers are its primary means of defence.

Grumman/General Dynamics EF-111A Raven

Widely known as the 'Spark Vark', the EF-111A provides the US Air Force with its non-lethal SEAD (suppression of enemy air defences) assets. The jamming system is based on that of the EA-6B Prowler, but features greater automation to enable only one electronic warfare officer to operate it. Compared to the Prowler, the EF-111 has far better performance, which allows it to operate more effectively in the strike escort role, especially when supporting high-performance jets such as the F-111 or F-15E. However, it does not have HARM-firing capability, which restricts it to non-lethal SEAD, whereas the Block 86 EA-6Bs can launch the AGM-88.

An underview emphasises the ghostly qualities of the EF-111. All of the jammers are housed in the canoe fairing. As all of the Ravens were converted from F-111As, they inherited the Triple Plow I intakes with large splitter plates.

The canoe fairing hinges open to allow rapid access to the jammers for maintenance.

RECEIVER ANTENNAS

Hostile radar emissions are detected by antennas in the SIR (System Integrated Receiver) pod mounted at the top of the fin (otherwise known as the 'football'). These face forwards, sideways and rearwards, and are augmented by further receivers lower down on the fin and blade antennas on the sides of the engine intake trunks. Receivers provide information to the central computer, which processes the data, analyses and prioritises the threats for display in the cockpit and automatic operation of the jamming system.

and the speed at which those countermeasures could be implemented, but it appears that cuts in defence spending may well curtail the extent of the improvement effort. However, even though updating may not be quite as ambitious as first hoped, there appears to be little likelihood of early or premature retirement, since the EF-111A is still the only dedicated jamming platform in the USAF inventory and is likely to remain unique in that capacity for the foreseeable future.

Reductions in the size of USAFE following the demise of the Warsaw Pact alliance included the withdrawal of the EF-111A squadron from Upper Heyford during 1992. The Raven force is now concentrated in the US under the control of Air Combat Command with the 27th Fighter Wing at Cannon AFB, NM, which now operates all the surviving F-111 variants.

On account of its jamming systems, the EF-111A is well-protected against missile attack. However, its best defence remains the sheer speed and acceleration available at all altitudes.

Protruding beneath the aircraft, these are covered by a 'canoe' radome that measures approximately 16 ft (5 m) in length. Other items of equipment associated with EW role include active and passive ECM systems, and the EF-111 also features an AN/ALR-23 infra-red warning system.

Unarmed warrior

Unlike other variants of the F-111 family, the EF-111A has no armament capability and is therefore forced to rely purely on performance and evasion in the event of running into hostile fighters. The EF-111A was committed to combat during Operation Desert Storm when it operated from bases at Taif, Saudi Arabia, with the 48th Tactical Fighter Wing (Provisional) and Incirlik, Turkey, with the 7440th Wing (Provisional). Employed mainly in a supporting role by disrupting hostile radars with its jamming, it did manage to emerge victorious in an aerial engagement with an Iraqi Mirage F1 on the first night of the air campaign, when skilful manoeuvring by a Raven pilot caused his pursuer to fly into the ground. This was, in fact, one of the first Iraqi warplanes to be destroyed during the war, although it appears that it was never officially accredited as a 'kill'.

Development of the EF-111A was initiated in 1972, but it was not until 1975 that Grumman received an $89.5 million contract covering the conversion of two prototypes, both of which flew for the first time in 1977. After lengthy and extensive testing of the sophisticated system, production-configured conversions eventually entered service with TAC's 366th TFW at Mountain Home AFB, ID, and others were subsequently assigned to USAFE's 42nd Electronic Combat Squadron at Upper Heyford, England.

Conversion total

A total of 42 aircraft was eventually brought to EF-111A Raven standard by Grumman and most of these are still operational, although one was lost during the Gulf War and at least one other is known to have been destroyed in a crash while assigned to the 42nd ECS in England. Survivors were earmarked for an extensive Service Improvement Program (SIP) which was intended to upgrade existing capability and enhance reliability to counter progressively more sophisticated radar threats.

Part of this work was intended to increase the number of hostile emitters that could be countered by the AN/ALQ-99E TJS

SPECIFICATION

Grumman/General Dynamics EF-111A Raven
generally similar to the General Dynamics F-111A except in the following particulars
Fuselage and tail: length 76 ft 0 in (23.16 m); height 20 ft 0 in (6.10 m)
Powerplant: two Pratt & Whitney TF30-P-3 each rated at 18,500 lb st (82.29 kN) with afterburning
Weights: operating empty 55,275 lb (25072 kg); normal take-off 70,000 lb (31752 kg); maximum take-off 88,948 lb (40347 kg)
Fuel and load: internal fuel 32,493 lb (14739 kg)
Speed: maximum speed at high altitude 1,226 kt (1,412 mph) 2272 km/h); maximum combat speed 1,196 kt (1,377 mph) 2216 km/h); average speed in combat area 507 kt (584 mph; 940 km/h)
Range: combat radius 807 nm (929 miles; 1495 km); unrefuelled endurance more than 4 hours 0 minutes
Performance: maximum rate of climb at sea level 3,300 ft (1006 m) per minute; service ceiling 45,000 ft (13715 m)

Guizhou (GAIC) JJ-7/FT-7

Guizhou Aviation Industry Corporation
PO Box 38, Anshun,
Guizhou 561000, China

Developed by the Guizhou Aviation Industry Corporation (GAIC) as a combat-capable two-seat fighter-trainer derivative of the Chengdu J-7 II single-seat fighter (which was, in turn, the result of incremental redesign of the licence-built MiG-21F-13), the **JJ-7**, or **Jianjiao-7**, was first flown on 5 July 1985. Closely resembling the tandem-seat MiG-21U, the JJ-7 has starboard-opening twin cockpit canopies, the aft cockpit being fitted with a retractable periscope and provision being made for a removable saddleback fuel tank. Powered by a 43.15-kN (9,700-lb st) dry and 59.8-kN (13,448-lb st) afterburning Chengdu WP-7B turbojet, the JJ-7 can carry a centreline ventral twin-barrelled 23-mm cannon pack plus two PL-2B AAMs, two 18-round 57-mm rocket pods or two 250-kg (551-lb) bombs.

The JJ-7 entered production for the **People's Republic of China** air force in 1987, simultaneously being offered with a GEC-supplied avionics suite for export as the **FT-7**. One of the first customers for the export model was the **Pakistan** air force, which procured 15 (as **FT-7Ps**). **Bangladesh** has also bought the type to supplement its two F-7 squadrons.

SPECIFICATION

Guizhou JJ-7/FT-7
Wing: span 7.154 m (23 ft 5.375 in); aspect ratio 2.2; area 23.00 m² (247.58 sq ft)
Fuselage and tail: length 14.874 m (48 ft 9.5 in) including probe; height 4.103 m (13 ft 5.5 in); tailplane span 3.74 m (12 ft 3.25 in); wheel track 2.692 m (8 ft 10 in); wheel base 4.807 m (15 ft 9.25 in)
Powerplant: one Liyang (LMC) Wopen-7B turbojet rated at 43.15 kN (9,700 lb st) dry and 59.82 kN (13,448 lb st) with afterburning
Weights: empty equipped 5330 kg (11,750 lb); normal take-off 7590 kg (16,733 lb); maximum take-off 8600 kg (18,959 lb)
Fuel and load: internal fuel 1891 kg (4,169 lb); external fuel up to one 800- or 400-litre (211- or 127-US gal) drop tank; maximum ordnance 500 kg (1,102 lb)
Speed: maximum level speed 'clean' at 12500 m (41,010 ft) 2175 km/h (1,172 kt; 1,350 mph)
Range: ferry range 1300 km (701 nm; 808 miles) with drop tank; range 1010 km (545 nm; 627 miles) with internal fuel
Performance: maximum rate of climb at sea level about 9000 m (29,530 ft) per minute; service ceiling 17300 m (56,760 ft); take-off run 900 m (2,953 ft) at normal take-off weight increasing to 1100 m (3,609 ft) at maximum take-off weight; landing run 1100 m

Most JJ-7/FT-7s have been produced for the Chinese air arms, but also for Pakistan and Bangladesh. The Pakistani aircraft (right) serves with No. 20 Squadron, while the Bangladeshi aircraft (left) wears the markings of Nos 5 'Supersonics' and 35 'Thundercats' Sqns.

Gulfstream Aerospace (Grumman)
Gulfstream I/TC-4A Academe

Gulfstream Aerospace Corporation
PO Box 2206, Savannah International Airport,
Savannah, GA 31402, USA

The **US Navy** adopted a version of the **Grumman Gulfstream I** twin-turboprop executive aircraft in December 1966, for use to train Intruder bombardier/navigators in the use of the DIANE nav/attack weapon systems of the A-6. A simulated A-6 cockpit was located in the rear of the cabin, together with four identical radar/navigation training consoles. Since entering service with VA-42 and VA-128, and with the USMC's VMAT-202, nine **TC-4C**s have been extensively updated to match latest A-6E avionic standards. A single **VC-4A** is used by the **US Coast Guard** as an executive transport, a role in which single 'G1s' are flown by **Greece** and **Venezuela**.

Gulfstream Aerospace (Grumman) Gulfstream I/TC-4A Academe

Left: The TC-4C is used as a trainer for A-6E bombardiers, and has an Intruder weapons system.

SPECIFICATION

Gulfstream Aerospace TC-4C Academe
Wing: span 78 ft 4 in (23.88 m); aspect ratio 10.05; area 610.30 sq ft (56.70 m2)
Fuselage and tail: length 67 ft 10.75 in (20.69 m); height 23 ft 4 in (7.11 m); tailplane span 25 ft 6 in (7.77 m); wheel track 24 ft 2 in (7.37 m); wheel base 19 ft 9.5 in (6.03 m)
Powerplant: two Rolls-Royce Dart RDa.7/2 Mk 529-8X turboprops each rated at 2,210 ehp (1648 ekW)
Weights: empty 24,575 lb (11114 kg); maximum take-off 36,000 lb (16330 kg)

Fuel and load: internal fuel 1,550 US gal (5867 litres); external fuel none; maximum payload 4,270 lb (1937 kg)
Speed: maximum speed at 15,000 ft (4570 m) 317 kt (365 mph; 587 km/h); maximum cruising speed at 25,000 ft (7620 m) 302 kt (348 mph; 560 km/h); economical cruising speed at 25,000 ft (7620 m) 259 kt (298 mph; 480 km/h)
Range: typical range at 30,000 ft (9145 m) 1720 nm (1,980 miles; 3186 km) or at 5,000 ft (1525 m) 995 nm (1,145 miles; 1843 km)
Performance: maximum rate of climb at sea level 1,900 ft (579 m) per minute; service ceiling 33,600 ft (10240 m); take-off distance to 35 ft (10.7 m) 3,000 ft

(914 m) at maximum take-off weight; landing distance from 50 ft (15 m) 2,100 ft (664 m) at maximum landing weight

This single Gulfstream I flies with the Greek air force's 356 'Iraklis' Mira on VIP/staff transport duties. It is based at Elefsina.

Gulfstream Aerospace (Grumman) Gulfstream II/VC-11A

The **Gulfstream II** long-range executive jet was built successively by Grumman, Grumman American and Gulfstream American between October 1966 and March 1980. Only one example, of 258 built, was sold as new for other than civil use. This was an example acquired as a VIP/staff transport by the **US Coast Guard** and designated **VC-11A**, becoming the first pure jet aircraft operated by the CG when delivered in July 1968. A few used Gulf-

stream IIs have been acquired by other military operators for communications and VIP transport duties, including the **US Army** (two VC-11As) and the air forces of **Morocco**, **Oman** and **Venezuela**.

SPECIFICATION

Gulfstream Aerospace Gulfstream II
Wing: span 68 ft 10 in (20.98 m); aspect ratio 5.97;

area 793.50 sq ft (73.72 m2)
Fuselage and tail: length 79 ft 11 in (24.36 m); height 24 ft 6 in (7.47 m); tailplane span 27 ft 0 in (8.23 m); wheel track 13 ft 8 in (4.16 m); wheel base 33 ft 4 in (10.16 m)
Powerplant: two Rolls-Royce Spey RB.168 Mk 511-8 turbofans each rated at 11,400 lb st (50.71 kN) dry
Weights: maximum take-off 57,500 lb (26081 kg); external fuel none
Speed: maximum level speed 'clean' at 25,000 ft

(7620 m) 508 kt (585 mph; 941 km/h); maximum cruising speed at optimum altitude 491 kt (565 mph; 909 km/h)
Range: range 3,005 nm (3,460 miles; 5568 km)
Performance: maximum rate of climb at sea level 5,050 ft (1539 m) per minute; service ceiling 43,000 ft (13105 m); take-off balanced field length 4,070 ft (1241 m) at maximum take-off weight; landing balanced field length 3,080 ft (939 m) at normal landing weight

Gulfstream Aerospace (Grumman) Gulfstream III/C-20/SRA-1

Of similar configuration to the Gulfstream II, the **Gulfstream III** was launched by Grumman American in 1976, its development and production becoming the responsibility of Gulfstream American in 1978 after Grumman sold its interest. The 19-seat Gulfstream III, which first flew on 2 December 1979, features a 24-in (61-cm) stretch and an improved wing with winglets. The **USAF** operates three Gulfstream IIIs as **C-20A**s, and eight **C-20B/C-20C**s (with basic AC instead of DC electrical systems) used by the 89th AW at Andrews AFB for VIP use. Generally similar transport versions are two **C-20D** 14-seat staff transports used by the **US Navy** and two **C-20E**s serving the **US Army**. Gulfstream IIIs are also used in VIP or Presidential transport role by the air forces of **Gabon** (Presidential Guard), **Italy**, **Ivory Coast**, **Mexico**, **Morocco**, **Oman**, **Saudi Arabia** and **Venezuela**.

Three special mission aircraft, designated **SMA-3**, were supplied to the **Royal Danish air force** in 1981/82, and equipped with quickly-convertible interiors to allow their use in a variety of roles including, in particular, fishery patrols. The three are operated by No. 721 Squadron, which also

flies Hercules from its base at at Vaerløse, near Copenhagen. One aircraft is usually detached to Greenland for fishery patrols and SAR support. Equipped as a surveillance and reconnaissance aircraft, a **Gulfstream SRA-1** demonstrator was flown on 14 August 1984 and two aircraft to this standard are operated by **India**, apparently on clandestine Elint missions.

SPECIFICATION

Gulfstream Aerospace Gulfstream III
Wing: span 77 ft 10 in (23.72 m); aspect ratio 6.48; area 934.60 sq ft (86.83 m2)
Fuselage and tail: length 83 ft 1 in (25.32 m); height 24 ft 4.5 in (7.43 m); tailplane span 27 ft 0 in (8.23 m); wheel track 13 ft 10 in (4.22 m); wheel base 35 ft 2 in (10.72 m)
Powerplant: two Rolls-Royce Spey RB.168 Mk 511-8 turbofans each rated at 11,400 lb st (50.71 kN)
Weights: manufacturer's empty 32,300 lb (14651 kg); typical operating empty 38,000 lb (17236 kg); maximum take-off 68,200 lb (30936 kg)
Fuel and load: internal fuel 28,300 lb (12836 kg);

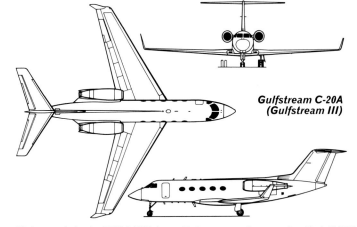

Gulfstream C-20A (Gulfstream III)

external fuel none; typical payload 1,600 lb (726 kg)
Speed: maximum cruising speed at 30,000 ft (9145 m) 501 kt (577 mph; 929 km/h); economical cruising speed at 30,000 ft (9145 m) 453 kt (522 mph; 840 km/h)
Range: 3,647 nm (4,200 miles; 6760 km)

Performance: maximum operating altitude 45,000 ft (13715 m); take-off balanced field length 5,700 ft (1737 m) at maximum take-off weight; landing run 3,400 ft (1036 m) at normal landing weight

Below: All four US services use the C-20 for staff transport duties.

Right: Denmark's G III force is used for SAR and fishery patrols in addition to transport.

Gulfstream Aerospace Gulfstream IV/C-20/SRA-4

First flown on 19 September 1985, the **Gulfstream IV** was developed from the G III, from which it differed primarily in having a 54-in (1.37-m) fuselage stretch, Rolls-Royce Tay in place of Spey engines, structural improvements, increased fuel capacity and a modernised cockpit. Like the G III, the G IV finds application as a VIP transport for military use, examples to date including a **C-20F** for the **US Army**, five **C-20G**s for the **US Navy** (two for active-duty, two for the Reserve and one for the **USMC**), and a single **C-20H** for the **USAF**. The C-20Gs delivered in 1994 are equipped with cargo doors and convertible passenger/cargo interiors. The US Navy C-20Gs serve with VR-48 at Andrews AFB, where the single C-20H will join earlier USAF C-20 models serving in the 89th MAW. One civil-registered Gulfstream IV serves in the quasi-military VIP transport squadron of the **Egyptian air force** at Cairo East, and another is used for high-altitude navaid checking by the Japanese ministry of transport. The Gulfstream IV is used additionally by the **Botswana** defence force (one), the **Irish Air Corps** (one), the

Turkish air force (three operated by 224 Filo for VIP transportation) and the **Swedish air force** (one for transport/training and two for Elint duty). The designation **SRA-4** refers to a proposed special-mission version of the Gulfstream IV, for such roles as EW support, electronic surveillance/reconnaissance, maritime patrol, ASW, medevac and priority cargo transport. A prototype/demonstrator was flown in 1988. The designation **EC-20F** referred to a proposed version for the US Navy FEWSG missions.

SPECIFICATION

Gulfstream Aerospace Gulfstream SRA-4
Wing: span 77 ft 10 in (23.72 m) over winglets; aspect ratio 6.0; area 950.39 sq ft (88.29 m²)
Fuselage and tail: length 88 ft 4 in (26.92 m); height 24 ft 10 in (7.57 m); tailplane span 32 ft 0 in (9.75 m); wheel track 13 ft 8 in (4.17 m); wheel base 38 ft 1.25 in (11.61 m)
Powerplant: two Rolls-Royce Tay Mk 611-8 turbofans rated at 13,850 lb st (61.61 kN)
Weights: manufacturer's empty 35,500 lb (16102 kg);

maximum take-off 73,200 lb (33203 kg)
Fuel and load: internal fuel 29,500 lb (13381 kg); external fuel none; maximum payload 6,198 lb (2811 kg) including 600 lb (272 kg) of expendables
Speed: never-exceed speed Mach 0.88; maximum cruising speed at 31,000 ft (9450 m) 509 kt (586 mph; 943 km/h); economical cruising speed at 41,000 ft (12500 m) 454 kt (523 mph; 841 km/h)
Range: operational radius typically 600 nm (691 miles; 1112 km) for a 6-hour patrol with a 6,198-lb (2811-kg) mission payload, or 1,000 nm (1,152 miles; 1853 km) for a 4.3-hour patrol with a 5,518-lb

In Swedish service the G IV is known as the Tp 102, three serving with F16M. This is the single transport version on strength.

(2503-kg) mission payload including six crew and one anti-ship missile
Performance: maximum rate of climb at sea level 4,000 ft (1219 m) per minute; service ceiling 45,000 ft (13715 m); take-off balanced field length 5,250 ft (1600 m); landing distance from 50 ft (15 m) 3,366 ft (1026 m) at normal landing weight

---

HFB (MBB) 320 Hansa

A product of the Hamburger Flugzeugbau before its merger into MBB (itself now a part of DASA), the **HFB 320 Hansa** is notable for its configuration, with a wing of moderate forward sweep. First flown on 21 April 1964 and intended for the corporate market, the seven- to 12-seat Hansa sold only in small numbers, and 16 of the 47 built were delivered to the **Luftwaffe**. Of these, eight used as transports were withdrawn in 1988; the other eight were converted to serve as ECM trainers and for airways calibration. At first flown by FVST 61, they are now operated by No. 323 Staffel in the mainly Tornado-equipped Jagdbomber-Geschwader 32 at Lechfeld.

SPECIFICATION

Hamburger Flugzeugbau HFB 320 Hansa
Wing: span 47 ft 4 in (14.46 m) over tiptanks; area 324.4 sq ft (30.14 m²)
Fuselage and tail: length 54 ft 6 in (16.61 m); height 15 ft 7.5 in (4.76 m); tailplane span 18 ft 2 in (5.55 m); wheel track 7 ft 9 in (2.36 m); wheel base 22 ft 1.5 in (6.74 m)
Powerplant: two General Electric CJ610-1 turbojets rated at 2,850 lb st (12.68 kN)
Weights: empty equipped 10,670 lb (4840 kg); maximum take-off 18,740 lb (8500 kg)
Fuel and load: internal fuel 7,341 lb (3330 kg);

Easily identified by its additional radomes and antennas, and Dayglo panels for high conspicuity, this is one of the HFB 320ECMs used by the Luftwaffe for EW training.

maximum payload 2,650 lb (1200 kg)
Speed: never-exceed speed Mach 0.83; maximum level speed at 26,250 ft (8000 m) 509 mph (819 km/h); economical cruising speed at 39,400 ft (12000 m) 449 mph (723 km/h)
Range: with maximum fuel, 760 lb (345 kg) payload at 39,400 ft (12000 m) and sufficient for diversion and reserves 1,450 miles (2335 km); with maximum

payload and sufficient for diversion and reserves 825 miles (1330 km)
Performance: maximum rate of climb at sea level 4,080 ft (1242 m) per minute; service ceiling 38,000 ft (11600 m); take-off run at 17,640 lb (8000 kg) 3,190 ft (970 m); take-off run to 35 ft (10.5 m) 3,190 ft (970 m); landing distance at 13,230 lb (6000 kg) 1,300 ft (395 m)

Harbin (HAMC) SH-5

*Harbin Aircraft Manufacturing Corporation
PO Box 201, Harbin,
Heilongjiang 150066, China*

The **SH-5**, or **Shuihong-5**, amphibious flying-boat was conceived in the mid-1960s as a maritime patrol and anti-submarine aircraft. Detail design was not completed, however, until February 1970, and the first flying prototype did not enter flight test until 3 April 1976. Some limited production of the SH-5 followed for the air component of the **People's Republic of China** navy, but the first four series aircraft were not handed over until a decade later, on 3 September 1986. These have since been operated from the Tuandao naval air base, Qingdao.

Powered by four Dongan (DEMC) WJ5A turboprops each rated at 3,150 ehp (2349 kW), the SH-5 has a flight crew of five plus three systems/equipment operators. Defensive armament consists of a twin-gun, remotely-controlled dorsal barbette, offensive weaponry including up to 6000 kg (13,228 lb) of depth charges, mines or bombs internally, plus external loads. The

latter may include up to four anti-shipping missiles suspended from wing hardpoints, each outer hardpoint being capable of lifting up to three lightweight torpedoes. SAR and water-bomber versions of the SH-5 have been evaluated, and a bulk cargo variant has been proposed. The Chinese were reportedly seeking an ASW avionics upgrade for the SH-5 in the early 1990s.

SPECIFICATION

Harbin SH-5
Wing: span 36.00 m (118 ft 1.25 in); aspect ratio 9.0; area 144.00 m² (1550.05 sq ft)
Fuselage and tail: length 38.90 m (127 ft 7.5 in); height 9.802 m (32 ft 2 in); tailplane span 10.50 m (34 ft 5.5 in); wheel track 3.754 m (12 ft 3.75 in); wheel base 10.50 m (34 ft 5.5 in)
Powerplant: four Dongan (DEMC) Wojiang-5A1 turboprops each rated at 3,150 ehp (2349 ekW)
Weights: empty equipped less than 25000 kg

(55,115 lb) for the SAR and transport roles, or 26500 kg (58,422 lb) for the ASW role; normal take-off 36000 kg (79,365 lb); maximum take-off 45000 kg (99,206 lb)
Fuel and load: internal fuel 13417 kg (29,579 lb); external fuel none; maximum ordnance 6000 kg (13,228 lb) carried internally or maximum payload 10000 kg (22,046 lb)
Speed: maximum level speed 'clean' at optimum altitude 555 km/h (300 kt; 345 mph); maximum cruising speed at optimum altitude 450 km/h (243 kt; 280 mph); minimum patrol speed at optimum altitude 230 km/h (124 kt; 143 mph)
Range: 4750 km (2,563 nm; 2,951 miles); endurance between 12 hours and 15 hours on two engines

The impressive SH-5 undertakes many maritime roles, including ASV, ASW, SAR, fire fighting and minelaying.

Performance: service ceiling 10250 m (33,630 ft); take-off run 548 m (1,798 ft) on water at maximum take-off weight; landing run 653 m (2,143 ft) on water at normal landing weight

---

Harbin Y-11/Y-12

The **Harbin Y-11** was developed as a general utility aircraft to replace **China**'s Antonov An-2/Harbin Y-5. The initial aircraft were powered by two indigenous Quzhou Huosai-6A 213-kW (285-hp) nine-cylinder radial piston engines based on the Ivchenko AI-14RF. These allowed the

aircraft to carry a payload of 940 kg (2,072 lb), which was raised to 1250 kg (2,755 lb) when HS6D engines were fitted. Eight passengers could be carried in addition to the two crew.

In order to give better single-engine performance the **Y-11B** was developed, with

350-hp (261-kW) Continental TSIO-550-B flat six engines. The prototype first flew on 25 December 1990 and deliveries began in 1992. The **Y-11BI** is similar, with further upgraded avionics.

The **Y-12** shares the same configuration as the Y-11, but is of larger overall size, with a bigger fuselage cross-section and a fuselage 'plug' ahead of the wings. The new cabin accommodated up to 17 passengers. It was originally to have been designated

Y-11T1, but the Y-12 designation was adopted before the first flight. The new aircraft was originally to have been powered by a pair of 400-shp (298-kW) Allison 250-B17B turboprops but these were displaced by 500-shp (373-kW) Pratt & Whitney PT6A-11 turboprops. This led to the adoption of the name **'Turbo Panda'** for overseas marketing. Payload/range capability is dramatically improved by comparison with the Y-11. The prototype made its maiden flight on 14 July 1982 and was followed by about 30 production aircraft, most of which were used for geological survey and mineral exploration.

The Y-12I was replaced on the production line by the **Y-12II**, built to international airworthiness standards, powered by 507-kW (680-shp) PT6A-27 engines, and with leading-edge slats deleted. Military customers for the Y-12II include **Sri Lanka** (nine, delivered from 1987), **Iran**, **Paraguay** (at least seven) and **Peru** (six).

SPECIFICATION

Harbin Y-12 II
Wing: span 17.235 m (56 ft 6.5 in); aspect ratio 8.7; area 34.27 m² (368.88 sq ft)
Fuselage and tail: length 14.86 m (48 ft 9 in); height 5.575 m (18 ft 3.5 in); elevator span 5.365 m (17 ft 7.27 in); wheel track 3.60 m (11 ft 9.75 in); wheel base

4.698 m (15 ft 5 in)
Powerplant: two Pratt & Whitney PT6A-27 turboprops each flat-rated at 680 shp (507 kW)
Weights: empty equipped 2840 kg (6,261 lb); operating empty 3000 kg (6,614 lb); normal take-off 4500 kg (9,921 lb) for agricultural use; maximum take-off 5300 kg (11,684 lb)
Fuel and load: internal fuel 1233 kg (2,718 lb); external fuel none; maximum payload 1700 kg (3,748 lb)
Speed: never-exceed speed at 3000 m (9,845 ft) 328 km/h (177 kt; 204 mph); maximum cruising speed at 3000 m (9,845 ft) 292 km/h (157 kt; 181 mph); economical cruising speed 3000 m (9,845 ft) 250 km/h (125 kt; 155 mph)
Range: 1340 km (723 nm; 832 miles)

Performance: maximum rate of climb at sea level 504 m (1,655 ft) per minute; service ceiling 7000 m (22,960 ft); take-off run 340 m (1,115 ft) at maximum take-off weight; take-off distance to 50 ft (15 m) 425 m (1,395 ft) at maximum take-off weight; landing distance from 50 ft (15 m) 500 m (1,640 ft) with

Sri Lanka's No. 2 Transport Wing operates six Y-12s from the base at Ratmalana.

propeller reversal at maximum landing weight; landing run 200 m (656 ft)

Harbin **Z-5/Z-6**

At the same time that the MiG-19 was selected by **China** for licence-production by Shenyang, production of the Mil Mi-4 'Hound' was entrusted to Harbin. Drawings arrived in 1958 and the prototype made its maiden flight on 14 December 1959, with certification following later in the same month. Like the J-6, the **Z-5** suffered

catastrophic quality control problems during the Great Leap Forward, and none was delivered.

Updated drawings were delivered in 1961, and the production tooling was completely rebuilt. The first 'acceptable' Z-5 made its maiden flight on 20 August 1963. The rotor blades of Chinese-built Mi-4s

were originally made from dragon spruce instead of pine, but metal rotor blades were soon developed. The first metal-rotored Z-5 made its maiden flight on 22 June 1966.

The Z-5 was built in several different versions, for which local designations remain unknown. The basic military transport usually had an underfuselage gondola containing a fixed, forward-firing machine-gun, which is missing from others, and from the square-windowed passenger transport. A version delivered to the PLA Navy may have had an undernose radome and other ASW sensors.

At least one Z-5 was re-engined with a Pratt & Whitney PT6T-6 Turbo Twin-Pac and flew for the first time in 1979. The **Z-6** was an unrelated single turboshaft helicopter, whose relationship to the Z-5 (if any) is uncertain. A total of 545 Z-5s had been built by the time production ceased in 1979, including 86 passenger carriers, seven agricultural aircraft, 13 SAR aircraft and two dedicated survey platforms.

The Harbin Z-5 forms the backbone of China's rotary-wing fleet, and is used for a wide variety of tasks. This example is seen sowing mines, fitted with chutes to slow their fall.

SPECIFICATION

Harbin Z-5
Rotor system: main rotor diameter 21.00 m (68 ft 11 in); main rotor disc area 346.36 m² (3,728.31 sq ft)
Fuselage and tail: length overall, rotors turning 25.02 m (82 ft 1 in) and fuselage 16.80 m (55 ft 1 in); height overall 4.40 m (14 ft 5.25 in)
Powerplant: one Harbin (HEF) Huosai-5A radial piston engine rated at 1,700 hp (1268 kW)
Weights: empty 5270 kg (11,618 lb); normal take-off 7200 kg (15,873 lb); maximum take-off 7800 kg (17,196 lb)
Fuel and load: internal fuel 1000 litres (264 US gal) plus provision for 500 litres (132 US gal) of auxiliary fuel in a cabin tank; external fuel none; maximum payload 1600 kg (3,527 lb)
Speed: maximum level speed at 1500 m (4,920 ft) 210 km/h (113 kt; 130 mph); maximum cruising speed at optimum altitude 160 km/h (86 kt; 99 mph)
Range: range 250 km (135 nm; 155 miles) with 11 passengers
Performance: service ceiling 5000 m (16,405 ft); hovering ceiling 700 m (2,295 ft) out of ground effect

Harbin **Z-9**

With the local name **Z-9 Haitun**, the Eurocopter AS 365N (described separately) is built under licence by Harbin for both civil users and all three air arms. The first batch of agreed production covered 50 aircraft, the later ones to AS 365N1 standard. The current version is the **Z-9A-100**, of which an anti-tank version (with 'Red Arrow 8' missiles) has been reported.

Hawker Siddeley (de Havilland) **Trident**

Developed for British European Airways, the Trident (initially de Havilland D.H.121) was a stalwart of the British airline's fleet for many years, and achieved some small export success. By far the most important sales were to **China**, which bought four **Trident 1Es**, 33 **Trident 2Es** and two **Trident 3Bs**. Some survive in Chinese air force service, most with the commercial division which operates under the China United Airlines title. Serving with this branch are a single 1E, seven 2Es and two 3Bs. Others may serve on VIP and staff transport duties with the regular air force.

Helio **H-395 Super Courier/U-10**

Noted for its excellent take-off and landing capabilities, the Helio range of light transport/utility aircraft originated with the **H-391 Courier** in 1953. More than 100 acquired by the USAF were more powerful four-seat **H-395 Super Courier** versions, designated **U-10A**, **U-10B** and **U-10D**; most were supplied through MAP to other nations or used in South East Asia. A handful remain in use, in the **Royal Thai air force** and the **Peruvian army,** where they are used for liaison duties. Five Super Couriers delivered to the Peruvian air force were fitted with interchangeable float and wheel landing gear.

231.00 sq ft (21.46 m²)
Fuselage and tail: length 30 ft 0 in (9.14 m); height 8 ft 10 in (2.69 m); tailplane span 15 ft 0 in (4.57 m); wheel track 9 ft 0 in (2.74 m); wheel base 23 ft 5 in (7.14 m)
Powerplant: one Textron Lycoming GO-480-G1D6 rated at 295 hp (220 kW)
Weights: empty 2,037 lb (924 kg); normal take-off 3,400 lb (1542 kg); maximum take-off 4,420 lb (2005 kg)
Fuel and load: internal fuel 60 US gal (227 litres) standard or 120 US gal (454 litres) optional plus provision for 150 US gal (568 litres) of auxiliary fuel; external fuel none
Speed: maximum level speed 'clean' at sea level 145 kt (167 mph; 269 km/h); maximum cruising speed at 8,500 ft (2590 m) 143 kt (165 mph; 265 km/h); economical cruising speed at optimum altitude 130 kt (150 mph; 241 km/h)
Range: ferry range 2,518 nm (2,900 miles; 4667 km); range 1,198 nm (1,380 miles; 2221 km) with optional

fuel or 573 nm (660 miles; 1062 km) with standard fuel
Performance: maximum rate of climb at sea level 1,150 ft (351 m) per minute; service ceiling 20,500 ft (6250 m); take-off run 335 ft (102 m) at maximum take-off weight for STOL or 700 ft (213 m) at maximum take-off weight for conventional use; take-off distance to 50 ft (15 m) 610 ft (196 m) at maximum take-off weight for STOL or 1,180 ft (360 m) at maximum take-off weight for conventional use; landing distance from 50 ft (15 m) 520 ft (158 m) at normal landing

weight for STOL or 665 ft (203 m) at normal landing weight for conventional use; landing run 270 ft (82 m) at normal landing weight for STOL or 355 ft (107 m) at normal landing weight for conventional use

Thailand's U-10 Couriers are a hang-over from the Vietnam era. Although obsolete, the sturdy airframe is still highly regarded for work in the jungle and operations from primitive airstrips.

SPECIFICATION

Helio H-295 Super Courier
Wing: span 39 ft 0 in (11.89 m); aspect ratio 6.5; area

Heliopolis **Gomhouria**

Heliopolis has been absorbed by the nationalised aviation industry, headquartered at the aircraft factory at Helwan. Kade and SAKR factories are still located at Heliopolis

The prototype Bücker Bü 181 Bestmann first flew in early 1939, and the type was produced in thousands as an advanced trainer for the Luftwaffe. Post-war production was undertaken in Czechoslovakia as the Zlin 281/381/C.6/C.106, and in Egypt as the **Heliopolis Gomhouria**, where several variants were developed for use as trainers by the Egyptian air force and other Arab air arms.

A simple, side-by-side, two-seat low-wing trainer with non-retractable tailwheel undercarriage, the Gomhouria was powered by the 105-hp (78.3-kW) Walter Minor engine (**Gomhouria Mks 1** and **5**), the 145-hp (109.2-kW) Continental C145 (**Gomhouria Mks 2, 3** and **4**) or the similarly-powered Continental O-300 (**Gomhouria Mk 6**). Other differences concerned the amount of internal fuel tank-

age and the provision of a 'bubble' canopy. About 300 were built in Egypt, and of these at least 100 are thought to still serve in the training role with the Egyptian air force.

SPECIFICATION

Heliopolis Gomhouria Mk 6
Wing: span 10.60 m (34 ft 9.3 in); aspect ratio 8.32; area 13.50 m² (145.32 sq ft)
Fuselage and tail: length 7.85 m (25 ft 9 in); height 2.05 m (6 ft 8.7 in); tailplane span 3.00 m (9 ft 10 in); wheel track 1.83 m (6 ft 0 in)
Powerplant: one Teledyne Continental O-300-A rated at 145 hp (108 kW)
Weights: empty equipped 520 kg (1,146 lb); maximum take-off 800 kg (1,764 lb)
Fuel and load: internal fuel 125 litres (33 US gal); external fuel none; maximum ordnance none

A typical Egyptian Heliopolis Gomhouria Mk 6, with bubble canopy and other refinements.

Speed: maximum level speed 'clean' at sea level 225 km/h (122 kt; 140 mph); cruising speed at 2000 m (6,560 ft) 205 km/h (110 kt; 127 mph)
Range: 780 km (421 nm; 485 miles)

Performance: maximum rate of climb at sea level 300 m (984 ft) per minute; service ceiling 6000 m (19,685 ft); take-off distance to 15 m (50 ft) 350 m (1,149 ft) at maximum take-off weight

Hiller **UH-12/H-23 Raven**

Hiller is now part of Rogerson Hiller

Based on an original design by Stanley Hiller in 1948, the **Hiller UH-12E** has been restored to production (under new ownership), having meanwhile passed through many stages of development and production. Well over 2,000 examples have been built for civil use or as **H-23 Ravens** for the US armed forces. Principal military users are the **Argentine army**, which has eight three-seat **UH-12ET**s powered by the Allison 250-C20B turboshaft for liaison duties, and the **Egyptian air force**, with

18 piston-engined UH-12E trainers. Current Hiller designs such as the **RH-1100** and new-model UH-12E are described more fully under a separate Rogerson-Hiller entry.

SPECIFICATION

Hiller UH-12E
Rotor system: main rotor diameter 35 ft 5 in (10.80 m); tail rotor diameter 5 ft 6 in (1.68 m); main rotor disc area 985.16 sq ft (91.52 m²); tail rotor disc area

23.76 sq ft (2.21 m²)
Fuselage and tail: length overall, rotors turning 40 ft 8.5 in (12.41 m) and fuselage 28 ft 6 in (8.69 m); height to top of rotor head 10 ft 1.25 in (3.08 m); skid track 7 ft 6 in (2.29 m)
Powerplant: one 340-hp (253.5-kW) Textron Lycoming VO-540 six-cylinder air-cooled piston engine derated to 305 hp (227.5 kW)
Weights: empty 1,759 lb (798 kg); maximum take-off 2,800 lb (1270 kg)
Fuel and load: internal fuel 46 US gal (174 litres) plus provision for 40 US gal (151.5 litres) of auxiliary

fuel in two fuselage tanks; external fuel none
Speed: never-exceed and maximum level speed at optimum altitude 83 kt (96 mph; 154 km/h); maximum cruising speed at optimum altitude 78 kt (90 mph; 145 km/h)
Range: ferry range 365 nm (420 miles; 676 km) with auxiliary fuel; range 187 nm (215 miles; 346 km) with standard fuel
Performance: maximum rate of climb at sea level 1,290 ft (393 m) per minute; service ceiling 16,200 ft (4940 m); hovering ceiling 10,800 ft (3290 m) in ground effect and 7,200 ft (2195 m) out of ground effect

Hindustan (HAL) **HT-2**

*Hindustan Aeronautics Ltd, PO Box 5150
15/1 Cubbon Re
Bangalore 560 001, India*

The first powered aircraft designed and built by HAL (Hindustan Aeronautics Limited), the **HT-2** first flew on 5 August 1951 and subsequently entered production to serve the **Indian Air Force** as its primary trainer. Such use ended in 1981, but 22 aircraft were retained at the IAF Elementary Flying School at Bidar for the 30-hour initial training course for army helicopter pilots, and these may remain in use. A conversion programme started in 1983 fitted Lycoming engines in place of the original Cirrus Majors.

SPECIFICATION

HAL HT-2
Wing: span 10.72 m (35 ft 2 in); aspect ratio 7.18; area 16.00 m² (172.23 sq ft)
Fuselage and tail: length 7.53 m (24 ft 8.5 in);

height 2.72 m (8 ft 11 in)
Powerplant: one Textron Lycoming O-320-H flat-four piston engine rated at 160 hp (119 kW)
Weights: empty equipped 1,540 lb (699 kg); maximum take-off 2,240 lb (1016 kg)
Fuel and load: external fuel none; maximum ordnance none
Speed: maximum level speed 'clean' at sea level 113 kt (130 mph; 209 km/h); cruising speed at sea level 100 kt (115 mph; 185 km/h)
Range: 278 nm (320 miles; 515 km); endurance 3 hours 30 minutes
Performance: maximum rate of climb at sea level 800 ft (244 m) per minute; service ceiling 16,500 ft (5030 m)

This Lycoming-engined Hindustan HT-2 was displayed at India's inaugural aerospace trade show at Yelahanka during December 1993. A handful reportedly remains in use.

Hindustan (HAL) **HJT-16 Kiran I/II**

The **HAL Kiran** (ray of light) was designed to meet an **Indian Air Force** requirement for a trainer similar to the RAF's Hunting Jet Provost. Design of HAL's first jet aircraft began in December 1959, and after subsequent development the prototype made its first flight on 4 September 1964. Intended as a replacement for the DH Vampire, the Kiran shared some of the features of the Jet Provost, including all-metal construction, side-by-side seating, a low wing and the 2,500-lb (11.1-kN) thrust Rolls-Royce Bristol Viper Mk 11 turbojet. In some respects it was more advanced, having a pressurised cockpit and ejection seats specified from the outset (Martin-Baker H4HA seats with zero-altitude capability were fitted).

After completion of a second prototype in August 1965 a pre-production batch of 24

aircraft was launched, the first of these being delivered in March 1968. These and the first series of full production aircraft were unarmed **Kiran Mk I**s, but provision was made in the **Kiran Mk IA** for the carriage of bombs or rocket pods on two wing points stressed to carry 500 lb (227 kg) each. A total of 118 Mk Is was built, of which seven went to the **Indian Navy** and the others to the IAF, primarily to serve at the Air Force Academy at Dundigal, Hyderabad. There, Kiran Is are now used for the first 95 hours of an all-through jet training course, followed by 120 hours of applied training on Mk IAs. Production of the Mk IA totalled 72, with at least four later transferred to the navy. Some interest from abroad was shown in the Kiran Mk 1, notably from Malaysia, but no orders ensued.

In September 1972 a go-ahead was given for an improved version, known as the **Kiran II**, to provide for more complete weapons and tactical training. Two Mk I airframes served as prototypes, and following

a protracted development period the first flew on 30 July 1976. The Kiran II introduced a pair of 7.62-mm machine-guns with 150 rounds each in the nose, a strengthened wing to accept four hardpoints, updated avionics, an improved hydraulic system and a more powerful Rolls-Royce Orpheus engine to replace the Viper II used in the Mks I and IA. Each hardpoint had a

A line-up of Kiran Is of India's Air Force Academy, at Dundigal. Pilots move to the Kiran after primary training/selection on the HPT-32 at Bamrauli or Allahabad. After 75 hours, cadets move on to the Kiran II or the Iskra, depending on whether they are to be streamed to fly a Western type or MiGs.

Left: Undernose blade antennas and blue tails identify these as Kiran IIs from the Air Academy's Bidar airfield.

Right: A line-up of Indian Navy Kirans at INS Hansa. These are used by the 'Phantoms' aerobatic team.

550-lb (250-kg) capacity and could carry a 50-lmp gal (227-litre) drop tank as an alternative to bombs or rocket pods. Installation of the Orpheus engine resulted in improved speed, climb rate and manoeuvrability. However, radius of action and night flying qualities were found to be unacceptable, and the type was not accepted by the IAF. A second prototype flew in February 1979, but it was not until March 1983 that development was officially completed, allowing deliveries to the IAF to begin in April 1985.

The last Kiran Mk II was delivered in March 1989, production eventually totalling

61 aircraft. Other than six for the Indian Navy, all went to the IAF, and are now used for a six-month course at Bidar prior to new pilots joining an Operational Fighter Training Unit. The Kirans diverted to the Navy serve with No. 551 Squadron (INAS 551), the Sea Harrier training unit.

SPECIFICATION

HAL HJT-16 Kiran Mk II
Wing: span 10.70 m (35 ft 1.25 in); aspect ratio 6.03; area 19.00 m² (204.52 sq ft)

Fuselage and tail: length 10.60 m (34 ft 9.5 in); height 3.635 m (11 ft 11 in); tailplane span 3.90 m (12 ft 9.5 in); wheel track 2.42 m (7 ft 11 in); wheel base 3.50 m (11 ft 6 in)
Powerplant: one HAL-built Rolls-Royce (Bristol Siddeley) Orpheus Mk 701-01 turbojet rated at 4,200 lb st (18.68 kN)
Weights: empty equipped 2995 kg (6,603 lb); normal take-off 4250 kg (9,369 lb); maximum take-off 5000 kg (11,023 lb)
Fuel and load: internal fuel 1775 kg (3,913 lb); external fuel up to two 227 litre (60-US gal) drop tanks; maximum ordnance 1000 kg (2,205 lb)
Speed: never-exceed speed 421 kt (484 mph; 780 km/h);

maximum level speed 'clean' at sea level 363 kt (418 mph; 672 km/h); maximum cruising speed at 15,000 ft (4570 m) 335 kt (386 mph; 621 km/h); economical cruising speed at 15,000 ft (4570 m) 225 kt (259 mph; 417 km/h)
Range: 397 nm (457 miles; 735 km) with standard fuel
Performance: maximum rate of climb at sea level 5,250 ft (1600 m) per minute; service ceiling 39,375 ft (12000 m); take-off run 540 m (1,772 ft) at maximum take-off weight; take-off distance to 50 ft (15 m) 730 m (2,395 ft) at maximum take-off weight; landing distance from 50 ft (15 m) 1440 m (4,725 ft) at normal landing weight

Hindustan (HAL) **HPT-32 Deepak**

Designed as the replacement for the HT-2 as the standard *ab initio* trainer used by the **Indian Air Force**, the **HAL HPT-32** switched from the former's tandem seating to the officially preferred side-by-side arrangement. Space was also provided at the rear of the cabin for an optional third seat, thus giving a limited secondary role for communications. In addition to its normal training functions of instrument flying, navigation exercises, night flying and formation work, the fully-aerobatic HPT-32 was also to be capable of fulfilling a wide range of tasks including observation, liaison, sport flying, SAR, supply dropping, target towing, etc., but protracted development limited its usefulness. Production of an initial batch of 88 is to be followed by a further 32, delivery of which was to begin in 1993. The first prototype flew on 6 January 1977, followed by a second over two years later. These proved unable to meet the specification, and it was not until several design changes (notably aerodynamic improvement

and a stringent programme of weight reduction) had been made that the aircraft was accepted for production. The definitive configuration was achieved with the third aircraft, flown on 31 July 1981.

Production deliveries began in March 1984 but the first official acceptance was delayed until 1985, when deliveries commenced to the Elementary Flying School at Bidar with the formal handing over of 12 aircraft. It was not until the beginning of 1988 that the first student course on the HPT-32 was introduced at the Air Force Academy, using its auxiliary Elementary Flying School at Bamrauli. From initial production, the Indian Navy has taken eight HPT-32s, used by INAS 550 at Cochin.

SPECIFICATION

HAL HPT-32 Deepak
Wing: span 9.50 m (31 ft 2 in); aspect ratio 6.01; area 15.01 m² (161.57 sq ft)

Fuselage and tail: length 7.72 m (25 ft 4 in); height 2.88 m (9 ft 5.5 in); tailplane span 3.60 m (11 ft 9.75 in); wheel track 3.45 m (11 ft 4 in); wheel base 2.10 m (6 ft 10.75 in)
Powerplant: one Textron Lycoming AEIO-540-D4B5 piston engine rated at 260 hp (194 kW)
Weights: basic empty 890 kg (1,962 lb); maximum take-off 1250 kg (2,756 lb)
Fuel and load: internal fuel 229 litres (60.5 US gal); external fuel none; maximum ordnance none
Speed: never exceed speed 240 kt (276 mph; 445 km/h); maximum level speed 'clean' at sea level 143 kt (164 mph; 265 km/h); maximum cruising speed at 10,000 ft (3050 m) 115 kt (132 mph; 213 km/h); economical cruising speed at optimum altitude 95 kt (109 mph; 176 km/h)
Range: 401 nm (462 miles; 744 km)
Performance: maximum rate of climb at sea level 335 m (1,100 ft) per minute; service ceiling 5500 m (18,045 ft); take-off run 345 m (1,132 ft) at maximum

Three piston-engined HPT-32 Deepaks in flight. The different colour schemes indicate that these aircraft serve with a test establishment, although the nearest is in Training Command trim.

take-off weight; take-off distance to 15 m (50 ft) 545 m (1,788 ft) at maximum take-off weight; landing distance from 15 m (50 ft) 487 m (1,598 ft) at normal landing weight; landing run 220 m (720 ft) at normal landing weight
g limits: -3 to +6

Hindustan (HAL) **HTT-34**

As a private venture, HAL fitted a 420-hp (313-kW) Allison 250-B17D turboprop in the third HPT-32 to provide an alternative to the piston-engined trainer. As the **HAL HTT-34**, the re-engined prototype flew on 17 June 1984 and a pre-production model with further modifications appeared in 1989. The HTT-34 is 0.35 m (1 ft 1.75 in) longer than the HPT-32 and has a smaller tail surface area. The lighter, but considerably more powerful, engine improves performance, increasing maximum level speed and service ceiling. A reduction in landing run to 200 m (656 ft) may be achieved by selecting reverse pitch on the three-bladed propeller. No orders were placed for the HTT-34 and production now appears unlikely, particularly in view of the develop-

ment of the HTT-35. Production standard aircraft were to have retractable gear.

SPECIFICATION

HAL HTT-34
Wing: span 9.50 m (31 ft 2 in); aspect ratio 6.01; area 15.01 m² (161.57 sq ft)
Fuselage and tail: length 8.07 m (26 ft 5.75 in); height 2.88 m (9 ft 5.5 in); tailplane span 3.60 m (11 ft 9.75 in); wheel track 3.45 m (11 ft 4 in); wheel base 2.10 m (6 ft 10.75 in)
Powerplant: one Allison 250-B17D turboprop rated at 420 shp (313 kW)
Weights: empty 1,909 lb (866 kg); maximum take-off 2,689 lb (1220 kg)
Fuel and load: internal fuel 229 litres (60.5 US gal);

One of the turboprop HTT-34 prototypes. Several of these are on charge with the ASTE (Aircraft and Systems Testing Establishment) at Bangalore.

external fuel none; maximum ordnance none
Speed: maximum level speed 'clean' at sea level 167 kt (192 mph; 310 km/h) and at 9,845 ft (3000 m) 143 kt (165 mph; 266 km/h)
Range: 332 nm (382 miles; 615 km); endurance 3 hours 8 minutes
Performance: maximum rate of climb at sea level

2,132 ft (650 m) per minute; service ceiling 25,000 ft (7620 m); take-off distance to 50 ft (15 m) 870 ft (265 m) at maximum take-off weight; landing distance from 50 ft (15 m) 1,526 ft (465 m) at maximum landing weight without propeller reversal or 656 ft (200 m) at maximum landing weight with propeller reversal
g limits: -3 to +6

Hindustan (HAL) **HTT-35**

Although the HTT-34 seems to have been dropped, Hindustan Aeronautics Ltd have not abandoned their attempts to produce a new turboprop-powered trainer for the Indian Air Force, to meet the IAF Air Staff Target 208. This details a replacement for both the HPT-32 and the HJT-16, inferring a requirement for more than 150 air-

craft. Unveiled in mock-up form at Avia India '93 in December 1993, the **HTT-35** is a conventional looking tandem-seat low-wing monoplane, with a distinctively hump-backed appearance and stepped cockpits covered by separate upward-hinging canopies. The retractable tricycle undercarriage retracts inwards (main units) and rear-

wards (nose gear). The pilots will sit on lightweight ejection seats. HAL hope to use either the 1150-shp Garrett TPE-331-12D (flat-rated to 1100 shp/819 kW) or the 1150-shp Pratt and Whitney Canada PT6A-62 (flat rated to 950 shp/707 kW) to power the new aircraft. HAL claim a maximum level speed of 290 mph (470 km/h) at sea level, with a stall speed in approach configuration of 80 mph (127 km/h). The take off distance to 50 ft (15 m) is 850 ft (260 m), and landing distance from (50 ft) 15m is (1900 ft) 580 m. Sea level rate of climb is calculated as 4000 ft (1220 m) per minute, and service ceiling as 29,500 ft (9000 m). The HTT-35 will be fully aerobatic, with a normal operating load factor of +6 to -3 and a fatigue life of 7,000 flying hours. Integral wing and fuselage tanks will carry 990 lb (450 kg) of fuel, with an inverted system allowing up to 30 seconds inverted flight. This gives a range of 790 miles (1270 km), and allows two high-density aerobatic/spinning sorties to be flown on a single load of fuel. Underwing hard-

points (stressed for loads of up to 550 lb/ 250 kg each) allow the carriage of bombs, gun or rocket pods for weapons training or counter-insurgency. Full-scale development awaits a government go-ahead, which HAL hopes to receive by mid-1994, leading to a first flight 24 months later.

The HTT-35 mock-up, displayed in December 1993, showed the indigenous trainer to have a conventional low-wing and stepped cockpit configuration, reminiscent of the Tucano and PC-9. In service it would replace both the HPT-32 and the HJT-16.

Hoffman **H 36 Dimona**

Wolf Hoffman Flugzeugbau KG, Sportflugplatz
D-8870 Günzberg/Ulm
Germany

First flying on 9 October 1980, at Königsdorf near Munich, the **H 36 Dimona** is a side-by-side two-seat motor glider built in Germany. Power comes from a 59.7-kW (80-hp) Limbach L 2000 EB1C engine, dri-

ving a Hoffman propeller. Low-vibration mountings are employed. The Dimona has a low-set wing, a T-tail and fixed sprung undercarriage, the wheels housed in spats. The wings can be folded back, to lay along

the sides of the fuselage. The cockpit is covered by an upward-hinging canopy, and has a baggage compartment and an 17.5-Imp gal (80-litre) fuel tank behind. This gives a range of about 620 miles (1000 km), with

a fuel consumption of 12 litres per hour at 75 per cent power (180 km/h). Top speed is 130 mph (210 km/h). Fourteen aircraft were purchased by the **Royal Thai air force** for training purposes.

IAI **1124 Westwind/SeaScan**

Israel Aircraft Industries Ltd
Ben Gurion International Airport, Tel Aviv
Israel 70100

After purchasing the design and production facilities for the **Model 1121 Jet Commander** from Rockwell in 1967, IAI further developed the executive twin jet into the **Models 1123** and **1124 Westwind**. Powered respectively by 3,100-lb st (13.7-kN) General Electric CJ610-9 turbojets and 3,700-lb st (16.4-kN) Garrett TFE731-3 turbofans, these two versions were produced almost entirely for civil use. One of each later entered service with the **Honduran air force**, and two Model 1124s serve in the **Chilean navy**, all in the VIP transport role. One was similarly used by President Idi Amin in Uganda and, in response to Uganda air force interest, IAI fitted machine-guns in place of tip tanks on one Model 1124, but these were removed when the deal fell through and the aircraft passed into service with the **Israeli Defence Force/Air Force**.

The IDF/AF also operates three **Model 1124N SeaScan** versions on behalf of the navy for maritime search and patrol mis-

sions. The Seascan carries a nose radar and has provision for a variety of other sensors, as well as two load-carrying pylons on the fuselage sides for torpedoes, missiles or other stores. A Litton AN/APS-504 provides 360° coverage. Four Model 1124s were operated by Rhein-Flugzeugbau until 1990 as target-tugs for the military services in Germany.

SPECIFICATION

IAI 1124N Sea Scan
Wing: span 43 ft 2 in (13.16 m) without tip tanks and 44 ft 9.5 in (13.65 m) with tip tanks; aspect ratio 6.51; area 308.26 sq ft (28.64 m²)
Fuselage and tail: length 52 ft 3 in (15.93 m); height 15 ft 9.5 in (4.81 m); tailplane span 21 ft 0 in (6.40 m); wheel track 11 ft 0 in (3.35 m); wheel base 25 ft 6.75 in (7.79 m)
Powerplant: two Garrett TFE731-3-1G each rated at 3,700 lb st (16.46 kN) dry
Weights: empty equipped 12,300 lb (5578 kg);

maximum take-off 23,500 lb (10660 kg)
Fuel and load: internal fuel 1,300 US gal (4920 litres); external fuel none
Speed: maximum level and maximum cruising speed 'clean' between sea level and 19,355 ft (5900 m) 470 kt (542 mph; 872 km/h); economical cruising speed at 41,000 ft (12500 m) 400 kt (460 mph; 741 km/h)
Range: ferry range 2,900 nm (3,339 miles; 5373 km); operational radius 1,380 nm (1,588 miles; 2555 km) for a 6.5-hour patrol at low altitude, or 2,500 nm (2,878 miles; 4633 km) for an 8-hour patrol at high altitude

This civil-registered Westwind was used for target facilities on behalf of the Luftwaffe, operating from Lübeck.

Performance: maximum rate of climb at sea level 5,000 ft (1524 m) per minute; service ceiling 45,000 ft (13715 m); balanced take-off field length 4,900 ft (1495 m) at maximum take-off weight; landing distance from 50 ft (15 m) 1,700 ft (518 m) at normal landing weight with thrust reversal

---

IAI **1125 Astra/Astra SP**

Based on the 1124 Westwind, the **IAI 1125 Astra** business jet introduces a low-mounted swept wing with more extensive use of composites materials. The revised wing-mounting arrangement allows for an improved cabin layout with increased headroom. The 2-in (5-cm) wider fuselage has a deeper profile and incorporates a stretch of nearly 2 ft (0.61 m). Only the Westwind's tail unit and Garrett TFE731-3A

powerplant have been retained. A prototype Astra flew on 19 March 1984 and deliveries began two years later. An **Astra SP** (with new avionics and aerodynamics) serves with the government of **Eritrea**.

SPECIFICATION

IAI 1125 Astra

Wing: span 52 ft 8 in (16.05 m); aspect ratio 8.8; area 316.60 sq ft (29.40 m²)
Fuselage and tail: length 55 ft 7 in (16.94 m); height 18 ft 2 in (5.54 m); tailplane span 21 ft 0 in (6.40 m); wheel track 9 ft 1 in (2.77 m); wheel base 24 ft 1 in (7.34 m)
Powerplant: two Garrett TFE731-3A-200G each rated at 3,650 lb st (16.24 kN) dry
Weights: operating empty 12,670 lb (5747 kg) with standard tankage or 12,790 lb (5801 kg) with optional tankage; maximum take-off 23500 lb (10659 kg)
Fuel and load: internal fuel 8,692 lb (3942 kg) plus provision for 673 lb (305 kg) of optional fuel in a 100-US gal (378.5-litre) tank in the forward part of the

baggage compartment; external fuel none; maximum payload 3,330 lb (1510 kg) declining to 3,230 lb (1465 kg) with auxiliary fuel tank installed
Speed: maximum cruising speed at 35,000 ft (10670 m) 465 kt (535 mph; 862 km/h)
Range: 3,110 nm (3,581 miles; 5763 km) with optional fuel and four passengers
Performance: maximum rate of climb at sea level 3,650 ft (1112 m) per minute; certificated ceiling 45,000 ft (13715 m); take-off balanced field length 4,980 ft (1518 m) at 22,700 lb (10296 kg); landing balanced field length 2,645 ft (806 m) at maximum landing weight

---

IAI **Arava**

The first wholly IAI-designed aircraft to reach production, the **Arava** was originally conceived in 1966 as a 20-seat multi-mission light twin-turboprop STOL aircraft, for both civilian and military customers. The compact design features a high-mounted wing with twin-tail booms and a simple fixed nosewheel landing gear, with single wheels on each unit. Flown in prototype form on 27 November 1969, the Arava was subsequently produced in civil (**Series 101, 102**) and military (**Series 201, 202**)

applications; almost all of about 100 built between 1972 and 1988 were for military users. Although intended as a replacement for the **Israeli air force**'s venerable Douglas C-47s, the Arava was not introduced in this capacity until the late 1970s (three leased 201s were operated during the 1973 Arab-Israeli war, however) when Series 201s were delivered. The type's ruggedness, capacious cabin, performance and ability to operate from rough strips make it extremely versatile, and usable for use in a variety of roles.

These aircraft were equipped for a variety of tasks (other than as troop transports) including maritime surveillance (equipped

with search/weather radar), and EW duties in a number of different configurations with pallet-mounted Elint and ESM packages, radomes, and tailcone-mounted rear scanner. Another EW version features a large number of blade antennas on tail booms, fuselage roof and wings. Active jamming is carried out when the aircraft is equipped with the Elta/EL-7010 jammer, for which an auxiliary generator is also installed. Primary IDF/AF Arava operator is No. 126 Squadron at Lod, Israel's main transport and special duties base. The **Royal Thai air force** similarly flies three for the surveillance/ ECM mission with 404 Squadron at Takhli.

As the final stage in Arava development,

IAI developed the Series 202 variant in 1977. This introduced an extended fuselage accommodating 30 fully-equipped troops, increased weights, a 'wet' wing and winglets. Initial deliveries began to the Israeli and other air forces in 1984-85. The Series 202 became a retrofit option for Aravas already in service. Both versions of the Arava may be armed with a pair of forward-firing, fuselage-mounted 12.7-mm (0.5-in) machine-guns and up to 12 82-mm (3.23-in) rockets carried on fuselage pylons.

Most of the 16 national air arms that acquired Aravas selected the Series 201 model for use as personnel and/or supply transports. Examples remain in service in this primary tactical and utility transport role in **Colombia**, **Ecuador** (army and navy air arms), **Guatemala**, **Honduras**, **Mexico**, **El Salvador**, **Swaziland** and **Venezuela** (army). At least one continues to serve in **Bolivia** for anti-drug patrols, and an ex-civil **Series 101B** in **Cameroon** is operated as a military/government VIP transport.

SPECIFICATION

IAI 201 Arava
Wing: span 68 ft 9 in (20.96 m); aspect ratio 10.06; area 470.18 sq ft (43.68 m²)
Fuselage and tail: length 42 ft 9 in (13.03 m); height 17 ft 1 in (5.21 m); tailplane span 17 ft 0.75 in (5.20 m); wheel track 13 ft 2 in (4.01 m); wheel base 15 ft 2 in (4.62 m)
Powerplant: two Pratt & Whitney Canada PT6A-34 each rated at 750 shp (559 kW)

Weights: basic empty 8,816 lb (3999 kg); maximum take-off 15,000 lb (6804 kg)
Fuel and load: internal fuel 440 US gal (1665 litres) plus provision for 540 US gal (2044 litres) of auxiliary fuel in two ferry tanks in the cabin; external fuel none; maximum payload 5,100 lb (2313 kg)
Speed: never-exceed speed 215 kt (247 mph; 397 km/h); maximum level speed 'clean' at 10,000 ft (3050 m) 176 kt (203 mph; 326 km/h); maximum cruising speed at 10,000 ft (3050 m) 172 kt (198 mph; 319 km/h); economical cruising speed at 10,000 ft (3050 m) 168 kt (193 mph; 311 km/h)
Range: 540 nm (622 miles; 1001 km) with a 3,500-lb (1587-kg) payload declining to 140 nm (161 miles; 259 km) with maximum payload
Performance: maximum rate of climb at sea level 1,290 ft (393 m) per minute; service ceiling 25,000 ft (7620 m); take-off run 960 ft (293 m) at maximum take-off weight; take-off distance to 50 ft (15 m) 1,520 ft (463 m) at maximum take-off weight; landing distance from 50 ft (15 m) 1,540 ft (469 m) at normal landing weight; landing run 820 ft (250 m)

Right: A camouflaged IAI Arava 201 of Colombia's Escuadron 712.

Right: Another operator of Arava 201s is the Papua New Guinea Defence Force. Three Arava 201s were grounded and withdrawn in 1989.

IAI Dagger (Nesher)

Until the 1967 Six Day War, Israel had come to depend upon the US and France for provision of combat aircraft. Following that war, however, the supply of Dassault Mirage 5Js was halted by an embargo. Faced with the continuing threat of conflict with its Arab neighbours, Israel set about producing its own combat aircraft.

As an interim expedient Israel Aircraft Industries (IAI) started production of an unlicensed copy of the Dassault Mirage 5, complete with its French-built Atar 09C turbojet, of which large stocks existed in the country. The task of building the Mirage without French co-operation was eased by espionage. Production drawings of the Atar were stolen from the Swiss factory which was licence-building the engine for Swiss-built Mirages, and many airframe production drawings were also stolen in France.

The new product was termed the **IAI Nesher** (eagle), and from the outset it was capable of mounting a pair of the indigenous Rafael Shafrir short-range air-to-air missiles (externally similar to the American AIM-9 Sidewinder but in fact a wholly new

The revised nose profile of a recently modified Argentine air force 'Finger' standard IAI Dagger.

An Argentine IAI Dagger in its original configuration, with the early (solid) nose shape painted semi-gloss black to simulate a large radome for a Mirage IIIE type radar.

Israel design). The gun armament of two 30-mm DEFA cannon was also retained. The new variant incorporated some indigenous avionics systems, and was fitted with a Martin-Baker Mk 6 ejection seat.

First flown in September 1969, the Nesher entered service with the **Heyl Ha'Avir** in time for the Yom Kippur War of October 1973, when some 40 aircraft saw action and Shafrir missiles achieved a success rate of more than 50 per cent.

The French imposed an arms embargo in the wake of the 1973 war, and this led directly to Project Black Curtain, which resulted in the IAI Kfir (described separately). This also led to the termination of the Nesher programme, after an estimated 51 **Nesher S** single-seaters and 10 **Nesher T** trainers had been completed. These aircraft were frequently used operationally in the long, undeclared war which raged on Israel's borders during the 1970s, but Kfir deliveries rendered them surplus to IDF/AF requirements by 1977.

Argentina, forced to shelve plans to acquire 80 Mirage IIIs (from an order totalling 94) for economic reasons, purchased 26 of the Neshers in 1978 under the export designation **Dagger** (including two two-seaters). These were joined by the rest of the surviving Neshers by 1982, bringing Argentine procurement to 39 **Dagger A** and four **Dagger B**s. They equipped II and III Squadrons (since redesignated I and II Squadrons) of 6° Grupo, VI Brigada Aérea, replacing ageing North American F-86 Sabres. Seventeen were lost during the 1982 Falklands War, during which they operated primarily in the fighter-bomber and

anti-shipping roles, pressing home their attacks with astonishing ferocity and a high degree of precision, although the effectiveness of their attacks was greatly reduced by poorly fused bombs, which often hit British ships without exploding. The survivors have since undergone a three-stage modification programme, which has provided Kfir-type avionics in a recontoured nose, with vortex generators, under the codenames 'Finger-I', '-II' and '-III'.

Argentina continues to operate about 20 IAI Daggers in the fighter-bomber and CAS roles.

IAI Kfir

Israel was the first export customer for the Dassault Mirage III, and used the type to great effect during the 1967 and 1973 wars with its Arab neighbours and during the lower intensity of hostilities. Despite its suc-

cess, **Israel** was aware of the shortcomings of the Mirage, which included very fast take-off and landing speeds and consequently long take-off and landing run, lack of thrust, and primitive avionics. This obvious need for improvement, coupled with arms embargoes, forced Israel first to upgrade its Mirages and then to build its own improved Mirage derivatives.

This process resulted first in Project Salvo, under which Israel's Mirage IIICJs were rebuilt and upgraded, and then in the IAI Nesher, an unlicensed Mirage 5 copy (see separate entry), and eventually in the **IAI Kfir** (lion cub). The development of the Kfir was made possible by Israel's purchase of the F-4 Phantom and its General Electric J79 engine. The first J79-engined Mirage

was a French-built two-seater, and this made its maiden flight on 19 October 1970, joined by a re-engined Nesher in September 1971.

The J79's 11 per cent greater mass flow and higher operating temperature necessitated the provision of enlarged air intakes and extensive heat shielding of the rear fuselage. A large air scoop was added to

IAI Kfir

The first Kfirs were not equipped with canards, and some had a round-tipped radome for their ranging radar. They were essentially little more than J79-engined Mirage 5s, equipped with Israeli avionics and built without a licence.

the leading edge of the tailfin for afterburner cooling. Other airframe changes included a strengthened undercarriage with longer stroke oleos.

There have been persistent reports that some Mirage IIICJs were re-engined with the J79, receiving the local name **Barak** (lightning), but such conversions seem unlikely and have never been photographed. A similar rumour concerned the production of a radar-nosed Kfir, this being caused by photographs of an early aircraft which had its forward fuselage painted black as though it were a radome. The more observant immediately noticed that the nose contours were unchanged, and the pitot position remained the same. The basic Kfir was produced in small numbers (27) and most were later upgraded to **Kfir C1** configuration, with small narrow-span fixed canards on the intakes and rectangular strakes behind the ranging radar, on the sides of the nose. Twenty-five survivors were later lent to the US Navy and US Marines for adversary training (between 1985 and 1989) as **F-21A**s.

The **Kfir C2** was the first full-standard variant, equipped with nose strakes and

A fully-armed Israeli Kfir C7, carrying bombs on the under-intake hardpoints which distinguish this variant. Kfirs remain in service with two IDF/AF front-line squadrons and an OCU, including No. 111 at Ovda and No. 144 at Hatzor.

large fixed canard foreplanes from the outset. The new variant also had a dogtooth wing leading edge. Canards and strakes were first flown on the J79-powered Mirage IIIB which had served as the Kfir prototype, during July 1974. These aerodynamic alterations improved turn and take-off performance along with controllability.

The Kfir C2 also introduced new avionics, including an ELTA M-2001B ranging radar. Other equipment includes an MBT twin-computer flight control system, angle of attack sensor vane on the port side of the forward fuselage (retrofitted to early aircraft), Elbit S-8600 multi-mode navigation and weapons delivery system (alternatively Elbit/IAI WDNS-141), Taman central air data computer and Israel Electro-Optics HUD. One hundred and eighty-five C2s and **TC2** trainers were built, and about 120 of these remain in service with four squadrons, and others are held in flyable storage.

After long delays in gaining US approval to re-export the J79 powerplant, 12 Kfir C2s were sold to **Ecuador** in 1982, and another 11 went to **Colombia** in 1988-89. Both export customers also took delivery of a pair of Kfir TC2s. Virtually all surviving Israeli Kfir C2s and TC2s were upgraded to Kfir **C7** and **TC7** standards, but it is uncertain as to whether any were built as new.

The C7 designation is applied to upgraded aircraft delivered from 1983 onwards. These incorporate a number of avionics improvements, and have what is effectively a HOTAS cockpit. Equipment improvements involve a WDNS-391 weapons delivery and navigation system, an Elbit 82 stores management system, armament control display panel, video subsystems and the ability to release 'smart' weapons. Aerial refuelling provision with either probe or receptacle is optional. Most C2s in IDF/AF service have been upgraded

to C7 standard, and the potential is present to replace ranging radar by an Elta EL/M-2021 I/J-band multi-mode radar as installed in Israel's F-16s. Not all C2s had RWRs – at least initially – but late-production machines have an Elisra SPS-200 comprising two hemispherical sensors under the lower forward fuselage and two on the fin, immediately above the rudder. Jamming pods such as the Elta E/L-8202 can be fitted on the port inboard wing pylon.

The only external difference is the provision of an extra pair of hardpoints under the engine intakes, bringing the total to nine and increasing warload to a maximum of 13,415 lb (6085 kg). An engine overspeed provision, referred to as 'combat plus', can be used to boost thrust to 18,750 lb st (83.41 kN) for brief periods.

During 1993, Israel began seeking export customers for its surplus Kfir C2/C7s, and to this end IAI proposed a further upgrade as the **Kfir C10**. Features of this version, benefitting from Lavi technology, include a new cockpit fit, new radar in an enlarged radome, more external fuel and provision for an IFR probe.

SPECIFICATION

IAI Kfir-C7

Wing: span 8.22 m (26 ft 11.6 in); canard foreplane span 3.73 m (12 ft 3 in); wing aspect ratio 1.94; wing area 34.80 m² (374.60 sq ft); canard foreplane area 1.66 m² (17.87 sq ft)
Fuselage and tail: length 15.65 m (51 ft 4.25 in) including probe; height 4.55 m (14 ft 11.25 in); wheel track 3.20 m (10 ft 6 in); wheel base 4.87 m (15 ft 11.7 in)
Powerplant: one IAI Bedek Division-built General Electric J79-J1E rated at 11,890 lb st (52.89 kN) dry and 18,75b st (83.40 kN) with afterburning
Weights: empty about 7285 kg (16,060 lb); normal take-off 10415 kg (22,961 lb); maximum take-off

Some early Kfir 1s were fitted with vestigial canards under the designation Kfir C1. Some of these were later lent to the US Navy and Marines as F-21As, and were used for dedicated adversary dissimilar air combat training. The US Navy aircraft and some USMC aircraft wore a two-tone grey scheme, while others retained Israeli camouflage.

16500 kg (36,376 lb)
Fuel and load: internal fuel 2572 kg (5,670 lb); external fuel up to 3727 kg (8,216 lb) in three 1700-, 1300-, 825- and 500-litre (449-, 343-, 218-, 159- or 132-US gal) drop tanks; maximum ordnance 6085 kg (13,415 lb)
Speed: maximum level speed 'clean' at 36,000 ft (10975 m) more than 1,317 kt (1,516 mph; 2440 km/h) or at sea level 750 kt (863 mph; 1389 km/h)
Range: ferry range 1,744 nm (2,000 miles; 3232 km) with one 1300-litre (343US gal) and two 1700-litre (449-US gal) drop tanks; combat radius 419 nm (482 miles; 776 km) on a hi-hi-hi interception mission with two Shafrir AAMs, one 825-litre (218-US gal) and two 1300-litre (343-US gal) drop tanks, or 476 nm (548 miles; 882 km) on a 1-hour CAP with two Shafrir AAMs, one 1700-litre (449-US gal) and two 1300-litre (343-US gal) drop tanks, or 640 nm (737 miles; 1186 km) on a hi-lo-hi attack mission with two 363-kg (800-lb and two 181-kg (400-lb) bombs, two Shafrir AAMs, and one 1300-litre (343-US gal) and two 1700-litre (449-US gal) drop tanks
Performance: maximum rate of climb at sea level 14000 m (45,930 ft) per minute; climb to 50,000 ft (15240 m) in 5 minutes 10 seconds with full internal fuel and two Shafrir AAMs; zoom climb ceiling 75,000 ft (22860 m); stabilised supersonic ceiling 58,000 ft (17680 m); take-off run 1450 m (4,757 ft) at maximum take-off weight; landing distance from 50 ft (15 m) 1555 m (5,102 ft) at 25,500 lb (11566 kg; landing run 1280 m (4,200 ft) at 25,500 lb (11566 kg)
g limits: +7.5

A Fuerza Aérea Colombiana Kfir C2, carrying Rafael Python AAMs underwing. The Colombian aircraft have been upgraded to virtually full C7 standards.

NOSE CONTOURS
All Kfirs, and many IAI-inspired Mirage upgrades, feature a long, slender nose packed with avionics and tipped by a small Elta EL/M-2001B ranging radar. The pitot is underslung, and small strakes are fitted to the sides of the nose. These improve controllability at high angles of attack by generating powerful vortices.

ARMAMENT
Ecuador's Kfirs are used primarily in the air defence and intercept role, although as part of a multi-role wing they do undertake training in the fighter-bomber role. The aircraft are normally armed with a pair of Rafael Shafrir IR-homing air-to-air missiles, the newer, more effective Python not having been supplied. Like all Kfirs and Dagger/Neshers, they have a pair of Rafael-built DEFA 553 30-mm cannon in the wingroots, each with 125 rounds of ammunition. In the ground attack role the aircraft can carry a variety of US, Israeli or French free-fall bombs, but do not have the extra under-intake hardpoints associated with the Kfir C7. The squadron is not believed to practise the use of PGMs or rockets.

CONFIGURATION
The Kfir retains the basic delta-winged configuration of the Mirage III/5/50, with canard foreplanes and small aerodynamic refinements to improve agility and take-off performance.

CANARD FOREPLANES
Ecuadorian Kfirs are fitted with the full-size fixed foreplanes associated with the Kfir C2 and C7. These reduce the take-off run by some 1,500 ft (457 m) and have a similarly dramatic effect on turn performance, reducing longitudinal stability by generating lift ahead of the centre of gravity.

WING
The Kfir's wing lacks the sawcut leading-edge slots of the Mirage and, instead, has extended outboard leading edges, giving a pronounced saw-tooth leading edge discontinuity.

IAI Kfir C2

Like Colombia's Kfirs, Ecuadorian aircraft are nominally Kfir C2s, but with many of the advanced avionics systems of the Kfir C7. Ecuador's Kfir unit is Escuadrón de Combate 2113, part of Grupo 211 at Taura, and its aircraft wear a triangular Kfir badge on the port side of the fin and the starboard side of the nose. The Grupo's other units fly the Jaguar and the Mirage F1. Escuadron 2113 equipped with Kfirs during 1982, and became operational in 1984. The squadron helped Colombian pilots convert to the Kfir during 1989.

CAMOUFLAGE
Ecuador's Kfirs wear a smart two-tone disruptive camouflage scheme, with light grey undersides. National insignia is applied above the port and below the starboard wing.

POWERPLANT
A single General Electric J79-J1E augmented turbojet, the most powerful production variant of the J79, powers the Kfir. Because it has a greater mass flow than the original Mirage's Atar engine, installation of the J79 necessitates bigger intakes, and increased operating temperatures require provision of a dorsal airscoop.

IAI Lavi TD

The **IAI Lavi** (young lion) was launched in February 1980 as a multi-role combat aircraft, and full-scale development began towards the end of 1982. With a prospective IDF/AF requirement for up to 300 aircraft, the FSD phase was to involve six prototypes, of which four would be two-seaters. After the first two of these (both two-seaters with their rear cockpits occupied by test equipment) had flown, on 31 December 1986 and 30 March 1987, respectively, the programme was cancelled, in the teeth of US opposition, budgetary problems and the availability of cut price F-16s. A third airframe was completed, as a true two-seater and using parts of the others, to serve as a technology demonstrator (TD) for advanced cockpit systems and as an equipment testbed. In this form, the **Lavi TD** first flew on 25 September 1989. This aircraft is still flying test sorties, and has been the force behind IAI's highly successful fighter upgrades.

The Lavi TD, completed as a genuine two-seater, was rolled out after cancellation of the programme and was intended as a demonstrator for IAI's advanced fighter technologies, which the company is applying by retrofit to a number of earlier aircraft types, and as an equipment testbed.

SPECIFICATION

IAI Lavi
Wing: span 8.78 m (28 ft 9.67 in); aspect ratio 1.83; area 33.05 m² (355.76 sq ft)
Fuselage and tail: length 14.57 m (47 ft 9.67 in); height 4.78 m (15 ft 8.25 in); wheel track 2.31 m (7 ft 7 in); wheel base 3.86 m (12 ft 8 in)
Powerplant: one Pratt & Whitney PW1120 rated at 13,550 lb st (60.27 kN) intermediate and 20,620 lb st

(91.72 kN) with afterburning
Weights: empty about 15,500 lb (7031 kg); normal take-off 22,025 lb (9991 kg); maximum take-off 42,500 lb (19277 kg)
Fuel and load: internal fuel 6,000 lb (2722 kg); external fuel up to 9,180 lb (4164 kg) in drop tanks; maximum external load 16,0000 lb (7257 kg) including 6,000 lb (2722 kg) of ordnance excluding AAMs
Speed: maximum level speed 'clean' above 36,000 ft (10975 m) 1,061 kt (1,222 mph; 1965 km/h); low-level penetration speed 538 kt (610 mph; 997 km/h) with two AAMs and eight 750-lb (340-kg) bombs
Range: combat radius 1,150 nm (1.324 miles; 2131 km) on a hi-lo-hi attack mission with two 1,000-lb (454-kg) or six 250 kg (113-kg) bombs, or 1,000 nm (1,151 miles; 1853 km) on a combat air patrol, or 600 nm (691 miles; 1112 km) on a lo-lo-lo attack mission
Performance: take-off run about 1,000 ft (305 m) at maximum take-off weight

Below: The second prototype Lavi, equipped with a bolt-on retractable inflight-refuelling probe, refuels from an A-4 Skyhawk tanker. The rear cockpit is full of test equipment.

IAI Tzukit

The name **Tzukit** (thrush) has been given by the **IDF/AF** to the **Fouga Magister** trainers and light strike aircraft, about 80 of which remain in service, primarily at the Hatzerim flying school. Original purchases of the Magister were 52 from France and 36 from the Bedek Division of IAI, with subsequent purchases from other

Magister users to maintain the inventory.
Starting in 1981, the **Advanced Multi-Mission Improved Trainer** (**AMIT**) programme resulted in approximately 80 Tzukits undergoing service life extension and modernisation at Bedek. The AMIT programme embraced some 250 modifications to extend service life by 5,000 hours and to improve systems throughout the airframe. Two prototypes were tested in 1981 before production conversions began. The Tzukit is powered by 4.7-kN (1,058-lb st) Turboméca

The Tzukit is an upgraded and modernised conversion of the basic Magister, and is operated by the IDF/AF's flying training school at Hatzerim.

Marboré VIC turbojets; its dimensions and performance are similar to those for the

Fouga CM 170-3 Super Magister (described separately).

IAI Phantom 2000 (Kurnass 2000)

The designation **Phantom 2000** (**Kurnass 2000**) is used in **Israel** for an upgrade programme embracing surviving examples of the McDonnell Douglas F-4E Phantom (more than 100), of which 204 were supplied from 1969 to 1976. First flown on 11 August 1987, the Phantom 2000 is structurally strengthened to extend the service life, systems are updated and a MIL STD 1553B dual redundant digital databus is fitted. Cockpit layout is improved and HOTAS installed. An advanced new avionics suite includes Norden/UTC MMRS multi-mode radar, a Kaiser wide-angle HUD and other items. The upgrade programme is handled by the Shaham Division of Bedek Aviation and redelivery to the IDF/AF began on 9 April 1989. A proposed re-engining programme with Pratt & Whitney PW1120 turbofans has been abandoned.

The Kurnass 2000 prototype seen here featured some features not funded for the upgraded aircraft delivered to the IDF/AF. The prototype flew with a Pratt & Whitney PW1120 engine in its starboard nacelle, and then with two of these advanced turbofans, appearing in this configuration at the 1987 Paris Air Salon. The funded upgrade includes an advanced Norden synthetic aperture radar, new avionics and structural modifications. Plans are afoot to retrofit a wrap-around frameless windscreen to upgraded Kurnass 2000s. Kurnass translates as 'heavy hammer'.

IAI/Elta Phalcon

Israel Aircraft Industries is no stranger to the Boeing 707. Over the last 20 years the company has maintained the type for the **IDF/AF**, and also been involved in many conversions for special purposes. These have included tankers with both hose/drogue and boom refuelling systems, signals intelligence platforms, command posts and other electronic specialists. For the last four years, IAI and its electronics

subsidiary, Elta, have been developing an airborne early warning version, named **IAI/Elta Phalcon.**
The name Phalcon relates to the AEW system, rather than the carrier aircraft, which could be virtually any large aircraft such as a 747 or C-130. Within the Phalcon system there are many options to suit customer requirements, including additional ESM, communications and reconnaissance

equipment.
At the heart of the system is the Elta EL/2075 phased-array radar. For full coverage there are four antenna arrays – two each side of the forward fuselage housed in giant cheek fairings, one in the nose in a bulbous radome, and one under the rear fuselage. The radomes do add considerable drag, eroding speed performance, but the main concern is for long endurance, which is not dramatically affected. The nose radome has a flattened underside for ground clearance, and its fitment has necessitated the re-siting of the two pitot probes

above the flight deck.
Each EL/2075 array consists of hundreds of fixed antennas, each with an individual transmit/receive module in the forward fuselage. They are electronically steered and scanned, and mounted on a floating bed so that flexing in the aircraft's structure does not affect their alignment. The radar works in L-band, and the electronic steering and power management computer allows it to be very flexible. Detection range is reported to be in the order of 400 km (250 miles) for fighter-sized targets, and around 100 such targets can be processed

by the Phalcon at any one time.

Fast scanning is possible, so that area coverage can be maintained while concentrating on an important target. To increase the detection range all power can be assigned in a specific direction. A sharp beam mode keeps track of a fast or manoeuvring target, and scan area can be limited to just the battle area, thereby increasing the scan rate in this region. Track initiation is in the region of two to four seconds, which is roughly a tenth that of rotodome-equipped platforms. Augmenting the radar are IFF, ESM/Elint and Comint suites, processed by a central battle management system for distribution to the 13 or so operator consoles in the main cabin. A command post option has a separate commander's cabin with a huge situation display.

It is likely that the **Israeli air force** operates some of its 707s in Phalcon configuration, and **South Africa**'s No. 60 Squadron is believed to operate two 707s equipped with a partial Phalcon system,

with just the side fairings and no nose radome. **Chile** is the first confirmed customer, specifiying a 260°-coverage system with side fairings and nose radome.

The prototype Phalcon, probably destined for Chile, appeared at the 1993 Paris air show. It is configured with three antenna arrays; a fourth can reportedly be added below the tail. Wingtip antennas serve the aircraft's extensive Elint/ESM system.

IAR (Sud/Aérospatiale) IAR-316B Alouette III

IAROM SA, c/o Technoimportexport SA
2 Doamnei St (PO Box 110)
Bucharest, Romania

Romania's state-owned Aeronautical Construction Enterprise (ICA) began production under licence of the **Aérospatiale SA 316B Alouette III** (described separately) in 1971. Built at Brasov, the **IAR-316B** conformed entirely to the French standard and was powered by the imported 870-shp (649-kW) Turboméca Artouste IIIB turboshaft. Production peaked at 24 Alouettes a year, and a total of about 230 was built. Of these, at least 45 were delivered to the **Aviatiei Militare Romane**, entering service with squadrons at Giarmata, Sibiu and Boboc, where they are used for anti-tank and liaison duties. In armed configuration, the helicopter could be fitted with stub wings carrying six AT-3

'Saggers' above and four 12-round rocket pods below. Machine-guns, normally 7.62-mm weapons, are fitted below the belly and in the starboard cabin door, and a roof-mounted sight can be fitted. The aircraft is also operated by the **Romanian navy**, which received at least six examples for liaison duties. The Alouette III provided the basis for development in Romania of the **IAR-317 Airfox**, described below.

A Romanian-built Alouette III. Romanian production has included large numbers of military versions, some of them armed with guns, rocket launchers and even 9M14 AT-3 'Sagger' ATGMs.

IAR IAR-317 Airfox

To provide a light anti-armour and military training helicopter for the Romanian air force and possible export, the ICA developed a new fuselage to combine with the basic Alouette III transmission and dynamics. As the **IAR-317 Airfox**, the first of three prototypes flew in April 1984, with a new slimline fuselage ahead of the main rotor mast seating a crew of two in tandem. Although the tailboom of the aircraft closely resembled that of the original Alouette III, the structure was completely new. The rear cockpit was raised to provide the pilot with a clear view over the gunner's head, and armour protection was fitted, as well as

toughened glass. A pair of 7.62-mm machine-guns was fitted to the lower front fuselage sides, and a load-carrying beam aft of the rear cockpit provided two or three attachment points each side for up to 750 kg (1,653 lb) of rocket pods, bombs, anti-armour missiles and AAMs. Testing of the Airfox prototypes did not lead to production orders and the project was not revived by the post-Ceausescu administration.

The IAR-317 Airfox is an Alouette III derivative with a low cross-section fuselage, optimised for the light anti-armour role.

IAR (Aérospatiale/Eurocopter) IAR-330L Puma

Under licence agreements with Aérospatiale, IAR in Romania established a production line for the **SA 330L Puma** in 1977 and by mid-1991 had completed 165 helicopters, with production continuing for civil and military customers. Exports have reportedly included some for the **South African Air Force**. The majority of IAR production was for the **Romanian air force**, and included an armed variant developed locally. This carries two 20-mm cannon in cheek pods on the lower front fuse-

lage sides, with ammunition in 540-round boxed belts in the cabin, and with steel tube mountings on each side of the main cabin (behind the entry doors) capable of carrying four rocket pods with eight 120-mm or 16 57-mm rockets, as well as four wire-guided AT-3 'Sagger' anti-armour missiles. Alternatively, up to four 7.62-mm GMP-2 machine-gun pods or four 100-kg (220-lb) bombs can be carried. In addition, pintle mountings are fitted for one machine-gun in each cabin doorway. Some aircraft have been seen

Some Romanian-built armed Pumas feature scabbed-on cannon on the sides of the forward fuselage, but this aircraft merely has outrigger pylons for rocket pods and AT-3 'Sagger' ATGMs.

IAR (Aérospatiale/Eurocopter) IAR-330L Puma

with a roof-mounted sight. A chin turret has also been designed as an option, either for a gun or for a TV/FLIR.

The **IAR-330L Puma** is powered by Turbomecanica (Romania) Turmo IVC turboshafts of 1,575 shp (1175 kW) each, but IAR is now working on the final development of the **Puma 2000**, featuring more powerful engines and a range of advanced equipment as standard or optional fit. First exhibited as a mock-up at the 1992 Farnborough show, the standard Puma 2000 has hands-off cyclic and stick (HOCS), helmet-mounted HUD, EFIS and MIL STD 1553 technology. The aircraft has an NVG compatible cockpit. Options include TV/FLIR for the surveillance role, a laser designator for target acquisition and a wide range of

weapons for anti-armour or infantry fire support missions. Israel's Elbit is primary avionics sub-contractor. The Puma 2000 will be offered as a new-build aircraft or as an upgrade based on the 330J or 330L.

Wearing Coast Guard colours and a striking bird-of-prey insignia, this IAR-330L demonstrator is unarmed, but is equipped with flotation gear and comprehensive navaids. Romanian licence-production of the Aérospatiale Puma began in 1977, primarily for the Romanian air force. A number of armed variants have been produced, and IAR actively markets the aircraft to military and civilian customers.

IAR IAR-823

After many years of producing foreign types under licence, most notably the **Yak-52** (produced only in Romania, and described under Aerostar) IAR began studies for an indigenous military training aircraft during the late 1960s. Although capable of seating five as a touring aircraft, the resulting **IAR-823** is more usually regarded as a two-seater in its role as a primary trainer for the **Romanian air force**. First flown in July 1973, the IAR-823 is powered by a 290-hp (216-kW) Textron Lycoming IO-540-G1D5 flat-six piston engine and is an entirely conventional low-wing monoplane with side-by-side seating for the instructor and trainee pilot (and an optional bench seat for three behind). Production deliveries began in 1974 and approximately 100 were in service by 1985, principally at the 'Aurel Vlaicu' Officer's Military School at Boboc. The IAR-823 is fully aerobatic and has provision for light practice weapons or drop tanks on two wing hardpoints.

The IAR-823 served as the basis for two more advanced trainer aircraft, neither of which reached production status. The first of these was the **IAR-825TP Triumf**, which combined the wing of the IAR-823 (strengthened for stores, but interchangeable with a standard IAR-823 wing) with a

new fuselage, tail unit and landing gear, and using a 680-shp (506-kW) Pratt and Whitney Canada PT6A-15AG turboprop, although the production version was to have used a more powerful 750-shp (558-kW) PT6A-25C. The new tandem cockpits were covered by a large rearward-sliding bubble canopy, giving a good all-round view. The prototype made its maiden flight on 12 June 1982. The **IAR-831 Pelican**, which made its public debut at the 1983 Paris Air Salon, was similar, but combined the airframe of the IAR-825TP with the original 290-hp Textron Lycoming IO-540-G1D5 piston engine of the IAR-823.

The IAR-831 Pelican combined the airframe of the turboprop-powered IAR-825TP with the original Lycoming piston engine of the IAR-823. It did not attain production status.

Above left: The basic IAR-823 is a five-seat tourer, used by the Romanian air force as a two-seat primary trainer.

Above: The turboprop-powered, tandem-seat IAR-825TP Triumf was based on the IAR-823 but did not enter production.

IAR IAR-99 Soim/-109 Swift

The **IAR-99 Soim** (hawk) was designed in the early 1980s in the Institutul de Aviatie at Bucharest and was put into production at Craiova by Intreprinderea de Avioane (IAv). In the reorganisation of the state aircraft industry following the collapse of the Ceausescu regime, the Craiova factory became a part of the Avioane subsidiary of the IAROM holding company.

A conventional design for a straight-wing single-jet aircraft, the Soim was conceived as a basic/advanced trainer with secondary ground attack/close support capability. Tandem seating in zero-zero ejection seats was arranged in a pressurised cockpit with the rear seat raised for improved forward view. For the armed role, provision was made for a removable ventral gun pod containing a 23-mm GSh-23 cannon with 200 rounds. Four wing hardpoints were each stressed for 250-kg (551-lb) loads, comprising bombs, rocket pods, machine-gun pods, AAMs, fuel tanks or similar ordnance.

Following the first flight on 21 December 1985, the IAR-99 entered service with the **Romanian Air Force** (AMR) in 1988 when an initial batch of 20 aircraft became operational at the Bacau flying school, replacing Aero L-29 Delfins, although the latter remain in service for weapons training.

The first IAR-99 Soim prototype, wears non-standard company livery. About 50 camouflaged IAR-99s now serve in the training role at Boboc.

Production of the Soim had reached about 50 by 1994, all for the AMR.

While production of the IAR-99 continues at a very low rate at Craiova following cuts in the military budget, consideration has been given to a modified version with the 4,870-lb st (21.7-kN) Viper 680 replacing the usual Viper 632, which is built in Romania. Jaffe Aircraft in the USA has sought to market an upgraded version outside of Romania. First announced in 1991, it was planned to incorporate major systems and completely updated avionics of Western origin, including a HUD and modern gunsight, with possible modification of the Viper engine to increase thrust. A further upgraded version was discussed with Israel Aircraft Industries in 1992. Designated **IAR-109 Swift**, planned modifications were primarily based on avionics improvements. After a gestation period of two years IAR publicly displayed the Swift for the first time at the Paris Air Show in 1993. This aircraft was originally built as an IAR-99.

SPECIFICATION

IAR-99 Soim (standard version for Romanian air force)
Wing: span 9.85 m (32 ft 3.75 in); aspect ratio 5.19; area 18.71 m² (201.4 sq ft)
Fuselage and tail: length 11.01 m (36 ft 1.5 in); height 3.90 m (12 ft 9.5 in); wheel track 2.69 m (8 ft 10 in); wheel base 4.38 m (14 ft 4.5 in)
Powerplant: one Turbomecanica Romanian-built Rolls-Royce Viper Mk 632-41M turbojet rated at

17.79 kN (4,000 lb st)
Weights: empty, equipped 3200 kg (7,055 lb); maximum take-off weight 4400 kg (9,700 lb)
Fuel and load: maximum usable fuel (internal) 1100 kg (2,425 lb); external fuel 350 kg (772 lb); payload 1000 kg (2,204 lb)
Speed: maximum Mach number 0.76; maximum level speed at sea level 865 km/h (467 kt; 537 mph)
Range: maximum range with internal fuel 683 miles (593 nm; 1100 km); lo-lo-hi 217 miles (189 nm; 350 km)
Performance: maximum climb rate at sea level 6,890 ft (2100 m) per minute; service ceiling 42,325 ft (12,900 m)

Ilyushin **Il-14 'Crate'**

Aviation Complex named after S.V. Ilyushin
125319 Moscow
Russia

Now thoroughly obsolete, the **Il-14** is the Eastern Bloc equivalent of the DC-3/C-47, and has enjoyed a similar success. Like the Dakota, it remains in service in small numbers with a number of air forces. Developed from the similar Il-12 'Coach', the Il-14 also has a tricycle undercarriage, giving the advantage of a level cabin on the ground, but has a stretched fuselage with accommodation for up to 28 passengers. First flown in 1952, the Il-14 entered service in 1954 and some 3,500 were built in the USSR, with further aircraft being licence-built in East Germany and as the **Avia 14** in Czechoslovakia.

A number of variants were produced, most military operators using the **Il-14P** with strengthened cabin floors, twin freight loading doors, provision for a parachute static line and observation blisters aft of the flight deck for a drop controller. The stretched **Il-14M** offered greater accommodation, and the **Il-14T** was a dedicated freighter (often being produced by conversion). In 1979 an ECM platform, reportedly allocated the codename **'Crate-C'**, was identified, but details of its service use are unavailable. A handful operated in the survey role, and some Czech machines had a stretched glazed nose for survey and mapping duties and were designated **Avia 14FG**. One of the latter survived until 1993 with the Czech air force. Other Il-14 survivors serve in **Albania**, **North Korea**, and **Poland** (including a survey aircraft),

SPECIFICATION

Ilyushin Il-14M 'Crate'
Wing: span 31.70 m (104 ft 0 in); aspect ratio 10.05; area 100.00 m² (1,076.43 sq ft)
Fuselage and tail: length 22.31 m (73 ft 2.25 in); height 7.90 m (25 ft 11 in)
Powerplant: two Shvetsov ASh-82T air-cooled radial piston engines each rated at 1,875 hp (1397 kW)
Weights: empty 12700 kg (27,998 lb); normal take-off weight 17700 kg (39,020 lb); maximum take-off 18500 kg (40,785 lb)
Fuel and load: internal fuel 6500 litres

(1,717 US gal); external fuel none; maximum payload 3300 kg (7,275 lb)
Speed: maximum level speed 'clean' at 2400 m (7,875 ft) 430 km/h (232 kt; 267 mph) and at sea level 400 km/h (217 kt; 248 mph); cruising speed at 3000 m (9,845 ft) 350 km/h (188 kt; 217 mph)
Range: 1500 km (809 nm; 932 miles) with 26 passengers or 400 km (216 nm; 249 miles) with maximum payload
Performance: climb to 5000 m (16,405 ft) in 8 minutes 30 seconds; service ceiling 6500 m (21,325 ft); take-off run 1020 m (3,346 ft); landing run 800 m (2,625 ft)

One of two Il-14s in service with 13th PLT at Krakow-Balice. Two further examples have been withdrawn. The surviving Polish Il-14s are configured for transport and photo-survey respectively.

Ilyushin **Il-18 'Coot'**

Designed as a sophisticated turboprop airliner for Aeroflot's domestic and shorter international routes, the **Il-18**, which first flew in July 1957, remains in service with a variety of civil and military operators worldwide. The initial production version accommodated 75 passengers, and could be powered until the 21st aircraft by Kuznetsov NK-4 or Ivchenko AI-20 turboprops, the latter engine subsequently being adopted as standard. The **Il-18B** introduced the AI-20K engine, with increased maximum take-off weight and accommodating 84 passengers. The **Il-18V** seated 89-100 passengers, and the **Il-18I** (later redesignated **Il-18D**) of 1964 seated 110-122 passengers, this being made possible by extending the pressurised cabin aft by deleting the former cargo hold in the tail. This variant also introduced more powerful AI-20M turboprops and increased fuel tankage in the centre-section. The contemporary **Il-18Ye** was identical, apart from lacking the extra fuel tankage.

Examples of most of these Il-18 variants have been supplied to a number of military operators for transport and VIP transport duties, but few remain in service today. Current military operators include **China**, **Congo**, **North Korea**, **Romania**, **Syria**, and **Vietnam**. A large number of nominally civilian Il-18s serve as equipment and avionics testbeds, in the experimental role, and the Gromov Flight Test Centre at Zhukhovskii has large numbers on charge. Some Aeroflot Il-18s seem to be used for military tasks, often being fitted with unusual antennas or equipment fairings, and at least one served as a meteorological research aircraft until replaced by an An-12.

SPECIFICATION

Ilyushin Il-18D 'Coot'
Wing: span 37.42 m (122 ft 9.25 in); aspect ratio 10.0; area 140.00 m² (1,507.00 sq ft)
Fuselage and tail: length 35.90 m (117 ft 9 in); height 10.17 m (33 ft 4 in); tailplane span 11.80 m (38 ft 8.5 in); wheel track 9.00 m (29 ft 6 in); wheel base

12.78 m (41 ft 10 in)
Powerplant: four ZMDB Progress (Ivchenko) AI-20M turboprops each rated at 3169 ekW (4,250 ehp)
Weights: empty equipped 35000 kg (77,160 lb); maximum take-off 64000 kg (141,093 lb)
Fuel and load: internal fuel 30000 litres (7,965 US gal); external fuel none; maximum payload 13500 kg (29,762 lb)
Speed: maximum cruising speed at 8500 m (27,890 ft) 675 km/h (364 kt; 419 mph); economical cruising speed at optimum altitude 625 km/h (337 kt; 388 mph)

The North Korean air force continues to operate the Il-18 as a freighter. North Korean transports are more often seen in 'airline' markings.

Range: 6500 km (3,508 nm; 4,039 miles) with maximum fuel or 3700 km (1,997 nm; 2,299 miles) with maximum payload
Performance: service ceiling 10000 m (32,810 ft); take-off run 1300 m (4,265 ft)

Ilyushin **Il-20/22 'Coot'**

The replacement of the basic Il-18 'Coot' on most Aeroflot routes resulted in a pool of redundant airframes suitable for conversion to military roles. The first such conversion to receive a separate NATO reporting name (**'Coot-A'**) is the **Il-20**, which is a dedicated Elint/radar reconnaissance aircraft seemingly based on the basic Il-18D airframe. Below the fuselage, projecting forward from a point just behind the wing leading edge, the aircraft carries a large, cylindrical underfuselage pod, about 10.25 m (33 ft 7 in) long and 1.15 m (3 ft 9 in) in diameter. The underside of the pod (apart from its streamlined nose and tail sections), through an arc of about 270°, consists of a single dielectric panel and is assumed to house some kind of SLAR. Smaller, more square-section pods, about 4.4 m (14 ft 5 in) long, are mounted on the forward fuselage just below the line of the cabin windows. These seem to have a small door towards the forward end, which can open to allow a camera or some other optical sensor to be used. Two large, very broad-chord trapezoidal blade antennas are mounted above the forward fuselage (some reports suggest these are associated with a satellite communications system), and other antennas

include three large blister fairings (the first teardrop-shaped, the next two more hemispherical) below the centre fuselage, on the centreline. Smaller antenna fairings are carried on the centreline further aft, and there are a number of dielectric panels flush with the fuselage and on the wingtips.

The Ilyushin **Il-22 'Coot-B'** is believed to be an airborne command post or communications relay variant of the Il-18. The aircraft can be identified by a cylindrical pod on the tailfin, and by an array of antennas (mostly blade) above and below the fuselage. The aircraft may also have a long cylindrical or canoe fairing under the belly, considerably smaller than those fitted to the 'Coot-A'. Such modified 'Coots' have been sighted at Zhukhovskii and Pushkin (the latter seems to be a location where former airliners are converted to this standard). Interestingly, most Il-22s retain Aeroflot markings although these are freshly re-applied after conversion. One serves in Ukrainian air force colours.

Unconfirmed reports suggest that the reporting name **'Coot-C'** has been allocated to a third Il-18 derivative, and that examples of this type have been intercepted by NATO interceptors.

Above: The Il-20 'Coot-A' is an Elint/radar recce derivative of the Il-18D, with a massive cylindrical SLAR under the belly.

Below: An Il-22 'Coot-B' at Pushkin, an airfield which is believed to specialise in the conversion of aircraft for Elint and EW roles.

Ilyushin **Il-28 'Beagle'/Il-28U 'Mascot'/**Harbin **H-5**

The **Il-28** was a jet-powered medium bomber which was built in enormous numbers and became Russia's equivalent to the British Canberra, being adapted to fulfil a variety of roles and serving with a large number of export customers. The final Il-28s were retired from Soviet service relatively recently, having ended their days as target tugs and ECM platforms. Some remain in surprisingly good condition on the dumps of vacated Soviet airfields in the former East Germany.

A handful of obsolete Il-28s may remain in use for second-line duties with a small number of air forces. Afghanistan, Hungary, Iraq, North Korea, Poland and Yemen are understood to have retired the aircraft in recent years, leaving **China** and **Romania** as the most likely users (in 1992, a handful of Romanian Il-28s were certainly still operational). Although China builds the Il-28 itself as the **Harbin H-5** it may also still have some Soviet-built aircraft on charge, and may have refurbished the ex-Albanian aircraft it swapped for a Harbin H-5 in the late 1970s.

In 1963, the Chinese aircraft industry initiated a programme under which the Ilyushin Il-28 light tactical bomber was to be manufactured without benefit of a licence from the Soviet Union. The People's Republic of China Air Force had received a number of Il-28 bombers from the Soviet Union, a fac-

tory at Harbin being assigned the task of repairing these and manufacturing some replacement parts. The programme of 'reverse-engineering' to copy the bomber was also assigned to Harbin. A prototype of the Chinese Il-28 flew as the H-5, or **Hongzhaji-5**, on 25 September 1966. H-5 production was launched in April 1967, and continued into the early 1980s, almost 2,000 allegedly having been built by the time that the programme terminated. This total included 186 examples of the **HJ-5** crew trainer, and variants included a tactical reconnaissance version, the **H-5R (or HZ-5)**, and dedicated torpedo-bombing and target-towing models. Exports included 18 H-5Rs to Romania, some 50 H-5s, H-5Rs and HJ-5s to North Korea, and one H-5 to Albania.

The H-5 remains in service in **Albania**, and in substantial numbers with China's Air Force and with the air component of the **People's Republic of China Navy**. The latter service also operates a number of H-5s adapted to carry Rushton low-level towed targets to simulate sea-skimming anti-shipping missiles. Data for the H-5 is essentially similar to that for the Ilyushin Il-28.

SPECIFICATION

Ilyushin Il-28 'Beagle'
Wing: span 21.45 m (70 ft 4.5 in) without tip tanks; aspect ratio 7.55; area 60.80 m² (654.47 sq ft)
Fuselage and tail: length, fuselage 17.65 m (57 ft 11 in) excluding tail cannon; height 6.70 m (21 ft 11.75 in); tailplane span 7.10 m (23 ft 3.5 in); wheel track 7.40 m (24 ft 3.5 in); wheel base about 8.10 m (26 ft 7 in)
Powerplant: two Klimov VK-1A each rated at 26.48 kN (5,952 lb st) dry
Weights: empty equipped 11890 kg (28,417 lb); normal take-off 18400 kg (40,564 lb); maximum take-off 21200 kg (46,738 lb)
Fuel and load: internal fuel 6600 kg (14,550 lb) including 200 kg (441 lb) in optional tip tanks; external fuel none; maximum ordnance 3000 kg (6,614 lb)
Speed: maximum level speed 'clean' at 4500 m (14,765 ft) 902 km/h (486 kt; 560 mph) or at sea level 800 km/h (432 kt; 497 mph); typical cruising speed at

A single H-5 remains operational with the Albanian air force, and Il-28s remain in use with the Romanian air force.

optimum altitude 876 km/h (472 kt; 544 mph)
Range: 2400 km (1,295 nm; 1,491 miles) at 10000 m (32,810 ft) declining to 1135 km (612 nm; 705 miles) at 1000 m (3,280 ft)
Performance: maximum rate of climb at sea level 900 m (2,952 ft) per minute; climb to 10000 m (32,810 ft in 18 minutes 0 seconds; service ceiling 12300 m (40,350 ft); take-off run 875 m (2,871 ft) at normal take-off weight or 1150 m (3,773 ft) at maximum take-off weight; landing run 1170 m (3,839 ft) at 14690 kg (32,385 lb)

Ilyushin **Il-38 'May'**

Although the **Il-38** is clearly derived from the Il-18 airliner, the extent of the changes to the new aircraft make it virtually certain that it is a new-build aeroplane, and not a conversion, with the same relationship to its airliner progenitor as the Orion has with the Electra or the Nimrod with the Comet. Certain components may be recovered from surplus Aeroflot Il-18s for re-use, such as wheels, and possibly even the aircraft's Ivchenko AI-20M turboprops and their propellers.

The basic Il-18 fuselage has been lengthened by about 4 m (13 ft 1.5 in), and the wings have been moved forward to compensate for the effect on aircraft centre of gravity of the new role equipment. Most of the original cabin windows have been removed, and the remainder have mostly been reduced in size. The Il-18's original passenger entry doors have all been removed, replaced by a new door on the starboard side at the rear of the cabin, where the Il-18's service door used to be. The flight deck and main cabin are separated by a pressure bulkhead. Other struc-

tural alterations include the provision of a MAD stinger projecting aft from the tailcone, and a pair of internal weapons/stores bays fore and aft of the wing structure.

The Il-38 has a standard weather radar in the nose, with its large search radar (NATO reporting name 'Wet Eye') in a distinctive, bulged radome below the forward fuselage, immediately aft of the nosewheel bay. The otherwise smooth skin is disrupted by a handful of antennas, heat exchanger outlets, and by large heat exchanger inlet pods and cable ducts just ahead of the wing.

The bulk of former Soviet Il-38s remain in use with the **AV-MF** (naval air arm). Some aircraft may actually be under **VVS** command however, in a similar fashion to maritime reconnaissance 'Bear-Ds', The only export customer is the **Indian Navy**, whose No. 315 Squadron operates five from INS Hansa at Dabolim, Goa. Il-38s encountered over the Mediterranean in Egyptian markings during the early 1970s were Soviet aircraft operating from Egyptian bases and wearing a 'flag of convenience'. The status of the Il-38 is uncertain, but con-

Based on the Il-18, but with a redesigned fuselage accommodating tandem weapons bays, radar and sonar, and a tail-mounted MAD, the Il-38 is Russia's most numerous ASW platform, augmented by a smaller number of Tu-142 'Bear-Fs'.

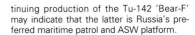

tinuing production of the Tu-142 'Bear-F' may indicate that the latter is Russia's preferred maritime patrol and ASW platform.

SPECIFICATION

Ilyushin Il-38 'May'
Wing: span 37.42 m (122 ft 9.25 in); aspect ratio 10.0; area 140.00 m² (1,507.00 sq ft)
Fuselage and tail: length 39.60 m (129 ft 10 in); height 10.16 m (33 ft 4 in); tailplane span 11.80 m (38 ft 8.5 in); wheel track 9.00 m (29 ft 6 in); wheel base 12.78 m (41 ft 10 in)
Powerplant: four ZMDB Progress (Ivchenko) AI-20M each rated at 3169 kW (4,250 shp)
Weights: empty equipped 36000 kg (79,365 lb); maximum take-off 63500 kg (139,991 lb)
Fuel and load: internal fuel 30000 litres (7,925 US gal) external fuel none
Speed: maximum level speed 'clean' at 6400 m (21,000 ft) 722 km/h (389 kt; 448 mph); maximum cruising speed at 8230 m (27,000 ft) 611 km/h (330 kt; 380 mph); patrol speed at 600 m (1,985 ft) 400 km/h (215 kt; 248 mph)
Range: ferry range 7200 km (3,885 nm; 4,474 miles); patrol endurance 12 hours 0 minutes
Performance: take-off run 1300 m (4,265 ft) at maximum take-off weight; landing run 850 m (2,789 ft at normal landing weight with propeller reversal

Ilyushin **Il-62 'Classic'**

With a T-tail, rear-engine configuration closely resembling that of the Vickers/BAC VC-10, the **Il-62** was the first Soviet long-range, four-engined jet airliner to enter service. Developed as a replacement for the turboprop-engined Tu-114 on Aeroflot's most prestigious international routes, the Il-62 made its maiden flight in January 1963, powered by Lyul'ka AL-7 turbojets, pending availability of the Kuznetsov NK8-4 engines used by production aircraft. The improved longer-range **Il-62M** is powered by Soloviev D-30KU turbofans, and with the previous cascade-type thrust reversers replaced by clamshell-type units. These were still only fitted to the outboard engines. The more powerful engines allowed operation at higher gross weights, and an extra fuel tank was installed in the fin. An internal redesign allowed up to 198

passengers to be accommodated.

Although the Il-62 frequently served as a Presidential aircraft in the **USSR**, the aircraft involved retained Aeroflot markings and were operated by civilian crews. They were specially modified for the role, however, with a long dorsal avionics fairing and satellite communications equipment. Recently, these aircraft have relinquished Aeroflot titles, and have been painted in a quasi-government colour scheme, with massive Rossiya (Russia) titles on the fuselage sides. There are no known red-starred Il-62s. The only known truly military Il-62s were three former Interflug aircraft (**Il-62Ms** and **MKs**) taken over by the **Luftwaffe** after reunification and operated by TG44 at Marxwalde, which became LTG65; the airfield was renamed Neuhardenburg. These aircraft were withdrawn from military

use and sold, leaving only the Russian VIP transports. Marketing of the Il-62 continues (particularly second-hand examples), and further military or government customers may yet emerge.

SPECIFICATION

Ilyushin Il-62M 'Classic'
Wing: span 43.20 m (141 ft 9 in); aspect ratio 6.68; area 279.55 m² (3,009.15 sq ft)
Fuselage and tail: length 53.12 m (174 ft 3.5 in); height 12.35 m (40 ft 6.25 in); tailplane span 12.23 m (40 ft 1.5 in); wheel track 6.80 m (22 ft 3.5 in); wheel base 24.49 m (80 ft 4.5 in)
Powerplant: four PNPP 'Aviadvigatel' (Soloviev) D-30KU each rated at 107.87 kN (24,250 lb st) dry
Weights: operating empty 71600 kg (157,848 lb); maximum take-off 165000 kg (363,757 lb)
Fuel and load: internal fuel 105300 litres (27,817 US gal); external fuel none; maximum payload 23000 kg (50,705 lb)
Speed: normal cruising speed at between 10000 and

The Luftwaffe's former Interflug Il-62s were recently withdrawn and sold. They were replaced by three Airbus A310s (also obtained from Interflug), in the transport role .

12000 m (32,810 and 39,370 ft) between 820 and 900 km/h (442 and 486 kt; 509 and 560 mph)
Range: 7800 km (4,210 nm; 4,848 miles) with a 5100 kg (11,243-lb) payload
Performance: take-off balanced field length 3300 m (10,827 ft) at maximum take-off weight; landing run 2500 m (8,202 ft) at normal landing weight

Ilyushin **Il-76 'Candid'**

The Il-76 was developed as a successor to the An-12 for both Aeroflot and the **Soviet air force**. Just as the USAF purchased the jet-engined C-141 to augment its propeller-driven Hercules transports, so the Soviet air force turned to a jet aircraft to augment (and eventually supersede) its An-12s. Like the USAF, the Soviets found that for certain tasks the turboprop transport was superior and the Il-76 has still not entirely supplanted the An-12, which will finally be replaced by the An-70T, another turboprop. Larger, heavier and more powerful than the C-141, the Il-76 uses extensive high lift devices, thrust reversers and a high flotation undercarriage to achieve much better short- and rough-field performance, at the expense of only slightly inferior payload and range.

The Ilyushin Il-76 displays several other examples of Soviet design philosophy, with most military versions having a gun turret with two twin-barrelled 23-mm cannon in the tail, and with all transport versions having a glazed navigator/drop master position in the lower part of the nose. The cargo hold is fully pressurised and has a titanium floor, with fold-down roller conveyors, and can be quickly reconfigured by using interchangeable passenger, freight or air ambulance modules. Three such modules (each 6.1 m/20 ft long and 2.44 m/8 ft wide) can be fitted, the passenger modules containing 30 passengers in four abreast seats.

Loading is accomplished using two internal overhead winches, each of which can use two 3000-kg (6,615-lb) or four 2500-kg (5,511-lb) hoists. The ramp itself can be used as a lift, with a capacity of up to 30000 kg (66,150 lb). The hold is compatible with international standard containers and pallets.

The first prototype (SSSR-86712) made its maiden flight on 25 March 1971, and by 1974 a development squadron was in service flying Il-76s equipped with tail gun turrets. Series production began in 1975 at Tashkent. More than 750 had been built by the beginning of 1993, and production continues at a rate of about 50 per year. The initial production version was the **Il-76**, which received the NATO reporting name **'Candid-A'**. The codename was retained for the developed **Il-76T** featuring additional fuel tankage in the wing centre-section. The final 'Candid-A' variant is the **Il-76TD** with uprated Soloviev D-30KP-1 engines, which maintain full power at higher outside air temperatures and give improved 'hot-and-high' take-off performance. One soundproofed and specially equipped Il-76TD is used as the support aircraft for Soviet Antarctic expeditions, flying via

Based on an Il-76MD airframe, this aircraft is one of two Il-76 command posts based at Zhukhovskii's LII Flight Research Centre. The aircraft differs from standard in having a large number of extra blade aerials, strakes, antenna pods and an enormous radome fairing above the cockpit.

An Il-76MD in full Soviet air force markings during a rare visit to Britain. The Il-76 largely replaced the An-12, and is in use in huge numbers. The military fleet can be augmented by Aeroflot aircraft.

Maputo in Mozambique. Some military export Il-76 customers, including Iraq, use 'Candid-As', often in addition to 'Candid-Bs'.

Other 'Candid-A' sub-types include four **Il-76LL** engine testbeds, which have tested a number of engines, including the D-236 propfan, the NK-86, the PS-90A and the D-18T turbofans, and the **Il-76DMP**, a one-off fire-bomber conversion carrying up to 44 tonnes of retardant in two cylindrical tanks in the hold, and with special aiming devices for accurate retardant delivery. The equipment can be installed or removed in four hours, and the tanks take about 12 minutes to fill. The tanks can be discharged simultaneously or in series in just over six seconds. The aircraft can also carry up to 384 meteorological cartridges (cloud-seeders) for 'weather modification', or 40 fire-fighting parachutists. Military or pseudo-military users of the 'Candid-A' include **Cuba** and **North Korea**.

Finally, the Moscow Aeroshow at Zhukhovskii in August 1992 revealed two new variants of the basic 'civil' Il-76. With no known Soviet designation two of the aircraft were clearly equipped for some kind of military airborne command post or range control role, despite their Aeroflot colour scheme. They had prominent dorsal canoe radomes above the forward fuselage, a trailing aerial fitting (like that fitted to the EC-130Q, and the 'Bear-J') projecting from the ramp area, and various blade antennas. Small aerial pods, similar to those fitted to the Boeing E-6A Mercury, were carried under the outer wing panels. There were also several examples of an aircraft which appeared to be similar to the A-50 'Mainstay', with a very similar rotodome above

the fuselage. All wore Aeroflot markings and are described in greater detail under the Ilyushin A-50 'Mainstay' heading.

The NATO reporting name **'Candid-B'** is used to identify dedicated military versions of the Il-76, which can be externally identified by the gun turret in the tailcone. Many military 'Candids' also have small ECM fairings between the centre windows at the front of the navigator's compartment, and on each side of the forward and rear fuselage. Packs containing 96 50-mm IRCM flares or chaff cartridges can also be scabbed onto the landing gear fairings and/or the sides of the rear fuselage. The first dedicated military variant was the **Il-76M**, which was equivalent to the civil Il-76T; with uprated D-30KP-1 engines, the designation **Il-76MD** is used. Twenty-four Il-76MDs delivered to **India** to equip one flight of No. 25 Squadron at Chandigarh and No. 44 Squadron at Agra bear the local name **Gajaraj** (King Elephant). Other foreign users are **Iraq**, **Libya** and **Syria**.

SPECIFICATION

Ilyushin Il-76M 'Candid-B'
Wing: span 50.50 m (165 ft 8 in); aspect ratio 8.5;

area 300.00 m^2 (3,229.28 sq ft)
Fuselage and tail: length 46.59 m (152 ft 10.25 in); height 14.76 m (48 ft 5 in)
Powerplant: four PNPP 'Aviadvigatel' (Soloviev) D-30KP each rated at 117.68 kN (26,455 lb st) dry
Weights: maximum take-off 170000 kg (374,780 lb)
Fuel and load: internal fuel about 81830 litres (21,617 US gal); external fuel none; maximum payload 40000 kg (88,183 lb)
Speed: maximum level speed 'clean' at optimum altitude 850 km/h (459 kt; 528 mph); cruising speed between 9000 and 12000 m (29,530 and 39,370 ft) between 750 and 800 km/h (405 and 432 kt; 466 and 497 mph)
Range: ferry range 6700 km (3,617 nm; 4,163 miles); range 5000 km (2,698 nm; 3,107 miles) with maximum payload
Performance: absolute ceiling about 15500 m (50,855 ft); take-off run 850 m (2,790 ft) at maximum take-off weight; landing run 450 m (1,475 ft) at normal landing weight

Ilyushin Il-76MD 'Candid-B'
generally similar to the Ilyushin Il-76M 'Candid-B' except in the following particulars:
Powerplant: four PNPP 'Aviadvigatel' (Soloviev) D-30KP-1 each rated at 117.68 kN (26,455 lb st) dry
Weights: maximum take-off 190000 kg (418,871 lb)
Fuel and load: external fuel none; maximum payload 48000 kg (105,820 lb)

Ilyushin **Il-78M 'Midas'**

The introduction of inflight-refuelling probes on some Soviet tactical aircraft notably the Su-24M and MiG-31, but also the Su-27IB, MiG-29K and Su-27P/PU) and the age of Russia's handful of Myasishchev M-4 'Bison' and Tu-16N 'Badger' tankers, led to the need for a new inflight-refuelling aircraft. Conversion of retired bombers was considered but, in the end, a tanker based on the Il-76 'Candid' (which was available in large numbers) was felt to be a better option.

The **Il-78M 'Midas'** is a three-point

tanker based on (or even converted from) the airframe of the Il-76MD military freighter. The aircraft is fitted with three Severin/UPAZ PAE external refuelling units, one under each wing and one mounted on the port side of the rear fuselage. The two underwing pods are reportedly sometimes removed on missions involving only a single

An Il-78 'Midas', unusually in full military markings, trails three hoses in front of its customer, a Tu-142MS 'Bear-H'.

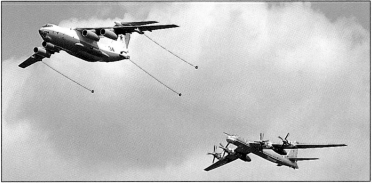

211

receiver aircraft. Pods are also carried by some tactical aircraft (usually Su-24s) operating in the 'buddy-buddy' role and consist of pylon-mounted square-section self-powered HDUs with a conical front which retracts to open an annular ram air intake, which in turn drives the turbine which powers the refuelling hose winch and fuel pump. The three HDUs can operate at a maximum rate of 2500 litres (550 Imp gal)

per minute (total 7500 litres/1,650 Imp gal per minute), which is a higher rate than Western HDUs can handle, and allows very fast refuelling of formations of tactical aircraft. Red and yellow lights are mounted on the back of each HDU and on the former tail turret, to allow radio-silent contacts.

Internally the Il-78M has a pair of enormous cylindrical tanks pallet-mounted in the hold. Together these contain 35 tonnes (of

the aircraft's 100-tonne total) and since they are distinct from the aircraft's own fuel system represent the total transferable fuel load. The observer sits in the former tail gunner's turret, but has no controls, communicating via radio link with the flight engineer who operates the refuelling controls. Receiver/tanker rendezvous is facilitated by a simple homing radar housed behind a broad flat aft-facing radome ahead of the

standard rear-loading ramp.

The former Soviet Union's only operational Il-78M regiment was based in the **Ukraine** and was retained by that country's air arm after it declared independence, leaving only a handful in Russian hands. Although most Il-78Ms have been noted in Aeroflot colours, at least one has been photographed in full **CIS** air force colours, with a two-digit regimental code.

Ilyushin **Il-86 'Camber'**

Although no military customers have been found for the basic **Il-86** wide-bodied 'Airbus', there is some evidence that a handful of these aircraft is operational in a military or quasi-military role. At least four have been seen at Zhukhovskii wearing full Aeroflot colours, but clearly modified for some kind of command post, missile tracking or avionics test role. Fitted with a huge dorsal canoe antenna above the forward fuselage, the aircraft also have a plethora of

blade aerials above and below the fuselage. Large pods (with dielectric antennas and cooling air intakes) are also carried under the wingroots.

This Il-86, despite its Aeroflot colours, is an airborne command post or range control aircraft. Cabin windows are faired over, and the aircraft carries underwing antenna pods and a massive dorsal radome.

Ilyushin **Il-102**

The **Ilyushin Il-102**, which made its first appearance at the 1992 Moscow Aeroshow, was developed as a competitor to the Su-25 'Frogfoot' and is still being marketed as such, despite its rejection by the Soviet air force and its anachronistic design. It is powered by a pair of non-afterburning RD-33I turbofans based on those used by the MiG-29. During 1992 Ilyushin even went so far as to issue a slim brochure on what they called the 'Il-102 Armoured Close Air Support Aircraft'.

The aircraft has its roots in the **Il-40 'Brawny'**, developed as a dedicated ground attack/close air support aircraft during the late 1940s, as an alternative to simply using obsolete jet fighters. Powered by a pair of RD-9F turbojets (as used in the MiG-19 and later, ironically, by the prototype

Su-25), the Il-40 was a heavily-armoured two-seater, the second seat being in a separate cockpit located adjacent to the trailing edge of the wing and occupied by a rearward-facing gunner, who controlled a remote gun turret in the tailcone. With its mixture of six underwing pylons and six inboard internal weapons bays inside the wing, the aircraft has obvious similarities with 1940s-vintage *shturmovik* ground attack aircraft. An NR-23 23-mm cannon (traversible to near vertical) was fitted for strafing ground targets. The prototype made its maiden flight on 7 March 1955, but flight tests revealed gun gas ingestion problems which were cured by extending the intakes forward to meet, side-by-side, at the nose. State acceptance tests were passed in January 1955, but the project was cancelled, and the five completed pre-production aircraft were scrapped, on Kruschchev's orders, later that year, in the belief that a dedicated jet *shturmovik* was unnecessary.

A single prototype may have survived.

The design was resurrected in the aftermath of the 1967 Six Day War, during which Israeli fighters armed with 30-mm cannon proved devastatingly effective as tank-killers, This led directly to the requirement which resulted in the Su-25, Sukhoi following the US approach of using a single-seat attack aircraft while Ilyushin opted for a two-seater. Under the designation **Il-42**, Ilyushin revised the original Il-40, only to have their design rejected summarily by the air force. The aircraft was redesignated Il-102, to disassociate it from the Il-40, and a prototype was constructed using company funds and borrowed equipment.

The new aircraft was externally very similar to the Il-40 of 1953, albeit with the tailplanes lowered and given dihedral, with wing fences removed, and with the previously bifurcated engine intakes cut back from the nose to a point level with the cockpit. Whether the Il-102 began life as an Il-40,

or used parts from an uncompleted Il-40, remains unknown. Orders to terminate the project were ignored, the OKB pressing on using the new designation 'Experimental Aircraft No.1' and the pretence that it was a pure research platform. The prototype made its maiden flight on 25 September 1982, and made 250 flights before it was grounded in 1984 when engine life expired (no funding being available for replacement or overhaul). The aircraft was represented to the air force in 1986 as a potential Su-25 replacement, the Su-25T being selected instead, and was shown at the 1992 Moscow Aeroshow, perhaps in an effort to remind the world of Ilyushin's long history as a military aircraft producer.

The sole Il-102 prototype. The aircraft is still being marketed by Ilyushin as a cheap ground attack platform, and to keep the OKB in the military aircraft business.

Ilyushin A-50 'Mainstay'/Il-976

The **'Mainstay'** was developed as a replacement for the Tupolev Tu-126 'Moss', the USSR's first AEW and AWACS platform. Like many early Western AEW aircraft, the 'Moss' was virtually ineffective over land, but was efficient enough to demonstrate the usefulness of an airborne radar station for providing early warning of enemy attack and for controlling defending fighters. Remarkably, development of what the Russians call SDRLO (Systyem Dalnovo Radiolocacio-mnovo Obnarushenya, or Long-Range Radio Location and Detection System) was actually terminated during the 1960s as an economy measure and was then restarted in the face of Western development of the E-3 Sentry.

The **A-50** has a rotodome (influenced more by that carried by the E-3 than that of the Tu-126) above the fuselage, with the nose glazing and tail turret removed and replaced by further radomes, and with a small dorsal canoe radome projecting forward from the leading edge of the wing centre-section. Large horizontal flat plates of unknown purpose are fitted to the rear of each undercarriage fairing.

The 'Mainstay' reportedly entered service during 1984, and after some teething troubles has proved successful and popular. The system's designers admit inferior radar range and multiple target tracking capability by comparison with the E-3, but claim better discrimination of objects and targets on the ground or of low-flying targets against ground 'clutter'. A particular bugbear for crews (used to the luxuriously-appointed 'Moss', which was a converted Tu-114 airliner) is the inferior conditions in which they must work. Noise levels are high, and toilet and galley facilities barely adequate. Rest bunks are not provided at all. Morale problems have been worsened by the move from the Baltic to Pechora in the polar region, where accommodation and facilities are poor even by Soviet standards. The move was made to allow the aircraft to meet threats from what one senior air force commander described as "the most dangerous direction."

Because the Soviet electronics industry lags behind that of the West and has no domestic market for home computers and computer games, equipment tends to be bigger and heavier, and achieving similar equipment performance has been an amazing leap, achieved only at the expense of lightness and simplicity. The separate command and control systems of the separate branches of the armed forces necessitates the installation of duplicate systems for

The Aeroflot colour scheme, glazed nose and wingtip pods identify this aircraft as an Il-976, a rotodome-equipped range control aircraft similar to the full standard A-50 'Mainstay'.

exchanging data, decoding IFF signals, etc. All decoding and interfacing is carried out on board, whereas much of the latter is done on the ground for the E-3 Sentry.

The weight of all the equipment is greater than had been anticipated, and landing gear limitations prevent the aircraft from taking off with a full fuel load, which reduces endurance by about half an hour. This problem is exacerbated by the fact that disturbed airflow from the rotodome makes it very difficult to use the nose-mounted inflight-refuelling probe, and only the most experienced pilots are cleared for the practice.

Inside the cabin a single large screen is used for controlling fighters, with smaller screens monitoring the tactical situation on the ground and in the air, and showing number and type of friendly and enemy aircraft, with details of course, speed, altitude, armament and fuel state. All the screens are fully-digitised colour CRTs, and show friendly forces in red and enemy in blue.

The aircraft's mission computer allows automatic communication of data to and from fighters and ground stations directly, and via satellite using datalinks. When connected to the aircraft's autopilot it can fly the aircraft through pre-programmed search patterns over programmed points on the ground. A-50s typically fly a figure-eight racetrack pattern at about 10000 m (33,000 ft) with 100 km (62 miles) between the centres of the two circles. During exercises the A-50s have demonstrated an ability to control MiG-31 interceptors, directing them onto incoming cruise missiles, while simultaneously supplying submarines with tactical information and controlling Tu-22M-3 'Backfire' bombers and other fighters.

During the Gulf War, two A-50s were deployed to a Black Sea airfield, where they maintained a single-aircraft, round-the-clock

watch over the war zone, able to see every take-off and cruise missile firing in Turkey and over most of Iraq. Further aircraft maintained a standing patrol over the Caspian Sea. Refuelling difficulties were surmounted and the aircraft were supported by 3MS-2 (Myasishchev M-4 'Bison') tankers.

A second rotodome-equipped version of the Il-76 is the **Il-976**, described by some sources as a one-off AEW testbed but in fact already available in considerable numbers, and also described as a range control and missile tracking platform. It may also be a forerunner of the A-50, used for AEW trials and for systems development. At least five aircraft, all wearing Aeroflot markings and civil registration numbers, were present at Zhukhovskii during the 1992 Moscow Aeroshow. The Il-976 differs from the A-50 in retaining the glazed nose of the Il-76, and the glazed tail turret, although the guns are replaced by a bulbous radome. The aircraft also lacks an inflight-refuelling probe and many of the A-50's minor antennas, but is fitted with fat cylindrical wingtip pods.

The A-50 is fitted with a rotodome above the trailing edge of the wing centre-section, and a dorsal canoe.

It has been reported that Beriev is responsible for converting Il-76s to AEW configuration, using equipment supplied by the Ministry of the Radio Equipment Industry, but it is not known whether this refers to the A-50 or the Il-976, or both. Iraq has developed similar AEW versions of the Il-76, which are described separately.

SPECIFICATION

Ilyushin A-50 'Mainstay'
generally similar to the Ilyushin Il-76M 'Candid-A' except in the following particulars:
Fuselage and tail: height 14.76 m (48 ft 5 in)

The definitive production A-50 has a horizontal winglet/blade antenna mounted on the rear part of the landing gear fairing.

IPTN (Eurocopter/MBB) NBO 105

Industri Pesawat Terbang Nusantara (Nusantara Aircraft Industries Ltd
PO Box 1562, Jalan Pajajaran 15
Bandung 40174, Indonesi

Nusantara Aircraft Industries Ltd (IPTN) in Bandung, Indonesia, produces the **Eurocopter BO 105** helicopter (described separately) under licence from Eurocopter Germany (previously MBB), for both military and commercial users. Between 1976 and 1987, IPTN built 100 **NBO 105**s, then changed to the **NBO 105S** model with a 25-cm (10-in) fuselage stretch and with provision for nose-mounted search or weather radar.

IPTN has developed a multi-purpose delivery system for the NBO 105, comprising fuselage-mounted provision for such armament as unguided rocket pods and machine-gun pods, or reconnaissance sensors including FLIR pods. Rocket-armed NBO 105s are included in the 16-strong inventory of this type flown by the Indonesian army (**TNI-AD**). Other military customers for the NBO 105 are the air force (**TNI-AU**) and navy (**TNI-AL**), although the latter's No. 200 Squadron found the type unsuitable for shipboard operation. The type is also used by the Indonesian **Polisi** and the **Royal Jordanian Air Force**.

A rocket-armed NBO-105 of the Indonesian army. The type also serves with the air force, navy, Polisi and with the Royal Jordanian Air Force.

IPTN (CASA) NC.212 Aviocar

IPTN in Indonesia has been building the **CASA C.212 Aviocar** (described separately) under licence since 1976, primarily to satisfy the domestic demand for both military and civil versions. The first 29 aircraft from the Bandung production line were equivalent to the Spanish **C.212 Series 100** model, with production subsequently changing to the Series 200 model, identified locally as the **NC.212-200**. The Indonesian air force (**TNI-AU**) received two Series 100s and eight Series 200s. These aircraft are used principally by No. 2 Squadron at Kemayoran in the transport role, and for communications duties by No. 4 Squadron at Malany. Both the army and the navy (**TNI-AD** and **TNI-AL**) received four NC.212-200s for routine transport operations; other possible roles include LAPES, SAR, airdropping, maritime patrol, medevac and photographic survey.

An Indonesian-built NC.212A-4 Aviocar in full air force camouflage. The type is used by the Indonesian air force, navy and army.

IPTN (Eurocopter) AS 330 Puma/NAS 332 Super Puma

IPTN assembled 11 **Aérospatiale AS 330J** Pumas in 1981/83 using components from French production, and subsequently delivered 10 to the Indonesian air force (**TNI-AU**), including two in VIP configuration. A batch of 18 Super Pumas then followed, equivalent to the AS 332C, and from this batch the Indonesian navy (**TNI-AL**) received four **NAS 332B** utility models for operation from support vessels used in amphibious operations. One VIP-configured NAS 332 was supplied to the Malaysian government. With the 19th Super Puma, production switched to the equivalent of the **AS 332L**, the version with cabin lengthened by 76.5 cm (30 in). The TNI-AU is among reported customers for this version, with at least one VIP transport on order.

Above left: An Indonesian-built AS 330J in service with the TNI-AU, one of 10 IPTN-built Pumas in use.

Above: Indonesian-built NAS 332F Super Pumas can carry Exocet ASMs and have a chin-mounted radar.

Iraqi Air Force Baghdad 1 and Adnan

Iraqi Air Force, Ministry of Defence
Bab Al Muadan
Baghdad, Ira

While Soviet conversions of the Ilyushin Il-76 'Candid' for the AEW role are described under the Ilyushin A-50 'Mainstay' heading, two Iraqi AEW conversions deserve separate treatment. The first AEW modification was named **Baghdad 1**, and was an Il-76MD (without tail turret) with the antenna of a Thomson-CSF Tigre surveillance radar mounted inverted behind a blister radome in place of the clamshell and upward-opening rear doors. The Tigre radar is licence-built in Iraq (usually truck-mounted) and signal processing was modified to deal with ground clutter for its new application. The radar is manned by four operators, gives a 180° sweep, and can detect, track and identify targets out to 190 nm (350 km; 218 miles). Unspecified problems with the Baghdad 1 led to the development of a second AEW aircraft, this one having a more conventional 9 m (29 ft 6 in) diameter rotodome atop the fuselage, but no tail turret. Details of this conversion, known as the **Adnan**, remain sketchy. At least three were produced by conversion and one was destroyed during a coalition air attack on Al Taqqaddum on 23 January 1991, the other two then fleeing to Iran, where they may remain.

The radome of one of the two Baghdad 1 Il-76 conversions, with a huge dielectric radome for the Thomson-CSF Tigre surveillance radar mounted in place of the rear loading doors. The aircraft proved unsuccessful, and Iraq instead developed a 'Mainstay' clone.

IRGC Fajr

Intended as a primary trainer, the **Fajr** (Dawn) was built by the Air Industries Division of the Islamic Revolutionary Guard Corps. Flown on 22 February 1988, the prototype (the first aircraft built in Iran since the Islamic revolution) was built based upon **Neico Lancair 235** plans. This was a kit-built US sport aircraft which flew in 1984.

SPECIFICATION

IRGC Fajr (Neico Lancair 235)
Wing: span 23 ft 6 in (7.16 m); area 76.00 sq ft (7.06 m2)

Fuselage and tail: length 19 ft 8 in (5.99 m); height 6 ft 1 in (1.85 m)
Powerplant: one Textron Lycoming O-235 four-cylinder horizontally opposed piston engine rated at 118 hp (88 kW)
Weights: basic empty 650 lb (295 kg); maximum take-off 1,275 lb (578 kg)

Speed: maximum level speed 'clean' at sea level 185 kt (213 mph, 343 km/h)
Range: 868 nm (1,000 miles; 1609 km)
Performance: maximum rate of climb at sea level 1,500 ft (457 m) per minute; take-off run 600 ft (183 m) at maximum take-off weight; landing run 600 ft (183 m) at maximum landing weight

Jodel (SAN) D.140 Mousquetaire/Abeille

Société des Avions Jodel
is currently inactive

The title Jodel is a contraction of the names of the type's test pilot, Eduard Joly, and its designer, Jean Delmontez. The Jodel company acted as a design bureau and provider of plans, licensing other companies and individuals to build its designs. The **Jodel D.140 Mousquetaire** was based on the **Jodel D.117** and this was licensed from Jean Delmontez by SAN (Société Aéronautique Normande), who developed the larger, four/five-seater D.140 family with a 180-hp (134 kW) Lycoming engine, revised tail surfaces and other improvements. The prototype was first flown in July 1958. Production of the **D.140E Mousquetaire IV**, with enlarged tail surfaces, an all-flying tail and modified ailerons, included 18 for the **French air force**, which went on to acquire 14 **D.140R Abeille**s. This has a cut-down rear fuselage with all-round vision canopy and glider-towing hook. Both types remain in use with the Armée de l'Air for recreation flying and (the D.140Rs) for glider-towing with GI 4/312 at Salon and the Ecole de Pupille de l'Air 349 at Grenoble. The D.140s are powered by 180-hp (134-kW) Lycoming O-360 four-cylinder piston engines.

This is one of the D.140R Abeille glider tugs operated by the Armée de l'Air at Salon and Grenoble. The similar D.140 is used for sport flying.

Kaman **SH-2F Seasprite**

Kaman Aerospace Corporation
Old Windsor Rd, PO Box No.2
Bloomfield, Connecticut 06002, USA

Originally designated **K-20** by Kaman, the Seasprite was conceived in response to a 1956 **USN** requirement for a high-speed, all-weather, long-range SAR, liaison and utility helicopter. The original **HU2K-1** made its maiden flight on 2 July 1959, and the type was redesignated **UH-2A** in 1962. Successive variants of the aircraft were progressively improved and updated, gaining a second engine (for greater safety margin for ship-based operations), dual mainwheels, and a four-bladed tail rotor, but retained their liaison, utility, SAR and combat rescue roles. All early variants have now been retired or, more often, converted to later standards. Production stopped after the delivery of the last **UH-2B**, bringing production to a total of 190 (all originally single-engined). These comprised four **YUH-2A** prototypes 84 UH-2As and 102 UH-2Bs. At least two were evaluated by the US Army. Further variants were all converted from existing airframes.

The helicopter was first used in the ASW role in October 1970, when the Navy selected the **SH-2D** as an interim LAMPS (Light Airborne Multi-Purpose System) platform. Externally, the SH-2D introduced an undernose radome housing a Litton LN 66 search radar, with an ASQ-81 MAD on the starboard fuselage pylon and a removable sonobuoy rack in the fuselage port side for 15 SSQ-47 active or SSQ-41 passive sonobuoys. Twenty were converted from **HH-2D**s, entering service in 1972.

Deliveries of the definitive **SH-2F**, which also bears the **LAMPS I** designation, commenced in May 1973. Its primary role is concerned with extending the area of protection provided by the outer defensive screen of a carrier battle group. The SH-2F introduced uprated General Electric T58-GE-8F engines, Kaman's advanced '101' rotor which gave a longer life (3,000 hours), improved performance, reliability and maintainability and a strengthened landing gear. A notable external difference concerned the tailwheel, which was relocated forwards, shortening the wheelbase by nearly 6 ft (1.83 m) for greater deck-edge clearance when operating from smaller warships. These modifications allowed the SH-2F to operate at higher all-up weights than the SH-2D. The SH-2F also featured an improved Marconi LN 66HP surface search radar, AN/ASQ-81(V)2 towed MAD bird on a starboard pylon and a tactical nav/comms system, necessitating a sensor operator in addition to the normal crew of two pilots. Offensive capability comprised two Mk 46 torpedoes to engage sub-surface threats. Eighty-eight aircraft were converted from earlier variants (using up virtually every surviving airframe), and 16 surviving SH-2Ds were also brought up to the same standard in a programme completed in 1982.

In March 1972 Kaman completed two **YSH-2E**s as testbeds for the Navy's LAMPS II programme with a new Texas Instruments APS-115 radar in a reconfigured nose. The programme was cancelled later the same year. Kaman proposed a derivative of the SH-2, known as the **Sealamp**, as a contender for the LAMPS III requirement that was eventually fulfilled by the SH-60B. The aircraft remained unbuilt, although several SH-2s were used to test LAMPS III systems and equipment.

Despite its failure to be selected as the LAMPS III platform, the Seasprite was retained for service aboard US Navy 'Knox'- and 'Kidd'-class frigates, the 'Truxton'-class cruisers and the first two 'Ticonderoga'-class cruisers. All but the first 'Belknap'-class cruisers carry SH-2Fs, as do the first and the third through to the 25th 'Oliver Hazard Perry'-class ASW frigates. Accordingly, the aircraft was reinstated in production during 1981, when the US Navy placed an order for the first batch of an eventual 60 new-build SH-2Fs, the last six being delivered as upgraded **SH-2G**s (described separately). Many of these aircraft, and some earlier SH-2Fs, received AN/ALR-66A(V)1 RWRs and AN/ALE-39 chaff/flare dispensers. In 1992 the SH-2F was operated by eight front-line and three Reserve HSL squadrons, but by the end of April 1994 post-Cold War defence cuts had reduced the force to two Reserve units, the last fleet squadron having been HSL-33. These units transitioned to SH-2Gs during 1994.

From 1987, 16 SH-2Fs received a package of modifications to allow them to operate in the Gulf. This included the provision of an AN/AAQ-16 FLIR under the nose, an AN/ALQ-144 IR jammer, AN/AAR-47 and AN/DLQ-3 missile warning and jamming equipment, and new radios. During the Gulf War of 1991, SH-2Fs tested the ML-30 Magic Lantern laser sub-surface mine detector. Two essentially similar ML-90 sets are also to be tested on SH-2s.

The SH-2F has been ordered by **Pakistan** (six aircraft, whose delivery has been halted by embargo), and has been offered to Egypt, Greece, South Korea, Portugal, Taiwan and Thailand. In Portugal and Korea the aircraft lost out to Westland's Super Lynx while Greece and Taiwan already have orders for the SH-60. Orders may still materialise from the other countries. The US Navy has already discovered the versatility and adaptability of the Seasprite airframe, and retired SH-2Fs, especially if brought up to SH-2G standards, would represent an excellent buy for many customers. The aircraft combines compact external dimensions, a rugged, dependable airframe and good handling characteristics.

This SH-2F of HSL-34 wears the high-visibility colour scheme associated with the SH-2F until very recently. No active-duty squadrons now fly the SH-2F, which has become a rare bird in US skies.

Many, but by no means all, SH-2Fs received an overall light grey tactical colour scheme in recent years. The SH-2F has already been ordered by Pakistan (whose aircraft are now embargoed) and may attract orders from other countries. In US service, the SH-2F is rapidly giving way to the re-engined and updated SH-2G. The original shape engine pods are clearly evident.

SPECIFICATION

Kaman SH-2F Seasprite
generally similar to the SH-2G Super Seasprite (see following page) except in the following particulars:

Rotor system: main rotor diameter 44 ft 0 in (13.41 m); tail rotor diameter 8 ft 2 in (2.49 m); main rotor disc area 1,520.53 sq ft (141.26 m²); tail rotor disc area 52.38 sq ft (4.87 m²)
Fuselage and tail: length overall, rotors turning 52 ft 7 in (16.03 m); height overall, rotors turning 15 ft 6 in (4.72 m) and to top of rotor head 13 ft 5 in (4.09 m); wheel base 16 ft 9 in (5.11 m)
Powerplant: two General Electric T58-GE-8F turboshafts each rated at 1,350 shp (1007 kW)
Weights: empty 7,040 lb (3193 kg); maximum normal take-off 12,800 lb (5805 kg); maximum overload take-off 13,300 lb (6033 kg)
Fuel and load: external fuel up to two 60-US gal (227-litre) auxiliary tanks; maximum ordnance 1,200 lb (544 kg)
Speed: maximum level speed 'clean' at sea level 143 kt (165 mph; 265 km/h); normal cruising speed 130 kt (150 mph; 241 km/h)
Range: maximum range 366 nm (422 miles: 679 km)
Performance: maximum rate of climb at sea level 2,440 ft (774 m) per minute; service ceiling 22,500 ft (6860 m); hovering ceiling 18,600 ft (5670 m) in ground effect and 15,400 ft (4695 m) out of ground effect

Kaman **SH-2G Seasprite**

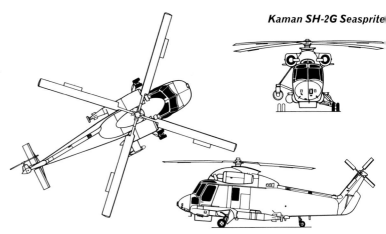

Continued development of Kaman's versatile **Seasprite** helicopter resulted in the appearance of the **SH-2G**. The prototype **YSH-2G**, which first flew on 2 April 1985, was simply a conversion of an **SH-2F** and served as a T700 engine testbed. This was the main modification from SH-2F standard, the SH-2G adopting a pair of General Electric T700-GE-701 turboshaft engines in lieu of the SH-2F's original T58-GE-8Fs. These deliver approximately 10 per cent more power, with commensurate performance benefits and 20 per cent lower fuel burn (allowing increased range), as well as improved reliability and maintainability. In addition, new composite main rotor blades with a service life of 10,000 hours are fitted.

Avionics improvements include MIL-STD 1553 digital databus, AN/UYS-503 onboard acoustic processor, AN/ASN-150 tactical management system and multi-function displays. The SH-2G is expected to retain the package of avionics modifications applied to 16 SH-2Fs for operations in the Gulf, including AN/ALQ-144 IR jammers, AN/AAR-47 missile warning equipment, AN/AAQ-16 FLIR, secure UHF/VHF radios and Magic Lantern laser equipment for sub-surface mine detection.

The SH-2G is also qualified for dipping sonar operations, ASM firing, FLIR sensors, rockets, guns (a 7.62-mm machine-gun may be pintle-mounted in each cabin doorway) and countermeasures. The Mk 50 lightweight aerial torpedo is expected to supersede the Mk 46 weapon currently in service. Two torpedoes may be carried, but a single example is more common. Mk 25 marine smoke markers are also carried in a compartment under the nose and are used to give crew members visual reference when prosecuting a sub-surface contact.

The first flight with full avionics occurred on 28 December 1989 and was followed by deliveries of six new-build examples ordered in FY 1987. The first production SH-2G was flown in March 1990. No further new production is planned and it is envisaged to retrospectively modernise more than 90 existing SH-2Fs to SH-2G standard, with 24 conversion kits ordered by January 1992. These will now serve with two **US Navy Reserve** light anti-submarine warfare helicopter squadrons, HSL-84 at North Island and HSL-94 at Willow Grove, the Seasprite having been prematurely retired from active-duty use in early 1994 as a result of defence cuts. The Seasprite's long term future is uncertain, since reductions in the HSL community may free up sufficient SH-60B airframes to re-equip the two units.

SPECIFICATION

Kaman SH-2G Super Seasprite
Rotor system: main rotor diameter 44 ft 4 in (13.51 m); tail rotor diameter 8 ft 1 in (2.46 m); main rotor disc area 1,543.66 sq ft (143.41 m²); tail rotor disc area 51.32 sq ft (4.77 m²)
Fuselage and tail: length overall, rotors turning 52 ft 9 in (16.08 m), fuselage excluding tail rotor 40 ft 0 in (12.19 m), and with nose and blades folded 38 ft 4 in (11.68 m); height overall, rotors turning 15 ft 0.5 in (4.58 m), and with blades folded 13 ft 7 in (4.14 m); stabiliser span 9 ft 9 in (2.97 m); wheel track 10 ft 10 in (3.30 m); wheel base 16 ft 10 in (5.13 m)
Powerplant: two General Electric T700-GE-401/401C turboshafts each rated at 1,723 shp (1285 kW)
Weights: empty 7,680 lb (3483 kg); maximum take-off 13,500 lb (6123 kg)
Fuel and load: internal fuel 276 US gal (1045 litres); external fuel up to two 100-US gal (379-litre) auxiliary tanks; maximum payload 4,000 lb (1814 kg)
Speed: maximum level speed 'clean' at sea level 138 kt (159 mph; 256 km/h); normal cruising speed 120 kt (138 mph; 222 km/h)
Range: maximum range 478 nm (500 miles; 885 km) with two auxiliary tanks; operational radius 35 nm (40 miles; 65 km) for a patrol of 2 hours 10 minutes with one torpedo or of 1 hour 30 minutes with two torpedoes; endurance 5 hours with two auxiliary tanks

Performance: maximum rate of climb at sea level 2,500 ft (762 m) per minute; service ceiling 23,900 ft (7285 m); hovering ceiling 20,800 ft (6340 m) in ground effect and 18,000 ft (5485 m) out of ground effect

The SH-2G is immediately recognisable by its redesigned engine nacelles, housing T700 turboshafts.

Kaman **K-MAX (MMIRA)**

Kaman's **K-MAX** was developed as a private venture for military and civil applications. The K-MAX was initially dubbed **Multi-Mission Intermeshing Rotor Aircraft** (MMIRA) and was designed primarily for the logging role and other external medium/heavylift missions, replacing Kaman's previous H-43 Huskie. First flown on 23 December 1991, it retains the classic Kaman configuration with two intermeshing 'teetering' rotors with Kaman's patented aerodynamic servo-flap rotor control. The transmission is based on the proven design from the H-43, although production gearboxes are taken from the higher power transmission of Kaman's SH-2 naval helicopter due to the K-MAX's greater power on/off cycles. Optimised for single-pilot operations, the prototype K-MAX is powered by a derated Textron Lycoming T53 turboshaft and can lift a 6,000-lb (2722-kg) external load out of ground effect at 8,000 ft (2438 m). Possible military missions include surveillance, communications, resupply and ordnance delivery, and the design is optimised for unpiloted drone operation and to be readily 'scaleable' for larger or smaller size.

SPECIFICATION

Kaman K-Max (MMIRA)
Rotor system: rotor diameter, each 47 ft 0 in (14.32 m); rotor disc area, total 3,469.89 sq ft (322.35 m²)
Fuselage and tail: length overall, rotors turning 50 ft 6 in (15.39 m); wheel track 11 ft 4 in (3.44 m)
Powerplant: one 1,800-shp (1343-kW) Textron Lycoming T5317A turboshaft flat-rated at 1,500 shp (1119 kW) for take-off and 1,340 shp (1007 kW) for continuous running
Weights: operating empty 4,100 lb (1859 kg); normal take-off 6,000 lb (2722 kg) without jettisonable load; maximum take-off 10,500 lb (4762 kg) with jettisonable load
Fuel and load: internal fuel 1,541 lb (699 kg); external fuel none; maximum payload 6,000 lb (2722 kg)
Performance: target hovering ceiling 8,000 ft (2440 m) out of ground effect with a 5,000-lb (2268-kg) slung load and fuel for 1 hour 30 minutes

The K-Max is suitable for a range of military roles, and can be flown as a manned helicopter or as a drone. Note the intermeshing rotors.

Kamov Ka-25 'Hormone'

Helicopter Scientific and Technology Complex named after N.I. Kamov
March 8th St
Lubertsy 14007, Moscow, Russia

The Ka-25 family of shipborne helicopters was the aircraft which put Nikolai Kamov's contra-rotating co-axial rotor configuration 'on the map'. The lack of an anti-torque tail rotor brought benefits of lightness and simplicity, and the co-axial rotors made possible a smaller overall rotor diameter. Designed to meet a 1957 **Soviet navy** requirement for a new shipborne ASW helicopter, the first member of the family was the Ka-20 'Harp', which initially flew during 1960 and which formed the basis of the operational 'Hormone'. The production **Ka-25BSh 'Hormone-A'** was of almost identical size and appearance, but was fitted with operational equipment and uprated 900-shp (671-kW) GTD-3F engines (from 1973 replaced by 990-shp/736-kW GTD-3Ms). It entered service in 1967.

Although the lower part of the fuselage is sealed and watertight, the Ka-25 is not intended for amphibious operations, and flotation bags are often fitted to the undercarriage for use in the event of an emergency landing on the water. The cabin is adequate for the job, but is not tall enough to allow the crew to stand upright. Progressive additions of new equipment have made the interior more cluttered. Primary sensors for the ASW mission are the I/J-band radar (NATO 'Big Bulge'), OKA-2 dipping sonar, a downward-looking 'Tie Rod' electro-optical sensor in the tailboom, and a MAD sensor, either in a recess in the rear part of the cabin or in a fairing sometimes fitted below the central of the three tailfins. A box-like sonobuoy launcher can also be scabbed on to the starboard side of the rear fuselage. Dye-markers or smoke floats can also be carried externally. Comprehensive avionics, defensive and navigation systems are fitted.

Armament is not normally carried, although the helicopter can be fitted with a long 'coffin-like' weapons bay which runs

A 'Hormone-B' with wheels retracted out of the way of the radar scan pattern. The round-bottomed radome is a distinctive recognition feature.

along the belly from the radome back to the tailboom, and small bombs or depth charges can be carried on tiny pylons just aft of the nosewheels. The underfuselage weapons bay can carry a variety of weapons, including nuclear depth charges. When wire-guided torpedoes are carried, a wire reel is mounted on the port side of the forward fuselage.

It has been estimated that some 260 of the 450 or so Ka-25s produced were 'Hormone-As', but only a handful remains, fulfilling secondary roles. Although the Ka-25BSh has been withdrawn from front-line use by the navies of the former USSR, small numbers were exported to **India**, **Syria**, **Vietnam** and former **Yugoslavia**, and most of these aircraft remain in use.

The second Ka-25 variant identified in the West was given the NATO reporting name **'Hormone-B'**, but its Soviet designation remains unknown. This variant is externally identifiable by its bulbous (instead of flat-bottomed) undernose radome and small (datalink?) radome under the rear fuselage. This is believed to have been used for acquiring targets and providing mid-course missile guidance, for ship- and submarine-launched SS-N-3 'Shaddock' and SS-N-12 'Sandbox' missiles. It may also allow the 'Hormone-B' to fulfil a secondary AEW role. On the 'Hormone-B' only, the four undercarriage units are retractable and can be lifted out of the scanning pattern of the radar. Today, modern missiles do not usually require mid-course guidance and targeting is usually achieved from greater stand-off ranges, often using long-range fixed-wing aircraft. The 'Hormone-B' thus has no direct replacement, and has been withdrawn from use in its primary role.

The final version of the Ka-25 is the **Ka-25PS**, allocated the NATO reporting name **'Hormone-C'**. Almost certainly converted from redundant 'Hormone-A' airframes, the Ka-25PS is best known as a search and rescue aircraft, although some sources suggest that it initially had a missile guidance role, operating in conjunction with 'Hormone-Bs'. Stripped of ASW systems, the Ka-25PS can carry a practical load of

freight or up to 12 passengers, making it a useful ship-to-ship or ship-to-shore transport and vertrep platform. A quadruple Yagi antenna (NATO 'Home Guard') fitted to many aircraft is reportedly used for homing onto the personal locator beacons carried by aircrew. Most Ka-25PSs also have searchlights, and a 300-kg (660-lb) capacity rescue winch. The Ka-25PS has largely been replaced by SAR versions of the Ka-27 'Helix'.

SPECIFICATION

Kamov Ka-25BSh 'Hormone-A'
Rotor system: rotor diameter, each 15.74 m (52 ft 7.75 in); rotor disc area, total 389.15 m² (4,188.93 sq ft)
Fuselage and tail: length of fuselage 9.75 m (32 ft 0 in); height overall 5.37 m (17 ft 7.5 in); stabiliser span 3.76 m (12 ft 4 in) including endplate surfaces; wheel track 1.41 m (4 ft 7.5 in) for the front unit and 3.52 m (11 ft 6.5 in) for the rear unit
Powerplant: two OMKB 'Mars' (Glushenkov) GTD-3F

A Ka-25BSh 'Hormone-A' stripped of ASW equipment and flotation gear for the COD role, carrying 12 passengers.

turboshafts each rated at 671 kW (898 shp) in early helicopters, or two OMKB 'Mars' (Glushenkov) GTD-3BM each rated at 738 kW (900 shp) in late helicopters
Weights: empty 4765 kg (10,505 lb); maximum take-off 7500 kg (16,534 lb)
Fuel and load: maximum payload 1300 kg (2,866 lb)
Speed: maximum level speed 'clean' at optimum altitude 209 km/h (113 kt; 130 mph); normal cruising speed at optimum altitude 193 km/h (104 kt; 120 mph)
Range: ferry range 650 km (351 nm; 404 miles) with auxiliary fuel; range 400 km (216 nm; 249 miles) with standard fuel

A Ka-25PS 'Hormone-C' search and rescue helicopter. The ventral pannier can be extended downwards by the addition of a bulged stores bay. Smoke floats and searchlights can be fitted.

Kamov Ka-26 'Hoodlum'

The **Ka-26 'Hoodlum-A'** was designed primarily as a multi-role civilian helicopter, and has been adapted for agricultural, firefighting, medevac, survey and light SAR duties. This versatility is largely a result of the helicopter's unusual configuration. The fully enclosed two-seat cabin is attached to a shallow upper fuselage which carries the rotor mast and two very short stub wings (or, perhaps more accurately, pylons) which carry the two Vedeneyev M14V-26 radial engines. Two slender tailbooms extend aft from this, carrying the tailplane and two massive endplate tailfins

and rudders. The resulting space below the rotor mast, between the engines and aft of the cockpit, can carry a variety of pods for passengers, stretchers or cargo, or a hopper for agricultural spraying, or a rescue hoist.

About 850 Ka-26s have been built, plus turbine-engined **Ka-126s** (described separately) built by IAR in Romania, but only a small handful have been procured by military customers, mainly for use in the liaison or border patrol roles. The type may be in service in **Benin**, **Bulgaria** and the **CIS**.

One of Hungary's Ka-26s. The type is still in military service in Bulgaria, and perhaps also in Benin and the CIS. Hungary is understood to have recently retired the last of its 'Hoodlums'.

Kamov Ka-26 'Hoodlum'

SPECIFICATION

Kamov Ka-26 'Hoodlum-A'
Rotor system: rotor diameter, each 13.00 m (42 ft 8 in); rotor disc area, total 265.5 m² (2,857.5 sq ft)
Fuselage and tail: length of fuselage 7.75 m (25 ft 5 in); height overall 4.05 m (13 ft 3.5 in) to top of rotor head; stabiliser span 4.60 m (15 ft 1 in); wheel track

0.90 m (2 ft 11.5 in) for front unit and 2.42 m (7 ft 11.5 in) for rear unit; wheel base 3.48 m (11 ft 5 in)
Powerplant: two VMKB (Vedeneyev) M-14V-26 air-cooled radial piston engines each rated at 242.5 kW (325 hp)
Weights: operating empty 1950 kg (4,299 lb) stripped, or 2085 kg (4,597 lb) for the freight role with cargo platform, or 2050 kg (4,519 lb) for the freight role with cargo sling, or 2100 kg (4,630 lb) for the

passenger role; normal take-off 3076 kg (6,781 lb) for the transport role; maximum take-off 3250 kg (7,165 lb)
Fuel and load: internal fuel 100 kg (220 lb) plus provision for 260 kg (573 lb) of auxiliary fuel; external fuel none; maximum payload 1100 kg (2,425 lb)
Speed: maximum level speed at optimum altitude 170 km/h (91 kt; 105 mph); maximum cruising speed at optimum altitude 150 km/h (81 kt; 93 mph); economical cruising speed at optimum altitude

between 110 and 90 km/h (59 and 49 kt; 68 and 56 mph) depending on role
Range: ferry range 1200 km (648 nm; 746 miles) with auxiliary fuel; range 400 km (215 nm; 248 miles) with standard fuel and seven passengers; endurance 3 hours 42 minutes
Performance: service ceiling 3000 m (9,845 ft); hovering ceiling 1300 m (4,265 ft) in ground effect and 800 m (2,625 ft) out of ground effect

Kamov **Ka-27/Ka-28/Ka-32 'Helix'**

Work on the Ka-27 family began in 1969, with Sergei Mikheyev taking over as chief designer after the death of Nikolai Kamov. A totally new design, the Ka-27 retains Kamov's proven coaxial contra-rotating rotor configuration, and has similar overall dimensions to the Ka-25. The availability of a new engine, Isotov's 2,000-shp (1486-kW) TV3, allowed the rotor to absorb double the power output without increasing the diameter or number of blades, but using new methods of construction, a new blade profile and greater blade area. This produced a much larger, more capable helicopter which uses the same amount of deck space as its predecessor, and which can use the same hangars, deck lifts, etc.

The first production variant was the **Ka-27PL 'Helix-A'**, which is the basic ASW version, designed as a replacement for the Ka-25BSh. The prototype made its maiden flight during December 1974, and operational evaluation began in late 1981. The aircraft has a larger fuselage than that of the Ka-25, and incorporates more composite materials and advanced alloys. The lower part of the fuselage is again sealed for buoyancy, and extra flotation equipment can be fitted in boxes on the lower part of the centre fuselage.

The aircraft usually carries a crew of three, with a pilot, navigator and observer or hoist operator behind. The Ka-27 is extremely stable and easy to fly, and automatic height hold, auto transition to and from the hover and autohover are possible in all wind conditions. The Ka-27PL has all the usual ASW and ESM equipment, including dipping sonar and sonobuoys (now carried inside the cabin) and with a new undernose radome housing a shallow rectangular scanner.

The civilian **Ka-32S** is basically similar, using its radar for SAR and ice reconnaissance duties. The borderline between military and civilian variants is not very clear, and some nominally civilian 'Aeroflot' aircraft have been seen operating from Soviet navy warships, while some obviously military aircraft have been exhibited wearing Ka-32 titles.

Export versions of the basic Ka-27PL are designated **Ka-28** and have been sold to **India** and **Yugoslavia**. Further military variants of the Ka-27 are optimised for the search and rescue role and include what appears to be a military version of the simplified civil **Ka-32T 'Helix-C'**, similarly lacking undernose radome but with flotation gear, external fuel tanks and a rescue winch.

The main SAR variant is the radar-equipped **Ka-27PS 'Helix-D'**. This almost inevitably carries external fuel tanks and flotation gear (seldom seen on Soviet 'Helix-As', but sometimes fitted to Ka-28s). A hydraulically-operated 300-kg (660-lb) capacity rescue winch is fitted above the cabin door, with associated downward-pointing floodlights under the port side of the nose and rear cabin. Directional ESM and IFF is

The Ka-28 is a downgraded export version of the Ka-27PL 'Helix-A' used by India, and also delivered to Yugoslavia (seen here).

A Ka-27PL seen without auxiliary tanks and flotation gear. It lacks the bulged pilot's window of late-production and export Ka-28s.

retained, but other operational equipment is deleted. An unidentified box-like fairing, with two protruding spherical objects, is carried below the end of the tailboom, aft of the gyro magnetic heads and Doppler box.

SPECIFICATION

Kamov Ka-27PL 'Helix-A'
Rotor system: rotor diameter, each 15.90 m (52 ft 2 in); rotor disc area, total 397.11 m² (4,274.63 sq ft)
Fuselage and tail: length of fuselage 11.30 m (37 ft 0.9 in) and with rotors folded 12.25 m (40 ft 2.25 in); height overall 5.40 m (17 ft 8.6 in) to top of rotor head; wheel track 1.40 m (4 ft 7 in) for the front unit and 3.50 m (11 ft 5.75 in) for the rear unit; wheel base 3.02 m (9 ft 11 in)
Powerplant: two Klimov (Isotov) TV3-117V turboshafts each rated at 1645 kW (2,205 shp)
Weights: basic empty 6100 kg (13,338 lb); operating empty 6500 kg (14,330 lb); normal take-off 11000 kg (24,251 lb); maximum take-off 12600 kg (27,778 lb)
Fuel and load: maximum payload 5000 kg (11,023 lb)
Speed: maximum level speed 'clean' at optimum altitude 250 km/h (135 kt; 155 mph); maximum cruising speed at optimum altitude 230 km/h (124 kt; 143 mph)
Range: ferry range 800 km (432 nm; 497 miles) with auxiliary fuel; endurance 4 hours 30 minutes
Performance: service ceiling 5000 m (16,405 ft); hovering ceiling 3500 m (11,485 ft) out of ground effect

Right: The Ka-27PS 'Helix-D' is a dedicated naval SAR aircraft.

Kamov **Ka-29TB 'Helix-B'/Ka-29RLD**

The **Ka-29TB** (Transportno Boyevoya) is a dedicated assault transport derivative of the Ka-27/Ka-32 family, intended especially for the support of **Russian navy** amphibious operations and featuring a substantially changed airframe. The first example was seen on the assault ship *Ivan Rogov* in 1987 and was initially assumed to be designated Ka-27B. The NATO reporting name **'Helix-B'** was allocated. Many of the new variants went unnoticed, and it was initially thought to be a minimum-change non-radar version of the basic Ka-27PL.

In fact, the Ka-29TB features an entirely new, much widened forward fuselage, with a flight deck seating three crew side-by-side, one of these acting as a gunner to aim the various rockets carried on the aircraft's braced pylons, and the four-barrelled 7.62-mm cannon hidden behind an articulated door on the starboard side of the nose. The location of the braced pylons precludes the fitting of external fuel tanks or flotation gear. The two-piece curved windscreen of the Ka-27 has given way to a five-piece unit, with three main flat plates at the front and two smaller, slightly blown quarterlights.

A long, braced, air data boom projects forward from the port side of the nose, which is painted black, and which may one day become some kind of radome. Under the nose the Ka-29TB has an electro-optical sensor to starboard and a missile guidance/illuminating radar pod to port, both being similar to devices seen on the Mil Mi-24 'Hind'. The EO sensor is probably a combined FLIR and low-light TV, and the radome is probably associated with the AT-6 'Spiral' missile. An ammunition link ejection chute is located under the nose farther to starboard. Another similarity with the Mil Mi-24 is the replacement of the original sliding cabin door with a horizontally-divided, outward-hinging two-piece door, and the provision of an IRCM jammer on the top of the fuselage/engine fairing.

The basic Ka-29TB airframe also serves as the basis for the **Ka-29RLD**, first seen during carrier trials aboard the *Kuznetsov*, for which a NATO reporting name has not yet been allocated. The two aircraft seen both wore Aeroflot titles, though one of them sported a two-tone grey camouflage scheme. The wider cabin section extends further back (to the rear undercarriage oleo) and ends more abruptly.

Both aircraft are fitted with a huge ventral pannier, which begins just aft of the black-painted nosecone and extends aft along the full length of the cabin, across virtually the full width of the fuselage. The APU seems to be relocated above the engine fairing, with an intake forward and an intake (pointing to starboard) aft. Both aircraft have a new narrow cabin door on the starboard side, just aft of the flight deck. This is horizontally divided and the lower section incorporates a built-in airstair. A square-shaped fairing replaces the window on the upper half.

Large rectangular panniers, of about the same cross-section as the standard flotation gear boxes but extending farther forward (past the nose gear) and aft to the main undercarriage, are fitted to the lower part of the cabin sides. One aircraft had further panniers mounted slightly higher aft of the main undercarriage. Finally, the aircraft has unidentified equipment within a tubular box-like structure mounted on the rear face of the cabin underside.

Despite their Aeroflot markings, these aircraft almost certainly represent the prototypes or development aircraft of a new ship-board AEW platform with planar array radar antennas in the ventral fairing. They are unlikely to retain the armament of the Ka-29TB.

Above: This Ka-29TB is armed with rocket pods and the unusual retractable nose cannon. A missile guidance pod is visible undernose.

Below: The Ka-29RLD has panniers on each side of the fuselage and below the cabin, perhaps containing a planar array radar antenna.

SPECIFICATION

Kamov Ka-29TB 'Helix-B'
generally similar to the Ka-27PL 'Helix-A' except in the following particulars:
Fuselage and tail: wheel base 3.00 m (9 ft 10 in)
Powerplant: two Klimov (Isotov) TV3-117VK turboshafts each rated at 1660 kW (2,226 shp)
Weights: basic empty 5520 kg (12,170 lb)
Speed: maximum level speed 'clean' at sea level 265 km/h (143 kt; 165 mph)
Range: 520 km (280 nm; 322 miles)

Kamov **Ka-50 'Hokum'**

Design of the **Ka-50 'Hokum'** began in 1977 under the direction of Sergei Mikheyev, designer general since 1974. The aircraft was developed as a rival to the Mil Mi-28 in the competition to provide a battlefield attack helicopter for the **Soviet armed forces**. This competition was provoked by the emergence of a new generation of Western battlefield helicopters and represented Kamov's second attempt to produce a land-based attack helicopter, the Ka-25F of 1966 having lost out to the Mil Mi-24. While Mil decided to follow the same overall philosophy as the McDonnell Douglas AH-64 Apache, Kamov worked out its own concept.

Realising that it would be difficult to achieve AH-64 levels of performance with Soviet heavyweight technology and equipment, and believing that Hughes (later McDonnell Douglas Helicopters) had got it wrong in some important respects, Kamov followed an individualistic course. Although the coaxial contra-rotating rotor had become something of a Kamov trademark, the design bureau explored other configurations but quickly came to the conclusion that the advantages of the layout outweighed any disadvantages. Much better agility, reduced vulnerability, compact airframe, benign handling characteristics, a lack of rpm limitations, the ability to take off and land regardless of wind speed and direction, and lower power losses were the crucial factors, while the disadvantages of difficult design problems could be solved by the bureau's considerable experience with the configuration (and probably by no other helicopter company). The conventional single rotor and anti-torque tail rotor configuration was not considered by Kamov, who felt it to be unacceptably vulnerable.

Kamov anticipated problems in keeping weight down, since heavier armour, more powerful armament and advanced sensors would all be required. As a strategic imperative, Kamov decided to work towards meeting the requirement with a single-seat helicopter, using their experience of automated systems on their naval helicopters, which had sophisticated autoland, autohover and even automatic formation flying equipment, together with datalinks for exchanging tactical information between aircraft and ships. Similar systems would clearly be useful in allowing a single-seat battlefield helicopter to operate successfully.

The single-pilot cockpit was successfully demonstrated on the testbench, and in a modified Ka-29TB. Early links with the Sukhoi OKB led to much interchange of ideas, especially concerning the Su-25 ground attack aircraft. At one stage the idea of adapting the Su-25 cockpit for the new helicopter was seriously considered, but eventually rejected. The first prototype made its maiden flight on 27 July 1982, before its rival, under the designation **V.80**. The competitive evaluation ended in October 1986 and the Ka-50 was selected in preference to the Mil Mi-28 due to its better agility, longer missile range, greater ammunition load, heavier armour and more accurate weapons delivery.

Mil's political influence, coupled with widespread lack of faith in the single-pilot concept, led to a three-phase competition that the Ka-50 won at every stage, although in late 1992 Mil still expected an army order of some sort for their helicopter. The first photographs of the Ka-50 were not released officially until early 1992, although the existence of the aircraft had been known since 1984, and Western analysts had produced some surprisingly accurate artist's impressions. The aircraft made a flypast at the

The unarmed third prototype (in silver finish) Ka-50 is seen in company with the much later Werewolf demonstrator, painted black for its role in a feature film.

August 1992 Moscow Aeroshow, but the first opportunity to study the aircraft was not afforded until September, when a Ka-50 was displayed statically at Farnborough.

The tube-launched, laser-beam-riding Vikhr (NATO AT-9 'Whirlwind') missile has a shaped-charge fragmentation warhead and both proximity and contact fuses, and is capable of penetrating reactive armour up to 900 mm (35 inches) thick. Its range exceeds that of most anti-aircraft systems, and it has proved extremely effective in trials. Sixteen can be carried and the proximity fuse and fragmentation jacket make it suit-

Kamov Ka-50 'Hokum'

able as a last-resort air-to-air weapon, although dedicated AAMs can also be carried. The missiles can be augmented by AS-12 'Kegler' guided missiles or by up to 80 unguided S-8 80-mm rockets in four B-8 pods, by a variety of bombs and by the built-in 30-mm 2A42 cannon. Developed for the BMP AFV, the gun has variable rates of fire and selective feed from two 250-round ammunition boxes (which can be separately loaded with armour-piercing and explosive rounds, allowing the pilot to select the type of ammunition he wishes to fire simply by selecting the correct box) and is extremely resistant to jamming, even in the dusty conditions encountered by armoured personnel carriers, let alone low-flying helicopters.

The gun is installed on the starboard side

of the fuselage, below the wingroot, this location being as close as possible to the helicopter's centre of gravity, and in the strongest and most rigid location to minimise the effect of recoil and to give the greatest possible accuracy. The gun is electro-hydraulically driven and can be traversed through 30° in elevation, and can also move 15° in azimuth.

Combat survivability is enhanced by infra-red suppressors in the exhausts, heavily armoured pressurised cockpit, foam-filled, self-sealing fuel tanks, and by the small size and compactness of the transmission and control systems by comparison with conventional helicopters, and by detailed features like the wide-diameter control rods, two-contour rotor blade spars and a high

degree of systems redundancy. Wingtip pods house Vympel UV-26 chaff/flare dispensers. In the event of a catastrophic hit, the pilot can use his Severin/Zvezda K-37 ejection seat. The ejection sequence begins with automatic rotor blade separation, then the doors blow off and a rocket pack extracts the seat.

SPECIFICATION

Kamov Ka-50 Werewolf 'Hokum'
Rotor system: rotor diameter, each 14.50 m (45 ft 6.9 in); rotor disc area, total 330.26 m² (3,555.00 sq ft)
Fuselage and tail: length overall, with rotors turning 16.00 m (52 ft 5.9 in), and fuselage excluding probe and gun 13.50 m (44 ft 3.5 in); height 5.40 m (17 ft 8.6 in)

The normal Russian land forces camouflage, as worn by Mi-8s and Mi-24s, is also applied to several of the Ka-50 prototypes. The coaxial rotors allow the aircraft to dispense with a tail rotor.

Powerplant: two Klimov (Isotov) TV3-117VK turboshafts each rated at 1660 kW (2,226 shp)
Weights: maximum take-off 7500 kg (16,534 lb)
Speed: maximum level speed 'clean' at optimum altitude 350 km/h (188 kt; 217 mph)
Range: combat radius about 250 km (135 nm; 155 miles)
Performance: maximum vertical rate of climb at 2500 m (8,200 ft) 600 m (1,969 ft) per minute; hovering ceiling 4000 m (13,125 ft) out of ground effect

Kamov (IAR) Ka-126 'Hoodlum-B'

A Ka-126 in Aeroflot colours. Military use of this IAR-built helicopter is uncertain, though the type clearly has potential to fulfil some more martial roles.

A multi-role light helicopter with both military and civil applications, the **Kamov Ka-126 'Hoodlum-B'** is a turbine-powered derivative of the **Kamov Ka-26** (described separately). A prototype was flown in the Soviet Union in 1986, followed by the first of a four-aircraft pre-production batch in October 1988. Production was assigned to the IAR factory at Brasov, Romania, where one of the pre-production aircraft was assembled and first flew on 31 December 1988. Orders for 1,000 were expected from the USSR, but only 12 were contracted before the collapse of the Soviet Union, and some unresolved problems with engine vibrations effectively brought the programme to an end. The first production aircraft flew in Romania on 14 February

1989. Seven Ka-126s had been delivered by IAR to Kamov by June 1992, with a few others then under construction at Brasov. Military use is uncertain.

SPECIFICATION

Kamov (IAR) Ka-126 'Hoodlum-B'
generally similar to the Kamov Ka-26 'Hoodlum-A' except in the following particulars:
Fuselage and tail: length of fuselage 7.775 m (25 ft 5.25 in); height overall 4.155 m (13 ft 7.5 in) to top of rotor head; stabiliser span 3.224 m (10 ft 7 in); wheel track 2.56 m (8 ft 4.75 in) for rear unit; wheel base 3.479 m (11 ft 5 in)
Powerplant: one OMKB 'Mars' (Glushenkov) TVD-100 turboshaft rated at 537 kW (720 shp)

Weights: maximum take-off 3250 kg (7,165 lb)
Fuel and load: internal fuel 800 litres (211 US gal); external fuel none; maximum payload 1000 kg (2,205 lb)
Speed: maximum level speed at optimum altitude 180 km/h (97 kt; 112 mph); maximum cruising speed at

optimum altitude 160 km/h (86 kt; 99 mph)
Range: range 650 km (351 nm; 404 miles) with standard fuel; endurance 4 hours 30 minutes
Performance: service ceiling 3800 m (12,470 ft); hovering ceiling 1000 m (3,280 ft) out of ground effect

Kawasaki C-1

*Kawasaki Heavy Industries Ltd
1-18 Nakamachi-Dori, 2-chome, Chuo-Ku
Kobe, Japan*

With a requirement to replace Curtiss C-46 Commando transport aircraft then in service, the **Japan Air Self-Defence Force** drew up its C-X specification for an indigenous replacement for a medium-sized troop and freight transport in the early 1970s. Nihon Aeroplane Manufacturing Company began its design in 1966, and even before approval of the full-size mock-up the company was contracted to build two **XC-1** flying prototypes plus a static test airframe. The first of the prototypes, assembled by Kawasaki, made its maiden flight on 12 November 1970, and the flight test programme of both prototypes was

completed by the Japan Defence Agency in March 1973. Following construction of two pre-production aircraft, a first contract was placed for 11 production **Kawasaki C-1** transports.

The C-1 is of conventional modern military transport design, featuring a high-wing monoplane configuration to maximise cabin volume, a fuselage with pressurised and air-conditioned flight deck and cabin/cargo hold, and a rear-loading ramp door which can be opened in flight. The landing gear is of retractable tricycle type, and the aircraft's two turbofan engines are pylon-mounted beneath the wings. The C-1 is operated by a

flight crew of five, and typical loads include 60 fully-equipped troops or 45 paratroops, up to 36 stretchers with attendants, and a variety of equipment or palletised cargo.

A collaborative project, the C-1 was built by Fuji (outer wings), Mitsubishi (centre/aft fuselage/tail surfaces), and Nihon (control surfaces/engine pods), with Kawasaki responsible for forward fuselage, wing centre-section, final assembly and testing. Production of the C-1 totalled 31 examples, including the four prototype/pre-production aircraft, with the last delivery on 21 October 1981. Although built to JASDF requirements, the C-1's maximum payload of

11900 kg (26,266 lb) limited its value and plans for variants did not materialise. The C-1 currently equips two squadrons (*hikotai*) of Support Command, JASDF, comprising the 402nd at Iruma and 403rd at Miho.

A C-1 airframe has been used by the JDA as a flying testbed for the MITI/NAL FJR-710 and Ishikawajima-Harima XF3 turbofan engines, the latter powering the T-4 trainer. More recently, Kawasaki has modified one as a **C-1Kai** ECM trainer, giving it a flat bulbous nose and tail radomes, an indigenous ALQ-5 ECM system and antennas beneath the fuselage. This serves alongside YS-11Es with the 501st Hikotai of the Electronic

Warfare Training Unit at Iruma. Proposed variants for inflight refuelling, electronic warfare, weather reconnaissance and mine-laying remained stillborn, as did a larger-capacity transport with a stretched fuselage. One aircraft served as the basis for the **NAL Asuka** (described separately), a dedicated quiet STOL testbed which flew with overwing engines and blown flaps.

SPECIFICATION

Kawasaki C-1

Wing: span 30.60 m (100 ft 4.75 in); aspect ratio 7.8; area 120.50 m² (1,297.09 sq ft)

Fuselage and tail: length 29.00 m (95 ft 1.75 in); height 9.99 m (32 ft 9.25 in); tailplane span 11.30 m (37 ft 1 in); wheel track 4.40 m (14 ft 5.25 in); wheel base 9.33 m (30 ft 7.75 in)

Powerplant: two Mitsubishi-built Pratt & Whitney JT8D-M-9 turbofans each rated at 14,500 lb st (64.50 kN) and fitted with thrust reversers

Weights: empty equipped 24300 kg (53,571 lb); normal take-off 38700 kg (85,317 lb); maximum take-off 45000 kg (99,206 lb)

Fuel and load: internal fuel 15200 litres (4,015 US gal); external fuel none; maximum payload 11900 kg (26,235 lb)

Speed: maximum level speed 'clean' at 25,000 ft (7620 m) 435 kt (501 mph; 806 km/h); maximum cruising speed at 35,000 ft (10670 m) 380 kt (438 mph; 704 km/h); economical cruising speed at 35,000 ft (10670 m) 355 kt (409 mph; 658 km/h)

Range: 1,810 nm (2,084 miles; 3353 km) with maximum fuel and a 2200-kg (4,850-lb) payload, or 700 nm (806 miles; 1297 km) with a 7900-kg (17,416-lb) payload

Performance: maximum rate of climb at sea level 3,495 ft (1065 m) per minute; service ceiling 38,000 ft (11580 m); take-off run 2,100 ft (640 m) at maximum take-off weight; take-off distance to 50 ft (15 m) 3,000 ft (914 m) at maximum take-off weight; landing distance from 50 ft (15 m) 2,700 ft (823 m) at 36860 kg (81,261 lb); landing run 1,500 ft (457 m) at 36860 kg (81,261 lb)

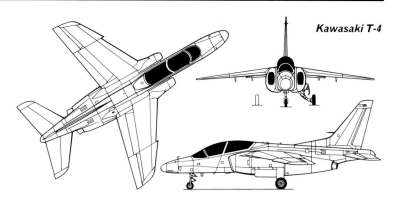

Above: A single Kawasaki C-1 was converted for the electronic warfare training role, with the indigenous TRDI/Mitsubishi XJ/ALQ-5 ECM system. The aircraft has several massive dielectric fairings and radomes.

Right: One of the standard transport C-1s serving with 403 Hikotai at Miho, part of Support Command. C-1 transports also fly with 402 Hikotai at Iruma, each unit having a mix of C-1s and NAMC YS-11s on charge. Squadron markings are carried on the tailfins of the C-1s.

Kawasaki **T-4**

With a similar high-winged configuration to the Dassault-Dornier Alpha Jet, the **Kawasaki T-4** was developed as an intermediate jet trainer (with a secondary liaison role) to replace the **JASDF**'s Lockheed T-33 and indigenous Fuji T-1A/B. Design studies were completed in 1982 and four prototypes (designated **XT-4**) were funded in 1984, the first of these making the type's maiden flight on 29 July 1985.

The T-4 is of entirely conventional design, featuring high subsonic manoeuvrability and docile handling characteristics. The tandem

The first and third T-4 prototypes in flight. The T-4 has now begun to replace the Fuji T-1 and Lockheed T-33 in the training role and as a liaison/hack aircraft.

stepped cockpits are fitted with standard dual controls and UPC (Stencel) SHIS-3J ejection seats. Visibility for instructor and pupil is excellent, with a wrap-around windscreen and a one-piece starboard-opening canopy. For the liaison role, a baggage compartment is fitted in the centre fuselage.

The T-4 is a collaborative venture, in which Fuji builds the rear fuselage, super-critical-section wings and tail unit, and Mitsubishi the centre fuselage and air intakes. Kawasaki builds only the forward fuselage, but is responsible for assembly and flight test. Virtually all components are indigenously built, and most are locally designed, including the 3,680-lb st (16.37-kN) Ishikawa-jima-Harima F3-IHI-30 turbofans. Single underwing pylons can carry a 450-litre (99-Imp gal) drop tank, and a centreline pylon can accommodate a target winch, air sampling pod, ECM pod or chaff dispenser.

Production deliveries began in September 1988 and by mid-1992 126 had been

Kawasaki T-4

ordered, and examples were in service with Nos 31 and 32 Squadrons at Hamamatsu and with some operational squadrons and wings as hacks, sometimes wearing a camouflage colour scheme.

Below: This Kawasaki T-4 wears the black panther badge of F-1-equipped 8 Hikotai, with which it serves as a hack, having replaced T-33s with F-1, F-4 and F-15 units.

Kawasaki (Boeing Vertol) KV-107

The **Boeing Vertol Model 107** tandem-rotor helicopter proved attractive for civil use in Japan, and in 1962 Kawasaki secured a manufacturing licence for the type. The first **Kawasaki (Boeing Vertol) KV-107** to be built under this arrangement was flown in May 1962, and in 1965 (following further negotiations) the Japanese company acquired from Boeing Vertol worldwide sales rights.

Since then Kawasaki has built several KV-107 versions, the **KV-107/II** range being powered by 1,250-shp (932-kW) General Electric CT58-110-1 turboshaft engines or licence-built Ishikawajima-Harima CT58-IHI-110-1 engines of similar output. The range includes the **KV-107/II-2** standard 25-passenger airline helicopter and the six/11-seat **KV-107/II-7** VIP transport. The first of the military variants was the **KV-107/II-3**, a mine countermeasures version for the **JMSDF** (two built). The **KV-107/II-4** tactical cargo/troop carrier for the **JGSDF** was more extensively produced (42 built including one fitted out as a VIP transport). This version has a strengthened floor and can accommodate 26 equipped troops on foldable seats or, alternatively, 15 casualties on stretchers. For the **JASDF** Kawasaki developed the **KV-107/II-5** long-range search and rescue helicopter (14 built) with external auxiliary fuel tanks (one each side), a domed observation window, four searchlights, a rescue hoist and an extensive nav/com system. During 1972-74 Kawasaki supplied eight aircraft to the **Swedish navy**; these are designated **Hkp 4C** and have Rolls-Royce Gnome H.1200 powerplants and Decca navigation systems installed in Sweden.

Current **KV-107/IIA** production has more powerful turboshafts for improved performance in 'hot-and-high' or VTOL oper-

ations. The range includes seven **KV-107/IIA-3**, 18 **KV-107/IIA-4** (four of them with external auxiliary fuel tanks), and 22 **KV-107/IIA-5** helicopters, these three versions being comparable respectively to the KV-107/II-3, -4 and -5. For **Saudi Arabia** Kawasaki has built one **KV-170/IIA-17** long-range passenger/cargo transport, seven **KV-107/IIA-SM-1** fire-fighters, four **KV-107/IIA-SM-2** aero-medical/rescue helicopters, two **KV-107/IIA-SM-3** transports, and three examples of the **KV-107/IIA-SM-4** air ambulance.

The Saudi aircraft still serve with the RSAF, and the Hkp 4Cs are retained by the Swedish navy's 11 Helikopterdivisionen at Berga, 12 Hkpdiv at Ronneby and 13 Hkpdiv at Säve, alongside Boeing Vertol-built aircraft. In the home country, KV-107s serve with the JASDF's Air Rescue Wing at Iruma

(with detachments), 11 Kokutai at Shimo-fusa (JMSDF), and with the JGSDF's Western Air Command at Takayubaru, 101 Hikotai (Naha), and 1 Helicopter Brigade (Kisarazu). These units are in the process of being replaced by other types, notably the Kawasaki-built CH-47J.

SPECIFICATION

Kawasaki KV-107IIA-4

Rotor system: rotor diameter, each 50 ft 0 in (15.24 m); rotor disc area, total 3,926.99 sq ft (364.82 m²)
Fuselage and tail: length overall, rotors turning 83 ft 4 in (25.40 m) and fuselage 44 ft 7 in (13.59 m); height to top of rear rotor head 16 ft 10 in (5.13 m); wheel track 12 ft 11 in (3.94 m); wheel base 24 ft 11in (7.59 m)
Powerplant: two 1,400-shp (1044-kW) General Electric CT58-140-1 or Ishikawajima-Harima (General

Electric) CT58-IHI-140-1 turboshafts each rated at 1,250 shp (932 kW) for continuous running
Weights: empty equipped 11,575 lb (5250 kg); normal take-off 19,000 lb (8618 kg); maximum take-off 21,400 lb (9706 kg)
Fuel and load: internal fuel 2,275 lb (1032 kg) plus provision for 7,835 lb (3554 kg) of auxiliary fuel in one 1,087-lb (493-kg) auxiliary and one 6,748-lb (3061-kg) extended-range tank; external fuel none; maximum payload 6,993 lb (3172 kg) at normal take-off weight
Speed: never-exceed speed 146 kt (168 mph; 270 km/h); maximum level speed at sea level 137 kt (158 mph; 254 km/h); maximum cruising speed at 5,000 ft (1525 m) 130 kt (150 mph; 241 km/h)
Range: 592 nm (682 miles; 1097 km) with auxiliary fuel; range 193 nm (222 miles; 357 km) internal fuel
Performance: maximum rate of climb at sea level 2,050 ft (625 m) per minute; service ceiling 17,000 ft (5180 m); hovering ceiling 11,700 ft (3565 m) in ground effect and 8,800 lb (2680 m) out of ground effect

This KV-107 wears the yellow and white scheme applied to JASDF aircraft, JGSDF KV-107s having dark blue undersides, yellow fuselage sides and white tops, and JMSDF aircraft being painted in dark blue and white. KV-107s also serve with the Swedish and Saudi armed forces.

Kawasaki-Boeing Vertol CH-47J Chinook

The **Kawasaki CH-47J** is Japan's licence-built version of the Boeing Vertol CH-47 Chinook (described separately). Two **Boeing CH-47C**s were delivered in 1986 to Japan, followed by a third in component form for assembly by Kawasaki. Two of these were for the **JGSDF**, and one for the **JASDF**. The first CH-47J, which is essentially similar to the advanced CH-47D standard, was subsequently delivered in late 1986.

The CH-47J filled Japan's mid-1980s HH-X requirement, which was drafted to find a replacement for the large numbers of Kawasaki-Vertol KV-107/II-5 helicopters in service with the JGSDF. An eventual requirement exists for up to 42 JGSDF Chinooks (36 ordered to date) for transport

duties and for 16 for the JASDF (all funded and ordered). Initial deliveries were made to the JGSDF's No.1 Helicopter Division (1 Heli Group) at Kisarazu and to the Air Training School's support squadron at Akeno. Twenty-three of the JGSDF aircraft had been delivered by the beginning of 1994. The Japanese Air Self-Defence Force has already received 15 CH-47Js for SAR duties and for the logistics support of remote radar sites. They serve with the Air Rescue unit at Iruma (with detachments elsewhere).

SPECIFICATION

Kawasaki (Boeing Vertol) CH-47J
generally similar to the Boeing (Boeing Vertol) CH-47D

Chinook except in the following particulars:
Powerplant: two Kawasaki (Textron Lycoming) T55-K-712 turboshafts each rated at 4,378 shp (3264 kW)

for take-off and 3,137 shp (2339 kW) for continuous running, in both cases driving a transmission rated at 7,500 shp (5593 kW) on two engines and 4,600 shp (3430 kW) on one engine

This is one of the first CH-47Js delivered to the JGSDF.

Kawasaki-Lockheed P-2J Neptune

After it had built 48 **P2V-7 Owashi** (Giant eagle) aircraft, equivalent to the **Lockheed P-2H Neptune**, for the JMSDF, Kawasaki developed the improved **P2V-7 Kai** with Ishikawajima-Harima-built T64-IHI-10 turboprops replacing the original Wright R-3350 piston engines, and with an all-new avionics suite giving much greater

operational capability. Additional power was provided by licence-built IHI-J3 auxiliary underwing turbojets. First flown on 21 July 1966, the P2V-7 Kai entered production as the **P-2J** and 82 were built by 1979. The aircraft had a 1.3-m (4-ft 2-in) fuselage stretch ahead of the wing, allowing seven operators to be carried in the forward compartment,

with three more aft of the wing spar. Rudder chord was increased by reducing taper, compensating for the extra length forward. They have finally been replaced in the ASW and maritime reconnaissance roles by P-3C Orions, the last squadron converting in late 1993, but a few special-purpose variants remain in **JMSDF** service. These include

the survivors from two **EP-2J**s equipped for Elint duties with HLR-105 and HLR-106 sensors, and four **UP-2J** support aircraft. The EP-2Js had their transparent nosecones replaced with solid radomes, and had a variety of underfuselage antennas too. The UP-2Js, first delivered in December 1979 are equipped to launch Firebee target drones and to tow targets, and carry missile seeker head simulators and jamming gear Like the EP-2Js, they are operated by the

81st Kokutai at Iwakuni. Others may serve with the 51st Kokutai, the JMSDF's dedicated test and trials unit at Atsugi.

The JMSDF retired its last front-line Neptunes from the 7th Kokutai in late 1993, but special-purpose versions and test aircraft remain active.

Kawasaki-Lockheed **P-3 Orion**

Kawasaki is prime contractor for the production under licence and assembly of the **Lockheed P-3C Orion** (described separately) for the **JMSDF**, which has a requirement for 110. Initial aircraft were to the US Navy's Update II standard, with Update III introduced subsequently and the more extensive 1993-Update IV revision using Japanese-made equipment. Lockheed built the first three JMSDF P-3Cs at Burbank, where the first aircraft was accepted on 29 April 1981, with subsequent delivery to Atsugi on 25 December.

Using Lockheed-supplied components for the next four aircraft, Kawasaki flew the first P-3C assembled in Japan on 17 March

1982, with delivery on 26 May for operational testing by the 51st Kokutai. Equipment of the first squadron, 6th Kokutai, began at Atsugi on 30 March 1983, followed by the 3rd Kokutai at the same base. Further P-3C squadrons are the 2nd and 4th at Hachinoe and the 1st and 7th at Kanoya, with a further squadron planned at Iwakuni. The 206th Kokutai at Shimofusa is responsible for conversion training. Orions have now entirely supplanted Neptunes in the ASW role.

Kawasaki has completed three Orions as **EP-3C**s to operate in the electronic surveillance role, as the first in a planned total of nine required for operation by 81st Kokutai

Large black dorsal and ventral radomes identify this aircraft as one of three EP-3C Elint aircraft. These all serve with the 81st Kokutai.

at Iwakuni. The low- and high- frequency detector systems for these aircraft are produced by NEC and Mitsubishi Electric in Japan. Further variants procured by the JMSDF are two **UP-3C** ECM trainers. A single dedicated **NP-3C** for navaid flight

checking was cancelled, and provision for the role was incorporated into the two UP-3Cs. The P-3Cs built by Kawasaki are powered by 4,910-ehp (3661-kW) Allison T56-IHI-14 turboprops produced in Japan by Ishikawajima-Harima.

Kawasaki (MDH) **OH-6D and OH-6J**

After the Hughes OH-6 had been adopted by the **JGSDF** as its standard observation helicopter and principal rotary wing type, a licence was acquired for its production in Japan by Kawasaki. The initial phase of the programme comprised the acquisition of 117 **OH-6J**s, commencing on 10 March 1969 and completed in 1979. Phase Two marked a switch from the

OH-6J, which was based on the US Army's **OH-6A Cayuse** light observation helicopter, to the **OH-6D**, which was based on the civil **Hughes Model 500D** and was distinguished by its 'T' tailplane with small endplates replacing the OH-6J's V-tail. McDonnell-built helicopters are described separately.

Kawasaki flew its first OH-6D on 2

December 1977 and production has been primarily for JGSDF, which ordered 153 for delivery by the mid-1990s. Both D and J models are widely distributed through the JGSDF, which has 13 squadrons (1 to 13 Hikotai inclusive) flying the helicopter in its intended observation role, as well as for training and other miscellaneous duties. OH-6s are also used in the scout role, oper-

ating in conjunction with the JGSDF's anti-tank AH-1s. These aircraft serve with No. 1 and No. 2 Anti Tank Squadrons. No. 1 Helicopter Brigade includes two KV-107/OH-6/CH-47-equipped units. In addition, the **JMSDF** acquired three OH-6Js in 1973/74 for the 211th Kyoiku Kokutai (Air Training Squadron) at Kanoya, and followed these with OH-6Ds for the same role.

Korean Air **Model 500/520**

Production of the **Hughes Model 500D** helicopter was the first major aircraft programme undertaken by the Aerospace Division of Korean Air, set up at Kim Hae in 1976. More than 300 have been built, in the basic Model 500D and armed **Model 500MD** versions, some 200 for the **Republic of Korea army and navy**. Fifty 500MDs for the army were equipped with Hughes BGM-71A TOW anti-tank missiles, while more than 100 Model 500Ds for the

observation/liaison role can carry a 40-mm grenade launcher. Replacement of the Model 500s is planned with the **Model 520MK Black Tiger**, based on the **McDonnell Douglas MD 520N** variant.

One of Korean Air's TOW-armed 500MDs of the Republic of Korea army in flight. The missile sight is mounted in the nose, and exhaust suppressors are also fitted.

Korean government-sponsored programmes

The Korean aircraft industry is involved in a number of ongoing government-sponsored programmes, with **Daewoo Heavy Industries**, **Korean Air** and **Samsung Aerospace** the key players. Straight licence manufacture and component making are still the most important activities, but the development of indigenous types, and of indigenous derivatives of other people's aircraft, is becoming of increasing importance. Daewoo is working as prime contractor on Korea's indigenous primary trainer, actually the nation's first indigenously designed military aircraft, created by a government agency. Under the designa-

tion **KTX-1**, the first of five prototypes, made its maiden flight in December 1991. The 750-shp (559 kW) Pratt & Whitney Canada PT-6A-25C engined second prototype, with increased dorsal fin area, a two-piece blown canopy and lightweight ejection seats, flew during 1992. Production aircraft may be re-engined with a 1,000-shp (746kW) Pratt & Whitney Canada PT6A-62 or a similarly rated Garrett TPE331. The requirement is for some 100 aircraft.

Daewoo's other activities include production of centre fuselage sections for Korean **F-16**s, **Dornier 328** fuselage shells, **Lynx** helicopter airframes, wing components for

Hawks and **Orion**s and rotor hubs for **Bell 212**s and **412**s. Daewoo is also the prime contractor for the proposed light scout helicopter, which should be a licence-built **Agusta A109CM** or **MBB BO 105CB**. The Agricultural Remote Control Helicopter requirement has been expanded to include some military surveillance roles, and may be met by a Daewoo-built derivative of the **Kamov Ka-37** drone. Another Daewoo helicopter project is the **MK-30**, a proposed licence-built derivative of the Mil Mi-17 with a refined airframe and recontoured Mi-26 type nose.

Korean Air, previously responsible for

F-5E production, maintenance and modifications of various military types, manufactures the Sikorsky S-70 under licence as the **UH-60P**, as well as the MD 520 discussed above. The company will also build centre and rear fuselages for the KTX-1 trainer. Samsung, which produces parts and subassemblies for a number of US-designed civil aircraft is the prime contractor for the Korean Fighter Programme under which 120 F-16Cs and Ds are being bought off-the-shelf (12), licence-assembled (36), and manufactured (72). The company is also developing the **KTX-2** indigenous jet trainer to replace ROKAF T-33s and T-37s.

Lake LA-4 Buccaneer, LA-250 Renegade and Seawolf

Derived indirectly from the C 1 Skimmer of 1948, the **Lake LA-4 Buccaneer** is a four-seat amphibian for the general aviation market, more than 1,300 of which have been built in several versions. Two LA-4s serve the **Royal Thai navy** for

general duties. The current standard version is the **LA-250 Renegade**, which featured a lengthened six-seat cabin and an uprated engine. In 1985, Lake introduced a military version of the Renegade, with surveillance, patrol and SAR among its design roles. This

variant was named **Seawolf** and introduced armament and radar options. Search radar can be fitted on the front of the (pusher) engine nacelle, and four Alkan wing hardpoints – one inboard and one outboard of each outrigger balance float – provide for up to 270 kg (594 lb) of stores such as SAR, ECM, gun, rocket or reconnaissance pods, external tanks, flares and practice bombs.

SPECIFICATION

Lake Seawolf

Wing: span 38 ft 4 in (11.68 m); aspect ratio 8.7; area 170.00 sq ft (15.79 m²)
Fuselage and tail: length 28 ft 4 in (8.64 m); height 10 ft 0 in (3.05 m); tailplane span 10 ft 0 in (3.05 m); wheel track 11 ft 2 in (3.40 m); wheel base 10 ft 3 in (3.13 m)

The Seawolf amphibian features a search radar mounted on the front of the engine.

Powerplant: one Textron Lycoming IO-540-C4B5 flat-six piston engine rated at 290 hp (216 kW)
Weights: empty 2,200 lb (998 kg); maximum take-off 3,450 lb (1565 kg)
Fuel and load: internal fuel 88 US gal (333 litres); external fuel up to two 31-US gal (117.3-litre) drop tanks; maximum ordnance 400 lb (181 kg)
Speed: never exceed speed 148 kt (170 mph; 274 km/h); maximum level speed 'clean' at 6,500 ft (1980 m) 139 kt (160 mph; 258 km/h); maximum cruising speed at 6,500 ft (1980 m) 132 kt (152 mph; 245 km/h); economical cruising speed at optimum altitude 110 kt (127 mph; 204 km/h)
Range: ferry range 1,500 nm (1,727 miles; 2780 km) with drop tanks; range 875 nm (1,008 miles; 1622 km) with standard fuel; endurance 14 hours 30 minutes with drop tanks or 8 hours 30 minutes with standard fuel
Performance: maximum rate of climb at sea level 900 ft (274 m) per minute; service ceiling 14,700 ft (4480 m); take-off run 880 ft (268 m) at maximum take-off weight on land, or 1,250 ft (381 m) at maximum take-off weight on water; landing run 755 ft (230 m) at normal landing weight on land and water

---

Learjet Inc
One Learjet Way, PO Box 7707,
Wichita, KS 67277, USA

Learjet (Gates) Models 24/25/35/36 and C-21

Some 200 examples of different models of the Learjet corporate twin-jet transport currently serve with military air arms. The **Learjet 24** is the smallest in the range, and the **Model 25** introduced a 52-in (1.32-m) fuselage plug to increase maximum seating from eight to 10. Both versions are powered by General Electric CJ610 turbojets. The **Model 35** is based on the Model 25, with a further 13-in (33-cm) stretch, greater wingspan and TFE731-2 turbofans. The **Model 36** was adapted as a long-range Model 35, with extra fuel in the fuselage, reducing standard seating from eight to six passengers.

Eighty-four **C-21A**s were acquired by the **USAF** in 1984, based on the commercial **Learjet 35A** version. The C-21A is used as an Operational Support Aircraft (including four by the ANG's 201st Airlift Squadron) to carry up to eight passengers or 3,153 lb (1593 kg) of cargo, and has a convertible interior for the casevac role.

The Learjet company (previously Gates, now a subsidiary of Bombardier in Canada) has developed several special mission versions of the Model 35/36, based on the basic designation **C-35/36**. The specialised variants include the **EC-35A** for EW training simulation and related roles; **PC-35A** for maritime patrol; **RC-35A** and **RC-36A** for photo and/or radar reconnaissance, surveillance and mapping; and **UC-35A** utility version for transport, navaid calibration, medevac and target towing.

Japan operates four aircraft under the designation **U-36A** (described separately under ShinMaywa). Flown by 81 Kokutai of 31 Kokugun at Iwakuni, these are equipped

USAF Learjets are assigned to wings for high-speed staff and light cargo transport. This C-21A wears the 'OF' codes of the 55th Wing.

to tow high-speed sleeve targets, missile seeker and jammer equipment in tip pods and ocean surveillance radar in an underbelly fairing, and have an expanded underwing stores capability. The **People's Republic of China** operates two RC-36As and three RC-35As, the latter SLAR-equipped for geological surveys. **Finland**'s three **Learjet 35A**s are similarly provided with a removable underbelly radar and underwing hardpoints, with facilities for target towing. **Germany** has four **Learjet 35A/36A** target tugs, civilian-operated to support the armed forces. Two Learjet 35As serve as VIP transports in the Royal Flight (No. 1 Squadron) of the **Royal Saudi air force**.

In the reconnaissance role, the RC-35A and RC-36A versions are equipped with long-range oblique cameras in the fuselage, and can carry other cameras in external pods and/or SLAR. Among the nations using Learjets primarily in the photo survey role are **Argentina**, with three Model 35s in the aerial photographic wing (1 EVR); **Brazil** with three (locally designated **R-35A**) flown by 1ª Esq in No. 6 Wing at Recife; **Chile**, which has two in its Aerial Photo-mapping Service; and **Peru**, with two each Model 36As and **Model 25B**s used by the Servicio Aerofotografico Nacional.

Examples of the earlier Learjet models are also used in the photo-reconnaissance, survey and mapping role by **Bolivia** (one each **Model 25B** and **Model 25D**), and **Ecuador** (one **Model 24D** with the Instituto Geographica Militar). Primarily in the communication and liaison role, the **Serbian air force** has one Learjet 25B. Model 24Bs are similarly used by the **Mexican navy** and Ecuador's Esc 41 of the Comando Aéreo de Transporte at La Carlota. In several countries specially-equipped Learjets are flown by civilian

contractors on behalf of the military, including Australia, Sweden, Switzerland, Thailand, the UK and the USA.

SPECIFICATION

Learjet 35A

Wing: span 39 ft 6 in (12.04 m) with tip tanks; aspect ratio 5.7; area 253.3 sq ft (23.53 m²)
Fuselage and tail: length 48 ft 8 in (14.83 m); height 12 ft 3 in (3.73 m); tailplane span 14 ft 8 in (4.47 m); wheel track 8 ft 3 in (2.51 m); wheel base 20 ft 2 in (6.15 m)
Powerplant: two Garrett TFE731-2-2B turbofans each rated at 3,500 lb st (15.57 kN)
Weights: empty equipped 9,838 lb (4462 kg); maximum take-off 18,300 lb (8301 kg)
Fuel and load: internal fuel 931 US gal (3524 litres);

Several operators use Learjets in the photo-mapping role. This camera-equipped Lear 25 serves with Bolivia.

external fuel none; maximum payload 3,500 lb (1588 kg)
Speed: never exceed speed Mach 0.83; maximum level speed at 25,000 ft (7620 m) 471 kt (542 mph; 872 km/h); maximum cruising speed at 41,000 ft (12495 m) 460 kt (529 mph; 851 km/h); economical cruising speed at 45,000 ft (13715 m) 418 kt (481 mph; 774 km/h)
Range: range 2,289 nm (2,634 miles; 4,239 km) with four passengers
Performance: maximum rate of climb at sea level 4,340 ft (1323 m) per minute; service ceiling 45,000 ft (13715 m); take-off balanced field length 4,972 ft (1515 m) at 18,300 lb (8301 kg); landing run 3,075 ft (937 m) at maximum landing weight

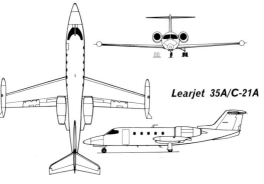

Learjet 35A/C-21A

LET L-410 Turbolet

Let Akciová Spolecnost
Uherské Hradisté, CR-686 04 Kunovice
Czech Republic

First flown on 16 April 1969, the **LET L-410 Turbolet** was the first aircraft of indigenous design to emerge from the Kunovice factory of the LET concern, set up in 1950. Intended as a light commuter transport, the L-410 achieved considerable success after some early difficulties, and was adopted by Aeroflot as its standard feeder-liner, as well as being exported to several East European countries and elsewhere. Between 1,000 and 1,100 L-410s were built, of which 318 were for the Soviet Union, primarily in the **L-410UVP** and **L-410UVP-E** versions. Some of these still fly with the **Russian** armed forces.

The L-410UVP, which flew for the first time on 1 November 1977, was distinguished by an increased wing span and vertical tail area, dihedral on the tailplane, improvements to the control system and other modifications. The L-410UVP was powered by two Motorlet M601B turboprops, as used in the earlier **L-410M**. After production of 495 of the UVP model by late 1985, LET changed to the UVP-E variant which had first flown on 30 December 1984. This introduced M601E engines, provision for extra fuel in wingtip tanks and some further control system and equipment improvements.

About 50 examples of the L-410M and (mostly) UVP were delivered for military use in the light transport and communications role. These were delivered to the **Bulgarian air force**, **Czechoslovak air force** (20) and **army** (two), **East Germany** (12), **Hungarian air force** and the **Libyan Arab Jamahiriya air force** (18). In East Germany, four L-410 UVPs were delivered to VS14, a liaison squadron, and eight to the

Otto Lilienthal Air Academy for multi-engine conversion. Following German unification, some or all of these L-410s were absorbed into the Luftwaffe. They were subsequently withdrawn from service and at least one was sold to the **Latvian air force**. **Slovenia** operates one for parachute training.

SPECIFICATION

LET L-410UVP-E Turbolet
Wing: span 19.48 m (63 ft 11 in) without tip tanks and 19.98 m (65 ft 6.5 in) with tip tanks; aspect ratio 10.79; area 35.18 m² (378.67 sq ft)
Fuselage and tail: length 14.424 m (47 ft 4 in);

height 5.83 m (19 ft 1.5 in); tailplane span 6.74 m (22 ft 1.25 in); wheel track 3.65 m (11 ft 11.5 in); wheel base 3.67 m (12 ft 0.25 in)
Powerplant: two Motorlet (Walter) M 601E turboprops each rated at 559 kW (750 shp)
Weights: empty 3985 kg (8,785 lb); operating empty 4160 kg (9,171 lb); maximum take-off 6400 kg (14,109 lb)
Fuel and load: internal fuel 1300 kg (2,866 lb); external fuel none; maximum payload 1615 kg (3,560 lb)
Speed: never exceed speed 357 km/h (192 kt; 222 mph); maximum level speed 'clean' at 4200 m (13,780 ft) 311 km/h (168 kt; 193 mph); maximum cruising speed at 4200 m (13,780 ft) 380 km/h (205 kt; 236 mph); economical cruising speed at 4200 m

Originally purchased by East Germany, this LET 410UVP now wears the colours of Latvia.

(13,780 ft) 365 km/h (197 kt; 227 mph)
Range: 1380 km (744 nm; 858 km) with maximum fuel or 546 km (294 nm; 339 miles) with maximum payload
Performance: maximum rate of climb at sea level 444 m (1,455 ft) per minute; service ceiling 6320 m (20,735 ft); take-off run 445 m (1,460 ft) at maximum take-off weight; take-off distance to 10.7 m (35 ft) 685 m (2,250 ft) at maximum take-off weight; landing distance from 9 m (30 ft) 480 m (1,575 ft) at normal landing weight; landing run 240 m (787 ft) at normal landing weight

---

Lisunov Li-2 'Cab'

A Soviet copy of the Douglas DC-3 (described separately) licensed before World War II, a few examples of the **Lisunov Li-2 'Cab'** remain in service in China. Initially designated **PS-84**, the aircraft was used by Aeroflot and the Red Army, which armed many of its aircraft, sometimes with a dorsal gun turret. The

original 671-kW (900-hp) Shvetsov M-62 radial engines were replaced by 746-kW (1,000-hp) Shvetsov ASh-62 engines on the post-war **Li-2P**, which became the major production variant and was supplied to the ADD (and later A-DVD) for short- and medium-range trooping in Eastern Europe and the USSR. It was estimated that about

1,000 aircraft remained in service with the Soviet air forces during the 1950s, although many of these probably doubled their duties as back-up on domestic Aeroflot services. Variants included the **Li-2G** civil and **Li-2T** military freighters, **Li-2PG** convertible trooper/freighter, **Li-2D** paratrooper and the **Li-2V** high-altitude version with 895-kW (1,200-hp) radials. Some of the Li-2Ps and Li-2Gs appeared with wing span reduced to 28.04 m (92 ft).

During the 1950s, as the Il-12 and Il-14

took over the majority of short-haul transport duties, the Li-2s underwent limited refurbishing for export among Communist Bloc air forces, the type being supplied in quantity to China, Poland, Bulgaria, Czechoslovakia, North Korea and Romania; in Hungary the type was named the **Teve** (camel), reflecting its utilitarian transport role. A few examples may remain in service in **China** and **North Korea**.

Lockheed C-5 Galaxy

Lockheed Martin Aeronautical Systems Company
86 South Cobb Drive, Marietta
GA 30063, USA

The **Lockheed C-5 Galaxy** heavy logistics transport is the workhorse of US strategic airlift and is flown by active, Reserve and Air National Guard units for the **US Air Force**'s Air Mobility Command. The C-5 originated with a 1963 USAF CX-HLS (Cargo Experimental-Heavy Logistics System) requirement for a capability to carry 250,000 lb (113400 kg) over 3,000 miles (4828 km) without air refuelling.

The Galaxy is a high-wing, T-tailed transport with four underwing pod-mounted TF39 turbofan engines and main undercarriage retracting into fuselage pods. The Galaxy's value for rapid deployment of large or heavy items of equipment has been demonstrated repeatedly. Key to the C-5's mission is its cavernous interior and 'roll on/roll off' capability with access to the vast cargo bay at both front and rear. The Galaxy has an upward-lifting visor nose which can be raised above the cockpit for loading/unloading, while standard clamshell doors accommodate loading/unloading at the rear of the aircraft.

The Galaxy's primary mission is to carry equipment and vehicles, although it can be configured for up to 363 passengers (73 on upper rear deck, 290 in main compartment). The upper deck houses the crew of five (two pilots, flight engineer, two load masters).

The **C-5A** first flew on 30 June 1968. The first operational C-5A was delivered on 17 December 1969, the last in May 1973. The C-5A suffered initially from wing crack problems and cost overruns but has served well after a teething period. Seventy-seven C-5As underwent a re-winging programme from 1981 to 1987, intended to increase service life to 30,000 hours. The wings are of virtually new design, apart from the moving services, and incorporated new aluminium alloy for greater corrosion resistance.

In the mid-1980s, the production line was reopened to meet an urgent USAF demand for additional heavy airlift capacity. Fifty **C-5B** models were built, essentially similar to the C-5A, but incorporating modifications and improvements resulting from operations with the C-5A. The C-5B dispensed with the C-5A's complex crosswind main landing gear and introduced improved AFCS (automated flight control system) and MADAR II (malfunction detection and analysis and recording system). The first

production C-5B was delivered on 8 January 1986 and deliveries were completed by April 1989.

On a typical mission, a Galaxy can carry 300,000 lb (136080 kg) to a range of 3,434 miles (5526 km). Typical loads include two MIA1 Abrams main battle tanks, four M551 Sheridan light tanks plus one HMMVW tactical vehicle, 16 ¾-ton trucks, 10 LAV-25 (light armoured vehicles), or a CH-47 Chinook helicopter. The aircraft provides the most ton-miles at the fastest speed of any

The C-5 Galaxy remains the USAF's most valuable airlift asset, serving with an Air Mobility Command wing on each coast and a training unit at Altus. The C-5's prodigious capacity and global reach make it crucial to the US rapid deployment forces.

Lockheed C-5 Galaxy

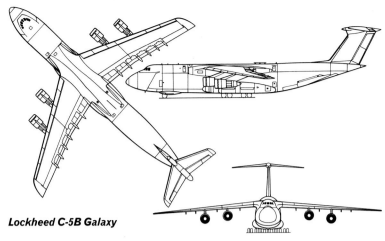

Lockheed C-5B Galaxy

The current camouflage scheme for Air Mobility Command airlifters is this 'proud grey'. This is considered to offer the best protection in the air and on the ground.

American airlifter. Although not usually assigned airdrop duties, the Galaxy can also drop paratroopers. On 7 June 1989, a C-5B air-dropped four M551 Sheridan tanks and 73 soldiers for a world record of 190,346 lb (86313 kg).

The C-5A/B serves with two Air Mobility Command Wings, the 60th AW at Travis AFB, CA, and the 436th AW at Dover, DE. Two Reserve squadrons (68th AS at Kelly AFB, TX, and 337th AS at Westover AFB, MA) and one Air National Guard squadron (137th AS at Stewart IAP, NY) fly C-5As, while four further Reserve units (301st/312th AS at Travis and 326th/709th AS at Dover) support the active-duty force through the Associate programme. Training

for the Galaxy fleet is provided by AETC's 97th Air Mobility Wing at Altus AFB, OK.

Known to crews as 'FRED', for Fantastic Ridiculous Economic Disaster, the C-5A/B has served admirably and economically in airlifts supporting US operations in Vietnam, Israel during the October 1973 War, and the Desert Shield/Storm effort of 1990-91. During Operation Desert Shield, C-5A/Bs flew 42 per cent of cargo and 18.6 per cent of passenger missions in an effort which exceeded in 17 days the total tonnage of the 65-week Berlin Airlift and totalled 15,800 missions with 498,900 passengers. One C-5A Galaxy of the 60th MAW (Travis AFB, CA) crewed by Reservists of the 433rd MAW (Kelly AFB, TX) crashed at Ramstein, Germany, on 29 August 1990, the only transport lost in the airlift.

Under the Pacer Snow project, two C-5s received a trial installation of ALE-40 flare dispensers and an AAR-47 missile warning system to provide a measure of self-

defence. The **C-5C** designation covers two Galaxies which have been modified with sealed front visor and strengthened interior for the carriage of satellites and space equipment.

Lacking the fatigue problem of its C-141B replacement, the Galaxy has no scheduled replacement and will remain in service until at least 2010.

SPECIFICATION

Lockheed C-5B Galaxy
Wing: span 222 ft 8.5 in (67.88 m); aspect ratio 7.75; area 6,200.00 sq ft (575.98 m²)
Fuselage and tail: length 247 ft 10 in (75.54 m); height 65 ft 1.5 in (19.85 m); tailplane span 68 ft 8.5 in (20.94 m); wheel track 37 ft 5.5 in (11.42 m); wheel base 72 ft 11 in (22.22 m)
Powerplant: four General Electric TF39-GE-1C turbofans each rated at 43,000 lb st (191.27 kN)
Weights: operating empty 374,000 lb (169643 kg);

maximum take-off 837,000 lb (379657 kg)
Fuel and load: internal fuel 332,500 lb (150815 kg); external fuel none; maximum payload 261,000 lb (118387 kg)
Speed: never exceed speed 402 kt (463 mph; 745 km/h) CAS; maximum level speed at 25,000 lb (7620 m) 496 kt (571 mph; 919 km/h); maximum cruising speed at 25,000 lb (7620 m) between 460 and 480 kt (552 and 564 mph; 888 and 908 km/h); economical cruising speed at 25,000 ft (7,620 m) 450 kt (518 mph; 833 km/h)
Range: 5,618 nm (6,469 miles; 10411 km) with maximum fuel or 2,982 nm (3,434 miles; 5526 km) with maximum payload
Performance: maximum rate of climb at sea level 1,725 ft (525 m) per minute; service ceiling 35,750 ft (10895 m) at 615,000 lb (278960 kg); take-off run 8,300 ft (2530 m) at maximum take-off weight; take-off distance to 50 ft (15 m) 9,800 ft (2987 m) at maximum take-off weight; landing distance from 50 ft (15 m) 3,820 ft (1164 m) at maximum landing weight; landing run 2,380 ft (725 m) at maximum landing weight

Lockheed **C-130 Hercules transport versions**

The **Lockheed C-130 Hercules** is the West's most popular and widely used military transport aircraft, in use for a wide range of airlift duties, and has been in pro-

duction longer than any other aircraft type in history. Huge numbers remain in service on every continent, and many operators have replaced early variants with newer versions.

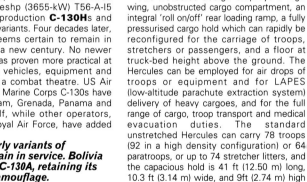

Left: A few early variants of Hercules remain in service. Bolivia operates this C-130A, retaining its USAF-style camouflage.

The **YC-130** prototype made its maiden flight on 23 August 1954, introducing the 3,250-eshp (2424-kW) Allison YT56A-1 turboprop engine, which has itself evolved into the 4,900-eshp (3655-kW) T56-A-I5 used today on production **C-130H**s and other upgraded variants. Four decades later, the Hercules seems certain to remain in production into a new century. No newer aircraft design has proven more practical at hauling people, vehicles, equipment and supplies within a combat theatre. US Air Force, Navy and Marine Corps C-130s have served in Vietnam, Grenada, Panama and the Persian Gulf, while other operators, including the Royal Air Force, have added

further combat experience to the aircraft's history. The number of countries operating C-130 variants now exceeds 60. The soundness of the basic Hercules design has led to a numerous versions optimised for gunship, rescue, tanker, drone-controller, reconnaissance and other missions.

The Hercules design employs a high wing, unobstructed cargo compartment, an integral 'roll on/off' rear loading ramp, a fully pressurised cargo hold which can rapidly be reconfigured for the carriage of troops, stretchers or passengers, and a floor at truck-bed height above the ground. The Hercules can be employed for air drops of troops or equipment and for LAPES (low-altitude parachute extraction system) delivery of heavy cargoes, and for the full range of cargo, troop transport and medical evacuation duties. The standard unstretched Hercules can carry 78 troops (92 in a high density configuration) or 64 paratroops, or up to 74 stretcher litters, and the capacious hold is 41 ft (12.50 m) long, 10.3 ft (3.14 m) wide, and 9ft (2.74 m) high at the lowest point.

The first two **YC-130A** prototypes came from the manufacturer's California 'Skunk Works', while more than 2,000 subsequent aircraft have been built in Marietta, Georgia. The first production **C-130A** flew on 7 April 1955, and deliveries to the US Air Force began in December of that year. All surviving C-130As now have four-bladed propellers, an extended tailcone housing a crash position indicator and AN/APN-59 radar in the reprofiled 'Pinnochio' nose, features originally associated with the later **C-130B**.

The Hercules is at its best operating into short, rough airstrips, proving its sturdiness and short-field ability. Seen during an airlift exercise, this is a C-130H of the Portuguese air force.

The C-130H-30 Super Hercules combines the stretched fuselage of the civilian L-100-30 with the military features of the C-130H. Cameroon bought this highly colourful example in 1982. The C-130H-30 can accommodate 92 paratroops instead of the regular aircraft's 64, or seven cargo pallets instead of the previous five.

The oldest version of the Hercules in widespread use in the early 1990s was the C-130B, which introduced engine improvements for the type's original T56-A-1A engine, increased fuel capacity and Hamilton Standard Model 54H60-91 13-ft 6-in (4.17-m) four-bladed hydromatic propellers. The C-130B variant did not usually carry wing pylons for external fuel, and had better radius, range and endurance than other variants whose external wing-tanks do not 'earn' their penalty in weight and drag. The Navy procured seven utility transport Hercules based on the C-130B and designated these **GV-1U** and later **C-130F**.

In 1961, production changed to the

A handful of WC-130H weather reconnaissance aircraft are operated by the USAF Reserve's 403rd Airlift Wing.

C-130E variant for the USAF and other users, introducing 4,050-eshp (3021-kW) T56-A-7 engines with increased power to improve take-off performance in hot weather or from airfields at high altitude. Maximum take-off weight went up from 124,200 lb (56336 kg) in the C-130A to 175,000 lb (79379 kg), this requiring strengthened wing spars, thicker skins and a reinforced undercarriage. The E model also introduced larger 1,360-US gal (5148-litre) external underwing tanks mounted between the inner and outer wings, and most Es have their forward cargo doors sealed. In service, the C-130E has been extensively upgraded and updated, with new avionics, a tactical precision approach system, and a self-contained nav system.

The Navy's **C-130G** was a utility transport version based on the C-130E. The four aircraft were later modified as TACAMO communications relay aircraft and were redesignated **EC-130G**. After replacement by the E-6A, three aircraft were returned to transport configuration (albeit with no cargo ramp) as **TC-130G**s, one now serving as the support aircraft for the 'Blue Angels' aerobatic team.

The current basic transport version, the C-130H, was developed for export customers, first flying in November 1964 and being delivered to the RNZAF in March

1965. The first delivery to the USAF occurred in April 1975. The new version has a redesigned and strengthened wing box, improved brakes and a new avionics suite, and is powered by improved T56-A-15 engines. Most lack provision for RATOG bottles. T56-A-15 powerplants and other features of the H model, including improved brakes and strengthened centre-wing design, have been retrofitted to many

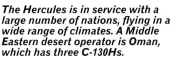

The Hercules is in service with a large number of nations, flying in a wide range of climates. A Middle Eastern desert operator is Oman, which has three C-130Hs.

earlier Hercules airframes. Some C-130H transports can be fitted internally for medical evacuation duties. Two Moroccan C-130Hs are fitted with SLAR pods on the port undercarriage fairing, and three USAF aircraft were extensively modified for participation in Operation Eagle Claw (the Iranian hostage rescue mission) with RATOG, aerodynamic improvements for better STOL performance and retro rockets for improved braking.

The C-130H served as the basis for a number of other variants, including the **C-130H(AEH)**, an airborne hospital aircraft used by Saudi Arabia, and the **C-130H-MP** maritime patroller supplied to Malaysia and Indonesia. The **C-130K** for Britain is essentially a C-130H with British avionics and equipment, incorporating some parts made by Scottish Aviation and fitted out by Marshalls of Cambridge, which has become perhaps the world's leading Hercules refurbishing and modification centre, apart from Lockheed itself. The RAF's 66 C-130Ks were delivered as **Hercules C.Mk 1**s, although subsequent modification

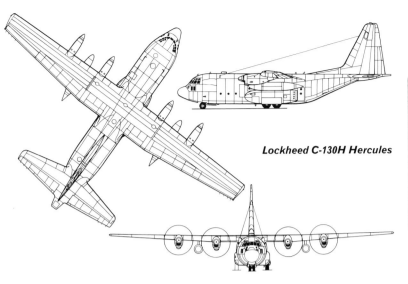

Lockheed C-130H Hercules

programmes have led to the allocation of new designations. During the Falklands War, 25 aircraft were fitted with inflight-refuelling probes to become **Hercules C.Mk 1P**s and six others received a hose drum refuelling unit and extra tanks in the hold to serve as tankers under the designation **Hercules C.Mk 1K**. Four of the tankers, and two C.Mk 1Ps used by No. 47 Squadron's Special Forces Flight, are equipped with wingtip-mounted Racal Orange Blossom ESM pods for surveillance tasks. The Special Forces support aircraft also have an extensive suite of defensive systems (including a Missile Approach Warning System) and an integrated INS/GPS. A single aircraft was converted for Meteorological Research duties under the designation **W.Mk 2**, and 30 have been stretched by insertion of fuselage plugs to become **C.Mk 3**s, redesignated **C.Mk 3P** when retrofitted with an inflight-refuelling probe. The 15-ft stretch (as used by the civilian **L-100-30**) increases maximum capacity from 92 to 128 troops. A prototype was converted by Lockheed, first flying on 3 December 1979, and was followed by aircraft converted by Marshalls. Similarly stretched C-130Hs were built for Algeria, Cameroon, Colombia, Dubai, France, Indonesia, Nigeria and Thailand, under the designation **C-130H-30** (the initial designation **C-130H(S)** was soon dropped).

A number of military operators use the civilian version of the Hercules, which bears the company designation **L-100**. Certificated in February 1965, the basic L-100 was broadly equivalent to the C-130E, without pylon tanks or military equipment. The **L-100-20** was given plugs fore (5 ft/1.52 m) and aft (3.3 ft/1.02 m) of the wing. The **L-100-30** has a full 15-ft fuselage stretch and is operated by Dubai, Ecuador, Gabon, Indonesia and Kuwait.

On a 'real life' tactical mission, the Hercules can haul a payload of people or cargo up to 38,702 lb (17555 kg) (C-130E) or 43,400 lb (19686 kg) (C-130H) to a range of 1,428 miles (2298 km) with a 45-minute fuel reserve and can make a tactical landing on an unprepared airstrip using 4,880 ft (1463 m) of landing roll. On famine relief missions into Somalia, C-130E/H transports with a reduced payload of 22,000 lb (9980 kg) routinely landed in 3,000 ft (930 m) of undeveloped airstrip. On other missions, a Hercules can carry five HMMWV tactical vehicles, five 8,818-lb (4000-kg) rectangular palletised freight containers, or three Land Rover-type vehicles and two trailers.

For airborne operations, the C-130E carries 64 fully equipped paratroopers to a radius of up to 710 miles (1142 km) for a combat air drop with a 45-minute fuel reserve. Most C-130 tactical airlift units are

The C-130 has been used for a huge variety of tasks other than the basic transport mission. Malaysia has three C-130H MPs used for maritime patrol. The secondary transport task is retained.

equipped with station keeping equipment to facilitate formation flying in daylight on tactical missions. Two USAF C-130E wings are equipped with AWADS (adverse weather aerial delivery system) to permit close formation flight during low-level airdrop operations at night and in bad weather.

Lockheed has developed a much-improved, high-technology Hercules designated **C-130J** and unofficially called **Hercules 2**. The C-130J proposal retains four engines rather than a twin-engined layout that was briefly contemplated, the new aircraft being powered by four Allison 2100 turboprop engines driving six-bladed, composite propellers. The C-130J, privately funded but responding to a US Air Force statement of need, has a two-man automated cockpit with four flat-panel liquid crystal displays, eliminating navigator and flight engineer crew positions. The wing will have no pylons or provision for external tanks, a return to the 'slick wing' configuration of the C-130B model. Many existing Hercules users are considering the aircraft as a potential replacement for their first generation C-130s, including the RAF, which has ordered the type as the **C.Mk 4** (long fuselage) and **C.Mk 5** (short). Lockheed is to deliver the first production C-130J in 1996.

Other sub-types closely based upon the above transport versions include the **TC-130A** trainer, the **JC-130A/B/F** and **NC-130A/B/E/H** test aircraft, the recce-configured **RC-130A**, the battlefield illumination **RC-130S**, the **VC-130B/H** VIP and staff transport, and the **WC-130B/E/H** weather reconnaissance ships.

Rescue, gunship, special forces, tanker, EW and ABCC variants are described separately.

SPECIFICATION

Lockheed C-130F Hercules
Wing: span 132 ft 7 in (40.41 m); aspect ratio 10.09;

area 1,745.00 sq ft (161.12 m²)
Fuselage and tail: length 97 ft 9 in (29.79 m); height 38 ft 3 in (11.66 m); tailplane span 52 ft 8 in (16.05 m); wheel track 14 ft 3 in (4.35 m); wheel base 32 ft 0.75 in (9.77 m)
Powerplant: four Allison T56-A-7 turboprops each rated at 4,050 ehp (3020 ekW)
Weights: empty equipped 69,300 lb (31434 kg); maximum take-off 135,000 lb (61236 kg)
Fuel and load: internal fuel 5,050 US gal (19116 litres); external fuel two 450-US gal (1703-litre) underwing tanks; maximum payload 35,700 lb (16194 kg)
Speed: maximum cruising speed at 30,000 ft (9145 m) 321 kt (370 mph; 595 km/h)
Range: range 4,210 nm (4,848 miles; 7802 km) with maximum fuel or 1,910 nm (2,199 miles; 3539 km) with maximum payload
Performance: maximum rate of climb at sea level 2,000 ft (610 m) per minute; service ceiling 34,000 ft (10365 m); take-off distance to 50 ft (15 m) 4,300 ft (1311 m) at maximum take-off weight

OPERATORS

1996 service status of transport-configured C-130s as follows (tanker and other versions detailed separately):
US Air Force (active-duty): approximately 200 C-130E/H serving with Air Combat Command (7th Wing – Dyess AFB, 23rd Wing – Pope AFB, 24th Wing – Howard AFB, 314th Airlift Wing – Little Rock AFB and 347th Wing – Moody AFB), AFSOC (353rd SOG – Kadena AB), PACAF (3rd Wing – Elmendorf AFB and 374th AW – Yokota AB) and USAFE (86th AW – Ramstein AB).
US Air National Guard: over 200 C-130E/H serving with 19 ANG units from the following states: Alaska (144th AS), Arkansas (154th TS – training unit), California (115th AS), Delaware (142nd AS), Georgia (158th AS), Kentucky (165th AS), Maryland (135th AS), Minnesota (109th AS), Missouri (180th AS), New York (139th AS), North Carolina (156th AS), Ohio (164th AS), Oklahoma (185th AS), Rhode Island (143rd AS), Tennessee (105th AS), Texas (181st AS), West Virginia (130th and 167th AS) and Wyoming (187th AS).
US Air Force Reserve: over 100 C-130E/H assigned to 12 squadrons: 700th AS/94th AW, 731st AS/302nd AW, 815th AS/403rd AW, 95th AS/440th AW, 357th AS/908th AW, 757th AS/910th AW, 758th AS/911th

Many C-130 operators have fire-fighting equipment for use in transport Hercules. This is a California ANG C-130E, demonstrating the MAFFS kit.

AW, 327th AS/913th AW, 328th AS/914th AW, 711th SOS/919th SOW, 64th AS/928th AW and 96th AS/934th AW.
US Navy: VR-53 and VR-54 (USNR) operate the C-130T from Martinsburg RAP and NAS New Orleans respectively. VRC-50 flies the C-130F from Andersen AFB, Guam. The 'Blue Angels' display team has a single support TC-130G transport, operated with US Marine Corps titles.
Algeria: C-130H (10), C-130H-30 (8) serving with 31ᵉ, 32ᵉ, 33ᵉ and 35ᵉ Escadrilles
Argentina: C-130B (2), C-130H (6), L-100-30 (1) serving with I Escuadrón, I Grupo
Australia: C-130E (12), C-130H (12) serving with Nos 36 and 37 Sqns at Richmond; C-130J on order
Belgium: C-130H (12) serving with 20 Smaldeel/Escadrille at Brussels
Bolivia: C-130A (7), C-130H (1) flying with Grupo Aéreo de Transporte 71 at La Paz and TAB
Brazil: C-130E (10), C-130H (4) serving with 1° Esq/1° GTT at Galeão and 2° Esq/1° GTT at Campo dos Alfonsos
Cameroon: C-130H (1)
Canada: CC-130E (19), CC-130H (11) serving with Nos 424 (SAR), 426 and 437 Sqns at Trenton, No. 413 Sqn at Greenwood (SAR), Nos 418 (SAR) and 435 Sqns at Namao. Five C-130Hs are tankers
Chad: C-130A (1), C-130H (1), C-130H-30 (1)
Chile: C-130B (4), C-130H (2) operated by Grupo de Aviación 10 at Santiago-Merino Benitez
Colombia: C-130B (5), C-130H (2) with the Escuadrón de Transporte at Bogota
Denmark: C-130H (3) flying with Eskadrille 721 at Vaerløse
Ecuador: C-130B (2), C-130H (1) serving with Ala de Transporte 11 at Quito-Mariscal Sucre
Egypt: C-130H (21), C-130H-30 (3). Two C-130Hs used in VIP role and two as electronic warfare platforms
France: C-130H (3), C-130H-30 (9) operated by Escadron de Transport 2/61 at Orléans-Bricy
Gabon: C-130H (1), L-100-20 (1)
Greece: C-130B (4), C-130H (11) with 356 Mira, 112 Ptérix at Elefsis
Honduras: C-130A (3)
India: order for 12 C-130H
Indonesia: C-130B (14), C-130H (3), C-130H-30 (5)

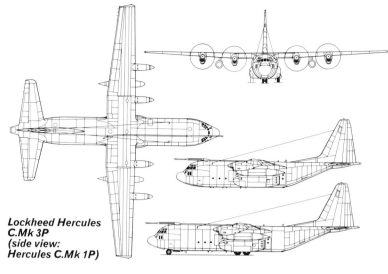

Lockheed Hercules C.Mk 3P (side view: Hercules C.Mk 1P)

flying with No. 31 Sqn at Jakarta-Halim and No. 32 Sqn at Malang

Iran: C-130H (approximately 10 believed serviceable)
Israel: C-130E (12), C-130H (9) serving with Nos 103 and 131 Squadrons
Italy: C-130H (12) with 50° Gruppo, 46ª Brigata at Pisa
Japan: C-130H (15) based with 401 Hikotai at Komatsu
Jordan: C-130B (2), C-130H (4) operated by No. 3 Sqn at Amman
Kuwait: L-100-30 (2) flown by No. 41 Sqn at Al al Salem
Libya: C-130H (7), L-100-20 (2), L-100-30 (2)
Malaysia: C-130H (5), C-130H-30 (1), C-130H-MP (3) serving with Nos 4 and 14 Sqns at Simpang
Mexico: C-130A (10) flying with Escuadrón Aéreo Transporte Pesado at Santa Lucia
Morocco: C-130H (17) based at Kenitra
Netherlands: C-130H-30 (2) with No. 334 Sqn at Eindhoven
New Zealand: C-130H (5) flying with No. 40 Sqn at Whenuapai; C-130J under consideration
Niger: C-130H (2) based at Niamey
Nigeria: C-130H (6), C-130H-30 (3) based at Lagos
Norway: C-130H (6) serving with No. 335 Skvadron at Gardermoen
Oman: C-130H (3) operated by No. 4 Squadron at Muscat/Seeb
Pakistan: C-130B (7), C-130E (4), L-100 (1) serving with No. 6 Tactical Transport Squadron at Rawalpindi and the Transport Conversion Squadron at Chakhala

Peru: C-130A (3), L-100-20 (5) flying with Grupo de Transporte 41 at Lima-Jorge Chavez
Philippines: C-130B 92), C-130H (2) flown by 222 Squadron at Mactan
Portugal: C-130H (4), C-130H-30 (2) serving with Esquadra de Transport 501 at Montijo
Saudi Arabia: C-130E (7), C-130H (21), VC-130H (4), C-130H AEH (3), L-100-30 (6). Transports flown by Nos 4 and 16 Sqns at Jeddah, VIP aircraft and air ambulances (including L-100-30s) operated by Saudia/No. 1 Sqn based at Riyadh
Singapore: C-130H (5) flying with 122 Sqn at Changi
South Africa: C-130B (7) based with No. 28 Sqn at Waterkloof
South Korea: C-130H (8), C-130H-30 (4) based at Seoul
Spain: C-130H (6), C-130H-30 (1) flying with Ala 31 at Zaragoza
Sudan: C-130H (6) based at Khartoum
Sweden: C-130H/Tp 84 (8) based with F7 at Satenas
Taiwan: C-130H (12) with a further 12 on order
Thailand: C-130H (7), C-130H-30 (6) operated by 601 Squadron at Bangkok-Don Muang

With Allison 2100 turboprops driving six-bladed propellers, and a new 'glass' cockpit, the C-130J is the latest generation Hercules, first flying in early 1996. The first aircraft from the line is for the Royal Air Force, which has 25 on order.

Tunisia: C-130H (2) based at Bizerte
Turkey: C-130B (6), C-130E (5), C-130H (1) operated by 222 Squadron at Erkilet
United Arab Emirates: C-130H (4), C-130H-30 (1), L-100-30 (1) flying from Bateen AB and Mindhat AB
United Kingdom: C.Mk 1P (25), C.Mk 3P (29). Operated by the Lyneham Transport Wing. Single W.Mk 2 in use with DRA Boscombe Down; 25 C.Mk 4/C.Mk 5 (C-130J-30/C-130J) on order
Uruguay: C-130B (2) based at Montevideo
Venezuela: C-130H (6) operated by Escuadrón 62 at Maracay-El Libertador
Vietnam: 13 C-130As put into use following North Vietnamese victory. A handful remain in open storage at Tan Son Nhut and Bien Hoa
Yemen: C-130H 92) based at Sana'a
Zaïre: C-130H (4) serving with 191ᵉ Escadrille

For strategic airlift tasks, the stretched C-130H-30 offers far greater payload capacity but with reduced field performance.

Lockheed **AC-130A/E/H**

Lockheed Martin Aircraft Services Company
1800 East Airport Drive, Ontario
CA 91761-0033, USA

A USAF need perceived from early experience in Vietnam was quick-reaction concentrated firepower for use against small targets, especially where defenders of isolated areas were subject to nocturnal attack. The first solution was the Gunship I conversion of the Douglas C-47 as the AC-47, known informally as 'Puff the Magic Dragon' or 'Spooky'. Initially fitted with three side-firing 7.62-mm (0.3-in) general-purpose machine-guns, they were soon refitted with three 7.62-mm multi-barrelled Miniguns.

With the system operational, there was a need to improve firepower, sensing equipment, targeting and armour. The Fairchild C-119 was adapted as the AC-119G Shadow and AC-119K Stinger with the 17th and 18th Special Operations Squadrons, respectively, while USAF's Aeronautical Systems Division began converting the 13th production C-130A (54-1626) to Gunship II standard in 1965. This involved installation of four 20-mm Vulcan cannon, four 7.62-mm Miniguns, flare equipment and improved sighting. This aircraft was tested operationally in Vietnam in late 1967, and LTV Electrosystems was awarded an immediate contract to modify seven JC-130A missile trackers to **Lockheed AC-130A** standard. Weaponry remained the same but these aircraft were fitted with an APQ-133 beacon tracker, an AN/APQ-136 MTI radar and a new analog computer, searchlight, sensors, target-acquisition and direct-view image intensifiers. Four were in service in Vietnam by the end of 1968 with the 14th Air Commando Wing operating from Ubon in

Puffs of smoke from this AC-130H show the forward 20-mm Vulcans firing and the aft 40-mm. The M102 105-mm howitzer is the heaviest weapon available.

The AC-130H fleet is assigned to the 16th Special Operations Squadron, and the unit has been very busy over Bosnia, flying from the Italian base at Brindisi.

Thailand. A further single C-130 was converted in the Surprise Package project with two 40-mm cannon replacing two of the 20-mm variety, and with computerised fire control. Nine more C-130A conversions were delivered to the same standards in the Pave Pronto programme, with Black Crow ignition sensor and a new AN/ASQ-24A Stabilised Tracking Set containing ASQ-145 LLTV and an AVQ-18 laser designator.

So successful was the project that 11 C-130E models were converted to **AC-130E** standard in the Pave Spectre programme. The aircraft were given heavier armour, better avionics including APQ-150 beacon tracking radar, and provision for more ammunition; from 1973 the 10 survivors were brought to **AC-130H** standard with the installation of uprated

T56-A-15 engines. The final developments for use in South East Asia were the fitting of a 105-mm howitzer and laser target designator in the Pave Aegis programme. At the end of the Vietnam War, remaining AC-130A/H aircraft returned to the US to serve with the 1st Special Operations Wing at Eglin AFB. AC-130Hs had their rear Miniguns deleted and do not usually carry forward Miniguns, either; from 1978 the aircraft were fitted with inflight-refuelling receptacles. The SOFI (Special Operations Force Improvement) programme of the early 1990s upgraded the sensors, fire control computers, ECM and nav/comms suite.

The AC-130 was used operationally again with the US occupation of Grenada in October 1983. and was later involved in operations in Panama (1989) and the Gulf (1991). Five AC-130Hs were used in Desert Storm to conduct night operations against ground targets. One aircraft was lost in the Gulf and another during operations over Somalia in 1994. AC-130Hs have also been on night patrol over Bosnia flying from Brin-

disi. The wing has renumbered as the 16th SOW.

The AC-130Hs remain in service with the 16th Special Operations Squadron at Hurlburt Field, but the AC-130As were retired in 1995. A new squadron (4th SOS) was established to operate the latest AC-130U, which is described separately.

SPECIFICATION

Lockheed AC-130E Hercules
generally similar to the C-130 except in the following particulars:

From the front an AC-130H displays its fearsome arsenal. The two 20-mm Vulcan cannon are similar to those found in USAF fighters, but have been modified to allow sustained firing. Each cannon has 3,000 rounds available.

Weights: empty 72,892 lb (33063 kg)
Speed: maximum speed at 30,000 ft (9145 m) 330 kt (380 mph; 612 km/h); cruising speed 320 kt (368 mph; 592 km/h)
Range: endurance 5 hours 0 minutes
Performance: maximum rate of climb at sea level 1,830 ft (558 m) per minute

Lockheed DC-130 Hercules

The **Lockheed DC-130 Hercules** is a drone controller aircraft employed for a variety of missions as a mother ship and launcher for RPVs, including some employed for reconnaissance in combat. These are carried on four underwing pylons.

Eight **DC-130A** aircraft (seven converted from C-130A, one converted from C-130D) were supplied to the US Air Force. DC-130As launched Combat Dawn reconnaissance RPVs in the Vietnam conflict and in a short-lived effort in Korea. Five of the USAF aircraft were subsequently transferred to the US Navy for drone target work. Three ex-**US Navy** DC-130As are

operated by Tracor Flight Systems for the Naval Air Warfare Center at Point Mugu, CA. These have AN/APN-45 tracking radar in an extended thimble nose, and can have an additional 'chin' radome for microwave guidance.

Seven similar **DC-130E**s were used for carrying reconnaissance drones during the Vietnam War, but all were subsequently converted back to transport configuration. A single **DC-130H** was converted from an HC-130H airframe during 1975-76, and was later redesignated **NC-130H**, although it continued to operate as a drone launcher and control aircraft. It now serves with the **USAF**'s 6514th Test Squadron at Hill AFB.

Three DC-130As are flown from Mojave in support of US Navy missile tests, used to launch drones from underwing.

Lockheed EC-130E Hercules

Several **Lockheed C-130 Hercules** variants currently in service carry the nominal designation **EC-130E**. This has given rise to much confusion over roles and numbers of aircraft, which the USAF has never ventured to clarify. All of these Hercules have a special operations role about which little detail is known. The only aircraft actually built with the EC-130E designation was a single C-130 intended for the USCG as a calibration aircraft. It had no underwing fuel tanks and had additional radio operator and navigation stations for checking the US Navy's worldwide LORAN beacon system. It has since been retired.

Several C-130Es were operated by the 7405th Operations Squadron at Frankfurt/Rhein-Main to undertake Sigint, Comint and Elint missions, mainly along the Berlin corridors. Outwardly, they were almost

indistinguishable from standard C-130Es but gained the unofficial designation EC-130E. They have been retired.

Three further versions of 'EC-130E' are operational today. The first of these is the Airborne Battlefield Command and Control Center (**ABCCC**) variant. This aircraft is the least sensitive EC-130E and attempts have been made to sell it to foreign customers. It first appeared in Vietnam, where it solved the problem of co-ordinating all the tactical information supplied by forward air controllers, flare ships and the troops on the ground. Ten aircraft were converted to accommodate the ASC-15 battle staff module in the fuselage. Of these, seven are currently in service. Four aircraft have been re-engined with T56A-15 engines and have inflight refuelling capability. From the module, up to 16 personnel and a comprehen-

The EC-130E ABCCC variant serves with the 355th Wing at Davis-Monthan. It uses palletised equipment complete with operator consoles to fly as a tactical airborne command post.

sive communication fit can command and organise the battlefield situation. The ram air scoop, on the port side, is used to provide cooling for its systems and is the most obvious clue to this aircraft's role. Two

new **ABCCC-III** capsules were delivered in January 1991. Fitted with satellite communication equipment, increased computer power and a JTIDS datalink, they controlled almost half the attack missions in the Gulf.

EC-130E Comfy Levi aircraft (above) are rarely seen with their full antenna suite fitted, and the exact nature of their mission is unknown. The antenna fit is occasionally seen on C-130s of transport units (right).

Five **EC-130E(CL)**s have been modified to undertake Elint (and probably jamming) missions codenamed Senior Scout. There is little outward indication of their special role, since mission equipment uses antennas that are fitted to removable doors and fairings. These highly secretive aircraft are colloquially known as 'Comfy Levis' and are operated by the 193rd SOS, PA ANG. In the cargo hold, mission specialists are carried in a pressurised capsule, similar to the ABCCC variant. For operations, these aircraft are flown to Andrews AFB where mission equipment is installed and mission crew are picked up, both coming from the National Security Agency at Fort Meade. Post-mission, the aircraft are demodified before they return to Harrisburg.

The 193rd SOS also operates the **EC-130E(RR)** 'Rivet Rider' Hercules alongside its EC-130E(CL)s. Four aircraft are tasked with 'Volant Solo' Comint and Sigint missions. They have the ability to tap into and rebroadcast radio or TV transmissions, for 'aid to the civil power' in times of emergency or during natural disasters, or for propaganda/psy war tasks. The latter role was highlighted by their deployment during the Gulf War. Outwardly, they are the most obviously modified EC-130Es, having a huge blade antenna on the fin leading edge, and a pair of large 'axe-head' antennas under the wing. They have undergone a major upgrading of their systems to allow colour TV broadcasting, and this upgrade has altered their appearance radically, adding two large bullet antennas on each side of the fin in place of the leading edge blade. All 'Rivet Rider' aircraft currently wear an overall two-tone grey colour scheme.

SPECIFICATION

Lockheed EC-130E Hercules
generally similar to the C-130E except in the following particulars
Weights: empty 72,892 lb (33063 kg); maximum payload 45,000 lb (20412 kg)
Speed: maximum speed at 30,000 ft (9145 m) 330 kt (380 mph; 612 km/h); cruising speed 320 kt (362 mph; 592 km/h)
Range: 4,080 nm (4,698 miles; 7560 km)
Performance: maximum rate of climb at sea level 1,830 ft (558 m) per minute

A current configuration EC-130E(RR) flies in formation with the older antenna fit (background).

Lockheed EC-130H Compass Call

The **Lockheed EC-130H Compass Call** is the latest of several electronic warfare versions of the familiar Hercules, 10 of which serve the US Air Force for communications intrusion and jamming duties. In both missions, EC-130Hs supplement earlier EC-130E aircraft (described separately). The EC-130H 'Compass Call' is used for stand-off jamming The aircraft is distinguished externally from other Hercules variants by the antennas housed in a pair of blister fairings fitted to the rear fuselage, and an array of wire antennas connected to a gantry suspended beneath the tail. All EC-130H 'Compass Call' aircraft are assigned to the 41st and 43rd Electronic Combat Squadrons of the 355th Wing at Davis-Monthan AFB, AZ.

The EC-130H has a large antenna array supported by the fin surfaces for jamming enemy communications.

Lockheed EC-130V Hercules

Following experience in using borrowed E-2 Hawkeyes in the anti-drug trafficking role, the US Coast Guard decided to procure its own AEW platform by converting an HC-130H (1721) to **EC-130V** configuration, with the Hawkeye's APS-145 radar mounted above the fuselage and three palletised operator's consoles inside the cabin. General Dynamics undertook the conversion, which first flew on 31 July 1991.

The aircraft went into service with USCG Clearwater, but following extensive evaluations on interdiction patrols lasting up to 10

hours, the programme was considered too costly and was cancelled. The single EC-130V was handed over to the **US Air Force** on 1 October 1993, for use in an undisclosed 'black' programme in the hands of the 6545th Test Squadron at Hill AFB, Utah.

The USCG scrapped the EC-130V on cost grounds, but the aircraft is still operated from Hill AFB on classified research projects by the US Air Force.

Lockheed HC-130 Hercules

Intended as a long-range search and rescue aircraft, the **Lockheed HC-130 Hercules** has served with the **US Air Force** and **US Coast Guard**. The earliest model, the **HC-130B** (formerly designated **R8V-1G**), is now out of service, leaving five current variants. Most numerous of these are the 43 **HC-130H**s delivered to the USAF between 1965 and 1966. These snub-nosed Hercules are fitted with a large distinctive radome for the AN/ARD-17 Cook Aerial Tracker above the forward fuselage and a large observation window in the port fuselage to locate satellite capsules during re-entry from orbit. Some aircraft still retain the nose-mounted arms of the Fulton STAR (surface-to-air recovery) gear. Eighteen similar aircraft were delivered to the USCG, without the AN/ARD-17 radome or the

Fulton STAR (although they retain the Fulton nose shape). A further 11 Hercules known as **HC-130H-7**s also carry Coast Guard colours. These are fitted with the standard C-130 'Pinocchio' nose but are otherwise identical to the HC-130H.

Intended as a combat-capable rescue aircraft, the **HC-130N** differed from the HC-130H in being equipped with inflight-refuelling HRUs underwing. Fifteen remain in USAF service. Soon after the introduction of this version came the **HC-130P**, which combines the appearance and ability of the HC-130H (including its Fulton STAR equipment and associated nose), with the air-to-air refuelling role of the HC-130N; 12 of

these aircraft remain in squadron service with the USAF and are used primarily to refuel rescue and special operations helicopters. In 1991 the first of a new-build version, the **HC-130H(N)**, was delivered to the 210th RQS, Alaska ANG, differing primarily from earlier aircraft in having extensively modernised avionics. This version lacks Fulton gear and AN/ARD-17 equipment, but is equipped with underwing HRUs. Other ANG units which operate HC-130s are the 129th RQS, California ANG and the 102nd RQS, New York ANG. AFRes HC-130s are operated by the 301st and 304th Rescue Squadrons of the 939th Rescue Wing, respectively based at Portland, OR, Homestead, FL, and Selfridge, MI. Active-duty Combat Shadows (codename for HC-130) fly with the 16th SOW, 352nd SOG, 353rd SOG and 919th SOW.

For standard combat rescue work (as opposed to Special Operations support) the HC-130 serves with three Air National Guard units, an Air Force Reserve Wing and one active-duty unit. Depicted here is one the Alaska ANG's HC-130H(N)s from the 210th Rescue Squadron, refuelling an HH-60G. The Alaskan aircraft were newly-built for the unit, based on the latest C-130H airframe and with the latest nav/comms equipment. Dedicated rescue equipment includes the addition of HRUs underwing for refuelling helicopters, and the ability to carry one or two auxiliary fuel tanks in the cabin. Like all HC-130s, they feature a large observation window in each side of the forward fuselage, equipped with a sheepskin-covered observer's seat.

SPECIFICATION

Wing: span 132 ft 7 in (40.41 m); aspect ratio 10.09; area 1,745.00 sq ft (162.12 m²)
Fuselage and tail: length 98 ft 9 in (30.10 m) with recovery system folded and 106 ft 4 in (32.41 m) with recovery system spread; height 38 ft 3 in (11.66 m); tailplane span 52 ft 8 in (16.05 m); wheel track 14 ft 3 in (4.35 m); wheel base 32 ft 0.75 in (9.77 m)
Powerplant: four Allison T56-A-15 turboprops each rated at 4,508 ehp (3362 ekW)
Weights: basic empty 72,611 lb (32936 kg); maximum normal take-off 155,000 lb (70307 kg); maximum overload take-off 175,000 lb (79379 kg)
Fuel and load: internal fuel 6,960 US gal (26344 litres); external fuel up to two 1,360-US gal (5146-litre) underwing tanks; maximum payload 43,811 lb (19872 kg)
Speed: maximum speed at 30,000 ft (9145 m) 325 kt

Among the USAF's combat SAR assets are 10 HC-130N/Ps assigned to the Reserve's 939th Rescue Wing.

(374 mph; 602 km/h); maximum cruising speed 318 kt (366 mph; 589 km/h); economical cruising speed

300 kt (345 mph; 556 km/h)
Range: with maximum internal and external fuel and 20,000-lb (9072-kg) payload 4,460 nm (5,135 miles; 8264 km); range with maximum payload 2,045 nm (2,356 miles; 3792 km)
Performance: maximum rate of climb at sea level

1,820 ft (555 m) per minute; service ceiling 33,000 ft (10060 m); take-off distance to 50 ft (15 m) 5,160 ft (1573 m) at maximum take-off weight; landing distance from 50 ft (15 m) 2,430 ft (741 m) at 100,000 lb (45360 kg)

AFSOC's HC-130s are undergoing the SOFI modification , distinguished by the addition of a FLIR turret under the nose. This aircraft is a 9th SOS HC-130N, wearing the latest two-tone scheme.

Lockheed KC-130 Hercules

The US Marine Corps required a tactical transport which could double as an inflight-refuelling tanker using the probe and drogue system. In August 1957 two US Air Force C-130As were borrowed and each fitted with two 506-US gal (1915-litre) tanks in the fuselage and two underwing pods containing the hose equipment. So successful were the trials that 46 **Lockheed KC-130F Hercules** were ordered for delivery from 1960. The KC-130F is based on the C-130B airframe, initially with Allison T56-A-7 engines but later re-engined

The KC-130H is the standard export tanker version with an HDU pod under each wing. Brazil had two delivered as such, and subsequently converted several C-130H transports to tanker status.

with the T56-A-16. An easily removable fuselage tank holding 3,600 US gal (13627 litres) is fitted, and the two equipment pods enable fuel transfer at the rate of 300 US gal (1136 litres) per minute. As well as the additional fuel, the tanker is able to transfer its own surplus fuel. Originally designated **GV-1**, the first production aircraft flew on 22 January 1960. The type currently equips VMGR-152, -252 and -352 of the USMC, and VR-22 of the USN.

To cope with attrition, the USMC ordered 14 **KC-130R** tankers based on the C-130H. These aircraft feature the T56-A-16 power-plant and pylon-mounted fuel tanks with an extra 2,720 US gal (10296 litres) of fuel. Fuelling of this variant is by a single point. Initial deliveries were to VMGR-352 at MCAS El Toro, CA. The most recent USMC variant is the **KC-130T**, 22 of which have

been ordered for USMC service. This model has updated avionics, a new search radar and improved navigation systems. The most recent deliveries have been of the **KC-130T-30** variant, with stretched fuselage.

Although not in service with US forces, the **KC-130H** (similar in most respects to the KC-130R) has been successfully exported to several countries. Foreign interest in the tanker Hercules has been high, as detailed below.

In the UK, the Falklands War resulted in an urgent RAF demand for increased tanker support. Marshalls of Cambridge, the UK support contractor for the Hercules, started work in May 1982 on converting a standard Hercules C.Mk 1 to tanker configuration. Four ex-Andover 900-Imp gal (4091-litre) tanks were fitted in the fuselage and a single Flight Refuelling Ltd FR.Mk 17B HDU was attached to the rear cargo ramp door. The first flight took place on 7 June 1982, and within three months four aircraft had been converted. Designated **Hercules**

C.Mk 1K, six such aircraft are operated by the Lyneham Transport Wing. Four aircraft have been subsequently fitted with wingtip ESM pods for surveillance duties.

Canada's CC-130H(T) tankers are basic H models with a 3,600-Imp gal (16365-litre) fuselage tank and FRL Mk 32B wing pods, installed by Northwest Industries.

SPECIFICATION

Lockheed KC-130F Hercules
generally similar to the C-130F Hercules except in the following particulars:
Powerplant: four Allison T56-A-16 turboprops each rated at 4,910 ehp (3661 ekW)
Fuel and load: maximum payload 3,600 US gal (13627 litres) of additional fuel in a removable cargo-hold tank
Speed: maximum cruising speed at 30,000 ft (9145 m) 330 kt (380 mph; 612 km/h); refuelling speed 308 kt (355 mph; 571 km/h)
Range: typical range to transfer 31,000 lb (14061 kg) of fuel 870 nm (1,002 miles; 1613 km)

OPERATORS

Argentina: KC-130H (2) with Grupo I
Brazil: KC-130H (5) with 1°/1° GTT
Canada: CC-130H(T) (5) with No. 435 Sqn
Indonesia: KC-130B (2) with No. 31 Sqn
Israel: KC-130H (3) with Nos 103/131 Sqn
Saudi Arabia: KC-130H (7) with Nos 4/16 Sqns
Singapore: KC-130B (4), KC-130H (1) with No. 122 Sqn
Spain: KC-130H (5) with Ala 31
United Kingdom: Hercules C.Mk 1K (6) , to be retired in mid-1996
US Marine Corps: VMGR-152 (KC-130R – MCAS Futenma), VMGR-234 (KC-130T, KC-130T-30 – NAS Glenview), VMGR-252 (KC-130F, KC-130R – MCAS Cherry Point), VMGRT-253 (KC-130F – MCAS Cherry Point), VMGR-352 (KC-130F, KC-130R – MCAS El Toro), VMGR-452 (KC-130T, KC-130T-30 – Stewart ANGB)

The only operator of a stretched tanker is the USMC, which flies the KC-130T-30 with VMGR-452.

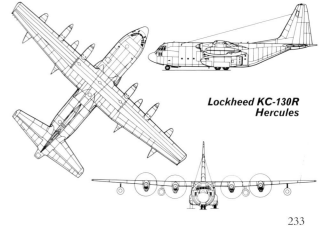

Lockheed KC-130R Hercules

Lockheed LC-130F/H/R

The Lockheed LC-130F/H/R Hercules transports are winterised aircraft designed for support operations (as denoted by the 'L' prefix) on the Antarctic ice shield and equipped with skis. LC-130F/H/R aircraft, with slightly redesigned fuselages, are designed for very long-range operations in polar environments. In flight, they can be distinguished by a nose fairing designed to hold the nose ski when retracted. All can be equipped with JATO (jet-assisted take-off) rockets for short-distance take-off from ice fields.

The C-130D was the first ski-equipped Hercules. These have been replaced by four **LC-130H** aircraft with the 139th Airlift Squadron, 109th Airlift Group, NY ANG at Schenectady, the only unit to operate LC-130s in the **USAF**.

The **LC-130F** was the first **US Navy** variant for Antarctic operations (based on the C-130B variant). Four joined VXE-6 'Puckered Penguins' in 1969. The squadron recovered one LC-130F in 1987 which had spent 16 years buried in snow and which resumed flying in the early 1990s. The **LC-130R** (six built) is the final ski-equipped Hercules and has joined the earlier version with VXE-6. It is powered by the 4,910-eshp (3663-ekW) T56-A-16 engine.

VXE-6 is based at NAS Point Mugu, but its ski-equipped LC-130s perform their primary mission in the Antarctic, supporting US scientific establishments, the major site being at McMurdo Sound. The aircraft deploy to the region during the Antarctic summer, returning to Point Mugu during the winter for training and servicing.

Below: The USAF's ski-equipped LC-130Hs are operated by the 139th Airlift Squadron/New York ANG, and are primarily tasked with support of Arctic installtions such as early warning radar sites.

SPECIFICATION

Lockheed LC-130R Hercules
generally similar to the C-130F Hercules except in the following particulars
Powerplant: four Allison T56-A-15 turboprops each rated at 4,508 ehp (3362 ekW)
Weights: empty equipped 78,492 lb (35604 kg); maximum take-off 175,000 lb (79380 kg)
Fuel and load: internal fuel 45,240 lb (20520 kg); external fuel up to 17,680 lb (8020 kg) in two 1,360-US gal (5148-litre) underwing tanks

Lockheed MC-130

US Air Force interest in variants of the Hercules tailored to the support of Special Forces began in the Vietnam War, when 17 C-130Es were converted to C-130E-I standard, with Fulton STAR recovery gear on the nose for the mid-air retrieval of agents from the ground. The system used a balloon which was inflated on the ground and sent aloft carrying a cable, to which the agent was attached. The C-130E-I snagged the cable between two forks which hinged forward from the nose, picking up the agent who was then winched in to the rear ramp. Fulton was not used in combat, but the aircraft themselves undertook special missions in night and adverse weather.

In the late 1970s the designation **MC-130E Combat Talon** was adopted as standard for the Special Forces Hercules, although 'Skyhook' EC-130E, C-130H(CT) and HC-130E had also been applied to some aircraft at some point. The basic MC-130E featured inflight-refuelling capability, uprated T56-A-15 engines, Omega and inertial navigation systems. There are three current sub-variants: the **MC-130E-C** (Clamp) which has Fulton STAR equipment and a nose radome extended downwards to house the radar in a lower position (below the Fulton gear); the **MC-130-Y** (Yank) which has a standard 'Pinocchio' nose; and the **MC-130E-S** (Swap) which is reportedly used for Sigint work.

MC-130Es feature the APQ-122(V)8 weather avoidance and long-range navigation radar, to which a terrain-following function has been retrofitted. Combined with a forward-looking infra-red sensor in a retractable turret, this allows the crew to penetrate hostile air space at night or in adverse weather at very low level and navigate accurately to a set position where Special Forces can be inserted by parachute, or supplied from the air. Makeshift landing strips can be used for the insertion of vehicles and retrieval of teams. An important task for the MC-130 is 'FARPing' (forward air refuelling point) for Special Forces helicopters, whereby the Hercules sets up at a landing strip and provides a fuel source for landing helicopters. MC-130Es can also carry the inflight-refuelling pods used by MH-53s and MH-60s.

Entering service is the **MC-130H Combat Talon II**, 26 of which are on order to augment and eventually replace the MC-130E fleet. These have new radar (APQ-170) in a revised radome, with a FLIR turret mounted underneath. Specialist equipment includes a low-level aerial delivery and container release system, and comprehensive defensive countermeasures. The aircraft are manufactured by Lockheed with minimal equipment, and delivered to IBM Federal Systems Division for the installation of mission equipment.

The first aircraft flew in December 1987, and began equipment flight trials at Edwards AFB in spring 1988. The 8th Special Operations Squadron of the 16th SOW received its first MC-130H in June 1990. The 15th SOS has since been formed to operate all operational US-based MC-130Hs. The 8th SOS retains MC-130Es, which also fly with the 1st SOS/353rd SOG at Kadena AB, Okinawa, while the 7th SOS/352nd SOG at RAF Mildenhall operates four MC-130Hs. The 58th SOW at Kirtland AFB flies four MC-130Hs for training and the 418th TS (412th TW) at Edwards AFB has a few examples for test and trials duties.

The MC-130H is the latest Special Operations version of the Hercules, readily identified by its enlarged radome. MC-130Hs from the Europe-based 352nd SOG have been used widely in Bosnia.

Lockheed MC-130H Combat Talon II

This MC-130H was one of the early aircraft, used for testing with the 418th Test Squadron at Edwards AFB. It is depicted during that time, when it wore the 'ED' tailcode. It is now assigned to the 15th Special Operations Squadron at Eglin AFB, Florida.

REAR RAMP
The ramp of the MC-130 can be opened in flight to air drop equipment, and has baffles to allow it to be opened at higher speeds than the ramps of standard variants. Combat Talon II crews regularly practise high-speed, low-level air-drop tactics to deliver loads with great accuracy. Alternative methods for delivering paratroops are HAHO (High-Altitude, High-Opening) and HALO (High-Altitude, Low-Opening). the first method allows troops to be dropped while the aircraft remains miles away from the drop zone, while the second gets troops on the ground in the shortest possible time.

CREW
The standard Hercules has a flight deck crew of three – two pilots and a navigator. The MC-130H adds an electronic warfare officer, and usually carries more than one loadmaster.

POWERPLANT
The MC-130H is powered by four Allison T56-A-15 turboprops, each developing 4,508 shp (3362 kW) and driving a Hamilton Standard 54H60 constant-speed propeller.

FUEL
Six integral wing tanks have a capacity of 6,960 US gal (26344 litres), to which are usually added two 1,360-US gal (5146-litre) underwing tanks. The MC-130H can carry HRU units underwing to refuel special forces helicopters in flight.

DEFENSIVE SYSTEMS
The Combat Talon II is exceptionally well protected against most threats. It carries ALQ-8 ECM pods underwing, ALR-69 radar warning receivers, ALQ-172 radar detector and jammer, APR-46 ESM, AAR-44 missile launch warning detector, QRC 84-02 IR jammer and internal chaff/flare dispensers.

LOW-LEVEL AVIONICS
In the enlarged nose radome is an Electronics and Space Corporation APQ-70 multi-mode radar. This provides ground mapping and weather detection functions, but is most useful as a terrain-following tool. In this mode it can look into turns to provide greater safety at very low level. Underneath the radome is a turret for the Texas Instruments AAQ-15 forward-looking infra-red. This can be slewed to flight vectors to provide visual back-up at night to the terrain-following radar.

An MC-130E-C kicks up the dust during a rough-field exercise. The 'Clamp' variant has a drooped radome for terrain-following radar, and forks for the Fulton recovery system. The MC-130E-Y 'Yank' lacks both the Fulton forks and the large radome. Most have been updated to Mod 90 standard with new mission computers and a wealth of avionics improvements, including the addition of a retractable FLIR under the nose.

SPECIFICATION

Lockheed MC-130E Hercules
generally similar to the C-130E except in the following particulars:
Weights: empty 72,892 lb (33063 kg)
Speed: maximum speed 318 kt (366 mph; 589 km/h); speed for personnel airdrop at 50 ft (15 m) 125 kt (144 mph; 232 km/h)
Range: 2,000 nm (2,303 miles; 3706 km)
Performance: maximum rate of climb at sea level 1,600 ft (488 m) per minute

Lockheed C-140 JetStar

The **Lockheed JetStar** was produced as a private venture to meet the US Air Force UCX requirement for a utility jet for crew readiness training, navaid calibration, transport and other duties. The prototype flew on 4 September 1957 powered by two Bristol Orpheus turbojet engines. Production aircraft have four Pratt & Whitney JT12-8 turbojets, wings fitted with a high-lift leading edge, twin-wheel landing gear and engine thrust-reversers. External tanks at mid-span were intended to be optional, but became standard. In October 1959 the USAF selected the JetStar as the **C-140**; the aircraft was also developed for the civilian executive jet market. Five were used by the Special Air Missions wing, and others by the Airways and Air Communications Service for inspecting overseas navaid calibration duties. The C-140 has been

retired from USAF service, but JetStars continue to fly on VIP transport duties with **Indonesia** (two), **Iran** (two), **Mexico** (1) and **Saudi Arabia** (two).

SPECIFICATION

Lockheed Model 1329-25 JetStar II
Wing: span 54 ft 6 in (16.60 m); aspect ratio 5.27; area 542.50 sq ft (50.40 m²)
Fuselage and tail: length 60 ft 5 in (18.42 m); height 20 ft 5 in (6.23 m); tailplane span 24 ft 9 in (7.55 m); wheel track 12 ft 3.5 in (3.75 m); wheel base 20 ft 7 in (6.28 m)
Powerplant: four Garrett TFE731-3 turbojets each rated at 3,700 lb st (16.46 kN) dry
Weights: operating empty 24,178 lb (10967 kg); maximum take-off 44,000 lb (19844 kg)
Fuel and load: internal fuel 2,686 US gal

Only a handful of JetStars are left in military service, operating as VIP/staff transports. Saudi Arabia still operates two.

(13953 litres); external fuel none; maximum payload 2,822 lb (1280 kg)
Speed: never exceed speed Mach 0.87; maximum level and maximum cruising speed 'clean' at 30,000 ft (9145 m) 475 kt (547 mph; 880 km/h); economical cruising speed at 35,000 ft (10670 m) 441 kt (508 mph; 817 km/h)
Range: range 2,770 nm (3,190 miles; 5132 km) with maximum fuel or 2,600 nm (2,994 miles; 4818 km) with maximum payload
Performance: maximum rate of climb at sea level 4,200 ft (1280 m) per minute; service ceiling 36,000 ft (10975 m); take-off distance to 50 ft (15 m) 4,950 ft (1509 m) at maximum take-off weight; landing distance from 50 ft (15 m) 4,180 ft (1274 m)

Lockheed C-141 StarLifter

First flown on 17 December 1963, the **Lockheed C-141A StarLifter** provided the **US Air Force** with a fast and capacious long-range jet transport with which it could replace the slow C-124 and narrow-cabin C-135 in service with the Military Air Transport Service. Drawing heavily on experience with the C-130 Hercules, the StarLifter featured a fuselage of similar cross-section (10 ft x 9 ft/ 3.05 m x 2.74 m), two large clamshell doors and a rear ramp that could be opened in flight for air-dropping, rear side parachute doors on both sides and an undercarriage housed in separate fairings.

Swept wings were adopted for high-speed cruise, with powerful high lift devices provided for good low-speed field performance. The C-141A was also fitted with an all-weather landing system. Power came from four podded TF33 turbofans, and all fuel was housed in integral wing tanks. The aircraft entered service in October 1964 and was soon impressed on the air bridge to South East Asia to supply the war effort in Vietnam, commencing squadron operations with MAC on 23 April 1965.

Not long after the C-141A entered ser-

Lengthening the StarLifter to produce the C-141B greatly increased the type's load-hauling capability, while the addition of a refuelling receptacle allowed global operations.

vice, it became obvious that its maximum payload of 70,847 lb (32136 kg) (or 92,000 lb/41731 kg on aircraft configured to carry LGM-30 Minuteman ICBMs) was rarely achieved, the aircraft 'bulking out' in terms of volume long before its weight limit was approached.

During the 1970s, the entire fleet (minus four **NC-141A** aircraft used for test purposes) was returned to Lockheed for an ambitious programme that involved 270 aircraft. A considerable stretch to the fuselage (totalling 23 ft 4 in/7.11 m) allowed the resultant **C-141B** to carry loads much closer to its design payload (overall cargo capacity has been increased by over 30 per cent). The programme added the equivalent of 90 new C-141s in terms of capacity at low relative cost. At the same time, Lockheed installed inflight-refuelling capability in a characteristic humped fairing above the

flight deck, providing the StarLifter with true global airlift capacity. The prototype **YC-141B** made its first flight on 24 March 1977 and Lockheed completed the final C-141B on 29 June 1982.

Throughout its career the StarLifter has been the workhorse of the US Air Force, flying regular supply missions around the world in addition to special requirements. The latter have included disaster relief, evacuations, aid delivery and missions in support of combat operations. Perhaps the StarLifter's finest hour came in the second half of 1990, when the entire fleet was instrumental in transporting much of the equipment for Desert Storm.

Of inestimable value to the US Air Force

is the StarLifter's sheer versatility. Like that of the Hercules, the C-141's main hold is fitted with tie-down points and floor cleats that allow it to be rapidly reconfigured for many missions. Palletised passenger seats can be fitted for 166 people, while by using canvas seats some 205 passengers or 168 paratroops can be carried. For a medevac mission, the StarLifter can carry, for instance, 103 litter patients and 113 walking wounded. Although most heavy equipment is moved by the C-5 Galaxy, the StarLifter can still carry a Sheridan tank, an AH-1 Cobra helicopter or five HMMWV vehicles. Thirteen standard cargo pallets can be admitted, and other loads can include aircraft engines, food supplies, fuel drums or nuclear weapons.

Thirteen C-141Bs of the 437th AW are equipped for the Special Operations Low Level (SOLL) role with increased surviviability measures, the most obvious being the addition of a FLIR turret beneath the nose.

Slowly being replaced by the McDonnell Douglas C-17A, beginning with the 437th Airlift Wing, the C-141B serves with the following active-duty squadrons: 19th/20th Airlift Squadrons (60th AW, Travis AFB, CA), 4th/7th/8th AS (62nd AW, McChord AFB, WA), 15th/16th AS (437th AW, Charleston AFB, SC), 6th/13th/18th AS (305th AMW, McGuire AFB, NJ) and the 57th AS (97th Air Mobility Wing, Altus AFB, OK) of AETC.

As active-duty units deactivate, the aircraft are being passed to reservist units. Air National Guard units currently equipped with the StarLifter are the 155th AS/164th AG of the Tennessee ANG at Memphis IAP, 183rd AS/172nd AG and the Mississippi ANG at Jackson MAP. The Air Force Reserve as the following squadrons: 300th/700th/701st AS (315th AW, Charleston AFB, 708th AS/710th AS (349th AMW, Travis AFB), 89th/359th AS (445th AW, Wright-Patterson AFB), 97th/313th/728th AS (446th AW, McChord AFB),

The elongated fuselage of the C-141B is graphically illustrated in this view. The StarLifter is slowly being replaced on active-duty units by the C-17, although it maintains an important position in the USAF airlift effort.

729th/730th AS (452nd AMW, March AFB), 756th AS (459th AW, Andrews AFB) and 335th/702nd/732nd AS (514th AMW, McGuire AFB). Finally, the 412th Test Wing at Edwards AFB, CA, still flies the short-fuselage NC-141A test aircraft, including one aircraft configured as an Advanced Radar Test Bed (ARTB) airborne laboratory.

Of current major concern is the rapid ageing of the C-141 fleet. There a number of reasons for this, most notably lower altitude operations imposed on certain special-missions and paradrops-tasked aircraft. The fatigue life of 45,000 hours specified in conversion to C-141B standard may be reduced due to wing cracks and other fatigue problems.

SPECIFICATION

Lockheed C-141B StarLifter
Wing: span 159 ft 11 in (48.74 m); aspect ratio 7.94; area 3,228.00 sq ft (299.88 m²)

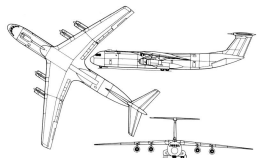
Lockheed C-141B StarLifter

After initial service in white and grey, the C-141 fleet adopted a 'lizard' scheme (illustrated). Now the fleet is being painted in an overall light grey.

Fuselage and tail: length 168 ft 3.5 in (51.29 m); height 39 ft 3 in (11.96 m); wheel track 17 ft 6 in (5.33 m); wheel base 66 ft 4 in (20.22 m)
Powerplant: four Pratt & Whitney TF33-P-7 turbofans each rated at 21,000 lb st (93.41 kN) dry
Weights: operating empty 148,120 lb (67186 kg); maximum take-off 343,000 lb (155580 kg)

Fuel and load: internal fuel 23,592 US gal (89305 litres); external fuel none; maximum payload 90,880 lb (41222 kg) at 2.25 g or 70,605 lb (32026 kg) at 2.5 g
Speed: maximum cruising speed at high altitude 492 kt (566 mph; 910 km/h); economical cruising speed at high altitude 430 kt (495 mph; 796 km/h)
Range: ferry range 5,550 nm (6,390 miles; 10280 km);

range 2,550 nm (2,936 miles; 4725 km) with maximum payload
Performance: maximum rate of climb at sea level 2,920 ft (890 m) per minute; service ceiling 41,600 ft (12680 m); take-off distance to 50 ft (15 m) 5,800 ft (1768 m) at maximum take-off weight; landing distance from 50 ft (15 m) 3,700 ft (1128 m) at normal landing weight

Lockheed (General Dynamics) F-16A/B Fighting Falcon

Lockheed Martin TAS
PO Box 748, Fort Worth
TX 761201, USA

The **Lockheed F-16 Fighting Falcon** is the most numerous fighter in the West. Many **F-16A/B**s have seen well over a decade's service, being modernised in operational capability upgrade programmes.

The Fighting Falcon was conceived as a lightweight 'no frills' fighter for air-to-air combat but despite this, and despite its small dimensions and light weight, has evolved into a versatile and effective multi-role workhorse. First flown on 20 January 1974, the service-test **YF-16** defeated Northrop's YF-17 in a fly-off competition. The first of eight FSD F-16A airframes flew in 1975, the first FSD F-16B in 1977. The two-seat version retains wing and fuselage dimensions of the single-seater while sacrificing 1,500 lb (680 kg) of fuel.

Nicknamed the 'Viper', the F-16 cuts a unique silhouette, with its shock-inlet air intake located under the forward fuselage below its pilot. The Falcon's unusual shape features wing/body blending and large leading-edge root extensions to enhance lift at high angles of attack. While its high Alpha capability is limited by comparison with that of the F/A-18 and the latest Russian 'super-fighters', its very high thrust to weight ratio, fast roll rate and high lift wing make it a very agile fighter. Among its once novel characteristics, the F-16 is statically unstable, relying upon a central computer and electronic FBW controls to remain controllable.

The F-16A pilot sits on a zero-zero ACES II canted to recline 30°. This improves average g tolerance and necessitates provi-

Israel still uses the F-16A in numbers, most aircraft having been fitted with extra local equipment, such as the large chaff/flare dispensers carried here.

sion of a limited-movement pressure-sensing sidestick controller in place of a conventional joystick. The cockpit has HUD and multifunction displays, and a one-piece canopy of blown polycarbonate with no windscreen and thus no framing forward of the pilot's shoulderline. This gives an incomparable all-round view, the F-16's most radically new feature and a great boon for dogfighting. The two-seat F-16B has full combat capability, but with reduced fuel capacity.

The F-16A/B is armed with a General Electric M61A1 Vulcan 20-mm cannon with 511 rounds, located on the port side at the

Right: Thailand has received two batches of F-16A/Bs, the first arriving in 1988 and the second in 1995. The latter batch, of which an example is illustrated, serves with 403 Squadron, the others with 103 Sqn.

Below: Among the satisfied customers for the F-16A is Indonesia. In the late 1990s surplus USAF aircraft will become available for sale to many countries, including those of Eastern Europe.

Left: The last unmodified F-16As in USAF service flew with the Air Force Reserve, like these 93rd FS examples.

Above: Pakistan's F-16 force is largely optimised for air defence. They have scored several kills in battles along the Afghan border.

Maverick missiles, and GBU-10 and GBU-15 guided weapons. Except for ADF variants (described separately), all F-16A/Bs now have air-to-ground work as their primary duty, with air combat important but secondary. Still, pilots praise the manoeuvrability, high *g* tolerance, heat-seeking missiles and gun, all which enable them to 'yank and bank' with an enemy fighter. Pilots are not pleased about what one flier calls "the conscious decision not to give it a radar missile" to fight beyond visual range, claiming that "we don't have a long enough spear to do battle with 'Floggers' and 'Fulcrums'."

NATO's search for an F-104 replacement led in June 1975 to the 'sale of the century' in which Belgium, Denmark, the Netherlands and Norway selected the F-16A/B. SABCA in Belgium was responsible for the manufacture of 221 aircraft mainly for Belgium and Denmark, while Fokker in Holland built 300 aircraft primarily for the Royal Netherlands Air Force and Norway. Some Dutch aircraft are equipped with a centreline tactical reconnaissance pod, and are designated **F-16A(R)**. Subsequent

blend between wing and fuselage. On a typical mission, an F-16A/B can carry as much as 16,700 lb (7575 kg) of ordnance, including Mk 20 Rockeye and CBU-87 cluster bombs, Mk 83 and Mk 84 500-lb (227-kg) and 1,000-lb (454-kg) bombs, AGM-65

Left: Tactical reconnaissance is the primary role of a few KLu aircraft, equipped with a centreline Orpheus camera pod.

Below: Like several overseas customers, Venezuela was offered the F-16/79, but eventually received F100-powered F-16A/B Block 15s.

OCUs have brought improvements to F-16A/Bs on both continents, while additional countries have taken the A model 'Viper' into their inventories. Many of these nations were initially offered the significantly inferior J79-powered **F-16/79**, but were able to buy the full-standard F100-engined F-16 when President Reagan relaxed some of the arms sales controls imposed by his predecessor.

Service entry

Delivery of operational USAF F-16A/Bs began in January 1979 to the 388th Tactical Fighter Wing at Hill AFB, UT. Despite teething troubles with engine malfunctions and structural cracks, the F-16 developed into a superb fighter-bomber. The F100-PW-100 engine encountered problems, including ground-start difficulties, compressor stalls, fuel-pump breakdowns and afterburner malfunctions, most of which were corrected early on in the aircraft's career. The F-15, which shared a common powerplant, suffered similar problems, an ironic development when this commonality was a powerful factor in the selection of the F-16 over the rival Northrop YF-17.

Versions of the F-16A were tested with APG-65 radar and J79 and YJ101 engines. In December 1975, the first YF-16 was rebuilt with twin canards added, to become the USAF Flight Dynamics Laboratory's **CCV** (Control-Configured Vehicle). General Dynamics converted the fifth FSD F-16A into the **AFTI** (Advanced Fighter Technology Integration) aircraft, or **AFTI/F-16A**. The AFTI/F-16A has a triplex digital flight-control system, larger vertical canard surfaces at the air intake, and a thick dorsal spine; this aircraft was used in recent close air support studies before being laid up by funding constraints. The **SCAMP** (Supersonic Cruise and Maneuvering Prototype), or **F-16XL** (described separately), was yet another special version with a 'cranked delta' wing. Two F-16XLs, a single- and a two-seater, have participated in various research efforts.

The F-16A/B was built in distinct production blocks numbered 1, 5, 10, and 15. Forty-three F-16A/B Block 1s (21 F-16As and 22 F-16Bs) can be distinguished from later Fighting Falcons by their black radomes. F-16A/B Block 5s numbered 126 (99 F-16As and 27 F-16Bs). F-16A/B Block 10 consists of 170 aeroplanes including 145 F-16As and and 24 F-16Bs, in addition to all surviving earlier machines which have been upgraded.

The F-16B has similar dimensions to the single-seater, and gives away no combat capability other than reduced range. This Danish example carries the badge of Esk 726.

F-16A/B Block 15 introduced the first important changes to the F-16. Noteworthy in Block 15 is the extended horizontal stabilator, or 'big tail', now standard on these and all subsequent Fighting Falcons. Pilots prefer the small tail for dogfighting but the big tail gives greater rudder authority when carrying a heavy ordnance load. Because of wing cracks and afterburner problems, the USAF retired all of its pre-Block 15 'small tail' ships in the early-1990s, making Block 15s the oldest F-16s in service. Block 15 comprises 457 American aircraft (410 F-16As, 47 F-16Bs), 270 of which were chosen for conversion to

F-16A/B ADF (described separately) with interceptor duties.

The OCU (Operational Capabilities Upgrade) programme, adopted by Belgium, Denmark, the Netherlands and Norway, improves the avionics and fire control systems, adds ring-laser INS and provides for the upgrading of the F100-PW-200 engine to F100-PW-220E. From 1988 exports were to Block 15 OCU standard, while surviving F-16A/Bs of the AFRes and ANG were upgraded with F100-PW-220Es. Further improvements planned for the F-16A/B include the MLU (Mid-Life Update) which brings the cockpit to Block 50 standard with wide-angle HUD and NVG

compatibility. New avionics include a modular mission computer, APG-66(V2A) radar and Navstar GPS. Options include wiring for intake-mounted FLIR and a helmet-mounted sight. The four European nations are customers for MLU aircraft, and the aircraft sold to Taiwan are also to a similar standard, known as Block 20. USAF aircraft will adopt some of the MLU features.

The first F-16A/B aircraft to be taken directly from USAF inventory for an overseas customer were ex-'Thunderbirds' aircraft transferred to Singapore in 1993 but retained at Luke AFB, AZ, for training of Singaporean pilots.

In December 1992 Lockheed purchased General Dynamics Tactical Military Aircraft Division, which was renamed Lockheed Fort Worth Company on 1 March 1993.

WEAPON OPTIONS

Standard armament includes internal 20-mm M61A1 Vulcan cannon with 511 rounds, and wingtip launch rails for AIM-9L/M/P Sidewinder missiles. Alternatives to Sidewinder are MATRA Magic 2 or Rafael Python 3. Centreline pylon stressed for 2,200 lb (1000 kg) at 5.5 g load or 1,200 lb (544 kg) at 9g, inboard wing pylons stressed to 4,500 lb (2040 kg)/ 2,500 lb (1134 kg), centre wing pylons stressed to 3,500 lb (1587 kg)/2,000 lb (907 kg) and outboard wing pylons (usually used for additional AIM-9 carriage) stressed to 700 lb (318 kg)/ 450 lb (204 kg). Most unguided weaponry is authorised for carriage, including Mk 82 bombs and cluster munitions on triple-ejector racks, or Mk 84 bombs carried singly on wing pylons. Guided weaponry includes AGM-65 Maverick anti-armour missile and Penguin anti-ship missile (Norway). Pakistani aircraft equipped with ATLIS laser-designator and Paveway LGBs. External fuel usually carried in 370-US gal (1400-litre) tanks on inboard pylons. ECM pods usually carried on centreline. KLu F-16A(R) carries Orpheus reconnaissance pod on centreline. GPU-5 Pave Claw cannon pod previously carried by NY ANG F-16As.

BLOCK 15
Also known as MSIP I, the Block 15 upgrades included a wider-span tailplane for greater control authority in out-of-control regimes and better stability, and a track-while-scan mode for the APG-66 radar giving better air-to-air capability.

Lockheed F-16A

Pakistan received 28 F-16As and 12 F-16Bs under the Peace Gate programme, the first being delivered in 1983. They are Block 15 aircraft powered by the F100-PW-200. This aircraft was used by Flt Lt Khalid Mahmood of No. 14 Squadron to shoot down an Afghan AF Sukhoi Su-22 on 3 November 1988. This was his third kill.

MARKINGS
Pakistani F-16s show a variation on the standard two-tone grey scheme, with a wide band around the centre of the aircraft and small patches on the tailplane. No squadron badges are worn.

ARMAMENT
In addition to the internal gun, this aircraft is armed with an air defence load of four Sidewinders. AIM-9Ls are carried on the wingtips, while the older-generation AIM-9P is carried on the outboard pylons.

ATTACK ARMAMENT
Pakistani F-16s are equipped for autonomous laser attacks using the French ATLIS acquisition/designation pod allied to US Paveway II bombs.

84717

RADAR
The APG-66 operates in X-band and offers ten modes covering air-to-air, air-to-ground and sea search. Some of the modes are frequency-agile to avoid jamming. The search angle is 120° in both azimuth and elevation.

Indonesia operates some of the most colourful F-16s. The aircraft were delivered to Block 15 OCU standard.

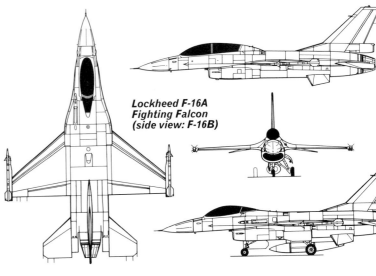

Lockheed F-16A Fighting Falcon (side view: F-16B)

OPERATORS

Deliveries of F-16A/Bs are as follows:
USAF: F-16A (664), F-16B (121) – survivors remain with the 412th Test Wing/Air Force Flight Test Center (Edwards AFB), 75th Air Base Wing (Hill AFB), 93rd Fighter Squadron (Homestead AFB), 182nd Fighter Squadron (Kelly AFB), 162nd Fighter Group (Tucson IAP, ANG training unit)

Belgium: F-16A (136), F-16B (24) – operated by 1, 2, 23, 31, 349 and 350 Sm/Esc, plus the OCS
Denmark: F-16A (54), F-16B (16) – operated by 723, 726, 727 and 730 Esk
Egypt: F-16A (34), F-16B (7) – operated by Nos 72 and 74 Sqns
Indonesia: F-16A (8), F-16B (4) – flown by No. 3 Sqn
Israel: F-16A (67), F-16B (8)
Netherlands: F-16A (177), F-16B (36) – flown by Nos 306, 311, 312, 313, 314, 315, 316, 322 and 323 Sqns, plus the KLu Test Groep
Norway: F-16A (96), F-16B (14) – flown by 331, 332, 334 and 338 Skv
Pakistan: F-16A (28), F-16B (12) – flown by Nos 9, 11 and 14 Sqns. Further 60 A/11 B embargoed and held

at Davis-Monthan AFB
Singapore: F-16A (6), F-16B (4) – flown by 140 Sqn. Nine aircraft leased from USAF for training.
Taiwan: 150 F-16A/B Block 20s on order
Thailand: F-16A (12), F-16B (6) Block 15s in initial batch, second batch of similar numbers of Block 15OCUs
Venezuela: F-16A (18), F-16B (6) – operated by 161 and 162 Esc

SPECIFICATION

Lockheed (General Dynamics) F-16A Fighting Falcon
generally similar to the F-16C Fighting Falcon except in the following particulars:
Fuselage and tail: height 16 ft 5.2 in (5.01 m); tailplane span 18 ft 0.34 in (5.495 m)

Powerplant: one Pratt & Whitney F100-P-100 rated at 14,670 lb st (65.26 kN) dry and 23,830 lb st (106.0 kN) with afterburning
Weights: operational empty 14,567 lb (6607 kg); typical combat take-off 22,785 lb (10335 kg); maximum take-off 33,000 lb (14968 kg)
Fuel and load: internal fuel 6,972 lb (3162 kg); external fuel up to 6,760 lb (3066 kg) in three 300-, 370-, 450- and 600-US gal (1136-, 1400-, 1703- and 2271-litre) drop tanks; maximum ordnance 15,200 lb (6894 kg)

Belgium is planning to put 48 of its F-16As through the MLU programme, with 24 further options depending on future defence budgets. The MLU adds a wide-angle HUD among other improvements.

Lockheed (General Dynamics) ADF F-16A/B Block 15

The **Lockheed (General Dynamics) ADF F-16A Block 15 (Air Defense Fighter)** is the only interceptor assigned to air defence of the North American continent; with the collapse of the Soviet Union, it is almost certainly the last.

The US Air Force decided in October 1986 to convert 270 F-16A/B Block 15 Fighting Falcons to **ADF** standard. The Cold War drove military plans, which called for 14 ANG (Air National Guard) squadrons to receive the ADF to defend North America from bombers and cruise missiles. This combat role had not been foreseen when the F-16 Fighting Falcon was developed and no American unit had operated the F-16 with a radar-guided missile or on a long-range intercept profile.

The ADF conversion is centred primarily

on upgrading the existing AN/APG-66 radar to improve small target detection and provide continuous-wave illumination (thus giving the ability to launch AIM-7 Sparrow BVR missiles). Further modifications include a night identification light in the port forward fuselage, advanced IFF, high frequency,

single side-band radio, improved ECCM and provision for GPS and AIM-120 AMRAAM missile datalink. The ADF F-16 can carry up to six AIM-7 or AIM-9 Sidewinder missiles and retains the internal 20-mm M61 cannon of the F-16A. The first successful launch of a Sparrow took place in February 1989.

Actual conversion of the ADF F-16s (completed in early 1992) was undertaken by the USAF's Ogden Air Materiel Area at Hill AFM, Utah, with General Dynamics-sourced modification kits. Development of the ADF F-16 was conducted at Edwards AFB in 1990 and was followed by operational test and evaluation with the 57th Fighter Weapons Wing at Nellis AFB, Nevada. The first service aircraft were assigned to the 114th Fighter Squadron, Oregon ANG, at Kingsley Field in Klamath

Distinguishing features of the ADF F-16 are the bulge on the fin/fuselage fairing and the searchlight on the port side of the nose. This aircraft is from the 179th Fighter Squadron, Minnesota ANG.

AVIONICS
As part of the ADF upgrade, avionics were upgraded for the intercept mission. Bendix/King ARC-200 HF/SSB radio is added for long-range communications in the single-seat ADFs, and provision is made for Navstar GPS. An AMRAAM datalink is provided, and Teledyne/E-Systems Mk XII advanced IFF is carried.

Lockheed (General Dynamics) F-16A Air Defense Fighter

Conversion of F-16A Block 15 aircraft to ADF standard covered 272 airframes, for service with 13 squadrons, including the training unit at Klamath Falls, Oregon. The operational units provide a chain of air defence alerts around the periphery of the United States. In the light of the present near-zero threat, the force is a prime candidate for massive cutbacks or even complete dissolution.

Portugal's 20 F-16A/Bs are to Block 15OCU standard with F100-PW-220E engines. They also have the full ADF fit, as they are intended for a primary air defence mission.

in order to allocate resources elsewhere.
  In addition to the ANG machines, the 17 F-16As and three F-16Bs supplied to Portugal for operation by 501 Esquadra are to ADF standard for the air defence mission.

ARMAMENT
The ADF can carry six air-to-air missiles on its outer pylons and wingtip launch rails. The standard load consists of four Sidewinders and two Sparrows, although AMRAAMs can be substituted for any of these. The internal M61A1 cannon is mounted in the port wingroot, with the ammunition housed in the central fuselage. The weapon is 6 ft 2 in (1.88 m) long and weighs approximately 265 lb (120 kg). Maximum rate of fire is 6,600 rounds per minute, and muzzle velocity is 3,400 ft (1036 m) per second.

Falls which trains ADF F-16A/B interceptor pilots. Operational ANG squadrons which fly the ADF are 194th FS/CA, 159th FS/FL , 169th FS/IL, 171st FS/MI, 179th FS/MN, 186th FS/MT, 119th FS/NJ, 136th FS/NY, 178th FS/ND, 198th FS/PR, 111th FS/TX and 134th FS/VT. In view of the lack of threat to the continental US, the Pentagon has been offering to disband them

WEAPON OPTIONS

Internal 20-mm M61A1 Vulcan cannon with 511 rounds. Wingtip and outboard wing pylons used for AIM-9 Sidewinder carriage. Often seen with AIM-9P on wingtip and AIM-9M on wing. Central wing pylon can carry AIM-7 Sparrow (ADF being only F-16 version with target illuminator for AIM-7). Inboard wing pylon usually reserved for fuel tanks. Alternatively six AIM-120 AMRAAM can be carried on the missile pylons, or a mix of any of the three missile types.

MARKINGS
The ADF wears the standard USAF two-tone grey camouflage. Most ANG units wear striking unit markings (none more so than this diving eagle of the 194th FS/144th FW/California ANG) and do not carry tailcodes. Those assigned to Puerto Rico and Illinois are outside the CONUS defence organisation, and wear ACC-style tailcodes.

SPOTLIGHT
Part of the ADF conversion was the fitment of a spotlight on the port side of the nose. This allows the ADF pilot to illuminate aircraft at night for visual identification or damage assessment purposes. The other main ADF distinguishing feature is the bulge on the fin/fuselage fairing. This houses the relocated rudder activators which were moved to make room for the HF radio.

RADAR
The ADF F-16A retains the Westinghouse APG-66, but this is uprated with a continuous-wave function to allow the launch of Sparrow missiles.

Lockheed (General Dynamics) F-16C/D Fighting Falcon

The **Lockheed (General Dynamics) F-16C** first flew on 19 June 1984. F-16C and two-seat **F-16D** models are distinguished by an enlarged base or 'island' leading up to the vertical fin, with a small blade antenna protruding up from it. This space was intended for the internal ASPJ (airborne self-protection jammer) which the USAF abandoned in favour of continuing use of external ECM pods.

Compared with earlier versions, the F-16C/D gives the pilot a GEC wide-angle HUD and a function keyboard control at the base of the HUD (located in a console to his left in earlier ships) and an improved data display with key items of information located at 'design eye' level for HOTAS flying. F-16C/Ds employ Hughes APG-68 multi-mode radar with increased range, sharper resolution and expanded operating modes, and have a weapons interface for the AGM-65D Maverick and AMRAAM missiles.

F-16C single-seat and combat-capable F-16D two-seat fighters introduced progressive changes, some installed at the factory and others as part of **MSIP II** (avionics, cockpit and airframe changes) and **MSIP III** (further systems installation) programmes, aimed at enhancing the Fighting Falcon's ability to fly and fight at night.

F-16C/D aircraft retain the unique, low-slung configuration of earlier Fighting Falcon variants, with fuselage-wing 'blending,' fly-by-wire controls, ACES II ejection seat, and a blown polycarbonate canopy which, in these later versions, has a gold tint because of its lining of radar-reflecting materials. F-16C/Ds retain the General Electric M61A1 Vulcan 20-mm cannon with 511 rounds and a capability for up to 16,700 lb (7575 kg) of ordnance, including most bombs and missiles in inventory.

Block 25 aircraft entered production in July 1984 and totalled 319, 289 F-16Cs and 30 F-16Ds. With Blocks 30/32 came the configured (formerly 'common') engine bay, with options for the GE F110-GE-100 (Block 30) or P&W F100-PW-220 (Block 32).

F-16C Blocks 30 and 40 are powered by the General Electric F110-GE-100 offering 28,984 lb (128.9 kN), while F-16C Blocks 32 and 42 Falcons introduced 23,840-lb

(106.05-kN) thrust Pratt & Whitney F100-PW-220s. This powerplant change brought a need to alter the contours of the F-16's air intake to accommodate the larger amount of air ingested. Because the change was not made initially, early F-16C/D Block 30s are 'small inlet' aeroplanes, the 1-ft (0.30-m) wider air intake having become standard for GE power on 'big inlet' ships after deliveries began. USAF F-16C/D delivery totals slightly favour the GE engine.

The introduction of the F100-PW-220 engine marks a maturing of the original F-16 powerplant. While the improved P&W engine is not as powerful as the GE powerplant, it is lighter and crew chiefs consider it 'smarter' and more dependable than earlier P&W models. In addition, Block 30/32 aircraft have the capability to carry AGM-45 Shrike and AGM-88A HARM anti-radiation missiles, and AIM-120 AMRAAM. Avionics hardware changes are also introduced with Block 30/32, which total 501 aircraft, comprising 446 F-16Cs and 55 two-seat F-16Ds. In addition to tactical squadrons, the F-16C/D Block 32 is flown by the USAF's Adversary Tactics Division on aggressor duties, and by the 'Thunderbirds' aerial demonstration team.

F-16C/D Block 40/42 **Night Falcon**s began to come off the Fort Worth production line in December 1988. This version introduces LANTIRN navigation and targeting pods, Navstar GPS navigation receiver, AGM-88B HARM II, APG-68V radar, digital flight controls, automatic terrain following and, as a consequence, increased take-off weight. Greater structural strength raises the Night Falcon's 9g capability from 26,900 lb (12201 kg) to 28,500 lb (12928 kg). The heavier all-up weight and the need to accommodate LANTIRN has resulted in larger landing gear, bulged landing gear doors and the relocation of landing lights to the nose gear door. Block 40/42 Night Falcons have been delivered to the USAF, Israel, Egypt, Turkey and Bahrain. A Block 42 F-16D equipped with AMRAAMs became the first USAF 'Viper' to score an air-to-air victory by downing an Iraqi MiG-25 on 27 December 1992. In 1994 F-16s shot down four Serbian aircraft over Bosnia.

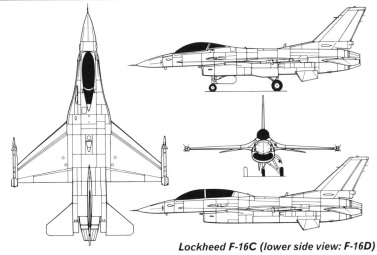

Lockheed F-16C (lower side view: F-16D)

A total of 249 F-16 Fighting Falcons was deployed to Operation Desert Storm and flew almost 13,500 sorties, the highest sortie total for any aircraft in the war, while maintaining a 95.2 per cent mission-capable rate, 5 per cent better than the F-16's peacetime rate. F-16s attacked ground elements in the Kuwaiti Theatre of Operations, flew anti-'Scud' missions, and destroyed military and chemical production facilities, and airfields.

In December 1991, General Dynamics began delivering F-16C/D Block 50 and 52 aircraft. First flight date for Block 50 was 22 October 1991. The first Block 50s went to the 388th Fighter Wing at Hill Air Force Base, UT, in 1992, followed by delivery to USAFE's 52nd FW. Block 50/52 'Vipers' introduced the Westinghouse AN/APG-68 (V5) radar with improved memory and more modes, new NVG-compatible GEC HUD, and improved avionics computer. Numerous other additions to Block 50/52 include a Tracor AN/ALE-47 chaff/flare dispenser, ALR-56M radar warning receiver, Have Quick IIA radio, Have Sync anti-jam VHF and full HARM integration.

These latest F-16s are powered by the

IPE (Improved Performance Engine) versions of GE and P&W engines, the 29,588-lb (131.6-kN) F110-GE-229 and 29,100-lb (129.4-kN) F100-PW-220, respectively. Problems arose with developmental test ships for the Block 52 programme in July 1991, and these had to be refitted with older F100 variants until the P&W IPE's fourth fan blade could be redesigned.

Around 100 USAF F-16C/D Block 50/52 aircraft are being raised to Block 50/52D standard, with provision for the ASQ-213 pod carried under the starboard side of the intake. This pod is known as the HARM Targeting System, and provides the F-16 with a limited 'Wild Weasel' defence-suppression capability to augment the dwindling F-4G force. Further USAF programmes include the **RF-16** tactical reconnaissance aircraft carrying an IR/EO sensor pod, fitment of head-steered FLIR sensor and helmet-mounted sights and modifications of Block 30/32/40/42 aircraft for the close air support/battlefield air interdiction mission.

In 1991, the USAF began studying an MRF (Multi-Role Fighter) which would replace the F-16 in the 21st century. The future of MRF is doubtful, especially since USAF F-16C/Ds (in contrast to ageing F-16A 'small tail' Block 10s) have relatively low airframe hours and will not need early replacement. The proposed Block 60/62 F-16 would utilise some technology developed for the F-22 to answer the MRF requirement.

The F-16C/D has been widely exported, as detailed in the operators list. Licensed production is undertaken by TAI in Turkey and Samsung Aerospace in South Korea.

Many F-16Ds delivered to Israel have been subsequently fitted with a very bulged spine, housing unidentified indigenous avionics reportedly associated with the

Below: The Night Falcon features the LANTIRN system carried in two pods under the intake. This provides FLIR, laser designation and terrain-following radar for precision all-weather attack.

Above: Bahrain's small air force is spearheaded by a force of 12 F-16C/D Block 40s.

Below: The F-16C/D is firmly established in the ANG, this aircraft being a 162nd FS two-seater.

Above: An F-16C from the 432nd FW in Japan drops inert bombs on a range. The aircraft is armed with AIM-120 AMRAAM, and carries a centreline ALQ-184 ECM pod.

Right: F-16s of the 389th FS, 366th Wing carry Mk 82 bombs on triple-ejector racks. The wing is the USAF's power projection unit, also flying B-1s, F-15s and KC-135Rs,

'Wild Weasel'/SAM-suppression role. Several IDF/AF units operate an 'F-16D-heavy' mix of F-16Cs and F-16Ds.

WEAPON OPTIONS

F-16C/D basically similar to F-16A/B, but with greater accent on 'smart' weapons. Block 50/52 aircraft have full AGM-88 HARM capability, while LANTIRN-equipped aircraft can autonomously launch GBU-10 and GBU-12 laser-guided bombs.

SPECIFICATION

Lockheed (General Dynamics) F-16C Fighting Falcon
Wing: span 31 ft 0 in (9.45 m) without tip-mounted AAMs and 32 ft 9.75 in; (10.00 m) with tip-mounted AAMs; aspect ratio 3.09; area 300.00 sq ft (28.87 m²)
Fuselage and tail: length 49 ft 4 in (15.03 m); height 16 ft 8.5 in (5.09 m); tailplane span 18 ft 3.75 in (5.58 m); wheel track 7 ft 9 in (2.36 m); wheel base 13 ft 1.5 in (4.00 m)
Powerplant: (see text for sub-variant) one General Electric F110-GE-100 turbofan rated at 27,600 lb st (122.77 kN) with afterburning or one Pratt & Whitney F100-P-220 turbofan rated at 23,450 lb st (104.31 kN) with afterburning
Weights: empty 19,100 lb (8663 kg) with F110 turbofan or 18,335 lb (8316 kg) with F100 turbofan; typical combat take-off 21,585 lb (9791 kg); maximum take-off 25,071 lb (11372 kg) for an air-to-air mission without drop tanks or 42,300 lb (19187 kg) with maximum external load
Fuel and load: internal fuel 6,972 lb (3162 kg);

external fuel up to 6,760 lb (3066 kg) in three 300-, 370-, 450- and 600-US gal (1136-, 1400-, 1703- and 2271-litre) drop tanks; maximum ordnance 20,450 lb (9276 kg) for 5-*g* manoeuvre limit or 11,950 lb (5421 kg) for 9-*g* manoeuvre limit
Speed: maximum level speed 'clean' at 40,000 ft (12190 m) more than 1,146 kt (1,320 mph; 2124 km/h) and at sea level 795 kt (915 mph; 1472 km/h)
Range: ferry range more than 2,100 nm (2,418 miles; 3891 km) with drop tanks; combat radius 295 nm (340 miles; 547 km) on a hi-lo-hi mission with six 454-kg (1,000-lb) bombs
Performance: maximum rate of climb at sea level more than 50,000 ft (15240 m) per minute; service ceiling more than 50,000 ft (15240 m); typical take-off run 2,500 ft (762 m) at MTOW; typical landing run 2,500 ft (762 m) at normal landing weight
***g* limits:** +9

OPERATORS

Deliveries of F-16C/D are as follows:
US Air Force: F-16C (1,009), F-16D (180) plus 229 F-16C/D Block 50/52 in process of delivery. Active-duty wings are the 20th FW (Shaw AFB), 23rd Wing (Pope AFB), 347th FW (Moody AFB), 366th Wing (Mountain Home AFB) and 388th FW (Hill AFB) in Air Combat Command (plus the 57th FWW at Nellis AFB and 79th TEG at Eglin AFB for test purposes), 58th FW (Luke AFB) in AETC, 8th FW (Kunsan AB), 51st FW (Osan AB), 354th FW (Eielson AFB) and 432nd FW (Misawa AB) in PACAF, and the 31st FW (Aviano AB), 52nd FW (Spangdahlem AB) and 86th Wing (Ramstein AB) in USAFE. Air Force Reserve units are the 457th FS/301st FW at Carswell AFB, 706th FS/926th FG at NAS New Orleans and 302nd FS/944th FG at Luke

AFB. Air National Guard units are 120th FS/CO, 124th and 174th FS/IA, 113th and 163rd/IN, 184th FG/KS, 188th FS/NM, 138th FS/NY, 112th and 162nd FS/OH, 125th FS/OK, 157th FS/SC, 175th FS/SD, 149th FS/VA and 176th FS/WI. Various test agencies also operate F-16s
Bahrain: F-16C Blk 40 (8), F-16D Blk 40 (4) – based at Sheikh Isa
Egypt: F-16C Blk 32 (36), F-16D Blk 32 (4), F-16C Blk 40 (40), F-16D Blk 40 (7) plus 46 TAI-built F-16C/D Blk 50 in process of delivery 1994
Greece: F-16C Blk 40 (34), F-16D Blk 40 (6) plus 40 F-16C/D in process of delivery 1994. Current squadrons are 330 and 346 Mira
Israel: F-16C Blk 30 (51), F-16D Blk 30 (24), F-16C Blk 40 (30), F-16D Blk 40 (30) – operated by 101 and 105 Sqns at Hatzor ('D-heavy' mix), 109, 110 and 117 Sqns at Ramat David and 102 and 105 Sqns at Nevatin
South Korea: F-16C Blk 32 (30), F-16D Blk 32 (10)

With its sophisticated weapon system, the F-16 can be used to replicate the latest Russian fighters for air combat training. This aircraft, painted to resemble a MiG-29, is one of a handful flown by the ATD/414th TS/57th Wing at Nellis AFB.

plus 120 F-16C/D Blk 52 on order – 12 built by Lockheed, 36 supplied as kits and 72 built by Samsung Aerospace
Turkey: F-16C Blk 30 (35), F-16D Blk 30 (9), F-16C Blk 40 (101), F-16D Blk 40 (15) plus 80 F-16C/D Blk 50. Local production by TAI. Current squadrons are 141, 142, 161 and 162 Filo with four more to form

A fully-armed Turkish F-16 patrols the skies over Bosnia during Operation Deny Flight.

The Block 50/52D F-16s are compatible with the ASQ-213 HARM Targeting System, carried on the intake. Around 100 are being produced to provide a stop-gap defence suppression capability.

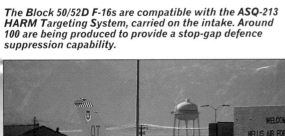

Lockheed (General Dynamics) F-16N Fighting Falcon

Requiring a highly-manoeuvrable supersonic aircraft for its adversary squadrons, the **US Navy** chose the F-16. Using the F-16C Block 30 as the basis, the **F-16N** is considerably downgraded, as it has no secondary operational function. The earlier APG-66 radar replaces the APG-68, and the cannon is removed. The wingtip rails can carry only AIS pods and AIM-9 acquisition rounds, although the other pylons remain available for stores. ALR-69 radar warning receivers are fitted, and there is some structural strengthening to resist the greater amount of high g forces encountered in the adversary mission.

Ordered in January 1985, 26 aircraft were delivered in 1987/88, for use with the Fighter Weapons School and VF-126 at NAS

Miramar, VF-43 at NAS Oceana and VF-45 at NAS Key West. VF-43 and VF-126 have since disbanded. Four of the 26 were **TF-16N** two-seaters. Most aircraft serve in a low-visibility three-tone air defence scheme with two-digit Soviet-style codes, but one was flown with a dark-green disruptive camouflage and Marine Corps titles.

Augmenting regular Navy types (A-4, F-14 and F/A-18) in the adversary role, the F-16Ns are the most exciting F-16s to fly, possessing the highest power/weight ratio of any variant. Titanium is used in key areas in place of aluminium to strengthen the airframe against the rigours of prolonged high-g flight.

Lockheed (General Dynamics) F-16XL/NF-16D/AFTI/F-16

The **Lockheed (General Dynamics) F-16XL** with its unique 'wedged' wing shape has flown intermittently at Edwards Air Force Base, CA, since 1982, first with the US Air Force and currently with **NASA**. The **SCAMP** (Supersonic Cruise and Maneuvering Prototype), or F-16XL, was conceived to increase weapons capacity, range and penetration speed of the F-16. The F-16XL's fuselage was lengthened to 54 ft 1.86 in (16.51 m) and grafted to a 'cranked-arrow' delta wing incorporating composite material to save weight while increasing area and allowing up to 17 stores stations. Tests confirmed greater lifting capability, range and manoeuvring capability with no corresponding penalty for the change in configuration which produced the design.

The two F-16XLs, a single- and two-seater, are former F-16A FSD aircraft; the first made its initial flight as an F-16XL on 3 July 1982. During evaluations at Edwards in 1984, the standard F-16 undercarriage with a maximum weight limit of 37,500 lb (17010 kg) was replaced with strengthened units allowing 48,000 lb (21772 kg) gross weight. The first F-16XL is powered by a Pratt & Whitney F100 afterburning turbofan, the second by a General Electric F110.

The US Air Force abandoned development of the F-16XL in the late 1980s. The aircraft was revived to compete for the production contract that was eventually won by the McDonnell F-15E 'Strike Eagle'. Had it been successful, operational F-16XLs would have been designated **F-16E** (single-seat) and **F-16F** (two-seat).

NASA took delivery of the single-seater on 10 March 1989 and of the two-seat aircraft on 14 February 1991. To carry out laminar-flow flight tests at sustained supersonic speeds, NASA modified both aircraft with a Rockwell-designed titanium wing section or 'active suction glove', which

siphons away turbulent boundary-layer air through millions of tiny laser-cut holes. A foam and fibreglass fairing blends the raised 'glove' into the wing's upper surface. On 2 December 1991, the F-16XL single-seater achieved laminar flow over a swept-wing aircraft for the first time at speeds up to nearly 1,200 mph (1932 km/h) and at altitudes above 40,000 ft (12384 m).

Other research-dedicated F-16s include the **AFTI/F-16** (advanced fighter technology integration) and the **NF-16D VISTA** (variable-stability inflight simulator test aircraft). The AFTI/F-16 is used by the Air Force Flight Test Center at Edwards AFB to research many fighter/CAS-related systems, and features an enlarged spine to house more equipment. The NF-16D VISTA is currently in the **F-16 MATV** (multi-axis thrust-vectoring) testbed configuration, fitted with the AVEN (axisymmetric vectoring engine nozzle) to its F110 engine.

Above: Designated NF-16A, the AFTI/F-16 is fitted with a wide variety of avionics for close air support trials.

Below: The two-seat F-16XL displays the unique planform of the variant, together with the laminar-flow section on the starboard wing.

SPECIFICATION

Lockheed (General Dynamics) F-16XL Fighting Falcon
Wing: span 34 ft 2.8 in (10.43 m); aspect ratio 1.77; area 663.00 sq ft (61.59 m²)
Fuselage and tail: length 54 ft 1.86 in (16.51 m); height 17 ft 7 in (5.36 m); wheel track 7 ft 9 in (2.36 m)
Powerplant: one Pratt & Whitney F100-P-100 turbofan rated at 14,670 lb st (65.26 kN) dry and 23,830 lb st (106.0 kN) with afterburning, or one General Electric F110-GE-100 turbofan rated at 27,600 lb st (122.77 kN) with afterburning
Weights: design mission take-off 43,000 lb (19505 kg); maximum take-off 48,000 lb (21773 kg)
Fuel and load: maximum ordnance 15,000 lb (6803 kg)
Speed: maximum level speed 'clean' at 36,000 ft (10975 m) 1,147 kt (1,321 mph; 2126 km/h)
Range: more than 2,500 nm (2,875 miles; 4630 km)
g limits: +9

Lockheed F-104 Starfighter

Some 2,221 single-seat **Starfighter**s were eventually built in the US, Canada, Europe and Japan in Lockheed's F-104 programme, which started in the early 1950s at C. L. 'Kelly' Johnson's renowned 'Skunk Works' at Burbank, CA. The first of two 10,200-lb (45.37-kN) Wright XJ65-W-6 (Sapphire)-powered **XF-104** prototypes started flying on 18 February 1954, in the hands of A. W. 'Tony' Le Vier. These were followed by 17 pre-production **YF-104A**s with definitive J79-GE-3A turbojets developing 14,800 lb st (65.83 kN) for take-off. The USAF procured 153 **F-104A**s and 77 **F-104C**s, although after at least 73 accident losses these were withdrawn from regular fighter units in 1968, and from the

Air National Guard in mid-1975. Most were transferred to the air forces of Jordan, Pakistan and Taiwan, all of whom used them in combat, but none now remains in service. Two-seat trainer variants of the F-104 are described separately.

Extensive modifications and installation of multi-role nav/attack systems and the improved 15,800-lb (70.28-kN) J79-GE-11A, coupled with US government-backed high-pressure salesmanship, secured for Lockheed in late 1958 an initial West German

A line-up of CF-104Gs of Turkey's 182 Filo. The Starfighter is in the process of being replaced by F-16s from local production.

contract for the new **F-104G** Starfighter, which spearheaded orders from other NATO countries in what quickly became known as 'the sale of the century'. This involved a massive European Starfighter licence-production programme by Belgium, Germany, Italy and the Netherlands, with

additional industrial participation from Canada, which also selected the **CF-104** as its next-generation fighter, and from Lockheed in the US. New **F/CF/RF-104G** Starfighters from this joint production were procured by Belgium (101), Canada (200), Denmark (40), the German Luftwaffe and

Within the ranks of RoCAF Starfighters are several RF-104G 'Stargazer' aircraft, serving with the 12th Special Missions Squadron, part of the 401st TCW at Taoyuan.

Marineflieger (749), Greece (45), Italy (125), the Netherlands (120), Norway (19), Spain (18), Taiwan (67) and Turkey (46). Starfighter production was also undertaken in Japan, where Mitsubishi built 210 Lockheed Model 683B **F-104J**s between 1962 and 1967 for the JASDF. These were retired from front-line service in March 1986, although four aircraft served until 1990 for trials duties. A number of F-104Js were stored and eight of these are being converted as target drones.

Many Starfighters were replaced in service from 1979 by more modern fighters, but large numbers were also transferred to US allies and other NATO countries. Major recipients included Greece, which eventually received at least 170 single-seat Starfighters from US and NATO sources, plus 60 ex-German F/RF-104Gs; Norway (18 surplus CAF CF-104s); Taiwan (53 ex-German/RDAF F-104Gs and at least 22 ex-JASDF F-104Js); and Turkey (230 F-104Gs/CF-104s, and 33 RF-104Gs). Some, particularly from Germany, were supplied in unairworthy condition for spares recovery, and most have since been retired.

In 1994, **Taiwan**'s RoCAF remained the biggest Starfighter operator, with seven tactical fighter squadrons and one reconnaissance unit using six so-called **RF-104G 'Stargazer'** aircraft. The F-104s form three wings at Hsinchu (41st, 42nd, 48th TFS), Ching Chuan Kang (7th, 8th, 28th and 35th TFS), and Taoyuan (12th Special Mission Sqn) air bases. In **Turkey**, the last F-104Gs were serving with 181 Filo at Diyarbakir and 193 Filo at Akhisar, while the CF-104G served with 182 Filo at Diyarbakir. Turkey also has one squadron of **F-104S**, a type which serves in numbers in **Italy**, and which is described separately under Alenia.

SPECIFICATION

Lockheed F-104G Starfighter
Wing: span 21 ft 11 in (6.68 m) without tip-mounted AAMs; aspect ratio 2.45; area 196.10 sq ft (18.22 m²)
Fuselage and tail: length 54 ft 9 in (16.69 m); height 13 ft 6 in (4.11 m); tailplane span 11 ft 11 in (3.63 m); wheel track 9 ft 0 in (2.74 m); wheel base 15 ft 0.5 in (4.59 m)
Powerplant: one General Electric J79-GE-11A turbojet rated at 10,000 lb st (44.48 kN) dry and 15,800 lb st (70.28 kN) with afterburning
Weights: empty equipped 14,082 lb (6387 kg); operating empty 14,903 lb (6760 kg); normal take-off 21,693 lb (9840 kg); maximum take-off 28,779 lb (13054 kg)

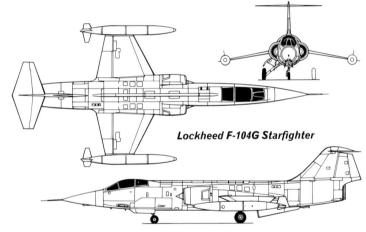

Lockheed F-104G Starfighter

Fuel and load: internal fuel 896 US gal (3392 litres); external fuel up to 955 US gal (3615 litres) in one 225-US gal (852-litre) drop tank, two 195-US gal (740-litre) drop tanks and two 170-US gal (645-litre) tip tanks; maximum ordnance 4,310 lb (1955 kg)
Speed: maximum level speed 'clean' at 36,000 ft (10975 m) 1,262 kt (1,453 mph; 2338 km/h); cruising speed at 36,000 ft (10975 m) 530 kt (610 mph; 981 km/h)
Range: ferry range 1,893 nm (2,180 miles; 3510 km) with four drop tanks; combat radius 648 nm

(746 miles; 1200 km) with maximum fuel or 261 nm (30 miles; 483 km) on a hi-lo-hi attack mission with maximum warload
Performance: maximum rate of climb at sea level 55,000 ft (16765 m) per minute; service ceiling 58,000 ft (17680 m); take-off 2,960 ft (902 m) at 21,840 lb (9906 kg); take-off distance to 50 ft (15 m) 4,600 ft (1402 m) at 22,840 lb (10360 kg); landing distance from 50 ft (15 m) 3,250 ft (990 m) at 15,900 lb (7212 kg); landing run 2,280 ft (695 m) at 15,900 lb (7212 kg)

Lockheed **TF-104 Starfighter**

Following development and production for the USAF from 1956 of 26 tandem two-seat **F-104B** and 21 **F-104D** Starfighter conversion trainers, Lockheed undertook the output, from its Burbank and Palmdale factories in California, of most similar trainer versions of the later F-104G series in the NATO and Japanese programmes. These included 38 **CF-104D**s for Canada, 30 **F-104F**s and 137 **TF-104G**s for the FRG, 20 **F-104DJ**s for Japan, and 29 TFs for MAP contracts (Denmark, four; Greece, six; Norway, two; Spain, three; Turkey, six; Taiwan, eight). Lockheed built 191 TF-104Gs for NATO use, also including 12 each for Belgium and Italy and 18 for the Netherlands. Some 68 of these were assembled in Europe from Lockheed-supplied kits, an extra 16 being delivered from

Fiat for the AMI, increasing overall two-seat F-104 production to 359. The TF-104G retains the single-seat version's weapons systems and associated avionics, including its F-15A NASARR radar but not its 20-mm Vulcan cannon, which has been replaced by extra fuel. In 1994 TF-104Gs were still operated in **Italy**, **Turkey** and **Taiwan** (alongside F-104DJs).

SPECIFICATION

Lockheed TF-104G Starfighter
generally similar to the Lockheed F-104G Starfighter except in the following particulars:
Fuselage and tail: wheel base 14 ft 5.5 in (4.41 m)
Weights: empty equipped 14,181 lb (6432 kg); maximum take-off 26,364 lb (11959 kg)

Fuel and load: internal fuel 700 US gal (2650 litres); maximum ordnance 2,744 lb (1245 kg)
Range: combat radius 515 nm (593 miles; 955 km) with maximum fuel
Performance: take-off run 2,260 ft (960 m) at 18,900 lb (8573 kg); take-off distance to 50 ft (15 m) 3,500 ft (1067 m) at 18,900 lb (8573 kg); landing

distance from 50 ft (15 m) 3,190 ft (972 m) at 15,424 lb (6996 kg) weight; landing run 2,215 ft (676 m) at 15,424 lb (6996 kg)

Taiwan has many TF-104Gs in its inventory, most with the OCU but some with operational units.

Lockheed F-117 Night Hawk

Lockheed Advanced Development Company
1011 Lockheed Way, Palmdale
CA 93599-3740, USA

Stealth technology had been under low-key development since the 1940s, but it was the effects of the Vietnam and Yom Kippur Wars which spurred a DARPA request in 1974 for development of a stealth aircraft. This used a mix of radar-absorbent materials, radar-reflective internal structure (re-entrant triangles that scatter radar energy away from the transmitter) and a similarly 'reflective' configuration to dramatically decrease radar cross-section to the point at which defences have insufficient time to react to a threat, or do not 'see' it at all. Overall faceting reflects radar energy in all directions, making the aircraft virtually invisible even to AWACS platforms, and the concept extends to the wing itself, the aerofoil section of which consists of two flat surfaces on the underside and three on the top of the wing. The avoidance of straight lines is continued on access panels and doors, many of which have serrated edges for the same reason. Cockpit transparencies are coated with gold. Radio aerials are retractable, and during peacetime the aircraft carry external radar reflectors and transponders.

The Lockheed 'Skunk Works', famed builder of the U-2 and SR-71, was awarded a development order in April 1976 for two sub-scale technology demonstrators. Under the codename Have Blue, the first of these aircraft made its maiden flight in 1977 from the secret test base at Groom Dry Lake, NV, with Bill Park at the controls. Although both Have Blue aircraft were lost, experience gained was sufficient to win Lockheed a contract to develop a full-scale operational tactical fighter, awarded on 16 November

1978 under the Senior Trend codename. Lessons from the Have Blue prototypes led to some major changes, most notably to the configuration of the tailfins, which were canted outboard instead of inboard. The first of five FSD prototypes flew on 18 June 1981 under the command of Hal Farley. These aircraft were not originally painted in the black colour scheme which is now synonymous with the **F-117**, some being grey and others decorated in a two-tone disruptive camouflage. The aircraft also had smaller tailplanes than production aircraft.

To reduce costs and maintain secrecy, components and equipment from other in-service aircraft were used wherever possible, allowing many F-117 costs to be buried in 'spares' listings for other types. Thus, the aircraft has an A-10A nose gear, F-15E mainwheels, a standard ACES ejection seat, and cockpit displays from the F/A-18 Hornet. The aircraft's arrow-like configuration demands the use of a digital fly-by-wire control system. Lockheed selected the F-16's GEC Astronics quadruplex system to actuate two-section elevons and all-moving 'ruddervons'.

Tonopah base

As production continued at a low rate, the USAF began establishing a base at Tonopah Test Range, not far from Groom Lake and almost as secluded. In October 1983 the first unit was declared operational, with about five F-117s and 18 A-7D Corsairs, which were flown for proficiency and as a security 'cover'. All flights were undertaken at night, necessitating considerable upheavals to the lifestyles of the crews.

The F-117 presents an unmistakable silhouette from any angle. Fly-by-wire computer control is central to the ability to create a stealthy shape that is also an effective flying machine.

This factor was a contributory factor to the two F-117 losses in the 1980s. It was not until November 1988 that the F-117 was officially acknowledged by the Pentagon, allowing the 'Black Jet' to begin flying daylight missions.

As early as October 1979, the US Air Force began the task of picking pilots for F-117 operations, carefully selecting the personnel on the basis of flying skill, character and background. The 4450th Tactical Group was formed in 1980 at Nellis AFB as the operational unit, and the first cadre of pilots joined in mid-1982, at the same time as the first production aircraft arrived. The unit was divided into four units, known as P-unit (flying A-7Ds as cover and as chase aircraft), I-unit ('Nightstalkers'), Q-unit ('Goatsuckers') and Z-unit ('Grim Reapers'). Later these were formed as squadrons, 'I'

becoming the 4450th Tactical Squadron, 'P' the 4451st TS, 'Q' the 4452nd TS and 'Z' the 4453rd Test and Evaluation Squadron.

In October 1989, the 4450th TG was redesignated as the 37th Tactical Fighter Wing, taking this designation from the George-based 'Wild Weasel' Phantom wing, whose squadrons amalgamated with the 35th TFW. The F-117 units realigned into three squadrons, the 415th TFS 'Nightstalkers', 416th TFS 'Ghostriders' and 417th Tactical Fighter Training Squadron 'Bandits'. In October 1991 the 37th was redesignated as a Fighter Wing, and similarly all three subordinate units became Fighter Squadrons. The unit retained the bird of prey badge of the 4450th Tactical Group, but superimposed this on the famous cross of the 37th TFW.

On 19 December 1989, the F-117 finally went into action during a two-ship attack on the Rio Hato barracks during the invasion of Panama. This small baptism of fire was overshadowed by the type's contribution to Desert Storm, when an eventual total of 42 aircraft flew from Khamis Mushait in Saudi Arabia on nightly missions against Iraq and

Left: As the F-117 is a 'hot ship' on landing, a drag chute is deployed from between the F-117's tails to reduce the landing roll. This aircraft is a test example serving with the 412th TW at Edwards AFB.

Below: A 49th FW F-117A flies over White Sands, near the wing's base at Holloman AFB. The relocation to Holloman completed the move out of the 'black' world.

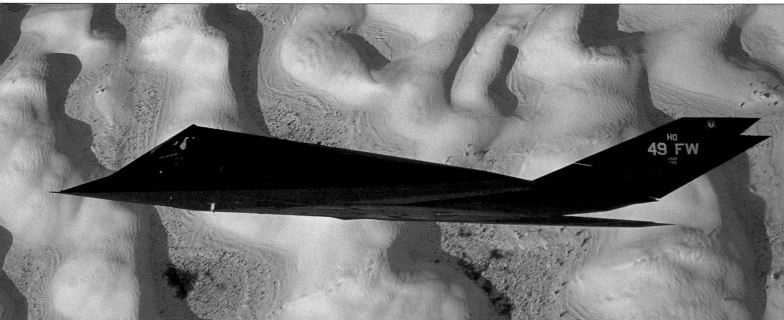

occupied Kuwait. Using its low observability to the full, the F-117 nightly penetrated the defences around Baghdad, and guided weapons with utmost precision against most of the key targets in the city, including the release of the first bomb of the war, against an air defence centre. As the availability of such targets dried up in the latter part of the war, the 'Black Jets' turned their sights on bridges and aircraft shelters. In a war that was a demonstration of Western technical capability, the F-117 was the undisputed star. Under the command of

Lieutenant Colonel Ralph W. Getchell, the 415th TFS was the first to deploy to the Gulf region, arriving at Khamis Mushait (known as 'Tonopah East') on 19 August 1990. The 416th TFS was sent out to Saudi Arabia in December, and the 37th TFW, commanded by Colonel Al Whitley, was further reinforced by a handful of aircraft and pilots from the 417th TFTS. A total of 1,271

A 412th TW F-117A displays the carriage of the GBU-27 2,000-lb class Paveway III laser-guided bomb.

FLY-BY-WIRE
The quadruplex flight control system is fed with precise air data from four nose probes.

ARMAMENT
The two weapon bays are equipped with a trapeze for the carriage of bombs up to 2,000 lb (907 kg). The laser-guided bomb is the standard weapon (either GBU-10 or GBU-27), but other weapons such as AGM-65 Maverick and AGM-88 HARM can be carried.

Lockheed F-117A Night Hawk

Arguably the best-known shape in the skies after Concorde, the F-117 equips the 49th Fighter Wing, serving with the 7th, 8th and 9th Fighter Squadrons. A handful are additionally used for test purposes. The force is intended for precision attacks against high-value targets, a capability it demonstrated with outstanding success in the Gulf War. The OCIP programme greatly improved the cockpit, adding full-colour MFDs and a moving-map display, while also adding an autothrottle and a pilot-activated 'panic' button that automatically restores the aircraft to straight and level flight from any attitude. Further immediate upgrades include a new FLIR/designator system, GPS and ring-laser gyro INS. In the future, radar may be added to improve bad-weather capability.

STEALTH FEATURES
Helped by its amazing shape, the F-117 defeats radars by the use of RAM over the entire surface. The use of mesh over the engine intakes and sensor ports make these appear as flat surfaces to radars, while dogtooth patterns are used to disrupt returns from doors and panels.

REFUELLING
The F-117 is equipped with a receptacle on the spine for boom refuelling. The small excrescence at the apex of the fuselage houses a small floodlight for illumination.

INFRA-RED SUPPRESSION
The exhaust nozzles are fashioned into narrow slits with vertical guide vanes to diffuse the hot efflux. These are surrounded by Space Shuttle-style heat tiles.

ACQUISITION/DESIGNATION SYSTEM
The F-117 pilot uses the highly-accurate INS for navigation to the target area, whereupon the forward-looking infra-red (mounted forward of the windscreen) is used to acquire the target from long range. Once the target has been locked-in to the system, the downward-looking infra-red system takes over, this sensor peering through a mesh in the lower side of the nose. The DLIR stays peering at the target throughout the attack phase, a boresighted laser designator supplying a 'sparkle' for the precision guidance of a laser-guided bomb.

Lockheed F-117 Night Hawk

*In addition to having a tiny radar
signature, the F-117 has a very low
infra-red signature, due to the use of
non-afterburning engines and a
wide, diffusing exhaust slot.*

combat missions was flown during Desert
Storm. On their return from the battle zone,
the Night Hawks became highly visible at
many air shows, and in 1992 completed
their move out of the 'black' world by moving to Holloman AFB, NM. In January 1992
the 37th FW changed its designation to
49th FW.

In US Air Force planning, the F-117 is
used for attacks against what the service
calls 'highly leveraged' targets. These are
targets whose destruction would have a far
greater effect on the defensive or offensive
capability of the enemy than just the physi-
cal damage caused. Such targets include
communications and command centres, air
defence sector centres, key bridges, airfields and the like.

Target acquisition

In order to attack such targets, the F-117
uses a highly accurate inertial navigation
system to put it in the right position to begin the attack. From there, the forward-looking infra-red is used to acquire the target.
Once acquired, the pilot aligns cross-hairs
on his FLIR screen over the target, and
locks the point into the weapons computer.
As the F-117 approaches its quarry, the target dips below the aircraft's nose, and the
locked-in image is handed over to the downward-looking infra-red sensor mounted
under the starboard side of the nose. This
remains continuously pointed at the target
image, using contrast auto-tracking techniques. Laser-guided bombs are released
at a computed point, and at some time during their free fall in the general direction of
the target a laser is used to designate the

impact point. This laser is boresighted with
the DLIR. The reflected laser energy is
picked up by the seeker head on the
weapon, and guides it to a direct hit.

After the Gulf War, Lockheed began an
Offensive Capability Improvement Program
(OCIP) for the 57 remaining F-117s (of 59
production aircraft and five pre-series aircraft delivered) with the aim of increasing
their combat effectiveness by reducing
cockpit workload. Two colour multi-function
displays are being added, together with a
moving map display. An LCD unit is to provide for data entry. Auto-throttles are incorporated, tied in to the navigation system,
which provide a time-over-target function
for accurate timing of attacks. An auto-
recovery facility is included to prevent spa-
tial disorientation in bad weather. Since
1984 aircraft had been upgraded with IBM
AP-102 computers in place of the Delco
M362Fs. A third phase of the improvement
programme will add a new infra-red acquisition and designation sensor in place of the
existing FLIR and DLIR (test-flown in 1992),
and will also provide a Honeywell ring laser
gyro INS and Collins GPS.

RAF and Luftwaffe interest in the F-117
has been claimed, and RAF exchange pilots
have flown the aircraft since 1987, perhaps
in exchange for occasional permission to
use British bases for the aircraft. A navalised derivative has been offered to the USN
as an interim strike aircraft pending the
introduction of the AX. Nicknamed 'Seahawk', this aircraft would be a derivative of
the basic F-117A with reduced-sweep folding wings, trapezoidal F-22-style conventional tailplanes, provision to carry weapons
externally, a Grumman F-14 undercarriage
and carrier landing system, and with an
arrester hook housed behind closing doors
in the belly.

There is no two-seat trainer version of
the F-117, although a crashed FSD F-117

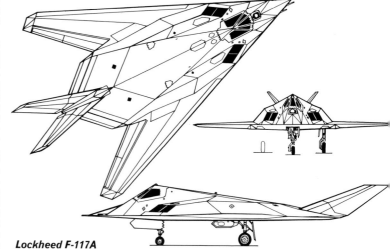

Lockheed F-117A

was proposed as the basis of a two-seat
prototype. Instead, pilots rely on very
sophisticated simulators and the use of a
handful of T-38s for proficiency training.

WEAPON OPTIONS

Although able to carry many different weapons, the
standard ordnance of the F-117 is the 2,000-lb (907-kg)
LGB, either in GBU-10 Paveway II or GBU-27 Paveway
III form. Each comes with two warhead options, the
standard Mk 84 or the BLU-109 penetration with
thicker, straight-sided walls. The GBU-27 was
developed especially for the F-117 for, although it has
the Paveway III guidance set, it has Paveway II-style
fins that can fit in the internal weapons bays of the
Night Hawk. The USAF is coy about the F-117's
weapons options, answering all questions with a
blanket "it can carry everything in the inventory",

refusing to discount the use of AAMs or even gun
pods. Some sources suggest that the AGM-65
Maverick, AGM-88 HARM and AIM-9 Sidewinder are
regularly carried, and there have been reports that
there is a proposal to adapt the aircraft to carry a
modified F-14-style TARPS pod internally.

SPECIFICATION

Lockheed F-117A Night Hawk
Wing: span 43 ft 4 in (13.20 m); aspect ratio about
4.3; area about 1,140.00 sq ft (105.9 m²)
Fuselage and tail: length 65 ft 11 in (20.08 m);
height 12 ft 5 in (3.78 m)
Powerplant: two General Electric F404-GE-F1D2 non-
afterburning turbofans each rated at 10,800 lb st
(48.04 kN)
Weights: empty about 30,000 lb (13608 kg);
maximum take-off 52,500 lb (23814 kg)
Fuel and load: maximum ordnance 5,000 lb (2268 kg)
Speed: maximum level speed 'clean' at high altitude
possibly more than Mach 1; normal maximum
operating speed at optimum altitude Mach 0.9
Range: combat radius about 600 nm (691 miles)
1112 km) with maximum ordnance
g **limits:** +6

*Apart from the test aircraft, all
F-117s are assigned to the 49th FW
at Holloman, which operates three
squadrons (7th/8th/9th FS), one of
which is primarily a training unit.
The small blades projecting from
the back of this aircraft serve the
communications suite, and are
retractable for operations. For
peacetime flying, F-117s usually
carry radar reflectors to aid air
traffic control.*

Lockheed **L-188 Electra**

Having provided the basis for Lockheed's successful development of the P-3 Orion maritime reconnaissance aircraft, the **L-188 Electra** medium-range turboprop airliner itself entered service in a similar role late in its service life. This resulted from a modification programme to fit APS-705 search radar and other appropriate equipment in four ex-commercial **L-188A**s in **Argentina**. These serve in 1ª EAE (No. 1 Naval Reconnaissance Squadron) as part of the Argentine navy's 6ª Escuadra Aéronaval at Trelew, one Electra having been modified (by IAI in Israel) for operations in the Elint/Sigint role. Three ex-civil **L-188PF Electra Freighters** also are in service with 1ª EASLM (Logistical Supply Squadron) as part of 5ª Escuadra Aéronaval at Ezeiza. Several air forces have made use of Electras in the Presidential, VIP and general transport role, and single examples remain in service in this capacity in **Bolivia** (operated by the quasi-military TAM airline) and in **Honduras**. Airliner Electras are able to accommodate 98 passengers in high-density configuration.

SPECIFICATION

Lockheed L-188A Electra
Wing: span 99 ft 0 in (30.18 m); aspect ratio 7.54; area 1,300.00 sq ft (120.77 m2)
Fuselage and tail: length 104 ft 6 in (31.85 m); height 32 ft 10 in (10.01 m); tailplane span 42 ft 10 in (13.06 m); wheel track 31 ft 2 in (9.50 m); wheel base 29 ft 9 in (9.07 m)
Powerplant: four Allison 501D-13/13A turboprops each rated at 3,750 shp (2796 ekW) or 501D-15 each rated at 4,050 shp (3020 ekW)
Weights: empty 57,400 lb (26036 kg); typical operating empty 61,500 lb (27896 kg); maximum take-off 116,000 lb (52664 kg)
Fuel and load: internal fuel 37,500 lb (17010 kg); external fuel none; maximum payload 26,500 lb (12020 kg)
Speed: maximum level speed 'clean' at 12,000 ft (3660 m) 389 kt (448 mph; 721 km/h); maximum

cruising speed at 22,000 ft (6705 m) 352 kt (405 mph; 652 km/h); economical cruising speed at optimum altitude 325 kt (374 mph; 602 km/h)
Range: 2,180 nm (2,510 miles; 4040 km) with maximum fuel or 1,910 nm (2,200 miles; 3540 km) with maximum payload
Performance: maximum rate of climb at sea level 1,670 ft (509 m) per minute; service ceiling 27,000 ft

Argentina has a fleet of Electras for transport, Elint and maritime patrol. This example has APS-504 radar.

(8230 m); balanced take-off field length 4,720 ft (1439 m) at maximum take-off weight; balanced landing field length 4,300 ft (1311 m) at normal landing weight

Lockheed **L-1011 TriStar**

A total of nine **Lockheed TriStar 500** airliners was acquired by the UK Ministry of Defence in 1982/84 (six ex-British Airways and three ex-Pan Am) and these aircraft form the equipment of the **RAF**'s No. 216 Squadron at Brize Norton. In the first phase of a major programme handled by Marshall of Cambridge (Engineering) Ltd, four of the BA aircraft were converted to **TriStar K.Mk 1** tanker/transports. The conversion involves installation of underfloor fuel tanks in the fore and aft baggage compartments, providing an additional 100,000 lb (45360 kg) and increasing the aircraft's total fuel capacity to over 300,000 lb (136080 kg), paired Flight Refuelling Ltd HDUs in the lower rear fuselage, and a closed-circuit TV camera to monitor refuelling. The HDUs can transfer fuel at the rate of 4,000 lb (1814 kg) per minute. A refuelling probe is fitted above the forward fuselage and full passenger seating (all seats facing forwards) provided throughout the cabin. The first flight was made on 9 July 1985.

Two of the four K.Mk 1s remain in service, with the remaining two aircraft and two newly-acquired TriStars having been further modified as **TriStar KC.Mk 1** tanker/freighters. The KC.Mk 1 was first flown in 1988 and introduces a 104 x 140-in (264 x 356-cm) front fuselage port side cargo door and freight handling system, to carry palletised cargo and 35 passengers. The floor is strengthened for high-density loadings.

Two of the ex-Pan Am TriStars serve as **TriStar C.Mk 2** troop transports without probes. Planned modifications were abandoned to fit the third aircraft with underwing Mk 32B pods containing HDUs as the **TriStar K.Mk 2** and it was delivered as a **TriStar C.Mk 2A** instead, with military avionics, a new interior and the troublesome digital autopilot replaced by an analog autopilot as fitted to the K.Mk 1 and KC.Mk 1. All RAF TriStars are being fitted with AN/ALR-66 radar warning receivers, but plans to fit underwing FRL Mk 32B pods appear to have been abandoned. One other TriStar 500 (ex-Air Canada) has been converted by Marshall of Cambridge for Orbital Sciences Corp. in the USA to serve as a launcher for the Pegasus Air-Launched Space Booster, itself to be used to launch small satellites into low Earth orbit. One VIP-configured TriStar 500 serves as a part of the **Jordanian Royal Flight**.

SPECIFICATION

Lockheed L-1011 TriStar K.Mk 1
Wing: span 164 ft 4 in (50.09 m); aspect ratio 7.63; area 3,541.00 sq ft (328.96 m2)
Fuselage and tail: length 164 ft 2.5 in (50.05 m); height 55 ft 4 in (16.87 m); tailplane span 71 ft 7 in (21.82 m); wheel track 36 ft 0 in (10.97 m); wheel base 64 ft 8 in (19.71 m)
Powerplant: three Rolls-Royce RB211-524B4 turbofans each rated at 50,000 lb st (222.41 kN)
Weights: basic empty 242,684 lb (110163 kg); maximum take-off 540,000 lb (244944 kg)
Fuel and load: internal fuel 213,240 lb (96724 kg) plus provision for 100,060 lb (45387 kg) of transfer fuel in two fuselage tanks; external fuel none
Speed: never exceed speed 435 kt (501 mph; 806 km/h) CAS; maximum cruising speed at 35,000 ft (10670 m) 520 kt (599 mph; 964 km/h); economical cruising speed at 35,000 ft (10670 m) 480 kt (553 mph; 890 km/h)

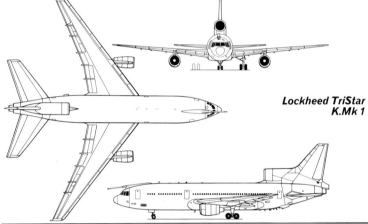

Lockheed TriStar K.Mk 1

Range: 4,200 nm (4,836 miles; 7783 km) with maximum payload
Performance: maximum rate of climb at sea level 2,820 ft (860 m) per minute; service ceiling 43,000 ft (13105 m); take-off balanced field length 9,200 ft (2804 m) at maximum take-off weight; landing balanced field length 6,770 ft (2063 m)

A No. 216 Sqn TriStar K.Mk 1 refuels a Tornado F.Mk 3 from one of its fuselage HDUs. The TriStar is excellent for fighter deployments: not only can it refuel the fighters all the way, but it can also carry squadron personnel and supplies.

Lockheed **P-3A/B Orion**

In August 1957, Type Specification No. 146 was issued by the **US Navy**, calling for a new anti-submarine aircraft to replace the Lockheed P-2 Neptune. The Lockheed proposal was based on the company's L-188 Electra medium-range passenger airliner. In May 1958 Lockheed was awarded a contract largely on the basis of the strength of the aircraft's structure and its size, which was sufficient to house an extensive array of detection systems. Lockheed modified the third Electra airframe (N1883) as the prototype with a tail-mounted MAD boom and a ventral bulge simulating a weapons bay. Following extensive adaptations (including a shortening of the fuselage), the aircraft made a successful maiden flight as the **YP3V-1** (later redesignated **YP-3A**) on 25 November 1959. The Navy ordered an initial batch of seven aircraft in October 1960, and the first of these (BuNo. 148883) flew in April of the following year. In 1962 the type was redesignated **Lockheed P-3A** and named **Orion**.

Several nations are acquiring surplus US Navy P-3A/Bs. Chile has taken delivery of eight to patrol its extensive coastline.

Lockheed P-3A/B Orion

Iberian Orions: above is a Portuguese P-3P,
while at left is a Spanish P-3A.

*Many early Orions have had mission
equipment removed (including the
MAD sting) and transport interiors
installed. This aircraft is a VP-3A
staff transport.*

The P-3A entered service in the summer
of 1962, with Patrol Squadron Eight (VP-8);
other units soon followed, and by December 1963 Lockheed had delivered over 50
Orions to eight squadrons. After the production of 109 P-3As, Lockheed incorporated
the DELTIC (Delayed Time Compression) installation in an improvement programme.
This doubled sonobuoy information-pro-
cessing capability and also incorporated
redesigned avionics. The first squadron to
receive the new **P-3A DELTIC** was VP-46
at Moffett Field, and within a short time
most aircraft had been retrofitted.

In the summer of 1965, after three years'
experience and with 157 P-3As built, Lockheed began production of a new variant.

The **P-3B** was fitted with more powerful
Allison T56-A-14 engines and was heavier
than its predecessor, mainly through having
provision for the AGM-12 Bullpup ASM,
although it retained basically the same
electronics fit. The P-3B secured the first
export orders and became operational with
the Royal New Zealand and Norwegian air
forces (five aircraft each), and with the
RAAF (10 aircraft). From 1977 the USN's
P-3Bs have been updated with improved
navigation and acoustic-processing equipment, and with provision for the AGM-84
Harpoon anti-ship missile. Production of the
P-3B ceased in 1969, following the introduction of its successor, the **P-3C** (described
separately).

P-3Bs have virtually been retired from
USN service, although some remain with
Reserve and trials units. P-3As were con-
verted to **RP-3A** standard (three aircraft)
for oceanographic reconnaissance use by
VXN-8, and to **WP-3A** standard (four air-

craft) for weather reconnaissance by VW-4.
Six early aircraft have been refitted for executive transport use as the **VP-3A**, while a
handful serve as aircrew trainers under the
designation **TP-3A**. Several early Orions
have been converted for utility transport
duties as **UP-3A**s and **UP-3B**s. Four P-3As
were transferred to the US Customs Service under the **P-3A(CS)** designation, and
others have been modified by Aero Union
as civilian fire-bombers. Special-purpose
variants are described separately.

New Zealand's aircraft have received
an avionics upgrade (the first by Boeing, five
more by Air New Zealand) and the new designation **P-3K**. The sixth was an ex-RAAF
P-3B. **Norway** acquired two ex-USN P-3Bs
in 1979 and one of these, plus one original
aircraft, remain in service as **P-3N**s for pilot
training, fishery protection and other duties.
The other five were transferred to **Spain** to
replace four leased USN P-3As and to augment the two surviving (of three originally)
P-3As purchased by Spain.

One of Australia's P-3Bs was lost in service, and one was transferred to New
Zealand in 1985. Four more were transferred to Lockheed in 1983, one becoming
the P-3 AEW & C prototype (described separately). The six surviving Australian aircraft
were upgraded to P-3C standard as **P-3P**s
and subsequently transferred to **Portugal**
in 1986. Australia plans to purchase three
surplus USN P-3Bs for training duties.

A number of new customers may take
delivery of surplus US Navy P-3As or P-3Bs,
Greece being a likely candidate. Two P-3As
and six UP-3As were held in storage against
a **Chilean** contract and were subsequently

delivered from March 1993 for coasta
patrol work. Three P-3As have been up
graded and redesignated **P-3T** (two) and
UP-3T (one) for **Thailand** as replacement
for the Grumman S-2 Tracker.

A summary of all Orion operators is pro
vided in the following P-3C entry.

Lockheed P-3B Orion
generally similar to the P-3C Orion except in the
following particulars:
Weights: empty 60,000 lb (27216 kg); normal take-off
127,200 lb (57697 kg); maximum take-off 134,000 lb
(60782)
Fuel and load: internal fuel 9,200 US gal
(34826 litres); maximum expendable load 15,000 lb
(6804 kg) as 7,252 lb (3290 kg) in the weapon bay and
7,748 lb (3514 kg) under the wings
Speed: maximum level speed 'clean' at 15,000 ft
(4575 m) 413 kt (476 mph; 766 km/h); economical
cruising speed at 25,000 ft (7620 m) 345 kt (397 mph;
639 km/h); patrol speed at 1,500 ft (457 m) 200 kt
(230 mph; 371 km/h)
Range: operational radius 2,200 nm (2,533 miles;
4076 km) with no time on station, or 1,680 nm
(1,935 miles; 3114 km) with 3 hours on station;
endurance at 1,500 ft (457 m) 12 hours 54 minutes on
four engines or 17 hours on two engines
Performance: maximum rate of climb at sea level
3270 ft (997 m) per minute; take-off run 3,700 ft
(1128 m) at maximum take-off weight; take-off
distance to 50 ft (15 m) 4,900 ft (1494 m) at maximum
take-off weight; landing distance from 50 ft (15 m)
2,420 ft (738 m) at design landing weight

Lockheed **P-3C Orion**

The **Lockheed P-3C Orion** is the US
Navy's primary land-based, anti-submarine warfare patrol aircraft. It retains the
airframe and powerplant installation of the
earlier P-3B. The first service-test **YP-3C**
'prototype' was actually a converted P-3B
and first flew on 18 September 1968. Since
then, the P-3C has been exported to Australia, the Netherlands, Norway, Japan,
Pakistan and South Korea.

With a crew of 10, the baseline P-3C carries out its mission of hunting submarines
using a comprehensive package of ASW
detection equipment. This includes APS-
115B search radar, ASQ-81 magnetic anomaly detector, AQA-7 DIFAR (Directional
Acoustics-Frequency Analysis and Recording) system, and AQH-4 multi-track sonar
tape recorder. The P-3C introduced an integrated ASW and navigation avionics system, including the AN/ASQ-114 computer,

*Iran received six P-3F Orions, which
combined features of both the B and
C models. Without a source of
spares, the fleet has dwindled to
just one or two airworthy specimens,
kept aloft by raiding the others.*

thus becoming the world's first ASW aircraft with a centralised computer. The first
US Navy squadron to operate the P-3C was
VP-30 in 1969. One hundred and eighteen
'baseline' aircraft have been succeeded by
approximately 150 upgraded 'Update' versions. The P-3 has 10 stores stations (three
under each outer wing panel and two on

each inner panel between the inner engine
and fuselage) and a bomb bay which can
carry a variety of ordnance including mines,
torpedoes, destructors, nuclear depth
charges, conventional bombs, practice
bombs and rockets. Search stores include
AN/ALQ-78 ESM pods, sonobuoys, smoke
markers and parachute flares.

The **P-3C Update I** (31 built) introduced
a sevenfold increase in computer memory
and AN/ARN-99(V)-1 Omega navigation in
place of the original LORAN. 'Baseline' and

Update I aircraft may be identified by a
undernose camera fairing with windows
The **P-3C Update II** (37 built) featured the
Cubic Corporation AN/ARS-3 Sonobuoy Ref
erence System, provision for carrying and
launching the AGM-84A Harpoon anti-ship
ping missile, an acoustic tape recording sys
tem and a Texas Instruments AN/AAS-3
IRDS (Infra-Red Detection System – a FLIF
housed in a retractable turret aft of the nose
radome). Since the AGM-84A Harpoon has
been added to its armament, the Orion has

250

Once highly colourful, the Orion fleet has surrendered to the drab grey Tactical Paint Scheme, as illustrated by this VP-16 aircraft from Jacksonville.

been given a secondary surface warfare role. This version was first delivered in August 1977. Update II.5 covered a further 24 US Navy P-3Cs with more reliable nav/comms suite, MAD compensation, standardised pylons and other improvements.

The definitive P-3C Orion variant is the **P-3C Update III**, fitted with an entirely new IBM AN/UYS-1 Proteus advanced acoustic signal processor and a new sonobuoy communications link. These enable the aircraft to monitor concurrently twice the number of sonobuoys as can the Update II.5 version. The Update III was the last production version and was first delivered in May 1984. Most baseline P-3Cs were later modified to **P-3C Update III Retrofit** standard.

Export P-3Cs included 10 Update IIs for Australia. These are equipped with the Anglo-Australian Barra acoustic data processor and indigenously developed Barra passive directional sonobuoys. Australia's second P-3C batch (a further 10 aircraft) comprised Update II.5s, but these are known locally as **P-3W**s. Ten of Australia's aircraft are receiving an Elta-developed ESM suite. The Netherlands (13) and Japan also received Update II.5s, a term also applied by the US Navy to embargoed Pakistani P-3Cs, although Lockheed calls these **Update II.75**s. P-3Cs for Norway and South Korea are Update IIIs.

Japan received three aircraft, plus a further four in component knocked-down kit form for assembly by Kawasaki (Japanese licence-built versions are described sepa-

rately). The Imperial Iranian Navy received six P-3Cs in 'baseline' standard (from an order placed in 1975) as **P-3F**s, and these were fitted with a receptacle for inflight refuelling. Due to chronic spares shortages, it is thought that only one or two are left airworthy. The Lockheed CP-140 Aurora, which resembles the P-3C externally, is built to Canadian specification with a different avionics fit. This variant is described separately.

The final P-3C for the US Navy was delivered on 17 April 1990. In 1991, Lockheed moved its Orion production line from Palmdale, CA, to Marietta, GA, with a start-up order announced on 10 December 1990 for eight P-3Cs for South Korea.

P-3C Orions have participated in all American military campaigns of their era. They played a key role in 1986 operations against Libya and in Operations Desert Shield/Storm. In the war with Iraq, Orion detachments flew 3,787 hours in 369 combat sorties. One P-3C of VP-19 was modified under the Outlaw Hunter programme for the OASIS (OTH Airborne Sensor Information System) mission. This is an over-the-horizon targeting platform which provides an overall battlefield plot for commanders. Two further Orions, OASIS I and II, have since been modified for this role.

Proposals to further improve the Orion have fallen victim to programme management troubles and budgeting constraints. To replace some Orions, the US Navy intended in the late 1980s to procure 125 **P-7A** or **LRAACA** (Long-Range Air ASW-Capable Aircraft), originally designated **P-3G**. The P-7A also was expected to go to Britain and Germany, to replace Nimrod MR.Mk 2 and Atlantic ASW aircraft. Powered by four 5,000-shp (3730-ekW) General Electric GE38 free-turbine powerplants driving five-bladed Hamilton Standard 15WF modular

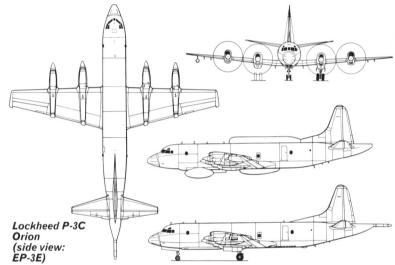

Lockheed P-3C Orion (side view: EP-3E)

composite propellers, the P-7A was never built and the programme was cancelled on 20 July 1990 due to cost overruns.

The US Navy then sought to proceed with the **P-3C Orion Update IV** (the avionics package once envisioned for the P-7A), to introduce improved ASW electronics to cope with quiet, deep-running Soviet submarines. A 10 July 1987 contract to Boeing temporarily took this stage of Orion improvement work away from Lockheed. The Boeing-built P-3C Update IV aircraft made its first functional flight test on 16 December 1991. Update IV included IBM AN/UYS-2 processor with increased sonobuoy capability, APS-137 imaging radar, AAS-36 IRDS, ALR-66(V)5 ASM, GPS navigation, and improved stores and weapons management sub-systems. Following a brief flight test programme, development of the P-3C Update IV was suspended on 13 October 1992.

With both P-7A and P-3C Update IV removed from its future planning, in May 1992 the US Navy authorised developmental funding for yet another advanced Orion, now called the **P-3H Orion II**, a 'stretched' and largely new aircraft based on the P-3C.

VP-40 is based at NAS Barbers Point in Hawaii to cover the Pacific, with regular deployments to the Far East. The squadron operates one of the OASIS/Outlaw Hunter Orions.

The Orion II is to have a new 6,000-shp (4476-ekW) turboprop engine of unspecified type and six-bladed composite propellers to give the aircraft greater fuel economy, range and time on station. The Orion II is unlikely to advance to the hardware stage without a Pentagon go-ahead for 125 aircraft, and/or revival of interest by Britain and Germany.

WEAPON OPTIONS

The Orion has a large weapons bay forward of the wing and 10 underwing hardpoints. Standard ASW weapons are Mk 46 or Mk 50 torpedoes, various depth bombs and destructors, or B57 nuclear depth charges. For the ASV role some P-3Cs are equipped to launch AGM-84 Harpoon, while all can carry underwing rocket pods.

SPECIFICATION

Lockheed P-3C Orion
Wing: span 99 ft 8 in (30.37 m); aspect ratio 7.5; area 1,300.00 sq ft (120.77 m²)
Fuselage and tail: length 116 ft 10 in (35.61 m); height 33 ft 8.5 in (10.27 m); tailplane span 42 ft 10 in (13.06 m); wheel track 31 ft 2 in (9.50 m); wheel base 29 ft 9 in (9.07 m)
Powerplant: four Allison T56-A-14 turboprops each rated at 4,910 ehp (3661 ekW)
Weights: empty 61,491 lb (27890 kg); normal take-off

Lockheed P-3C Orion

Left: Australia purchased 20 P-3Cs in two batches, of which 19 still fly with 92 Wing, divided between Nos 10 and 11 Sqns. An ESM update used Israeli equipment, while local equipment includes the Barra sonobuoy. The second batch (Update II.5) is designated P-3W to avoid confusion with the earlier Update II aircraft.

Above: With a large slice of the North Sea and Atlantic to cover, the Netherlands purchased 13 P-3C Update II.5s to replace its elderly Neptunes. The force is concentrated at Valkenburg with the MARPAT (Maritime Patrol) group, although one aircraft is detached to Keflavik in Iceland on a rotational basis.

135,000 lb (61235 kg); maximum take-off 142,000 lb (64410 kg)
Fuel and load: internal fuel 62,500 lb (28350 kg); external fuel none; maximum expendable load 20,000 lb (9072 kg)
Speed: maximum level speed 'clean' at 15,000 ft (4575 m) 411 kt (473 mph; 761 km/h); economical cruising speed at 25,000 ft (7620 m) 328 kt (378 mph; 608 km/h); patrol speed at 1,500 ft (457 m) 206 kt (237 mph; 381 km/h)
Range: operational radius 2,070 nm (2,383 miles; 3835 km) with no time on station or 1,346 nm (1,550 miles; 2494 km) with 3 hours on station
Performance: maximum rate of climb 1,950 ft (594 m) per minute; service ceiling 28,300 ft (8625 m); take-off run 4,240 ft (1292 m) at maximum take-off weight; take-off distance to 50 ft (15 m) 5,490 ft (1673 m) at maximum take-off weight; landing distance from 50 ft (15 m) 5,490 ft (1673 m) at design landing weight

OPERATORS

The operators list covers all variants of the P-3.
US Navy: VP-1/4/9/17/47 (P-3C) NAS Barbers Point
VP-5/16/24/30/45/62 (P-3C) NAS Jacksonville
VP-8/10/11/23/26 (P-3C) NAS Brunswick
VP-46/91 (P-3C) NAS Moffett Field
VP-65 (P-3C) NAWS Point Mugu
VP-68 (P-3C) NAF Washington
VP-40/69 (P-3C) NAS Whidbey Island
VP-92 (P-3C) NAS South Weymouth
VP-30 (TP-3A, VP-3A, P-3C) NAS Jacksonville
VP-60/90 (P-3B) NAS Glenview
VP-64 (P-3B), VP-66 (P-3B, EP-3J) NAS Willow Grove
VP-67 (P-3B) NAS Memphis
VP-93/94 (P-3B) NAF Detroit
VP-94 (P-3B) NAS New Orleans
VPU-1 (P-3B) NAS Brunswick
VPU-2 (UP-3A, P-3B, P-3C) NAS Barbers Point
VQ-1 (UP-3A, UP-3B, EP-3E) NAS Agana

VQ-2 (UP-3B, EP-3E) NAS Rota
VRC-30 (UP-3A) NAS North Island
VX-1 (P-3C) NAS Patuxent River
ETD (TP-3A, UP-3A, VP-3A) NAS Barbers Point
NAS Bermuda (UP-3A)
NS Keflavik (UP-3A)
NAS Sigonella (VP-3A)
NRL (RP-3A, P-3B) NAS Patuxent River
NAWC-23 (P-3B, NP-3B, P-3C) Dallas-Love Field
NAWC-AD Patuxent River (P-3B, P-3C)
NAWC-AD Point Mugu (RP-3A)
NAWC-AD Warminster (UP-3A, P-3C)
US other agencies: US Customs Service (P-3A, P-3AEW) CSS Corpus Christi
US Forestry Service (P-3A) fire-bombers with Hawkins and Power, Black Hills Aviation and Aero Union
NASA (P-3B) Wallops Island
NOAA (WP-3D) Miami
Australia: P-3C (9), P-3W (10) – Nos 10 and 11 Sqns at RAAF Edinburgh
Canada: CP-140 (18), CP-140A (3) – aircraft of Nos

404, 405 and 415 Sqns pooled at CFB Greenwood, remainder at CFB Comox with No. 407 Sqn
Chile: P-3A (2), UP-3A (6)
Greece: expected to receive five P-3A and one UP-3A
Iran: six P-3Fs delivered, but only one or two remain airworthy
Japan: 109 P-3Cs procured for JMSDF. All but the first three built by Kawasaki (described under that manufacturer). Two converted to EP-3C and one to UP-3C
Netherlands: P-3C (13) – pooled under MARPAT Group for use by Nos 320 and 321 Sqns, and 2 OCU
New Zealand: P-3K (6) – serve with No 5 Sqn at Whenuapai
Norway: P-3C (4), P-3N (2) – operated by 333 Skvadron at Andoya
Pakistan: P-3C (3) – embargoed
Portugal: P-3P (6) – with Esquadra 601 at Montijo
South Korea: P-3C (8) – on order, first received 1994
Spain: P-3A (2), P-3B (5) – with Ala 22 at Jerez
Thailand: P-3T (2), UP-3T (1) – with 2 Sqn at U-Tapao

Lockheed P-3 AEW

Lockheed produced a prototype AEW & C (Airborne Early Warning & Control) aircraft as a private venture in 1984 using a **P-3B Orion** airframe reacquired from the RAAF. Flight testing began on 14 June 1984 with a 24-ft (7.32-m) rotodome mounted above the rear fuselage, and was continued in 1988 after installation of a full General Electric AN/APS-138 radar system. Export orders did not materialise, but the prototype conversion, initially fitted with AN/APS-125 radar, was delivered to the **US Customs Service** for anti-narcotics patrols on 17 June 1988. Options on three further aircraft were subsequently taken up by US Customs. These aircraft were also based on ex-RAAF P-3B airframes but were fitted with the AN/APS-138 system; deliveries took place in 1989, 1992 and 1993, respec-

In its fight against drug-smuggling, the US Customs Service employs eight Orions, four of them equipped with AEW radar as 'Blue Sentinel' aircraft. The 'slick' P-3s are fitted with the F-15's APG-63 fire control radar.

tively. These are augmented by four 'slick' P-3As equipped with APG-63 fire control radar on loan from the US Navy. The APG-63, as fitted to the F-15 Eagle interceptor, replaces the P-3A's AN/APS-80 radar in these **P-3A(CS)** aircraft.

SPECIFICATION

Lockheed P-3 AEW & C Orion
generally similar to the Lockheed P-3C Orion except in the following particulars:

Weight: maximum take-off 127,500 lb (57833 kg)
Fuel and load: maximum ordnance none
Speed: economical cruising speed at 30,000 ft (9145 m) 200 kt (230 mph; 370 km/h)
Range: endurance 14 hours

Lockheed EP-3 Orion

In order to maintain an up-to-date appraisal of the naval strengths of potentially hostile nations, the **US Navy** employs a fleet of specially-modified P-3s to perform the electronic intelligence-gathering role. These aircraft use receivers to gather data from foreign vessels and analyse the radars and other

electronic equipment in order to produce an electronic 'fingerprint' of the vessel. In this way, the vessel's warfighting capabilities can be catalogued, and it can be rapidly identified in the future. The electronic Orion fleet can also undertake regular Sigint duties against land-based and airborne targets.

The designation **EP-3A** has been applied to several airframes used for electronic research platforms in a variety of configurations (including a modified P-3A serving as an electronic aggressor). Two P-3As were converted to **EP-3B** standard in 1969 as Elint aircraft, known as 'Batrack'. These were fitted with direction-finding equipment and communications interception and recording equipment, replacing the ASW gear. Mission equipment was housed in a

large, retractable, ventral radome, dorsal and ventral 'canoe' fairings and a modified tailcone. EP-3Bs served with Fleet Air Reconnaissance Squadron (VQ-) 1 at NAS Agana, Guam, seeing service in Vietnam. Four **EP-3E** aircraft followed for VQ-1, these featuring improved systems, and six EP-3Es were converted for sister squadron VQ-2 at NAS Rota, Spain, operating in support of the Atlantic fleet. The EP-3E is easily distinguished by the large, flattened 360°

The EP-3E (and the similar replacement EP-3E-II) is the US Navy's principal Elint-gathering platform, tasked primarily with 'fingerprinting' foreign vessels.

adome under the forward fuselage, truncated tailboom, long dorsal and ventral canoes, and numerous additional small antennas. The array of antennas serves a comprehensive onboard suite, known collectively as the 'Aries' system. This has as its main constituent parts an ALD-8 radio direction finder, ALQ-110 signals-gathering system, ALR-52 frequency-measuring receiver and ALR-60 communications recorder. Both EP-3Bs were brought up to EP-3E standard.

As the elderly EP-3E airframes neared the end of their service lives, the US Navy opted for a CILOP (conversion in lieu of procurement) programme to update the fleet. Accordingly, 12 P-3Cs were stripped of ASW gear and had the original 'Aries' systems from the EP-3Bs and EP-3Es installed instead, together with some improvements. The aircraft emerged as **EP-3E-II**s, and continue to serve with both VQ-1 at Agana, Guam, and VQ-2 at Rota, Spain.

Additional Orions have carried the EP-3 designation for trials and EW aggressor work. At least one P-3A was converted as

an **EP-3A** to serve with various naval research facilities, including evaluation squadron VX-1, on trials work. Another EP-3A was converted to provide jamming for fleet exercises, this aircraft serving with VAQ-33 at NAS Key West. It has since been joined by an **EP-3J**, with internally- and pod-mounted jamming equipment. VAQ-33's Orions were used to provide heavy ECM environments in which naval defences could be exercised.

Both aircraft are now in EP-3J configuration, serving with VP-66 at NAS Willow Grove.

EP-3As which served the PMTC were redesignated as RP-3s, and are described separately.

SPECIFICATION

Lockheed EP-3E Orion

generally similar to the P-3C Orion except in the following particulars:
Speed: maximum level speed at 15,000 ft (4575 m) 380 kt (437 mph; 703 km/h); patrol speed 180 kt (207 mph; 333 km/h)
Range: operational radius 2,200 nm (2,533 miles; 4076 km) with no time on station
Performance: maximum rate of climb at sea level 2,175 ft (663 m) per minute; service ceiling 28,000 ft (8535 m)

Lockheed NP-3/RP-3/WP-3

In addition to the EP-3, TP-3, UP-3 and VP-3 described above, the **US Navy** and related agencies operate a small number of other special-mission Orions. The **RP-3A** designation is applied to seven PMTC (now Naval Air Warfare Center – Aircraft Division, NAWS Point Mugu, CA) Orions (four previously known as EP-3As), including two aircraft modified with SMILS (Sonobuoy Missile Impact Locating System) and three with 'Billboard' tail modifications (applied by Hayes International and Tracor during 1982/83). All seven aircraft have EATS (Extended Area Test System) equipment, but the 'Billboard' tail adds a Raytheon Rotman-lens phased-array antenna in an extension of the fin leading edge, allowing the aircraft to receive and rebroadcast EATS data. Their

Three of NAWC-AD's RP-3A aircraft carry the 'billboard' antenna in a giant fin extension.

role is to monitor and support naval weapons trials over the Pacific. The US Navy's VXN-8 used a handful of **RP-3A**, **RP-3C** and **RP-3D** Orions on behalf of the US Naval Oceanographic Office for a variety of research programmes related to ocean currents, and acoustic and thermal properties, but these were retired in 1993.

A single **NP-3B** is used for trials by a Naval Air Systems Command test unit at Love Field, and a single P-3C has been modified with optical windows in the belly for a laser generator and receiver for the Tactical Airborne Laser Communication Program.

Two aircraft with an X-band radar in their tailcones and a C-band radar in a large ventral radome were built as **WP-3D**s using P-3C-type airframes and engines. These aircraft have extra observation windows and

new pitot static booms on nose and port wingtip, and are used by the **National Oceanic and Atmospheric Administration** for weather research and hurricane hunting from their Miami base.

Lockheed CP-140 Aurora

Externally closely resembling the US Navy's P-3C Orion (described separately), the **Lockheed CP-140 Aurora** is the version of the Orion purchased in 1976 by the **Canadian Armed Forces**. Internally, the 11-seat Aurora is configured to Canadian requirements, and is equipped with an avionics system based on that of the S-3A Viking, including APS-116 search radar, ASQ-501 MAD and AN/AYK-10 computer. Provision was also made in the weapons bay for Canadian-specified ordnance loads, including eight Mk 44/46 torpedoes. Lockheed flew the first CP-140 on 22 March 1979 and completed delivery of the 18 on

order in July 1981, allowing replacement of the CP-107 Argus in CAF service. The Auroras are flown by four squadrons: VP-404 (originally VT-404 for training), VP-405 and VP-415, all at Greenwood and sharing 14 aircraft, plus VP-407 at Comox with the remaining four. Paramax systems has submitted an unsolicited bid to the Department of National Defence for a C$750-million CP-140 upgrade covering acoustic sensors, radar, ESM and communications and navigation equipment, as well as a refurbishment/ SLEP to allow the fleet to operate to 2010 or beyond. Other Canadian companies are competing for the upgrade contract.

The CP-140A Arcturus is an austere version, described in the following entry.

SPECIFICATION

Lockheed CP-140 Aurora
Wing: span 99 ft 8 in (30.37 m); aspect ratio 7.5; area 1,300.00 sq ft (120.77 m²)
Fuselage and tail: length 116 ft 10 in (35.61 m); height 33 ft 8.5 in (10.29 m); tailplane span 42 ft 10 in (13.06 m); wheel track 31 ft 2 in (9.50 m); wheel base 29 ft 9 in (9.07 m)
Powerplant: four Allison T56-A-14 turboprops each rated at 4,910 ehp (3661 ekW)
Weights: empty 61,491 lb (27892 kg); normal take-off 135,000 lb

(61236 kg); maximum take-off 142,000 lb (64411 kg)
Fuel and load: internal fuel 9,200 US gal (34826 litres); external fuel none; maximum ordnance 20,000 lb (9071 kg)
Speed: maximum cruising speed at optimum altitude 395 kt (455 mph; 732 km/h)
Range: ferry range 4,500 nm (5,182 miles; 8339 km); operational radius 1,000 nm (1,152 miles; 1853 km) for an 8.2-hour patrol
Performance: maximum rate of climb at sea level 2,890 ft (881 m) per minute; service ceiling 28,250 ft (8610 m); take-off distance to 50 ft (15 m) 6,000 ft (1829 m) at maximum take-off weight; landing distance from 50 ft (15 m) 3,200 ft (975 m) at normal landing weight

Both pictures: The three Greenwood Aurora squadrons (404, 405 and 415) draw aircraft from a pool of 14 owned by the BAMEO. The remaining four are with 407 Sqn at Comox. Supporting the fleet are the Maritime Proving and Evaluation Unit, and the Aurora Software Development Unit, both at Greenwood.

Lockheed **CP-140A Arcturus**

Ordered by **Canada** in August 1989 and the last examples of the P-3 family built at Burbank before the final assembly line was transferred to Marietta, the **CP-140A Arcturus** is an austere special-duty variant of the CP-140 Aurora (described separately). Stripped of all ASW equipment, the Arcturus has two principal roles. The first is crew training for the Aurora fleet, and the second is environmental, Arctic sovereignty and fishery patrols, for which it carries AN/APS-134 radar and other appropriate sensors and flight systems. Delivery of three CP-140As to the BAMEO at Greenwood was completed in September 1991. The use of these aircraft releases the Aurora fleet to concentrate on their ASW activities.

Outwardly similar to the CP-140 Aurora, the Arcturus can be distinguished by the lack of certain antennas.

Lockheed **S-3 Viking**

The **Lockheed S-3 Viking** is the **US Navy**'s carrier-based, fixed-wing ASW aircraft. Designed to meet the US Navy's 1964 VSX (experimental carrier-based ASW aircraft) requirement, the first service-test **YS-3A** (of eight built) made its maiden flight on 21 January 1972 at Palmdale, CA. Conventional in design for a carrier-based warplane, the Viking is a high-wing, twin-turbofan aircraft with hydraulically-folding wings, and pressurised accommodation for its crew of four (comprising pilot, co-pilot, tactical co-ordinator and acoustic sensor operator). Based on an August 1969 contract, Lockheed manufactured the Viking in partnership with Vought, which designed and built wings, tail unit, landing gear and engine pods.

The original production **S-3A** variant is equipped with a Univac AN/AYK-10 digital computer, Texas Instruments AN/APS-116 radar and Texas Instruments OR-89 FLIR. The heart of the Viking's ASW suite is a Texas Instruments AN/ASQ-81 magnetic anomaly detector sensor housed in a retractable tailboom. The Viking carries 60 sonobuoys in its aft fuselage and has a ventral bomb bay and wing ordnance stations able to house bombs, torpedoes or depth charges. The first S-3A Viking went to VS-41 'Shamrocks', the first FRS for the type, located at North Island, CA, and was received in February 1974. VS-21 'Fighting Redtails', also at North Island, became the first fleet squadron to operate the type in July 1974. Lockheed built a total of 179 production S-3As, delivering the last aircraft in August 1978.

The improved **S-3B** variant is the result of a weapons system improvement pro-

Fleet ASW squadrons are equipped with the S-3B version, with improved systems and Harpoon anti-ship missile capability.

gramme launched in 1981, which retains the Viking airframe and engines but adds improved acoustic processing, expanded ESM coverage, increased radar processing capabilities, a new sonobuoy receiver system, and provision for AGM-84 Harpoon air-to-surface missiles. All but identical in outward appearance to the S-3A, the S-3B can be distinguished by a small chaff dispenser located on its aft fuselage. Nearly all existing S-3As have been upgraded to S-3B status at naval air depots. Except for a few S-3As scattered among the two training and two fleet air reconnaissance squadrons, the entire Viking force now consists of the upgraded S-3B model.

The seventh YS-3A was modified to become the **US-3A** carrier onboard delivery aircraft, envisioned as a replacement for the piston-engined Grumman C-1 Trader and first flown on 2 July 1976. In all, six US-3A Vikings, stripped of ASW equipment and transformed into 'people haulers', have been used to complement the turbine-powered Grumman C-2A Greyhound. Lockheed also modified the fifth YS-3A to test the aircraft as the **KS-3A** tanker. The dedicated tanker variant has not been produced, although operational Vikings have been adapted as part-time tankers with the same 'buddy-buddy' refuelling store.

Developed to meet the Cold War threat posed by the Soviet fleet of quiet, deep-diving nuclear submarines, the S-3 fought in Operation Desert Storm against an enemy which possessed no submarines. The S-3A/B Viking proved an exceedingly effective conventional bomber when employed against Iraqi radar stations, anti-aircraft batteries, small vessels in the Persian Gulf and other targets. On a typical mission on 20 February 1991, an S-3B of VS-32 'Maulers',

A VS-32 S-3B lands carrying a D-704 refuelling pod.

operating from USS *America* (CV-66), employed its own inverse SAR and FLIR, plus guidance from the cruiser USS *Valley Forge* (CG-50), to despatch an Iraqi combat vessel with a stick of three Mk 82 500-lb (227-kg) bombs.

Several special mission variants of the S-3B are in service or development. The **Outlaw Viking** is modified with OASIS III equipment to provide an over-the-horizon targeting and theatre control platform. The **Gray Wolf** S-3B features a Multi-Mode Radar System (comprising ISAR and SAR modes), laser ranger, digital camera system and infra-red. This is intended for littoral surveillance and tracking of 'Scud'-type missile launches. The deployed **Viking Beartrap** has an Elint processing capability in addition to its normal suite, while **Orca** is the name of one Viking used for testing advanced ASW systems such as the Intrum Extended Echo Ranger (IEER) and an ASW laser ranger integrated with some of the Gray Wolf's equipment, including a wing-mount-

ed synthetic aperture radar pod. Orca is believed to be able to detect minefields.

Several Vikings are currently involved in anti-drug trafficking duties in the Caribbean using camera systems, FLIR and hand-held sensors. The **Calypso** S-3B is a proposal for a dedicated anti-smuggling variant, with many of the Gray Wolf systems including ISAR, SAR, IRST and cluster ranger. Finally it has been reported that under the code name Project Aladdin, so-called **Brown Boy** Vikings have been used to drop acoustic sensors to monitor ground movements in Bosnia, similar to the use of such sensors in the Igloo White programme in South East Asia.

WEAPON OPTIONS

The S-3B has two internal weapon bays on the 'corners' of its fuselage, able to carry four Mk 46 or 50 torpedoes, four Mk 36, 62 or 82 bomb/destructors, or two B57 nuclear depth charges (no longer carried on US carriers). A wing pylon outboard of each nacelle is able to carry two Mk 52, 55, 56 or 60 mines, six Mk 36, 62 or 82 destructor/bombs, six Mk 7 cluster dispensers, six ADM-141 decoys, six rocket pods, six flare dispensers or two AGM-84 Harpoons or AGM-84E SLAM. In the refuelling role the D-704 pod is carried under the port wing, with a 300-US gal (1135-litre) fuel tank to starboard.

SPECIFICATION

Lockheed S-3A Viking
Wing: span 68 ft 8 in (20.93 m); width folded 29 ft 6 in (8.99 m); aspect ratio 7.88; area 598.00 sq ft (55.56 m²)
Fuselage and tail: length overall 53 ft 4 in (16.26 m) and with tail folded 49 ft 5 in (15.06 m); height overall 22 ft 9 in (6.93 m) and with tail folded 15 ft 3 in (4.65 m); tailplane span 27 ft 0 in (8.23 m)
Powerplant: two General Electric TF34-GE-2 turbofans each rated at 9,275 lb st (41.26 kN) dry
Weights: empty 26,650 lb (12088 kg); normal take-off 42,500 lb (19277 kg); maximum take-off 52,540 lb (23832 kg)
Fuel and load: internal fuel 12,863 lb (5753 kg); external fuel two 300-US gal (1136-litre) drop tanks; maximum ordnance 7,000 lb (3175 kg) including 4,000 lb (1814 kg) carried internally
Speed: maximum level speed 'clean' at sea level 439 kt (506 mph; 814 km/h); maximum cruising speed

RADAR
The large nose radome houses the Texas Instruments APS-137(V)1 ISAR (inverse synthetic aperture radar). ISAR technology allows the long-range classification of ship types, while the radar uses pulse compression and a fast scan rate to eliminate sea clutter and therefore improve periscope detection capability. There are eight modes: small target detection, high-altitude long-range ocean surveillance, short-range search and rescue, medium-resolution ship classification, high-resolution classification and battle damage assessment, navigation/coast-mapping, weather detection and self-test.

SONOBUOY LAUNCHERS
The 60 ejector ports are inclined backwards so that the buoys hit the surface below the point from which they were fired.

ASW SENSORS
In addition to the radar, the S-3B uses MAD and sonobuoys to detect and track submarines. The MAD 'sting' is deployed from the tailcone, while up to 60 sonobuoys are carried, ejected through ports in the lower fuselage. A Hazeltine ARR-78 system receives sonobuoy signals, which are processed by the AYS-1 Proteus system. ALR-76 ESM provides passive detection of hostile radar systems.

CREW
The Viking is operated by a crew of four, all seated on McDonnell Douglas Escapac 1-E ejection seats. Two pilots sit side-by-side, handling flight control and navigation. Behind them sit the mission crew of Tactical Co-ordinator ('Tacco'), who controls the search and attack portion of the mission, and Sensor Operator ('Senso'). Both are provided with a small window in the cabin side.

Lockheed S-3B Viking

The S-3 Viking is carried aboard each carrier to perform the outer-zone anti-submarine mission, patrolling at long distance from the carrier while the SH-60F Ocean Hawk or SH-3 Sea King handles the inner-zone defence. In addition to this primary role, the S-3B is tasked with secondary duties of inflight-refuelling (with the D-704 refuelling pod depicted here) and various forms of attack. These include anti-ship (with AGM-84 Harpoon), stand-off precision (with AGM-84E SLAM), surface attack (with general-purpose or cluster weapons) and mine-laying. ASW weapons include various destructors and depth charges, torpedoes, captive torpedoes and the B57 nuclear depth charge. The latter is no longer carried in the magazines of US Navy carriers, but remains available for contingencies.

FUEL
Internal fuel capacity (in the inner wing structure and top of the fuselage) is 1,900 US gal (7190 litres), which can be augmented by two 300-US gal (1136-litre) drop tanks. A retractable refuelling probe deploys from above the cockpit.

FLIR
One of the main attack sensors is the Texas Instruments OR-89/AA FLIR. This is mounted in a retractable turret located behind doors in the lower port fuselage beneath the flight deck.

WING-FOLDING
In order to take up the minimum amount of room on the carrier deck, and to fit the deck-edge elevators and hangars, the S-3 has a unique wing-folding arrangement. The wings hinge immediately outboard of the engine pylons, but stagger to lie against each other across the aircraft's back. The tall fin folds to port.

optimum altitude more than 350 kt (403 mph; 649 km/h); patrol speed at optimum altitude 160 kt (184 mph; 296 km/h)
Range: ferry range more than 3,000 nm (3,454 miles; 5558 km); operational radius more than 945 nm (1,088 miles; 1751 km); endurance 7 hours 30 minutes
Performance: maximum rate of climb at sea level more than 4,200 ft (1280 m) per minute; service ceiling more than 35,000 ft (10670 m); take-off run 2,200 ft (671 m) at maximum take-off weight; landing in 1,600 ft (488 m) at 36,500 lb (16556 kg)

Six US-3A Vikings serve with VRC-50 in the Pacific on utility transport duties. Two were originally designated S-3A(COD). A dedicated tanker version was not proceeded with.

Lockheed ES-3A Viking

The **Lockheed ES-3A Viking** is a carrier-based Elint aircraft modified from the S-3A with over-the-horizon surveillance equipment similar to that fitted to the land-based Lockheed EP-3A Aries II. The **US Navy** has procured 16 ES-3As, converted by Lockheed at NAS Cecil Field, FL.

In the ES-3A, the co-pilot position is replaced by a third sensor station and the bomb bays have been modified to accommodate avionics. The ES-3A introduces a new radome, direction-finding antenna and other equipment in a dorsal 'shoulder' on the fuselage, an array of seven receiving antennas on its underfuselage, a cone-shaped omnidirectional Elint antenna on each side of the fuselage just forward of the horizontal stabiliser, and AN/ALR-76 ESM antennas forward and aft of the wingtips.

An ES-3A of VQ-6, the Atlantic Fleet carrierborne Sigint squadron. The US Navy was without a seagoing electronic surveillance aircraft from the withdrawal of the EA-3B in November 1987 until the arrival of the ES-3A in 1991.

Two US Navy squadrons deploy eight ES-3As each on carriers, generally in pairs. VQ-5 'Sea Shadows' stood up on 15 April 1991 at NAS Agana, Guam. VQ-6 'Black Ravens' was established in August 1991 at NAS Cecil Field.

Lockheed began the ES-3A programme with a 'proof of concept' aircraft lacking internal systems and, on 1 October 1990, began conversion of 15 ES-3As at Cecil. An ES-3A 'first flight' on 15 May 1991 involved the 16th aircraft, the sole production airframe modified by Lockheed at Palmdale, CA. The next 'production' ES-3A flew at Cecil on 21 January 1992.

Lockheed SR-71

Withdrawn from USAF service in 1990, the **Lockheed SR-71 Blackbird** reconnaissance aircraft, once the world's highest performance military aircraft, continues to play a role for research. Three SR-71s were originally placed in storage at Palmdale for the USAF, but these are believed to be no longer recoverable. A further three, comprising two **SR-71A**s and a dual-control **SR-71B**, were transferred to **NASA** and now form part of the research fleet at the Ames-Dryden Flight Research Facility based at Edwards AFB. In 1994 the possibility of returning the NASA aircraft to front-line USAF service was under review.

A proposal concerns the use of the SR-71 as a launch platform for lightweight space vehicles, using the aircraft as, in effect, reusable first stage.

Although shrinking budgets forced the USAF to retire the SR-71, these three continue to fly from Edwards AFB with NASA-Dryden.

Lockheed T-33

With approximately 6,750 aircraft built, the **Lockheed T-33A** is by far the most successful jet trainer yet developed for service anywhere in the world, and it says much for the durability of the 'T-bird' that many aircraft remain airworthy around the world today, more than 40 years after the type first flew. The oldest aircraft in the USAF inventory is a much-modified **NT-33A** which is still flying at Wright-Patterson AFB on research tasks in mid-1994.

A logical development of the single-seat **F-80** (the first jet-powered fighter to become operational with the US Army Air Forces), the T-33A actually began life in the late 1940s as the **TF-80C**, a stretched tandem two-seater trainer version of the F-80.

Following introduction to service with the US Air Force in the closing stages of the 1940s, the 'T-bird' was soon being built in numbers that far outstripped those of the F-80, and it ultimately became the USAF's standard jet trainer type, equipping flying schools for several years. Just under 700 extensively modified examples of the T-33A were diverted to the US Navy, initially known as the **TO-2** and soon redesignated **TV-2 SeaStar** (**T-33B** from late 1962).

In addition to being extensively used by the USAF and US Navy, the T-33A found a ready market overseas, many of the aircraft built being supplied to friendly nations under the Military Assistance Program. Countries which acquired the T-33A in this way included France, Greece, Italy, the Philippines, Portugal, Spain, Taiwan, Thailand, Turkey and West Germany. Licence production was undertaken by Canada, which completed 656 Nene-engined **CL-30 Silver Star** aircraft, and by Japan, which assembled 210, many of them still engaged in training duties today.

Although viewed basically as a trainer, Lockheed's jet has performed other roles,

Left: Thailand uses a large fleet of T-33s mainly for advanced training. A handful of RT-33s are on strength.

Right: In Europe both Greece and Turkey retain the T-33 for 'hack' and training work. This Turkish machine is on the strength of the Konya base flight.

Above: In JASDF service the T-33 is mainly assigned to HQ flights and in support of front-line units.

Above: Canada's surviving CT-133s are mostly used as either EW aggressors (illustrated) or in the target facilities role, serving with 414 Sqn.

Left: No. 2 Sqn, Pakistan air force, operates the camera-equipped RT-33A.

modest number of aircraft being fitted with a camera nose and electronic equipment in the aft cockpit in order to perform reconnaissance functions. Designated **RT-33A**, these single-seaters were produced mainly for MAP operators including France, Italy, the Netherlands, Pakistan, Thailand and Turkey. A version armed for interdiction and close support was the **AT-33A**, of which numbers are still in service.

Another important role was that of target drone, the US Navy being perhaps the major operator and destroyer of drone-configured 'T-birds'. Often controlled by a **DT-33** director, the **QT-33** took part in numerous weapons test projects, most of the converted aircraft meeting a fiery end over the range areas of the Pacific Missile Test Center and the Naval Weapons Center at Point Mugu and China Lake, respectively.

More recently, the Skyfox Corporation has proposed remanufacturing the T-33A as a twin-turbofan advanced trainer, employing externally-mounted Garrett TFE731 engines. Extensive redesign of the fuselage and empennage forms part of the modernisation process, but so far no customers have been found for the resulting **Skyfox**, the prototype of which flew in June 1983.

SPECIFICATION

Lockheed T-33A
Wing: span 38 ft 10.5 in (11.85 m); aspect ratio 6.44; area 234.00 sq ft (21.81 m²)
Fuselage and tail: length 37 ft 9 in (11.51 m); height 11 ft 8 in (3.55 m)
Powerplant: one Allison J33-A-35 turbojet rated at 5,400 lb st (24.02 kN)
Weights: empty equipped 8,365 lb (3794 kg); normal take-off 12,071 lb (5475 kg); maximum take-off 15,061 lb (6832 kg)
Fuel and load: internal fuel 353 US gal (1336 litres) plus provision for 460 US gal (1741 litres) in two tip tanks; external fuel none; maximum ordnance none

Speed: maximum level speed 'clean' at sea level 521 kt (600 mph; 966 km/h); cruising speed at optimum altitude 395 kt (455 mph; 732 km/h)
Range: ferry range 1,107 nm (1,275 miles; 2050 km) with tip tanks; range 890 nm (1,025 miles; 1650 km) with internal fuel
Performance: maximum rate of climb at sea level 4,870 ft (1484 m) per minute; service ceiling 48,000 ft (14630 m)

OPERATORS

T/AT-33s survive with the following air arms: Bolivia (32), Canada (local designation **CT-133**, 60 including about 30 in storage), Ecuador (23), Greece

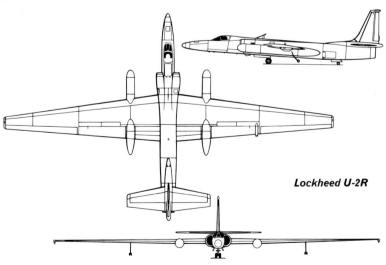

Canada's test establishment, the AETE at Cold Lake, operates five CT-133s, including aircraft calibrated to act as chase planes. This example is used for ejection seat trials.

(about 40), Iran (10), Japan (over 100), Mexico (40), Pakistan (10 and four RT-33s), Philippines (3), South Korea (33), Thailand (over 30 and four RT-33s), Turkey about 50) and Uruguay (11 including six AT-33As).

Lockheed **U-2R**

In its original form, the **Lockheed U-2** first flew with Tony LeVier at the controls on 4 August 1955, from the secret Groom Dry Lake test facility in Nevada. A highly successful reconnaissance career for the early variants ensued, overshadowed by the shooting-down over Sverdlovsk of a CIA aircraft flown by Francis Gary Powers in May 1960. Despite the setback to the programme, the U-2 was still seen as a highly useful reconnaissance tool with its ability to loiter for hours at high altitude, making it an excellent platform for the gathering of electronic intelligence in addition to long-range oblique photographs.

As powered by the J75 engine, the first-generation U-2s were airframe-limited, so Lockheed began the development of a much larger aircraft to provide far greater sensor carriage on the same power. The result was the **U-2R**, which first flew from Edwards North Base on 28 August 1967. This closely resembled the early aircraft in layout, but was larger in overall dimensions, offering the ability to carry large amounts of

intelligence-gathering equipment and much greater range/endurance by way of large internal fuel carriage in the huge 'wet' wings. At the same time, the new design alleviated many of the aerodynamic flaws of the first generation, making the U-2R much less tricky to fly.

A first batch of 12 aircraft was completed, equally distributed between the **US Air Force** and the CIA. The former mostly flew in South East Asia, while the latter operated from Taiwan over Communist China. In 1974 the agency aircraft passed to the US Air Force, and joined a global reconnaissance effort that has been maintained ever since.

In November 1979, the production line reopened to provide 37 new airframes. The initiative for this was the **TR-1A** programme, which used the U-2R airframe as a platform for the ASARS-2 battlefield surveillance radar. The TR-1A was also seen as a platform for the PLSS radar location system, and for signals intelligence-gathering equipment as carried by the U-2R. TR-1As were

intended for use in Europe and deployed to RAF Alconbury and the 17th Reconnaissance Wing, but the presence was progressively withdrawn as the Cold War threat diminished. The TR-1 designation was

Lockheed U-2R

finally dropped to recognise the fact that the aircraft were virtually identical to the U-2Rs.

The new-build batch contained 25 aircraft designated TR-1A, and seven designated U-2Rs as attrition replacements from the

Lockheed U-2R

Lockheed began to replace J75 turbojet with GE F101-GE-F29 turbofans. First flown in a TR-1A in March 1989, this powerplant is derived from the B-2's F118 engine, and is in the 18,500-Lb st (83.9-kN) class. The F101 confers a 15 per cent increase in endurance, restores operational ceiling to above 80,000 ft (24380 m) and improves supportability across USAF bases, the U-2 being the last USAF aircraft to fly under J75 power.

SPECIFICATION

Lockheed U-2R

Wing: span 103 ft 0 in (31.39 m); aspect ratio 10.6; area about 1,000.00 sq ft (92.90 m2)

Fuselage and tail: length 62 ft 9 in (19.13 m); height 16 ft 0 in (4.88 m)

Powerplant: one Pratt & Whitney J75-P-13B turbojet rated at 17,000 lb st (75.62 kN) dry

Weights: basic empty without powerplant and equipment pods less than 10,000 lb (4536 kg); operating empty about 15,500 lb (7031 kg); maximum take-off 41,300 lb (18733 kg)

Fuel and load: internal fuel 7,649 lb (3469 kg); external fuel none; sensor weight 3,000 lb (1361 kg)

Speed: never exceed speed Mach 0.8; maximum cruising speed at 70,000 ft (21335 m) more than 373 mph (430 mph; 692 km/h)

Range: maximum range about 5,428 nm (6,250 miles; 10060 km); maximum endurance 12 hours

Performance: maximum rate of climb at sea level about 5,000 ft (1525 m) per minute; climb to 65,000 ft (19810 m) in 35 minutes; operational ceiling 80,000 ft (24385 m); take-off run about 650 ft (198 m) at MTOW; landing run about 2,500 ft (762 m) at maximum

Above: For the real-time global transfer of data, some U-2Rs are fitted with the Senior Span satellite communications equipment, housed in a teardrop fairing on a dorsal pylon.

Left: Three U-2RT trainers are on strength with the 9th Reconnaissance Wing for conversion training and check rides.

three theatre detachments to cover the Mediterranean, Far East and Europe. These are, respectively, at RAF Akrotiri, Cyprus (Det 2), Osan AB, South Korea (Det 3) and RAF Alconbury, England (OL-UK), each usually operating two aircraft. Additionally, U-2s have been stationed at Taif, Saudi Arabia (OL-CH – Operating Location-Camel Hump), since the first days of the Desert Shield military build-up following the Iraqi invasion of Kuwait in August 1990. In 1994 the U-2s were still regularly flying monitoring missions in that theatre, continuing an impressive record established before and during the war. Regular surveillance of Bosnia was also being maintained.

While new sensors are continually being developed for the U-2R fleet, airframe modifications were limited until 1992, when

NASA operates three ER-2s as high-altitude research and sensor platforms. These fly with NASA-Ames at Moffett Field.

outset. Three two-seat trainers were included in the batch, these comprising two **TR-1B**s and a single **U-2RT**. All three are identical, and the TR-1Bs have now adopted the U-2RT designation. Finally, two aircraft were completed as **ER-2**s for use as earth resources monitoring aircraft by NASA-Ames. These were later joined by an ex-TR-1A.

In configuration, the U-2R resembles a powered glider. The high aspect ratio wings confer extraordinary range and altitude performance, while the slender fuselage houses the engine, cockpit and bicycle undercarriage. The main undercarriage is retractable, but the wings are supported by plug-in 'pogo' outriggers. These fall free on take-off, leaving the aircraft to come to rest on one wingtip at the end of its landing run. The wingtips incorporate skids, above which are radar warning receivers.

Sensors are carried in the detachable nosecone (with different-shaped cones for different sensor fits), a large 'Q-bay' behind the cockpit for the carriage of large cameras, smaller bays along the lower fuselage and in two wing 'super pods', which are removable. Sensors include a wide range of recorders for Comint and Elint, imaging radars, radar locators and high-resolution cameras. A common configuration is the Tactical Reconnaissance System (TRS) fit, which features ASARS-2 radar in extended nosecone, side-looking radars in 'super pods' and a large farm of Sigint antennas on the 'super pods' and rear fuselage.

Recorded intelligence can be transmitted via datalink to ground stations, and at least three aircraft are equipped to carry the Senior Span satellite communications antenna in a huge teardrop radome mounted on a dorsal pylon. This allows the transmission of recorded intelligence across global distances in near real-time.

Missions vary according to requirements, but often reach 10 hours in duration. The standard profile is to fly racetrack patterns at altitudes around 75,000 ft (22860 m). On approach, the U-2R pilot is aided by another pilot in a Ford Mustang chase car (the 'mobile') who provides landing instruc-

tions as the U-2R settles back to earth. Despite the aerodynamic refinements applied to the second-generation U-2, it remains a particularly tricky aircraft to land, being very prone to weather-cocking due to the central main undercarriage and large fin, and with a high tendency to float due to the very low wing loading and high idle speed of the engine.

All U-2s serve with the 9th Reconnaissance Wing headquartered at Beale AFB, CA, where they previously shared the base with the Mach 3+ SR-71. The primary flying unit is the 99th Reconnaissance Squadron, augmented by the 1st RS(T) which undertakes training and flies the U-2RT trainers. This squadron previously flew the SR-71, while the U-2 training function was undertaken by the 5th SRTS. The 9th RW has

Below: In common with other Air Combat Command aircraft, the 9th Wing's U-2Rs wear tailcodes and a unit fin-band.

Lockheed/Boeing F-22

*YF-22 originally Lockheed/General Dynamics/Boeing.
GD's fighter division at Fort Worth
subsequently purchased by Lockheed*

The **Lockheed/Boeing F-22** is the **US Air Force**'s replacement for the F-15 Eagle. Intended to be the leading American air-to-air fighter in the early part of the 21st century, the F-22 meets a USAF requirement for long-range cruise at supersonic speeds without afterburning (supercruise), and makes use of low-observables (LO), or stealth technology, to defeat advanced radar defence systems.

The F-22 emerged from the free-spending Reagan years (1981-89) when the USAF sought an F-15 Eagle replacement. In 1984, the USAF formalised a requirement for a fighter capable of supersonic flight in the region of Mach 1.5 without afterburning, with a range greater than that of the F-15, and with vectoring and reversing engine nozzles for STOL performance.

Lockheed YF-22A and Northrop YF-23A candidates were developed for this ATF (Advanced Tactical Fighter) contest, initially in a 'black' programme accessible only to those with compartmentalised security clearances. Boeing and General Dynamics teamed with Lockheed; the former's company-owned Boeing 757 was modified to become an avionics flying laboratory for the F-22 programme. The first YF-22A, powered by General Electric YF120 engines, made its first flight on 29 September 1990. The second YF-22A, powered by Pratt & Whitney YF119 engines, flew on 30 October 1990. The competing Northrop YF-23 also

flew in both GE- and P&W-powered examples. On 23 April 1991, the USAF announced its choice of the F-22 for the ATF production contract. The decision in favour of the P&W engine came soon after.

The F-22 uses thrust vectoring to manoeuvre at high angles of attack in air-to-air combat: two-dimensional engine nozzles can be vectored 20 per cent up or down at any power setting. Coupled with large leading-edge wing flaps and overall low wing loading, the nozzles permit manoeuvre at low speeds and high flight angles.

The angular YF-22 has a comparatively large, diamond-shaped wing, splayed twin vertical tails and large horizontal tails. The wing is almost a delta, with 48° of sweep on the leading edge, a nearly straight trailing edge, and a very small tip chord. The wing blends into the fuselage to provide a lifting body area. Engine air intakes are located astride a short, tapered nose, which houses the cockpit and most of the avionics. The inlet ducts curve inward and upward, shielding the front faces of the engine from direct illumination by radar. Radar-absorbent materials are employed in the forward fuselage and cockpit canopy.

The pilot sits upright on a zero-zero ACES II seat beneath an unbroken bubble-style canopy and has a panel of liquid-crystal colour displays and HUD. Extensive use is made of VHSIC (very high-speed integrated circuits), common modules and high-speed

Lockheed/Boeing YF-22

data buses. The avionics suite makes use of voice command/control, VHSIC 1750 computer, shared antennas, advanced data fusion/cockpit displays, INEWS (integrated electronic warfare system), ICNIA (integrated communications, navigation, identification avionics) and fibre-optics data transmission. The integrated avionics suite maximises the pilot's situational awareness, allowing him to fully exploit the aircraft's

many high-technology systems.

The F-22 is intended to cruise at supersonic speed to a high-risk area and engage opposing aircraft beyond visual range but, if necessary, to be able to outmanoeuvre them at closer range. Details have not been released concerning the radar, which will be crucial to the F-22 in BVR engagements, although it will have a fixed, phased-array antenna. A 20-mm cannon is mounted internally in production F-22s for closer-in combat. The F-22's lower fuselage has a weapon bay with serrated edges to house four AIM-120 AMRAAM missiles. The aircraft also has lateral weapon bays just aft of the engine inlets for four AIM-9M

Left: The F119-powered YF-22 manoeuvres at speed. For the second stage of its flight trials a military serial was worn, in place of the civilian N22YX used for the first stage of Dem/Val. Note the Pratt & Whitney badge on the intake, and the 'Skunk Works' badge on the fin.

Below: Looking every inch a fighter, the F-22 design is a careful blend of manoeuvrability, performance, advanced avionics and stealthiness. The two YF-22 prototypes fully validated the design concept.

Lockheed/Boeing F-22

Sidewinders. Other planned production changes made in a desire for economy include a relaxation in rear hemisphere 'stealthiness'.

In September 1991, the USAF acknowledged that the F-22 would exceed its projected weight goal by 10,000 lb (4536 kg) and will weigh 20 per cent more than the target weight of 50,000 lb (22680 kg). A Martin-Marietta IRST for the F-22 was postponed due mainly to cost considerations. Flight testing of the YF-22 resumed on 30 October 1991 at Edwards AFB, but was discontinued after the second YF-22, the only example then flying, crashed at Edwards on 25 April 1992.

Engineering and manufacturing development work will occupy the period 1992-96. In the FSD F-22 programme, the manufacturers will produce seven single-seat **F-22A** aircraft and two two-seat **F-22B** aircraft, the first due to fly in 1996. The production aircraft will differ significantly from the YF-22s, with revised shapes applied to the nose, wings and tail surfaces. The all-important alignment of surfaces (for low radar cross-section) has been altered with leading-edge sweepback reduced from 48° to 42°, with an additional edge added to the wing planform. The tailplane is revised, although overall wing and tailplane areas remain unchanged. The engine intakes are moved farther back, and the nose profile enlarged to house the radar. The vertical tails are reduced in size and the wingroot thickness decreased. Air-to-ground capability is being added with provision to carry the Joint Direct Attack Munition and the Tri-Service Stand-off Attack Missile.

The USAF had planned originally to order 750 ATFs, with production from 1994. Following the 1990 Major Aircraft Review, production was to begin in 1996, saving $1.26 billion, for a total of 648 aircraft (one-third earmarked for air defence) with maximum production rate being changed from 72 per year in 1999 to 48 per year in 2001. By 1994 the figure stood at 442 aircraft for service entry in 2003/04. The 325th FW at Tyndall AFB, FL, may become the first F-22 operator for training, followed by the 1st FW at Langley AFB, VA, as the first front-line unit. Based on the F-22 design, the swing-wing **NATF** was proposed for the US Navy to replace the F-14 Tomcat. The programme was subsequently cancelled in 1993.

ALIGNMENT
Key edges of the F-22's shape are on the same alignment. This vastly reduces radar cross-section. The YF-22's principal alignment was 48°, that of the F-22A being 42°.

CONTROL SURFACES
The leading-edge flaps deflect 3° up and 35° down, the trailing-edge flaperons 20° up and 40° down, the ailerons +/- 20°, the tailplanes 30° up and 25° down, and the rudders +/- 30°.

AIR-TO-AIR ARMAMENT
The F-22 will have a primary armament of four AIM-120 AMRAAM missiles housed in two bays in the lower fuselage. The bay doors have serrated edges fore and aft to preserve the low radar cross-section. Short-range missiles are housed in two bays in the side of the engine intake trunks, again with dogtooth edges for the double doors. At present the AIM-9M would be carried, but under development is the AIM-9X, based on either the 'Boa' tail-control or 'Boxoffice' canard configurations. Missiles are carried on 'revolutionary' launch rails, which eject the weapon into the air stream from out of the bays before the motor fires. Gun armament, not fitted to the YF-22, will be a long-barrelled version of the trusty M61A1 20-mm Vulcan cannon.

AIR-TO-GROUND WEAPONS
The F-22 will have four underwing pylons for the carriage of fuel tanks or weapons. The main weapon will be the pylon-carried AGM-137 TSSAM, while the JDAM (Joint Direct Attack Munition) will be carried in the AMRAAM bays.

Lockheed/Boeing YF-22 PAV No. 1

Since the F-104, Lockheed has been out the fighter business but now, with the F-22 programme and the purchase of G[ ] F-16 production facility, the company is the forefront. Two YF-22s were built, along with two Northrop/McDD YF-23s, for the ATF Dem/Val competition. One aircraft of each pair was powered by the Pratt & Whitney YF119 and one by the General Electric YF120. This aircraft is t[ ] GE-powered PAV (prototype air vehicle) No. 1. The YF-22/YF119 combination wa[ ] eventually selected, chiefly on the grounds of the least development risk factor, but also on cost. Nevertheless, t[ ] huge price tag of the F-22 has seen procurement totals tumble, and may ye[ ] see the programme cancelled or severel[ ] curtailed. Production aircraft will featur[ ] considerably revised surfaces, with double-cropped wing planform, smaller fins, wider nose profile and squarer tailplanes.

INTAKES
The diamond-shaped intakes follow the same alignments as the other surfaces to preserve stealth characteristics, while the serpentine trunks shield the compressor face from prying radars. A pronounced lip on the upper edge aids high-Alpha ingestion. Auxiliary doors are on top of the intakes.

AVIONICS TESTBED
Boeing is using the 757 prototype to test F-22 systems. It is currently being modified to 'Catfish' configuration with an F-22 wing section mounted at zero incidence above the forward fuselage, with an F-22 nose on the front.

With a large gantry mounting a spin recovery parachute, the General Electric YF120-powered YF-22 shows off its agility, and the complicated control surfaces. These include full-span leading-edge manoeuvring flaperons, small ailerons and larger flaperons. The horizontal tail surfaces are all-moving and are aided in pitch control by the vectoring nozzles. All surfaces, including the nozzles, are controlled by a digital triplex fly-by-wire system.

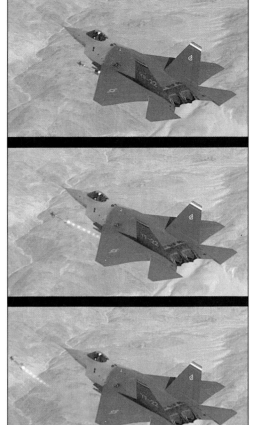

During the YF-22 Dem/Val phase, test pilot Jon Beesley launched an AIM-9 Sidewinder.

For longer-range engagements the AIM-120 will be carried, seen here being launched from the lower fuselage bay. JDAM air-to-ground munitions will also be carried in the lower weapon bays.

POWERPLANT
The F-22 will be powered by two F119-PW-100 engines of roughly 35,000 lb (155 kN) thrust. These are low bypass ratio turbofans, with a two-shaft design. The fan has three stages, while the compressor is a multi-stage unit turning in the opposite direction. The turbine consists of single low- and high-pressure stages turning in opposition.

ONICS
F-22 is the first aircraft with fully grated avionics, with a Hughes common grated processor at the heart of the tem. The radar is a Westinghouse low bability-of-intercept unit which offers long-ge detection without giving away the ition of the F-22. A Sanders/General ctric EW system and TRW comm/nav/ident tem are all controlled by the CIP. Data is sented to the pilot on four advanced liquid-stal colour MFDs and a HUD.

AIRBRAKE
A dorsal airbrake was fitted to the YF-22, but will not be incorporated on production aircraft. Instead, the rudders will be differentially deployed to a maximum of 30° for aerodynamic braking.

SPECIFICATION

Lockheed/Boeing YF-22A
Wing: span 43 ft 0 in (13.11 m); aspect ratio about 2.2; area about 840.00 sq ft (78.04 m²)
Fuselage and tail: length 64 ft 2 in (19.56 m); height 17 ft 7 in (5.36 m)
Powerplant: two Pratt & Whitney F119-P-100 turbofans each rated at 35,000 lb st (155.69 kN) with afterburning
Weights: empty more than 30,000 lb (13608 kg); maximum take-off 58,000 lb (26308 kg)
Speed: maximum level speed 'clean' at optimum altitude Mach 1.58 in supercruise mode and at 30,000 ft (9145 m)

Mach 1.7 in afterburning mode
Performance: service ceiling 50,000 ft (15240 m)
g limits: +7.9

Lockheed/Boeing F-22A
generally similar to the Lockheed/Boeing YF-22A except in the following particulars:
Wing: span 44 ft 6 in (13.56 m); aspect ratio 2.36
Fuselage and tail: length 62 ft 1 in (18.92 m); height 16 ft 5 in (5.00 m)
Weights: maximum take-off 60,000 lb (27216 kg)

Right: An artist's impression of the production F-22A displays the revised wing and tailplane plans, the fatter nose and the cut-back intakes.

EXHAUST
The exhaust nozzles are of the two-dimensional convergent-divergent type, incorporating vectoring to increase field performance and pitch/turn rate.

LTV (Vought) A-7 Corsair II

LTV renamed Vought Aircraft Company in 1992
9314 West Jefferson Boulevard, PO Box 655907
Dallas, TX 75265-5907, USA

First flying on 27 September 1965, the A-7 **Corsair II** was developed for the US Navy light attack mission, and early variants were active in the Vietnam War from carrier decks. The Corsair II is now out of front-line US Navy service. The type was adopted by the US Air Force for the close air support/battlefield air interdiction role as the **A-7D**, which differed primarily in being powered by a licence-built Rolls-Royce Spey turbofan (Allison TF41). The first A-7D flew on 26 September 1968, and this variant also saw service in South East Asia. A total of 459 was built.

After being replaced on active-duty service by the Fairchild A-10, A-7Ds were issued to Air National Guard units, where the type continued to have a productive career. In January 1981 the two-seat **A-7K** made its first flight, the 31 built being issued only to Guard units.

In order to keep the aircraft viable in the 1990s, Vought began development of the **A-7F** version, which involved a radical reworking of the ANG machines with P&W F100 afterburning turbofans, lengthened fuselage and updated avionics. This programme was cancelled after two prototype conversions had flown, and in the early

1990s the aircraft began a rapid withdrawal from Guard service. The last retired in 1993.

With the US Navy, 11 **TA-7C** trainers and **EA-7L** EW trainers survived a grounding order and continue to serve with test units at Point Mugu and Patuxent River.

Exports of the Corsair were limited, sales to Pakistan and Switzerland having been thwarted. **Portugal** received 50 aircraft in two batches from 1981 onwards. These are rebuilt Navy A-7A/Bs, and are designated in FAP service as the **A-7P** and **TA-7P**, the latter a two-seat derivative. The remaining 31 A-7Ps and six TA-7Ps are operated by Esquadra 302 and 304 at Monte Real with maritime strike as the primary role, using AGM-65 Maverick missiles. **Greece** purchased 60 **A-7H** and five **TA-7H** aircraft, and these are based on the Navy's **A-7E** variant with TF41 engine. Some 49 still serve, flying with 347 Mira at Larissa and 340/345 Mira at Soudha. Like Portuguese A-7Ps, the primary role is anti-shipping. The fleet has been bolstered by the transfer of 36 ex-US Navy aircraft, mostly A-7Es but also including a handful of TA-7C trainers. The sale of 18 ex-US Navy A-7Es to the **Royal Thai Navy** was agreed in 1994.

The pugnacious A-7 continues to provide sterling service, principally on anti-ship duties, to two Mediterranean NATO operators: the Greek and Portuguese air forces. Portuguese A-7Ps are equipped to carry the ALQ-131 ECM pod.

*LTV (Vought)
A-7D Corsair II
(lower side
view: A-7K)*

SPECIFICATION

Vought A-7D Corsair II

Wing: span 38 ft 9 in (11.81 m); width folded 23 ft 9 in (7.24 m); aspect ratio 4.0; area 375.00 sq ft (34.83 m²)
Fuselage and tail: length 46 ft 1.5 in (14.06 m); height 16 ft 0.75 in (4.90 m); tailplane span 18 ft 1.5 in (5.52 m); wheel base 18 ft 1.5 in (4.83 m)
Powerplant: one Allison TF41-A-1 turbofan rated at 14,500 lb st (64.50 kN)
Weights: basic empty 19,127 lb (8676 kg); operating empty 19,915 lb (8988 kg); maximum take-off 42,000 lb (19050 kg)
Fuel and load: internal fuel 9,263 lb (4202 kg); external fuel up to four 300-US gal (1136-litre) drop tanks; maximum ordnance 20,000 lb (9072 kg) theoretical, 15,000 lb (6804 kg) practical with reduced internal fuel and 9,500 lb (4309 kg) with maximum internal fuel
Speed: maximum level speed 'clean' at sea level 606 kt (698 mph; 1123 km/h); maximum speed at 5,000 ft (1525 m) 562 kt (646 mph; 1040 km/h) with 12

Mk 82 bombs or 595 kt (685 mph; 1102 km/h) after bomb release
Range: ferry range 2,485 nm (2,861 miles; 4604 km) with maximum internal and external fuel or 1,981 nm (2,281 miles; 3,671 km) with internal fuel; combat radius 620 nm (714 miles; 1149 km) on a hi-lo-hi mission
Performance: maximum rate of climb at sea level 15,000 ft (4572 m) per minute; service ceiling 42,000 ft (12800 m); take-off run 5,600 ft (1705 m) at MTOW

Vought A-7K
generally similar to the A-7D except in the following particulars:
Fuselage and tail: length 48 ft 11.5 in (14.92 m)

McDonnell Douglas A-4 Skyhawk

Initial design and manufacture of the A-4 by Douglas.
McDonnell Douglas Corporation formed
with McDonnell on 28 April 1967

A classic warplane by any criterion, the small and compact **A-4 Skyhawk** first flew in prototype form on 22 June 1954, and entered service with the **US Navy** in October 1956. It provided that service, and the **Marine Corps**, with their principal light attack platform for many years. Total production of all variants reached 2,960.

The early **A-4A/B/C** variants were powered by the Wright J65 turbojet and differed

in levels of avionics and engine power. The **A-4E** introduced the Pratt & Whitney J52 turbojet, and the **A-4F** featured a large dorsal hump to contain extra avionics, this being retrofitted to some earlier models. The **A-4G** was built for the Royal Australian Navy, while the **A-4H** was tailored to the requirements of the **Israeli air force**, featuring a revised fin and a braking parachute. The **A-4K** was supplied to **New Zealand** and the **A-4KU** to **Kuwait**, while the

The A-4K is the mainstay of the RNZAF, 14 single-seat aircraft serving with Nos 2 and 75 Sqns. The main improvement of the Kahu upgrade was the addition of APG-66NZ radar.

A-4L was a rebuilt A-4C for the US Navy Reserve. **A-4N**s were similar to the A-4H but featured uprated avionics, including an HUD. The last major production model was the **A-4M**, based on the A-4F but with numerous updates including the A-4H fin, brake chute and J52-P-408A engine. Most of the surviving aircraft have been updated to prolong their lives. The various two-seat variants are described separately.

With the original operator, there are few single-seat Skyhawks left, these mostly serving with aggressor squadrons. The major variant is the A-4F, which has been stripped of most of its attack avionics, including removal of the dorsal hump, and is known as the **'Super Fox'**. These serve, augmented by two-seat aircraft and the later stripped-down A-4M **'Super Mike'**, with adversary units, including the naval Fighter Weapons School ('Top Gun') at NAS Miramar. The A-4M model remains in use with three USMC Reserve squadrons (VMA-124, 131 and 322), but these are being phased out swiftly.

Overseas operators

In foreign service, there are seven operators. **Argentina** operates refurbished A-4B/Cs as the **A-4P** (air force) and **A-4Q** (navy), numbers remaining being 29 and five, respectively. The fleet has been bolstered by the transfer beginning in 1993 of 36 ex-USMC A-4Ms and two-seat OA-4Ms (described separately). **Indonesia** operates two squadrons of refurbished ex-Israeli A-4Es, one at Madiun (11 Sqn) and one at Pekanbaru (12 Sqn). Israel itself retains some 70 A-4Ns, probably now relegated to training or reserve use, and perhaps some A-4Hs, although most of these aircraft may be stored. Kuwait's A-4KU aircraft were used during the Gulf War in 1991, and it is thought 18 (of 30 delivered) remain in use, although these are likely to be sold in the near future, with Chile an interested party.

Malaysia has a fleet of Skyhawks designated **A-4PTM** (Peculiar To Malaysia). In 1979, the RMAF bought 88 former US Navy A-4C/Ls in storage, planning to overhaul and conduct an ambitious upgrade for 70 of them. This was later abandoned on cost grounds, and Grumman refurbished them to produce 40 A-4PTMs (comprising 34 single-seaters and six **TA-4PTM** trainers). These aircraft can potentially carry AGM-65 Mavericks for air-to-surface missions, and AIM-9s for air-to-air combat. Two Kuantan-based squadrons (Nos 6 and 9) operate the 34 surviving aircraft, although these will probably be withdrawn as the RMAF receives its BAe Hawk 100s and 200s. Neighbour **Singapore** has the most capable Skyhawks, having substantially upgraded a large number of surplus A-4B/Cs as **A-4S**s. These

Israel still operates A-4N Skyhawks. They are fitted with lengthened jetpipes to reduce IR signature.

Grumman updated 40 ex-US Navy Skyhawks for Malaysia, which are designated A-4PTM. They serve with Nos 6 and 9 Squadrons at Kuantan on the east coast.

are described in greater detail under the heading Singapore Aerospace.

New Zealand is the final foreign user, flying 14 A-4Ks alongside two-seaters. These have been upgraded with new avionics under Project Kahu, including APG-66NZ radar, Ferranti HUD/WAC, ALR-66 RWR, ALE-39 chaff/flare dispenser, ring-laser gyro INS and HOTAS controls. The radar is similar to that fitted to the F-16, but with a reduced-size scanner to fit the Skyhawk's contours and an additional sea-search mode for anti-shipping attacks. New weapon options include AGM-65 Maverick, AIM-9 Sidewinder, GBU-16 LGB and CRV-7 rockets. A-4Ks serve with No. 75 Sqn at Ohakea, and No. 2 Sqn at RAN Nowra in Australia, where they provide a joint-national force for naval support. All foreign operators also fly two-seat trainer versions, which are described separately.

SPECIFICATION

McDonnell Douglas A-4M Skyhawk II
Wing: span 27 ft 6 in (8.38 m); aspect ratio 2.91; area 260.00 sq ft (24.155 m2)
Fuselage and tail: length 40 ft 3.5 in (12.27 m) excluding probe; height 15 ft 0 in (4.57 m); tailplane span 11 ft 3.5 in (3.44 m); wheel track 7 ft 9.5 in (2.38 m)
Powerplant: one Pratt & Whitney J52-P-408 turbojet rated at 11,200 lb st (50.0 kN) dry
Weights: empty 10,465 lb (4747 kg); normal take-off 24,500 lb (11113 kg)
Fuel and load: internal fuel 4,434 lb (2011 kg); external fuel up to three 300-US gal (1136-litre) drop tanks; maximum ordnance 9,155 lb (4153 kg)
Speed: maximum level speed 'clean' at 25,000 ft with a 4,000-lb (1814-kg) warload (7620 m) 560 kt (645 mph; 1,038 km/h) or 'clean' at sea level 595 kt

*McDonnell Douglas TA-4J Skyhawk
(side view: A-4M)*

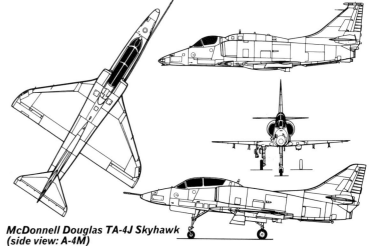

(685 mph; 1102 km/h)
Range: ferry range 1,785 nm (2,055 miles; 3,307 km); combat radius 295 nm (345 miles; 547 km) with a 4,000-lb (1814-kg) warload
Performance: maximum rate of climb at sea level 10,300 ft (3140 m) per minute; service ceiling 38,700 ft (11795 m); take-off run 2,730 ft (832 m) at 23,000 lb (10433 kg)

Above: US Navy use of the single-seat Skyhawk is restricted to a few examples with adversary units. This 'Super Mike' serves with VF-126.

Below: A-4Ms remain in the attack role with USMC Reserve, but are due for retirement in 1994/95.

McDonnell Douglas **TA-4 Skyhawk**

Although it was an easy aircraft to convert to, the Skyhawk was a natural basis for a two-seat trainer version, although such a variant was not introduced until some way into the production run. The first major Skyhawk trainer model was the **TA-4E/F**, which first flew on 30 June 1965, featuring two cockpits in tandem with a single canopy, and some combat capability (although the dorsal avionics hump could not be fitted). Related variants were the **TA-4G** for Australia, **TA-4H** for **Israel**, **TA-4K** for **New Zealand**, and **TA-4KU** for **Kuwait**. The **EA-4F** was an electronic warfare aggressor for US Navy squadron VAQ-33. The **OA-4M** was the sole two-seater based on the A-4M, and was used by the USMC for forward air control duties. Although retired from USMC service, some OA-4Ms are

included in the 36-Skyhawk batch delivered to **Argentina** from 1994.

The definitive two-seater was the **TA-4J**, of which 292 were built new and several converted from TA-4Fs. This was a simplified version lacking cannon armament and combat capability. In **US Navy** service this is the major operational model, being used in the advanced training role, including carrier qualification, by squadrons VT-7 (NAS Meridian, MI), VT-21 and 22 (NAS Kingsville, TX), and VT-24 and 25 (NAS Chase Field, TX). The main training fleet is being replaced by the T-45 Goshawk. A small number of TA-4Js and Fs serve with utility composite squadrons, USMC units, and with adversary squadrons.

Overseas, the two-seaters remain with **Indonesia** (two TA-4Hs), Israel (30-plus

TA-4Hs and ex-US Navy TA-4Js), Kuwait (one TA-4KU), **Malaysia** (10 TA-4PTMs), New Zealand (six TA-4Ks) and **Singapore** (12 **TA-4S**s). Many of these have been updated under the same programmes running for the single-seat aircraft. The trainers of Singapore are unique in so far as they are converted from single-seat aircraft with an additional, separate cockpit instead of the single two-place cockpit of the other trainer variants.

SPECIFICATION

McDonnell Douglas TA-4F Skyhawk
generally similar to the McDonnell Douglas A-4M Skyhawk II except in the following particulars:
Fuselage and tail: length 42 ft 7.25 in (12.98 m);

height 15 ft 3 in (4.65 m)
Powerplant: one Pratt & Whitney J52-P-8A turbojet rated at 9,300 lb st (41.3 kN)
Weights: empty 10,602 lb (4809 kg); normal take-off 15,783 lb (7159 kg)
Fuel and load: internal fuel 660 US gal (2498 litres)
Speed: maximum level speed 'clean' at sea level 586 kt (675 mph) 1086 km/h)
Range: ferry range 1,910 nm (2,200 miles; 3540 km); normal range 1,175 nm (1,353 miles; 2177 km)
Performance: maximum rate of climb at sea level 5,750 ft (1753 m) per minute; take-off run 3,380 ft (1030 m) at 23,000 lb (10433 kg)

McDonnell Douglas TA-4J Skyhawk
generally similar to the McDonnell Douglas TA-4F Skyhawk except in the following particulars:
Powerplant: one Pratt & Whitney J52-P-6 turbojet rated at 8,500 lb st (37.7 kN)

No. 2 Sqn RNZAF acts as the Skyhawk OCU and also undertakes the naval target facilities role, based at Nowra in Australia. It has three TA-4Ks on strength, all fully upgraded with the Kahu modifications, including APG-66NZ radar, a derivative of the unit fitted to the F-16.

Above: Large numbers of TA-4Js serve the US Navy as advanced trainers. This aircraft serves with VT-7.

Below: Singapore's TA-4S conversion trainers are unique in having separate cockpits.

McDonnell Douglas **C-9 Nightingale/Skytrain II**

*Douglas Aircraft Company
3855 Lakewood Boulevard
Long Beach, CA 90846, USA*

Experience gained in the early stages of American involvement in the Vietnam War highlighted the need for a medium-range aeromedical transport, and as a relatively low-cost expedient an initial order for eight 'off-the-shelf' commercial **McDonnell Douglas DC-9 Series 30** twin rear-turbofan airliners was placed, to be set aside for military conversion. Modifications included the provision of a special-care compartment, galleys and toilets fore and aft, and the addition of a third access door 11 ft 4 in (3.45 m) wide in the front fuselage with inbuilt hydraulic ramp to facilitate the loading of litters. Accommodation was provided for up to 40 litters and 40 ambulatory patients, two nurses and three aeromedical attendants.

With these features, the first **McDonnell Douglas C-9A Nightingale** was

rolled out on 17 June 1968 and delivered to Scott AFB two months later; subsequent aircraft served with the 375th Aeromedical Airlift Wing of **USAF**'s MAC (now 375th AW of AMC), and later with the 55th AAS of the 435th Tactical Airlift Wing (now 86th Wing at Ramstein). Later orders brought the total deliveries to 21, in addition to three **C-9C** executive transports flown by the 89th Military Airlift Wing at Andrews AFB, MD. In addition to these operators, the C-9 is flown by the 374th AW at Yokota, while the 73rd AAS is an AFRes Associate unit at Scott, supplying aircrew to augment the active-duty crews.

A subsequent version of the DC-9 was developed as the **C-9B Skytrain II**, ordered by the **US Navy** as a fleet logistic transport. Combining features of both the DC-9 Series 30 and 40, a total of 19 aircraft was delivered for use by Navy logistic support squadrons in the USA and two to the **US Marine Corps'** Station Operations and Engineering Squadron at Cherry Point MCAS, NC. The US Navy subsequently purchased 10 similar DC-9-30s, the combined fleet serving with VR-46/51/52/55/56/57/58/59/60/61/62. Two similar military aircraft, which

retain the **DC-9-32CF** designation, were delivered to the **Kuwaiti air force**, being convertible as either passenger or freight transports. One was lost during the Gulf War, but has since been replaced in No. 41 Squadron by a **McDonnell Douglas MD-83** aircraft, this much later variant featuring a stretched fuselage, updated cockpit and JT8D-219 engines. **Italy** operates two **DC-9-32**s on VIP transport duties.

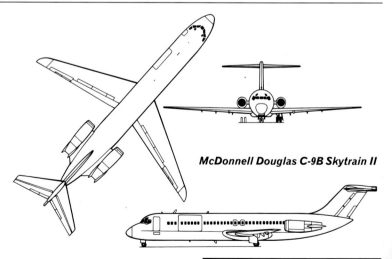

McDonnell Douglas C-9B Skytrain II

A pair of DC-9-32s serves with the AMI's 306° Gruppo, 31° Stormo for VIP transport duties. They are based at Roma-Ciampino.

SPECIFICATION

McDonnell Douglas C-9A Nightingale
Wing: span 93 ft 5 in (28.47 m); aspect ratio 8.71; area 1,000.70 sq ft (92.97 m²)
Fuselage and tail: length 119 ft 3.5 in (36.37 m); height 27 ft 6 in (8.38 m); tailplane span 36 ft 10.25 in (11.23 m); wheel track 16 ft 6 in (5.03 m); wheel base 53 ft 2.5 in (16.22 m)

Powerplant: two Pratt & Whitney JT8D-9 turbofans each rated at 14,500 lb st (64.5 kN)
Weights: empty 57,190 lb (25940 kg); maximum take-off 121,000 lb (54885 kg)
Fuel and load: internal fuel 3,679 US gal (13925 litres); external fuel none; maximum payload 31,125 lb (14118 kg)
Speed: never exceed speed 537 kt (618 mph; 995 km/h); maximum cruising speed at 25,000 ft 7620 m) 490 kt (564 mph; 907 km/h); economical cruising speed between 30,000 and 35,000 ft 9145 and 10670 m) 443 kt (510 mph; 821 km/h)
Range: ferry range 1,980 nm (2,280 miles; 3669 km); range at economical cruising speed at 30,000 ft (9145 m) 1,670 nm (1,923 miles;

3095 km), or with full accommodation 1,290 nm (1,485 miles; 2390 km)
Performance: maximum rate of climb at sea level 2,900 ft (885 m) per minute; service ceiling 37,000 ft (11280 m); take-off distance to 35 ft (10.7 m) 7,400 ft (2256 m) at maximum take-off weight; landing distance from 50 ft (15 m) 4,720 ft (1439 m) at normal landing weight

The C-9 is used by the USAF for aeromedical duties, equipped for emergency treatment and evacuation. This example serves with the 20th Air Ambulance Squadron at Yokota.

McDonnell Douglas KC-10A Extender

The **McDonnell Douglas KC-10A Extender** strategic tanker/transport is based on the **DC-10 Series 30CF** commercial freighter/airliner and was obtained off the shelf to satisfy the ATCA (Advanced Tanker Cargo Aircraft) requirement. It emerged victorious in a competition with Boeing's Model 747 in December 1977 when the **USAF** indicated its intention to procure 16 examples, but the number on order rose substantially in December 1982, when the USAF placed a multi-year contract covering a further 44 aircraft. The first example of the Extender made its maiden flight on 12 July 1980 and deliveries to the Air Force at Barksdale, CA, commenced in March 1981, presaging a six-month period of operational testing in which all aspects were exhaustively evaluated. Just over seven years later, the 60th and last KC-10A was formally handed over on 29 November 1988.

Originally allocated solely to Strategic Air Command, the KC-10A was (and still is) frequently flown by Air Force Reserve crews under the so-called 'Associate' programme. The type was not fitted with thermal blast screens, nor 'hardened' against electromagnetic pulse effects, as it was not designed to to undertake Emergency War Order missions. Rather, the ATCA requirement was mainly concerned with supporting tactical rather than strategic forces.

The recent major USAF reorganisation that witnessed the elimination of SAC has resulted in examples of the Extender being redistributed among elements of Air Mobility Command and Air Combat Command. Apart from a single example that was destroyed in a fire on the ground in September 1987, all KC-10As continue to serve with units located at Barksdale AFB, LA, and March AFB, CA (both units with the 722nd Air Refueling Wing), and Seymour Johnson AFB, NC (4th Wing).

Changes from commercial DC-10 standard include provision of an inflight-refuelling receptacle above the cockpit, improved cargo-handling system and some military avionics. The most visible evidence of modification for the ATCA role is the McDonnell Douglas Advanced Aerial Refuelling Boom (AARB) sited beneath the aft fuselage. The refuelling operator's station is equipped with a periscope observation system and rear window for wide field of view. The KC-10's boom is fitted with digital FBW control and provides greater capability than the type fitted in the KC-135. The boom is rated for a fuel transfer rate of 1,500 US gal

The KC-10 was procured primarily to support fighter deployments, being able to carry fuel, supplies and personnel. The type has proved extremely useful in both pure tanker and transport roles. These aircraft, demonstrating the previous charcoal grey and current mid-grey schemes, serve with the 4th Wing at Seymour Johnson AFB.

(5678 litres) per minute. The 'flying boom' is the preferred Air Force method of transferring fuel in flight, but the Extender is also fitted with a hose-and-reel unit in the starboard aft fuselage and can thus refuel Navy and Marine Corps aircraft during the same mission. This dual capability makes it much more versatile than the KC-135, which has to be configured for one or other option on the ground.

Twenty KC-10s are fitted with wing-mounted pods so that three receiver aircraft may be refuelled simultaneously with the probe-and-drogue system. Trials of this configuration were undertaken with the last Extender to be built, which was fitted with a pair of Flight Refuelling Ltd Mk 32B hose-drum units. Seven bladder fuel cells have been installed in the lower fuselage baggage compartments, and comprise three forward cells and four aft of the wing. These contain a total of 117,829 lb (53446 kg) of fuel, equivalent to approximately 18,125 US gal (68610 litres), and are interconnected with the aircraft's basic fuel system. Total onboard fuel is available either for transfer to other aircraft or for extended range. The KC-10 is able to transfer 200,000 lb (90718 kg) of fuel to a receiver 1,910 nm (2,200 miles; 3540 km) from its home base and return to base.

Other notable aspects are the 8 ft 6 in x 11 ft 8 in (2.59 m x 3.56 m) cargo door on the port side of the fuselage, a feature that allows the KC-10A to undertake conventional strategic transport missions carrying standard USAF pallets, bulk cargo or wheeled vehicles. In this role, maximum cargo ca-

pacity is 169,409 lb (76843 kg), which it can carry over an unrefuelled range of 3,797 nm (4,370 miles; 7031 km). Since it is also able to receive fuel in flight, it can effectively operate non-stop to any point on the globe, with the most important limiting factor likely to be crew duty restrictions. A modification introduced an onboard loading system to allow the KC-10 to operate from austere locations without the need for the prepositioning of ground loading equipment.

Finally, the aircraft may perform missions that call upon the Extender to undertake

aspects of both the tanker and transport functions in a single mission. For example, when accompanying deploying fighters, this is achieved during the transit by the provision of inflight-refuelling support. In addition, technicians, administrative staff and vital ground equipment can also be carried in the cabin, which is able to accommodate up to 75 personnel and 17 cargo pallets.

Two McDonnell Douglas DC-10s were procured secondhand from Martinair by the Royal Netherlands air force, but were temporarily leased back to the airline. These aircraft are being converted by McDonnell Douglas to **KDC-10** tanker configuration and will return to service in 1995 with 334 Squadron at Eindhoven.

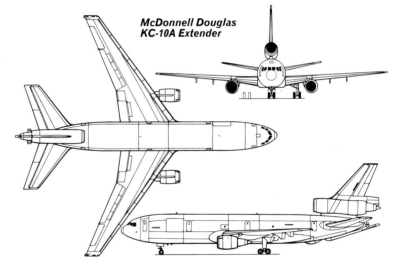

McDonnell Douglas KC-10A Extender

McDonnell Douglas KC-10A Extender

SPECIFICATION

McDonnell Douglas KC-10A Extender
Wing: span 155 ft 4 in (47.34 m); aspect ratio 6.8; area 3,861.00 sq ft (358.69 m²)
Fuselage and tail: length 181 ft 7 in (55.35 m); height 58 ft 1 in (17.70 m); tailplane span 71 ft 2 in (21.69 m); wheel track 34 ft 8 in (10.57 m); wheel

base 72 ft 5 in (22.07 m)
Powerplant: three General Electric CF6-50C2 turbofans each rated at 52,500 lb st (233.53 kN)
Weights: operating empty 240,065 lb (108891 kg) as a tanker or 244,630 lb (110962 kg) as a cargo transport; maximum take-off 267620 kg (590,000 lb)
Fuel and load: aircraft basic fuel system 238,236 lb (108062 kg); fuselage bladder fuel cells 117,829 lb (53446 kg); total internal fuel 356,065 lb (161508 kg);

external fuel none; maximum payload 169,409 lb (76843 kg) of cargo
Speed: never exceed speed Mach 0.95; maximum level speed 'clean' at 25,000 ft (7620 m) 530 kt (610 mph; 982 km/h); maximum cruising speed at 30,000 ft (9145 m) 490 kt (564 mph; 908 km/h)
Range: nominal range with 100,000 lb (45400 kg) payload 6,000 nm (6,905 miles; 11,112 km); maximum range with maximum cargo 3,797 nm (4,370 miles;

7032 km); ferry range 9,993 nm (11,500 miles; 18507 km)
Performance: maximum rate of climb at sea level 2,900 ft (884 m) per minute; service ceiling 33,400 ft (10180 m); take-off balanced field length 10,400 ft (3170 m) at maximum take-off weight; landing balanced field length 6,130 ft (1868 m) at maximum landing weight

McDonnell Douglas **C-17 Globemaster III**

On 29 August 1981 McDonnell Douglas was chosen to proceed with a design to fulfil the **USAF**'s **C-X** requirement for a new heavy cargo transport. Although the aircraft has suffered a protracted development programme – it is planned to achieve IOC in early 1995 – it is set to revitalise the US strategic airlift effort. The requirement called for the provision of intra-theatre and theatre airlift of outsize loads, including armoured vehicles, directly into a combat zone. This required an aircraft with a cabin

The C-17 entered service with the aptly-numbered 17th Airlift Squadron. The first aircraft wears the legend 'Spirit of Charleston'.

offering large-volume capacity, ease of loading/unloading for wheeled or tracked vehicles, and good short-field performance.

McDonnell's winning design was designated **C-17A** and named **Globemaster III**. It exhibits a classic military transport aircraft configuration – high wing, rear-fuselage loading ramp and undercarriage housings on each side of the fuselage. However, it has such advanced-technology features as winglets, supercritical wing section and high-performance turbofans. Short-field performance is aided to some extent by an externally-blown flap system similar to that demonstrated on the McDonnell Douglas YC-15 prototype, in which the trailing-edge flaps are extended into the exhaust flow

from the engines during take-off and landing to contribute to STOL performance. The usefulness of all these STOL features was negated to some extent when rough field capability was deleted as an economy measure. However, the C-17 can routinely operate from airfields previously denied to jet-powered transports. Reverse thrust on the F117 engines (similar to those which power the Boeing 757 airliner) allows the aircraft to reverse up a shallow slope or turn around on a narrow runway.

The C-17 has a flight crew of two, a loadmaster, and provision for 102 troops/paratroopers on stowable seats in the cabin, which can carry, for example, 48 litters, three AH-64A Apache helicopters, or air-

droppable platforms of up to 110,000 lb (49895 kg). The cockpit is state-of-the-art, with four multi-function displays and an HUD for each pilot. Flight control is effected by fly-by-wire, and the pilots have a control column rather than the conventional yoke.

After an earlier FSD schedule had been abandoned, the single prototype (T-1) of the C-17A flew on 15 September 1991, followed by the first three production examples comprising P-1 on 18 May, P-2 on 23 June and P-3 on 7 September 1992. A total of 10 aircraft was flying by February 1994. A symmetrical wing failure of the static test aircraft necessitated an extensive and costly stiffening and strengthening modification (with subsequent weight and performance penalties). An interim wing will be introduced to P-13 and subsequent aircraft and a new redesigned wing from aircraft between P-32 and P-38.

Deliveries to the 17th AS at Charleston AFB, SC, began in June 1993 to replace the C-141B StarLifter. Testing was continuing with the 412th Test Wing (417th TS) at Edwards AFB. Cold-weather trials were accomplished at Eielson AFB, AK. Total planned procurement is 120, although cancellation remains possible and further cutbacks in procurement are likely. By early 1994, 40 C-17s had been funded.

SPECIFICATION

McDonnell Douglas C-17A Globemaster III
Wing: span 165 ft 0 in (50.29 m) basic and 171 ft 3 in (52.20 m) between winglet tips; aspect ratio 7.16; area 3,800.00 sq ft (353.02 m²)

Below: Landing at Edwards, the first production C-17 displays the large flaps that are central to the aircraft's STOL performance.

PASSENGER CARRIAGE
The C-17 is equipped with 54 tip-up seats along the sides of the cargo hold, to which can be added a further 48 along the centreline for a maximum of 102 fully-equipped troops. Alternatively, the hold can be reconfigured with 100 pallet-mounted seats, for a maximum of 154 troops. In the medical evacuation role, 48 litters can be mounted on 12 four-litter stanchions.

McDonnell Douglas C-17 Globemaster III

AIRDROP
Paradropping capability from the rear ramp includes up to 110,000 lb (49895 kg) on multiple platforms, 60,000 lb (27215 kg) on a single platform or 102 paratroops. Eleven 463L pallets can be airdropped, including two carried on the rear ramp.

MAIN CABIN
The main compartment measures 68 ft 2 in (20.78 m) in length, including the load-bearing rear ramp, and has a volume of 20,900 cu ft (592 m³). The height under the wing centre-section is 12 ft 4 in (3.76 m) and the maximum loadable width is 18 ft 0 in (5.49 m). An internal loading system runs the full length of the hold, and can be operated by the single loadmaster. In addition to outsize equipment, 18 standard 463L freight pallets can be carried.

...EL
...el is held in six main
...egral wing tanks,
...uated between the main
...ars and extending for
...tually the full span of
... wing. Total capacity is
...108 US gal (102614
...es). A refuelling
...ceptacle is located
...ove the flight deck.

Fuselage and tail: length 174 ft 0 in (53.04 m); height 55 ft 1 in (16.79 m); tailplane span 65 ft 0 in (19.81 m); wheel track 33 ft 8.5 in (10.27 m); wheel base 65 ft 9.5 in (20.05 m)
Powerplant: four Pratt & Whitney F117-P-100 turbofans each rated at 41,700 lb st (185.49 kN)
Weights: operating empty 269,000 lb (122016 kg); maximum take-off 580,000 lb (263083 kg)
Fuel and load: internal fuel 27,108 US gal (102614 litres); maximum payload 172,200 lb (78108 kg); typical payload 124,000 lb (56245 kg) on an inter-theatre logistics mission at a 2.25-*g* load factor increasing to 153,300 lb (69535 kg) on a heavy logistics mission at a 2.5-*g* load factor
Speed: maximum cruising speed at low altitude 350 kt (403 mph; 648 km/h) CAS; airdrop speed at sea level between 115 and 250 kt (132 and 288 mph; 213 and 463 km/h) or at 25,000 ft (7620 m) between 130 and 250 kt (150 and 288 mph; 241 and 463 km/h)
Range: ferry range with maximum fuel and no payload 4,700 nm (5,412 miles; 8710 km); range with a 124,000-lb (56245-kg) payload 2,800 nm (3,225 miles; 5190 km), or with a 160,000-lb (72575-kg) payload 2,400 nm (2,765 miles; 4445 km); radius with an 81,100-lb (36786-kg) payload 500 nm (575 miles; 925 km) or with a 124,000-lb (56245-kg) payload 1,900 nm (2,190 miles; 3520 km)
Performance: service ceiling 45,000 ft (13715 m); take-off field length with 167,000-lb (75750-kg) payload 7,500 ft (2286 m); landing field length with 167,000-lb (75750-kg) payload 3,000 ft (914 m) with thrust reversal

POWERPLANT
The four F117-PW-100s give a total thrust of 166,800 lb (742.2 kN). The engine is similar to the PW2040 which powers several versions of the Boeing 757 airliner, offering high thrust with excellent fuel economy.

FLIGHT CONTROL
The General Electric quadruple-redundant fly-by-wire system controls outboard ailerons and eight overwing spoilers for roll control, two rudder sections for yaw, four elevator sections for pitch, and full-span leading-edge slats and trailing-edge hinged flaps for high lift.

FLAPS
The single-piece flaps employ propulsive-lift technology. Engine exhaust is blown back at the flap, and through the hinge slot, so that a sheet of air is deflected down either side of the flap. This allows steep approaches at 116 kt (215 km/h; 133 mph) with a 15 ft (4.5 m) per second sink rate.

McDonnell Douglas C-17A Globemaster III

The design of the C-17 was driven by the need to carry large items, such as tanks and helicopters, on strategic airlift tasks, while at the same time retaining the ability for tactical delivery profiles, including LAPES and short landings into austere airfields. Vital equipment can be delivered much closer to the front line than with existing strategic airlifters, which need full-length runways, while present tactical transports cannot carry such large items. Consequently, the C-17 has a voluminous and easily accessible cargo hold, but has outstanding STOL and ground-manoeuvring qualities. In the air the aircraft is far more responsive and agile than the C-141 and C-5, as it is required to operate closer to the front line.

...REW
...he C-17 is flown and
...avigated by two
...lots. The loadmaster
...as a work station at
...e forward end of the
...old deck. Two
...dditional seats are
...rovided on the flight
...eck for observers or
...lief aircrew.

USAF
80265

McDonnell Douglas **F-4D Phantom II**

McDonnell Aircraft Company
Box 516, St Louis
MO 63166, USA

The **F-4D** was the first purpose-designed USAF **Phantom II** variant. Specifically optimised for air-to-ground operations, it retained the basic airframe and engines of the **F-4C** but incorporated extensively modified avionics. A smaller, lighter, partly solid-state APQ-109 radar giving air-to-ground ranging replaced the F-4C's APQ-100 unit, and the ASN-63 replaced the ASN-48 inertial navigator. McDonnell manufactured a total of 825 F-4Ds.

The F-4C and F-4D have been retired from US service (all F-4Ds had been withdrawn from fighter intercept groups of the Air National Guard by 1992). The F-4D was exported to **Iran**, where some survivors of 32 delivered from 1968 are still flying, although serviceability is questionable. The final major user is **South Korea**, which has approximately 60 F-4Ds (the majority ex-USAF) as part of the 11th Fighter Wing at Taegu, comprising the 110th TFS (detach-

ed to Kunsan) and the 151st TFS. The last batch was equipped with Pave Spike laser designator pods for all-weather weapons delivery. Primary weapons comprise AIM-7E/ AIM-7F Sparrow and AIM-9N AAMs for interception duties, and AGM-65A Maverick AGMs for air-to-surface tasks.

In addition to their primary air-to-ground tasking, armed with laser-guided bombs and Mavericks, the F-4Ds of the 11th TFW, RoKAF, undertake target-towing duties. The dart target is reeled out behind the Phantom.

SPECIFICATION

McDonnell Douglas F-4D Phantom II
Wing: span 38 ft 4.875 in (11.71 m); aspect ratio 2.82; area 530.00 sq ft (49.24 m2)
Fuselage and tail: length 58 ft 3.25 in (17.76 m); height 16 ft 3 in (4.95 m); tailplane span 17 ft 11.5 in (5.47 m); wheel track 17 ft 10.5 in (5.30 m); wheel base 23 ft 4.5 in (7.12 m)
Powerplant: two General Electric J79-GE-15 turbojets each rated at 10,900 lb st (48.49 kN) dry and 17,000 lb st (75.62 kN) with afterburning
Weights: basic empty 28,976 lb (13144 kg); maximum

take-off 59,247 lb (26874 kg)
Fuel and load: internal fuel 1,972 US gal (7465 litres); external fuel up to 8,830 lb (4005 kg) in one 600-US gal (2271-litre) and two 370-US gal (1401-litre) drop tanks; maximum ordnance 16,000 lb (7257 kg)
Speed: maximum level speed 'clean' at 40,000 ft (12190 m) 1,290 kt (1,485 mph; 2390 km/h); cruising

speed at optimum altitude 510 kt (587 mph; 945 km/h)
Range: ferry range 1,520 nm (1,750 miles; 2816 km) with drop tanks; combat radius 730 nm (841 miles; 1353 km)
Performance: maximum rate of climb at sea level 48,000 ft (14630 m) per minute; service ceiling 59,400 ft (18105 m)

McDonnell Douglas **F-4E/F Phantom II**

The **McDonnell F-4E Phantom II** is the definitive version of the Phantom and currently serves half a dozen air arms in the strike role. While no longer the primary fighter in any air force, the F-4E retains some useful capabilities, although only Israel and South Korea are upgrading this version. The F-4E resulted from experience gained in air-to-air engagements over North Vietnam. It was first flown on 30 June 1967, and entered service in 1968. With 1,397 examples manufactured, the F-4E became the most numerous version, and serves with the air forces of Egypt, Greece, Iran, Israel, South Korea and Turkey. The F-4E has been withdrawn from the US Air Force (apart from the Luftwaffe training unit), AFRes and ANG, but some may be converted to drone configuration.

The F-4E is distinguished from other Phantom variants by its internal centreline General Electric M61A1 Vulcan or 'Gatling' 20-mm cannon with 640 rounds in an undernose fairing, and a new Westinghouse

AN/APQ-120 solid-state radar fire control system housed in a longer nose. The F-4E also introduced a seventh 104-US gal (394-litre) fuselage fuel tank, although the impact of this is reduced by the addition of self-sealing to the fuel tanks, an innovation that reduces capacity from 1,364 to 1,225 US gal (5164 to 4636 litres). Powered wing folding was removed, and a slotted stabilator was added to increase tailplane authority. During production of the F-4E various improvements were added, including a leading-edge TISEO electro-optical sensor and leading-edge slats that dramatically improved instantaneous turn performance. Though outclassed by newer fighters such as the F-15, which have more capable and longer-range radar and greater manoeuvrability, the F-4E retains an air-to-air capability, with AIM-7 Sparrow and AIM-9 Sidewinder AAMs in addition to its cannon. It is now, however, more often used in the air-to-ground role carrying guided and unguided ordnance. Standard weapons include the

AGM-65 Maverick. Korea uses the Phantom as an LGB launch platform, having been supplied with eight Pave Tack target acquisition/laser designation pods for all-weather precision attack. Some of Israel's Phantoms are believed to be equipped for the defence suppression role.

Israel's original **F-4E 'Super Phantom'** upgrade was to have been powered by Pratt & Whitney PW1120 engines. This aspect of the upgrade has not been proceeded with, but Israel has upgraded 50 of its surviving F-4Es under the designation **Kurnass 2000** (described separately under the heading IAI).

The multi-role F-4E served as the basis for the dedicated interceptor **Mitsubishi F-4EJ** (described separately). This was originally intended to be a lightweight single-seat version of the F-4E, and had the seventh fuel tank, Sparrow capability and inflight-refuelling equipment removed (the latter was later reinstated). The tailplane was unslot-

ted. Although conceived as an interceptor the F-4F was also employed in the fighter bomber role by two wings. The F-4F first flew on 18 May 1973 and 175 were built. The Luftwaffe has pursued an ambitious upgrade programme to keep the F-4F competitive and has applied the first stage of the **ICE** (Improved Combat Efficiency, or **KWS** – Kampfwehrsteigerung) upgrade to 150 surviving F-4Fs. The upgrade adds a new laser inertial gyro, GEC CPU-143/A digital air data computer and a new databus. One hundred and ten interceptors (originally 75) are scheduled to receive the second phase with APG-65 radar, AEG radar displays, Hughes cockpit displays, an improved IFF system, Litton ALR-68(V)-2 RWR, smokeless engines, a new fire control computer and Frazer Nash ejector launchers for four belly-mounted AMRAAM missiles. The resulting **F-4F ICE** is AIM-120 AMRAAM capable, and the first guided firing was made on 22 November 1991. This upgraded variant has re-entered service with JG 71 and JG 74.

WEAPON OPTIONS

Standard air-to-air load consists of internal M61A1 20-mm Vulcan cannon, four AIM-9 Sidewinders carried on shoulder rails either side of the inboard wing pylon and four AIM-7 Sparrows in semi-recessed bays under the fuselage. Luftwaffe ICE aircraft can carry AIM-120 AMRAAM in place of AIM-7. Fuel tanks usually carried on outboard wing pylons, leaving inboard pylon free for air-to-ground weapons carriage. Large variety of air-to-ground weapons available, including rocket pods, gun pods, 'iron' and cluster bombs, AGM-65 Maverick, laser-guided bombs (used in conjunction with AVQ-23 Pave Spike designator carried in forward Sparrow well or, for Korea, the AVQ-26 Pave Tack pod) and Shrike anti-radiation missiles. Israeli aircraft can launch Gabriel anti-ship missile.

Left: An F-4E from 7 Ana Jet Üs touches down at Erhac. The wing has three Phantom squadrons, of which one (173 Filo) is the type OCU for the Turkish air force.

Below: Luftwaffe F-4Fs are being upgraded to ICE standard, with improved avionics, AIM-120 missiles and a modern radar (APG-65). A light grey camouflage is being adopted for air defence work, as demonstrated by this JG 74 aircraft.

SPECIFICATION

McDonnell Douglas F-4E Phantom II
Wing: span 38 ft 4.875 in (11.71 m); aspect ratio 2.82; area 530.00 sq ft (49.24 m2)
Fuselage and tail: length 63 ft 0 in (19.20 m); height 16 ft 5.5 in (5.02 m); tailplane span 17 ft 11.5 in (5.47 m); wheel track 17 ft 10.5 in (5.30 m); wheel base 23 ft 4.5 in (7.12 m)
Powerplant: two General Electric J79-GE-17A turbojets each rated at 11,810 lb st (52.53 kN) dry and 17,900 lb st (79.62 kN) with afterburning
Weights: basic empty 30,328 lb (13757 kg); mission empty 31,853 lb (14448 kg); combat take-off 41,487 lb (18818 kg); maximum take-off 61,795 lb (28030 kg)
Fuel and load: internal fuel 12,290 lb (5575 kg); external fuel up to 8,830 lb (4005 kg) in one 600-US gal (2271-litre) and two 370-US gal (1401-litre) drop tanks; maximum ordnance 16,000 lb (7258 kg)
Speed: maximum level speed 'clean' at 36,000 ft

Left: Two of the Greek Phantom squadrons are given a ground attack role, while the third is tasked with air defence.

Below left: Egypt received Phantoms from 1979, following the shift in allegiance from East to West. Orange stripes prevented confusion with Israeli F-4s.

(10975 m) 1,290 kt (1,485 mph; 2390 km/h); cruising speed at maximum take-off weight 496 kt (571 mph; 919 km/h)

Range: ferry range 1,718 nm (1,978 miles; 3184 km); defensive counter-air combat radius 430 nm (495 miles; 797 km); interdiction combat radius 618 nm (712 miles; 1145 km); area interception combat radius 683 nm (786 miles; 1266 km)

Performance: maximum rate of climb at sea level 61,400 ft (18715 m) per minute; service ceiling 62,250 ft (18975 m); take-off run 4,390 ft (1338 m) at maximum take-off weight or 3,180 ft (969 m) at 53,814 lb (24410 kg); landing run 3,780 ft (1152 m) at

maximum landing weight or 3,520 ft (1073 m) at 35,143 lb (15937 kg)

OPERATORS

Egypt: 32 F-4Es are in service with the 76th and 88th Squadrons of the 222nd TFB at Cairo-West
Germany: 150 F-4Fs fly with JG 71 (Wittmundhafen), JG 72 (Hopsten), JG 73 (Laage) and JG 74 (Neuburg). Some serve with the trials organisation ETD 61. The fleet is undergoing ICE/KWS upgrade
Greece: 48 F-4Es remain from the initial Greek procurement, being augmented by 28 ex-USAF aircraft. They serve with 337 Mira, 110 Ptérix at Larissa and 338/339 Mira, 117 Ptérix at Andravidha
Iran: 177 F-4Es were delivered prior to the Islamic revolution. About 40 Phantoms of all variants remain in service, many of which are F-4Es
Israel: 140 F-4Es fly with four squadrons. Aircraft are being updated to Kurnass 2000 standard
Japan: 129 F-4EJ Kais serve with 301 Hikotai (Hyakuri), 302 Hikotai (Naha), 306 Hikotai (Komatsu) and the Air Proving Wing at Gifu
South Korea: 59 F-4Es serve with the 152nd and 153rd TFS, assigned to the 17th TFW at Chognjiu
Turkey: 166 F-4Es with 111/112 Filo at Eskisehir, 131/132 Filo at Konya and 171/172/173 Filo at Erhac. Fleet due for upgrade, possibly to ICE standard with new radar and AIM-120 missile
United States: Seven F-4Es in use with the 20th FS/ 49th FW at Holloman AFB for training Luftwaffe crews

McDonnell Douglas **F-4G Wild Weasel V**

Widespread use in Vietnam of Soviet-supplied SA-2 'Guideline' SAMs was only partly countered by the use of aircraft such as the Douglas EB-66 and Grumman EA-6B by the **USAF** and US Navy, respectively, and subsequent efforts were made to develop more capable anti-radar platforms. Greater success attended development of North American F-100s and Republic F-105s in the radar suppression role. This effort culminated in the adoption for a similar task of the **McDonnell Douglas F-4 Phantom II**, with its higher performance and strike capabilities. A total of 36 temporarily converted **F-4C Wild Weasel IV** aircraft were in service by 1972 (unofficially designated **EF-4C**), employing Westinghouse ECM pods in conjunction with AGM-45 Shrike anti-radiation missiles. Such aircraft frequently accompanied routine strike missions by standard F-4Cs.

In due course a much more extensive modification programme was undertaken. McDonnell produced a total of 116 **F-4G** aircraft (known initially as **Advanced Wild Weasel** or **Wild Weasel V**) by modifying F-4Es from production Block 42 onwards when they were returned for life-extension programmes. Changes included deletion of the integral M61A1 cannon and installation of a McDonnell Douglas APR-38 RHAWS, much of the component avionics for which are located in a long cylindrical fairing on top of the aircraft's fin. Associated with the APR-38 is a Texas Instruments computer, whose purpose is to accommodate varying future circumstances without demands for

additional electronic hardware in an already densely-packed aircraft (there are no fewer than 52 antennas distributed throughout the airframe).

Self-defence weaponry is confined to a pair of Sparrow AAMs in the rear fuselage recesses (and perhaps a pair of AIM-9s if pylon stations are available), one of the forward pair normally being occupied by an ECM pod such as ALQ-131. For the 'lethal SEAD' (suppression of enemy air defences) role, the APR-38 (and upgraded APR-47 system now carried) is compatible with the AGM-45 Shrike, AGM-65 Maverick EO-guided missile and AGM-88 HARM, and features automatic and blind weapon firing. Cockpit displays include annotated threat symbology, while reaction to priority threats is automatically initiated. Aircraft in service today have been re-equipped with LORAN, while restressing of the fuselage store mounting enables the McDonnell Douglas F-15-type centreline fuel drop tank to be carried; this is cleared to 5*g* when full, compared with 3*g* of the F-4's customary tank. The AGM-88 HARM, carried in pairs on the main wing pylon, is now the universal weapon of the F-4G, which remains the only aircraft that can employ all the operating modes of the missile.

After highly successful operations in Desert Storm, the F-4G will most likely remain in service with the USAF for some years. Only two squadrons remain opera-

tional with the type: the 561st FS at Nellis AFB, NV, and the 190th FS of the Idaho ANG at Boise. The 189th TF at the latter base undertakes training on the type. In 1994 the first of approximately 100 F-16C/ F-16D Block 50/52Ds equipped with the ASQ-213 HARM Targeting System pod entered service, augmenting the dwindling F-4G force. Nevertheless, it will be some time before the F-4G's unique capabilities can be completely replaced.

SPECIFICATION

McDonnell Douglas F-4G Phantom II
generally similar to the McDonnell Douglas F-4E Phantom II except in the following particulars:
Weights: empty equipped 29,321 lb (13300 kg); maximum take-off 62,390 lb (28300 kg)
Speed: maximum level speed 'clean' at 40,000 ft (12190 m) 1,290 kt (1,485 mph; 2300 km/h); cruising speed at maximum take-off weight 496 kt (571 mph; 919 km/h)
Range: ferry range 1,718 nm (1,978 miles; 3184 km); combat radius 520 nm (599 miles; 964 km)

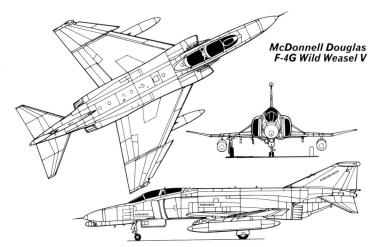

McDonnell Douglas F-4G Wild Weasel V

The 190th FS/Idaho ANG began conversion to the F-4G in June 1991, and is now one of only two units operating the type. Both take turns manning detachments in the Middle East. Replacement of the F-4G is a hotly-debated issue, and neither the new F-16/HTS or planned F-15C/PDF combination provides the same capability as offered by the current F-4G. Both are hampered by single-pilot operation; one of the main reasons for the success of the F-4G is the dedicated and highly experienced EWO in the backseat.

McDonnell Douglas RF-4 Phantom II

Representing a radical departure from the basic F-4B/C fighter, a reconnaissance version of the Phantom II was first flown as a **YRF-4C** demonstrator (of two prototypes) on 8 August 1963. This was followed on 18 May 1964 by the first flight of a production **RF-4C** aircraft. The RF-4C is a multi-sensor aircraft employed primarily for day reconnaissance and was used operationally in this role in Vietnam. McDonnell manufactured a total of 503 RF-4Cs.

Optical cameras, radar and electronic reconnaissance equipment and infra-red sensors are housed in a modified nose which increases the length of the aircraft by 33 in (84 cm) compared with the F-4B/C fighter versions. The F-4C's fire control radar was replaced by a smaller Texas Instruments AN/APQ-99 for mapping, and terrain and collision avoidance. Diverse sensors can be accommodated in the nose and forward fuselage. Twenty-four RF-4Cs are fitted with the AN/ALQ-125 TEREC (Tactical Electronic Reconnaissance) sensor for locating electronic emitters. Twenty-four others employ the LOROP suite, consisting of KS-127 optical camera with 66-in (167-cm) focal length. Other RF-4C/Es have carried various combinations of medium- to long-range and oblique reconnaissance cameras, including one KS-72 or KS-87 forward oblique-framing camera plus one KA-56A low-altitude and one KA-55A high-altitude panoramic camera. Unique to reconnaissance Phantoms is the AN/ARN-101 digital avionics navigation/reconnaissance system, supplemented recently by a new navigation/weapons deliv-

In USAF service the RF-4C was largely flown by the ANG during the latter years of its service life. The 106th RS/AL ANG (illustrated) and 192nd RS/NE ANG still retained the type in mid-1994, but were due for a change of type and role. This aircraft carries self-defence AIM-9P Sidewinders .

ery system and ring-laser gyro. Night capability was added with provision for photo-flashes, with one or two ejectors on the upper rear fuselage.

On a typical mission, an RF-4 will cruise at medium altitude for a KS-127 LOROP day photographic 'sweep' of a target region, this camera providing a slant range of up to 55 miles (89 km) on missions flown at 30,000 ft (9144 m). Although the RF-4 is usually unarmed, some users have added AIM-9M/AIM-9P Sidewinder missiles for self-defence capability.

The RF-4C is the last dedicated fast-jet tactical reconnaissance aircraft in US service, where it operates with two **Air National Guard** squadrons in Alabama and Nevada. RF-4Cs from the Alabama ANG and the last active-duty squadron (from Zweibrücken in Germany) were used during Operation Desert Storm, flying from Sheikh Isa and Incirlik. The Alabama aircraft were equipped with KS-127 LOROP cameras with 66-in (168-cm) lenses. The RF-4C has been exported to two customers. Up to 27 have been delivered to **South Korea** from 1988, all aircraft having been transferred from USAF stocks, along with AN/ALQ-131 jamming pods. The RF-4C equips the 131st TRS/39th TRG of the 10th Tactical Fighter Wing at Suwon. **Spain** received a total of 12 RF-4Cs (locally designated **CR.12**), currently equipping 123 Escuadron at Torrejón within Ala 12. These have been steadily updated with AN/APQ-172 terrain-following radar, laser INS, new ECM systems, new electro-optical sensors and real-time data-links, as well as inflight-refuelling probes similar to those installed on Israeli aircraft.

The **RF-4E** was developed as an export version of the RF-4C, primarily for the German **Luftwaffe**. The aircraft combines the airframe and engine of the early unslatted F-4E with the reconnaissance nose of the RF-4C, although some sensitive RF-4C systems were not installed. Its more fuel efficient J79-GE-17 engines improved range

and radius of action. The prototype was first flown on 15 September 1970 and a total of 150 aircraft was eventually built. German RF-4Es were retired in 1992. Additional operators comprise **Greece**, **Iran**, **Israel** and **Turkey**. Greece and Turkey each received eight new-build aircraft and these are being supplemented by surplus Luftwaffe RF-4Es. Israeli RF-4s are equipped with indigenous reconnaissance and avionics equipment and are armed with Shafrir, Python or Sidewinder missiles for self-defence. Under the Peace Jack codename, General Dynamics examined the use of the enormous HIAC-1 LOROP camera with the Phantom. Several USAF aircraft could carry a pod-mounted camera, but three Israeli F-4Es were converted to take the HIAC-1 in an enlarged nose. Redelivered to Israel in 1978 and designated **F-4E(S)**, one of these aircraft may still be in use. The **JASDF** purchased 14 reconnaissance Phantoms, actually built to a similar standard as the RF-4C. These were designated **RF-4EJ** and have been upgraded by Mitsubishi. Seventeen F-4EJ interceptors are being converted to a different RF-4EJ standard without camera noses but with pod-mounted camera, SLAR or Elint systems. Japanese RF-4Es

and RF-4EJs upgraded by Mitsubishi are described separately.

Now virtually obsolete despite a mid-life upgrade programme, which replaced AN/APQ-99 radar with AN/APQ-172, the RF-4C is no longer cost-effective, but the USAF has no ready substitute for its TEREC, LOROP and other capabilities. The overseas RF-4E fleet is more recent, so some examples will remain in service into the next century.

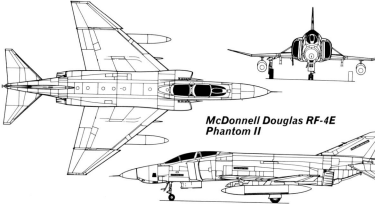

McDonnell Douglas RF-4E Phantom II

Spain received 12 ex-USAF RF-4Cs. Eight are still in use with Ala 12 at Torrejón.

SPECIFICATION

McDonnell Douglas RF-4C Phantom II
Wing: span 38 ft 4.875 in (11.71 m); aspect ratio 2.82; area 530.00 sq ft (49.24 m2)
Fuselage and tail: length 62 ft 11 in (19.17 m); height 16 ft 6 in (5.03 m); tailplane span 17 ft 11.5 in (5.47 m); wheel track 17 ft 10.5 in (5.30 m); wheel base 24 ft 9 in (7.54 m)
Powerplant: two General Electric J79-GE-15 turbojets each rated at 10,900 lb st (48.49 kN) dry and 17,000 lb st (75.62 kN) with afterburning
Weights: basic empty 28,276 lb (12826 kg); maximum take-off 58,000 lb (26308 kg)
Fuel and load: internal fuel 1,771 US gal (6704 litres); external fuel up to one 600-US gal (2271-litre) and two 370-US gal (1401-litre) drop tanks; maximum ordnance 16,000 lb (7257 kg), generally not carried
Speed: maximum level speed 'clean' at 40,000 ft (12190 m) 1,267 kt (1,459 mph; 2348 km/h) and at sea level 780 kt (898 mph; 1445 km/h)
Range: ferry range 1,520 nm (1,750 miles; 2816 km) with drop tanks; combat radius 730 nm (841 miles; 1,353 km)
Performance: maximum rate of climb at sea level 48,000 ft (14630 m) per minute; service ceiling 59,400 ft (18105 m)

348 Mira of the Elliniki Aeroporia (Greek air force) shares Larissa with two F-4E Phantom fighter squadrons. Greece operates seven of its original RF-4E batch, subsequently augmented by 18 ex-Luftwaffe aircraft.

McDonnell Douglas **F-15A/B Eagle**

The **McDonnell Douglas F-15 Eagle** air superiority fighter and interceptor is in service today in its original configuration and in two multi-stage improvement programme (MSIP) versions. The Eagle is widely viewed as setting the world standard for the primarily BVR air-to-air mission it performs, and has sufficient agility and the right armament to be able to hold its own in a close-in dogfight. Today, even unmodified early **F-15A/B** models remain among the world's most potent and capable fighters.

The F-15 Eagle programme dates from 1965 when the USAF issued its FX requirement for a long-range tactical air superiority fighter to replace the F-4. While the concept was being refined, hard-learned lessons from Vietnam were incorporated. In 1968, when the Required Operational Capability for the F-15 was issued, the aircraft was defined as a dedicated air-to-air fighter, a single-seat long-range BVR interceptor which would be able to dogfight. The F-15 was thus to be a fighter specifically tailored for the long-range air superiority role, marking a change in policy from the emphasis on multi-mission capabilities in earlier procurement of the F-4 and F-111. Vietnam experience pointed towards the need for twin engines, two crew (eventually not adopted) and an internal gun. The 1968 RFP added a requirement for a ferry range sufficient for deployment to Europe without tanker support and a maximum speed of at least Mach 2.5. This last inexplicable and very difficult requirement was technically achieved (albeit at huge cost), although an armed F-15 is limited to Mach 1.78.

McDonnell won the competition to build the F-15 (against proposals from North American and Fairchild-Republic), and the initial contract called for 10 single-seat development **F-15A**s (often erroneously referred to as **YF-15**s), two twin-seat development **TF-15A**s and eight Category II FSD aircraft. The first F-15 made its maiden flight on 27 July 1972, the first two-seater following on 7 July 1973. Initial plans called for the procurement of 729 more F-15A/Bs, 143 as attrition replacements. A total of 355 production F-15As was eventually built, together with 57 two-seat **F-15B**s. The F-15B is fully mission capable, though it lacks the F-15A's AN/ALQ-135 ECM and is 800 lb (364 kg) heavier than the single-seater.

The weapon load, range and endurance requirements were resolved by adopting an aircraft of large overall dimensions. The large wings give a remarkably low wing loading and confer a surprising degree of agility. The wings employ conventional outboard ailerons and unblown inboard two-position flaps, but have no high-lift devices such as slats or computer-controlled combat flaps. The Eagle's aerodynamic design was very advanced by the standards of the day, and some modifications were needed to the original configuration flown on the first development aircraft. To reduce severe buffet encountered in transonic testing, the innovative spine-mounted airbrake (originally fitted with a small dorsal strake) was increased in size and its extension angle reduced. The trailing edges of the wingtips were cropped, while the tailplane was notched (equipped with dogtooth leading edges) to cure flutter problems.

More serious than these minor aerodynamic problems were difficulties experienced with the Eagle's Pratt & Whitney F100-PW-100 engine, and with the X-band

Hawaii's 199th Fighter Squadron is the principal air defence for the islands, flying the F-15A. The Guard unit is gained by PACAF in time of war. Two of the CONUS-based ANG Eagle squadrons (Massachusetts and Oregon) are dedicated to air defence, while the other three are battlefield air superiority units.

Hughes APG-63 coherent pulse-Doppler radar, both of which were designed specifically for the Eagle. To minimise asymmetric handling problems, the engines are mounted close together and, to prevent damage to one engine causing reciprocal damage to the other, they are separated by a titanium keel. This provides a very rigid, very simple engine mount and allows rapid engine changes to be achieved. An engine change under operational conditions has been demonstrated in some 20 minutes.

The F-15A has an advanced and sophisticated avionics system, with the main radar supplemented by an AN/ALR-56 RWR, and an AN/ALQ-128 EW warning system. These are backed up by a Northrop AN/ALQ-135 internal countermeasures set.

The F-15 pilot sits high up and well forward on a McDonnell Escapac IC-7 ejection seat under a large blown canopy, with excellent all-round view. The cockpit itself is well laid out, but is equipped only with analog instruments, with no CRT MFDs. An HUD and a variety of control column- and throttle-mounted controls give true HOTAS operation of all important systems. The Eagle was designed to fight in the HOTAS mode, the pilot receiving all necessary information from his HUD and cueing the weapons system without having to look down into the cockpit to make switch selections or monitor instruments.

Delivery to TAC

The operational career of the Eagle began with the first delivery of an F-15A to Tactical Air Command's 1st Tactical Fighter Wing at Langley AFB, VA, on 9 January 1976. The 36th TFW at Bitburg, Germany, received the Eagle in April 1977. Other operators have included the 21st FW (Elmendorf AFB, AK), 33rd FW (Eglin AFB, FL), 49th FW (Holloman AFB, NM), 57th Fighter Weapons Wing (Nellis AFB, NV) and 32nd FG (Soesterberg, Holland). Other wings have subsequently acquired the improved **F-15C/D** variant (described separately).

The first F-15s to engage in combat operations were blooded by Israel on 27 June 1979 when they claimed five MiG-21s of the Syrian air force. Four FSD F-15As were delivered to Israel during 1976 under Operation Peace Fox III, and these were later joined by 19 refurbished F-15As and a pair of F-15Bs. These serve with 133 Squadron at Tel Nov. Ten more ex-Louisiana ANG F-15As were supplied after Desert Storm in return for Israel's co-operation during the Gulf War. On 7 June 1981, Israeli Eagles escorted F-16 Fighting Falcons on the long-range strike against Iraq's Osirak nuclear reactor, and were heavily involved in the 1982 'turkey shoot' over the Bekaa Valley.

During the 1980s, the F-15A entered service with three TAC air defence squadrons in the interceptor role and was to have been the carrier aircraft for the ASAT (anti-satellite) weapon; development of the latter was cancelled, but aircraft continue to be

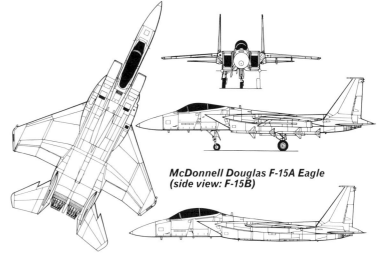

McDonnell Douglas F-15A Eagle (side view: F-15B)

'wired' for it. The three fighter interceptor squadrons disbanded during 1988-91, passing their aircraft on to three ANG units (one in Hawaii) which fulfil the same role. Other ANG squadrons fly the F-15A in the tactical fighter role.

The original Eagle two-seater was modified to become the **SMTD** (STOL/Maneuver Technology Demonstrator), equipped with canard foreplanes and Pratt & Whitney two-dimensional vectoring nozzles that can deflect through 20° up and down and provide reverse thrust. The SMTD demonstrator flew on 7 September 1988. The aircraft used its vectored thrust and canards to improve low-speed performance. The result was an aircraft able to operate on a much shortened runway – an important consideration in wartime, when fixed airfields are likely to be cratered and under constant attack. After a three-year programme, the SMTD Eagle made its 138th and final flight on 12 August 1991, making a short night landing under a simulated 200-ft (61-m) ceiling in total darkness.

In the 1990s, with relatively few 'new-build' aircraft being ordered, the USAF is improving its F-15A/B fighters through an ambitious MSIP. This follows a far more modest MSIP of the early 1980s that resulted in only minor improvements to the aircraft. Developed jointly by the manufacturer and the Warner Robins Logistics Center in Georgia, the current MSIP endeavour for the F-15A/B (similar to, and carried out in conjunction with, MSIP for F-15C/D models) replaces the proven APG-63 with more advanced Hughes APG-70 look-down/shootdown radar, new avionics and digital central computers replacing the F-15A/B's original analog computers.

F-15A/B Eagles emerging from MSIP differ from F-15C/D models only in lacking the latter's radar warning receiver antenna located next to the horizontal stabiliser and

the 2,000 lb (907 kg) of extra fuel carried by the F-15C. MSIP F-15A/B aircraft replaced non-MSIP F-15C/D models with the 32nd TFG, Soesterberg, Holland, in June 1992.

WEAPON OPTIONS

Standard Eagle weaponry is one M61A1 Vulcan 20-mm cannon with 940 rounds, four AIM-9M Sidewinders on wing pylon shoulder launchers and four AIM-7M Sparrows on the lower 'corners' of the fuselage. Older AIM-7/9 variants are still in use, while the AIM-120 AMRAAM is available to MSIP and F-15C/D aircraft. Secondary ground attack capability is virtually never employed.

SPECIFICATION

McDonnell Douglas F-15A Eagle
generally similar to the McDonnell Douglas F-15C Eagle except in the following particulars:
Powerplant: two Pratt & Whitney F100-PW-100 turbofans each rated at 14,670 lb st (65.26 kN) dry and 23,830 lb st (106.0 kN) with afterburning
Weights: operating empty 28,600 lb (12973 kg); normal take-off 41,500 lb (18884 kg) on an interception mission or 54,400 lb (24675 kg) with three 600-US gal (2271-litre) drop tanks; maximum take-off 56,000 lb (25401 kg)
Fuel and load: internal fuel 11,600 lb (5260 kg); external fuel up to 11,895 lb (5395 kg) in three 600-US gal (2271-litre) drop tanks; maximum ordnance 16,000 lb (7257 kg)
Range: ferry range more than 2,500 nm (2,878 miles; 4631 km) with drop tanks
Performance: landing run 2,500 ft (762 m) at normal landing weight with a brake parachute

OPERATORS

Israel: currently operates an estimated 35 F-15As and two F-15Bs with 133 Sqn at Tel Nov. Ten early Eagles

were transferred from the Louisiana ANG to Israel from October 1991 following the Gulf War
United States: 325th FW, Tyndall AFB (AETC)
WR-ALC, Robins AFB (AFMC)
101st FS/102nd FG, MA ANG, Otis ANGB
110th FS/131st FW, MO ANG, St Louis-Lambert Field
122nd FS/159th FG, LA ANG, NAS New Orleans
123rd FS/142nd FG, OR ANG, Portland IAP
128th FS/116th FW, GA ANG, Dobbins AFB
199th FS/154th CG, HI ANG, Hickam AFB

An Israeli F-15A wears the badge of 133 Squadron, the unit which flies the early variants from Tel Nov. These aircraft were heavily committed to the fighting over the Bekaa Valley when the type claimed 40 kills over Syrian MiGs for no losses. The eagle's head is a recent addition to the inside of the fins.

McDonnell Douglas **F-15C/D Eagle**

The **F-15C** followed the F-15A on the St Louis production line and made its first flight on 26 February 1979. It represents an improved and updated derivative of the basic fighter. The two-seat **F-15D** similarly succeeds the F-15B trainer. F-15C/D Eagles came off the production line with the improved, lightweight Hughes APG-63 X-band pulse-Doppler radar with reprogrammable signal processing, and with provision for 750-US gal (2389-litre) CFTs (conformal fuel tanks) on the sides of the intakes.

Formerly known as FAST (fuel and sensor, tactical) packs, first demonstrated in 1974 and subsequently sold to Israel, the CFTs cannot be jettisoned but their contents can be dumped, and the fuselage Sparrow stations they displace are duplicated on the outside of the pack itself. Plans for FAST packs containing 'Wild Weasel' avionics equipment, rocket motors and recce equipment were eventually abandoned, and the CFT designation confirms the change to fuel-only.

The prime armament of the baseline F-15C/D remains the AIM-7/9 AAM combination, and the same 20-mm M61A cannon is retained. The F-15C was intended to be powered by the more powerful Pratt & Whitney F100-PW-220 engine, although early aircraft retained the -100 powerplant. Minor changes were made to the undercarriage, allowing gross weight to be increased to 68,000 lb (30845 kg). Software changes increased the scope of the 9*g* envelope, an important modification since F-15As had effectively been limited to 7.33 *g* under

Left: An F-15C of the RSAF's No. 13 Squadron leaves Dhahran during a Desert Storm mission. Two Mirage F1 kills were credited to a Saudi pilot during the conflict.

Below: The 18th Wing is based at Kadena on the Japanese island of Okinawa, and is the main USAF unit in the Pacific Rim region. It flies three squadrons of F-15Cs, alongside a KC-135 tanker squadron and an E-3 Sentry unit.

COCKPIT
The pilot sits on a McDonnell Douglas ACES II ejection seat, under a stretched acrylic canopy. Data is presented on a McDonnell Douglas AVQ-20 head-up display and a Honeywell vertical situation display including a CRT for presenting radar and attitude information.

McDonnell Douglas F-15C MSIP Eagle

The F-15 has been the USAF's premier fighter since the late 1970s, and has enjoyed ongoing improvements to keep it at the front of the air superiority race. The most recent development is the MSIP (Multi-Stage Improvement Program), which replaces the APG-63 radar with the APG-70, among a host of other improvements to aircraft and weapon systems. MSIP aircraft were available to the 58th TFS, 33rd TFW for their deployment to Desert Storm. Flying from Tabuk, the squadron was responsible for the majority of coalition kills over the Iraqi air force, claiming a total of 16 victories. This aircraft was marked for the wing commander, Colonel Rick Parsons, and wore the legend 'Gulf Spirit'. This was applied pre-war in recognition of the 33rd's base at Eglin, on the Gulf Coast of Florida. The three Iraqi flags marked the kills scored by the aircraft (one MiG-23 shot down by Captain David G. Rose on 29 January 1991 and two Su-22s shot down by Captain Anthony R. Murphy on 7 February). The single star marks the victory scored by Colonel Parsons over an Su-22 on the same day, when he was flying 85-0104.

FUEL
The basic internal capacity is 2,070 US gal (7836 litres), to which can be added 1,464 US gal (5542 litres) in the CFTs and three 610-US gal (2309-litre) drop tanks.

ARMAMENT
For many years, the standard missile armament comprised four AIM-9 Sidewinders on the wing launch rails and four AIM-7 Sparrows on the fuselage 'corner' stations. During the latter part of the Gulf War, the AIM-120 AMRAAM was carried (although not used), and this weapon is now used widely by the F-15C, replacing the Sidewinders on the wing launch rails. The internal M61A1 cannon is provided with 920 rounds.

MSIP
Apart from the addition of APG-70 radar, MSIP covers the replacement of the weapons control panel with a single colour display, enhanced ALQ-135 countermeasures and ALR-56C RWR, addition of ALE-45 chaff/flare dispenser and Magnavox EW warning system, provision for JTIDS and a four-fold increase in central computer memory, with three times the processing speed.

POWERPLANT
Early F-15Cs were fitted with F100-PW-100 engines, but most were delivered with F100-PW-220s, nominally rated at 23,830 lb (106 kN) thrust with afterburning.

Formerly an F-111F operator, the 48th FW at Lakenheath now flies F-15Cs and F-15Es.

most circumstances. Changes to the F-15C add about 600 lb (272 kg) to the aircraft's empty weight.

Initial F-15C deliveries were made to the 18th Tactical Fighter Wing at Kadena AB, Okinawa, commencing in September 1979. F-15C/D models later replaced F-15A/Bs with the 1st, 33rd and 36th TFWs and with the 32nd Fighter Squadron at Soesterberg, although the latter unit traded its F-15Cs for MSIP F-15As during 1991. The F-15C/D has also equipped the 57th Fighter-Interceptor

Squadron at NS Keflavik, Iceland.

First blood for the F-15C was drawn during a period of border tensions when two Saudi Arabian F-15Cs shot down two Iranian F-4E Phantoms over the Persian Gulf on 5 June 1984, possibly the only time one McDonnell fighter scored an aerial victory over another. Israeli F-15Cs may also have notched up kills prior to Desert Storm. When the US launched Operation Desert Shield on 6 August 1990, the 1st TFW at Langley AFB, VA, deployed F-15C/D Eagles

of its 27th and 71st Tactical Fighter Squadrons at very short notice. Forty-eight Eagles made the longest non-stop fighter deployment in history, flying between 14 and 17 hours from Langley to Dhahran with six to eight inflight refuellings en route. The early arrival of the Eagles may have helped deter Iraq from moving immediately against Saudi oil fields.

In September 1990, the 33rd TFW from Eglin AFB, FL, deployed its 58th TFS with F-15C Eagles to Tabuk, Saudi Arabia. The 36th TFW at Bitburg, Germany, deployed F-15Cs to Tabuk and to Incirlik AB, Turkey. The 32nd TFS from Soesterberg, Holland, also deployed to Incirlik. When the war against Iraq began on 17 January 1991, the US had five F-15C air-to-air (and two F-15E strike) squadrons in the field. Most air-to-air

McDonnell Douglas F-15C/D Eagle

F-15s of the Alaska-based 3rd Wing display the old light grey scheme and the current 'Mod Eagle' darker grey low-visibility scheme.

engagements were fought by F-15Cs of the 58th TFS, part of the 33rd TFW, which scored 17 air-to-air victories, mainly during CAPs and fighter sweeps. Eagles also flew longer missions to escort strike aircraft. Quick turn-arounds were a major factor in achieving high sortie rates, and the F-15C exceeded expectations. No F-15C/Ds were lost during Desert Shield/ Storm. More than 2,200 missions totalling some 7,700 hours of combat time were logged, resulting in 32 aerial victories, two of them scored by a Saudi pilot of the RSAF's No. 13 Squadron. AMRAAM was sometimes carried, but was not used in combat.

During the 1990s, F-15 Eagles will continue to undergo staged improvements to radar and internal systems. Firmly committed to the F-22, the USAF appears to have abandoned plans for a scaled-down, improved Eagle known as **F-15XX**, but an MSIP for the F-15C/D, similar to that applied to earlier F-15A/B aircraft, is under way. This upgrade programme replaces the APG-63 with APG-70 radar, increases onboard computer memory to 1,000 K, trebles processing speed, multiplies central computer capacity by 300 per cent, and adds many improved avionics items. MSIP replaces the original weapons panel with a single Honeywell colour TV display. All F-15C/Ds are acquiring Tracor AN/ALE-45 chaff/flare dispensers located behind the nosewheel door, also found on the F-15E. Northrop AN/ALQ-135 enhanced internal countermeasures, Loral AN/ALR-56C RWR and a Magnavox EW warning system are all incorporated, and JTIDS 2 terminals are to be retrofitted. The MSIP F-15C/D is also compatible with the AIM-120 AMRAAM, which is belatedly replacing the AIM-7M Sparrow as the principal armament for the C/D model Eagle. The MSIP-II changes were flight-tested during December 1984, and were applied on production aircraft (beginning with 84-001) during June 1985. F-15C/D aircraft are projected to be operational in the fighter role until at least 2005.

When F-22s enter service in numbers, the displaced F-15Cs are scheduled to be reworked for the defence suppression role. This aircraft is known as **F-15/PDF (Precision Direction Finder)**, and the first contracts for this programme have been awarded. The aircraft is intended to supplement F-4Gs and F-16C/Ds in the 'Wild Weasel' role early in the next century.

The F-15C/D has been exported to favoured nations Israel, Japan and Saudi Arabia, as detailed under the operators. Japanese **F-15J** fighters (but not the two-seat **F-15DJ** trainers) are built by Mitsubishi and are described separately.

SPECIFICATION

McDonnell Douglas F-15C Eagle
Wing: span 42 ft 9.75 in (13.05 m); aspect ratio 3.01; area 608.00 sq ft (56.48 m²)
Fuselage and tail: length 63 ft 9 in (19.43 m); height 18 ft 5.5 in (5.63 m); tailplane span 28 ft 3 in (8.61 m); wheel track 9 ft 0.25 in (2.75 m); wheel base 17 ft 9.5 in (5.42 m)
Powerplant: two Pratt & Whitney F100-PW-220 turbofans each rated at 14,670 lb st (65.26 kN) dry and 23,830 lb st (106.0 kN) with afterburning

Weights: operating empty 28,600 lb (12793 kg); normal take-off 44,630 lb (20244 kg) on an intercept mission with four AIM-7 Sparrow AAMs; maximum take-off 58,470 lb (26521 kg) with three 610-US gal (2309-litre) drop tanks or 68,000 lb (30844 kg) with conformal fuel tanks
Fuel and load: internal fuel 13,455 lb (6103 kg); external fuel up to 9,750 lb (4423 kg) in two CFTs and 11,895 lb (5395 kg) in three 600-US gal (2271-litre) drop tanks; maximum ordnance 16,000 or 23,600 lb (7257 or 10705 kg) without or with CFTs respectively
Speed: maximum level speed 'clean' at 36,000 ft (10975 m) more than 1,433 kt (1,650 mph; 2655 km/h); cruising speed at optimum altitude 495 kt (570 mph; 917 km/h)
Range: ferry range with drop tanks more than 2,500 or 3,100 nm (2,879 or 3,570 miles; 4633 or 5745 km) without or with CFTs respectively; combat radius on an interception mission 1,061 nm (1,222 miles; 1967 km); endurance 5 hours 15 minutes with CFTs or 15 hours with flight refuelling
Performance: maximum rate of climb at sea level more than 50,000 ft (15240 m) per minute; service ceiling 60,000 ft (18290 m); absolute ceiling 100,000 ft (30480 m); take-off run 900 ft (274 m) at normal take-off weight; landing run 3,500 ft (1067 m) at normal landing weight without a brake parachute
g limits: -3 to +9

McDonnell Douglas F-15D Eagle
generally similar to the McDonnell Douglas F-15C Eagle except in the following particulars:
Weights: operating empty 29,400 lb (13336 kg)

OPERATORS

United States: 408 F-15Cs and 62 F-15Ds delivered. Current operators are 1st Fighter Wing (Langley AFB, VA), 33rd Fighter Wing (Eglin AFB, FL), 35th Wing (NS Keflavik, Iceland), 366th Wing (Mountain Home AFB, ID) of ACC, 325th Fighter Wing (Tyndall AFB, FL) of AETC, 3rd Wing (Elmendorf AFB, AK) and 18th Wing (Kadena AB, Okinawa) of PACAF, and 48th Fighter Wing (RAF Lakenheath, England) and 52nd Fighter Wing (Spangdahlem AB, Germany) of USAFE. Test and trials units include 57th FW (Nellis AFB, NV), 79th TEG (Eglin AFB, FL) and 412th Test Wing (Edwards AFB, CA)
Israel: 18 F-15Cs and eight F-15Ds supplied under Peace Fox III programme to equip 106 Sqn at Tel Nov. Five additional aircraft supplied in 1991. Israeli aircraft have the F-15A's IC-7 ejection seat in place of ACES II
Japan: two F-15J and 12 F-15DJ built by McDonnell, further single-seat aircraft built by Mitsubishi for a total of 223. These serve with 201/203 Hikotai at Chitose, 202 Hikotai/Hiko Kyodotai at Nyutabaru, 204/305 Hikotai at Hyakuri, 303 Hikotai at Komatsu, 304 Hikotai at Tsuiki
Saudi Arabia: 46 F-15Cs and 16 F-15Ds supplied under original Peace Sun programme. Total of 62 included two attrition replacments, as the US stipulated that no more than 60 F-15s could be operated by Saudi Arabia. This was rescinded during the Gulf War when 24 F-15C/Ds were hastily transferred from USAFE stocks. Peace Sun VI covered the delivery of a further nine F-15Cs and three F-15Ds from August 1991. Eagle units are No. 5 Sqn at Taif, No. 6 Sqn at Khamis Mushait, Nos 13 and 42 Sqns at Dhahran

Japanese two-seat F-15DJs are built by the parent company rather than by Mitsubishi. This example serves with the aggressor unit (Hiko Kyodotai) at Nyutabaru.

McDonnell Douglas **F-15E Eagle**

All F-15s were built with air-to-ground capability, and are wired for the carriage of air-to-ground ordnance. They were originally intended as dual-role aircraft, but the ground attack role was abandoned in 1975 and the relevant software was never incorporated. Trials of an air-to-ground F-15 began during 1982, when McDonnell Douglas modified the second TF-15A as the **'Strike Eagle'**, funding the project itself. The aircraft was conceived as an ETF (Enhanced Tactical Fighter) replacement for the General Dynamics F-111 and was cho-

sen in preference to the 'cranked wing' F-16XL Fighting Falcon. The 'Strike Eagle' demonstrator was joined by an F-15C and an F-15D which conducted trials with a variety of fuel and ordnance loads, usually with CFTs fitted. The resulting **F-15E** was given the go-ahead on 24 February 1984, and the first production aircraft made its maiden flight on 11 December 1986. McDonnell's 'Strike Eagle' name was not adopted, though some unofficial epithets such as 'Beagle' (Bomber Eagle) and 'Mud Hen' have been used on occasion.

In introducing new avionics and equipment for a 'mud-moving' role not assigned to earlier variants, the F-15E is very much a second-generation Eagle. The aircraft intro-

duced redesigned controls, a wide field of vision HUD, and three CRTs that provide multi-purpose displays of navigation, weapons delivery and systems operations.

The F-15E has nuclear delivery capability in the form of the B61 tactical weapon, seen here on an Eglin test aircraft. The wing- and fuselage-mounted ciné cameras record the weapon separation.

COCKPIT
The F-15E has a state-of-the-art cockpit, the pilot having a wide-angle HUD and three MFDs. The WSO has four MFDs. All vital flight and attack inputs are made via an upfront controller and stick/throttle controls.

ARMAMENT
This F-15E is loaded for a close air support/battlefield air interdiction mission with 14 SUU-30H cluster bombs. The AIM-9s are for self-defence. Lakenheath F-15Es also carry AIM-120 AMRAAM from the outer launch rail, with Sidewinders on the inner.

McDonnell Douglas
F-15E Eagle

Mirroring the USAF's quest for greater flexibility and efficiency in an era of vastly reduced expenditure, the F-15E is arguably the world's most capable operational warplane. In the air-to-ground role its superb avionics and sensors allow it to undertake precision attacks with heavy loads in any conditions, yet once it is relieved of the encumbrance of attack ordnance it handles just like any fighter Eagle. Strike/attack is its primary role, but its air-fighting prowess allows it to be far more survivable over hostile territory where there is a heavy air threat. F-15Es are based with theatre units in Alaska and Europe, with a rapid-reaction composite wing at Mountain Home and a dedicated F-15E wing at Seymour Johnson. The force is seen as a highly credible deterrent to meet quickly-evolving situations, and would be in the vanguard of any USAF deployment in a crisis. This aircraft is marked for the wing commander of the 48th Fighter Wing, which swapped its four squadrons of F-111Fs for two of F-15Es in 1992.

CFTs
The conformal fuel tanks each hold 723 US gal (2737 litres) of fuel, and have a continuous pylon (with three attachment points) and three stub pylons for the carriage of weapons.

LANTIRN NAV POD
The LANTIRN system consists of the AAQ-13 navigation pod on the starboard intake and AAQ-14 targeting pod on the port. The AAQ-13 consists of a wide-angle FLIR, which projects an image on the pilot's HUD, and a Texas Instruments terrain-following radar, which interfaces with the aircraft's autopilot system to provide safe low-level flight in all conditions.

LANTIRN TARGETING POD
The AAQ-14 is used for attacks, and contains a wide/narrow field-of-view forward-looking infra-red for target acquisition, laser designator/rangefinder, stabiliser system, multi-mode tracker and an automatic IR Maverick hands-off system. At the rear of both LANTIRN pods are air intakes to serve the cooling systems.

CANNON
The M61A1 cannon is mounted in the starboard wingroot, armed with 512 rounds. In the port wingroot is the refuelling receptacle.

RADAR
At the heart of the F-15E's capability is the APG-70 radar, a vastly-improved version of the F-15C's APG-63. As well as improved air-to-air modes, the APG-70 offers a high-resolution synthetic aperture mapping mode allowing highly accurate 'patch maps' to be taken of a target area, which in turn allow precise designation of the desired aimpoint.

POWERPLANT
Initial F-15E deliveries were powered by the P&W F100-PW-220 engine rated at 23,450 lb (104.3 kN) thrust. Later aircraft, like this one, are fitted with the F100-PW-229 IPE, offering 29,100 lb (129.4 kN) thrust.

This 412th TW F-15E displays the LANTIRN pods and the bomb carriage along the conformal fuel tanks.

The rear-cockpit WSO employs four multi-purpose CRT terminals for radar, weapon selection and monitoring of enemy tracking systems. The WSO also operates an AN/APG-70 synthetic aperture radar and Martin-Marietta LANTIRN navigation (AN/AAQ-13) and targeting (AN-AAQ-14) pods. The navigation pod incorporates its own terrain-following radar, which can be linked to the aircraft's flight control system to allow automatic coupled terrain-following flight. The targeting pod allows the aircraft to self-designate GBU-10 and GBU-24 laser-guided bombs. Basic flight controls are also provided. Both pilot and WSO sit in tandem on ACES II zero-zero ejection seats.

Power for the new variant was initially provided by F100-PW-220 turbofans, as used by the F-15C, with a digital engine control system, but this was soon replaced under the Improved Performance Engine programme, whereby paired GE F110-GE-129 and P&W F100-PW-229 engines were flown in F-15Es under competitive evaluation; the Pratt & Whitney engine was eventually selected. Since August 1991 (F-15E serial 90-0233) the new engine has been fitted on the production line, and other aircraft

McDonnell Douglas F-15E Eagle

Powerplant: two Pratt & Whitney F100-P-220 turbofans each rated at 14,670 lb st (65.26 kN) dry and 23,830 lb st (106.0 kN) with afterburning or, in aircraft built after August 1991, two F100-PW-229s each rated at 17,800 lb st (79.18 kN) dry and 29,100 lb st (129.45 kN) with afterburning; option of two General Electric F110-GE-129s each rated at 17,000 lb st (75.62 kN) dry and 29,000 lb st (129.0 kN) with afterburning

Weights: operating empty 31,700 lb (14379 kg); maximum take-off 81,000 lb (36741 kg)

Fuel and load: internal fuel 13,123 lb (5952 kg); external fuel 21,645 lb (9818 kg) in two CFTs and up to three 610-US gal (2309-litre) drop tanks; maximum ordnance 24,500 lb (11113 kg)

Speed: maximum level speed 'clean' at high altitude more than 1,433 kt (1,650 mph; 2655 km/h); cruising speed at optimum altitude 495 kt (570 mph; 917 km/h)

Range: ferry range 3,100 nm (3,570 miles; 5745 km) with CFTs and drop tanks, or 2,400 nm (2,765 miles; 4445 km) with drop tanks; combat radius 685 nm (790 miles; 1270 km)

Performance: maximum rate of climb at sea level more than 50,000 ft (15240 m) per minute; service ceiling 60,000 ft (18290 m); landing run 3,500 ft (1067 m) at normal landing weight without braking parachute

The 366th Wing operates a mixed force of types as the USAF's rapid-reaction, power-projection 'super wing'. Offensive muscle comes from the B-52, F-16C and F-15E, the latter flown by the 'Bold Tigers' of the 391st Fighter Squadron.

will be retrofitted. To suit the F-15E for the rigours of the low-level role, the aircraft was structurally redesigned for a 16,000-hour life and loads of up to 9 *g*. More use was made of superplastic forming and diffusion bonding of titanium in the rear fuselage, engine bay and on some panels. The fuel tanks have been filled with reticulated foam, reducing capacity to 2,019 US gal (7643 litres).

In 1988, the 405th Tactical Training Wing at Luke AFB, AZ, became Tactical Air Command's replacement training unit for the F-15E Eagle aircraft, a role since taken over by the 58th Fighter Wing in Air Education and Training Command. The first operational F-15Es were delivered to the 4th TFW, Seymour Johnson AFB, NC, replacing F-4Es.

On 12 August 1990, as the US began Operation Desert Shield, F-15E Eagles from the 336th TFS, 4th TFW, deployed to Al Kharj air base, Saudi Arabia. F-15Es of that wing's 335th TFS followed. During Desert Storm, F-15Es were assigned strike missions against a variety of targets, including five/six-hour sorties in search of 'Scud' missile launch sites. Two F-15E Eagles were lost in combat during 2,200 sorties totalling 7,700 hours.

The USAF was authorised to procure 209 F-15Es, all of which have been delivered. In 1991, the Secretary of Defense overruled USAF leaders who wanted to keep the F-15E Eagle in production. Although the F-15E is an exceedingly potent warplane for the strike mission, critics point out that its low wing-loading produces a rough ride, especially for the backseater, and that the F-15E's payload is less than that of the 30-year-old F-111. The US Air Force wanted to

keep the production line open to 'bridge' a hoped-for additional purchase from Saudi Arabia directly from inventory.

WEAPON OPTIONS

The primary mission of the F-15E is air-to-ground strike, for which it carries a wide range of weapons on two underwing pylons, underfuselage pylons and 12 bomb racks mounted directly on the CFTs. The F-15E carries up to a maximum of 24,250 lb (11000 kg) of tactical ordnance, including Mk 82 500-lb (227-kg) (26) or Mk 84 2,000-lb (907-kg) (7) bombs; or GBU-10 (7), GBU-12 (15) or GBU-15 (2) guided weapons. GBU-15s are accompanied by an AN/AXQ-14 datalink pod carried on the centreline. The aircraft also carries 25 CBU-52, -58, -71, -87, -89, -90, -92 or -93 bombs. The AGM-65 Maverick can be carried, on single or triple launchers on the two underwing pylons only. The F-15E is also capable of carrying up to five B57 or B61 nuclear bombs. Specialist weapons include the AGM-

88 HARM for defence suppression, and the AGM-130, a powered version of the GBU-15 EO-guided bomb. As a dual-role warplane, the F-15E has air-to-air capability and, like its air-superiority predecessors, is able to engage enemy aircraft beyond visual range with four AIM-7M Sparrows or eight AIM-120 AMRAAMs. The F-15E also has four AIM-9 Sidewinder missiles and a 20-mm M61A1 Vulcan six-barrelled cannon with 512 rounds of ammunition. The centreline and wing pylons are often reserved for the carriage of 600-US gal (2270-litre) fuel tanks.

SPECIFICATION

McDonnell Douglas F-15E Eagle

Wing: span 42 ft 9.75 in (13.05 m); aspect ratio 3.01; area 608.00 sq ft (56.48 m²)

Fuselage and tail: length 63 ft 9 in (19.43 m); height 18 ft 5.5 in (5.63 m); tailplane span 28 ft 3 in (8.61 m); wheel track 9 ft 0.25 in (2.75 m); wheel base 17 ft 9.5 in (5.42 m)

OPERATORS

Air Combat Command: 4th Wing (Seymour Johnson AFB, NC), 57th Wing (Nellis AFB, NV), 366th Wing (Mountain Home AFB, ID), Air Warfare Center (Eglin AFB, FL)

Air Education and Training Command: 58th Fighter Wing (Luke AFB, AZ)

Air Force Materiel Command: 412th Test Wing (Edwards AFB, CA)

Pacific Air Forces: 3rd Wing (Elmendorf AFB, AK)

USAF Europe: 48th Fighter Wing (RAF Lakenheath, England)

The 46th Test Wing at Eglin uses F-15Es for weapons trial work with the 40th TS. This aircraft carries the AGM-130, essentially a GBU-15 electro-optical guided bomb with a rocket booster strapped on. For long range guidance, the AXQ-14 datalink pod is carried on the centreline.

McDonnell Douglas **F-15F/H/I/S/XP** Eagle

McDonnell has proposed several versions of the F-15 Eagle which have not yet been ordered into production. A low-cost USAF alternative to the Lockheed F-22, the lightweight **F-15XX**, was abandoned in 1992. Other designations were applied to studies for export versions of the dual-role F-15E, primarily for **Saudi Arabia**.

The **F-15F** was a single-seater optimised for air-to-air duties, but based on the F-15E,

with the same airframe, engines, CRT-equipped cockpit and AN/APG-70 radar, although the latter has its attack and high-resolution synthetic aperture ground mapping modes deleted. No provision was made for LANTIRN pods. Saudi Arabia originally requested the supply of 24 of these aircraft, with 48 dual-role two-seaters.

The **F-15H** was probably the paper proposal for a dual-role aircraft, 48 of which

would have been delivered with the 24 F-15Fs. This was to have retained most of the capabilities of the F-15E without all of the latter's equipment, including the twin-podded LANTIRN system.

The **F-15XP** designation was applied to the F-15F and F-15H in the original Congressional notification documents, as a general term to cover new-generation Saudi F-15s. The term is no longer used, since Saudi Ara-

bia is now to receive 72 examples of a new two-seat, dual-role Eagle, under the designation **F-15S**. All will be two-seaters, again based on the F-15E airframe but with downgraded avionics and downgraded LANTIRN pods. The design calls for a simplified Hughes APG-70 radar without computerised radar mapping. CFTs are deleted, thereby reducing the F-15S's combat radius. A similar variant, designated **F-15I**, has gained an initial order for 26 from **Israel**, in the face of stiff competition from a modified, long-range strike version of the Lockheed F-16 Fighting Falcon.

McDonnell Douglas F/A-18A/C Hornet

Emerging victorious in the Navy's Air Combat Fighter programme that pitted the General Dynamics YF-16 against the **Northrop YF-17** in the mid-1970s, the **Hornet** was a more sophisticated navalised derivative of the Northrop contender (originally designed to meet the USAF's ACF requirement). It was at first intended to be produced in two distinct versions: specifically, the **F-18** fighter and the **A-18** for strike/attack tasks. Eventually, a single common aircraft was selected for both missions (replacing US Navy A-7s and US Marine Corps F-4s) and was given the designation **F/A-18**, although a land-based version, the **F/A-18L**, was to have been available for export. Under the original agreement, McDonnell was to have design leadership and the larger workshare of the naval versions, and Northrop that of the land-based versions. The export success of the naval F/A-18 to land-based customers eventually led to major disagreements and even a lawsuit between the partners.

These problems were eventually solved, and were never allowed to interfere with the aircraft itself. Responsibility for development and production of the F/A-18 has always been shared by McDonnell Douglas and Northrop, with the former company being the dominant partner. To speed the development process, a batch of 11 aircraft was ordered for trials purposes and nine of these were ultimately completed as single-seaters. The designation **YF/A-18** has sometimes been unofficially applied, although technically the aircraft were not prototypes but pre-production aircraft. The first example made its maiden flight on 18 November 1978, and the remainder had all joined the test programme by March 1980.

Production of the initial **F/A-18A** version eventually totalled 371 and delivery of these began in May 1980, with early examples being allocated to the US Navy's operational test and evaluation force. Subsequent assignment to elements of the Navy and Marine Corps was spearheaded by the formation of a Navy training squadron at Lemoore, CA, but the first fully operational Hornet units were from the Marine Corps. Fighter-attack squadron VMFA-314 'Black Knights' led the way in August 1982, returning to El Toro from Lemoore and being declared operational on 7 January 1983.

The service entry of the new type made a huge impact that exceeded many expectations. The F/A-18 offered much greater weapons delivery accuracy than its predecessors, and was a genuinely multi-role aircraft, able to out-bomb the A-7 and to out-turn the F-14. Suddenly, the fleet's attack aircraft was in many ways also its finest fighter. The term 'Swing Fighter' has often been applied, referring to the pilot's ability to switch from the air-to-ground role to air-to-air or defence suppression duties literally at the push of a button. The aircraft's dog-fighting capability is remarkable, the high-lift wing and leading-edge extensions conferring excellent high-Alpha capability and turn performance. Similarly, the APG-65 radar, which has become the benchmark fighter radar, is as effective at putting bombs on target as it is at detecting and engaging multiple airborne targets (fighter-sized targets can be picked up at ranges of over 80 nm/148 km). Air-to-air capability is enhanced by a well-designed cockpit with three multi-function CRT-type displays and true HOTAS controls, which help the pilot maintain situational awareness. In the air-to-ground role the F/A-18 can carry a Martin-Marietta laser spot tracker on the starboard underfuselage

Illustrating the Hornet's versatility, a pair of Marine Hornets carries iron bombs and AGM-88 defence suppression missiles. Both carry FLIR pods on the starboard intake pylons for night attack.

pylon, with a Ford Aerospace AN/AAS-38 FLIR or a Hughes AN/AAR-50 TINS to port.

Some of the Hornet's success may be attributed to its 16,000-lb st (71.2-kN) General Electric F404-GE-400 low-bypass turbofans, developed from the YJ101 engine of the YF-17. These have proved reliable and fuel-efficient, but are to be replaced by the derived 17,600-lb st (78.3-kN) F404-GE-402 EPE/IPE (Enhanced/Improved Performance Engine).

Navy service

The first US Navy squadron, VFA-113, soon followed VMFA-314 and accepted its first Hornet in August 1983. Accompanied by VFA-25, VFA-113 made the initial operational deployment as part of Carrier Air Wing 14 aboard USS *Constellation* during 1985. By the time they returned to the West Coast, several more squadrons were well advanced with conversion to the Hornet, the type replacing F-4 Phantoms with the Marines and A-7 Corsairs with the Navy.

Four Hornet squadrons aboard USS *Coral*

Right: Spain's Hornets serve with two wings (Ala 15 illustrated) for both air defence and attack roles. Specialist equipment includes Harpoon and HARM.

Sea (two Navy and two Marine Corps) participated in the El Dorado Canyon attack against targets in Libya in April 1986 when they were mainly employed in defence suppression. This marked the operational debut of both the F/A-18 and the AGM-88A HARM. Hornets from both the Navy (nine squadrons) and Marines (seven squadrons) were heavily committed to action during Desert Storm in 1991. Then, they were predominantly concerned with attack tasks, but they also flew combat air patrol missions. Two bomb-laden Hornets were responsible for the destruction of a pair of Iraqi F-7s on the first day of the war, continuing with their strike mission after despatching their enemies.

The F/A-18A was superseded on the St

Anti-ship capability is available thanks to the AGM-84 Harpoon missile, two of which can be carried. The AGM-84E SLAM version is available for long-range precision attack against ground targets.

Louis line by the **F/A-18C**, which remains the production single-seat model in 1994, some 355 examples having been ordered. The first F/A-18C (163427) made its maiden flight on 3 September 1986. Changes were made to weapons capability, so that the F/A-18C becomes the first Hornet variant compatible with the AIM-120 AMRAAM and with imaging infra-red Maverick missiles. The F/A-18C was also designed with provision for installation of the proposed (and

McDonnell Douglas F/A-18A/C Hornet

UNIT
VFA-87 'Golden Warriors' traded A-7s for F/A-18Cs in July 1987. In 1992 the squadron transitioned to Lot 14 Night-Attack Hornets. The squadron is shore-based at NAS Cecil Field, FL.

POWERPLANT
The basic F/A-18C featured the General Electric F404-GE-400 low-bypass turbofan, rated at 16,000 lb (71.2 kN) thrust with afterburning. From early 1992, the standard engine became the F404-GE-402 EPE (Enhanced Performance Engine), developing 17,600 lb (78.3 kN) thrust.

In addition to regular Fleet duties, the Hornet is routinely called upon to act in an aggressor role. Shown above is a VFA-37 aircraft carrying ALQ-167 ECM pods to provide an EW environment for realistic training, while below is a VFA-303 aircraft in an air combat adversary scheme, with black fin silhouette to represent a MiG-29.

cancelled) **RF-18A** interchangeable recce nose, with hardpoints, wiring and EMI shielding. It is fitted with a new CRT engine monitor display and has received an avionics upgrade with new AN/ALR-67 RHAWS. The type had provision for the cancelled AN/ALQ-165 airborne self-protection jammer (interchangeable with AN/ALQ-126B), and features revisions to mission computer equipment with enhanced built-in test facilities, increased memory and faster processing. These necessitated improvements to the ECS (Environmental Control System).

The new avionics give the F/A-18C its only external distinguishing characteristics, a five-pronged antenna array for the ALR-67 on the gun bay door, with small fairings on the sides of the nose and on the trailing edge of the fin, and similar ALQ-165 antennas on the gun bay access door, nose gear door, on top of the nose and behind the canopy. The F/A-18C also introduced the Martin-Baker NACES in place of the SJU-5/6 ejection seat and is fitted with small strakes above the LERXes designed to reduce buffet on the vertical tailfins and to improve yaw control at very high angles of attack. These strakes have since been retrofitted to virtually all surviving Hornets.

After 137 baseline F/A-18Cs had been delivered, production switched to a night-attack capable version (retaining the designation F/A-18C), the package of equipment including compatibility with GEC Cat's Eyes

pilot's night vision goggles, a Hughes AN/AAR-50 TINS pod presenting its thermal picture of the terrain ahead in the Kaiser AN/AVQ-28 raster HUD, externally-carried Loral AN/AAS-38 targeting FLIR pod, and colour MFDs. The latter were joined by a new Honeywell colour digital moving map, which replaced the projected moving map display used previously, freeing the aircraft from having to be loaded with bulky film for projection. The first example (163985) was delivered to the NATC at Patuxent River, MD, on 1 November 1989.

Multi-mode radar

The Hornet's flexibility and versatility enable it to undertake interception, air superiority and strike/attack tasks with equal facility. One of the key factors in this flexibility is the radar. The Hughes AN/APG-65 multimode digital fire control unit has become a standard in fighter radars and can operate with equal effectiveness in air-to-air and air-to-surface modes. Future changes to the Hornet avionics suite include substitution of the Hughes AN/APG-73 radar in place of the same company's AN/APG-65 unit. This enhanced radar embodies new signal and data processors, a different bandwidth and an upgraded receiver/exciter. The first APG-73-equipped Hornet flew on 15 April 1992, and production aircraft have been fitted with the new radar since June 1994.

The F/A-18's unrivalled versatility makes

it a real force multiplier in any carrier air wing, and current plans are increasing the type's importance, by deploying US Marine Corps F/A-18 squadrons on board US Navy carriers at the expense of A-6 and S-3 assets. The diminishing threat from cruise missile-carrying, very long-range strategic bombers means that carriers no longer have to stand-off so far from an enemy coast, and the F/A-18's relatively short range (often deliberately overstated by the aircraft's opponents) is less of a problem. In fact, a clean F/A-18 can out-distance a clean F-4, and even with fuel tanks can carry a greater bombload than the A-7, over the same range. The Hornet's accuracy also means that it can achieve more over the target on less fuel. In the air combat role, the F/A-18's high dry thrust means that it can outstay aircraft like the F-14, which rely more heavily on using afterburner. Hornet pilots seldom reach 'bingo' state (break off an engagement due to reaching minimum fuel) first.

The Hornet's versatility has led to substantial export sales. Canada was the first foreign customer and has taken delivery of 98 single-seaters. These are known as **CF-18A**s by McDonnell and as **CF-188A**s by the operator, although it should be noted that the name Hornet is used only unofficially, since the French language equivalent, 'Frelon', could be confused with the Aérospatiale helicopter of the same name. Deliveries were accomplished between October 1982 and September 1988. The Canadian aircraft are virtually standard F/A-18As, except in being fitted with a spotlight on the port side of the nose (for identifying aircraft during night intercepts), a new ILS and in having provision for the carriage of LAU-5003 rocket pods. These were followed by an Australian order negotiated in 1981, whereby local assembly, and later production, was undertaken of 57 **AF-18A**s by ASTA; these were handed over during 1985-90 as replacements for the Mirage. The aircraft are being updated to F/A-18C standard, and can launch AGM-85, AGM-88

and Paveway II laser-guided bombs. Spain originally evaluated the YF-17 but eventually opted to purchase 60 **EF-18A**s for the Ejercito del Aire, with delivery from 1986 to 1990. Spanish Hornets are operated under the local designation **C.15**. Like Australian Hornets, the Spanish EF-18As are being upgraded to near C model standard.

Subsequent export contracts have all been for the F/A-18C variant and comprise 32 for Kuwait, which were delivered by September 1993; 26 for Switzerland with deliveries due to start in 1995 (after a national referendum which endorsed the purchase); 57 for Finland, again with deliveries set to run from 1995. Finnish Hornets will be supplied in knock-down form by McDonnell Douglas and assembled locally by Valmet. Israel is continuing to look at the F/A-18 as a potential A-4/F-4 replacement, and has evaluated the type.

The F-18 has now entirely supplanted the A-7 and F-4 in US Navy and Marine Corps service. These two organisations currently possess more than 40 first- and second-line Hornet strike/fighter (VFA) and Marine fighter-attack (VMFA) squadrons. In addition, it also serves with several support squadrons in the adversary and electronic aggressor roles, and with test agencies. The F/A-18 has also been the mount for the Navy's 'Blue Angels' aerial display team since the end of the 1986 season.

WEAPON OPTIONS

In keeping with its multi-role capability, the Hornet is equipped with nine external stores stations, enabling it to carry a wide range of ordnance. For air-to-air missions, missile armament includes AIM-120 AMRAAM, AIM-7 Sparrow and AIM-9 Sidewinder, in addition to a nose-mounted Vulcan M61A1 20-mm cannon with 570 rounds of ammunition. For strike missions, options include precision-guided munitions

Left: Canada has four operational CF-188 squadrons, augmented by an OCU. The fleet has true dual-role taskings, including air defence alerts in the north of the country.

Below: Australian Hornets carry a wide variety of stores, and are able to carry the AAS-48 FLIR/laser designation pod.

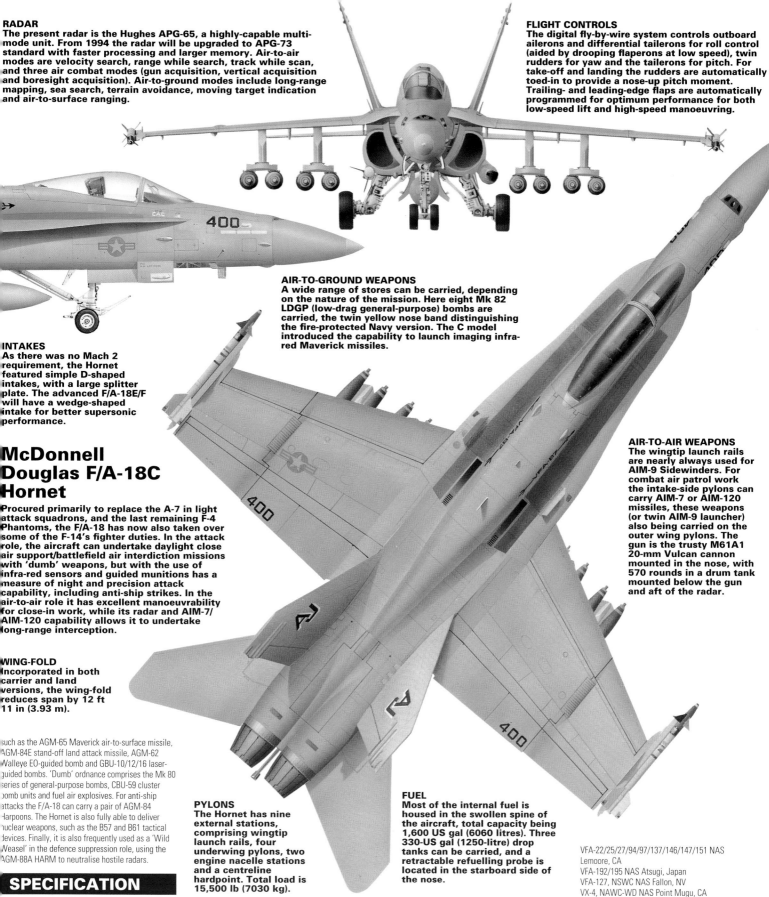

RADAR

The present radar is the Hughes APG-65, a highly-capable multi-mode unit. From 1994 the radar will be upgraded to APG-73 standard with faster processing and larger memory. Air-to-air modes are velocity search, range while search, track while scan, and three air combat modes (gun acquisition, vertical acquisition and boresight acquisition). Air-to-ground modes include long-range mapping, sea search, terrain avoidance, moving target indication and air-to-surface ranging.

FLIGHT CONTROLS

The digital fly-by-wire system controls outboard ailerons and differential tailerons for roll control (aided by drooping flaperons at low speed), twin rudders for yaw and the tailerons for pitch. For take-off and landing the rudders are automatically toed-in to provide a nose-up pitch moment. Trailing- and leading-edge flaps are automatically programmed for optimum performance for both low-speed lift and high-speed manoeuvring.

INTAKES

As there was no Mach 2 requirement, the Hornet featured simple D-shaped intakes, with a large splitter plate. The advanced F/A-18E/F will have a wedge-shaped intake for better supersonic performance.

AIR-TO-GROUND WEAPONS

A wide range of stores can be carried, depending on the nature of the mission. Here eight Mk 82 LDGP (low-drag general-purpose) bombs are carried, the twin yellow nose band distinguishing the fire-protected Navy version. The C model introduced the capability to launch imaging infra-red Maverick missiles.

McDonnell Douglas F/A-18C Hornet

Procured primarily to replace the A-7 in light attack squadrons, and the last remaining F-4 Phantoms, the F/A-18 has now also taken over some of the F-14's fighter duties. In the attack role, the aircraft can undertake daylight close air support/battlefield air interdiction missions with 'dumb' weapons, but with the use of infra-red sensors and guided munitions has a measure of night and precision attack capability, including anti-ship strikes. In the air-to-air role it has excellent manoeuvrability for close-in work, while its radar and AIM-7/AIM-120 capability allows it to undertake long-range interception.

AIR-TO-AIR WEAPONS

The wingtip launch rails are nearly always used for AIM-9 Sidewinders. For combat air patrol work the intake-side pylons can carry AIM-7 or AIM-120 missiles, these weapons (or twin AIM-9 launcher) also being carried on the outer wing pylons. The gun is the trusty M61A1 20-mm Vulcan cannon mounted in the nose, with 570 rounds in a drum tank mounted below the gun and aft of the radar.

WING-FOLD

Incorporated in both carrier and land versions, the wing-fold reduces span by 12 ft 11 in (3.93 m).

such as the AGM-65 Maverick air-to-surface missile, AGM-84E stand-off land attack missile, AGM-62 Walleye EO-guided bomb and GBU-10/12/16 laser-guided bombs. 'Dumb' ordnance comprises the Mk 80 series of general-purpose bombs, CBU-59 cluster bomb units and fuel air explosives. For anti-ship attacks the F/A-18 can carry a pair of AGM-84 Harpoons. The Hornet is also fully able to deliver nuclear weapons, such as the B57 and B61 tactical devices. Finally, it is also frequently used as a 'Wild Weasel' in the defence suppression role, using the AGM-88A HARM to neutralise hostile radars.

PYLONS

The Hornet has nine external stations, comprising wingtip launch rails, four underwing pylons, two engine nacelle stations and a centreline hardpoint. Total load is 15,500 lb (7030 kg).

FUEL

Most of the internal fuel is housed in the swollen spine of the aircraft, total capacity being 1,600 US gal (6060 litres). Three 330-US gal (1250-litre) drop tanks can be carried, and a retractable refuelling probe is located in the starboard side of the nose.

SPECIFICATION

McDonnell Douglas F/A-18C Hornet
Wing: span 37 ft 6 in (11.43 m) without tip-mounted AAMs and 40 ft 4.75 in (12.31 m) with tip-mounted AAMs; width folded 27 ft 6 in (8.38 m); aspect ratio 3.5; area 400.00 sq ft (37.16 m²)
Fuselage and tail: length 56 ft 0 in (17.07 m); height 15 ft 3.5 in (4.66 m); tailplane span 21 ft 7.25 in (6.58 m); wheel track 10 ft 2.5 in (3.11 m); wheel base 17 ft 9.5 in (5.42 m)
Powerplant: two General Electric F404-GE-400 turbofans each rated at 16,000 lb st (71.17 kN) with afterburning or, in aircraft built from early 1992, F404-GE-402 turbofans each rated at 17,700 lb st (78.73 kN) with afterburning
Weights: empty 23,050 lb (10455 kg); normal take-off 36,710 lb (16652 kg) for a fighter mission or

51,900 lb (23541 kg) for an attack mission; maximum take-off about 56,000 lb (25401 kg)
Fuel and load: internal fuel 10,860 lb (4926 kg); external fuel up to 6,732 lb (3053 kg) in three 330-US gal (1250-litre) drop tanks; maximum ordnance 15,500 lb (7031 kg)
Speed: maximum level speed 'clean' at high altitude more than 1,033 kt (1,190 mph; 1915 km/h)
Range: ferry range more than 1,800 nm (2,073 miles; 3336 km) with drop tanks; combat radius more than 400 nm (460 miles; 740 km) on a fighter mission, or 575 nm (662 miles; 1065 km) on an attack mission, or 290 nm (340 miles; 537 km) on a hi-lo-hi interdiction mission
Performance: maximum rate of climb at sea level 45,000 ft (13715 m) per minute; combat ceiling about

50,000 ft (15240 m); take-off run less than 1,400 ft (427 m) at maximum take-off weight

McDonnell Douglas F/A-18A Hornet
generally similar to the F/A-18C Hornet except in the following particulars:
Weights: normal take-off 33,585 lb (15234 kg) for a fighter mission; maximum take-off 48,253 lb (21888 kg) for an attack mission

OPERATORS

In 1994 the units operating all Hornet variants (including two-seaters) were as follows:
US Navy (active-duty): VFA-15/37/81/82/83/86/87/105/106/131/132/136 NAS Cecil Field, FL

VFA-22/25/27/94/97/137/146/147/151 NAS Lemoore, CA
VFA-192/195 NAS Atsugi, Japan
VFA-127, NSWC NAS Fallon, NV
VX-4, NAWC-WD NAS Point Mugu, CA
VX-5, NAWC-WD NAS China Lake, CA
NAWC-AD, USN TPS NAS Patuxent River, MD
'Blue Angels' NAS Pensacola, FL
US Navy Reserve: VFA-203 NAS Cecil Field, FL
VFA-204 NAS New Orleans, LA
VFA-303 NAS Lemoore, CA
VFA-305 NAS Point Mugu, CA
US Marine Corps (active-duty): VMFA-115/122/251/312/451, VMFA(AW)-224/332/533 MCAS Beaufort, SC
VMFA-314/323, VMFAT-101, VMFA(AW)-121/225/242 MCAS El Toro, CA
VMFA-212/232/235 MCAS Kaneohe Bay, HI
US Marine Corps Reserve: VMFA-112 NAS Dallas, TX
VMFA-134 MCAS El Toro, CA
VMFA-142 NAS Cecil Field, FL

McDonnell Douglas F/A-18A/C Hornet

Eight F/A-18As and a single F/A-18B are assigned to the US Navy's 'Blue Angels' aerobatic team. The aircraft have civilian nav/comms gear, smoke-generating equipment and no cannon.

McDonnell Douglas F/A-18B/D/D(RC) Hornet

Development of a two-seat version of the Hornet was undertaken concurrently with that of the single-seater, following the McDonnell Douglas/Northrop contender's victory over the rival General Dynamics F-16 in the US Navy's Air Combat Fighter contest of the mid-1970s. In consequence, two examples of the **TF-18A** (initial designation, later replaced by **F/A-18B**) featured in the original contract which covered procurement of a batch of 11 prototype aircraft for RDT&E tasks.

Basically identical to the F/A-18A, the B model introduced a second seat in tandem for a modest six per cent penalty in fuel capacity. Otherwise, the F/A-18B was unaltered, possessing identical equipment and near-identical combat capability, with the latter being a factor in the change of designation.

Subsequent procurement of the F/A-18B for service with Navy and Marine Corps units ended with the 40th production example, and this version has never been employed by front-line forces. Apart from a few examples assigned to test agencies, the F/A-18B serves only with VFA-106.

The second two-seat Hornet version was the **F/A-18D**, which is broadly similar to the single-seat F/A-18C. Thirty-one baseline aircraft were procured before production changed to the night attack-capable F/A-18D, which has the same avionics improvements as the night-attack F/A-18C. All FY 1988 and subsequent F/A-18Cs and F/A-18Ds have been to this standard, the first night-attack F/A-18D going to Patuxent River on 14 November 1989. This variant is a special night attack two-seat Hornet which has replaced the Grumman A-6 Intruder with the USMC's VMA(AW) units (All Weather Attack Squadrons). Originally dubbed **F/A-18D+**, the aircraft features 'uncoupled' cockpits, usually with no control column in the rear cockpit (although one can be refitted) and with two sidestick weapons controllers.

The Hornet was first proposed as a reconnaissance platform early in its career and it was initially envisaged that single-seaters would be modified to accept an interchangeable recce package in the nose occupying the space normally taken up by the M61A1 cannon. This contained a Fairchild-Weston KA-99 panoramic camera and a Honeywell AN/AAD-5 linescan, with provision for various other cameras. The first prototype was used as the aerodynamic prototype for the reconnaissance Hornet, with the bulged undernose sensor pallet and associated camera windows. An F/A-18A (161214) was modified more comprehensively, receiving full recce equipment, under the designation **RF-18** (or more correctly, **F/A-18(R)**), first flying in its new configuration on 15 August 1984.

The increasing trend towards the use of digitised reconnaissance sensors, which

Left: Kuwait's Hornet order included eight KAF-18D two-seaters.

Below: The Marines use the F/A-18D for fast FAC duties in addition to training. This aircraft, from El Toro-based training outfit VMFAT-101 'Sharpshooters', lets fly with 5-in Zuni rockets. These weapons, carried in four-round LAU-10 pods, can be used for target-marking with white phosphorus warheads.

FLIR SENSOR
Carried on the starboard intake is an infra-red sensor pod. The F/A-18 has a choice of the Ford Aerospace AAS-38, chiefly for target acquisition, or the Hughes AAR-50 TINS (thermal imaging navigation set) for low-level night flying. Later versions of the AAS-38 incorporate a laser designator.

LST/SCAM
The Martin-Marietta ASQ-173 pod on the port intake contains a laser spot tracker in the nose for attacking targets designated by other sources, and a strike camera in the rear section for rapid damage assessment.

allow the real-time use and/or transmission of reconnaissance information, led to the development of a new variant for the US Marine Corps. The modified **F/A-18D(RC)** version was originally intended to have the same recce nose as the single-seat reconnaissance Hornet, but also to use the ATARS pod that contains a Loral AN/UPD-8 high resolution synthetic aperture SLAR, and is able to transmit imagery in real time by datalink. The old-style recce nose was abandoned and ATARS was redesigned to be able to be packaged into the nose, but delivery of the F/A-18D(RC) to VMFA(AW)-225 in February 1992 marked only the delivery of aircraft wired for ATARS. ATARS itself is still under test, although a correctly ballasted F/A-18 has flown. Today VMFA(AW)-225's aircraft have only the radar and digital moving map (and the Mark One Eyeball) with which to carry out the

McDonnell Douglas F/A-18D(RC) Hornet

Central to the USMC's drive for a two-type fixed-wing tactical force, the Hornet has not only replaced the F-4 Phantom and A-4 Skyhawk, it has supplanted the A-6 Intruder. For the latter's precision attack role, the two-seat F/A-18D is required, the second crew member being concerned with operating the sophisticated avionics/sensor suite. Whereas most two-seat Hornets are used for training, those of the USMC are optimised for an offensive role, with no flight controls in the backseat but full weapon systems controls.

ZUNI ROCKET
Widely used in Vietnam, the 5-in (12.7-cm) Zuni is still employed for attack and target-marking. Fired from the LAU-10 pod, current Zunis have the 80-lb (36-kg) Mk 71 Mod 1 motor and a variety of warhead options. High-explosive and white phosphorus are the favourites for FAC missions, while a flare can be used for night illumination.

FAST FAC
One role the two-seat Hornet is used for is fast forward air control, the backseater controlling other attack aircraft over the battlefield. Targets are marked with rockets carried in four-round pods under each wing, while the aircraft carries a forward-looking infra-red and laser spot tracker on the intake pylons.

UNIT
VMFA(AW)-225 is known as the 'Vagabonds'. It received its first **F/A-18D(RC)** aircraft on 14 February 1992.

recce mission. IOC is optimistically slated for FY94. The current requirement covers 48 aircraft, which will all be able to assume conventional fighter/attack duties, the conversion process being undertaken in several hours.

Production of two-seat Hornets has also been undertaken for the export market and all customers to date have obtained or ordered some for training purposes. Equipment and designations vary somewhat, according to local needs, but these machines are basically similar to their USN/USMC equivalents. Deliveries were undertaken to **Australia** (18 **ATF-18A**s, fundamentally an F/A-18B), **Canada** (40 **CF-18B**s designated **CF-188B**), **Kuwait** (eight **KAF-18D**) and **Spain** (12 **EF-18B**s operated as **CE.15**s). The F/A-18D variant has been ordered by prospective F/A-18C operators, these comprising **Finland** (seven), and **Switzerland** (eight). Uniquely, **Malaysia** has bought only the two-seat model.

NIGHT VISION
In addition to the FLIR systems available, the F/A-18D's cockpit is compatible with GEC-Marconi Cat's Eyes night-vision goggles.

RECONNAISSANCE
The F/A-18D(RC) is intended to fulfil the tactical reconnaissance mission, but by 1994 no suitable equipment had been provided.

REAR COCKPIT
The missionised backseat is equipped with two 5-in (12.7-cm) colour MFDs in addition to a colour moving map display. The system is operated by two sidestick weapons controllers. The cockpit can be reconfigured with flight controls for pilot training if required.

TWO-SEAT HORNET
Fitting the extra cockpit has no effect on the Hornet's fighting capacity other than to reduce fuel by approximately 6 per cent. This is caused by having to relocate some avionics displaced by the second seat. Overall dimensions are unchanged.

SPECIFICATION

McDonnell Douglas F/A-18B Hornet
generally similar to the F/A-18A Hornet except in the following particulars:
Weights: normal take-off 33,585 lb (15234 kg) for a fighter mission; maximum take-off 47,000 lb (21319 kg) for an attack mission
Fuel and load: internal fuel reduced by less than six per cent to accommodate second seat
Range: ferry range with internal and external fuel 1,900 nm (2,187 miles; 3520 km); combat radius 550 nm (634 miles; 1020 km/h) on an attack mission

SERVICE
Seven US Marine Corps squadrons fly the two-seat Hornet, the type having replaced the A-6E. The first three, including VMA(AW)-225, were established at MCAS El Toro. The Atlantic squadrons at Beaufort followed, while some F/A-18Ds were delivered to the training squadron, VMFAT-101 at El Toro.

DEFENCES
The Hornet is well protected with ALR-50/67 RWRs, ALE-39/47 chaff dispensers and ALQ-126B deception ECM. After cancellation of the ASPJ, a new jamming system is being sought.

281

McDonnell Douglas F/A-18E/F

Originally proposed during 1991 as a replacement for the abandoned A-12 Avenger project, the latest variants of the Hornet are presently under development with a view to flying for the first time in 1995 and attaining IOC in 1999. As with preceding variants, single- and two-seat versions have been proposed, with the respective designations **F/A-18E** and **F/A-18F**.

The resulting aircraft have been extensively redesigned and are fundamentally stretched versions of the current production F/A-18C/D models, featuring a 2-ft 10-in (86-cm) plug inserted in the fuselage, as well as increased span and wing area and enlarged horizontal tail surfaces. The LERXes have also been significantly increased in area. Gross weight is expected to rise by approximately 10,000 lb (4536 kg). These changes will allow an additional 3,000 lb (1361 kg) of internal and 3,100 lb (1406 kg) of external fuel capacity, resulting in an increase in range of approximately 38 per cent.

Further improvements are aimed at enhancing survivability and include measures intended to reduce radar cross-section. Performance benefits arising from the adoption of more powerful General Electric F414-GE-400 turbofan engines will be mainly related to payload capability, both new versions possessing two extra hardpoints (giving a total of 11) for the carriage of ordnance. As a result, maximum external payload will rise by some 2,250 lb (1020 kg)

to 17,750 lb (8050 kg). The F/A-18E/Fs have distinctive, sharply raked rectangular-section air intakes, which replace the old D-shaped intakes of previous models. The F414 is a derivative of the F404 and is closely related to the F412 developed for the ill-fated A-12. It will have a new afterburner with longer high-temperature life. With the current two-dimensional F/A-18E/F inlet, thrust growth will be limited to about 10-15 per cent, but an extra 30 per cent thrust could theoretically be provided.

Current avionics planning anticipates more than 90 per cent commonality with the F/A-18C version, but the primary radar sensor will be the Hughes AN/APG-73, an improved version of the APG-65 with enhanced data-processing capability. The radar entered flight tests in April 1992 and has also been installed in production F/A-18Cs and F/A-18Ds in place of the existing AN/APG-65 unit with effect from June 1994. In addition to its suitability for the fighter and strike/attack missions, the F/A-18E will be compatible with the pod-mounted Martin-Marietta ATARS for the recce role.

SPECIFICATION

McDonnell Douglas F/A-18E Hornet
Wing: (approximate) span 41 ft 10.25 in (12.76 m) without tip-mounted AAMs and 44 ft 8.5 in (13.62 m) with tip-mounted AAMs; width folded 30 ft 7.25 in

(9.32 m); aspect ratio 3.51; area 500.00 sq ft (46.45 m²)
Fuselage and tail: length 60 ft 1.25 in (18.31 m); height 15 ft 9.5 in (4.82 m)
Powerplant: two General Electric F414-GE-400 turbofans each rated at 22,000 lb st (97.86 kN) with afterburning
Weights: empty 30,600 lb (13880 kg); maximum take-off 66,000 lb (29937 kg)
Fuel and load: internal fuel 14,400 lb (6531 kg); external fuel up to 9,780 lb (4436 kg) in three 480-US gal (1818-litre) fuel tanks; maximum ordnance 17,750 lb (8051 kg)
Speed: maximum level speed 'clean' at high altitude more than 1,033 kt (1,190 mph; 1915 km/h)
Range: combat radius 591 nm (681 miles; 1095 km)

An artist's impression of the F/A-18E shows the lengthened fuselage, enlarged wings, greater-area LERX and extra pylons. Another major feature of the variant is the wedge-shaped engine intakes.

on a hi-hi-hi interdiction mission with four 1,000-lb (454-kg) bombs, two AIM-9 Sidewinder AAMs and two fuel tanks, or 486 nm (560 miles; 901 km) on a hi-lo-hi interdiction mission with the same stores, or 150 nm (173 miles; 278 km) on a 135-minute maritime air superiority mission with six AAMs and three fuel tanks
Performance: combat ceiling about 50,000 ft (15240 m)

McDonnell Douglas/British Aerospace AV-8B Harrier II

For all its attributes, the original BAe (Hawker Siddeley) Harrier was no more than an armed derivative of the original P.1127 technology demonstrator, and Kestrel trials aircraft. Strong USMC interest in the Harrier in 1968 was followed by an initial order for 12 AV-8As. (US use of these early-generation Harriers is described separately.) Service with four Marine Corps squadrons confirmed the Harrier's early promise, but also demonstrated the limitations of the basic design. Anglo-American design studies for a successor with a supercritical wing were eventually halted, BAe pulling out of the project in March 1975 citing 'insufficient common ground' as the reason. Eventually, the Marines backed a development of an advanced model of the Harrier, designated **AV-8B**, which was

The standard day-attack AV-8B is identified by a clean nose profile, this example serving with VMA-223. The USMC plans to upgrade these aircraft to Plus configuration with uprated engine and APG-65 radar.

intended to offer a larger warload and better range/endurance characteristics There followed considerable political wrangling and some revised thinking over future requirements on the part of the Marines before what was known for a time as the **'Super Harrier'** project became a reality in the early 1980s.

While the original designers of the Harrier concentrated on developing an enlarged, advanced metal wing, which could be retrofitted to existing Harrier airframes, the American former 'junior partner' on the AV-8A pressed ahead with its own second-generation new-build Harrier. This was intended as a new production aircraft from the outset, and not as an upgrade of existing AV-8As. The new design was based around a new, larger-area carbon-fibre supercritical wing, but also incorporating carbon-fibre in other airframe areas and completely revising the cockpit, with HOTAS controls and a higher seating position for the pilot, all without a significant increase in engine power, but with advanced aerodynamic devices to increase

lift. First flown on 9 November 1978, fitted to the 11th AV-8A (which thereby became the first of two **YAV-8B**s), the new wing had 14.5 per cent more area and 20 per cent greater span, with a reduced leading-edge sweep of 10°. The greater area allowed six hardpoints to be fitted. The carbon-fibre construction allowed a 331-lb (150-kg) weight saving by comparison with the original metal wing. More efficient air intakes and carbon-fibre fuselage sections allowed a further equivalent weight saving of 750 lb (340 kg). The British-built rear fuselage remains of metal construction, for heat resistance, and is virtually unchanged, as is the undercarriage.

Engine improvements

Following the testing of four pre-series FSD **AV-8B**s from November 1981, the USMC took delivery of the first production aircraft which was handed over during 1983. The first 12 (like the four FSD aircraft) were powered by F402-RR-404 engines and had double rows of inlet suction relief doors, while later aircraft had the 21,450-lb

st (95.42-kN) F402-RR-406 (Pegasus 11-21, equivalent to the RAF's Mk 105). From the 44th airframe (162747) a digital engine control unit was fitted to AV-8Bs and TAV-8Bs, while from the 197th (163874) the 23,800-lb st (105.87-kN) F402-RR-408 (Pegasus 11-61) is fitted. Procurement was cut from 342 to 336 and then to 328 aircraft. Later defence cuts reduced the total to 280 aircraft, although an additional purchase of six attrition replacements following Operation Desert Storm increased procurement to 286. Originally this figure did not include two-seat **TAV-8B** trainers (described separately), although these were subsequently incorporated on the McDonnell Douglas production line.

From the 167th airframe (163853), all USMC AV-8Bs were made capable of conducting night-attack operations with the installation of GEC FLIR, a head-down display, a colour moving map and an improved HUD. The terms **Night Attack Harrier II** or **Night Attack AV-8B** are sometimes applied unofficially. The first delivery of this variant was to VMA-214 on 15 September 1989. During Desert Storm, the AV-8B was operated by USMC squadrons VMA-231, 311 and 331, and by six aircraft operating as Detachment B of VMA-513. Seven AV-8Bs were lost in combat during Desert Storm, mainly to SAMs, the type having been heavily engaged on ground support strikes. VMA-331 was disestablished during 1992, but the remaining units will continue to play a vital part in US Marine Corps aviation. Plans to withdraw some of the US Navy's conventional carriers may well lead to an increased role for the AV-8B, which can provide air support from smaller platforms.

The 205th production single-seater (164129) was the first fully equipped example of the improved **AV-8B Harrier II Plus** variant, and the true prototype for the new variant. It made its inaugural flight on 22 September 1992, although 161397, the second FSD AV-8B, had already flown as an aerodynamic prototype, with a dummy radome and inert AIM-120 AMRAAM missiles. Equipped with the Hughes AN/APG-65 radar (with an antenna cropped by 2 in/5 cm

WORKSHARE
AV-8B construction is split roughly 60/40 in favour of McDD, which builds the forward and forward-central fuselage, tailplane, wing and underfuselage strakes. BAe builds the rear-central and rear fuselage, tail and reaction-control system.

FLIGHT CONTROL
At normal airspeeds, the AV-8B has standard control surfaces comprising hydraulically-actuated ailerons and tailplane, and mechanically-actuated rudder. For high lift, the ailerons droop to augment single-slotted flaps. In very low-speed flight, control is effected by reaction control valves ('puffer jets') located in the nose, tail and wingtips and, of course, by the four thrust-vectoring nozzles. Extra lift is gained by creating a 'box' under the central fuselage out of the gun pods (or strakes), the airbrake and a retractable dam. This captures a cushion of jet air that bounces back off the ground, enabling the aircraft to take off vertically at the same weight at which it can hover.

DISPENSERS
An unusual feature of the AV-8B is the upward-firing chaff/flare dispensers scabbed on to the upper fuselage. Further dispensers are located under the rear fuselage.

ARMAMENT
This AV-8B carries a typical close air support load with two anti-armour Maverick missiles and two Mk 7 cluster bomb dispensers. The AIM-9M Sidewinders are standard for self-defence. Fire bombs (napalm) and fuel-air explosive weapons were also used during the Gulf War.

McDonnell Douglas/ British Aerospace AV-8B Harrier II Night Attack

For direct support of troops on the ground, the US Marine Corps chose the AV-8B. The Harrier II is of great value, as it can happily operate from assault carriers or from makeshift landing strips on the beach-head, close to the fighting. This close proximity to the action allows a force of AV-8Bs to generate a large number of sorties, highly important to the task of close air support, where air power is required over the battlefield for as long a period as possible. Initial AV-8B deliveries were seen as daytime-only attack aircraft, but the Night Attack Harrier, as depicted here, introduced full low-light capability. The small protuberance ahead of the windscreen houses a GEC forward-looking infra-red, while the pilot is issued with night-vision goggles, the cockpit instruments then being made compatible with their use.

CANNON SYSTEM
Housed in the two underfuselage pods, the gun system consists of a pod containing a GAU-12/A Equaliser cannon, and the other a linear linkless 300-round feed system. A fairing crosses the fuselage to carry the rounds to the gun. The Equaliser has five barrels of 25-mm calibre, with a maximum rate of fire of 4,200 rpm. Muzzle velocity is 1097 m per second. Round options are APDS (armour-piercing discarding sabot), API (armour-piercing incendiary), HEI (high-explosive incendiary) and TP (training practice).

MARKINGS
The two-tone grey camouflage with low-visibility markings has been adopted as standard. This aircraft is from VMA-211 'Wake Island Avengers'.

to fit the AV-8B's fuselage cross-section), the Harrier II Plus retains the overnose FLIR sensor (although this is repackaged in a broader, squarer section fairing) and is otherwise externally identical to late production AV-8Bs. The provision of radar gives compatibility with the AIM-7 Sparrow and AIM-120 AMRAAM, endowing a BVR kill capability for the first time. It also allows the use of AGM-84 Harpoon missiles in the anti-shipping role. The last 27 aircraft of the US Marine Corps order were to have been built to this standard, but this total was reduced to 24, three of which will now be delivered to Italy. The first Plus (164542) was delivered in early 1993. In addition, 114 pre-

Night Attack AV-8Bs will be converted to Harrier II Plus configuration. These will retain only their existing wings, tail surfaces and undercarriage.

Foreign customers
Two other nations with a NATO maritime commitment have also purchased AV-8Bs, these countries being Spain and Italy. Since 1977 the Spanish navy has embarked the AV-8S Harrier (locally designated **VA.1 Matador**) on the carrier *Dedalo*. With the commissioning of the carrier *Principe de Asturias* in 1989, the Arma Aérea de la Armada embarked 12 **EAV-8B**s as part of an expanded air group which included a mix

of AV/TAV-8Ss. The Spanish navy also ordered 13 AV-8B Harrier II Plus variants in November 1992, for initial delivery in late 1995, and the surviving EAV-8Bs are likely to be upgraded to the same standard. A two-seat TAV-8B had been ordered in March 1992 to supplement its two remaining TAV-8S models.

Italy's procurement of AV-8Bs followed a protracted political debate, but in May 1989 two TAV-8Bs were finally purchased, to enhance the main pilot training programme in the US by the Marine Corps. These aircraft were delivered in August 1991 and the first batch of three AV-8B Harrier II Plus aircraft was ordered in July 1991, followed by

a further 13 in November 1992. Italy has an option on eight more of these aircraft. Based at Luni, the Harriers will also embark on the carrier *Giuseppe Garibaldi*. In 1994, **Thailand** requested information on AV-8Bs for its new helicopter-carrier.

WEAPON OPTIONS

The AV-8B has three pylons under each wing, stressed to 2,000 lb (907 kg), 1,000 lb (454 kg) and 630 lb (286 kg) respectively. The outboard pylon is usually used for AIM-9 Sidewinder carriage, leaving the inner two for various air-to-ground weaponry, including Mk 7 cluster bomb dispensers, Mk 82/83 bombs, LAU-10/

The first operator of the AV-8B Plus is VMA-542 at Cherry Point. In addition to the radar, the nose also features FLIR in a flattened fairing.

68/69 rocket pods, AGM-65 Maverick, CBU-55/72 fuel-air explosive, Mk 77 fire bombs and GBU-12/16 LGBs, the latter requiring designation from another source. The centreline hardpoint is used for an ALQ-167 ECM pod. Two fuselage packs contain a five-barrelled 25-mm GAU-12 cannon (port) and ammunition tank for 300 rounds (starboard). These are replaced with aerodynamic strakes when not fitted. The Harrier II Plus adds two extra missile pylons for Sidewinders, and the ability to launch AMRAAM, Sparrow and Harpoon missiles.

SPECIFICATION

McDonnell Douglas AV-8B Harrier II
Wing: span 30 ft 4 in (9.25 m); aspect ratio 4.0; area 238.7 sq ft (22.18 m²) including two 4.35-sq ft (0.40-m²) LERXes or, in aircraft delivered from December 1990, 243.40 sq ft (22.61 m²) including two 6.70-sq ft (0.62-m²) LERXes
Fuselage and tail: length 46 ft 4 in (14.12 m); height 11 ft 7.75 in (3.55 m); tailplane span 13 ft 11 in (4.24 m); outrigger track 17 ft 0 in (5.18 m)

Powerplant: one Rolls-Royce F402-RR-406A turbofan rated at 21,450 lb st (95.42 kN) dry or, in aircraft delivered from December 1990, one Rolls-Royce F402-RR-408 turbofan rated at 23,800 lb st (105.87 kN)
Weights: operating empty 13,968 lb (6336 kg) including pilot and unused fuel; normal take-off 22,950 lb (10410 kg) for 7-g operation; maximum take-off 31,000 lb (14061 kg) for 1,330-ft (405-m) STO or 18,950 lb (8596 kg) for VTO
Fuel and load: internal fuel 7,759 lb (3519 kg); external fuel up to 8,070 lb (3661 kg) in four 300-US gal (1136-litre) drop tanks; maximum ordnance 10,800 lb (4899 kg) with -406A engine or 13,235 lb (6003 kg) with -408 engine
Speed: maximum level speed 'clean' at sea level 575 kt (662 mph; 1065 km/h)
Range: ferry range 1,965 nm (2,263 miles; 3641 km) with empty tanks dropped; combat radius 90 nm (103 miles; 167 km) with a 1-hour loiter after 1,200-ft (366-m) STO with 12 Mk 82 Snakeye bombs, or 594 nm (684 miles; 1001 km) on a hi-lo-hi attack mission after 1,200-ft (366-m) STO with seven 500-lb (227-kg) Mk 82 Snakeye bombs and two 300-US gal (1136-litre) drop tanks, or 627 nm (722 miles; 1162 km) on a deck-launched interception mission with two AIM-9 Sidewinders and two drop tanks; combat air patrol radius 100 nm (115 miles; 185 km) for a 3-hour patrol
Performance: maximum rate of climb at sea level 14,715 ft (4485 m) per minute; service ceiling more

than 50,000 ft (15240 m); STO run 1,437 ft (435 m) at maximum take-off weight; landing run 0 ft (0 m) at up to 19,937 lb (9043 kg)
g limits: -3 to +8

OPERATORS

US Marine Corps: VMA-223/231/542, VMAT-203 MCAS Cherry Point, NC
VMA-211/214/311/513 MCAS Yuma, AZ
US Navy: NAWC-AD NAS Patuxent River, MD

NAWC-WD NAS China Lake, CA
Italy: two AV-8B, 13 AV-8B Plus and three TAV-8B in the process of delivery. Option on eight more. Assembly of some aircraft undertaken by Alenia.
Spain: 12 EAV-8B for Eslla 9. One TAV-8B and eight EAV-8B Plus on order. Earlier aircraft to be brought to Plus standard.

Spain operates its Harrier fleet from the shore base at Rota, and aboard the carrier Principe de Asturias. *Note the GAU-12 cannon pod.*

McDonnell Douglas/British Aerospace TAV-8B Harrier II

Some while after the decision to go ahead with the AV-8B Harrier II programme, the **US Marine Corps** resolved that it would need a two-seat conversion trainer version of the second-generation aircraft, to which the designation **TAV-8B** was allocated. The target for USMC acquisition was 28 aircraft, but only 26 were procured, all serving with the type conversion unit VMAT-203 at MCAS Cherry Point, NC. The other two aircraft were delivered to **Italy**. The first aircraft made its initial flight on 21 October 1986, and the first was delivered to the Marines in March 1987. A subsequent sale was made to **Spain** (one aircraft ordered in 1992). The RAF has ordered the similar **Harrier GR.Mk 10**, described separately.

Principal differences between the two-seat TAV-8B and the AV-8B involve the forward fuselage, which is 3 ft 11-in (1.2-m) longer to accommodate the two-man cockpit. The rear seat is considerably raised to provide excellent visibility for the instructor.

As part of Italy's Harrier II order, the AMI received a pair of TAV-8Bs from the USMC FY89 production. The single-seat aircraft are to radar-equipped 'Plus' standard.

To offset the reduced stability caused by the longer fuselage, the vertical fin is increased in area by adding 1 ft 5 in (0.43 m) to the height and widening the chord by straightening the lower portion of the leading edge. Internal fuel is reduced by 453 lb (205 kg). As the TAV-8B is intended purely as a conversion trainer, it has only one pylon under each wing for practice weapons, and routinely carries fuselage strakes in place of the cannon.

SPECIFICATION

McDonnell Douglas TAV-8B Harrier II
generally similar to the McDonnell Douglas AV-8B Harrier II except in the following particulars:
Fuselage and tail: length 50 ft 3 in (15.32 m)
Weights: operating empty 15,542 lb (7050 kg) including pilot and unused fuel
Fuel and load: internal fuel 7,306 lb (3314 kg)

McDonnell Douglas/British Aerospace T-45 Goshawk

In 1981, the US Navy selected a modified version of the **British Aerospace Hawk** trainer as its **T45TS** (Training System). This highly significant programme aims to produce up to 600 jet pilots annually throughout the 1990s and into the 21st century. Concurrent with the last phases of Hawk flight testing prior to its RAF service debut, the US Navy began a three-year study into new trainer requirements that would, ideally, combine the handling qualities of the intermediate T-2B/C Buckeye and the advanced TA-4J Skyhawk. A saving in flight hours and costs was seen to be possible with the right new aircraft and, in 1978, an evaluation of available types was made with the intention of undertaking what had become the VTXTS programme. The Hawk was judged to be superior to existing US Navy trainers and its rivals on a number of counts, including fuel consumption, and in November 1981 the British trainer was duly selected. FSD funding followed in 1984 and an engineering development contract was awarded in May 1986 to the prime US contractor McDonnell Douglas. The principal sub-contractor is British Aerospace, which retains responsibility for manufacture of wings, centre and rear fuselage, fin, tailplane, windscreen, canopy and flying controls.

As first proposed, there were to be two variants, a 'wet' **T-45A** model fitted for carrier operation and a 'dry' model **T-45B** restricted to land-based training and dummy carrier landing practice. Subsequent confirmation of the practicality of extending the lives of both the T-2 and TA-4J led to a decision for the US Navy to acquire only the T-45A, with full carrier qualification.

In order to tailor the basic **Hawk Mk 60** airframe to stringent US Navy requirements for operations from a carrier, a number of changes have been made. The airframe has been strengthened to withstand the inevitable stresses of carrier operations, including the severe sink-rates encountered on a pitching deck. The forward fuselage

The first T-45A demonstrates the considerable aerodynamic differences between it and basic Hawks, including full-span slats, twin airbrakes and 'smurfs' forward of the tailplane. The hefty nosewheel strut has a catapult launch bar and twin wheels.

has a deeper profile to accommodate a new strengthened twin nosewheel undercarriage unit, which is also compatible with the US Navy's steam catapults with catapult launch bar and holdback. The main gear is also redesigned, with longer-stroke oleos. The fin height has been increased by 6 in (15.2 cm), tailplane span has been increased by 4 in (10.2 cm) and a single ventral fin has been added. The Hawk's single ventral airbrake has been replaced by two fuselage side-mounted units (of composite construction), while 'smurfs' (side mounted unit horizontal root tail fins – small curved surfaces forward of each tailplane) eliminate airbrake-related pitch-down during low-speed gear-up manoeuvres. The T-45 has new electrically actuated and hydraulically operated full-span leading-edge slats and a new aileron/rudder interconnect.The aircraft is also provided with an arrester hook (deployable to 20° on each side of the centreline) and US Navy standard cockpit instrumentation and radios, the crew sit on Martin-Baker Mk 14 NACES ejection seats and the fuel system is revised. The aircraft's overall appearance is otherwise similar to other two-seat Hawks, apart from squared-off wingtips, which do not alter overall span, and a broader-span square-tipped horizontal tail.

Although the strengthening programme was necessary for the carrier role, the T-45A (renamed **Goshawk** to avoid confusion with the US Army Hawk missile) will remain land-based, flying to a training carrier as required. The US Navy has stated that it expects each T-45A to undertake 38,000 field landings, 16,000 carrier landings and over 1,000 seaborne launchings. Initial carrier qualifications with the two Douglas-built, F405-RR-400L (Adour 861-49) engined FSD prototypes and McDonnell-built, F405-RR-401 (Adour 871) engined pre-production aircraft began aboard *John F. Kennedy* on 4 December 1991. The first St Louis-built T-45 made its maiden flight on 16 December 1991, and deliveries to the Navy began when the prototypes went to Patuxent River in October 1990. Even though the Adour 871 provides some 30 per cent more thrust than the original engine, there were for many years plans to re-engine the aircraft again, with a variety of American-built candidate engines. The 268 aircraft required (plus 24 simulators, and 34 computer-aided instruction devices) will be delivered to Naval Air Stations at Kingsville (VT-21/22/23

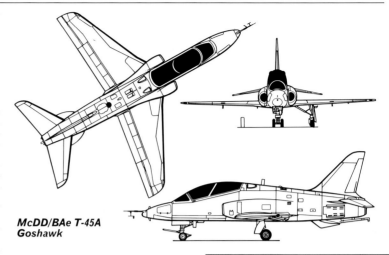

McDD/BAe T-45A Goshawk

of Training Wing 2) and NAS Meridian (VT-7 of Training Wing 1). It is planned to incorporate a digital, glass cockpit with two colour MFDs from the 97th aircraft, and a prototype will fly during 1995. Introduction of the T-45 will result in the training task being accomplished with 25 per cent fewer flying hours using 42 per cent fewer aircraft and 46 per cent fewer personnel.

WEAPON OPTIONS

Provision is made for a single pylon under each wing for the carriage of practice bomb rack, rocket pods or extra fuel. Centreline pylon can also carry stores for weapons training role. Rear cockpit has CAI gunsight.

SPECIFICATION

McDonnell Douglas/British Aerospace T-45A Goshawk
Wing: span 30 ft 9.75 in (9.39 m); aspect ratio 5.3; area 176.90 sq ft (16.69 m²)
Fuselage and tail: length 39 ft 3.125 in (11.97 m) including probe; height 14 ft 0 in (4.27 m); tailplane span 15 ft 0.75 in (4.59 m); wheel track 12 ft 9.5 in (3.90 m); wheel base 14 ft 1 in (4.29 m)
Powerplant: one Rolls-Royce/Turboméca F405-RR-401 turbofan rated at 5,845 lb st (26.00 kN)
Weights: empty 9,399 lb (4263 kg); maximum take-off 12,758 lb (5787 kg)
Fuel and load: internal fuel 2,893 lb (1312 kg);

Training Wing 2 received the first operational T-45As at Kingsville, the Goshawk replacing TA-4Js.

external fuel up to two 156-US gal (591-litre) drop tanks; maximum ordnance none
Speed: maximum level speed 'clean' at 8,000 ft (2440 m) 538 kt (620 mph; 997 km/h)
Range: ferry range on internal fuel 1,000 nm (1,152 miles; 1854 km)
Performance: maximum rate of climb at sea level 6,982 ft (2128 m) per minute; service ceiling 42,250 ft (12875 m); take-off distance to 50 ft (15 m) 3,744 ft (1189 m) at maximum take-off weight; landing distance from 50 ft (15 m) 3,900 ft (1189 m) at maximum landing weight
g limits: -3 to +7.33

McDonnell Douglas Helicopters **AH-64A/B Apache**

*McDonnell Douglas Helicopter Company
5000 East McDowell Road, Mesa
AZ 85205-9797, USA*

Formulated in the early 1970s, the US Army's requirement for an advanced attack helicopter (AAH) visualised an aircraft operating in a front-line environment and suitable for a day/night/adverse weather, anti-armour role. In the first part of a two-phase programme, Bell and Hughes were selected to build two flight-test prototypes for competitive evaluation, respectively the YAH-63 and **YAH-64A** (first flying on 30 September 1975). However, it was Hughes' **Model 77** submission that was declared the winning contender on 10 December 1976. A further four air vehicles (one ground test and three flight-test prototypes) were built for Phase 2, primarily concerned with full engineering development and evaluation of advanced avionics, electro-optical and fire-control systems, along with concurrent development of the airframe. Noteworthy modifications to production standard included swept tips on the main rotor blades, low-set (relocated) all-moving tailplane, increased-height vertical fin and adoption of 'Black Hole' infra-red suppression system. It was not until 26 March 1982 that final production approval was given with the issue of a US Army contract for an initial batch of 11 **Hughes AH-64A Apache** helicopters. The first production aircraft was subsequently delivered in January 1984, the same month Hughes became a division of McDonnell Douglas. The name was changed to McDonnell Helicopter Company on 27 August 1985.

The Apache is a tandem, two-seat conventional helicopter with advanced crew protection systems, avionics and electro-optics, plus weapon-control systems that include nose-mounted Martin-Marietta AN/AAQ-11 TADS/PNVS (Target Acquisition and Designation Sight/Pilot Night-Vision Sensor). TADS consists of a FLIR, TV camera, a laser spot tracker and a laser range-

Apaches make much use of the FARP (Forward Air Refueling Point) concept, ground-loitering close to the battle area. From the FARP they can rapidly re-enter the fray, fully armed and fuelled.

finder/designator, and is used for target search and designation, and as a back-up night-vision sensor for the pilot. PNVS is an articulated FLIR which permits nap-of-earth flight at night, providing thermal images to the pilot's monocular sight. The gunner sits in the front seat, with the pilot 19 in (49 cm) higher in the rear cockpit. Both use various sophisticated sensors and systems to detect and attack targets, including the IHADSS (Integrated Helmet And Display Sight System) which provides a monocular helmet-mounted designator/sight. The co-pilot/gunner has primary responsibility for firing both gun and missiles, but can be overridden by the pilot in the backseat. Teledyne Ryan is responsible for the manufacture of the Apache's fuselage, tail, wings, cowling, canopies and other components.

Terrain-masking flight

In combat, the AH-64A flies nap-of-the-earth, using terrain masking. In some scenarios, OH-58C Kiowa or OH-58D Kiowa Warrior scout helicopters spot and designate targets and assist in communications to position AH-64As to engage armour and other ground forces. In joint exercises, Apaches have worked effectively with US Air Force A-10 'Warthogs', dividing up the tank-killing mission to make an adversary's task more difficult.

Survivability is enhanced by the use of armour, the design having been required to survive 12.7-mm hits fired from anywhere in the helicopter's lower hemisphere, plus 20°, and to remain airborne for 30 minutes after such a hit. Most critical systems are protected against 23-mm cannon hits. The crew is protected by lightweight boron armour shields, and the undercarriage, cockpit and seats are designed to give a 95 per cent chance of surviving ground impacts at sink rates up to 42 ft (12.9 m) per second. The gun mounting is designed to collapse into the fuselage between the pilots' seats in the event of a crash landing. The engines, which feature integral particle separators and integral exhaust cooling, are widely separated and the key components are armour protected. The Litton Precision Gear Divi-

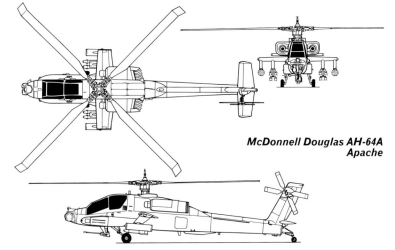

*McDonnell Douglas AH-64A
Apache*

sion transmission can run for over an hour without oil, and the gearboxes and shafts are designed to run for a similar time after ballistic damage. The transmission is isolated from flight loads by a sleeve which contains the main rotor drive shaft. The helicopter is aerobatic and can be flown down to 0.5 *g*.

Total AH-64A procurement by the US Army stands at 813 helicopters (plus prototypes), comprising 807 planned production aircraft and six attrition replacements for AH-64As lost during Desert Storm. The US Army hoped to upgrade 254 AH-64As to **AH-64A+** or **AH-64B** standard, but this was cancelled in 1992. This was an interim step (coming ahead of the more advanced **AH-64D**, described separately), with modest, near-term improvements based on Operation Desert Storm experience. Modifications included addition of GPS for accurate navigation, SINCGARS radios, extended-range fuel tanks, and new rotor blades. TADS/PNVS and the M230 gun were to have been modified to improve reliability,

The Middle East proved a rich market for the Apache, with sales to Egypt, Israel, Saudi Arabia and the UAE (illustrated).

maintainability and accuracy. The AH-64B's in-the-field modification would have included retrofitted General Electric T700-GE-701C engines. These replaced the -701 in production AH-64s from aircraft 604 (89-0192).

The AH-64A demonstrated its capabilities on ferrying missions on a 4 April 1985 flight, carrying four 230-US gal (870-litre) fuel tanks and flying 1,175 miles (1891 km). On 22 June 1985, six Apaches were loaded into a C-5A Galaxy to demonstrate the capability, since used frequently, to deploy the battlefield helicopter overseas via strategic airlift. Two can be carried in a C-141 and three in the C-17.

The first fully-fledged Apache combat unit was the 3/6th Cavalry at Fort Hood, TX, beginning in July 1986. Soon afterwards, AH-64As were delivered to the 1/3rd Aviation Brigade, 2nd Armored Division, also at Fort Hood, followed by half a dozen more stateside units. In Europe, AH-64As joined the 3/1st Avn, 1st Armored Division at Hanau and the 3/227th Avn, 3rd Armored Division at Illesheim, plus other units. The Army National Guard became an operator of the AH-64A Apache, commencing with 1989 deliveries to the 1/130th Aviation Brigade at Raleigh-Durham, NC. Throughout its operational history, the AH-64A has suffered from adverse publicity, especially in 1987 after a fleet-wide grounding which followed a fatal 21 August 1987 crash at Fort Rucker. Questions of reliability have been raised several times by the General Accounting Office and other agencies.

Various air-to-air missiles have been test-launched from the Apache, including the AIM-9 Sidewinder (illustrated). AAMs have yet to be carried regularly. Another missile option is the visually similar AGM-122 Sidearm anti-radar weapon, which is derived from early AIM-9s.

The first combat deployment of the Apache came with the 82nd Airborne Division's 1st Aviation Battalion's participation in Operation Just Cause in Panama during December 1989/January 1990. More recently, Apaches were employed to devastating effect during Operations Desert Shield/Desert Storm. On 17 January 1992, AH-64As fired the first shots of the war, attacking Iraqi radar sites, and thus opening up a radar-free corridor for coalition air strikes against Baghdad and other targets. Several US Army units employed AH-64As successfully in the anti-tank role in the desert. During the final land offensive of the war, Apaches destroyed 81 tanks and 23 other vehicles and assisted in the capture of 3,200 Iraqi prisoners. Sadly, however, Apaches also figured in two friendly-fire incidents in which coalition troops were killed.

WEAPON OPTIONS

The Apache's principal payload consists of up to 16 AGM-114A Hellfire long-range, laser-guided anti-tank missiles, carried on four pylons under stub wings. Early plans to arm the AH-64 with TOW anti-tank missiles were halted when development of the Hellfire proceeded more rapidly than expected, the missile being adopted as the chosen weapon in 1976. The first successful Apache firing of an AGM-114 took place on 18 March 1979. Operations began at Fort Rucker, AL, and Fort Eustis, VA, in January 1985.

Other weaponry includes pods of 19 2.75-in (70-mm)

Apache on the warpath: this AH-64A displays a typical warload of eight Hellfires and two 19-round Hydra 70 rocket pods. Note the TADS/PNVS sensor array in the nose.

Hydra 70 rockets. Standard fixed armament comprises a 30-mm M230 Chain Gun cannon with 1,200 rounds, mounted under the forward fuselage. Normal rate of fire is 625 rounds per minute. NATO ADEN/DEFA 30-mm ammunition can be used in place of the normal HE or HEDP ammunition. Although US Army doctrine does not foresee the AH-64A engaging fixed-wing warplanes or opposing helicopters, the Apache has been tested with a variety of air-to-air weapons, including AIM-9L Sidewinder, AIM-92A Stinger and MATRA Mistral; the air-to-air capability of the M230 cannon is also being improved. For defence suppression, the Sidearm missile can be employed.

SPECIFICATION

McDonnell Douglas Helicopters AH-64A Apache
Rotor system: main rotor diameter 48 ft 0 in (14.63 m); tail rotor diameter 9 ft 2 in (2.79 m); main rotor disc area 1,809.56 sq ft (168.11 m²); tail rotor disc area 70.00 sq ft (6.13 m²)
Wing: span 17 ft 2 in (5.23 m) clean or 19 ft 1 in (5.82 m) over empty weapon racks
Fuselage and tail: length overall, rotors turning 58 ft 3.125 in (17.76 m) and fuselage 49 ft 1.5 in (14.97 m); height overall 15 ft 3.5 in (4.66 m) to top of air data sensor, 14 ft 1.25 in (4.30 m) over turning tail rotor and 12 ft 7 in (3.84 m) to top of rotor head; stabiliser

span 11 ft 2 in (3.40 m); wheel track 6 ft 8 in (2.03 m); wheel base 34 ft 9 in (10.59 m)
Powerplant: two 1,696-shp (1265-kW) General Electric T700-GE-701 turboshafts each derated for normal operations or, from 604th helicopter, two General Electric T700-GE-701C turboshafts each rated at 1,800 shp (1342 kW)
Weights: empty 11,387 lb (5165 kg); normal take-off 14,445 lb (6552 kg) at primary mission weight or 17,650 lb (8006 kg) at design mission weight; maximum take-off 21,000 lb (9525 kg)
Fuel and load: internal fuel 2,550 lb (1157 kg); maximum ordnance 1,700 lb (771 kg)
Speed: never exceed speed 197 kt (227 mph; 365 km/h); maximum level speed 'clean' and maximum cruising speed at optimum altitude 158 kt (182 mph; 293 km/h)
Range: ferry range 918 nm (1,057 miles; 1701 km) with drop tanks; range 260 nm (300 miles; 428 km) with internal fuel; endurance 3 hours 9 minutes with internal fuel
Performance: maximum vertical rate of climb at sea

level 2,500 ft (762 m) per minute; service ceiling 21,000 ft (6400 m); hovering ceiling 15,000 ft (4570 m) in ground effect and 11,500 ft (3505 m) out of ground effect
***g* limits:** -0.5 to +3.5

OPERATORS

US Army: total procurement totals 813, including six Gulf War attrition replacements. Over 50 had been lost by 1994
Egypt: 24 aircraft on order with delivery commencing in 1994
Greece: 12 on order for delivery from 1995
Israel: 18 ordered from the manufacturer, delivered from September 1990. 24 ex-US Army aircraft delivered in 1993. Local name **Petan**
Saudi Arabia: 12 aircraft delivered from 1993
United Arab Emirates: 20 aircraft delivered 1993-94
Further interest: from Kuwait, South Korea and UK

McDonnell Douglas Helicopters AH-64D/Longbow Apache

In 1995 the **AH-64D Apache** is to become the third version of the US Army's principal attack helicopter to enter service, but will at first lack the Longbow radar/missile system fitted to the more advanced **AH-64D Longbow Apache** that is due to follow in 1997. The **AH-64C** designation was to have been applied to upgraded AH-64As that do not carry the Longbow radar. However, this was abandoned in early 1994, and all aircraft in the modernised fleet will be known as AH-64D.

The US Army's plan for an upgraded Apache fleet calls for conversion of 535 (or 750 according to some sources) existing AH-64A helicopters out of its total of 813 procured, of which 227 will be Longbow Apaches with the fire control radar fitted. In 1992, McDonnell Douglas converted four AH-64s with Longbow millimetric-wave fire control radar and Hellfire Longbow missile seekers to act as proof-of-concept aircraft for the AH-64D. Following completion of the Army's Longbow Apache critical design review in November 1991, and flight tests of an aerodynamically representative radome in March 1991, the prototype AH-64D Longbow Apache developmental aircraft made its first flight on 15 April 1992, although functioning radar was not flown until late 1993 (on the second prototype). The first RF Hellfire firing from an Apache followed soon after. Two AH-64C prototypes were also flown. Five aircraft will undergo a five-month Force Development Test and Evaluation during late 1994, and all six prototypes will then be used in the January-March initial operational test and evaluation.

McDonnell Douglas also has received limited funding to accelerate development of the AH-64D to enable production deliveries to begin in mid-1995, two years ahead of the fully-equipped AH-64D Longbow Apache. The AH-64D and AH-64D Longbow Apache are identical except for radar and engine. The Longbow Apache will be distinguished by the mast-mounted location of its MMW radar and will also have 1,800-shp (1342-kW) General Electric T700-GE-701C engines in

place of the -701 now fitted. The -701C has an emergency rating of 1,940 shp (1447 kW).

The Longbow radar (also being fitted to some of the new RAH-66 Comanches) will be integrated with the helicopter's avionics and with a new RF (radio frequency) seeker-equipped version of the AGM-114 Hellfire ATGM. Some 13,000 of these are to be built, all but 2,000 earmarked for the AH-64. The new radar will allow missiles to be fired in an autonomous fire-and-forget mode. The current laser-guided Hellfire requires external designation (e.g. by an OH-58D scout) or can be used in conjunction with the TADS, in which case it is a line-of-sight, non fire-and-forget weapon. Longbow radar scans through 270°, in 90° sectors, or through 360° in the air-to-air mode. Twelve targets can be detected, classified and prioritised simultaneously, and targets will be classified by six categories: tracked vehicle, wheeled vehicle, air defence, rotary-wing aircraft, fixed-wing aircraft and unknown. The radar can see through the fog and smoke that currently foils IR or TV sensors. An improved Data Modem will be more efficient than the present Automatic Target Handover System. The rotating antenna weighs 300 lb (136 kg).

The AH-64D will also incorporate a range of improvements in targeting, battle management, communications, weapons and navigation systems, including Plessey AN/ASN-157 Doppler, a new integrated GPS/INS, and EMI protection, some of which are to be finalised as the programme progresses. The cockpit will be improved, with new glass displays and symbology, and electrical power generation will be doubled. The forward avionics bay is expanded, and the undercarriage fairings are extended forward to accommodate some of the new equipment. The AH-64D's terrain-profiling

Apart from the Longbow radar mounted on the rotor mast, the AH-64D is distinguished by the fuselage-side fairings, which are enlarged to cover the wingroot and extend to the nose.

feature will enable the crew to navigate nap-of-the-earth, and sensor cueing will allow precise pre-pointing of the target acquisition system in order to zero-in on targets for rapid identification. Additionally, the Longbow interferometer will sense enemy air defence threats from any angle and alert the crew.

The first batch of AH-64Ds (308 or 523 on present plans) will have provision for both -701C engines and Longbow radar, so that either or both can be retrofitted easily if funding permits. It will have the targeting element of the Longbow system, and will carry RF Hellfire, allowing it to operate in conjunction with the later, fully-equipped AH-64D for total fire-and-forget capability.

One potential export customer for the Longbow Apache is the British army, although the aircraft's very high price might mean that the basic AH-64A would be

more likely to be selected. Any Apache variant faces strong competition from the upgraded AH-1 Cobra Venom, and a host of other attack helicopters. Longbow Apache deliveries are expected to begin in mid-1996.

SPECIFICATION

McDonnell Douglas AH-64D Longbow Apache generally similar to the McDonnell Douglas AH-64A Apache except in the following particulars:
Fuselage and tail: height overall 16 ft 1 in (4.90 m) to top of mast-mounted radome and 14 ft 1.25 in (4.30 m) to top of turning tail rotor
Powerplant: two General Electric T700-GE-701C turboshafts each rated at 1,800 shp (1342 kW)
Performance: maximum vertical rate of climb at sea level 2,530 ft (771 m) per minute; hovering ceiling 17,210 ft (5245 m) in ground effect and 13,530 ft (4125 m) out of ground effect

McDonnell Douglas Helicopters (Hughes) Model 369/OH-6 Cayuse

Requiring a new light observation helicopter (LOH) to replace Bell and Hiller types then in service, the **US Army** drew up a specification in 1960. This stipulated high performance, turboshaft power, easy maintenance and low purchase cost. All the major manufacturers submitted proposals, but only three designs were evaluated: the Bell YHO-4, Hiller YHO-5 and **Hughes YHO-6**. Flown initially on 27 February 1963, the redesignated **YOH-6A Cayuse** was selected on 26 May 1965 after a seven-month evaluation. The LOH mission led to the type's popular 'Loach' nickname.

Although Hughes had little experience with helicopters (its Model 269 then being at an early production stage), the Model 369 offered some notable features, including an egg-shaped cabin and innovative four-bladed rotor that endowed excellent manoeuvrability. The use of four blades obviated the need for a heavy and complex rotor control system by reducing rotor loads considerably.

First deliveries were made in September 1965 to the US Army, and the initial contract was for multi-year procurement of 714 aircraft. Production ended with 1,434 built in three slightly differing configurations. The production **OH-6A** was widely used in Vietnam, where 658 were lost in combat and a further 297 in accidents. The OH-6 could be armed with an XM27E1 7.62-mm machine-gun or an XM75 40-mm grenade launcher on the port side, with a flexibly mounted gun in the starboard cabin door. The US Army then reopened the LOH competition, which led to the Bell OH-58 Kiowa assuming the role (selected in preference to the **OH-6D**, a designation later used for a Japanese variant). This allowed wholesale transfers of OH-6As to the Reserve and National Guard. A package of modifications to airframe, transmission, avionics and equipment by the Mississippi AVCRAD led to the adoption of the designation **OH-6B** (or **Series IV**) for many modified aircraft. The modifications include re-engining with the 420-shp (313.32-kW) T63-A-720 engine with 'Black Hole' exhaust suppression, and provision of an undernose FLIR, wirestrike protection and an adjustable landing light. The prototype first flew during May 1988.

Some later airframes were manufactured to **MH-6B** and **MH-6C** configuration for Special Forces support, and as **EH-6B** Special Forces command and control and Elint/Sigint platforms and **AH-6C** light attack aircraft, all serving with the Army's 160th Special Operations Aviation Regiment. Twenty-three MH-6Bs were built as new, of which three were converted later to MH-6C configuration. Four EH-6Bs were built, and two were converted as MH-6Bs and one was later converted to AH-6C configuration. Approximately 14 AH-6Cs were built, comprising 11 delivered in May, August and October 1969, plus three converted MH-6Bs and a converted EH-6B.

This is an ex-US Army OH-6A now serving with Colombia's Escuadrón Aérotactico 511. This unit is one of the Fuerza Aérea Colombiana's most active participants in the unending war against the drug runners and growers. Unarmed OH-6As are augmented in Escuadrón 511 by armed versions of the MD500 and MD530, while rotary-wing training is carried out on the similar Model 500C.

These aircraft probably functioned as interim equipment pending delivery of the dedicated Special Forces AH/MH-6 variants of the **MD500** and **MD530** (described separately). All Special Forces H-6s were powered by the 400-shp (298.4-kW) Allison 250-C20 engine, with black hole IR suppressors, although retaining the V tail. They also had NVG-compatible cockpits and provision for a turret-mounted FLIR. The MH-6B and MH-6C had external pylons for two gun pods, or 'people platforms' seating up to four passengers. The AH-6C was usually equipped with an M27 cannon to port and a seven-round Mk 66 or Hydra rocket pod to starboard, but could carry two gun pods, up to four rocket pods or four BGM-71 TOW missiles. The early Special Forces variants are now out of service. Some surviving MH-6Bs were passed first to the 1/245th Aviation Battalion of the Oklahoma ArNG for continued Special Operations use, and then, stripped of special equipment, to A Company of the 1/132nd Aviation Battalion of the Oklahoma National Guard. They were finally retired in 1992.

The first-generation H-6 has now been declared obsolete, so its continued support receives no Army funding. Guard units can continue to operate the type by using state funds, some states having opted to do this. OH-6s are also operated by a number of Federal and State agencies, including the US Border Patrol and the State Department.

The Model 369/OH-6 is still operated by **Bahrain** (two), **Brazil** (four), **Colombia** (11), **Dominican Republic** (one), **Honduras** (four), **Nicaragua** (two) and **Taiwan** (six), and further aircraft may be exported as they are withdrawn from US Army National Guard service. Hughes became part of

McDonnell Douglas helicopters and its aircraft were accordingly renamed from August 1985, and were given new MD suffixes to their Hughes Model numbers.

SPECIFICATION

McDonnell Douglas Helicopters OH-6A Cayuse
Rotor system: main rotor diameter 26 ft 4 in (8.03 m); tail rotor diameter 4 ft 3 in (1.30 m); main rotor disc area 544.63 sq ft (50.60 m²); tail rotor disc area 14.19 sq ft (1.32 m²)
Fuselage and tail: length overall, rotors turning 30 ft 3.75 in (9.24 m) and fuselage 23 ft 0 in (7.01 m); height to top of rotor head 8 ft 1.4 in (2.48 m); skid track 6 ft 9 in (2.06 m)
Powerplant: one 317-shp (236.5-kW) Allison T63-A-5A turboshaft derated to 252.5 shp (188 kW) for take-off and 214.5 shp (160 kW) for continuous running
Weights: empty equipped 1,229 lb (557 kg); normal take-off 2,400 lb (1089 kg); MTOW 2,700 lb (1225 kg)
Fuel and load: internal fuel 61.5 US gal (232 litres)
Speed: never exceed and maximum level speed at sea level 130 kt (150 mph; 241 km/h); economical cruising speed at sea level 116 kt (134 mph; 216 km/h)
Range: ferry range 1,355 nm (1,560 miles; 2510 km); range at 5,000 ft (1525 m) 330 nm (380 miles; 611 km)
Performance: maximum rate of climb at sea level 1,250 ft (381 m) per minute; service ceiling 15,800 ft (4815 m); hovering ceiling 11,800 ft (3595 m) in ground effect and 7,300 ft (2225 m) out of ground effect

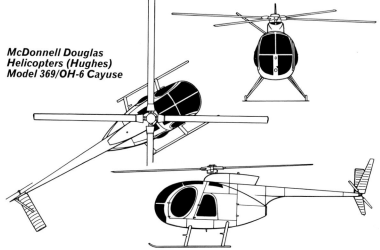

McDonnell Douglas Helicopters (Hughes) Model 369/OH-6 Cayuse

McDonnell Douglas Helicopters (Hughes) MD500

During the production run of the OH-6A for the US Army, Hughes also continued to build and market the aircraft for the civilian market, as the **Hughes 500**. The basic Model 500 was little more than a civilianised OH-6, spawning a sizeable family of related helicopters that has seen much service in military markings, although only a few examples have been operated by US services. The 500 differed primarily in having a more powerful engine, the 317-shp (236.5-kW) Allison 250-C18A turboshaft (derated to 243 shp/181.3 kW maximum continuous or 278 shp/207.4 kW for take-off), increased fuel and a revised interior. A dedicated 'hot-and-high' variant intended primarily for export was the **Model 500C**.

The first military variant was the **Model 500M Defender**, which was supplied initially (in 1968) to Colombia. This version was also licence-built for the **JGSDF** by Kawasaki as the **OH-6J** (subsequent Japanese versions are described separately), and by Nardi in Italy as the **NH500M** and the **NH500MC**, the latter a 'hot-and-high' variant. Spain bought a variant known as the **Model 500M/ASW** with MAD bird and the provision to carry torpedoes.

Hughes continued to develop the aircraft, producing an aircraft known simply as **'The Quiet One'** by fitting an early OH-6A with a five-bladed main rotor, a four-bladed tail rotor and a blanketed and muffled engine and exhaust. Airspeed was improved by

20 kt (23 mph; 37 km/h), payload was increased by 600 lb (272 kg) and the aircraft proved significantly quieter, running at 67 per cent of the usual rotor rpm. Its existence was revealed in April 1971. A second aircraft was fitted with a computer-controlled vibration-suppression system in 1982. Slightly later, a second early OH-6A was converted as the **OH-6C** with an uprated 400-shp (298.4-kW) Allison 250-C20 turboshaft, a modified T-tail, and the five-bladed main rotor. It achieved a speed of 173 kt (200 mph; 322 km/h). Neither aircraft was put into production, but both tested features later incorporated into the Models 500, 520 and 530. The **MD520/530** series is described separately.

The next basic variant was the civilian **500D**, which introduced a slow-turning five-bladed rotor with the characteristic 'coolie hat' fairing over the rotor head, and a T-tail. Kawasaki manufactured this model under licence for the JGSDF under the designation **OH-6D**, the type also being licence-built in Argentina, Italy and Korea. Various military variants were developed from the 500D, the basic military equivalent being the **500MD Defender** with armour protection and IR exhaust suppression. This is available in several different configurations, each with a different designation. Thus, the **500D Scout Defender** has provision for rockets and gun pods, while the **500MD/ASW Defender** has nose-mounted search radar offset to port, a towed MAD bird on a fuselage-side pylon and a heightened undercarriage to allow the carriage of torpedoes. The **500MD/TOW**

Right: The Royal Jordanian air force uses eight Model 500Ds for rotary-wing training, after potential helicopter pilots have been graded and screened on the Scottish Aviation Bulldog. The type serves with No. 5 Squadron, part of the King Hussein Air College at Mafraq. Fixed-wing pilots move from the Bulldog to the T-37 or CASA C.101, which are also based at Mafraq.

Below: The Philippine air force operates both Model 500MGs and Model 530MGs, this aircraft serving with the 15th Strike Wing's 18th Tactical Air Support Squadron at Sangley Point. The 15th Strike Wing also includes Sikorsky S-76 gunships, and OV-10 Broncos, but the last armed T-28s have now been retired.

Defender is an anti-tank version with TOW missiles on outrigger pylons and a nose-mounted sight; the similar **500MD/MMS-TOW Defender** has equivalent missile capability but introduces a mast-mounted sight. The **500MD Quiet Advanced Scout Defender** had the same armament with a four-bladed quiet tail rotor and other noise reduction features.

A handful of the Special Operations aircraft used by the US Army's 160th Special Operations Aviation Regiment at Fort Campbell are understood to have been based on the MD500D and MD500MD with the 250-C30 engine of the MD530F. These are designated **EH-6E**, **MH-6E** and **AH-6F**, and may have been joined by the eight

MD500Es reportedly delivered to the US Army's Systems Command during early 1985. The EH-6E (four built, one converted to MH-6E) was an Elint/Sigint/command post aircraft, while the MH-6E (15 new builds and one ex-EH-6E) and AH-6F (nine built, plus one for evaluation by USAF SOCOM) designations reportedly cover an insertion and an attack version, respectively based upon the 500D (flown from the left-hand seat) and 500MD. Both are believed to retain (or to have reverted to) the original rounded nose contours of early MD500s, since this is felt to be more crashworthy and much better suited to NVG operations. The AH-6F has a mast-mounted sight and provision for the M230 Chain Gun, as used

by the AH-64. Pairs of Stinger air-to-air missiles can also be carried. Survivors are understood to have been converted to later marks, described separately under the MD520/530 entry. The **Model 500MD Defender II** is an uprated model available in all the above options but with a quieter, slow-turning four-bladed tail rotor.

Leading the next generation was the **Model 500E**, with a revised, pointed nose profile, improved tailplane endplate fins, more spacious interior and Allison 250-C20B engine. The specialist military models are designated **500MG Defender**. Further improvement led to the **MD530**, which is described separately.

SPECIFICATION

McDonnell Douglas Helicopters Model 500
Rotor system: main rotor diameter 26 ft 4 in (8.03 m); tail rotor diameter 4 ft 3 in (1.30 m); main rotor disc area 544.63 sq ft (50.60 m²); tail rotor disc area 14.19 sq ft (1.32 m²)
Fuselage and tail: length overall, rotors turning 30 ft 3.75 in (9.24 m) and fuselage 23 ft 0 in (7.01 m); height 8 ft 1.5 in (2.48 m) to top of rotor head; skid track 6 ft 9 in (2.06 m)
Powerplant: one 317-shp (236-kW) Allison 250-C18A turboshaft derated to 278 shp (207 kW) for take-off and 243 shp (181 kW) for continuous running
Weights: empty 1,088 lb (493 kg); normal take-off 2,550 lb (1157 kg); maximum take-off 3,000 lb (1361 kg)
Fuel and load: internal fuel 64 US gal (242 litres)
Speed: maximum level speed at 1,000 ft (305 m) 132 kt (152 mph; 244 km/h); economical cruising speed at optimum altitude 117 kt (135 mph; 217 km/h)
Range: 267 nm (307 miles; 606 km)
Performance: maximum rate of climb at sea level 700 ft (518 m) per minute; service ceiling 14,400 ft

(4390 m); hovering ceiling 8,200 ft (2500 m) in ground effect and 5,300 ft (1615 m) out of ground effect

OPERATORS

Argentina: 11 500Ds, two with the Coast Guard
Bahrain: 500Ds
Bolivia: 10 500Ms
Colombia: eight 500Ds, two 500s, two 500Es, and four or six 500MG NightFoxes
Costa Rica: two 500Ds
Cyprus: two 500s
Denmark: 12 500Ms of 15 delivered
El Salvador: four 500Ms plus three 500s delivered
Finland: two 500Ds
Greece: 20 NH500s
Indonesia: 12 500Cs
Iraq: impressed civilian 500Ds and 500F
Israel: 36 500MDs
Italy: 50 NH500s
Japan: six OH-6Ds with the JMSDF, 164 OH-6Ds and 65 OH-6Js with the JGSDF
Jordan: eight 500Ds
Kenya: two 500Ds, 15 500MDs, 15 500MD/TOWs, eight 500Es and eight 500MGs
Mauritania: five 500Ms
Mexico: four 500Es used for training by the navy
North Korea: 66 500Es, 20 500Ds and a single 300C were delivered via a West German dealer before the breach of US embargoes was discovered and halted
Philippines: 27 500MDs and 28 530MG Defenders now being delivered
South Korea: the survivors of 34 US-built 500MD/TOWs, plus some 25 locally-built 500M/ASWs with the navy and 144 500MDs and 50 500MD/TOWs with the army
Spain: 10 500M/ASWs, of 12 delivered from April 1972
Taiwan: 12 500MD/ASWs
United States: 4 US Army EH-6E, 16 MH-6E and 10 AH-6F all probably converted to later standards

---

McDonnell Douglas Helicopters MD520/530 & MD520/530N

The McDonnell Douglas MD500E formed the basis of a new family of 'Loach' variants. The first of these was the **MD530F Lifter**, which was first flown on 22 October 1982, primarily intended for civilian customers. Along with subsequent conventional 520 and 530 variants, it featured a fully articulated five-bladed main rotor, with 1 ft (30 cm) greater diameter, and a tail rotor with 2 in (5 cm) greater diameter. The 530 is powered by a 650-shp (484.9-ekW) Allison 250-C30 turboshaft engine derated to 425 shp (317 ekW). The **MD530F Lifter** is also assembled under licence by Korean Air (described separately). Since the first delivery on 20 January 1984, some have gone to military users such as the Chilean army. Dedicated military variants

derived from the MD530F include the **MD530MG Defender**, which was flown in prototype form on 4 May 1984, and which has subsequently been ordered by **Mexico** (10 for the air force), **Bolivia** (20), **Colombia**, and the **Philippines** (30). Those delivered to Bolivia are reportedly dubbed **MD530MG Black Falcon**.

In military guise, the MD530 is lightweight, versatile and highly survivable, and has both military and paramilitary (police, etc.) applications. Weapons and sensor fits are tailored to the point attack and anti-armour roles, and for scout and day/night surveillance duties. The integrated crew station offers the pilot a head-up mode called HOLAS (hands on lever and stick) giving the pilot head-up/hands-on control of all

weapons selection and delivery, communications and flight controls, essential in combat and similar to the HOTAS controls found in modern fast jets. The system is based around the Racal RAMS 3000, which also allows nap-of-earth and all-weather flight. A CDU (control and display unit) consisting of a high-definition monochrome MFD with keyboard can be used for flight planning, navigation and systems management, as well as for selecting frequencies. A three-seat front bench makes provision for a normal complement of two pilots and an observer.

The full standard MD530MG has options for a mast-mounted TOW sight, FLIR, RHAW gear, IFF and a laser rangefinder, and can be armed with Hughes TOW 2

missiles, 2.75-in unguided rockets, General Dynamic Stinger AAMs and a McDonnell Douglas Chain Gun. Avionics include a Decca Doppler navigator (with Racal Doppler velocity sensor), an Astronics Corporation autopilot, and a GEC/Ferranti FIN 1110 AHRS. A **Nightfox** version, with NVG-compatible cockpit and a FLIR Systems Series 2000 Thermal Imager, is available for low-cost night surveillance and attack missions, while a more austerely equipped **530MG Paramilitary Defender** is available for police, border patrol, narcotics interdiction and other roles.

Today the MD520 and MD530 are inevitably associated with the revolutionary NOTAR (No Tail Rotor) concept, although few production aircraft have been delivered

McDonnell Douglas Helicopters MD520/530 & MD520/530N

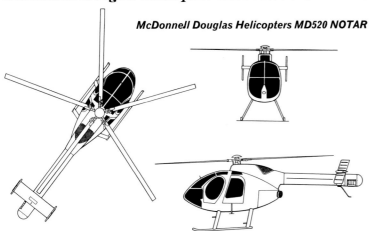

McDonnell Douglas Helicopters MD520 NOTAR

The Model 530MG, known as the 'Black Falcon', can carry rocket or gun pods, and may be fitted with exhaust suppressors. This aircraft serves with the Fuerza Aérea Colombiana.

with this type of tail and none has yet been delivered to military customers. The **MD520N** and the as-yet-unbuilt **MD530N** sub-variants both dispense with a conventional tail rotor in favour of the trademarked NOTAR system, an anti-torque tail boom that has experienced several design modifications. It has a variable-pitch fan mounted in the forward end, driven by a shortened tail rotor drive shaft and absorbing no more power. This produces an air stream which pressurises the boom interior to about 0.5 psi (0.034 bars) and vents pressurised air through a 0.33-in (0.85-cm) wide slot in the starboard side (a second slot was added later). This blown efflux unites with the main rotor downwash and is 'blown' down the side of the tailboom (the Coanda effect) as though it were a wing, generating a sideways thrusting force – 'lift' – which counteracts the main rotor's torque. A jet thruster with air exits to port and starboard allows pressurised air not vented through the slot to be ejected in either direction to provide control in yaw. This is operated via the pilot's 'rudder pedals', which move concentric fixed and moveable cones to block off one or other (or both) of the air exits.

The MD520N is the first widely-produced NOTAR variant, but owes its origin to a Hughes-initiated test programme employing an OH-6A. This testbed was first flown after conversion on 17 December 1981 as a testbed for the blown-air NOTAR system and subsequently has been modified several times, receiving an MD500E-type forward fuselage and eventually being upgraded to the current advanced NOTAR configuration. The NOTAR testbed was funded in part by DARPA and by the US Army Applied Technology Laboratory, and the original NOTAR boom was built by Aircraft Engineering Corporation of Paramount, CA.

The true MD520N prototype first flew 1 May 1990, with a production aircraft taking to the air on 28 June 1991. The MD530N prototype flew on 29 December 1989, but McDonnell Douglas did not proceed with certification of this variant, which has remained dormant, although it has formed the basis for military variants. The production MD520N is powered by a 450-shp (335.7-

ekW) Allison 250-C20R-2 turboshaft engine derated to 375 shp (279.75 ekW). Typically, the MD520N/530N offers a combat radius of around 160 miles (257 km) with a 1,600-lb (726-kg) payload for a variety of missions depending on configuration. The manufacturer has orders for about 160 examples, and many have been delivered to police forces.

Special variants

The US Army has taken delivery of a number of aircraft reportedly based on the non-NOTAR MD530FF with a unique part-glass instrument panel and a reinforced power train with a Kaflax shaft. They are reportedly equipped to a standard similar to the MD530MG, but with the original rounded nose contours of earlier MD500s. These are designated **MH-6H** (16 identified, all converted from EH-6E, MH-6E and AH-6F airframes) and **AH-6G** (five new build, seven converted from AH-6Fs) and are generically known as **'Little Birds'** They serve with the 160th Special Operations Aviation Regiment at Fort Campbell, and perhaps with 1 Battalion/245th Special Operations Aviation Group of the Oklahoma ArNG at Tulsa.

The AH-6G is a gunship, with a removable quick ordnance mounting system (known as a 'plank'), while the transport/insertion MH-6H has a so-called 'people plank' that allows the aircraft to carry three Special Operations soldiers externally on each side of the cabin. This is the same equipment as that fitted to the Kiowa Scout and is necessary because the rear cabin is occupied by radios and navigation systems, sometimes including Soviet-built GPS gear. In the MH-6, which is highly stable in the hover, the 'people plank' can also be used as a sniping platform by a Special Forces operative armed with a 0.50-calibre (12.7-mm) rifle.

All surviving 'Little Birds', perhaps including the AH-6Fs and MH-6Es, reportedly totalling 36 Model 500/520/530s, were to be upgraded to a common dual-role standard under the designation **MH-6J**. This was originally to have included conversion to NOTAR configuration, but this part of the

upgrade has reportedly been cancelled after trials of the first two NOTAR aircraft (perhaps designated **MH-6N** and **AH-6N**) showed that the new tailboom concept was less well-suited to the Special Operations role. A NOTAR allows the aircraft to hover 'tail-in-the-trees' and allows pedal turns at up to 90 kt, but limits maximum speed and dramatically increases fuel consumption.

The designation MH-6J may now apply to MH-6Es (currently at least four) brought up to the new standard, while **AH-6J** may be applied to new-build aircraft (at least seven). Many of the systems, avionics and equipment items reported for the MH-6J are already fitted to earlier 'Little Bird' variants, including a folding tailboom (to facilitate transport inside fixed-wing transport aircraft) and optional internal fuel tanks. These include a 29-US gal (110-litre) Robertson T-tank or a larger 62-US gal (236-litre) Goliath fuel tank package. These can be augmented by 30-US gal (114-litre) 'half tanks' carried externally. Armament can include M134 7.62-mm Miniguns, Aerocrafter 0.5-in (12.7-mm) machine-gun pods, or podded BEI Hydra 70-mm (2.75-in) rockets. A Litton AIM-1 laser designator and a Hughes AN/AAQ-16 FLIR can also be fitted, and the installations for these items of equipment are understood to be purpose-designed on the MH-6J, whereas earlier 'Little Birds' had them scabbed on at depot level in jury-rigged mountings. A FLIR-2000, similar to that carried by Britain's SAS Agusta 109s, can also be fitted.

The MD530N, with NOTAR features, offers about 40 per cent more power for hot-weather, high-altitude performance. McDonnell Douglas (which in any event

was seeking in mid-1994 to sell its Mesa AZ, helicopter division) has indicated tha it does not intend to proceed with th MD530N version and has instead launche the MD900 Explorer for the civil market.

SPECIFICATION

McDonnell Douglas Helicopters MD520N generally similar to the McDonnell Douglas Helicopters Model 530MG Defender except in the following particulars:
Fuselage and tail: length overall, rotor turning 28 ft 6 in (8.69 m) and fuselage 25 ft 0 in (7.62 m); height overall 9 ft 10.75 in (3.01 m) to top of rotor head with extended skids or 9 ft 0 in (2.74 m) to top o rotor head with standard skids; stabilizer span 6 ft 9.5 in (2.07 m); skid track 6 ft 6 in (1.98 m)
Weights: empty 1,636 lb (742 kg); normal take-off 3,350 lb (1519 kg); maximum overload take-off 3,850 l (1746 kg)
Fuel and load: internal fuel 404 lb (183 kg); external fuel none; maximum payload 2,214 lb (1004 kg)
Speed: never exceed speed 152 kt (175 mph; 281 km/h); maximum cruising speed at sea level 135 kt (155 mph; 249 km/h)
Range: range 217 nm (250 miles; 402 km) with standard fuel; endurance 2 hours 24 minutes
Performance: maximum rate of climb at sea level 1,850 ft (564 m) per minute; service ceiling 14,175 ft (4320 m); hovering ceiling 9,035 ft (2,755 m) in groun effect and 5,045 ft (1540 m) out of ground effect

With a crewman perched on its people platform, but without exhaust suppressors fitted, an MH-(of the 160th Special Operations Aviation Regiment hover-taxis just above the runway.

Martin/General Dynamics RB-57F

The success of the **British Aerospace (English Electric, BAC) Canberra** (described separately) can be gauged not only by its long production run and many export customers, but also by the fact that it was selected by the US Air Force over indigenous American competitors and was manufactured under licence as the **Martin B-57**. The name **'Night Intruder'** was coined, but 'Canberra' was always more widely used. B-57s served the USAF for many years as nuclear-armed bombers,

night intruders, interdictors, target tugs, electronic aggressors, weather ships and survey and reconnaissance platforms. B-57s fought long and hard over Vietnam, and were exported to Taiwan (in small numbers) and to Pakistan, which added to the B-57's combat record by participating in the 1971 war with India. A handful of Pakistani B-57s served in the target facilities role into the 1980s, outlasting the final US Air National Guard **EB-57E**s (used in a similar role) by a handsome margin.

Remarkably, a pair of B-57s remains active today. Both are examples of the extensively modified **RB-57F**, production of which involved an almost complete redesign. Twenty aircraft were converted to **RB-57F** standard by General Dynamics for the weather and high-altitude reconnaissance roles, following the groundwork laid by the **RB-57D**, another dedicated high-altitude recce platform which had a similar long-span wing but which was otherwise less radically modified. The Canberra already had superb high-altitude performance, but this was improved by the addition of greater wing area and extra engine thrust. Four of the RB-57Fs were dedicated

reconnaissance platforms, but the other had a more limited reconnaissance fit an were also capable of sampling airborn radioactive particles. The RB-57F was pow ered by a pair of 18,000-lb st (80.1-kN) Pra & Whitney TF33-P-11A turbofans, whic gave almost twice the thrust of the origin B-57 powerplant. These were augmente by a pair of underwing Pratt & Whitney J6(P-9 turbojets each rated at 3,300 lb st (14 kN), which were started after take-off an which 'cut in' at 42,000 ft (12800 m). The contributed 2,500 ft (760 m) to the aircraft 64,000-ft (19507-m) ceiling. Four underwir pylons were provided for carriage of store equipment pods, although two were usual used for the turbojets. The original wing was replaced by a completely new three-spar wing, incorporating honeycomb construction and with marked anhedral, and of almost doubled span at 122 ft 5 in (37.32 m). The fuselage fuel tank was deleted to accommodate equipment, all fuel being carried in the wings outboard of the engines, giving a typical mission range of 2,563 nm (2,950 miles; 4748 km). The tailfin was also increased in size to improve asymmetric handling and to damp out Dutch roll.

After retirement from the US Air Force, three RB-57Fs were taken on charge by **NASA** for high-altitude experiments from the Johnson Space Center at Ellington ANGB, TX. One was retired in September 1982, but the other two remain active, fulfilling a wide variety of roles. One is fitted with a NASA Universal Pallet System housing cameras, an X-band SLAR and a five-channel multi-spectral scanner, with a variety of other sensors and navigation aids. A handful of B-57s of other marks (including a B-57B used for gust response research) have now been retired by NASA.

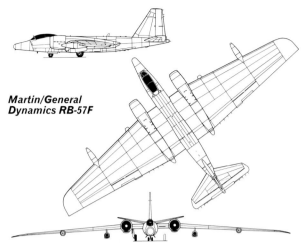

Martin/General Dynamics RB-57F

One of NASA's hardworking RB-57Fs flies near its Ellington ANGB home. The RB-57F's high-altitude performance and capacious fuselage make it a useful research tool.

Maule **M-4 to M-7**

Originating in 1968, the **Maule M-4** gave rise to a family of derivative designs in the classic high-wing single-engined lightplane configuration, featuring a fixed tailwheel undercarriage and 'razorback' glass-fibre fabric over a metal tube frame. The original M-4 was built in a number of forms, with various engine options, and with floats and cargo door options. The M-5 was introduced in 1975, with larger tail surfaces, extended flaps and other improvements. The M-6 was a one-off prototype which had new multi-position flaps and a larger cabin, while the M-7 introduced new engine options. Over 1,600 have been built, primarily for civil use, but with many being supplied to police, border patrol and other quasi-military operators. The contemporary, tricycle-undercarriage **MX-7-180 Star**

Rocket has been purchased by the **Royal Thai air force** (20) and the **Aviación de la Armada de Mexico** (Mexican navy) (12) for use in the basic training role.

SPECIFICATION

Maule MX-7-180 Star Rocket
Wing: span 30 ft 10 in (9.40 m); aspect ratio 6.0; area 157.90 sq ft (14.67 m²)
Fuselage and tail: length 23 ft 6 in (7.16 m); wheel base 15 ft 10 in (4.82 m) in tailwheel configuration
Powerplant: one Textron Lycoming O-360-C1F flat-four piston engine rated at 180 hp (134 kW)
Weights: basic empty 1,350 lb (613 kg); maximum take-off 2,500 lb (1134 kg)
Fuel and load: internal fuel 40 US gal (141 litres) plus provision for 30 US gal (113.5 litres) of auxiliary

fuel in outer wing fuel tanks; external fuel none
Speed: maximum level speed 'clean' at sea level 134 kt (154 mph; 248 km/h); maximum cruising speed at optimum altitude 126 kt (145 mph; 233 km/h)
Range: ferry range 977 nm (1,125 miles; 1810 km) with auxiliary fuel; range 560 nm (645 miles; 1038 km) with standard fuel

This aircraft is a Maule Patroller of the Georgia State Patrol.

Performance: maximum rate of climb at sea level 1,200 ft (366 m) per minute; service ceiling 15,000 ft (4570 m); take-off run 200 ft (61 m) at MTOW; landing run 500 ft (152 m) at maximum landing weight

Max Holste MH.1521M **Broussard**

The **Max Holste MH.1521M Broussard** is a single-engined, six-seat, general utility aircraft powered by a 450-hp (335.6-kW) Pratt & Whitney R-985 radial air-cooled engine. It is a high-wing, rigidly-braced monoplane with fixed tailwheel undercarriage and twin fins and rudders. At least nine former French territories in Africa

received Broussards for the use of their developing air forces upon the granting of independence. Of these, only **Burkina Faso** and, possibly, the **Central African Republic**'s air forces remain operators. Another serves in the communications role for the French **Aéronavale**, and two are used in **Argentina** for military parachute training.

DCAN, the French Board of Naval Dockyards and Weapons, operates a single MH.1521 Broussard for communications from Cuers.

Mikoyan-Gurevich **MiG-15 'Fagot' and MiG-15UTI 'Midget'**

The USSR's first operational swept-wing jet fighter, the **Mikoyan-Gurevich MiG-15** was built in huge numbers and became the Warsaw Pact's standard fighter. The estimated total of 3,000 included licence-built examples from Czechoslovakia and Poland, but not China, where large numbers of Russian-built aircraft were erroneously assumed to have been built as the Shenyang J-2, which in fact never existed. Made possible by Britain's short-sighted gift of examples of its latest turbojet engines (in particular the Rolls-Royce Nene with centrifugal-flow compressor) which were quickly copied and improved, the MiG-15 fought in Korea, where its poor showing was much more a reflection of pilot quality and training than of any inherent superiority of the US North American F-86 Sabre.

Production of a **MiG-15UTI** two-seat trainer (and limited conversion of single-seaters to this standard) totalled about 5,000 aircraft, and followed production of the improved single-seat **MiG-15bis**. The provision of an extra cockpit reduced internal fuel capacity, so external fuel tanks of various sizes are inevitably carried under the wing. Armament is not fitted as standard, although a single NR-23 23-mm cannon or UBK-Ye 12.7-mm machine-gun can be fitted, with 80 or 150 rounds of ammunition, respectively.

In 1994 the only positively confirmed operator of the Soviet-built MiG-15 was

Albania's Valona Air Academy still operates 12 single-seat Soviet-built MiG-15bis, of 26 delivered, together with 12 MiG-15UTI trainers.

Mikoyan-Gurevich MiG-15 'Fagot' and MiG-15UTI 'Midget'

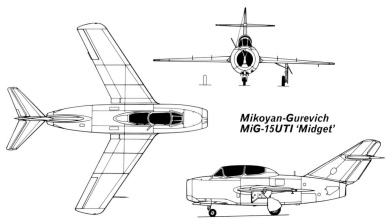

Mikoyan-Gurevich MiG-15UTI 'Midget'

Albania, whose Valona-based air academy operates 12 MiG-15bis and 12 MiG-15UTI trainers, although some of the latter were built in Czechoslovakia. Single-seat MiG-15s and MiG-15bis may continue to serve in **China**, **Cuba** and **Romania**, as advanced tactical trainers. The MiG-15UTI is believed to remain in service with **Algeria**, **Angola**, **Romania**, **Syria** and **Vietnam** for training duties, while one or two may remain on charge in the **Congo**, **Egypt**, **Guinea Bissau**, **Guinea Republic**, **Mali**, **Mongolia**, **Nigeria** and **Yemen** as hacks or as conversion trainers for MiG-17s.

SPECIFICATION

Mikoyan-Gurevich MiG-15UTI 'Midget'
Wing: span 10.085 m (33 ft 1 in); aspect ratio 4.93; area 20.60 m² (221.74 sq ft)
Fuselage and tail: length 10.11 m (33 ft 2 in); height 3.70 m (12 ft 1.7 in)
Powerplant: one Klimov RD-45F turbojet rated at 22.26 kN (5,004 lb st)
Weights: empty equipped 3724 kg (8,210 lb); maximum take-off 5400 kg (11,905 lb)
Fuel and load: internal fuel 900 kg (1,984 lb); maximum external load 1588 kg (3,500 lb)
Speed: maximum level speed 'clean' at 3000 m (9,843 ft) 1015 km/h (548 kt; 631 mph)
Range: ferry range 1054 km (569 nm; 655 miles) with drop tanks; range 680 km (367 nm; 423 miles) with standard fuel
Performance: climb to 5000 m (16,405 ft) in 2 minutes 36 seconds; service ceiling 14825 m (48,640 ft); take-off run 600 m (1,969 ft) at maximum take-off weight; landing run 740 m (2,428 ft) at normal landing weight

---

Mikoyan-Gurevich MiG-17 'Fresco'

Development of the **MiG-17** began in 1949 and was intended to address the shortcomings of the MiG-15, especially its high-speed handling characteristics. The production MiG-17 was preceded by a number of converted MiG-15s that acted as prototypes and introduced a larger tail unit, a lengthened rear fuselage, a thinner, more highly swept wing, revised airbrakes and other changes. The MiG-17 began to reach operational test units during late 1951 and soon demonstrated its superiority over the MiG-15, relegating the earlier aircraft to ground attack duties. The MiG-17 itself progressively went over to the ground attack role when newer fighters were introduced during the late 1950s. The basic MiG-17 was allocated the reporting name **'Fresco-A'**, while the improved **MiG-17F** with uprated engine became the **'Fresco-C'**. Interceptor variants equipped with radar included the cannon-armed **MiG-17PF 'Fresco-D'** with RP-1 'Scan Can' or RP-5 'Scan Odd' radar, and the **MiG-17PM 'Fresco-E'** with all guns removed, RP-2U radar, and an all-missile (RS-2U or AA-1 'Alkali') armament.

More than 8,000 MiG-17s were manufactured in the USSR. About 1,000 more were built in Poland under the local **LIM-5** and **LIM-6** designations, some variants having extensive modifications and improvements. The last Polish aircraft were retired from service during 1991/92. Although the decline of the MiG-17 has been very rapid, significant numbers remained in service well into the 1980s; East German MiG-17Fs, for example, were finally retired in 1986. Today,

Soviet-built MiG-17s may remain in service only with **Algeria**, the **Congo**, **Cuba**, **Guinea Bissau**, **Guinea**, **Madagascar**, **Mali**, **Mozambique**, **Romania**, **Syria**, **USA** (with the USAF's secret 'Red Hats' squadron at Groom Lake), **Vietnam** and **Yemen**.

SPECIFICATION

Mikoyan-Gurevich MiG-17F 'Fresco-C'
Wing: span 9.628 m (31 ft 7 in); aspect ratio 4.1; area 22.60 m² (243.27 sq ft)
Fuselage and tail: length 11.264 m (36 ft 11.5 in); height 3.80 m (12 ft 5.5 in); wheel track 3.849 m (12 ft 7.5 in); wheel base 3.368 m (11 ft 0.5 in)
Powerplant: one Klimov VK-1F turbojet rated at 29.50 kN (5,732 lb st) dry and 33.14 kN (7,451 lb st) with afterburning
Weights: empty equipped 3930 kg (8,664 lb); maximum take-off 6069 kg (13,380 lb)
Fuel and load: internal fuel 1170 kg (2,579 lb); external fuel up to 655 kg (1,444 lb) in two 400- or 240-litre (106- or 63-US gal) drop tanks; maximum ordnance 500 kg (1,102 lb)
Speed: limiting Mach No. 1.03; maximum level speed 'clean' at 3000 m (9,845 ft) 1100 km/h (594 kt; 684 mph) or at 10000 m (32,810 ft) 1071 km/h (578 kt; 666 mph); 900 km/h (486 kt; 559 mph) limit with drop tanks
Range: ferry range 2020 km (1,091 nm; 1,255 miles) with drop tanks; combat radius 700 km (378 nm; 435 miles) on a hi-lo-hi attack mission with two 250-kg (551-lb) bombs and two drop tanks
Performance: maximum rate of climb at sea level 3900 m (12,795 ft) per minute; climb to 5000 m

Mikoyan-Gurevich MiG-17M 'Fresco'/LIM-6

Cuba is believed to maintain a small number of Russian-built MiG-17s in service, though they may recently have been grounded through spares shortages and economic problems. They are probably allocated to a reserve or advanced training unit.

(16,405 ft) in 2 minutes 36 seconds at dry thrust or 1 minute 48 seconds at afterburning thrust; service ceiling 15000 m (49,215 ft) at dry thrust and 16600 m (54,460 ft) at afterburning thrust; take-off run 590 m (1,936 ft) at normal take-off weight; landing run 850 m (2,789 ft) at normal landing weight

---

Mikoyan-Gurevich MiG-19 'Farmer'

The **MiG-19** enjoyed a relatively short production run (about 2,500 aircraft) and a brief service life, having the misfortune to arrive on the scene between the MiG-17 and MiG-21. First flown on 5 January 1954, the MiG-19 was capable of supersonic level flight, reportedly achieving Mach 1.33 before the F-100 notched up its Mach 1.09 record. The aircraft entered service in early 1955. Successive variants included the **MiG-19S** with slab tailplane, more powerful engines and three NR-30 cannon; the **MiG-19SF** with uprated engine; the radar-equipped **MiG-19P**; the all-missile-armed **MiG-19PM**; and a host of research aircraft and testbeds. Most of the MiG-19s still in service worldwide are Chinese-built **Shenyang J-6s**, although a handful of Russian-built aircraft may still be in service in **China** itself, and perhaps also in **Cuba** with a reserve unit, although spares shortages may have grounded the latter.

SPECIFICATION

Mikoyan-Gurevich MiG-19SF 'Farmer-C'
Wing: span 9.00 m (29 ft 6.3 in); aspect ratio 3.24; area 25.00 m² (269.11 sq ft)
Fuselage and tail: length 14.64 m (48 ft 0.4 in) including probe and 12.54 m (41 ft 1.7 in) excluding probe; height 3.885 m (12 ft 9.0 in); wheel track 4.156 m (13 ft 7.6 in)
Powerplant: two MNPK 'Soyuz' (Tumanskii) RD-9BM turbojets each rated at 25.50 kN (5,732 lb st) dry and 32.36 kN (7,275 lb st) with afterburning
Weights: nominal empty 5760 kg (12,698 lb); normal take-off 7600 kg (16,755 lb); maximum take-off 9100 kg (20,062 lb)
Fuel and load: internal fuel 1800 kg (3,968 lb) or 2170 litres (573 US gal); external fuel up to two 1520-, 800-, 300- or 200-litre (401.5-, 211-, 79- or 53-US gal) drop tanks; maximum ordnance 500 kg (1,102 lb)
Speed: maximum level speed 'clean' at 10000 m (32,810 ft) 1452 km/h (783 kt; 902 mph)

Range: ferry range 2200 km (1,186 nm; 1,366 miles) with two 800-litre (211-US gal) drop tanks; combat radius 685 km (370 nm; 426 miles) on a hi-hi-hi interception mission with maximum ordnance and two 800-litre (211-US gal) drop tanks

Performance: maximum rate of climb at sea level 6900 m (22,638 ft) per minute; service ceiling 17900 m (58,725 ft); take-off run 515 m (1,690 ft) with afterburning; landing run 600 m (1,969 ft) with brake parachute

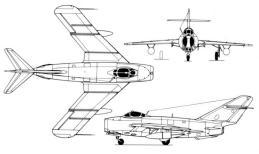

Mikoyan-Gurevich MiG-19M 'Farmer'

Mikoyan-Gurevich MiG-21 'Fishbed' early variants

The original concept of the **MiG-21** was for a simple, lightweight fighter, in which sophistication and considerations of endurance and firepower were sacrificed for outright performance. The production MiG-21 was preceded by a series of prototypes, some with swept wings and others with delta-wing planforms. The 40 pre-production **MiG-21F** (**Ye-6T** or **Type 72**) fighters were allocated the reporting name **'Fishbed-B'**, but the first full production version was the **MiG-21F-13 'Fishbed-C'**, or **Type 74**. The first 114 MiG-21F-13s had a narrow-chord vertical tail, but all had their armament reduced from two to one NR-30 cannon, on the starboard side, with underwing pylons for two guided AA-2 'Atoll' AAMs or rocket pods. Fuel capacity increased from 2280 litres (602 US gal) to 2550 litres (674 US gal).

The **MiG-21P** (**Ye-7**) **'Fishbed-D'** dispensed with the cannon armament altogether, and introduced a modified fuselage, with a longer nose and larger inlet centrebody for its TsD-30T R1L 'Spin Scan' radar. The canopy and spine were also modified with a distinctive bulge immediately aft of the cockpit, narrowing to the standard early spine farther aft. Internal fuel was increased to 2750 litres (726 US gal). The MiG-21P was followed by the R-11F2-300-engined **MiG-21PF (Type 76)** with pitot probe relocated to the top of the nose. The MiG-21PF introduced a new system for controlling the variable intake centrebody, which accommodated the new RP-21 Sapfir radar. Late production sub-variants introduced a still broader-chord tailfin, with a brake chute fairing at the base of the rudder, and reintroduced a gun, in the shape of an external GP9 cannon pod. NATO allocated these aircraft the reporting name **'Fishbed-E'**. The **MiG-21FL** was primarily intended for export, and while it was externally identical to the late MiG-21PF it had less powerful R-2L radar and the original R-11F-300 engine. Fuel capacity was increased to 2900 litres (766 US gal). Approximately 200 were built under licence in India.

The final versions which can be considered part of the 'first generation' were the **Type 94** sub-variants, the **MiG-21PFS** and the **MiG-21PFM 'Fishbed-F'**, externally similar to the late MiG-21PF and MiG-21FL but having a two-piece canopy with a fixed windscreen instead of the single-piece forward-hingeing canopy which acted as a blast shield on ejection. They also introduced blown SPS flaps, a cruciform brake chute, and the R-11F2S-300 engine. Addition of the RP-21M radar gave compatability with the semi-active RS-2US (K-5M) missile.

A surprising number of early 'Fishbeds' remain in service. India, for example, retains large numbers of MiG-21FLs in at least three front-line squadrons. Many early 'Fishbeds' are presently being converted as unmanned target drones for use at the Akhtubinsk test centre in Russia.

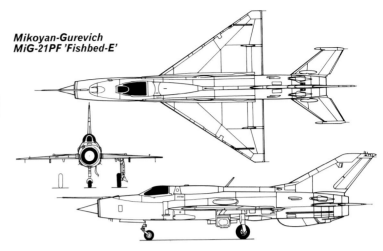

Mikoyan-Gurevich MiG-21PF 'Fishbed-E'

SPECIFICATION

Mikoyan-Gurevich MiG-21PFM 'Fishbed-F'
Wing: span 7.154 m (23 ft 5.7 in); aspect ratio 2.23; area 23 m² (247.5 sq ft)
Fuselage and tail: length 15.76 m (51 ft 8.5 in) including probe; length 12.285 m (40 ft 3.9 in) excluding probe and centrebody; height 4.125 m (13 ft 6.2 in); wheel track 2.787 m (9 ft 1.75 in); wheel base 4.71 m (15 ft 5.5 in)
Powerplant: one MNPK 'Soyuz' (Tumanskii) R-11F2S-300 turbojet rated at 38.26 kN (8,600 lb st) dry and 60.57 kN (13,613 lb st) with afterburning, and provision for two SPRD-99 solid-propellant booster rockets each rated at 24.50 kN (5,511 lb st)
Weights: empty 5350 kg (11,795 lb); normal take-off 7820 kg (17,240 lb); maximum take-off 9080 kg (20,018 lb), or 8800 kg (19,400 lb) on rough strip
Fuel and load: internal fuel 2650 litres (700 US gal); external fuel up to one 490-litre (130-US gal) drop tank; maximum ordnance 500 kg (1,102 lb)

Speed: maximum level speed 'clean' at 11000 m (36,090 ft) 2125 km/h (1,146 kt; 1,320 mph)
Range: ferry range more than 1300 km (704 nm; 808 miles) with 800-litre (211-US gal) drop tank
Performance: maximum rate of climb at sea level with two missiles and 50 per cent fuel more than 7500 m (24,600 ft) per minute; service ceiling 19000 m 62,335 ft); take-off run 850 m (2,790 ft); landing run 550 m (1,800 ft) at normal landing weight with SPS and brake chute

This MiG-21FL of India's No. 8 Squadron wears a temporary dark green fin for ACM training.

Mikoyan MiG-21 'Fishbed' second-generation models

Later MiG-21 variants moved progressively further away from the original lightweight fighter concept, gaining more internal fuel, heavier armament and increasingly more sophisticated avionics. All had R-11F2S-300 or R-13-300 engines, blown SPS flaps, pitot probes offset to the right of the centreline, two-piece canopies and broad-chord tailfins, as seen on some earlier aircraft. For the first time, all also had four underwing pylons, although initially only two of these were compatible with guided AAMs.

The first of the new generation was the **MiG-21R (Type 94R)**, a dedicated recce aircraft based on the MiG-21PFM, but with a new, enlarged dorsal fairing and with provision for carrying a variety of centreline reconnaissance pods, containing either optical or TV cameras, IR and laser sensors or SLAR. Codenamed **'Fishbed-H'** by NATO, some examples of the MiG-21R have ECM/ESM equipment in wingtip pods.

The **MiG-21S** (**Type 95**) was a fighter based on the MiG-21R airframe, with new RP-22 radar and with a GP-9 gun pod under the belly instead of a recce pod. It was followed by the R-13-300-engined **MiG-21SM** (**Type 15**), which also introduced a gunsight optimised for manoeuvring in high-*g* combat, and the improved GSh-23L cannon in a fixed installation recessed into the belly, instead of in the removable GP-9 gondola. Small rectangular fences were fitted below the auxiliary intakes in front of the wing-roots to prevent gun gas ingestion. The **MiG-21M** (**Type 96**) was an export version of the SM, with the older R-11F2S-300 engine. The aircraft was built under licence in India. The **MiG-21MF 'Fishbed-J'** (**Type 96F**) was a MiG-21M derivative for VVS use, powered by the R-13-300 engine, and fitted with the SMs RP-22 radar. It introduced AAM capability on all four underwing pylons, and was initially identifiable by the rear-view mirror above the canopy, although this was later retrofitted to many MiG-21Rs, MiG-21SMs and MiG-21Ms. The **MiG-21MT** (**Type 96T**) introduced the more-powerful R-13F-300 engine but only 15 were built.

The MiG-21M was built only for export, first by the Moscow Znamaya Truda factory, and then under licence by HAL in India. This aircraft wears the markings of No. 101 Squadron 'Falcons'.

Mikoyan MiG-21 'Fishbed' second-generation models

This Czech air force MiG-21R carries a centreline optical reconnaissance pod.

The **MiG-21SMT 'Fishbed-K' (Type 50)** was fitted with a unique dorsal spine of huge dimensions, holding some 900 litres (238 US gal) of fuel, although this reduced stability so much that capacity had to be reduced by 50 per cent.

Large numbers of MiG-21Rs, MiG-21Ms and MiG-21MFs remain in service, including many with the non-Soviet air forces of the former Warsaw Pact. In the CIS itself it

would seem likely that these variants, and the MiG-21SMT, have all been retired, although one or two may still be in use at trials or experimental establishments. More are almost certainly in storage, and some may have been converted as unmanned target drones. Many of the proposed Western retrofit programmes for the MiG-21, promoted by companies like IAI and GEC, would be most likely to be applied to these MiG-21 variants.

Note: We use only those designations used by the Mikoyan OKB and Russian air force, and have ignored speculative Western designations like PFMA. All MiG-21 operators (all variants) are listed in the MiG-21bis entry.

SPECIFICATION

Mikoyan Gurevich MiG-21MF 'Fishbed-J'
Generally similar to the MiG-21PFM except in the following particulars:

Powerplant: one MNPK 'Soyuz' (Tumanskii/Gavrilov) R-13-300 turbojet rated at 39.92 kN (8,972 lb st) dry and 63.66 kN (14,307 lb st) with afterburning
Weights: empty 5350 kg (11,795 lb); normal take-off 8150 kg (17.967 lb) with four AAMs and three 490-litre (129-US gal) tanks; maximum take-off 9400 kg (20,723 lb)
Fuel and load: internal fuel 2200 kg (4,850 lb) or 2600 litres (687 US gal); external fuel up to 1470 litres (387 US gal) in three drop tanks; maximum ordnance 2000 kg (4,409 lb)
Speed: maximum level speed 'clean' at 11000 m (36,090 ft) 2230 km/h (1,203 kt; 1,385 mph); maximum level speed at sea level 1300 km/h (703 kt; 807 mph)
Range: ferry range 1800 km (971 nm; 1,118 miles) with three drop tanks; combat radius 370 km (200 nm 230 miles) on a hi-lo-hi attack mission with four 250-kg (551-lb) bombs, or 740 km (400 nm; 460 miles) on a hi-lo-hi attack mission with two 250-kg (551-lb) bombs and drop tanks
Performance: maximum rate of climb at sea level 7200 m (23,622 ft) per minute; service ceiling 18200 m (59,711 ft); take-off run 800m (2,625ft)

Mikoyan-Gurevich MiG-21bis

The third generation **MiG-21bis** is the most advanced and most capable production variant, although by modern standards its lack of BVR missile capability, limited radar range, mediocre low-speed handling and poor endurance limit its usefulness. Various upgrades are being offered for the aircraft, most of them centred around replacing the radar and modernising the cockpit. A similar proposed indigenous upgrade, shown in mock-up form in 1992, would add a new pulse-Doppler radar and AA-10 'Alamo' and AA-11 'Archer' AAM compatibility.

The MiG-21bis was developed as a multi-role fighter for Frontal Aviation, with better close combat capability through improved avionics and the ability to carry the new R-60 AA-8 'Aphid' AAM. It was optimised for air combat at lower altitudes, against slower, more agile opponents, and had an enhanced ground attack capability. It can carry four UV-16-57 rocket pods, or four 240-mm (9½-in) rockets, or two 500-kg (1,102-lb) and two 250-kg (551-lb) bombs. Equipped with improved Sapfir-21 radar and powered by the 69.65-kN (15,653-lb) Tumanskii R-25-300 engine, the MiG-21bis features a completely redesigned dorsal spine which looks little different from that fitted to most second-generation 'Fishbeds', but which holds nearly as much fuel as even the huge spine of the MiG-21SMT.

The NATO reporting name **'Fishbed-L'** was allocated to the first version of the MiG-21bis, which entered service in February 1972. **'Fishbed-N'** was applied to later production aircraft (retaining the same Soviet designation) which had an undernose 'Swift Rod' ILS antenna and improved avionics. The 'Fishbed-N' was built under licence in India between 1980 and 1987. Another version of the MiG-21bis was optimised for the nuclear strike role, but no designations or NATO reporting name are known.

It is believed that about 60 MiG-21bis remain in service with a Russian tactical reconnaissance regiment, having replaced older 'Fishbed-Hs', and reportedly carrying the same reconnaissance pods. Other aircraft may still be in service in an advanced training role. Elsewhere, the MiG-21bis enjoys a much firmer hold on life, serving in large numbers with many operators.

SPECIFICATION

Mikoyan-Gurevich MiG-21bis 'Fishbed-L'
generally similar to the Mikoyan-Gurevich MiG-21MF 'Fishbed-J' except in the following particulars:
Powerplant: one MNPK 'Soyuz' (Tumanskii) R-25-300 turbojet rated at 40.2 kN (9,038 lb st) dry and 69.65 kN (15,653 lb st) with afterburning, with an emergency

regime rating of 97.12 kN (21,825 lb st) above Mach 1 and at heights up to 4000 m (13,123 ft) for periods of up to three minutes. Provision for two 24.52-kN (5,511-lb st) SPRD-99 solid rocket boosters
Weights: empty 5450 kg (12,015 lb); normal take-off 8725 kg (19,235 lb); maximum take-off 9800 kg (21,605 lb) or 8800 kg (19,400 lb) on rough strip, or 10400 kg (22,928 lb) with KT-92D wheels and 058 tyres
Fuel and load: internal fuel 2880 litres (760 US gal); external fuel up to 1750 litres (462 US gal) in three drop tanks; maximum ordnance 2000 kg (4,409 lb)
Speed: maximum level speed 'clean' at 13000 m (42,650 ft) 2175 km/h (1,177 kt; 1,351.5 mph)
Range: 1470 km (795 nm, 913 miles) at 10000m (32,800 ft) with one 800-litre (211-US gal) drop tank
Performance: maximum rate of climb at sea level with two missiles and 50 per cent fuel more than 13800 m (45,275 ft) per minute; service ceiling 17500 m (57,415 ft); take-off run 830 m (2,720 ft);

landing run 550 m (1,800 ft) at normal landing weight with SPS and brake chute

OPERATORS

Operators of all MiG-21 variants are listed below:

Afghanistan: 322 Regiment at Bagram may have as many as four squadrons of MiG-21s on charge, with up to 65 aircraft. Large numbers of late-mark MiG-21s, including examples of the MiG-21bis, were transferred from the Soviet air force
Albania: Albania's MiG-21s are all believed to be obtained from Chinese sources
Algeria: Three regiments operated examples of the MiG-21F, MiG-21M and MiG-21bis
Angola: Up to 70 MiG-21U, MiG-21M and MiG-21bis
Azerbaijan: Less than 10 MiG-21s are in use
Bangladesh: A handful of MiG-21MFs may remain in use with No. 5 Squadron, alongside Chinese-built aircraft from Pakistan
Byelorussia: Late series MiG-21s may remain active, at least for advanced training
Bulgaria: Bulgaria's air force includes at least one MiG-21 regiment, Polk 28000 at Graf Ignatievo. This operates the MiG-21bis and MiG-21UM. Other variants are still in service with regiments at Balchik, Jambol East and Uzundjovo and with training units at Dolna Metropolija, Kamen and Ruse, including the MiG-21M (18), MiG-21U (17) and MiG-21R (6)
Burkina Faso: About eight MiG-21s were delivered during the mid-1980s
Cambodia: The MiG-21bis fighters and MiG-21U trainers of Unit 701 are believed to have been grounded
Congo: About a dozen of the 16 MiG-21s delivered in 1986 remain in service
Croatia: Two MFs and a bis were acquired when JRV pilots defected to Croatia, at least one of these having subsequently been lost. Twenty more from Ukrainian sources are believed to be based at Pula
Cuba: Analysts believe that Cuba still operates the MiG-21F (30), MiG-21M/MF (35), MiG-21PFM (40), MiG-21bis (80), and MiG-21U/UM (18)
Czech Republic: Czechoslovakia received large numbers of early MiG-21s, many being built under licence by Aero. These included an estimated 150 MiG-21F-13s (62 survivors wfu in the late 1980s), 30

India's Hindustan Aeronautics Ltd built the Mikoyan MiG-21bis under licence and it continues to form the backbone of Indian air defence, equipping seven or eight squadrons. An ambitious upgrade with modern radar, ECM and other systems is planned. This aircraft, wearing yellow stripes for similar-type air combat training, serves with No. 24 Squadron 'Hunting Hawks' at Ambala, midway between Delhi and Amritsar.

MiG-21PFs (15 survivors wfu in the late 1980s), 50 MiG-21PFMs (35 survivors wfu in 1991), 25 MiG-21Rs (21 operational in 1993) and 120 MiG-21MFs (about 106 operational in 1993). These single-seaters were augmented by an unknown number of MiG-21Us (all retired by 1992), eight MiG-21USs and 30 MiG-21UMs. Before the division of Czechoslovakia, the country's air order of battle included the 9th Fighter-Bomber Regiment at Bechyne, the 47th Reconnaissance Regiment with MiG-21Rs and Su-22s at Hradec Kralove, with further MiG-21 squadrons at Zatec (part of the 1st Fighter Regiment) and Mosnov (82nd Independent Attack Squadron). After division, following reorganisation, all MiG-21MFs, Rs and USs and UMs were combined within a single regiment at Prerov, but may be retired by mid-1995

Ethiopia: The collapse of the Mengistu regime in May 1991 left the air force in tatters, many aircraft having flown to neighbouring states with their defecting aircrew, and others being abandoned on their airfields where they fell victim to vandalism, souvenir hunting or simple neglect. Before the collapse, Ethiopia had an estimated 60 MiG-21Ms, with five MiG-21U trainers

Finland: The first export customer for the MiG-21, Finland replaced its MiG-21F-13s with new MiG-21bis airframes delivered during 1980-81. Fourteen single-seaters serve with HavLlv 31 at Kuopio Rissala

Germany: The MiG-21s inherited from East Germany have now been retired, even from test and evaluation units, and are being scrapped or retired to museums under the terms of the CFE treaty

Guinea Republic: Seven MiG-21s may be in service with a fighter squadron at Conakry. These aircraft were supplied in return for landing rights for Tu-95 and Tu-142 'Bears'

Guinea Bissau: There are reports that MiG-21s have replaced MiG-17s with the sole combat unit at Bissalanca

Hungary: Although Kécskemet's two MiG-21MF squadrons are now re-equipping with the MiG-29, the MiG-21bis remains in service with one squadron of the Stromfeld Aurel Regiment at Pápa and with both squadrons of the Kapos Regiment at Taszár. An upgrade is likely

India: Despite the influx of more modern fighters like the MiG-29 and Mirage 2000, the MiG-21 remains the backbone of India's fighter strength with 830 (including 580 built locally) having been delivered. The MiG-21bis serves with Nos 3, 4, 15, 21, 23, 24, 26 and 37 Squadrons, the MiG-21M with Nos 17, 32, 35, 45, 101 and 108 Squadrons, and the MiG-21FL (and perhaps PFM) with Nos 8, 29, 30, 51 and 52 Squadrons. A variety of types serves with MOFTU at Tezpur for advanced training, and each squadron usually includes a handful of two-seat trainers

Indonesia: Indonesia operated MiG-21s before its break with the USSR during the 1960s

Iran: Believed to operate only Chinese-built 'Fishbeds'

Iraq: Before the Gulf War, Iraq's air force included 70 single-seat Soviet-built MiG-21s (probably MiG-21Ms and PFMs) with a dozen two-seaters and some 75 Chengdu F-7s. The number remaining is uncertain

Kazakhstan: Late series MiG-21s may remain active,

This battered-looking MiG-21bis is typical of those now serving with the Vietnamese People's Air Force. A handful are camouflaged in blue and grey, but most wear an overall scheme of light grey, often with faded, peeling insignia and serial numbers.

at least for advanced training

Laos: Two squadrons of MiG-21bis fighters operated from Wattay (Vientiane) but have now been grounded by lack of spares and support problems

Mongolia: Twelve 'Fishbeds', probably MiG-21MFs, are believed to be in use

Mozambique: Despite having been offered for sale, the 30-strong MiG-21 force, once split between squadrons at Beira, Nacala and Nampula, continues to fly from Nampula

Myanmar: Believed to operate only Chinese-built 'Fishbeds'

Nigeria: A fleet of about 28 MiG-21bis or MF fighters and two trainers is in service

North Korea: North Korea operates some 150 MiG-21s, believed mainly to be PFs and PFMs

Pakistan: Operates only Chengdu F-7s

Poland: Before the dissolution of the Warsaw Pact, Poland had nine MiG-21-equipped fighter regiments (1 PLM, 2 PLM, 9 PLM, 10 PLM, 11 PLM, 28 PLM, 34 PLM, 41 PLM, 62 PLM, and one tactical reconnaissance regiment, 32 PLRT), with more MiG-21s in use for advanced training with 23 Flying School at Deblin. 2 PLM and 34 PLM have now disbanded, but large numbers remain in use

Romania: Romania is the first MiG-21 user to have placed a contract for the upgrade of its aircraft (with Elbit). About 100 single-seaters remain in use, with some 12 or more trainers, in two to four air defence regiments. These include 86 Regiment at Borcea Baraganu and another at Caracal-Deveselu

Russia: Late series MiG-21s may remain active, at least for advanced training and perhaps for reconnaissance

Slovakia: Seventy Slovak MiG-21MFs, USs and UMs (and perhaps a handful of MiG-21PFs and even F-13s) serve with the Sliac-based 1st Fighter Regiment's second and third squadrons, alongside MiG-29s

Somalia: Six MiG-21MFs and a pair of MiG-21UMs remained active until grounded by the recent civil war, of an unknown number of aircraft delivered from 1974

Sri Lanka: Operates only Chengdu F-7s

Sudan: Nine MiG-21s (perhaps PFs) may be in

Sudanese service

Syria: Despite very heavy losses (especially over the Bekaa), Syria continues to be a major 'Fishbed' operator, with about 250 on charge

Tanzania: Believed to operate only Chengdu F-7s

Uganda: Five surviving MiG-21Ms may be in storage.

Ukraine: A handful of late series MiG-21s may remain active, for advanced training, but most Ukrainian MiG-21s (which totalled 195 in early 1994) are in storage or being scrapped under the terms of the CFE agreement

United States of America: The USAF's 4477th Fighter Squadron ('Red Hats') at Groom Lake has operated a variety of MiG-21 variants, acquired from Israel, Egypt and other sources

Vietnam: The MiG-21bis and MiG-21UM serve with the 920th Fighter Training Wing at Phu Cat, and with the 921st, 925th, 927th, 929th, 931st, 933rd and 935th

Fighter Wings, respectively based at Da Phuc, unknown, Kep, unknown, Yen Bai, unknown, Phu Cat and unknown. These are split between three divisions, the 370th 'Hai Van' Fighter Division, headquartered at Da Nang, the 371st 'Thang Long' Fighter Division, headquartered at Da Phuc, and the 372nd Fighter Division, headquartered at Tho Xuan

Yemen: The merger of North and South Yemen in 1990 resulted in a fleet of 70 MiG-21M and MiG-21bis fighters from North Yemen forming the backbone of the new combined air arm

Yugoslavia: Most of Yugoslavia's MiG-21R, MiG-21M and MiG-21bis aircraft were inherited by the federal (Serbian) air force

Zambia: Zambia's 16 aircraft, delivered in 1980-82, are believed to be MiG-21MFs

Zimbabwe: Believed to operate only Chengdu F-7s

*Mikoyan-Gurevich
MiG-21bis 'Fishbed-L'*

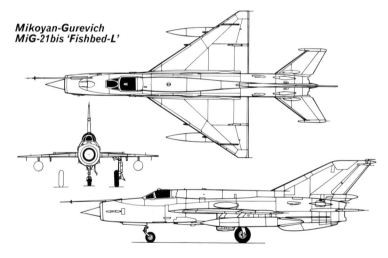

Mikoyan-Gurevich MiG-21U/US/UM 'Mongol'

Proposed two-seat trainer versions of the MiG-19 and MiG-17 did not reach production, but it soon became apparent that the MiG-15UTI would be inadequate for the conversion training of MiG-21 pilots. Mikoyan accordingly designed a two-seat trainer version, based on the MiG-21F-13 'Fishbed-C'. Armament and radar were deleted, although provision was made for a ventral gun pack and it also had two under-wing pylons. The aircraft was fitted with a one-piece airbrake below the forward fuselage and the pitot boom was repositioned above the nose. The instructor's cockpit was added behind the normal cockpit, and both were covered by separate sideways-hingeing canopies. Internal fuel was reduced to 2,350 litres (620 US gal).

The new trainer first flew, as the **Ye-6U**, on 17 October 1960, and entered production as the **MiG-21U (Type 66)**. Early produc-

tion aircraft had the original narrow-chord fin and had a brake chute at the rear of the ventral fin. The basic MiG-21U received the ASCC reporting name **'Mongol-A'** and was built by Znamya Truda between 1964 and 1968.

On the **MiG-21US 'Mongol-B' (Type 68** or **Ye-66B)**, built at Tbilisi between 1966 and 1970, the increased-chord tailfin was introduced from the start, along with the fin trailing-edge brake chute fairing, improved ejection seats, a bigger spine rais-

ing internal fuel capacity to 2450 litres (647 US gal), a retractable periscope and SPS flaps. The **MiG-21UM (Type 69)** introduced updated instruments, autopilot and

This is a late series MiG-21U of No. 8 Squadron, Indian Air Force. The basic MiG-21U equates to early single-seaters like the MiG-21F-13 and MiG-21FL.

*Mikoyan-Gurevich
MiG-21UM 'Mongol'*

Mikoyan-Gurevich MiG-21U/US/UM 'Mongol'

This Hungarian MiG-21UM is seen after a post-overhaul test flight, before the reapplication of camouflage and serial number. The nose-mounted AoA sensor and instructor's periscope are evident.

avionics (as fitted to the MiG-21R and subsequent single-seaters), and was fitted with an AoA sensor on the starboard side of the nose. It was built at Tbilisi from 1971.

Today MiG-21 trainers serve with most operators of the single-seat 'Fishbed' (see operators list with MiG-21bis entry) as conversion and continuation trainers,. However, in India and in the former USSR, MiG-21 trainers also serve as dedicated advanced flying training, pre-OCU/OTU aircraft.

SPECIFICATION

Mikoyan-Gurevich MiG-21US 'Mongol-B'
generally similar to the Mikoyan-Gurevich MiG-21PFM

except in the following particulars:
Fuselage and tail: length 14.41 m (47.27 ft), 12.18 m (39 ft 11.5 in) without probe and inlet centrebody; wheel track 2.69 m (8 ft 10 in); wheel base 4.81 m (15 ft 9.2 in)
Weights: normal take-off 8000 kg (17,636 lb)
Fuel and load: internal fuel 2030 kg (4,475 lb); maximum ordnance 1000 kg (2,204 lb)
Speed: maximum level speed 'clean' at 13000 m (42,650 ft) 2175 km/h (1,175 kt; 1,352 mph)
Performance: maximum rate of climb at sea level 6900 m (22,638 ft) per minute; service ceiling 17700 m (58,070 ft); take-off run 900 m (2,953 ft); landing run 550 m (1,800 ft) at normal landing weight with SPS and brake chute
Range: 1460 km (790 nm; 907 miles) with 800-litre (211-US gal) drop tank

Mikoyan-Gurevich MiG-23S/M/MF/MS 'Flogger-A/B/E'

Widely dismissed in the West as obsolete and ineffective, the remarkable **MiG-23/-27 'Flogger'** family has proved extremely versatile and robust, with an impressive performance. Its reputation has been severely damaged by a number of actions in which downgraded export variants, flown by ill-trained pilots using inflexible tactics, have been shot down without inflicting any loss themselves, most notably over the Bekaa Valley in 1982. Recent evaluations of the aircraft by Western pilots have led to some revised opinions, and the more recent versions of the aircraft have emerged with a much enhanced reputation.

Development of the MiG-23 began during the early 1960s, as a replacement for the MiG-21. Greater payload, range and firepower were clearly needed, along with more powerful onboard sensors to free the pilot from the constraints imposed by tight GCI control. The new fighter would clearly be larger and heavier, but the USSR was determined that this should not impose longer take-off distances.

Two approaches to the problem of giving their new fighter a degree of STOL capability were explored, both producing flying prototypes. A prototype with a delta wing and two 23.05-kN (5,180-lb st) Koliesov RD-36-35 lift jets, and with SPS flaps and a 76.52-kN (17,195-lb st) R-27F-300 primary engine, was designated **Model 23-01** (**MiG-23PD** NATO reporting name **'Faithless'**), while the **Model 23-11** was a version with variable-geometry wings. The 'swing-wing' concept was adopted to satisfy the conflicting requirements of high-speed flight and good low-speed airfield performance. Powered by a Tumanskii R-27F-300 turbojet, the 23-11 made its maiden flight on 10 April 1967, one week after the 23-01. The 23-11 had a multitude of high-lift devices, includ-

ing full-span four-section trailing-edge flaps, leading-edge slats and two-section spoilers, and these, in conjunction with the powerful engine, gave a useful STOL performance. The 23-11 demonstrated take-off runs of 320 m (1,050 ft) and a landing roll of 440 m (1,444 ft).

The 23-11 was ordered into production as the **MiG-23S** with a more powerful 98.1-kN (22,046-lb st) R-27F2M-300 engine, but without the intended Sapfir radar. Instead, the RP-22 'Jay Bird' of the MiG-21S was fitted, giving a very recognisable short radome and removing BVR capability. The aircraft was also fitted with a TP-23 IRST. Fifty were built between mid-1969 and the end of 1970 and were used for operational trials before production switched to the **MiG-23M**, dubbed **'Flogger-B'** by NATO. This featured the intended pulse-Doppler Sapfir-23 ('High Lark') radar and new fire control system and autopilot. The MiG-23M could fire the R-23 AA-7 'Apex' semi-active radar-homing missile. A new 122.63-kN (27,557-lb st) Soyuz (Tumanskii) R-29-300 (with shorter jetpipe) was fitted, while at the same time the aircraft's horizontal tail surfaces were moved aft, giving a very different appearance. A fourth fuel tank was added in the rear fuselage. A new Type 1 wing, with an extended leading edge, was introduced, this having a pronounced 'dogtooth' inboard. Leading-edge slats were deleted (the Type 2 wing), then reintroduced in 1973 with the Type 3 wing.

MiG-23Ms were delivered to Frontal Aviation as MiG-21 replacements, operating mainly in the battlefield air superiority role, but with an important secondary ground attack capability. Others went to the IA-PVO, where they augmented MiG-21s, Su-9s, Su-11s and Su-15s in the air defence role. Two downgraded export versions of the

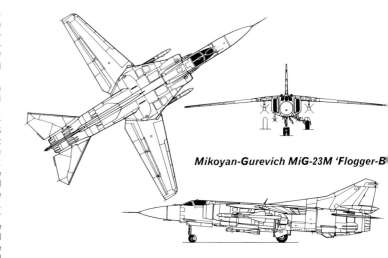

Mikoyan-Gurevich MiG-23M 'Flogger-B'

Above: Romanian MiG-23MFs wear a wide variety of colour schemes, and equip three front-line interceptor regiments. They are augmented by a single squadron of MiG-29 'Fulcrums'.

Below: The MiG-23M and MF can be identified by their large dorsal fin fillet and full-size 'High Lark' radar. This aircraft belongs to No. 224 Squadron, Indian Air Force, based at Adampur.

MiG-23M were produced, the second gaining the new reporting name **'Flogger-E'**. The **MiG-23MS** was a substantially downgraded version with MiG-21-type 'Jay Bird' radar in a short radome, with no BVR missile capability. The **MiG-23MF** was less radically sanitised and retained the 'High Lark' fire control radar, AA-7 'Apex' missile capability and 'Flogger-B' reporting name of the MiG-23M, and was delivered to Russia's Warsaw Pact allies, then later to Syria, Angola, Iraq, India and Libya.

Operators of all fighter/interceptor variants are listed in the MiG-23ML/P/MLD 'Flogger-G/K' entry.

SPECIFICATION

Mikoyan-Gurevich MiG-23MF 'Flogger-B'
Wing: span swept 7.779 m (25 ft 6.5 in); span spread 13.965 m (45.9 ft); area swept 34.16 m² (367.7 sq ft); area spread 37.35 m² (402 sq ft)
Fuselage and tail: length 16.7 m (54.8 ft); wheelbase 5.772 m (18.9 ft); wheel track 2.658 m 8.8 ft); height 4.82 m (15.8 ft)
Powerplant: one Soyuz (Tumanskii) R-29-300 turbojet rated at 78.45 kN (17,635 lb), 112.76 kN

Originally designed as a substantially downgraded export aircraft, with MiG-21-type 'Jay Bird' radar (note the small white radome), the MiG-23MS 'Flogger-E' was also used in small numbers by Frontal Aviation, probably for advanced training. Today, the recipients of front-line Russian-built fighters tend to receive almost full-standard versions, and the kind of radically downgraded export version typified by the MiG-23MS is no longer produced.

(25,348 lb) with afterburner
Weights: empty 8200 kg (18,077 lb); normal take-off 15750 kg (34,722 lb); maximum take-off 20670 kg (45569 lb) with three external tanks
Fuel and load: internal fuel 4700 litres (1,242 US gal); external fuel 2370 litres (626 US gal); maximum ordnance 1600 kg (3,527 lb)

Speed: maximum level speed at 12500 m (41,010 ft) 2490 km/h (1,348 kt; 1,547 mph): maximum speed with 16° sweepback 935 km/h (506 kt; 581 mph)
Range: estimated ferry range 2996 km (1,624 nm; 1,864 miles); estimated hi-lo-hi radius of action 323 nm (600 km; 372 miles)
Performance: estimated service ceiling 17500 m

(57,414 ft); estimated take-off run 580-600 m (1,902-1,968 ft); estimated landing run at normal landing weight with brake chute 750 m (2,460 ft); estimated time to 11000 m (36,084 ft) 1 minute 24 seconds
g limits: +8 up to Mach 0.85; +7 above Mach 0.85

Mikoyan-Gurevich MiG-23ML/P/MLD 'Flogger-G/K'

L ike most Soviet fighters, the MiG-23 has been subject to a constant programme of improvements and refinements, resulting in a succession of variants. The **MiG-23ML 'Flogger-G'** (allocated the OKB designation **23-12**) was intended to have improved handling, especially at high angles of attack, enhanced manoeuvrability and higher g limits. It featured a lightened airframe, with the fourth fuselage fuel tank removed and with the dorsal fin fillet deleted. More power was provided by installing the Soyuz (Tumanskii) R-35-300 engine. Strengthened three-section leading-edge slats were fitted.

Airframe and engine improvements were accompanied by an improved radar, the lightweight SP-23L, which had a new dogfight mode, and improvements to the defensive avionics suite. A new IRST was also fitted. The MiG-23ML has been delivered to Frontal Aviation and to a number of export customers including Syria, North Korea, Czechoslovakia and East Germany. A very similar aircraft, designated **MiG-23P** (**23-14**), is used by the PVO and has a new digital computer that allows the aircraft to be automatically steered onto its target from the ground, cueing the pilot to engage afterburner and launch weapons. Israeli evaluation of a defecting Syrian MiG-23ML showed the aircraft to be a match for the F-16 in some respects.

Super 'Flogger'

The MiG-23ML also serves as the basis for the further improved **MiG-23MLD**, codenamed **'Flogger-K'** by NATO, and known as the **23-18** to the OKB. The new version, reportedly produced by conversion of MiG-23ML airframes, incorporates vortex generators on the pitot probe and notches in its vestigial leading-edge root extensions. These notches generate powerful vortices at high angles of attack, improving high-Alpha handling and increasing Alpha limits. New automatic leading-edge slats are also fitted, these deploying to optimise handling and manoeuvrability at all angles of attack. Large chaff/flare dispensers can be fitted above the rear fuselage, and these are linked to the new RWR system. A new IFF system is fitted, and a missile-firing simulator allows economic training. Further modifications include swivelling pylons under the outboard wing panels, which move to remain aligned with the airflow even when the wings are swept. On other

MiG-23 variants these pylons can only be used with the wings fully forward, and are thus rarely fitted.

Some reports suggest that the 'Flogger-K' is compatible with the new R-73 AA-11 'Archer' IR-homing missile, or perhaps even with the long-range AA-10 'Alamo', but this cannot yet be confirmed. Either of these missiles would represent a major increase in capability over the armament of previous MiG-23 variants. No MiG-23MLDs have been exported.

SPECIFICATION

Mikoyan-Gurevich MiG-23ML 'Flogger-G'
generally similar to the MiG-23MF except in the following particulars:
Fuselage and tail: length 15.65 m (51 ft 3.7 in) excluding probe (0.08 m/3 in shorter than MiG-23M)
Powerplant: one Soyuz (Tumanskii) R-35-300 turbojet rated at 83.88 kN (18,849 lb st) dry and 127.5 kN (28,660 lb st) with afterburning
Weights: normal fuel 14700 kg (32,407 lb); maximum take-off 17800 kg (39,242 lb)
Fuel and load: internal fuel 4250 litres (1,122 US gal); external fuel 2400 litres (632 US gal); maximum ordnance 2000 kg (4409 lb)
Speed: maximum speed at 72° sweepback 2500 km/h

Mikoyan-Gurevich MiG-23MLD 'Flogger-K'

(1,349 kt; 1,553 mph); at 16° sweepback 940 km/h (507 kt; 584 mph)
Range: ferry range 2820 km (1,521 nm; 1,752 miles) with drop tanks
Performance: service ceiling 18000 m (59,055 ft); take-off run 1200-1300 m (3,937-4,265 ft); time to 11000 m (36,089 ft) 1 minute 12 seconds
g limits: +8.5 below Mach 0.85 and +7.5 above Mach 0.85

OPERATORS

Afghanistan: Reports of Afghan MiG-23s may refer to Soviet aircraft stationed in that country, and perhaps temporarily operated with Afghan markings, although there are persistent reports that MiG-23MFs equipped the 322nd Fighter Interceptor Regiment at Bagram

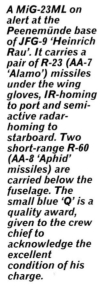

A MiG-23ML on alert at the Peenemünde base of JFG-9 'Heinrich Rau'. It carries a pair of R-23 (AA-7 'Alamo') missiles under the wing gloves, IR-homing to port and semi-active radar-homing to starboard. Two short-range R-60 (AA-8 'Aphid' missiles) are carried below the fuselage. The small blue 'Q' is a quality award, given to the crew chief to acknowledge the excellent condition of his charge.

Mikoyan-Gurevich MiG-23ML/P/MLD 'Flogger-G/K'

This fully modified MiG-23MLD of the 83rd Fighter Regiment is based at Altes Lager in Germany. Chaff/ flare dispensers are carried above the rear fuselage.

Algeria: Algeria operates some 20 MiG-23 fighters, (MiG-23MFs or MSs), alongside UB trainers
Angola: Angola's 80-strong MiG-23 fleet includes MiG-23MLs, and, reportedly, MFs and MSs as well as BN fighter-bombers and UB trainers
Byelorussia: The Byelorussian republic has 50 MiG-23s at Machulisch and Baranovich
Bulgaria: Eighty MiG-23MFs (and reportedly some MiG-23MLs delivered as attrition replacements) serve with the fighter regiment at Dobroslavtzi (which may be designated Polk 24900). Other MiG-23s serve at Bozhurishte
China: China is believed to have received between two and four (and perhaps many more) MiG-23s from Egypt in return for spares support for that nation's MiG-21s after its break with the USSR. They were

minutely examined, and technology acquired in the process was used in the J-8 and stillborn J-9 programmes
Cuba: Cuba is believed to have received about 20 MiG-23MS 'Flogger-Es' in 1977, together with a few MiG-23UBs, and perhaps later augmented by a number of MiG-23MFs
Czech Republic: Czechoslovakia took delivery of 12 MiG-23MFs and 18 MiG-23MLs for the 1st Fighter Regiment at Ceske Budejovice. Ten MiG-23UBs were also delivered. Slovakia did not take its allocated one-third of the MiG-23s on the division of Czechoslovakia into separate Czech and Slovak Republics. The Czech Republic is reportedly making its MiG-23MFs compatible with the MATRA Magic missile, and is actively looking to upgrade the aircraft further. With the withdrawal of the nine MiG-29s (judged too small a number to be viable) in late 1994, the MiG-23MFs will form the backbone of Czech air defence
Egypt: About 16 MiG-23s were delivered in 1974, but were passed to the USA and China following the split with the USSR

Ethiopia: A handful of MiG-23UBs were delivered to support Ethiopia's fighter-bomber MiG-23BMNs (which may actually be BMs or BKs)
Germany: An original batch of MiG-23MFs (delivered in 1978) and eight MiG-23UBs were augmented by 28 MiG-23MLs delivered during 1982 and 1983. Twelve MFs remained in use at reunification. Several aircraft were flown by the Luftwaffe for evaluation following the reunification of the two Germanies, and others were supplied to the RAF and US Air Force for evaluation
Hungary: Nine of the 12 MiG-23MFs delivered remain in service with the Saman squadron of the Stromfeld Aurel wing at Pápa, with three of four MiG-23UBs transferred from Frontal Aviation
India: Forty MiG-23MFs were acquired in 1982 as interim fighters pending the delivery of MiG-29s. The survivors remain in use with No. 224 Squadron, No. 223 having converted to the MiG-29 in 1989. Fifteen MiG-23UBs were delivered primarily to support the MiG-23BN and MiG-27 fighter-bomber force
Iraq: Iraq's MiG-23 fleet, severely depleted by the Gulf War, included MiG-23MS, MF(?) and ML fighters, and UB trainers. Eight were shot down during the war, eight fled to Iran, and many more were destroyed on the ground
Libya: Libya has received more than 150 MiG-23s, some of which were transferred to Sudan. About 85 fighters (MS, MF and ML) remain in use, with 15 trainers
North Korea: An initial 1984 batch of eight MiG-23MLs has been augmented by further deliveries, giving a total force of about 60 MiG-23s, including a handful of MiG-23UBs
Poland: About 28 survivors of 45 MiG-23MFs serve with 28 PLM at Slupsk, with about four MiG-23UBs
Romania: Some 30 MiG-23MFs and eight MiG-23UBs are in service with the 32nd and 57th Fighter Regiments at Timisoara and Constanta

Russia: Despite the widespread introduction of the MiG-29, MiG-23s remain in service in large numbers. Air forces withdrawn from Czechoslovakia, Germany and Poland all included MiG-23MLD fighter regiments, which joined other MiG-23 regiments in Russian-based Frontal Aviation, and Russian-based PVO regiments
Sudan: Libyan MiG-23s transferred to Sudan during 1987 may have been fighter-bombers or fighters. Between six and 12 remain in use
Syria: Many of the initial batch of MiG-23MS fighters were lost to the IDF/AF (especially over the Bekaa in 1982) and replacements have included MiG-23MFs and MLs. MiG-23UB trainers are also in service. About 100 fighter/trainer 'Floggers' are in service
Turkmenistan: Turkmenistan has a number of MiG-23s, some of which it has tried to sell to raise foreign currency. Whether its single combat squadron will have MiG-23s remains uncertain
Ukraine: About 230 MiG-23s remain active with the air defence force in the new republic, but not with the air force itself, apart from a handful of MiG-23UBs used as trainers by MiG-29 regiments. The air defence force, part of the PVO during USSR days, has Southern, Western and Central Regions, and MiG-23s serve with the 737th IAP at Chervanoglinskoe (Southern Region), and with the 179th IAP and 894th IAP at Stryy and Ozernoe (Western Region)
United States of America: The USAF's ex-Egyptian MiG-23s, augmented by three ex-East German aircraft (three MiG-23MLs), serve in the adversary tactics development role
Vietnam: About 30 MiG-23s were delivered to replace MiG-19s in the interceptor role during 1985/86. These may be MiG-23MLs
Yemen: Ex-South Yemeni MiG-23s have been described by different sources as MiG-23BN fighter-bombers and as MiG-23ML fighters. About 25 remain in use

Mikoyan-Gurevich MiG-23UB 'Flogger-C'

Because the handling characteristics of the MiG-23 were so different from those of other aircraft in the Soviet inventory, development of a two-seat trainer version was authorised in May 1968, six months after the the go-ahead had been given for the single-seat aircraft. Photographs of the second prototype, often described as a simple two-seat conversion of the MiG-23S, seem to show an aircraft with the definitive rear fuselage contours of the MiG-23M but with the original wing, and with no 'dogtooth' on the leading edge. The **MiG-23UB** prototype (allocated the NATO reporting name **'Flogger-C'**, and known to the bureau as the **23-51**) made its maiden flight in May 1969, three years before the first MiG-23M. This may perhaps indicate that the two-seater's rear-located tailplane and short jetpipe were adopted for the new single-seater.

Although never intended to have the Sapfir radar, the MiG-23UB was always supposed to be used for both pilot conversion and weapons training, and even to have a restricted combat capability, within the limitations imposed by the weapons carried. Accordingly, a separate guidance and illuminator pod for the AA-7 'Apex' missile was fitted in a conical fairing on the starboard wingroot. Production aircraft all have the 'clawed' No. 3 wing (compatible with the carriage of outboard underwing fuel tanks on non-swivelling pylons), and the two tandem cockpits are covered by separate upward-hinging canopies. The instructor is provided with a retractable periscope to give a better view forward on approach. All

two-seaters are fitted with an AoA limiter or an AoA warning system, together with a comprehensive avionics suite featuring improved navaids and a sophisticated system which allows the backseater to simulate emergencies and threats for the student pilot in the front cockpit.

All MiG-23, 23BN and MiG-27 operators also use the MiG-23UB, and the type, which was phased out of production at Irkutsk in 1978, also serves with many Russian MiG-29 and Su-27 units.

This MiG-23UB served as a trainer with the 33rd IAP at Wittstock, one of the MiG-29-equipped fighter regiments assigned to the Group of Soviet Forces in Germany. These tended to use MiG-23UBs to augment their MiG-29UB trainers.

Weights: empty 8700 kg (19,179 lb); normal take-off 15740 kg (34,700 lb); maximum take-off 18000 kg (39,682 lb)
Fuel and load: internal fuel 4000 kg (8,818 lb); external fuel 2400 litres (634 US gal)
Range: radius of action 700 km (377 km; 434 miles)
Performance: service ceiling 18000 m (59,055 ft); take-off run 1200-1300 m (3,837-4,265 ft); landing roll 1200-1300 m (3,837-4,265 ft)
g limit: +7

A Mikoyan MiG-23UB of No. 10 Squadron, Indian Air Force, takes off in full burner. No. 10 Squadron operates MiG-23BN fighter-bombers. There are no external differences between the two-seaters used by fighter and fighter-bomber squadrons, but there may be equipment changes.

Mikoyan-Gurevich MiG-23B/BK/BM/BN 'Flogger-F/-H'

Mikoyan began studies of a 'jet *Shtur-movik*' during 1969, to meet a Frontal Aviation requirement for a cheap, mass-produced attack aircraft offering the same level of capability as the Anglo-French SEPECAT Jaguar. Mikoyan assumed that an entirely new subsonic design would be necessary. The resulting MiG-27-11 combined the basic airframe of the MiG-21bis with an ogival delta wing (as used on Mikoyan's A-144 Analog and Tupolev's Tu-144) and side-mounted intakes. An alternative supersonic design, the MiG-27Sh, used a wing similar to that of the Jaguar. Economic constraints forced Mikoyan to examine the possibility of using a derivative of the MiG-23S, whose supersonic dash capability was felt to be a useful bonus. How the new design fitted in with the Su-25 'Frogfoot' being developed by Sukhoi to meet essentially the same role remains unclear. Mikoyan allocated a new designation (**Model 32**) but the air force retained a MiG-23 designation, perhaps feeling that funding for a new aircraft would be harder to obtain.

The original MiG-23 had been developed as a multi-role tactical fighter, and the ability to operate from primitive, semi-prepared airstrips had been stressed from the start. The aircraft's rugged airframe, strong under-

The MiG-23BN was essentially an attack derivative of the basic 'Flogger-B' fighter, with the same airframe and engine.

carriage, powerful engine and variable-geometry wing thus made it extremely suitable for conversion or adaptation to the fighter-bomber role. The use of a swing wing, in particular, allowed high straight line performance (with wings swept aft), while also endowing excellent low-speed handling characteristics, turn performance and short take-off/landing distances.

The basic **MiG-23B** (**32-24**) was based on the airframe of the MiG-23S, but with a new, more sloping nose giving the pilot an improved view forward and downward, and with a 112.78-kN (25,353-lb st) Lyul'ka AL-21F-300 powerplant in a shortened rear fuselage, again with the horizontal tailplane shifted rearward, as on the MiG-23M. Also like the MiG-23M, the new ground attack variant featured the No. 2 wing and was later fitted with the the No. 3 wing. Radar was not installed, and instead the new aircraft had a PrNK Sokol 23S nav/attack system. Armour was scabbed on to the sides of the forward fuselage, to protect the pilot, and the fuel tanks were fitted with an inert gas injection fire protection system. A missile illuminator (starboard) and a TV camera (port) were housed in bullet-like fairings on the wingroot gloves. The TV camera was later removed from most MiG-23 fighter-bombers. Piotr Ostapenko flew the first prototype on 20 August 1970, making the aircraft the third production version to fly, after the MiG-23S and MiG-23UB.

Twenty-four MiG-23Bs were built before

production finally switched to an improved variant. The **MiG-23BN** (**32-23**), featured an upgraded PrNK Sokol 23N nav/attack system, and was powered by a slightly derated

Above: The nose contours of a MiG-23BN reveal the undernose 'Swift Rod' and laser rangefinder window in the 'chisel nose'.

299

Mikoyan-Gurevich MiG-23B/BK/BM/BN 'Flogger-F/-H'

With the canopy cracked open for ventilation, an East German MiG-23BN taxis out for a mission at Drewitz. JBG 37 'Klement Gottwald' disbanded on the reunification of the two Germanies, although a handful of its aircraft were briefly retained for evaluation.

version of the Soyuz (Tumanskii) R-29B-300 engine. The MiG-23BN was intended to have been the first attack version, but was delayed by equipment and engine problems. It introduced the leading-edge bullet fairings on the fixed wing gloves that are usually associated with the AS-7 'Kerry' ASM. The MiG-23B and MiG-23BN share the NATO reporting name **'Flogger-F'**, and all seem to have a simplified jetpipe, which is more like that fitted to the MiG-27 than the standard MiG-23M jetpipe.

The MiG-23B and MiG-23BN proved disappointing in service, and many were subsequently upgraded to **MiG-23BK (32-26)** or **MiG-23BM (32-25)** standards, or exported, mainly to Third World customers. Cuban attack MiG-23s are 'Flogger-Fs', without the intake-mounted RWR fairings, for example, while German and Czech aircraft, designated MiG-23BNs, have these fairings and are thus 'Flogger-Hs'. Improved avionics were desperately needed, and two new fighter-bombers were quickly developed, both sharing the same **'Flogger-H'** reporting name. This was assigned because they

had new RWR fairings on the lower 'corners' of the fuselage, just ahead of the nose-wheel bay. The first of the new variants was the MiG-23BK, which had the same nav/attack system and laser rangefinder as the MiG-27K. The MiG-23BM was similar, but with the same PrNK Sokol 23M nav/attack system as the MiG-27D. Confusingly, the MiG-23BN designation seems to have been adopted as an overall service designation, sometimes being applied to aircraft designated BM or BK by the bureau. Many of the export 'Flogger-Hs' are usually described as MiG-23BNs, and were perhaps built as such, but are actually to MiG-23BK standards. Such aircraft include East Germany's MiG-23BKs, whose documentation described them as **MiG-24BNs**. Bulgarian, Czech, Indian and Iraqi 'Flogger-Hs' look identical, although many of the latter have fixed inflight-refuelling probes above the nose, almost identical to those fitted to the Mirage F1, and perhaps supplied by the same French manufacturer.

WEAPON OPTIONS

The MiG-23B series can carry a variety of guided and unguided weapons on underwing and underfuselage pylons. The aircraft also has a secondary reconnaissance capability, using podded sensors which are most frequently attached to one of the under-intake pylons. Hardpoints are provided under the forward fuselage, on the bottom 'corners' of the

rear fuselage and under the wing gloves. These can be used to carry the full range of podded and unpodded rockets, the UV-32-57 and newer S-8 rocket pods (respectively containing 32 57-mm rockets and 20 80-mm rockets) being favourite MiG-23BN weapons. The KMG-U bomblet dispenser can be carried, together with 50-kg (110-lb), 100-kg (220-lb), 250-kg (551-lb) or 500-kg (1,102-lb) freefall bombs. The bullet fairing on the starboard wing glove is believed to house a command guidance antenna for guided ASMs like the AS-7 'Kerry'. Internal armament consists of a GSh-23L 23-mm twin-barrelled cannon, as fitted to earlier fighter versions. This is carried in a semi-conformal gondola below the fuselage, just aft of the nosewheel bay. For strafing missions, this weapon can be augmented by UPK-23-250 cannon pods, or the SPPU-22 with traversable barrels.

SPECIFICATION

Mikoyan MiG-23BN 'Flogger-F'
generally similar to the MiG-23MF except in the following particulars:
Fuselage and tail: length 15.35 m (50.36 ft); wheelbase 5.9 m (19.35 ft); wheel track 2.73 m (2.9 ft)
Powerplant: one Soyuz (Tumanskii) R-29B-300 turbojet rated at 77 kN (17,310 lb) or 110 kN (24,728 lb) with afterburner
Weights: empty 10700 kg (23,589 lb); normal take-off 16750 kg (36,926 lb); maximum take-off 18850 kg (41,556 lb)
Fuel and load: internal fuel 5380 litres (1,421 US gal); maximum external fuel 2370 litres (626 US gal); maximum ordnance 3000 kg (6,613 lb)

Speed: maximum level speed at 11000 m (36,089 ft) 1900 km/h (1,025 kt; 1,180 mph); maximum level speed at sea level 1350 km/h (728 kt; 838 mph)
Range: ferry range 1350 km (728 nm; 838 miles); radius of action 550 km (296 nm; 341 miles)
Performance: service ceiling 16800 m (55,118 ft); take-off run 650-700 m (2,132-2,296 ft); landing run at normal landing weight with brake chute 800-850 m (2,262-2,788 ft); time to 11000 m (36,089 ft) 1 minute 42 seconds
g limits: +7 up to Mach 0.85; +6 above Mach 0.85

OPERATORS

Algeria: Algeria operates some 40 MiG-23BNs (which may actually be, or have been upgraded to, MiG-23BM or BK standards) in two squadrons
Angola: Angola's 80-strong MiG-23 fleet includes MiG-23 BN fighter-bombers (which may actually be, or have been upgraded to, MiG-23BM or BK standards)
Bulgaria: About 40 MiG-23BNs (which may actually be, or have been upgraded to, MiG-23BM or BK standards, and which are certainly 'Flogger-Hs') serve the 25th Bomber Regiment at Sadovo (which may alternatively be known as Polk 38790)
Cuba: Cuba is believed to operate 35 MiG-23BNs 'Flogger-Fs' in three squadrons at Guines and Santa Clara
Czech Republic: On the division of Czechoslovakia into separate Czech and Slovak Republics, the new Czech Republic retained all 28 surviving MiG-23BNs (of 32 delivered) for the 28th Fighter-Bomber Regiment at Caslav
Egypt: About 16 MiG-23s, including an unknown number of fighter-bombers, were delivered in 1974, and were later passed to the USA and China
Ethiopia: Ethiopia operates about 36 fighter-bomber MiG-23BNs (which may actually be BMs or BKs) with the 3rd Air Regiment at Dire Dawa and Debre Zeit
Germany: Eighteen MiG-23BNs (which may actually be, or have been upgraded to, MiG-23BM or BK standards, and which were reportedly known locally as MiG-24s) remained in service at reunification. Some were briefly flown in Luftwaffe markings for evaluation
India: Ninety-five MiG-23BNs were delivered from December 1980, allowing the re-equipment of Nos 10, 31, 220 and 221 Squadrons, which remain active
Iraq: Iraq's MiG-23 fleet included about 70 MiG-23BNs, but four fled to Iran during the Gulf War, several were impounded while on overhaul in Yugoslavia and Germany, and many more were destroyed on the ground. Many were fitted with Mirage F1-style refuelling probes and were compatible with the AS-14 'Kedge' ASM
Libya: Libya took delivery of some 40-50 MiG-23BNs (which may actually be, or have been upgraded to, MiG-23BM or BK standards), 35-38 of which remain in service with a regiment at El Adem. These may have been fitted with Mirage F1-style refuelling probes
Nigeria: Reports that Nigeria received some 40 MiG-23BNs and 10 UBs cannot be confirmed
Russia: MiG-23Bs, MiG-23BNs, BMs and BKs have been retired from front-line service, but a handful may be in use for test or trials duties
Sudan: Libyan MiG-23s transferred to Sudan during 1987 may have been fighter-bombers or fighters. Between six and 12 remain in use
Syria: Some sources suggest that Syria has about 60 MiG-23BNs (which may actually be, or have been upgraded to, MiG-23BM or BK standards)
United States of America: The USAF's ex-Egyptian MiG-23s included some MiG-23BNs
Yemen: 25 ex-South Yemeni MiG-23s have been described by different sources as MiG-23BN fighter-bombers and as MiG-23ML fighters. About 25 remain in use

This Indian Air Force MiG-23BN carries four UV-16-57 rocket pods, giving a total of 64 57-mm rockets. It wears the tiger's head insignia of No. 220 Squadron 'The Desert Tigers'.

Mikoyan-Gurevich MiG-25 fighter variants

The **MiG-25** was developed as a panic response to the American North American XB-70 Valkyrie strategic bomber, whose Mach 3 performance and very high altitude capability threatened to present Soviet air defences with almost insoluble problems. When development of the Valkyrie was halted in 1961, work on the MiG-25 was well advanced, and the USSR continued with the project, perhaps knowing that a Mach 3-capable reconnaissance aircraft, the Lockheed A-11 (later SR-71), was about to begin flight tests.

In designing an aircraft for sustained flight at Mach 3, the biggest problem facing the design bureau was the so-called heat barrier. It had been estimated that while a MiG-21 flying at Mach 2.05 with an outside air temperature of 0°C (32°F) would encounter nose temperatures of 107°C (225°F), the air friction of an aircraft flying at Mach 3 would generate temperatures of almost 300°C (572°F), well above the maximum temperature (130°C/266°F) that aluminium could withstand.

Those parts of the airframe which would have to withstand the greatest heat, such as the nose and leading edges, had to be of titanium construction, but many other areas that could theoretically have been made of riveted aluminium, such as the wing skins (which served as fuel tanks and were thus cooled by their contents) had to be made of welded steel because no suitable heat-resistant sealant could be found, and because there was a shortage of skilled riveters. Structural design of a Mach 3 aircraft posed enormous problems and demanded the use of advanced metallurgy and new welding processes to develop heat-resistant alloys and to avoid cracking and other problems. Eventually, 80 per cent of the aircraft was of tempered steel, 11 per cent of aluminium alloys and eight per cent of titanium. Similarly, no less than 76.5 per cent of assembly was by different types of welding, with conventional riveted joints making up only 23.5 per cent.

The aerodynamic problems posed by an aircraft designed to operate at sustained Mach 3 speeds were no less acute. In order to achieve satisfactory levels of stability and good manoeuvrability without sacrificing speed or altitude performance, the design bureau selected a novel configuration with large, highly-swept thin wings, sophisticated variable lateral air intakes, and canted twin tailfins. The wing leading-edge sweepback angle is not constant, with slightly more inboard (42°30') than outboard (41°). In order to provide adequate range and endurance, about 70 per cent of the aircraft's volume consists of fuel tanks, giving the prototype an internal capacity of 17660 litres (4,666 US gal).

Advanced cooling and insulation systems had to be developed for the engines, avionics and cockpit. The success of these features can be gauged by the fact that at maximum speed the pilot remains comfortable, yet the canopy above him is too hot to touch with the naked hand. Development of the **Ye-155P** interceptor was finally approved in February 1962, and the prototype **Ye-155P-1** made its maiden flight on 9 September 1964, after the first MiG-25 reconnaissance version, which had been designed after it. The aircraft was powered by a pair of 100-kN (22,500-lb) Mikulin (later Tumanskii) R-15B-300 turbojets with a life of 150 hours, and fitted with a Smertch-A radar, known to NATO as 'Fox Fire'. This

With twin cruciform brake chutes streamed, a MiG-25PU taxis in after a training mission. The instructor sits in the forward cockpit, displacing the radar, giving the pupil exactly the same view as he would have in the single-seat MiG-25.

The lack of an undernose IRST sensor identifies this Libyan MiG-25 as a 'Foxbat-A'. Libya has some 60 MiG-25 fighters, augmenting a smaller number of recce aircraft. These serve with a three-squadron regiment at Tripoli.

had a detection range of 54 nm (100 km; 62 miles) and a tracking range of 27 nm (50 km; 31 miles). The aircraft carried two R-40 air-to-air missiles, in mixed pairs of R-40R and R-40T semi-active radar- and IR-homing versions. Look-down capability was virtually non-existent.

Performance was up to expectations, and in March 1965, under the cover designation **Ye-266**, an early aircraft was used to shatter several of the records set by the Lockheed SR-71. Between 1965 and 1977, the Ye-266 and **Ye-266M** eventually made 21 FAI-notified record-breaking flights, setting nine records which still remained unbroken in 1994.

For the production **MiG-25P 'Foxbat-A'** the tailfin area was reduced and planned canard foreplanes were abandoned, as were the small wingtip tanks and winglets. Armament was increased from two to four R-40 (AA-6 'Acrid') missiles, comprising two each with infra-red and radar-homing seeker heads. The landing weight was so high that twin brake chutes had to be fitted, production aircraft eventually using either 60-m² (646-sq ft) conical or 50-m² (538-sq ft) cruciform chutes. Production began in 1969, but the aircraft did not enter full air force service until 1973, having been plagued by engine and control problems. Even in service, the MiG-25 was subject to severe operating limitations, which strictly constrained the amount of time that could be spent at very high speeds, and which limited the use of full engine power.

The ultimate **MiG-25PD 'Foxbat-E'** fighter variant entered production in 1978, and featured a new RP-25 look-down/shoot-down radar (similar to that fitted to the MiG-23M) and an undernose IRST. The engines were replaced by more powerful R-15BD-300s whose lives were extended to 1,000 hours, and provision was made for a 5300-litre (1,400-US gal) belly tank. Surviving Soviet 'Foxbat-As' were brought up to the same standard from 1979, under the designation **MiG-25PDS**. Some of the latter aircraft received a 250-mm (10-in) plug in front of the canopy to allow a retractable IFR probe to be fitted, although inflight refuelling was not (and is still not) a regular part of front-line PVO operations. Normal armament comprises two R-40s and four R-60 (AA-8 'Aphid') AAMs. The PD/PDS upgrade has restored the MiG-25's viability, however, and some are expected to serve into the next millennium.

Right: The MiG-25PD 'Foxbat-E' prototype lacks an undernose IRST and is currently in storage at the Zhukhovskii Flight Research Centre. Red stars along the intake represent successful missile firings.

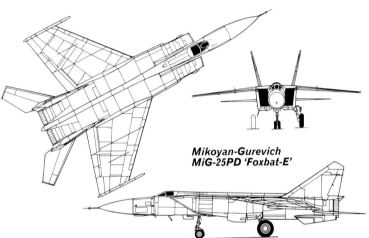

Mikoyan-Gurevich
MiG-25PD 'Foxbat-E'

The added fuselage plug of the MiG-25PDS can clearly be seen aheac of the windscreen in this view of 'Rec 45'. The 'scallop' below the nose is a black-painted anti-glare patch which surrounds the IRST sensor in order tc maintain a constant temperature, anc to not transmit reflections to the IRST.

Gulf War. Fuller user details are given in the operators section of the MiG-25R entry.

SPECIFICATION

Mikoyan-Gurevich MiG-25PDS 'Foxbat-E'
Wing: span 14.015 m (45 ft 11.75 in); aspect ratio 3.2; area 61.40 m² (660.93 sq ft)
Fuselage and tail: length 23.82 m (78 ft 1.75 in) or, in aircraft modified with IFR capability, 24.07 m (78 ft 11.67 in); height 6.10 m (20 ft 0.25 in); wheel track 3.85 m (12 ft 7.5 in); wheel base 5.14 m (16 ft 10.5 in)
Powerplant: two MNPK 'Soyuz' (Tumanskii) R-15BD-300 turbojets each rated at 109.83 kN (24,691 lb st) with afterburning
Weights: normal take-off 36720 kg (80,952 lb) with four R-40s and 100 per cent internal fuel
Fuel and load: internal fuel 14570 kg (32,121 lb); external fuel up to 4370 kg (9,634 lb) in an underbelly tank; maximum ordnance 4000 kg (8,818 lb)
Speed: maximum level speed 'clean' at 13000 m (42,650 ft) Mach 2.8 or 3000 km/h (1,619 kt; 1,864 mph) and at sea level 1200 km/h (647 kt; 745 mph)
Range: with internal fuel 1730 km (933 nm; 1,075 miles) subsonic or 1250 km (675 nm; 776 miles) supersonic; endurance 2 hours 5 minutes
Performance: climb to 20000 m (65,615 ft) in 8 minutes 54 seconds; service ceiling 20700 m (67,915 ft); take-off run 1250 m (4,101 ft) at normal take-off weight; landing run 800 m (2,624 ft) at normal landing weight with brake chutes
g limits: +4.5 supersonic

The **MiG-25PU 'Foxbat-C'** two-seat conversion trainer was rolled out in 1968. It lacks radar and has no combat capability. The type features a new forward cockpit for the instructor stepped down in front of the standard single-seat cockpit. The MiG-25P and MiG-25PU have been exported to Algeria, Iraq, Libya and Syria. Remarkably, an Iraqi MiG-25 is believed to have shot down a USN F/A-18 during the

This MiG-25 serves as an ejection seat testbed, with an open rear cockpit surrounded by a built-up blast screen. Based at Zhukhovskii, it serves alongside other MiG-25s used in test and research roles.

Mikoyan-Gurevich **MiG-25 reconnaissance variants**

Although the MiG-25 was originally designed as an interceptor, it had obvious potential as a reconnaissance platform. The prototype recce aircraft, the **Ye-155R-1**, made its maiden flight six months before the prototype fighter, on 6 March 1964. During flight trials of the three Ye-155Rs, the original wingtip tanks with vertical finlets were soon discarded and replaced by smaller anti-flutter masses, and 'letterbox'-shaped dielectric panels on the nose were made deeper and more square. Tail surfaces were also enlarged and the R-15B-300 engines were replaced by R-15BD-300s.

As the **MiG-25R**, the reconnaissance version passed its state acceptance tests in 1969, and series production began at Gorky in April 1969. The MiG-25R had five camera ports in the nose, one vertical and four oblique, with small square flush antennas further forward on the sides of the nose, probably serving some kind of SLAR. Three cameras would usually be carried, one vertical and two oblique, the latter having 300-mm and 650-mm lenses, allowing them to cover swathes of land equal to two-and-a-half times and five times the aircraft altitude, respectively.

Even before the aircraft entered front-line service, a trials unit with four MiG-25Rs was deployed to Egypt for operational reconnaissance missions over Israel. These operated under the cover designation **X-500**, flying at speeds of up to Mach 2.83 (flight at this upper limit was officially limited to eight minutes), although one pilot took his aircraft to Mach 3 to avoid Israeli SAMs and the time

limit was frequently broken. The aircraft enjoyed a four-year immunity from interception, between their deployment in 1971 to their withdrawal in 1975, despite a lack of security which meant that the IDF/AF was forewarned of virtually every mission.

The original MiG-25R was replaced on the production line by the **MiG-25RB 'Foxbat-B'** in 1970, this type remaining in production until 1982. The MiG-25RB was a dual-role reconnaissance bomber, with a new Peleng automatic bombing system, the Soviet Union's first operational inertial navigation system, and a Doppler to measure speed and drift. These allowed the aircraft to release its bombs from altitudes in excess of 20000 m (65,617 ft) at supersonic speeds. Four underwing hardpoints were provided for 500-kg (1,102-lb) bombs, with another two under the fuselage. Alternatively, a single nuclear weapon could be carried. The standard camera bay remained but the SRS-4A Elint system was slightly

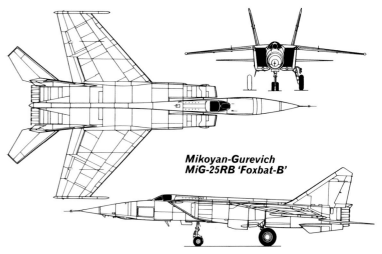

Mikoyan-Gurevich MiG-25RB 'Foxbat-B'

The Indian Air Force's No. 102 Squadron operates five MiG-25RBs (of six delivered) and also has a pair of MiG-25RU trainers.

This MiG-25RBF, identifiable by the small dielectric panels in place of camera ports, served with the Soviet Forces in Germany, based first at Werneuchen and later at Welzow.

improved. All surviving Soviet MiG-25Rs were brought up to MiG-25RB standards. Further models which are understood to have retained their cameras included the **MiG-25RBS** with the new Sabla radio location system. This variant entered service in 1972, and was produced until 1977. From 1981 many of these aircraft received new equipment and were allocated a new designation of **MiG-25RBSh**. The MiG-25RBS was replaced on the production line by the **MiG-25RBV**, with further improved equipment, and by the MiG-25RBV with SRS-9 Virazh Elint equipment. From observation of an aircraft described as a MiG-25RBV in Germany during 1992, this variant appears to have all but its vertical camera port faired over, but is otherwise externally identical to the MiG-25RB and MiG-25RBS.

The basic MiG-25RB also formed the basis of a model dedicated to Elint duties, with its optical sensors replaced by a variety of passive receivers and active SLAR systems. It is unclear whether the NATO **Foxbat-D'** reporting name covers all such versions, or just those with an enlarged SLAR antenna on the side of the nose, further aft. The first 'camera-less' 'Foxbat' was the **MiG-25RBK**, which has the usual flush antennas and cameras removed and replaced by much larger, longer dielectric panels on the sides of the cockpit stretching forward from a point immediately under the windscreen. These antennas reportedly serve the new Kub SLAR. The aircraft lacks even the vertical camera port, and the underside of the nose is completely smooth. The MiG-25RBK entered service in 1972 and remained in production until 1980.

The final variant is the **MiG-25RBF**, variously described as an RB brought up to RBK standards, or as a new production aircraft which replaced the RBK on the production line, with expanded jamming capability.

There is less doubt about the MiG-25RBF's appearance, fortunately. The aircraft lacks the large SLAR antennas of the RBK, instead having reverted to the small dielectric panels farther forward, as carried on the MiG-25RB and other variants. In place of oblique camera windows, the RBF has four small, symmetrically arranged, rectangular dielectric panels. The vertical camera window seems to be retained.

Unusually, the reconnaissance 'Foxbat' has its own dedicated two-seat trainer, designated **MiG-25RU**. This has no operational equipment, but does seem to have a constant-sweep wing leading edge. By comparison with 'fighter' MiG-25s, all reconnaissance aircraft have slightly reduced wingspan and a leading edge with constant sweep, instead of the fighter's 'cranked' leading edge. Camera-equipped MiG-25RBs have been exported to Algeria, Bulgaria, India, Iraq, Libya and Syria.

SPECIFICATION

Mikoyan-Gurevich MiG-25RB 'Foxbat-B'
generally similar to the Mikoyan-Gurevich MiG-25PDS 'Foxbat-E' except in the following particulars:
Wing: span 13.42 m (44 ft 0.25 in)
Weights: normal take-off 37000 kg (81,570 lb); maximum take-off 41200 kg (90,829 lb)
Fuel and load: internal fuel 15245 kg (33,609 lb); maximum ordnance 3000 kg (6,614 lb)
Range: ferry range with underbelly tank 2400 km (1,295 nm; 1,491 miles) subsonic or 2130 km (1150 nm; 1,323 miles) supersonic; range with internal fuel 1865 km (1,006 nm; 1,158 miles) subsonic or 1635 km (882 nm; 1,015 miles) supersonic
Performance: climb to 19000 m (41,885 ft) in 6 minutes 36 seconds 'clean' or 8 minutes 12 seconds with 2000 kg (4,409 lb) of bombs; service ceiling 21000 m (68,900 ft)

OPERATORS

Algeria: A single squadron is understood to operate some 16 MiG-25P interceptors and four MiG-25RB recce aircraft, although some reports estimate a total of 36 MiG-25s delivered

Azerbaijan: The Azeris seized several unserviceable MiG-25PD interceptors left behind when Russia withdrew from Nasosnaya air base, and also took over five MiG-25RBs. Their status is uncertain
Byelorussia: About 60 MiG-25PDs and MiG-25Rs of various types are believed to be in service
Bulgaria: Spares shortages and economic considerations have grounded Bulgaria's Tolbukhin/Dobritch-based MiG-25RBs since July 1991
Egypt: Egyptian markings were applied to Soviet MiG-25RBs operating from Egyptian bases during the early 1970s, but the type was never officially on charge
India: Five of the six MiG-25RBs delivered still serve with No. 102 Squadron, along with two MiG-25RUs
Iraq: Some 20 MiG-25s may have survived the Gulf War, several having been destroyed on the ground, two in the air, and at least one more lost to the USAF after the war, in January 1993
Kazakhstan: MiG-25RBs and other recce variants serve with the 39th RAP at Balkesh

A MiG-25RBK 'Foxbat-D' gets airborne, followed by a camera-equipped MiG-25RB 'Foxbat-B'. The MiG-25RBK has a large dielectric panel on each side of the nose, serving a SLAR, and has no undernose camera ports.

Libya: Libya's fleet of MiG-25s includes 60 fighters (MiG-25Ps and PDs), with five trainers and five RBs
Russia: Russia retains a number of MiG-25 regiments, especially in the reconnaissance role. MiG-25R squadrons were among the last units withdrawn from both Poland and Germany
Syria: Thirty MiG-25Ps are augmented by some five MiG-25PUs and six MiG-25RBs
Ukraine: MiG-25RBs and other recce variants serve with the 48th RAP at Kolomyya, while MiG-25PDs serve the Air Defence Force's 933rd IAP at Dnepropetrovsk (Voloskoye)

Mikoyan-Gurevich **MiG-25BM 'Foxbat-F'**

The **MiG-25BM** is a dedicated defence suppression aircraft, based on the airframe of the MiG-25RB and designed for high-level, long-range, stand-off, anti-radar missions. This unusual approach was chosen because the traditional 'low down and dirty' close-in tactics used by American 'Wild Weasel' defence suppression aircraft were felt to impose an unacceptable and unnecessary degree of vulnerability. Development began in 1972, and the aircraft was produced between 1982 and 1985.

The primary armament of the MiG-25BM is the Kh-58 (NATO AS-11 'Kilter'), four of which are carried on the underwing pylons.

The 'Kilter' is a conventional-looking anti-radiation missile, with cruciform clipped-delta wings and smaller moving tailfins of similar shape. The missile has a passive radar-homing head, a 129-kg (285-lb) blast fragmentation warhead, and a solid fuel rocket motor which gives a range in excess of 30 miles (48 km). The new anti-radar Kh-31 may be a suitable replacement, offering higher speed and a longer reach.

MiG-25BMs observed in service have their noses painted to represent the radomes of fighter MiG-25s, and when the first photos of the aircraft emerged this led some Western analysts to assume that a

large nose radar was fitted. More recent photos show that a MiG-25R-type nose is fitted, with similar flush dielectric antennas on the sides. It is now almost certain that these cover passive emitter location devices. The aircraft often carry the huge (5300-litre; 1,400-US gal) underfuselage auxiliary fuel tanks often associated with the MiG-25PD 'Foxbat-E'.

Clad in partial pressure suits, the crew of a MiG-25BM stand in front of their high-altitude defence suppression aircraft. The nose is painted to simulate an AI radome.

Mikoyan MiG-27 'Flogger-D/-J'

Because it was seen by Western intelligence agencies first, the **MiG-27** was for many years regarded as the first ground attack derivative of the 'Flogger' family, and the MiG-23B variants were regarded as later, less sophisticated, cheaper versions. In fact, the MiG-23B/BN/BK/BM were interim types which filled the gap until the definitive MiG-27 could enter service. The earlier aircraft actually gained a later NATO codename because it was not recorded by Western observers until after the MiG-27, largely because it had never reached squadron service with the front-line Group of Soviet Forces in Germany, where Soviet tactical aircraft were usually first sighted.

The MiG-27 designation was originally applied to a number of clean-sheet-of-paper studies drawn up by the Mikoyan OKB to meet the requirement eventually fulfilled by the Su-25. During the 1950s and 1960s the advent of the tactical nuclear weapon had apparently removed the need for dedicated close-support aircraft, Frontal Aviation instead relying on supersonic fighter-bombers delivering single weapons against troop concentrations, bridges or other high-value targets. US experience in Vietnam showed the limitations of such aircraft when forced to operate with conventional weapons, and the *Shturmovik* role was rediscovered. The September 1967 Exercise Dneipr showed that the elderly subsonic MiG-17 was a more effective conventional close air support/battlefield air interdiction aircraft than the MiG-21 or Su-7, although the supersonic fighters clearly had a role to play in attacking targets farther behind enemy lines. The OKB simultaneously worked on two designs under the MiG-27 designation, drawing up a subsonic **MiG-27Sh** (similar in configuration to the Anglo-French Jaguar) and a supersonic delta-winged MiG-27. In the event Sukhoi produced the Su-25 to fulfil the *Shturmovik* role, and financial considerations forced the OKB to produce a MiG-23-based fighter-bomber reusing the MiG-27 designation.

The new aircraft featured simplified, but slightly larger, 'bulged' air intakes, without the large variable intake ramps of previous 'Flogger' variants. The simplified two-position afterburner nozzle is externally similar to the nozzle fitted to MiG-23BMs and BKs. These modifications improve fuel economy and dramatically reduce weight, at the expense of absolute top speed performance. To improve the aircraft's warload, an extra (seventh) hardpoint was added on the centreline, and the original underfuselage

pylons were moved out to the intake ducts to allow wider stores to be carried. The two pylons on the sides of the rear fuselage, behind the main undercarriage, first fitted on the MiG-23B series, were retained, and may have been stressed to carry heavier stores. They are seldom used, however, since they impose a limit on the amount of fuel that can be carried because of centre of gravity considerations. A new six-barrelled GSh-6-30 30-mm cannon with 260 rounds of ammunition replaced the 23-mm cannon, which had often been described as inadequate for strafing ground targets and which carried only 200 rounds. The new mounting imposed a greater drag penalty than a podded gun, but had some advantages. Access for armourers and maintenance personnel was improved, and the risk of dangerous gases building up within the fuselage was completely avoided.

Further cannon armament can be added in underwing pods, including the UPK-23 23-mm cannon pod and the SPPU-22 gun pod that contains a 23-mm cannon with barrels which can be depressed for strafing ground targets in level flight. The full range of guided and unguided bombs and rockets

can be carried, including the new KMG-U bomblet dispenser and various tactical nuclear weapons. Mikoyan is not coy about this capability, listing the option between references to 500-kg (1,102-lb) bombs and napalm tanks. The aircraft can also be used in the tactical reconnaissance role, and some front-line Soviet MiG-27s have been

The original MiG-27K introduced a laser rangefinder in the nose, but retained the undernose 'Swift Rod' ILS antenna.

photographed with a reconnaissance pod on the starboard under-intake pylon. Plans are afoot to add a measure of defence suppres-

Above: The MiG-27 usually uses a single cruciform brake chute, as seen here. The MiG-27 can operate from rough, semi-prepared strips, thanks to its variable-geometry wing and strong undercarriage.

Left: Wearing a Guards badge on the intake, and carrying an unidentified pod below the starboard intake (perhaps a guidance/datalink pod for an ASM?), a Lärz-based, yellow-coded MiG-27D 'Flogger-J' taxis in after a mission.

sion capability, with the Kh-31 anti-radar missile having been spotted on some test and trials aircraft. Heavier than any other 'Flogger' variant, the MiG-27 required a redesigned undercarriage and large, high-pressure tyres. This necessitated the provision of new bulged main undercarriage doors.

The original MiG-27 and similar **MiG-27K 'Flogger-D'** were ordered into production directly off the drawing board, and the prototype (a converted MiG-23BM airframe) made its maiden flight during 1972 in the hands of Valery Menitsky, later to become OKB chief test pilot. Early examples were soon in service with the Group of Soviet Forces in Germany, equipping regiments at Mirow, Finsterwalde and Altenburg. Eventually, the MiG-27 equipped four of the 16th Air Army's fighter-bomber regiments, at Lärz, Grossenhain, Finsterwalde and Brand. The MiG-27 also served with the 59th Air Army in Hungary. The 'straight' MiG-27 (perhaps delivered without cannon armament) was very soon replaced by the MiG-27K, equipped with the PrNK-23K nav/attack system and a Fone laser rangefinder/target tracker mounted behind a small window in the nose. The MiG-27K was capable of automatic night or bad weather blind bombing with a very high degree of accuracy. RWR and ECM equipment is highly automated, and a new stores management system gives the pilot greater flexibility in selecting and using weapons.

There are several sub-variants of the aircraft known to NATO as **'Flogger-J'**, all equipped with the PrNK-23M nav/attack system, and 'Pelenga' weapons system giving compatability with PGMs and guided ASMs. All have wing glove bullet fairings removed and with extended wing leading-edge root extensions. The latter were added to serve as a location for the forward hemisphere RWR antennas, but also have the beneficial side effect of improving high-Alpha handling. All 'Flogger-Js' have a new Klen (maple) laser rangefinder in place of the MiG-27K's Fone unit. The 'Swift Rod' ILS antenna was moved from below the nose to the port side of the nose, opposite the pitot. Maximum take-off weight is increased to 20670 kg (45,569 lb).

There is some confusion as to the Soviet designations of some of the aircraft. The first of the 'Flogger-Js' was the new-build **MiG-27M**, which has an enlarged laser window in the nose, below a dielectric 'pimple' which protrudes forward from its upper 'lip'. Some externally identical aircraft (reportedly produced through conversion of ordinary MiG-27s) allegedly bear the Soviet air force designation **MiG-27D**. This variant incorporates the RSBN-6S navigation system, which is associated with the nuclear strike role. The twin pitot probes which serve the nav/attack system are mounted

Above: The pimple nose identifies this aircraft as a MiG-27K 'Flogger-J2'. A fresh coat of paint has rendered the scabbed-on cockpit armour especially visible.

Right: An Indian Air Force MiG-27L of No. 9 Squadron ('Wolfpack') in flight. Indian MiG-27s are broadly similar to the MiG-27D or MiG-27K.

high on the nose, providing the main recognition features between the basic MiG-27D/MiG-27K 'Flogger-J' and the **MiG-27K 'Flogger-J2'**. The latter variant was produced as a new-build aircraft, and by conversion of MiG-27s, MiG-27Ds and perhaps MiG-27Ms. It has a noticeable fairing below the nose, with a broad rectangular window for a FLIR system, and an upper window for the laser target designator. The new system is a member of the Kaira family, equivalent to the equipment used on the Su-24M. The twin pitots are mounted low on the nose and the 'pimple' radome is enlarged.

The Soviet Union exported its most capable bombers and strike aircraft only to a handful of its most-trusted Warsaw Pact allies and a few most-favoured client states. Thus, like the Su-24 'Fencer', the MiG-27 has not been made widely available to foreign customers. The only exception so far has been India, which actually builds the MiG-27 under licence, operating a version which it calls the MiG-27M or **Bahadur** (Valiant), but which Mikoyan refers to as the **MiG-27L**. The aircraft has the same nose contours as the MiG-27M/D, with only a single window in the undernose fairing, and shares the same 'Flogger-J' reporting name, and not the 'Flogger-J2' reporting name of the MiG-27K. The first Indian-assembled example was rolled out in October 1984, and the first MiG-27L using Indian-built sub-assemblies was rolled out on 11 January 1986. India's requirement is for 165 aircraft to equip six squadrons, five of which had formed by the end of 1992. All are now operational with the type.

The MiG-27 received its baptism of fire in Afghanistan where a regiment of MiG-27Ds was deployed to Shindand for offensive operations against Mujahideen guerrilla positions. Flying their first mission on 31 October 1987, the MiG-27s flew intensively until withdrawn on 15 February 1989. Overwing chaff/flare dispensers were hurriedly fitted as a result of this combat experience. The MiG-27 is said to be much more capa-

ble than its main rival, the Su-17M-4 'Fitter-K', but its more demanding handling characteristics, relative fragility and less easy maintenance reportedly make it less popular. The drawdown in defence spending following the end of the Cold War has affected Russia as much as any other nation, and the MiG-23BN and MiG-27 are likely to be casualties of the current policy of reducing the number of different aircraft types in service, which will see older single-engined types like the MiG-27 and Su-17 replaced by newer, twin-engined tactical aircraft like the Su-24, MiG-29 and Su-27.

SPECIFICATION

Mikoyan MiG-27 'Flogger-D'

Wing: span 13.97 m (45 ft 9.8 in) spread and 7.78 m (25 ft 6.25 in) swept; aspect ratio 5.22 spread and 1.77 swept; area 37.35 m2 (402.05 sq ft) spread and 34.16 m2 (367.71 sq ft) swept

Fuselage and tail: length 17.08 m (56 ft 0.25 in) including probe; height 5.00 m (16 ft 5 in); tailplane span 5.75 m (18 ft 10.25 in); wheel track 2.66 m (8 ft 8.75 in); wheel base 5.772 m (18 ft 11.25 in)

Powerplant: one MNPK 'Soyuz' (Tumanskii) R-29B-300 turbojet rated at 78.45 kN (17,637 lb st) dry and 112.77 kN (25,353 lb st) with afterburning

Weights: empty equipped 11908 kg (26,252 lb); normal take-off 18100 kg (39,903 lb); maximum take-off 20300 kg (44,753 lb)

Fuel and load: internal fuel 4560 kg (10,053 lb); external fuel up to three 790-litre (209-US gal) drop tanks; maximum ordnance more than 4000 kg (8,818 lb)

Speed: maximum level speed 'clean' at 8000 m (26,245 ft) 1885 km/h (1,017 kt; 1,170 mph) or at sea level 1350 km/h (728 kt; 839 mph)

Range: combat radius 540 km (291 nm; 335 miles) on a lo-lo-lo attack mission with two Kh-29 ASMs and three drop tanks, or 225 km (121 nm; 140 miles) with two Kh-29 ASMs

Performance: maximum rate of climb at sea level 12000 m (39,370 ft) per minute; service ceiling 14000 m (45,930 ft); take-off run 950 m (3,117 ft) at maximum take-off weight; landing run 1300 m (4,265 ft) at normal landing weight without brake

chute or 900 m (2,953 ft) at normal landing weight with brake chute

g limits: +7.0

OPERATORS

Byelorussia: Five MiG-27s are believed to be in service in Byelorussia, though they may be scrapped to comply with CFE limitations

India: MiG-27s serve with Nos 2, 9, 18, 22, 31 and 222 Squadrons, which are nominally based at Hindan, Halwara and Hashimara. India has ordered 165, progressively incorporating more and more local content (and eventually being fully licence-built) to replace the Su-7, Marut and Ajeet

Kazakhstan: The 11th Fighter-Bomber Division augments its Su-24 strike regiment with two MiG-27 units, the 129th IBAP at Taldy Kurgan and the 134th IBAP at Zhang Iztobe

Turkmenistan: MiG-27s were among the aircraft offered for sale by Turkmenistan, and probably will not be among the 32 aircraft retained for the air arm's planned single fighter regiment

Russia: The MiG-27M remains in service in significant numbers, although it is being rapidly withdrawn from use to comply with CFE treaty limitations and to allow the air force to standardise on more modern, twin-engined tactical aircraft. Large numbers of MiG-27s were withdrawn to European Russia and the Far East from both Hungary (regiments at Debrecen and Kunmadaras) and East Germany (the 19th IBAP at Lärz, the 116th IBAP at Brand, the 296th IBAP at Grossenhain and the 339th at Finsterwalde), joining significant numbers of regiments already based in Russia

Ukraine: In 1992 Ukraine tried to sell 27 surplus MiG-27Ks for $16 million each, at which time it had 49 of these aircraft on strength, all reportedly withdrawn from front-line service and held at the 117th Aircraft Repair Factory at Lvov, the 562nd Aircraft Repair Factory at Odessa or, more ominously, at the 6221st Aircraft Destruction Base

Uzbekistan: A regiment of MiG-27s at Chirchik has been used to support government forces engaged in the civil war in neighbouring Tadjikistan and remains under central CIS control

Mikoyan MiG-29 'Fulcrum-A' (9-12)

Comparisons between the **MiG-29** (initially allocated the internal OKB designation **9-12**) and the American Lockheed (General Dynamics) F-16 are perhaps inevitable, since both fulfil the same broad tactical fighter role, both are extremely agile high-performance aircraft optimised for dogfighting, both have been widely exported, and both were designed to meet requirements for a 'lightweight fighter'.

The MiG-29 which is recognised today was derived from a study for a heavier fighter (also designated MiG-29) designed to counter the F-15 under the Perspektivnyi Frontovoi Istrebeitel ('prospective frontal fighter') competition. The Mikoyan OKB proposed following the US example, with both heavy and light fighters complementing each other to meet the requirement. Its arguments were accepted and the requirement was redrafted to cover two quite separate aircraft. The new Soviet air forces' requirement for a Logkii Frontovoi Istrebityel ('lightweight front-line fighter') was issued in 1972, and Mikoyan successfully submitted a smaller version of the original design, the **MiG-29D** (Dubler – double), while Sukhoi submitted the T-10 proposal to meet the Tyazholyi Frontovoi Istrebityel requirement.

The new Soviet air force LFI requirement detailed a replacement for Frontal Aviation's MiG-21s and MiG-23s, Su-7s and Su-17s. The new fighter was to be capable of destroying enemy fighters in air combat, destroying enemy bombers and reconnaissance aircraft, and escorting friendly bombers and attack aircraft. The aircraft would also have an important secondary ground attack role. A production order was placed at the same time as the Technical Assignment was issued, meaning that the MiG-29 never received an in-house I- ('Ye-') designation.

The increasing importance of low-level penetration by attack aircraft made lookdown/shoot-down capability vital, while the growing importance of ECM made a capacity for independent action similarly important. The aircraft was from the start designed to be able to beat the new generation of US fighters (the F-14, F-15, YF-16 and YF-17) in air combat, and to restore the tarnished reputation of Soviet fighters incurred by heavy losses in the Middle East. Finally, a measure of rough-field/dispersed site capability was felt to be essential. Detailed design work began in 1974, the year that the F-15 entered service and that the YF-16 first flew.

While the MiG-29's configuration is superficially similar to those of the F-14, F-15, YF-17 and Su-27, it is different in many important ways, although common problems make some common solutions inevitable. Starting with a blended high-lift, low-drag wing and forebody, Mikoyan added twin canted fins, widely flared wing leading-edge root extensions and widely spaced twin engines with carefully tailored intakes to maximise high angle-of-attack capability. The original MiG-29 had been broadly similar, but with a faired-in MiG-25-type cockpit and with MiG-25-type engine intakes on each side of a conventional fuselage, with no inter-engine tunnel.

While some have criticised the MiG-29 for its supposedly crude finish in places, there can be no doubt that its aerodynamic design is extremely advanced, giving unmatched low-speed and high-Alpha handling characteristics, which can be invaluable

The earliest production MiG-29s had ventral fins below the vertical fins and tailplanes, and lacked the fin leading-edge extension chaff/flare dispensers fitted to later MiG-29s. These early aircraft were retrofitted with broad-chord rudders and pitot-mounted vortex generators after entry into service.

Above: Trailing its distinctive cruciform drag chute, a MiG-29 lands at Rissala during an exchange visit to Finland during 1986. The aircraft represents the initial definitive production standard. It has no ventral fins, and has narrow-chord rudders and an undernose 'Swift Rod' ILS antenna, but does have the fin leading-edge flare dispensers.

Right: The very first production series MiG-29s had an unusual debris deflector ahead of the nosewheels. Some are still used for trials, like this aircraft, which has a MiG-29M-type embedded radio compass antenna in the canopy.

in a 'close-in' engagement. The electro-mechanical flight control system has no 'hard limits', allowing the pilot briefly to override pitch and *g* limiters when tactically necessary, by deliberately pulling through a stick stop to enter that area of the flight envelope where departure becomes progressively more likely. Ample aerodynamic warning is given before the aircraft departs. When it does, the MiG-29 is reluctant to spin and recovers when pro-spin controls are released. Sophisticated aileron/rudder interconnects gradually phase out aileron at increasing angles of attack.

Flying controls are mainly conventional, and are hydraulically controlled. Computer-controlled full-span manoeuvre flaps occupy the wing leading edge, with plain flaps inboard and ailerons outboard on the trailing edge. The horizontal tail surfaces are all-moving.

To allow the aircraft to operate from primitive forward airfields, the low-mounted intakes are fitted with large doors that close on start-up, open only after the aircraft has rotated on take-off, and close again when the mainwheels touch on landing. These prevent the ingestion of mud, snow or other debris. While the main intakes are closed, air is drawn in through spring-loaded louvres in the top of the wingroots. Flight is possible at speeds of up to 800 km/h (432 kt; 500 mph) with the main intakes closed.

The MiG-29 broke much new ground for Mikoyan, with advanced aerodynamics, avionics, systems and even materials. The new aircraft made extensive use of advanced, lightweight aluminium-lithium alloys, which allowed fewer fasteners and bolts to be used, with savings in weight and production complexity. The operational life of the MiG-29

airframe, however, is believed to be significantly shorter than equivalent Western aircraft types.

The MiG-29 is powered by a pair of Sargisov (Leningrad/Klimov, formerly Isotov) RD-33 afterburning turbofans. These produce considerably more augmented thrust than equivalent Western aircraft types, but slightly less in dry power. This can make the aircraft more reliant on using afterburner in some circumstances, increasing fuel consumption. The latest versions of the engine have a full-authority digital engine-control system, and a sophisticated stall prevention/relight system. The engine is understood to have a four-stage fan (with fixed stator vanes) and a nine-stage high-pressure compressor (with variable stators on the first three stages). The time between overhauls is reportedly 350 hours.

This quartet of Indian MiG-29s is drawn from Nos 28 and 47 Squadrons. Coloured tail units are used to differentiate friend from foe during non-dissimilar air combat training. Each aircraft carries an R-60 AA-8 'Aphid' acquisition round.

Eleven prototypes (9-01 to 9-11) were built, the first flying initially on 6 October 1977. Two of them were lost in engine-related accidents. Spotted by a US satellite at Ramenskoye in November 1977, the aircraft was allocated the provisional reporting name **'Ram-L'**. The prototypes were followed by eight pre-production aircraft (9-12 to 9-19). Frontal Aviation evaluation commenced in 1983, and the aircraft began to enter service soon afterwards, initially with the Kubinka and Ros regiments. Early reliability problems were soon solved, and MTBF figures rose from 2.3 hours to 5.7 hours by 1988, while mission-capable rates rose from 65 per cent to 90 per cent over the same period.

The 'bald' MiG-29 designation covers most of the single-seat fighters delivered so far, although a host of improvements have been incorporated, some of them giving the aircraft involved a distinctive appearance and which might have been expected to lead to allocation of a new service designation (see **'Fulcrum-C'** entry). Small ventral fins, initially fitted to the prototype after its first flight, were deleted after a small batch of production aircraft (probably about 100) had been completed, at the same time as overwing chaff/flare dispensers were fitted in extensions to the tailfin leading edges. Extended-chord rudders and pitot-mounted vortex generators were adopted in the late 1980s, and were retrofitted to all service aircraft (including some of the earliest standard ventral-finned machines which remained in use even in 1994).

In the fighter role, the MiG-29 carries six underwing missiles, with two BVR R-27R/AKU-470 AA-10 'Alamo-As' inboard (usually both semi-active radar homing, but sometimes with one IR-homing 'Alamo-B') and four R-60/AA-8 'Aphid' or AA-11 'Archer' short-range IR-homing AAMs outboard. These are backed up by an internal lightweight GSh-301 single-barrelled 30-mm cannon, which replaced a twin-barrelled weapon on the first prototype.

The fire-control system is a sophisticated sensor, with data gathered by the aircraft's sensors being datalinked to a ground station or AWACS aircraft. The radar is extremely powerful and can easily overwhelm the pilot with information, and filtering and software techniques are inadequate for on-board threat prioritisation. The need to keep contact with an external agency limits the MiG pilot's capacity for independent action, and imposes a degree of inflexibility. ('Freelance' operations and independent search are, however, seen as desirable, and are stressed much more in current doctrine.)

The MiG-29 has two sensors for target acquisition. The first is the N-019 pulse-Doppler radar, which has previously been misidentified as the HO-93, the HO-193 and the NO-193, confusion arising because the Cyrillic letter 'H' is in fact an English 'N', and the '3' is an 'E' (for export), and because on a Farnborough demonstrator a hyphen was misplaced. The radar is known to NATO as 'Slot Back'. A measure of passive target acquisition capability is afforded by the IRST, which has a collimated laser rangefinder. This can be used to detect, track and engage a target while leaving the radar in a passive (non-emitting) mode, ready to be 'turned on' if contact is lost (if the target goes into cloud, for instance) or to fire a semi-active radar-homing missile. All the while, the target aircraft's RWR will not detect the MiG-29's unwelcome attentions.

For close-in engagements, a helmet-mounted sight (which works by sensing the pilot's head position) can be used to cue IR-homing missiles onto an off-boresight target. This is extremely useful in conjunction with the very agile R-73 (AA-11 'Archer') AAM, although firing at an angle well off the nose dramatically reduces missile range.

Primarily designed for fighter/air superiority duties, the MiG-29 nonetheless has an important secondary ground attack role. It is therefore able to carry a variety of bombs, rockets and missiles on the inboard and central underwing pylons, although the outboard pylons are believed to be reserved for the carriage of R-60 (AA-8 'Aphid') or R-73 IR-homing AAMs. Many Frontal Aviation MiG-29 regiments are believed to incorporate a nuclear strike squadron, whose aircraft can carry a single 30-kT RN-40 nuclear bomb on the port inboard pylon. A handful of MiG-29 regiments have even been assigned a primary air-to-ground role, including at least one of the units now under Ukrainian command. For ferrying, fuel tanks can be carried under the inboard

A Soviet air force MiG-29 undergoes servicing; with its radome removed, the unusual twist-cassegrain antenna of the 'Fulcrum's' N-019 'Slot Back' radar is revealed. The MiG-29 is remarkably maintainable but operators have to suffer a short time-between-overhauls, plus poor after-sales support and spares availability.

MiG-29 'Fulcrum-A'

Mikoyan MiG-29 'Fulcrum-A' (9-12)

A Czech MiG-29 reefs into a 'burner climb. The Czechoslovakian and East German air forces had their MiG-29s delivered in brown and green camouflage, applied to only a handful of Soviet MiG-29s. The Czech Republic is selling the MiG-29s it inherited on the division of Czechoslovakia.

underwing pylons, augmenting the tank carried on the centreline, which is stressed to 9 g.

About 450 'Fulcrums' are estimated to be in service with the VVS (more than 300 were in service with the Soviet air forces in East Germany alone during 1990), with 50 more in AV-MF service. Byelorussia, Kazakhstan, Moldova and Ukraine account for some 350 more. An estimated 380 have been delivered to export customers. Total production, including UBs and 'Fulcrum-Cs', probably stands at 1,250-1,350.

The Moscow Aircraft Production Organisation is presently offering a programme of modifications to MiG-29 operators that is aimed at improving the aircraft's combat potential. This programme would bring any 'Fulcrum-A' to virtual MiG-29S or MiG-29SE standard. These variants are described separately under the 9-13 'Fulcrum-C' entry. The modifications include making the inboard underwing pylons compatible with a pair of 1150-litre (304-US gal) fuel tanks (this modification has already been applied to some 40 per cent of Russian MiG-29s, including the factory demonstrators and most of those aircraft based in Germany and Hungary). Other improvements include the provision of compatibility with the new

This MiG-29 wears old-style Yugoslav markings, which have been replaced on some aircraft by a horizontally banded roundel on the intake (blue, white and red, descending) and a similar fin flash on the tail.

R-77 (AAM-AE) active radar homing missile and simultaneous two-target engagement capability. The flight control system is modified to allow the aircraft to reach higher angles of attack (30°+), and Western navaids can be installed. A new radio with the standard international emergency frequency of 243 MHz is also provided. Finally, the inboard underwing pylons are restressed for the carriage of up to four 500-kg (1,102-lb) bombs each, in tandem side-by-side pairs.

MAPO hopes to offer a retrofitted in-flight-refuelling probe, a ground mapping radar mode and compatibility with anti-radar, TV- and laser-guided ASMs in 1995.

WEAPON OPTIONS

In service, the MiG-29 is used primarily in the air-to-air fighter role. Its primary BVR armament is the R-27 (AA-10 'Alamo'), two of which may be carried on the inboard underwing pylons. The 'Fulcrum' usually carries the short-burn semi-active radar-homing R-27R ('Alamo-A') sometimes with one example of the similar IR-homing R-27T ('Alamo-B'), or sometimes as a pair of semi-active radar-homing missiles. The 'Fulcrum' is believed to be compatible with later long-burn versions of the R-27, but these have not been noted in released photographs and may have been given to long-range PVO interceptor Su-27s as a priority. Early reports that the MiG-29 could carry the AA-9 'Amos' are completely unfounded. When it first entered service, the MiG-29 usually carried R-60 (AA-8 'Aphid') short-range IR-homing missiles on the centre and outboard underwing pylons, but these have largely been replaced by the more capable R-73 RM2D (AA-11 'Archer'), a short-range IR-homing dogfight missile of exceptional agility, which has been rated by some experts as being superior to any Western equivalent. Some MiG-29s, especially those supplied to Warsaw Pact export customers, have been seen with 'cheap' AA-8s outboard, a pair of AA-11s on the centre pylons and AA-10s inboard. Some foreign customers (Cuba, Iran, Iraq and Syria, for example) may not have received AA-11s at all. In the future, MiG-29s will probably receive the active-homing R-77 ('AMRAAMski'), if it enters service, but

this will require some modifications. In the fighter-bomber role, MiG-29s have been seen carrying the B-8W 20-round 80-mm rocket pod and the older UV-32-57 32-round 57-mm rocket pod on inboard and/or centre underwing pylons. The S-24 240-mm rocket can be carried singly on the same pylons. The MiG-29 is believed to be compatible with the B-13 five-round 130-mm rocket pod, although use of this pod has not yet been confirmed. 'Fulcrum' ground attack weapons which can be confirmed include FAB-250ShN and -500ShN, FAB-250M-46 and -500M-46 and FAB-250M-62 and -500M-62 general-purpose bombs, and a range of specialised weapons. These included cluster bombs like the RBK-250 and -500, containing AO-2.5 RTM fragmentation munitions, BETAB concrete penetrators, PTAB-1M anti-armour munitions, ShOAB-0.5 anti-personnel mines, or SPBE anti-armour bomblets. The reusable KMGU-2 sub-munition dispenser carries AO-2.5 fragmentation bombs, which are dispensed through the container's rotary doors downwards, or to either side, depending on how the KMGU-2 container is mounted. BETAB-250 or -500 concrete-piercing bombs, BRAB-200, -220 and -500 armour-piercing bombs, FOZAB-500 incendiary bombs, ODAB-500 FAE bombs, and the deadly OFZAB-500 fragmentation/incendiary bomb are also compatible with the MiG-29.

SPECIFICATION

Mikoyan MiG-29 'Fulcrum-A'
Wing: span 11.36 m (37 ft 3.25 in); aspect ratio 3.4; wing area 38.00 m² (409.04 sq ft)
Fuselage and tail: length 17.32 m (56 ft 9.85 in) including probe; height 4.73 m (15 ft 6.2 in); tailplane span 7.78 m (25 ft 6.25 in); wheel track 3.10 m (10 ft 2 in); wheel base 3.67 m (12 ft 0.5 in)
Powerplant: two Klimov/Leningrad (Isotov/Sarkisov) RD-33 augmented turbofans each rated at 49.42 kN (11,111 lb st) dry and 81.39 kN (18,298 lb st) with afterburning
Weights: operating empty 10900 kg (24,030 lb); normal take-off 15240 kg (33,598 lb); maximum take-off 18500 kg (40,785 lb)
Fuel and load: internal fuel 3200 kg (7,055 lb) 4300-4365 litres (1,136-1,153 US gal); external fuel one 1500-1520 litre (396-402 US gal) centreline tank and (on some Soviet aircraft) two 1150-litre (303-US gal) underwing ferry tanks; maximum ordnance 3000 kg (6,614 lb)
Speed: maximum level speed 'clean' at 11000 m (36,090 ft) 2445 km/h (1,319 kt; 1,519 mph) or at sea level 1500 km/h (810 kt; 932 mph)
Range: ferry range 2100 km (1,134 nm; 1,305 miles) with three tanks; range 1500 km (810 nm; 932 miles) with internal fuel
Performance: maximum rate of climb at sea level 19800 m (64,961 ft) per minute; service ceiling 17000 m (55,775 ft); take-off run 250 m (820 ft) at normal take-off weight; landing run 600 m (1,969 ft) at normal landing weight with brake-chute
g limits: +9 below Mach 0.85 and +7 above Mach 0.85

An Iraqi MiG-29 takes off before Desert Storm. Iraqi 'Fulcrum' strength was severely depleted by the Gulf War, with losses in air-to-air combat and on the ground to coalition airfield attacks, together with the non-return of aircraft which fled to Iran for sanctuary.

OPERATORS

Afghanistan: Before the fall of the Kabul regime, there were negotiations for the supply of MiG-29s
Byelorussia: At least one MiG-29 regiment has been based in Byelorussia, at Minsk for many years, and this has been joined by the 787th IAP from Finow in Germany, which withdrew to Ros. A further regiment is based at Baranovich
Bulgaria: The MiG-29 equips two fighter regiments at Rawnetz and Jambol. An estimated 22 (including four two-seaters) were delivered in 1990
China: There are persistent reports that China intends ordering MiG-29s to augment its Su-27s. It has already bought RD-33 engines to upgrade its J-7s
Cuba: An initial batch of seven MiG-29s was delivered to San Antonio de los Banos during 1990. Deliveries are believed to have reached about 16 aircraft. A requirement for 36 MiG-29s is unlikely to be fulfilled
Czechoslovakia: Eighteen MiG-29s and two MiG-29UBs were delivered to Czechoslovakia for the 11th Fighter Regiment at Zatec. Delivery of the rest of the 40-aircraft order was halted by economic problems. On the division of Czechoslovakia, the MiG-29s were divided evenly between the new Czech and Slovak Republics
Czech Republic: With only nine MiG-29s and a single UB (since written off) remaining after the split with Slovakia, the Czech Republic assessed that this was not sufficient to form a viable unit and moved the aircraft from Zatec to Ceske Budejovice to join the air arm's MiG-23s. It was eventually decided to sell the MiG-29s to Slovakia, Israel or Iraq, and the aircraft were grounded from 1 July 1994 pending disposal
Germany: Twenty MiG-29s and four MiG-29UBs were delivered to the first and second *Staffeln* of JFG 3 'Vladimir Komarov' at Preschen from May 1988 An order for 32 more MiG-29s was cancelled after reunification, on payment of a massive penalty clause The aircraft were absorbed into the Luftwaffe (as a redesignated single-*Staffel* JG-3) and will eventually move to Laage to join a squadron of Phantoms as JG 73. MiG-29s also flew with WTD 61 for evaluation and trials, and some aircraft were loaned to friendly air forces for evaluation. A front-line fighter squadron, JG 3 has also operated successfully as an adversary unit, and was heavily involved in preparing coalition aircrew for Operation Desert Storm
Hungary: Twenty-two MiG-29s and six MiG-29UBs were delivered to Hungary in lieu of debt repayments from October 1993. These will re-equip the 'Puma' and 'Wasp' squadrons of the Kécskemet-based Vitez Szenfgyörgyi Deszo Regiment, and will be declared operational in September 1994
India: An initial batch of 45 single-seat MiG-29s (sometimes referred to as MiG-29Bs) and five UBs (no 42 single-seaters and eight UBs reported elsewhere)

was delivered to equip Nos 28 and 47 Squadrons at Poona. A second batch of 20 MiG-29s (all single-seaters) went to No. 223 Squadron at the same base. An attrition/top-up batch of 10 aircraft has now reportedly been ordered, and an order for up to 30 MiG-29Ms is under consideration

Iran: Iran received 14 MiG-29s in 1990, and gained either four or eight more when Iraqi aircraft fled to Iran for sanctuary during Desert Storm

Iraq: An estimated 36 MiG-29s (of some 50 delivered) survived the Gulf War, though spares shortages and the withdrawal of Russian advisors leave their status in some doubt. Five were shot down during Desert Storm and one during Southern Watch, and others were destroyed on the ground. Iraq claims that eight MiG-29s fled to Iran, while Iran admits to receiving four

Kazakhstan: Air force units in Kazakhstan remain under CIS (Russian) command and control and include the 715th IAP with MiG-29s at Lugovaya

Kyrgizia: The independent republic of Kyrgizia declared its sovereignty over Frunze-Lygovaya near the capital at Rishkek. This was used for MiG-29 conversion training for pilots from foreign customer nations and may have a based regiment

Malaysia: Malaysia has ordered 18 MiG-29s (including six two-seaters) which are expected to be variants of the MiG-29S, although pre-conditions set by the Malaysians would seem to exclude anything less capable than the MiG-29M

Moldova: Moldova took over some 34 MiG-29s from the 86th IAP (an AVMF fighter regiment) but had only four MiG-29-qualified pilots. The aircraft were used in bombing attacks on the breakaway Pridnestrovskaya Republic, and one was lost to a SAM. Moldova wishes to exchange its MiGs for more useful attack helicopters and has approached Russia and Romania

Turkmenistan: Turkmenistan includes the Mary training range complex, which may have a based MiG-29 regiment.

North Korea: The 57th Fighter Regiment at Onchon operates an estimated 30 MiG-29s (delivered in 1988)

Poland: The first squadron of No. 1 PLM operates nine single-seat MiG-29s and three UBs from its Minsk-Mazowiecki base. These were delivered in 1989 and 1990

Romania: The 57th Fighter Regiment's 2nd Esquadrilla operates 14 single-seat MiG-29s and a pair of UBs from Constanta-Mihail Kogalniceanu. These were delivered in 1989

Russia: A number of MiG-29 regiments are based in Russia. The 234th 'Proskurovskii' Guards IAP at Kubinka includes one expanded squadron of MiG-29s (of almost regimental strength and including the 'Swifts' aerobatic team). Other Russia-based regiments include the 176th IAP at Ruslan AB, Tskhakaya, and another at Primorsko-Akhtarsk. Six of the eight MiG-29 regiments formerly based in Germany have also returned to bases in Russia, the other two flying to bases in Byelorussia

and Ukraine. The 33rd IAP at Wittstock and the 733rd IAP at Pütnitz-Damgarten returned to Anreapol, while the 31st 'Nilopolskyi' Guards IAP from Alt Lonnewitz returned to Zernograd. The destinations of the 35th IAP from Zerbst, the 73rd 'Sevastapolski' IAP from Merseburg and the 968th Guards IAP from Altenburg are unknown. The 19th Guards Fighter-Bomber Regiment replaced its MiG-27s with MiG-29s when it returned from Germany and is based at Milerovo near Rostov. At least 14 regiments were equipped with the 'Fulcrum-A' by 1989

Serbia: Serbia inherited all 14 MiG-29s and both MiG-29UBs from the former Yugoslavia. These still equip the 204th Fighter Regiment's 127th Fighter Squadron at Batajnica, near Belgrade

Slovakia: Slovakia took over nine single-seat MiG-29s and a single UB on the division of Czechoslovakia. These were assigned to the 1st Fighter Regiment's 1st Fighter Squadron at Sliac and have been augmented by five ex-Ukrainian MiG-29s (including a single UB). Slovakia may buy further MiG-29s (from the Czech Republic or from Ukraine) or may take more from Russia in lieu of debt repayments

Syria: Twenty-four MiG-29s delivered in 1987 have reportedly been joined by two or three further batches of 24 aircraft each, and some 50 more are on order

Ukraine: The Ukrainian air force controls three air armies, with 185 MiG-29s in four regiments. The 5th Air Army, headquartered at Odessa, controls the 85th

This approach-configured MiG-29 is laden with R-27R AA-10 'Alamo' and R-73 AA-11 'Archers' underwing.

IAP at Starokonstantinov (which returned from Köthen in Germany) and the 642nd IBAP (a fighter-bomber unit) at Marlynovskoye, while the Lvov-headquartered 14th Air Army includes the 114th IAP at Ivano-Frankovsk. The autonomous air defence force's Western Region includes the 92nd IAP at Mukochevo. A handful of aircraft have been sold (e.g. to Slovakia). More MiG-29s are based at Mirgorod and Valsilkov

USA: The USAF evaluated two or three MiG-29s borrowed from the Luftwaffe, and there have been reports that secondhand MiG-29s may be procured for adversary training and tactics development

Yugoslavia: Fourteen single-seat MiG-29s and two UBs were delivered to the the 204th Fighter Regiment's 127th Fighter Squadron at Batajnica, near Belgrade, during October 1987 (see under Serbia)

Zimbabwe: A 1987 £125 million order for 12 MiG-29s was reportedly allowed to lapse

Others: The MiG-29 has been evaluated by Finland, Jordan, South Korea, Switzerland and a number of other nations. In Finland and Switzerland the MiG-29 lost out to the F/A-18, largely through its perceived lack of support infrastructure, and Jordan was unable to fund its intended purchase. A Taiwanese order was reportedly refused by the Russian government

Mikoyan MiG-29UB 'Fulcrum-B' (9-51)

SPECIFICATION

Due to its performance and handling characteristics, the MiG-29 clearly needed a two-seat conversion trainer variant. The extra weight of the second cockpit and the reduction in internal fuel tankage made it operationally limited, so the N-019 radar was deleted. Instead, the **MiG-29UB** (OKB designation **9-51**) trainer has a sophisticated weapons system and emergencies simulator, allowing the instructor to generate appropriate HUD and radar scope symbology in the front cockpit.

To minimise drag, the rear seat is not raised significantly. It was felt that an unobstructed view forward for the instructor was not a priority, with a small retractable periscope making up the deficiency.

The relatively low ratio of two-seat trainers delivered can be explained by the ease

of conversion to the MiG-29 from other Soviet Bloc fighters, and by the practice of converting aircrew from customer nations in

the Soviet Union itself. Most operators have a few two-seat aircraft, usually assigned to front-line units.

Mikoyan MiG-29UB 'Fulcrum-B'
generally similar to the Mikoyan MiG-29 'Fulcrum-A' except in the following particulars:
Fuselage and tail: length 17.42 m (57 ft 2 in)

A MiG-29UB 'Fulcrum-C' trainer wearing East German markings takes off from its Preschen base.

Mikoyan MiG-29 (9-13) and MiG-29S (9-13S) 'Fulcrum-C'

NATO allocated the new reporting name **'Fulcrum-C'** for aircraft fitted with a bulged and extended spine, which reportedly houses both fuel and avionics, and which may also be applied through retrofit. Internal fuel is increased by provision of a larger No. 1 fuel tank, though different sources disagree as to the size of the increase (75, 130, 175 or 240 litres/20, 34, 46 or 63 US gal, according to different Mikoyan documents). Soviet sources suggest that the 'Fulcrum-C' is still simply designated **MiG-29**, although the nickname 'Gorbatov' (hunchback) is commonly used.

The first 'fatbacked' MiG-29 was **9-13**, the second pre-production aircraft, which first flew on 23 December 1980, in the hands of V. M. Gorbunov. At one time the 'Fulcrum-C' seemed to be slowly replacing the 'Fulcrum-A' in **VVS** service, but the two types continued in production alongside one another and often serve in the same units (occasionally with the very early ventral-finned MiG-29s). Pilots report that apart from endurance, there is no difference in flying/operating characteristics, although some sources suggest that the 'Fulcrum-C' has an enhanced ground attack capability and/or provision for an active jammer. Certainly the 9-13 has redesigned wingtips which appear to accommodate new RWR antennas. No 'hunchbacked' 'Fulcrum-Cs' have been exported yet, though Malaysia's MiG-29s may prove to be based on the 'Fulcrum-C'.

The 9-13 forms the basis of the improved **MiG-29S** (**9-13S**), which was designed as an increased-capability version of the standard MiG-29. According to Mikoyan, the MiG-29S represents "what happened when we squeezed all we could from the basic MiG-29 airframe." The new variant has a modified flight control system, using small computers to improve stability and controllability, and the control surfaces have greater deflection. Alpha and *g* limits are increased. All MiG-29S features can be incorporated by upgrading existing 'Fulcrum-Cs', and MAPO is aggressively marketing a similar upgrade for export 'Fulcrum-As'.

The MiG-29S introduces revised radar/weapons system algorithms and software (and it is believed that processing capacity has been increased) to allow for the simultaneous tracking and engagement of multiple targets. The modified radar is redesignated N-019M. Operational capability has been enhanced by fitting a new sighting system, and more recently by making provision for the active homing AAM-AE 'AMRAAMski'. The first MiG-29S made its maiden flight during 1984, and three prototypes were followed by new production aircraft and conversions. Two *polk* (squadrons) are in service.

The designation **MiG-29SE** has been applied to an export version of the MiG-29S. This has a slightly downgraded radar (the

Right: One of the MiG-29S prototypes, this aircraft has a modified flight control system and upgraded radar, plus provision for Western avionics and underwing fuel tanks. A staged programme of modifications will allow the aircraft to carry up to 4000 kg of external stores. An inflight-refuelling probe and laser-, TV- and radar-guided ASMs will be added from 1995.

Right: The unique contours of the 'Fulcrum-C's enlarged fuselage spine led to the allocation of a new NATO reporting name, although the OKB designation is unchanged.

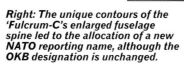

N-019ME) which retains multiple-target tracking and which may give compatibility with AAM-AE. An aircraft displayed at Le Bourget in June 1993 was not a MiG-29SE, but was a standard MiG-29 serving as a testbed, with a full standard MiG-29SE cockpit, new navaids and English language captions. Some sources have suggested that the MiG-29S was the first MiG-29 variant plumbed for the carriage of underwing fuel tanks, but this is untrue, since many Soviet 'Fulcrum-As' have been seen carrying these for ferry flights. The MiG-29S may, however, be the first variant stressed to carry underwing tanks in combat, or to have provision for extra pylons (like the MiG-29M and MiG-29K, which are described separately) to allow tanks to be carried without sacrificing weapons, and is the first export model offered with underwing tanks. External warload is doubled by the simple expedient of restressing the inner underwing pylons to carry up to four 500-kg (1,102-lb) bombs in side-by-side tandem pairs.

The end of the Cold War has led to a dramatic down-scaling of MiG-29 production, both for the VVS and for export customers. Production in Moscow (at the Labour Banner factory) and in Nizhny Novograd continues at a very low rate, adding to a June 1993 stockpile which totalled about 100 unsold aircraft. A July 1993 Malaysian order for the MiG-29 may have been for some of these aircraft upgraded to MiG-29SE standards, or for MiG-29Ms. The 18 aircraft on order include some two-seaters (perhaps as

Right: Although the spine of the 'Fulcrum-C' is considerably enlarged, it contains only 75-240 litres of extra fuel.

many as six). Hungary's MiG-29s have been described as MiG-29Ss by some sources, but are actually standard 'Fulcrum-As'.

SPECIFICATION

Mikoyan MiG-29S
generally similar to the Mikoyan MiG-29 'Fulcrum-A'

except in the following particulars:
Weights: normal take-off weight 15300 kg (33,730 lb): maximum take-off weight 19700 kg (42,680 lb)
Fuel and load: internal fuel 4440-4540 litres (976-998 US gal), external fuel 3,800 litres (1,004 US gal): maximum ordnance load 4000 kg (8,818 lb)
Range: ferry range 2900 km (1,566 nm; 1,802 miles) with three drop tanks

Below: The brown and green ground attack colour scheme worn by some Russian and Ukrainian MiG-29s (mainly 'Fulcrum-Cs', but including some early ventral-finned 'Fulcrum-As') is very similar to that applied to Czech and East German air force aircraft. This Russian 'Fulcrum-C' carries a Guards badge, perhaps indicating previous service at Kubinka, but was photographed at Zhukhovskii, where it serves the LII Gromov Flight Research Centre as a development and test aircraft.

Below: This unusual two-tone green camouflage, seen on a pair of MiG-29s (this one a 'Fulcrum-C') departing from Ribnitz-Damgarten during May 1994, may be the latest MiG-29 fighter-bomber colour scheme, or may have been entirely experimental and applied at unit level. One of the 733rd IAP's three squadrons was believed to have a primary fighter-bomber role.

Mikoyan MiG-29M (9-15)

Many Western analysts initially attributed the **MiG-29M** (**9-15**) designation to the big-spined MiG-29 fighter known to NATO as 'Fulcrum-C'. In fact, although the MiG-29M does incorporate a similar, large fuselage spine, the designation is applied to a completely new multi-role 'Fulcrum' variant that incorporates a quadruplex analog FBW control system (triplex in roll and yaw) and a modernised cockpit with two CRT displays. A heavier analog system was selected in preference to a digital system for simplicity and to provide greater protection from electro-magnetic damage.

The aircraft has a new N-010 radar (related to the Zhuk) with a new flat plate antenna like that of the AN/APG-65 in place of the original aircraft's cassegrain antenna. The new radar has a 400 per cent improvement in data processing capability and provides many new modes, especially for air-to-ground use, and gives automatic terrain-following capability. The MiG-29M also has a refined and updated IRST, similar to that fitted to the naval 'Fulcrum'. This reportedly has better sensor cooling, giving much increased detection range, and is collimated with a TV camera and powerful laser for designating targets for 'smart' air-to-air and air-to-ground weapons. The MiG-29M was once described as a one-off technology demonstrator, but in fact six prototypes have been built and are intended to lead to a new production variant.

Described by the bureau as being "based around the aerodynamically stable MiG-29 airframe, but different in every respect," the MiG-29M incorporates a number of major airframe changes and innovations. The leading-edge root extensions are redesigned, with a sharp leading edge, and overwing intake louvres are omitted, with the old solid anti-FOD doors in the main intakes being replaced by meshed grilles. This has allowed a dramatic increase in fuel capacity, with a 2550-litre (674-US gal) welded aluminium-lithium alloy tank replacing the original No. 1 and No. 2 tanks, and the space occupied by the old overwing intakes and their ducts, and by part of the cannon ammunition tank, which is of reduced capacity.

Equipped with four hardpoints under each wing, the MiG-29M can carry a wide range of weapons. This aircraft is seen carrying eight of the new Vympel R-77 'AMRAAMskis'. The R-77 is a medium-range AAM with active radar homing, giving true fire-and-forget capability. By comparison with the standard MiG-29, the MiG-29M has aerodynamic refinements and is structurally redesigned, with a recontoured radome and reshaped spine.

The integral wing tanks are also increased in capacity. Interestingly, the auxiliary air intakes have been painted on to some prototypes to confuse observers. Welded Al-Li is also used in the forward fuselage. Such structures do not require fasteners, resulting in increased volume that is used either for fuel or avionics black boxes. Greater use is also made of composites, with new engine intake ducts and access covers, and a new increased-area dorsal airbrake, of honeycomb construction. The new airframe has a design life of 2,500 flying hours, extendable to 4,000 hours. The overhaul interval has been extended to 1,000 hours.

The new spine accommodates a new chaff/flare dispenser, leading to the deletion of the leading edge extensions fitted to the standard aircraft's fins. The fins themselves have a slightly modified trailing edge, giving improved low-speed handling characteristics. The bulged spine continues to a new, slightly flattened tailcone, which still contains the braking parachutes. The twin upper and lower airbrakes have been replaced by a much larger one-piece airbrake on the

spine. The opportunity has also been taken to raise the pilot's seat, and this has necessitated a slight redesign of the canopy, which is slightly longer and rather more bulged. An antenna for the ARK radio compass is embedded in the canopy aft of the pilot's K-36D ejection seat.

The original MiG-29 was always hampered by its short range and endurance, and was sometimes unkindly referred to as a "fighter for use over the airfield beacon." The MiG-29M has an increase in internal fuel capacity of over 33 per cent (to a similar tankage to the McDonnell Douglas F/A-18C Hornet), giving a 33 per cent improvement in operational radius. The increased weight of the MiG-29M demands a reinforced (but externally unchanged) undercarriage, and the provision of twin braking parachutes, each of 13 m² (140 sq ft) area, replace the original 17 m² (183 sq ft) chute.

The MiG-29M features a slightly modified wing which shares the same span as the original MiG-29 wing but with new wingtips housing a different ECM/RWR system. The ailerons are of extended span. The tailplane

is more radically modified, with a significant increase in chord (and area) on the trailing edge but no increase in span. The tailplane has a small dogtooth on the leading edge, but this is much less prominent than has been shown in some Western artists' impressions. Other external changes include an extended and reconfigured rear fuselage (this allowing the centre of gravity to be moved aft), removal of the undernose sensor/equipment fairing and a recontoured (and possibly shortened) radome which lacks the distinctive double curvature on its leading edge.

The bulged spine of the MiG-29M is not the same as that fitted to the 'Fulcrum-C' and terminates in an entirely new 'beaver tail'. The aircraft also features increased-span ailerons, which extend out almost to the wingtips. The lack of overwing auxiliary intake louvres and the sharp-edged leading-edge root extensions (LERXes) are also noteworthy.

Mikoyan MiG-29M (9-15)

The first MiG-29M prototype may have been converted from the pre-production aircraft 9-15, and first flew in its new guise on 25 April 1986. The MiG-29M is now powered by uprated RD-33K engines, which first flew on 1 November 1989. These have a new four-stage fan, and second-stage compressor with variable stators in front of the first stage. These give a useful increase in thrust to 86 kN (19,400 lb st) with afterburning. To provide greater mass flow on take-off the intakes have small downward-hinging sections on the lower lip. Engine life and TBO figures have also been improved. Performance figures for the MiG-29M are little changed, although the new flight control system has significantly improved the aircraft's already formidable high angle-of-attack capability.

Like the MiG-29K, the aircraft has eight underwing hardpoints, and these are used to carry the new long/medium-range AAM-AE ('AMRAAMski') and a variety of other weapons, including for the first time laser-guided and TV-guided air-to-surface missiles

like the Kh-25 and Kh-31. The two inboard pylons on each wing are each stressed to carry stores of up to 1000 kg (2,204 lb), and the outboard pair to carry 500 kg (1,102 lb) of stores. New 2500-litre (660-US gal) fuel tanks (of the same length and width as standard tanks, but deeper and more slab-sided) are reportedly under development, together with auxiliary missile launch rails for the fuel tank pylons. Ammunition capacity for the internal 30-mm cannon has been reduced to 100 rounds.

During 1990 the VPK commission reportedly refused certification because of radar problems, although earlier FBW control system problems have apparently now been solved, and the aircraft has reportedly successfully completed state acceptance trials, unlike the troubled Su-35, production of which has temporarily ceased. Central funding for the MiG-29M may not have been obtained (although 1994 reports suggested that a small batch would be obtained by the **Russian air forces** in place of some of the more expensive Su-35s), and Mikoyan

is therefore actively looking for an international partner to put the aircraft into production. Recent orders by **Malaysia** and **India** may be for the MiG-29M, and India would be an obvious production partner. The 28 January 1993 Indian contract reportedly covered 30 single-seat MiG-29Ms and six MiG-29M two-seaters with the same CRT-equipped cockpit, and perhaps with radar. These were to be built by MAPO and supplied complete and in kit form for assembly by HAL. Negotiations reportedly took place with Lucas Aerospace for the provision of FADEC systems for the Indian MiG-29Ms. By June 1994, further details emerged of a $750 million Russian offer to supply these 36 aircraft, funding the first 10 through a state bank loan, and the remaining aircraft through a commercial loan. If finalised, this deal will allow development of the MiG-29M to be completed. The $385 million Malaysian contract incorporated with it a number of stringent conditions and requirements that seem to be impossible to fulfil except with a modified MiG-29M, although these

aircraft are expected to be MiG-29SEs which may not even be based on the 'Fulcrum-C'. The designation **MiG-33** may be applied to such an aircraft if it reaches production and Russian air force service, but the most senior bureau personnel aver that to use the designation now is incorrect.

SPECIFICATION

Mikoyan MiG-29M
generally similar to the Mikoyan MiG-29 'Fulcrum-A' except in the following particulars:
Fuselage and tail: length 17.37 m (57 ft 0 in) including probe
Powerplant: two Leningrad/Klimov (Isotov/Sarkisov) RD-33K turbofans rated at 53.95 kN (12,125 lb st) dry, 86.33 kN (19,400 lb st) with afterburning, and with an 'emergency regime' rating of 92.22 kN (20,725 lb st)
Fuel and load: internal fuel 5000 kg (6,250 litres; 1,651 US gal); maximum ordnance 4500 kg (9,921 lb)
Range: 2000 km (1,080 nm; 1,243 miles) with internal fuel; 3200 km (1,728 nm; 1,988 miles) with external fuel tanks

Mikoyan **MiG-29K (9-31), MiG-29KU and MiG-29KVP**

Because it shares so many features and systems with the MiG-29M, the development programme of the **MiG-29K (9-31)** has been achieved using only two prototypes, although a handful of early 'Fulcrum-As', including some with ventral fins, have received arrester hooks and a carrier landing system for trials, and for training naval pilots at the naval airfield at Saki in the Crimea. Designated **MiG-29KVP**, these aircraft lack folding wings and do not have the MiG-29K's fully strengthened undercarriage, so cannot routinely operate from a carrier, where a pitching deck can dramatically increase landing loads. One of these aircraft was also involved in the early trials, probably making a series of touch-and-go landings to familiarise test pilots with the deck of the *Tbilisi*. Some sources have suggested that the MiG-29KVP was originally developed as a naval fighter in its own right, although it quickly became apparent that greater fuel capacity and wing area, and improved high lift devices, would be desirable, and a new start was made using the MiG-29M airframe as a basis.

The Mikoyan design bureau claims to have been working on a naval MiG-29 derivative for some 10 years, in order to provide a multi-role fighter to serve aboard the *Kuznetsov* and her sister carriers. The first of two MiG-29K prototypes made its

The first MiG-29K prototype is about to take the wire on the carrier Kuznetsov. The square-section arrester hook and large double-slotted flaps are clearly evident.

maiden flight on 23 June 1988, in the hands of Takhtar Aubakirov. Based on the airframe of the MiG-29M, the big-spined MiG-29Ks similarly lack the usual 'Fulcrum' overwing chaff/flare dispensers, and have a similar, single large airbrake further forward on the spine. Like the MiG-29M, the naval variant also has revised tailfins.

The heavy intake door system has been removed (presumably to save weight) and has been replaced by lighter meshed grilles. The overwing auxiliary intakes have also gone, allowing the space they previously occupied to be taken by a large fuel tank of aluminium-lithium construction, of approximately 2550-litre (674-US gal) capacity.

The MiG-29K prototypes were 'navalised' by the substitution of an arrester hook for the braking parachute, and by the provision of a strengthened undercarriage. Maximum braking deceleration is 4.5 *g*. Equipment changes seem to include a new defensive ECM system (with bulged wingtips apparently housing passive receivers) and a new IRST sensor (which may be different in detail to that fitted to the MiG-29M). The prototypes have a solid IRST ball with a small window, this housing a test camera to record carrier approaches. The radome is of more curved profile, without the slightly concave conical leading edge of the 'Fulcrum-A' radome. This is more aerodynamically efficient and indicates that the new N-010 radar is fitted.

A retractable inflight-refuelling probe is fitted below the port side of the windscreen and the aircraft apparently incorporates various corrosion-protection measures.

The MiG-29K also has an entirely new wing, of slightly greater chord at the root and with slightly reduced leading edge sweep. The aircraft retains the extended-span ailerons of the MiG-29M, and has extended wingtips, giving greater overall span. New, broader-chord, double-slotted trailing-edge flaps are fitted, these projecting farther aft than the ailerons even when retracted. The aircraft has eight underwing hardpoints that can carry the same range of air-to-air and air-to-ground weapons as the MiG-29M, as well as the anti-ship version of Kh-31 or the new Kh-35 'Harpoonski' anti-ship missile.

For trials aboard the *Tbilisi* (as it then was) '311' initially made 20 launches (using the vessel's 15° ski jump, and running up against the unique deck restrainers, since no catapults are fitted). The MiG-29K landed

The MiG-29KVP served primarily as a trials aircraft for ski-jump and arrester gear development.

on *Tbilisi* after the first Su-27K, but did make the first fixed-wing launch from the new ship. Approaches are flown at some 130 kt (150 mph; 241 km/h) (also quoted as 124 kt/143 mph/230 km/h) and about 14° of Alpha, some 25 kt (29 mph; 46 km/h) lower and 3° higher than a normal approach. The usual glide slope is 4°. The RD-33K engine provides useful extra thrust, making the missed approach/go-around case less critical

The second MiG-29K wore an overall dark grey camouflage. The increased-span, increased-chord wing of the -29K can be seen in this view of the aircraft.

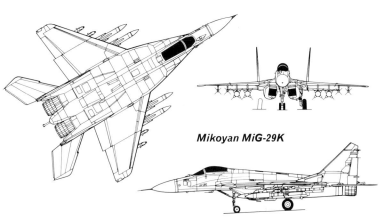

Mikoyan MiG-29K

cal. The third and fourth proposed carriers have now been abandoned, or scrapped. The second, *Varyag*, is almost complete, but its fate remains uncertain. China and India have both been quoted as possible purchasers and Russia itself still wants to take the vessel into service, but cannot do so while Ukraine contests the ownership of the vessel. The sudden reduction in carrier numbers, coupled with funding problems, has reduced the requirement for carrier-based fighters, and the original plan to have a mix of multi-role **MiG-29K**s and dedicated Su-27K interceptors may now have been abandoned in favour of using a single type. If this is the case, the MiG-29K would have been the most useful type, by virtue of

its multi-role capability and small size. Politics, however, always favoured the Sukhoi aircraft, which was selected for production (although this has now ceased, and the MiG-29K is reportedly being reconsidered).

Since the view from the rear cockpit of the MiG-29UB is inadequate for operations from aircraft-carriers (even without the increased angle of attack used on a carrier approach), Mikoyan proposed a new two-seat trainer variant for naval training. Designated **MiG-29KU**, the aircraft incorporated the same naval modifications as the MiG-29K (folding wings, removal of the intake doors, corrosion resistance, etc.) with a new stepped cockpit, covered by separate bubble canopies, with the instructor's cock-

pit forward, in the former radar bay as in the MiG-25U. The MiG-29KU reached model stage but has since been abandoned.

India is a possible export customer for both the MiG-29K and the MiG-29KU, since it hopes to acquire a third (conventional) aircraft-carrier. A second possible export customer is China, which continues to show interest in acquiring the *Varyag*. The future of the MiG-29K seems to have been dealt a fatal blow by recent moves to standardise Soviet tactical aircraft production on the Su-27, although the MiG-29K's relatively untroubled development, multi-role capability and smaller size (allowing more aircraft to be carried in the hangar deck or spotted on the main deck) make it the navy's preferred option and the natural choice if only one carrierborne fighter is to be procured. The recent cessation of Su-27/Su-27K/Su-35 production at Komsomolsk may lend credence to early 1994 reports that the aircraft's future had been reconsidered.

The view shows the second MiG-29K prototype at the LII Gromov Flight Research Centre at Zhukhovskii. It is laden with X-31 anti-radar missiles inboard and R-73 AAMs outboard, and has its IFR probe extended.

SPECIFICATION

Mikoyan MiG-29K
generally similar to the Mikoyan MiG-29M except in the following particulars:
Wing: span 12.00 m (39 ft 4 in); span (folded) 7.80 m (25 ft 7 in); area 41.6 m2 (447.77 sq ft)
Fuselage and tail: length 17.27 m (56 ft 8 in)
Weights: normal take-off 18480 kg (40,705 lb); maximum take-off 22400 kg (49,340 lb)
Speed: maximum level speed 'clean' at 11000 m (36.089 ft) 2300 km/h (1,242 kt; 1,430 mph)
Range: 1600 km (866 nm; 994 miles) with internal fuel; 2900 km (1,570 nm; 1,802 miles) with external fuel tanks

Mikoyan **MiG-31 'Foxhound'**

The **MiG-31** (Item 01) was developed as part of an overall programme to revitalise Soviet air defences to meet the threat posed by NATO low-level strike aircraft and cruise missiles. It was clear that Frontal Aviation's MiG-29s and the PVO's Su-27s would not be in service before the mid-1980s, and as an interim measure several existing aircraft were upgraded with new radar and weapons systems. The MiG-31 has often been assumed to be a similar low-risk upgrade of the MiG-25 but, actually, the new aircraft was always intended to complement the Su-27 in service, providing ultra-long-range intercept capability

This MiG-31 development aircraft is armed with four R-33s in the belly recesses and two older R-40Rs underwing.

and filling the gaps in Russia's ground-based radar chain. In fact, the MiG-31 nearly had a very different configuration to the MiG-25, since the original E-155MP design was a swing-wing, single-finned aircraft similar in configuration to the MiG-23, but with a large, square-section fuselage similar to that of the MiG-25, and with large folding ventral fins below the rear fuselage. This design, and an even more ambitious tailless

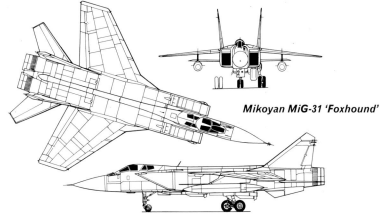

Mikoyan MiG-31 'Foxhound'

The MiG-31M features a wraparound one-piece windscreen, a neat retractable inflight-refuelling probe and underfuselage missile recesses for up to six R-37 missiles. This prototype also carried finned wingtip ESM/ECM pods.

delta (still secret because it eventually formed the basis of the 1-42's aerodynamic configuration) were eventually rejected in favour of a configuration more closely based on the MiG-25. This design, the **Ye-155M**, was a MiG-25 derivative intended to explore ways of improving the 'Foxbat's' speed and range. The aircraft served as a testbed for the 132-kN (29,762-lb) R-15BF-2-300 engine, and later the Soloviev D-30F-6, a high bypass turbofan used by the MiG-31, but plans to incorporate structural improvements were dropped. Several records were beaten by the aircraft during 1975, operating under the cover designation **Ye-266M**.

The new interceptor was closely based on this trials aircraft, originally bearing the designation **Ye-155MP**, and was expected to enter service as the **MiG-25MP**. A two-seater, the new interceptor also featured a new undercarriage, with side-by-side nose-wheels and offset tandem mainwheels. The rear wheel on each oleo was located outboard of the oleo, so that on snow it did not follow in the furrow of compacted snow left by the front wheel. This arrangement also spread the weight and reduced wear on un-hardened runways. New airbrakes were fitted, located ahead of the undercarriage and opening diagonally downwards from the 'corners' of the fuselage. The wing planform was subtly changed, with small leading-edge root extensions and no wingtip anti-flutter weights.

The basic Ye-155MP trials aircraft was originally one of a family of variants. The unbuilt **Ye-155MF**, for example, was a similar aircraft with side-by-side seats in a broader nose, intended for the defence suppression role, and there is also believed to have been a reconnaissance version.

The Ye-155MP interceptor made its maiden flight on 16 September 1975, and was clearly the two-seat 'Super Foxbat' described by defecting MiG-25 pilot Victor Belenko in 1976. He claimed this was strengthened for supersonic flight at low level and fitted with a new look-down/shoot-down radar giving genuine anti-cruise missile capability.

During 1977, a satellite observed the new aircraft destroy a low-flying target while itself flying at 20,000 ft (6096 m), and in a later test despatching an RPV at 70,000 ft (21336 m) while itself at 55,000 ft (16764 m). Series production of the MiG-31 began

at Gorki (now Nizhny Novgorod) in 1979, the new designation having been adopted to acknowledge that this was a very new aircraft, with new capabilities. Production aircraft began entering PVO service during 1982. The production aircraft had refined leading-edge slats and relocated airbrakes. Some very long-range flights were demonstrated during operational trials, including a gruelling five-hour CAP and a flight over the North Pole during tests of the navigation system. This included the Omega-equivalent Marshrut and the LORAN-like Tropik.

At the heart of the MiG-31 is its SBI-16 (S-800) 'Zaslon' radar, codenamed 'Flash Dance' by NATO. This uses a unique, fixed, phased-array antenna, which points its beam electronically. This allows the full fuselage diameter to be used, increasing radar range, and provides faster and more accurate beam pointing. Mikoyan claims rear hemisphere coverage to 120° on each side of the centreline. Ten targets can be tracked simultaneously, and four can be engaged at once. These can be automatically selected by the mission computer, which assigns priorities to all threats. Mikoyan claims a detection range of 200 km (125 miles) for a fighter-sized target, and a tracking range of 120 km (75 miles).

Even more impressively, groups of four MiG-31s can operate together, with only the leader linked to the AK-RLDN ground-based automatic guidance network, joined to his wingmen by datalink and covering a swathe of territory 900 km (560 miles) across. The formation leader can automatically control his wingmen, assigning them to engage threats according to the tactical situation. The aircraft also features a sensitive IRST to provide an emission-free alternative to radar.

The MiG-31 is fitted with a GSh-6-23 six-barrelled 23-mm Gatling-type cannon, with 260 rounds of linkless ammunition, scabbed on to the rear fuselage, just behind the starboard main undercarriage unit, and can carry two R-40 (AA-6 'Acrid') or four R-60 (AA-8 'Aphid') missiles under the wing. Its primary armament is the R-33 (AA-9 'Amos'), a long-range semi-active radar homing missile which bears some resemblance to Hughes' AIM-54 Phoenix AAM. Fully armed and fully fuelled, at its maximum take-off weight of 100,000 lb (45360 kg) the MiG-31 grosses as much as three AV-8B Harrier IIs.

Some improvements were added during the course of production (which amounted to 280 aircraft) at Gorky's IGAZ Sokol plant. Later MiG-31s are fitted with a semi-retractable inflight-refuelling probe just below the windscreen on the port side, and the two underwing pylons have been increased to four. Some sources suggest that plans exist for the outer pair to be

'plumbed' for the carriage of underwing drop tanks, as on the MiG-31D.

The **MiG-31M** (Item 05), which has yet to receive a production order, is an improved interceptor variant built only in prototype form (eight aircraft, at least some converted from production MiG-31s), in at least two configurations. All feature a new radar, whose recontoured radome droops by 7° by comparison with the old aircraft, and whose scanner has a diameter of 1.4 m (4 ft 6 in) (compared with 1.1 m/3 ft 6 in). This new radar may have a conventional scanner in place of the original Zaslon's fixed, phased array antenna.

The new variant also has new R-37 missiles (up to six of which can now apparently be carried below the fuselage), and can simultaneously engage up to six targets, but the cannon has been removed. All aircraft also have provision for a non-retractable IRST below the nose, and have lost their intake-mounted RWR antennas. Development began in 1983 under K. Vasilichenko, and the first MiG-31M (a converted production MiG-31) was delivered to Zhukhovskii for flight trials in March 1984.

MiG-31M modifications

All MiG-31Ms have a redesigned rear cockpit, with no periscope or control column (a sidestick is provided for emergency use), but with three colour CRT MFDs. There are two wingtip configurations, one with rounded tips and one with finned ECM pods. The MiG-31M features a host of aerodynamic and structural refinements and modifications, which increase maximum take-off weight to 52000 kg (114,638 lb). A fully retractable inflight-refuelling probe is mounted on the starboard side, and large cylindrical pods can be carried on the wingtips, with upper and lower vertical winglet fins or blade antennas. The tail unit is of raised height, and there are a number of aerodynamic improvements to the tailfin trailing edge/fuselage intersection. Fin LERXes were also revised, although these are now understood to have reverted to the original shape. The nose gear doors have been redesigned, with a pair of side-hinging doors and no forward-hinging front door. Handling at high angles of attack has been improved by the addition of longer, curving extensions to the wingroot leading edge, and the aircraft reportedly features a new digital flight control system. The overwing fences have been reduced in height. The MiG-31M also has a deeper, more bulged spine, with increased fuel capacity in three saddle tanks (an extra 300 litres/79 US gal), smaller windows for the rear cockpit and a one-piece canopy over the pilot's cockpit. A new one-piece windscreen has also been

provided. It is believed that at least eight prototypes have been constructed (or perhaps converted from earlier aircraft).

The big spine, new cockpit and non-retractable IRST of the MiG-31M have all been adopted on the new **MiG-31D** (Item 12), which retains the original 1.1-m (3-ft 6-in) radar diameter, and which has interchangeable wingtips (rounded or podded). The new variant, designed under the leadership of A. Belosvet, is also compatible with the new R-37 missile, a round-nosed derivative of the R-33 (AA-9 'Amos') with folding stabilisers, and can carry four R-77s ('AMRAAMski') under the wing. The outboard underwing pylons are plugged for the carriage of 2250-litre (594-US gal) fuel tanks. It seems likely that the MiG-31D will never become a production aircraft, but has already been produced by conversion of existing MiG-31s since 1991 under the designation **MiG-31BS** (Item 01BS). One last MiG-31 sub-variant which reached prototype stage was the Item 07, a dedicated satellite killer which was to have been armed with a Soviet equivalent of the US ASAT missile. Two prototypes were converted from production MiG-31s, with flat bellies, no underwing pylons, and a shortened, ballasted nose that lacked radar. They were produced during 1987.

SPECIFICATION

Mikoyan MiG-31 'Foxhound'

Wing: span 13.464 m (44 ft 4 in); area 61.6 m² (663 sq ft)

Fuselage and tail: overall length 22.688 m (74 ft 6 in); height 6.2 m (20.3 ft)

Powerplant: two PNPP (Soloviev) D-30F6 turbofans each rated at 93.19 kN (20,944 lb st) or 152.06 kN (34,171 lb st) with afterburner

Weights: empty 21825 kg (48,115 lb); normal take-off 41000 kg (90,388 lb); maximum take-off 46200 kg (101851 lb)

Fuel and load: internal fuel 16350 kg (36,045 lb); maximum external fuel 5000 litres (1,320 US gal)

Speed: maximum level speed at 17500 m (57,400 ft) 3000 km/h (1,620 kt; 1,865 mph); maximum level speed at sea level 1500 km/h (810 kt; 932 mph); economical cruising speed Mach 0.8; limiting Mach No. 2.83

Range: ferry range 3300 km (1,780 nm; 2,050 miles); Mach 2.35 radius of action 720 km (388 nm; 447 miles) unrefuelled; Mach 0.85 radius of action 1200 km (648 nm; 745 miles) unrefuelled, 2200 km (1,185 nm; 1,365 miles) with one inflight refuelling

Performance: service ceiling 20600 m (67,585 ft); take-off run 1200 m (3,937 ft) at maximum take-off weight; landing run at normal landing weight with brake chutes 800 m (2,624 ft); time to 1000 m (3,280 ft) 7 minutes 45 seconds

g limits: +5 at supersonic speed

Mikoyan 701 and 1-42

These **Mikoyan 701** and **1-42** designations were revealed in 1988 by Rostislav Belyakov, Designer General of the Mikoyan OKB, although since then he has both denied and admitted them. The 1-42 was said to be broadly equivalent to the EFA and Rafale in concept, role, weight, configuration and size, and was developed (perhaps from one of the Ye-155 designs discarded during the development of the MiG-31) to meet the air force's requirement for an MFI, or Mnogofunkstsionalniy Istrebityel (multirole fighter). The Sukhoi Su-37 (described

separately), which has reportedly been abandoned, may have been intended as a competitor to this aircraft. Rumours suggest that one, and perhaps two, 1-42 prototypes are in an advanced stage of construction in the factory at Nizhny Novgorod, but that funding problems and the non-availability of the intended Saturn/Lyul'ka engines have prevented their completion. The Russian air force has stated that it remains fully committed to the programme and will attempt to make available additional funding, but Lyul'ka remains coy about the progress of

the unnamed engine. A brochure released at the 1993 Paris air show revealed a very crude sketch of a tailless twin-finned fighter with side-by-side engines, and this may represent the 1-42 basic configuration. Other earlier artists' impressions showed an aircraft which more resembled the F-22, but with inward-canted tailfins.

The Mikoyan 701 was developed to meet the MDP, or Mnogofunkstsionalniy Dalniy Perevkhvatchik (multi-role long-range interceptor) requirement, perhaps in competition with a Sukhoi design known as the Su-32.

The aircraft is a long, slender, tailless deltawinged aircraft with intakes mounted above the fuselage and internal weapons bays. The fighter version has tandem cockpits, while a bizjet derivative has a side-by-side flight deck. Neither are believed to have progressed beyond the drawing board.

Although both Mikoyan and Sukhoi have hinted that they have flown aircraft more advanced than the MiG-29 and Su-27, they have on other occasions also claimed that the MiG-29M and Su-33 are their most advanced flying aircraft.

Mil Mi-1 'Hare'

Moskovskii Vertoletnay Zavod Imieni M.L. Milya,
2 Sokolnichyesky Val,
107113 Moscow, Russia.

The **Mil Mi-1** three/four-seat light liaison helicopter first flew in 1948 and is similar in size and configuration to the Sikorsky S-51. Also built under licence in Poland, the Mil Mi-1 appeared in several different variants, including a dual-control trainer. Powered by an AI-26 radial engine, driving a three-bladed wooden main rotor, the Mil Mi-1 proved a popular light utility and train-

ing helicopter, and was widely exported. A handful may remain in service in the states of the former **USSR**, in **Cuba** and in **China**.

SPECIFICATION

Mil Mi-1 'Hare'
Rotors: main rotor diameter 14.3 m (46.9 ft); main

rotor disc area 161.56 m² (193.32 sq ft)
Fuselage and tail: length overall 16.95 m (55.6 ft); height 3.30 m (10.8 ft)
Powerplant: one Ivchenko AI-26W piston engine rated at 422 kW (566 hp)
Weights: empty 1800 kg (3,968 lb); normal take-off 2300 kg (5,070 lb); maximum take-off 2400 kg (5,291 lb)
Fuel and load: internal fuel 260 litres (68.6 US gal);

external fuel 160 litres (42.2 US gal); maximum payload 300 kg (661 lb)
Speed: maximum level speed at 2000 m (6,561 ft) 185 km/h (99 kt; 114 mph); maximum level speed at sea level 170 km/h (91 kt; 105 mph)
Range: ferry range 620 km (334 nm; 385 miles);
Performance: maximum rate of climb at sea level 6.5 m (21.3 ft) per second; service ceiling 3000 m (9,842 ft)

Mil Mi-4 'Hound'

Design of the **Mil Mi-4 'Hound'** transport helicopter was initiated in 1951 and the first example was flown in August 1952. It was soon put into production, initially for Aeroflot, as the passenger-carrying **Mil Mi-4P**, and later for use by the Soviet armed forces in assault and troop transport roles. Of conventional design, the Mi-4 has rear clamshell doors to simplify loading of vehicles and cargo and a radial piston engine mounted in fuselage nose, similar to the contemporary Sikorsky S-55/Westland Whirlwind. The initial four-bladed wooden rotor caused many problems, and it was not until 1954 that blade life was extended to 300 hours; in 1960, all-metal parallel-chord blades were introduced.

Several military versions of the Mil Mi-4 were built. The basic **'Hound-A'** assault transport could carry 14 fully-equipped troops, 1600 kg (3,527 lb) of stores, or underslung loads. Many 'Hounds' were converted to other roles, including armed assault versions fitted with a ventral cannon gondola initially designed for an observer or naviga-

tor), the ASW-configured **'Hound-B'**, and the **'Hound-C'** ECM platform. When production ended in 1969, about 3,500 of all variants had been built in the USSR, mostly for military service, and an additional 1,000 were produced in China as the **Harbin Z-5** (described separately). Small numbers of 'Hound-As' remain active, with **Albania** and perhaps in **Afghanistan, Algeria, Angola, Bangladesh, Bhutan, China, Cuba, Egypt, Ethiopia, Guinea, Iraq, Mongolia, North Korea, Sudan, Syria, Vietnam** and **Yemen**.

SPECIFICATION

Mil Mi-4 'Hound-A'
Rotor system: main rotor diameter 21.00 m (68 ft 11 in); main rotor disc area 349.49 m² (3,761.88 sq ft)
Fuselage and tail: length overall, rotors turning 25.02 m (82 ft 1 in) and fuselage 16.80 m (55 ft 1 in); height overall 4.40 m (14 ft 5.25 in)
Powerplant: one Shvetsov ASh-82V radial piston engine rated at 1,700 hp (1268 kW)

Weights: empty 4900 kg (10,802 lb); normal take-off 7150 kg (15,763 lb); maximum take-off 7550 kg (16,645 lb)
Fuel and load: internal fuel 960 litres (254 US gal) plus provision for 500 litres (132 US gal) of auxiliary fuel in cabin tank; maximum payload 1000 kg (2,204 lb)
Speed: maximum level speed at 1000 m (3,281 ft) 200 km/h (108 kt; 124 mph); maximum level speed at sea level 175 km/h (94 kt;109 mph); maximum cruising speed at optimum altitude 160 km/h (65 kt; 99 mph)
Range: 650 km (351 nm; 404 miles)

Performance: service ceiling 5500 m (18,045 ft); hovering ceiling 700 m (2,295 ft) out of ground effect

Albania operates a mix of Russian-built Mi-4s and Chinese Harbin Z-5s, all of which have been retrofitted with Chinese metal rotor blades. This Mi-4, now in use as an air ambulance with Albania's Sixth Regiment, used to be dictator Enver Hoxha's personal aircraft.

Mil Mi-6 'Hook-A'

Development of the **Mil Mi-6** began in 1954 in response to Aeroflot and VVS requirements for a large transport helicopter. When it made its maiden flight in late 1957, it was the world's largest rotary-wing aircraft, but despite this size it retained the basic helicopter configuration. More significantly, it was also the first turbine-powered helicopter to enter production in the USSR. The Mi-6 immediately began to demonstrate its capabilities by demolishing records, and by becoming the first helicopter to exceed 162 kt (300 km/h; 186 mph). The Mi-6 featured

an optional detachable stub wing, which offloaded the rotor by some 20 per cent in cruising flight, with attendant benefits on fuel consumption and endurance. Five prototypes were followed by an initial production batch of 30, most of which went to the air force.

The standard **Mil Mi-6T 'Hook-A'** can carry 65 passengers on tip-up seats along the cabin sides and additional bench seats along the centreline, or 75 in a high-density configuration of 15 five-abreast forward-facing rows. In the medevac role, up to 41

stretchers can be carried. Clamshell doors are provided at the rear, with hydraulically operated loading ramps and an 800-kg (1,764-lb) capacity internal winch for cargo handling. The floor is stressed for loads of up to 2000 kg/m² (409 lb/sq ft). The hold is 11.72 m (38 ft 6 in) long and 2.65 m (8 ft 7 in) wide, with height varying between 2.00 and 2.64 m (6 ft 6 in and 8 ft 6 in). A maximum load of 12000 kg (26,455 lb) can be carried internally. Alternatively, an external cargo hook allows underslung loads of up to 9000 kg (19,800 lb) to be carried. A total of 800 'Hooks' had been built when production ended in 1981.

There are various civilian variants, including the **Mil Mi-6P** with square windows, and fire-fighting and flying crane versions. Special military versions are described separately under the Mi-6VKP heading.

All military 'Hooks' fly with a flight crew of five, comprised of two pilots, a flight engineer, a radio operator and a navigator (who sits in the glazed nose). The latter doubles as a gunner, since many military Mil Mi-6s

are fitted with a nose-mounted 12.7-mm Afansanayev machine-gun, and some (notably some Peruvian 'Hook-As') have a podded weather radar below the nose. The aircraft has reportedly been exported to **Algeria, Angola, Egypt, Ethiopia, Iraq, Indonesia, Laos, Peru, Pakistan, Poland, Syria, Vietnam** and **Zambia**. Although the Mi-6 has been withdrawn from service in Ethiopia, Indonesia, Pakistan, Poland and Vietnam, many remain operational elsewhere. Even in **Russia**, where the much newer, even larger Mil Mi-26 'Halo' is in service, the ageing 'Hook' remains highly prized.

SPECIFICATION

Mil Mi-6A 'Hook'
Rotor system: main rotor diameter 35.00 m (114 ft 10 in); tail rotor diameter 6.30 m (20 ft 8 in); wing span 15.30 m (50 ft 2.5 in); main rotor disc area 962.11 m² (10,356.43 sq ft); tail rotor disc area 31.17 m² (335.55 sq ft); wing area 35.00 m² (376.75 sq ft)
Wing: span 15.30 m (50 ft 2.5 in); area 35.00 m² (376.75 sq ft)
Fuselage and tail: length overall, rotors turning 41.74 m (136 ft 11.5 in) and fuselage 33.18 m (108 ft 10.5 in) excluding nose gun and tail rotor; height

This Mil Mi-6 'Hook' was assigned to the Group of Soviet Forces in Germany, based at Oranienburg, near Berlin.

overall 9.86 m (32 ft 4 in); wheel track 7.50 m (24 ft 7.25 in); wheel base 9.09 m (29 ft 9.75 in)
Powerplant: two PNPP 'Aviadvigatel' (Soloviev) D-25V (TV-2BM) turboshafts each rated at 4101 kW (5,500 shp)
Weights: empty 27240 kg (60,055 lb); normal take-off 40500 kg (82,285 lb); maximum take-off 42500 kg

(93,700 lb) for VTO
Fuel and load: internal fuel 6315 kg (13,922 lb) plus provision for 3490 kg (7,965 lb) of auxiliary fuel in two cabin tanks; maximum external fuel 3490 kg (7,965 lb) in two auxiliary tanks; maximum payload 12000 kg (26,455 lb)

Speed: maximum level speed 'clean' at optimum altitude 300 km/h (162 kt; 186 mph); maximum cruising speed at optimum altitude 250 km/h (135 kt; 155 mph)
Range: ferry range 1450 km (782 nm; 900 miles) with auxiliary fuel; range 1000 km (539 nm; 621 miles) with

external tanks and a 4500-kg (9,921-lb) payload or 620 km (334 nm; 385 miles) with internal fuel and an 8000-kg (17,637-lb) payload
Performance: service ceiling 4500 m (14,765 ft); hovering ceiling 2500 m (8,200 ft) in ground effect

Mil **Mi-6VKP 'Hook-B' & Mil Mi-22 'Hook-C'**

Possessing excellent performance, ready availability and capacious fuselage, the Mil Mi-6 has been adapted in small numbers for special duties. Two separate versions have been identified to date, both being described as airborne command posts. It may be more accurate to call the aircraft air-mobile command posts, since it seems likely that they function as command posts only on the ground. The nose-mounted Afanaseyev 12.7-mm machine-gun is deleted in both variants.

The Mi-6VKP 'Hook-B' is an airborne command post and has a cluster of 'swept-T' blade antennas around the tailboom, with a tubular antenna further forward and a heat exchanger pod on the starboard cabin side. This aircraft has a vertical (fold down?) rod-like antenna below the engine exhaust.

The first such variant is the **Mil Mi-6VKP 'Hook-B'**, which is packed with electronic equipment and bristles with unidentified antennas. Four blade antennas are arranged round the corners of the rear part of the tailboom, and in front of these is a large rectangular, tubular antenna frame which hangs below the forward part of the tailboom. The aircraft has a number of extra blade and whip antennas above and below the fuselage, and some examples are also fitted with a vertical upright rod antenna projecting from the port side of the fuselage, just aft of the forward entrance door. This may 'fold down' to a horizontal position when in use. The 'Hook-B' also has a small, horizontal drum-like fairing on the starboard side, just ahead of the former clamshell door hinge line, and just behind the entrance door. The extensive electronic equipment inside the cabin necessitates the provision of a heat exchanger, which is mount-

ed on the starboard side of the fuselage, forward of the main undercarriage, and this seems to prevent the aircraft from carrying an auxiliary fuel tank on that side.

'Hook-C', which is apparently designated **Mil Mi-22** by the manufacturers, is a second command post variant and features an entirely different antenna array. It more closely resembles the standard 'Hook-A', with auxiliary fuel tanks on both sides, but with a new underfuselage antenna farm, and with a single large swept blade antenna above the rear fuselage, roughly level with the top corner of the clamshell door, closest to the hinge line. Some 'Hook-Cs' have been seen carrying horizontally a large 'spear-like' device on the main under-

carriage legs. Some sources suggest that this might be a separate antenna designed to be erected on the ground. It is believed that both command post 'Hooks' have their clamshell doors sealed, and it is thought that neither can easily be reconfigured for transport duties. Neither 'Hook-B' nor 'Hook-C' has been exported, all aircraft serving in **Russia**, and in the states of the former **Soviet Union**.

The 'Hook-C' has a single large blade antenna above the tailboom, with an antenna farm below the cabin. This aircraft also carries an unidentified antenna on the starboard undercarriage outrigger.

Mil **Mi-8/17 'Hip-C' and 'Hip-H' – transport variants**

Combat proven in the Middle East, East Africa, Afghanistan, Angola, Mozambique and Nicaragua, the 'Hip' has proved rugged and dependable, and large numbers remain in use today. Design of the **Mi-8** was initiated in 1960 as a second-generation, turbine-engined derivative of and replacement for the Mil Mi-4, using the same tailboom, main rotor and tail rotor. The small size of the Isotov turboshaft engine permitted the engine to be moved from the nose to a position above the cabin, allowing the cockpit to be relocated to the nose and making possible a simpler transmission system. The cabin was much bigger, even though external dimensions were little changed, and could seat twice as many passengers (28 instead of the Mi-4's 14).

The single-engined prototype (**'Hip-A'**) was powered by a 2,700-shp (2013-kW) Soloviev turboshaft and made its maiden flight during 1961, but proved slightly underpowered and was quickly followed by a twin-engined prototype (**'Hip-B'**), which introduced the Isotov TV2 turboshafts. The production **'Hip-C'** introduced a new five-bladed main rotor, essentially a scaled-down copy of the Mi-6 rotor. The first production version was the **Mil Mi-8P**, a civilian passenger/freight transport which retained the rectangular cabin windows of the prototype, as did the **Mi-8S**, a passenger-carrying airliner with armchair-style seats, a toilet and galley. The Mi-8S has also seen service with many air forces as a VIP transport, and some have their clamshell doors removed and

replaced by a one-piece fairing to improve soundproofing and reduce draughts.

More popular with military customers is the **Mil Mi-8T**, the standard utility transport. This introduced small, circular cabin windows, and had rail-mounted seats (like the Mi-8P) that allowed the interior to be rapidly reconfigured. Early Mi-8Ts were fitted with 1,500-shp (1119-kW) engines, but most were powered by the 1,700-shp

(1268-kW) Isotov TV2-117A. The Mi-8T can be equipped with outriggers carrying four pylons, each capable of carrying a UV-16-57 rocket pod. Many aircraft have had these outrigger pylons strengthened to carry the larger UV-32-57 pod, or bombs of up to 250 kg (551 lb).

Mi-8Ts have been fitted with various other items of equipment. Finnish aircraft have an undernose weather radar and

pylon-mounted searchlight, while Egyptian aircraft have British-made sand filters. Angolan and Ethiopian Mi-8Ts, on the other hand, have the same PZU filters as are normally fitted to the Mi-17.

To improve performance, especially under 'hot-and-high' conditions, or with an engine out, the Mi-8 was re-engined with 1,950-shp (1454-kW) Isotov TV3-117MT engines to produce the **Mil Mi-17**, dubbed

This standard Soviet air force 'Hip-C' is equipped with a winch above the cabin entry door and with outriggers for the carriage of weapons. Unusually, the aircraft does not have chaff/flare dispensers. Despite the introduction of the up-engined Mi-17 'Hip-H', the Mi-8 remains in widespread service with the air force and with army aviation, in a very wide variety of roles.

'Hip-H' by NATO. With one engine inoperative, the other can produce up to 2,200 shp (1641 kW). The new aircraft has PZU dust filters in the engine intakes, and the tail rotor is relocated from starboard to port, changing its direction of rotation and becoming a tractor rather than a pusher unit. The aircraft also has a new titanium alloy rotor hub and an all-new gearbox. Payloads remain unchanged at 4000 kg (8,818 lb) (internal) or 3000 kg (6,614 lb) (underslung), but performance is considerably improved, and fuel consumption is reduced. Export customers often use the civilian Mil Mi-17 designation, but the CIS and Russian air forces have retained the **Mil Mi-8MT**, or **Mi-8TV** designations depending on equipment fit. Former Soviet military 'Hip-Hs' are often fitted with extra cockpit armour, IR jammers, chaff/flare dispensers and even bulky EVU exhaust gas diffusers. The 'Hip-H' can also carry the same six-pylon outrigger as the **'Hip-E'** and **'Hip-F'** armed variants (described separately), and some have been fitted with machine-guns in flexible nose mountings.

Because of its relatively capacious cabin, availability, reliability and performance, the Mil Mi-8 and Mil Mi-17 have been adapted to fulfil a number of different roles, boosting the numbers in service. Examples of the 'Hip' have been exported widely, to virtually every country which operates an aircraft of Soviet origin. Operators of all 'Hips', including EW and specialised sub-types, are detailed in the operators section below.

SPECIFICATION

Mil Mi-8T 'Hip-C'

Rotor system: main rotor diameter 21.29 m (69 ft 10.25 in); tail rotor diameter 3.91 m (12 ft 9.875 in); main rotor disc area 356.00 m² (3,832.08 sq ft); tail rotor disc area 12.01 m² (129.25 sq ft)

Fuselage and tail: length overall, rotors turning

25.24 m (82 ft 9.75 in) and fuselage 18.17 m (59 ft 7.375 in) excluding tail rotor; height overall 5.65 m (18 ft 6.5 in); wheel track 4.50 m (14 ft 9 in); wheel base 4.26 m (13 ft 11.75 in)

Powerplant: two Klimov (Isotov) TV2-117A turboshafts each rated at 1104 kW (1,481 shp)

Weights: typical empty 7160 kg (15,784 lb); normal take-off 11100 kg (24,471 lb); maximum take-off 12000 kg (26,455 lb)

Fuel and load: standard fuel 1870 litres (494 US gal); external fuel 980 litres (258 US gal); maximum payload 660 kg (1,455 lb)

Speed: maximum level speed at sea level 250 km/h (134 kt; 155 mph)

Range: ferry range 930 km (501 nm; 577 miles); radius of action 350 km (188 nm; 217 miles)

Performance: maximum rate of climb at sea level 4.5 m (14.7 ft) per second; service ceiling 4500 m (14,760 ft); hovering ceiling 1900 m (6,235 ft) in ground effect and 800 m (2,625 ft) out of ground effect

OPERATORS

All Mi-8 variants:

Afghanistan: Mi-8s and Mi-17s serve with 375 and 377 Combat Helicopter Regiments at Bagram and Mazar-E-Sharif, under the control of disparate warlords.

Algeria: Mi-8 (12) and Mi-17?

Angola: 40+ survivors of 42 Mi-8 and 18 Mi-17 delivered.

Armenia: Mi-8 or Mi-17, small numbers.

Bangladesh: In No. 1 Squadron at Chittagong, five Mi-8s are being replaced by five new Mi-17s. Another Mi-8 serves in the VIP role with No. 31 Squadron at Dhaka.

Byelorussia: Large numbers remain in service. Most variants are in use.

Bhutan: Mi-8 (2)

Bulgaria: Bulgaria operates Mi-8s (7) and Mi-17s (19) with a transport regiment at Krumovo.

Cambodia: Cambodia is believed to have been an Mi-8/-17 operator.

China: Mi-8 (30)

Congo: Mi-8 (2)

Croatia: Croatia may have inherited some Mi-8s from the former Yugoslavia, and is understood to have purchased more (perhaps including Mi-17s) from the Ukraine.

Cuba: Mi-8 (20 of 40 delivered) and Mi-17 (16)

Czech Republic: After the division of Czechoslovakia the Czech Republic retained 32 Mi-8 and 31 Mi-17 transports, together with two Mi-8PPAs and a single Mi-9. These serve with the 3rd DLP at Kbely and the 11th VRP at Line, and with the border police.

Egypt: Mi-8 (50+ of 120 delivered)

Ethiopia: Mi-8 (35) – status uncertain since fall of Mengistu.

Finland: Seven surviving Mi-8s serve with the Kuljetuslentolaivue at Utti.

Germany: The Luftwaffe has now retired the last of the Mi-8s which it inherited from East Germany. LSK/LV Mi-8s were operated with KG-3 at Cottbus, KG-5 at Basepohl (mainly Mi-8TBKs), MHG-18, THG-34 at Brandenburg-Briest, LTG-65 at Marxwalde and MFG-28 at Perow.

Guinea Bissau: Mi-8 (single aircraft now w/o?)

Guyana: Mi-8 (3)

Hungary: 29 Mi-8s and eight Mi-17s (including a single Mi-9 and two Mi-17P EW aircraft) fly with the Bakony Combat Helicopter Wing at Szentkirályszabadja and the Szolnok transport brigade at Szolnok.

India: The survivors of 140+ Mi-8s and Mi-17s serve with Nos 107, 109, 110, 111, 117, 118, 119, 120, 121, 128, 129, 130, 151 and 152 helicopter units.

Iraq: Mi-8 (100)

Kazakhstan: Large numbers remain in service. Most variants are in use.

Laos: Mi-8 (9 of 10 delivered)

Libya: Mi-8 (7 of 12 delivered)

Madagascar: Mi-8 (2)

Mali: Mi-8 (1)

Moldova: Small numbers (8) in service.

Mongolia: Mi-8 (10-12)

Mozambique: Mi-8 (6 of 15 delivered)

Nicaragua: Mi-8TBK (10 delivered), Mi-17 (15 delivered)

North Korea: Mi-8/-17 (20 to 70)

Pakistan: Pakistan's Army Aviation Corps operates 10 Mi-8s (of 12 delivered), these serving No. 4 Squadron at Dhamial, Rahwali and Gilgit.

This fully equipped Russian air force 'Hip-H' features scabbed-on cockpit armour, IR jammer and chaff/flare dispensers, and is armed with 80-mm rocket pods.

Paraguay: At least one Mi-8 delivered for the army

Peru: The survivors of 51 Mi-8s and 27 Mi-17s serve with the army, and with the air force's Escuadróns 332 and 441 at Lima-Callao.

Poland: 50+ Mi-8s and -17s serve with the 103 PL at Warszawa-Bemowo, with the 37th PST at Leznica-Wielka, and with the 36th SPLT at Warsaw-Okecie.

Romania: 25 Mi-8Ps and Mi-17s serve with the MAI/Polita at Banease, and with a FAR unit at Alexini.

Russia: Large numbers remain in service. Most variants are in use.

Slovakia: After the division of Czechoslovakia, Slovakia retained nine Mi-8 and 19 Mi-17 transports, together with an Mi-8PPA. These serve with squadrons at Sliac, Piestany, Malacky and Prerov.

Sri Lanka: Mi-17 deliveries (3?) have reportedly commenced recently.

Sudan: Mi-8 (4 of 10 delivered)

Syria: Mi-8/-17 (100+ including 'Hip-J/-K')

Tadjikistan: 10 Mi-8 ordered

Turkmenistan: One Mi-8 in government service, perhaps more with air force?

Ukraine: Large numbers remain in service, although some have been offered for sale. Most variants are in use.

United States of America: The US Army operates some Soviet-built helicopters, with at least one Mi-8.

Uzbekistan: One Mi-17 in government service, perhaps more with air force

Vietnam: Between 30 and 50 Mi-8s and Mi-17s serve with the 916th Helicopter Transport Regiment at Hoa Lac.

Yemen: Unification of the two Yemens brought together 25 North Yemeni 'Hips' and 30 South Yemeni examples. The type was used by both sides in the 1994 civil war.

Yugoslavia: 50 Mi-8s with 780th TRE and 787th TRE, under Serbian command

Zambia: Seven Mi-8s were delivered, but at least five have have been withdrawn from use.

Mil **Mi-8TB 'Hip-E' and Mi-8TBK 'Hip-F'**

Early experience with the 'Hip-C' armed assault version of the Mi-8 validated the airborne assault concept, and Mil subsequently developed a dedicated 'Hip' variant. The **Mi-8TB** is a minimum-change derivative of the basic Mi-8T transport helicopter, with a 12.7-mm Afanasayev machine-gun in a flexible mounting in the bottom of the nose, operated by the flight engineer. This

replaces the lower of the central two transparencies in the nosecone. The aircraft is also fitted with redesigned braced outriggers that each have three underslung pylons capable of carrying a UV-32-57 rocket pod, 250-kg (557-lb) bomb or equivalent. Above the outer two pylons are launch rails for the 9M17 Falanga (AT-2 'Swatter') anti-tank missile, which is aimed by the co-pilot

via a gyro-stabilised sight. When fully armed, the 'Hip-E' can carry only 14 troops and a limited fuel load, but packs an impressive punch. With a full attack load of six UV-32-57 rocket pods (192 57-mm rockets) and four 'Swatters', the Mi-8TB is more heavily armed than the Mi-24 'Hind'. Former **Soviet** Mil Mi-8TBs have now largely been replaced by similarly armed 'Hip-Hs'.

The related **Mil Mi-8TBK** was built for export to **East Germany**, because the Falanga missile had not been cleared for export. Instead, **'Hip-F'** had six 'overwing' launch rails for the 9M14M Malyutka (AT-3 'Sagger') anti-tank missile on its six-pylon outriggers. The aircraft served with the East German air force and navy, and some transferred to the **Luftwaffe** after reunification.

Others were exported to **Nicaragua**. Some **Yugoslav** Mil Mi-8s may also have been locally modified to carry the AT-3.

SPECIFICATION

Mil Mi-8TB 'Hip-E'
generally similar to the Mil Mi-8 'Hip-C' except in the following particulars:
Weights: empty 7422 kg (16,362 lb); normal take-off 11564 kg (25,494 lb)
Fuel and load: maximum auxiliary fuel 915 litres (242 US gal); maximum ordnance 1821 kg (4,015 lb)
Speed: maximum speed at sea level 245 km/h (132 kt; 152 mph)
Range: ferry range 930 km (502 nm; 578 miles); radius of action 200 km (108 nm; 124 miles)

This is one of the Mi-8TBK 'Hip-Fs' used by the East German navy (Volksmarine). 'Hip-Fs' transferred to the Luftwaffe after reunification have now all been retired.

Mil **Mi-8/9/17 'Hip-D/G/J/K'**

The Mi-8's performance and capacious cabin, plus the plentiful availability of surplus airframes, make it a natural choice for conversion to other roles. Many 'Hips' of various types are in front-line service with the air forces of the former Soviet Union, acting as ECM jamming platforms, command posts and Elint aircraft. The first special-purpose Mi-8 variant identified by NATO was the **Mi-8PS 'Hip-D'**. Fitted with long rectangular boxes on its outriggers, the aircraft also has a pair of canted tubular antennas above the rear fuselage, and a V-shaped antenna mast under the tailboom supporting an unusual twin wire antenna. The aircraft has been described as a radio relay platform, or as an airborne command post. The tubular antennas above the fuselage bear some resemblance to one of the aerials carried by the 'Hook-B' command post.

The **Mil Mi-9 'Hip-G'** is a further command post and radio relay aircraft, and may have been designed as a replacement for the 'Hip-D', although both remained in front-line service with the Group of Soviet Forces in Germany until their departure in 1994. Alternatively, the 'Hip-G' may have been intended primarily for export, since it was delivered to **East Germany**, **Hungary** and **Czechoslovakia**. The Mil Mi-9 has the smaller clamshell doors (with vertical hinge line) associated with the Mi-8S and earlier Mi-8 variants. It also has an unusual 'hockey stick' antenna under the tailboom, with another under the port clamshell door.

The **Mil Mi-8SMV** bears the NATO reporting name **'Hip-J'** and is believed to operate in the ECM jamming role. Clearly based on the standard Mi-8T airframe, 'Hip-J' has a small bulge under the co-pilot's window, and has two vertical 'handle' antennas and two box-like fairings on the fuselage sides. The **Mil Mi-8PPA 'Hip-K'** is a dedicated communications jammer, and is very distinctive in appearance. Very large but quite shallow box fairings are fitted on the fuselage sides, and a complex antenna array is mounted behind these, adjacent to the former clamshell doors. These antenna arrays consist of a fine square mesh on a rectangular tubular framework, with six cross dipole antennas, in three vertical rows of two, projecting from short plinths which

Above: The Mi-8PS 'Hip-D' is a dedicated airborne command post/relay aircraft, and usually operates in conjunction with the Mi-9 in many army aviation regiments.

Right: The Mi-9 is a command post and bristles with antennas, including two distinctive 'hockey sticks' under the tailboom and rear fuselage. Several have been exported, to Czechoslovakia, Hungary and East Germany.

stand proud from the tubular framework. A side-by-side row of six heat exchangers is located below the forward fuselage. The Mi-8PPA is in service in **Russia** and the **Czech Republic**.

Right: Hungary may be the only operator of the 'Hip-H (EW)', an Mi-17 airframe carrying equipment based on that used by the Mi-8PPA, but with a new antenna array.

Below: This Czech Mi-8PPA is a dedicated communications jamming aircraft.

This is one of the Czech air force's two unidentified special-purpose Mi-17s. The purpose of the four drum-like fairings is unknown.

Although it bears obvious similarities to the Mi-8PPA 'Hip-K', the **Mil Mi-17P** or **Mil Mi-17PP** is known to NATO simply as the **'Hip-H (EW)'**. Based on the Mil Mi-17 airframe, this communications jammer has the same row of heat exchangers under the forward fuselage, and the same box-like fairings on the fuselage sides. In

place of the mesh and dipole antenna array, the new variant has a solid array which seems to consist of shallow circular drum antennas set into a slightly square concave fairing. The solid array is slightly larger than that fitted to 'Hip-K' and has eight vertical rows of four drum antennas, with four more drums set in a smaller square mounted on the tailboom, adjacent to the Doppler box.

The **Czech Republic** operates two radically modified Mil Mi-17s which have no NATO reporting name and no known designation. These carry two huge drum-like fair-

ings, mounted one behind the other. Both are carried vertically upright on special outriggers on each side of the fuselage. There are several blade antennas above the tailboom, and the cabin contains two operator's stations, each with a large display screen, keyboard and oscilloscope.

SPECIFICATION

Mil Mi-9 'Hip-G'
generally similar to the Mil Mi-8 'Hip-C' except in the

The Mi-8SMV 'Hip-J' is an ECM and Elint platform. The Soviet Group of Forces in Germany included six of these aircraft, based at Cochstedt, close to the inter-German border.

following particulars:
Weights: empty 7500 kg (16,534 lb); normal take-off 11000 kg (24,250 lb)
Fuel and load: internal fuel 2615 litres (691 US gal)
Range: 480 km (259 nm; 298 miles); radius of action 200 km (108 nm; 124 miles)

Mil Mi-10 'Harke'

The **Mil Mi-10 'Harke'** is a specialised flying crane version of the Mil Mi-6 Hook'. First flown in 1960 as the **V-10** prototype, the Mil Mi-10 **'Harke-A'** in production form has the same powerplants, transmission system and rotors as the Mi-6, with a shallower fuselage. This supports a very tall, very wide track (6.01 m/19.7 ft front, 6.92 m/22.7 ft rear) quadricycle landing gear which allows the helicopter to be taxied with almost any load carried underslung between the undercarriage units (ground/underfuselage clearance is 3.75 m/12.3 ft). Alternatively, wheeled loading platforms can be rolled under the aircraft and clipped to the undercarriage units. Twenty-eight passengers can be carried internally, or freight can be loaded via a door on the starboard side. The **Mil Mi-10K 'Harke-B'** has a shortened, narrower-track undercarriage,

but has a ventral gondola with a backward-facing seat, allowing a second pilot to hover the aircraft accurately over a load and to operate the hoist. Small numbers of both types may remain available to the **Russian military**.

SPECIFICATION

Mil Mi-10K 'Harke-B'
Rotor system: main rotor diameter 35.00 m (114 ft 10 in); tail rotor diameter 6.30 m (20 ft 8 in); main rotor disc area 962.11 m2 (10,356.43 sq ft); tail rotor disc area 31.17 m2 (335.55 sq ft)
Fuselage and tail: length overall, rotors turning 41.89 m (137 ft 5.5 in) and fuselage 32.86 m (107 ft 9.75 in); height overall 7.80 m (25 ft 7 in); wheel track 5.00 m (16 ft 4.75 in); wheel base 8.74 m (28 ft 8 in)

Powerplant: two PNPP 'Aviadvigatel' (Soloviev) D-25VF turboshafts each rated at 4847 kW (6,500 shp)
Weights: empty 24680 kg (54,409 lb); maximum take-off 38000 kg (83,774 lb)
Fuel and load: internal fuel 8670 litres (19,114 lb) including auxiliary fuel in two cabin tanks; external fuel none; maximum payload 14000 kg (30,864 lb)
Speed: maximum cruising speed at optimum altitude

Mil Mi-10 flying cranes are nominally operated by Aeroflot, but are often tasked by the Russian military.

250 km/h (135 kt; 155 mph)
Range: ferry range 795 km (429 nm; 494 miles) with auxiliary fuel
Performance: service ceiling 3000 m (9,845 ft)

Mil Mi-14PL 'Haze-A'

It soon became apparent that the Mil Mi-8 could form the basis of a replacement for the many Mi-4 'Hounds' in service with the AV-MF in the ASW and SAR roles. Accordingly, a new version was developed with a boat-like hull, flotation gear and other improvements, resulting in the **Mil Mi-14**, which was allocated the new NATO reporting name **'Haze'**. Development commenced in 1968, resulting in a prototype, the **V-14**, in 1973. The production **Mil Mi-14PL** (NATO **'Haze-A'**) is a dedicated ASW platform, with a towed APM-60 MAD, OKA-2 dipping sonar, sonobuoys and a retractable Type 12-M search radar. Early Mi-14PLs had undercarriage doors, but these were soon deleted. To improve controllability in hovering flight, the more powerful TV3-117 engine of the Mi-17 was adopted during production, and the tail rotor changed sides from starboard to port. However, there was no change of reporting name or designation. The latest 'Haze-As' have a relocated APM-60D MAD and various other improvements, including a new IFF system, and are designated **Mi-14PLM**.

The Mi-14PL has been exported to **Bulgaria**, **Cuba**, **Libya**, **Poland** and **Syria**. One Polish aircraft has been modified for SAR training under the designation **Mi-14PX**.

SPECIFICATION

Mil Mi-14PL 'Haze-A'
Rotor system: main rotor diameter 21.29 m (69 ft 10.25 in); tail rotor diameter 3.91 m (12 ft 9.875 in); main rotor disc area 356.00 m2 (3,832.08 sq ft); tail rotor disc area 12.01 m2 (129.25 sq ft)
Fuselage and tail: length overall, rotors turning 25.32 m (83 ft 1 in) and fuselage 18.37 m (60 ft 3.0 in); height overall 6.93 m (22 ft 9 in); wheel base 4.13 m (13 ft 6.5 in)
Powerplant: two Klimov (Isotov) TV3-117A turboshafts each rated at 1268 kW (1,700 shp) in earlier helicopters, or two Klimov (Isotov) TV3-117M turboshafts each rated at 1417 kW (1,900 shp) or TV3-117MT turboshafts each rated at 2245 kW (1,950 shp) in later helicopters
Weights: empty 8902 kg (19,625 lb); maximum take-off 14000 kg (30,864 lb)
Fuel and load: standard fuel 1450 kg (3,197 lb) or 3530 litres (933 US gal) in one internal and two external tanks; auxiliary fuel up to 1420 kg (3,131 lb) or 465 litres (123 US gal) in one or two cabin tanks
Speed: maximum level speed 'clean' at optimum altitude 230 km/h (124 kt; 143 mph); maximum cruising speed at optimum altitude 215 km/h (116 kt; 133 mph); economical cruising speed at optimum altitude 205 km/h (110 kt; 127 mph)
Range: ferry range 1135 km (612 nm; 705 miles) with

Above: The Mi-14PLM has a revised avionics fit, and its APM-60 towed magnetic anomaly detector (MAD) bird is mounted lower on the rear fuselage. Revealed in 1989, it retains the NATO ASCC 'Haze-A' reporting name. The Mi-14PLM may be a new-build aircraft, or may have been produced by conversion of redundant Mi-14PLs. No Mil Mi-14PLMs have been exported.

auxiliary fuel; range 925 km (499 nm; 575 miles) with standard fuel; endurance 5 hours 56 minutes
Performance: service ceiling 4000 m (13,123 ft); initial rate of climb 468 m (1,535 ft) per minute; time to 1000 m (3,281 ft) 2 minutes 18 secs

Above: This German Mi-14PL is painted in dark blue maritime camouflage. The 'Haze-A' has an internal heat exchanger for its air conditioning system.

Mil Mi-14BT 'Haze-B'

The **Mil Mi-14BT 'Haze-B'** is a dedicated minesweeping helicopter, delivered only to the **AV-MF** and the **Volksmarine** but then transferred to the Luftwaffe. About 25 'Haze-Bs' were built, six of these going to the East German navy. Mine-sweeping trials were carried out in 1983, and production Mi-14BTs were deployed on multinational mine clearing operations during the early 1980s. The aircraft has never been widely deployed, however, the Russian navy and its allies preferring to use surface vessels for the mine countermeasures (MCM) role.

Externally, the Mil Mi-14BT can be distinguished by its lack of a towed MAD, and by having its SKW heating and ventilation system mounted in a pod on the starboard side of the cabin, above the windows. A further distinguishing feature is a broad strake running below the windows on the same side. The aircraft also has a small box under the tailboom, forward of the Doppler box, which houses a searchlight designed to illuminate the mine-clearing sled's launch and recovery at night. Some Mil Mi-14BTs have small windows in the lower part of the rear fuse-

The Mi-14BT is a dedicated mine countermeasures helicopter, equipped to tow various types of mine-clearing sled. On the Mi-14BT the SKW heating system is relocated to a pod scabbed on to the starboard side of the cabin. This East German Mi-14BT was converted to SAR duties but retains the external configuration of the 'Haze-B'. The Mi-14 has not been retained by the Luftwaffe.

lage, to allow the MCM operator to watch the mine-clearing sled.

The Mi-14BT 'Haze-B' can tow at least three different types of sled, usually doing this while flying at between 15 and 20 m (50 and 65 ft). An electromagnetic sled towing electrical cables is used against magnetic mines, while a noise-generating sled is used against acoustic mines and a sled tow-

ing small detonators is used against contact mines. Several of the East German Mi-14BTs were withdrawn from mine countermeasures duties and were converted for SAR duties prior to reunification, and all were offered for sale shortly after their transfer into Luftwaffe hands. Their fate remains uncertain. Some have emerged as civilian water-bombers for use in the fire-fighting role.

SPECIFICATION

Mil Mi-14BT 'Haze-B'
generally similar to the Mil Mi-14PL 'Haze-A' except in the following particulars:
Weights: empty 8800 kg (19,400 lb)

Mil Mi-14PS 'Haze-C'

The **'Haze-C'** is a dedicated search and rescue variant for the **AV-MF**, based on the airframe of the Mil Mi-14BT, with the same external air conditioning/heat exchanger pod and fuselage strake, but also with a widened cabin entry door, an increased capacity rescue winch and pop-out articulated searchlights in the nose. No MAD is fitted, but the Mil Mi-14BT's MCM sled illuminating searchlight is retained. Some Polish aircraft have an extra downward-shining searchlight in a nose 'beak',

and some former Soviet aircraft carry a survey camera in a third box under the tailboom. Poland is the only export customer.

SPECIFICATION

Mil Mi-14PS 'Haze-C'
generally similar to the Mil Mi-14BT 'Haze-B' except in the following particulars:
Fuselage and tail: fuselage length 18.78 m (61 ft 7.5 in)

This Russian AV-MF Mi-14PS has the unusual nose-mounted searchlight 'beak' fairing fitted to late production examples. The main cabin entry door (on the port side) is of much increased width, and is equipped with a swing-out internal rescue winch. Some aircraft have a camera box below the rear part of the tailboom.

Mil Mi-24 'Hind-A', 'Hind-B' and 'Hind-C'

The original **Mil Mi-24** was developed as a flying armoured personnel carrier, carrying a squad of soldiers and providing its own defensive and suppressive fire, and relying on speed for protection. It was optimised for moving troops forward quickly, either in support of an armoured push or participating in independent airborne assaults. The Mil Design Bureau carefully studied US experience in Vietnam, and concluded that speed and firepower were essential in a battlefield helicopter.

To hasten development, the Mil Mi-24 was designed around the same 1,700-shp (1268-kW) TV2-117A engines and dynamics system as the Mil Mi-8, but with a new airframe and a new smaller tail rotor, which turned at higher speed. The new cabin seated eight, in two back-to-back rows of four, with access via horizontally split outward-opening doors. The windows could be opened and incorporated firing supports for the occupants' AK-47 assault rifles. The crew were housed in an extensive greenhouse, with an engineer/gunner forward to aim the 12.7-mm machine-gun, and pilot and navigator side-by-side further aft.

From the start, the Mil Mi-24 was fitted with stub wings (similar to those fitted to the Mi-6 'Hook'), the purpose of which was to generate lift in forward flight, thereby offloading the main rotor and leaving more power available to carry weapons and provide greater speed. The wings also reduced turning radius and acted as a convenient

point to mount weapons of various types.

The prototype made its maiden flight during 1970 and was designated **V-24** or **A.10**. It, and two pre-production aircraft (also A.10s), had wings with no anhedral and were codenamed **'Hind-B'** by NATO because their existence was discovered after that of the production Mil Mi-24. One of the pre-production aircraft is reported to have tested an enclosed fan or fenestron tail rotor, similar to that fitted to the Aérospatiale Gazelle. The A.10s established a number of rotary-wing world speed, altitude and time-to-climb records, in the hands of both male and female pilots, by eventually reaching a remarkable 198.8 kt (368.4 km/h; 228.9 mph).

The production **'Hind-A'** entered front-line service with the **Group of Soviet Forces in Germany** during 1973, and was fitted with anhedral stub wings. These retained underwing pylons, but also had vertical endplates which served as the mounting for two missile launch rails for the 9M117P Falanga (AT-2 'Swatter') missile. A missile guidance/illuminator pod was mounted below the fuselage and a camera gun was recessed into the leading edge of the port inner pylon. During the production run of the 'Hind-A', the TV3-117 engine (as used by the Mil Mi-17) was introduced, and this led to the tail rotor being repositioned from the starboard side of the tailboom to the port. Late-model 'Hind-As' also received a panel with seven external strengthening ribs on the rear fuselage. An unarmed ver-

sion of the aircraft used for training, with no gun, undernose blister and missile rails, was dubbed **'Hind-C'** by NATO.

Only a handful of these early 'Hinds', if any, remain in service, and those that do serve as trainers or hacks. Early Mil Mi-24s were not widely exported, but examples were noted in service in **Afghanistan**, **Algeria**, **Libya** and **Vietnam**. Some of these export aircraft have even been photographed with PZU intake filters, normally associated with later variants.

A more comprehensive list of current op-

erators of early 'Hinds' is given in the Mil Mi-24D 'Hind-D' operators section.

SPECIFICATION

Mil Mi-24 'Hind-A'
generally similar to the Mil Mi-24 'Hind-D' except in the following particulars:
Speed: maximum level sspeed 'clean' at optimum altitude 320 km/h (173 kt; 199 mph)
Performance: maximum rate of climb at sea level 900 m (2,953 ft) per minute

This early Mil Mi-24 'Hind-A' is fully armed with rocket pods and wingtip AT-2 'Swatter' ATGMs. Early aircraft had a starboard side tail rotor.

Mil Mi-24D 'Hind-D' and Mi-24V 'Hind-E'

O perational experience with the initial Mil Mi-24s soon showed that the original concept was slightly flawed. The type's ground attack potential was clearly reduced when carrying troops, and it was realised that this task was better suited to less agile helicopters like the Mil Mi-8. As the Mi-24's transport role declined in importance, anti-tank capability became progressively more important. It soon became apparent that the greenhouse canopy of the 'Hind-A' gave less than perfect all-round visibility, and yet offered the crew little protection. To develop another new battlefield helicopter was unnecessary, since in many respects the basic Mi-24 design had proved outstanding.

The solution was to redesign the Mi-24 with an entirely new nose, with heavily armoured tandem cockpits for the pilot (rear) and gunner (front). These were covered by bubble canopies, with bullet-proof armoured glass windscreens. The pilot's cockpit canopy incorporated a large door which opened to starboard, while the front canopy hinged sideways to port. Besides ease of access, the new arrangement gave a much smaller frontal area, improved visibility and reduced drag.

Under the nose was fitted a stabilised turret housing a completely new four-barrelled JakB 12.7-mm Gatling gun. This has a very high rate of fire (about 4,000 rpm), and in its new turret could be traversed through 70° on each side of the centreline, elevated by 15° and depressed through 60°. The gun is normally aimed from the front cockpit, but the turret can be locked fore-and-aft, allowing the pilot to fire the gun using a fixed sight.

New sensors

Beside the new gun turret were a missile guidance pod (to port) and an electro-optical device, normally covered by armoured doors, but apparently serving as a laser rangefinder and designator. Further inputs to the weapons system come from the sensitive pitch and yaw vanes mounted on the long air data boom projecting from the forward cockpit. These sense sideslip and relative wind, allowing accurate weapons aiming. Aft of the cockpit the aircraft was unchanged, the flight engineer sitting in the narrow 'corridor' between the cockpit and the cabin. The cabin itself retained its seats and horizontally-split doors, but came to be regarded as a space for stowing missile reloads rather than for carrying passengers. The new variant received the bureau desig-

The Mi-24V is fitted with endplate launch rails for the 9M114 Shturm (AT-6 'Spiral') ATGM, and has a new command guidance antenna below the port side of the nose. This aircraft carries S-8 80-mm rocket pods underwing.

This Russian Mi-24D is one of the few 'Hind-Ds' remaining in front-line service during 1993/94, when this aircraft was in use by the Group of Soviet Forces in Germany. Russian army aviation regiments generally use the 'Hind-E'.

nation **Mil Mi-24A**, but some sources suggest a military designation of **Mil Mi-24D**. Export variants are designated **Mil Mi-25**. The NATO reporting name is **'Hind-D'**.

The 'Hind-D' was soon replaced in service by the outwardly similar **Mil Mi-24V 'Hind-E'**, which introduced wingtip launch rails for the tube-launched AT-6 'Spiral' missile. This accelerates faster than the older missile, has a range about 1000 m (3,280 ft) greater, and generates less smoke and flare on launch and in flight. It also necessitated the fitting of a new enlarged missile guidance pod. A HUD replaced the pilot's reflector gunsight. The Mil Mi-24V is the major current production version, and its export sub-variants are designated **Mil Mi-35**. The Mil Mi-24V also forms the basis for the **Mil Mi-24P**, **Mil Mi-24RCh** and **Mil Mi-24K** variants (described separately). Since the war in Afghanistan, Mil Mi-24Vs have been fitted with a variety of defensive systems, including IR jammers, dispensers for IRCM flares and chaff cartridges, and even exhaust suppressors to reduce the aircraft's IR signature. These, however, impose a significant drag penalty, and are not usually fitted in peacetime.

An unarmed version of the 'Hind-D' has been developed for training purposes. Reportedly designated **Mil Mi-24DU**, its gun turret has been faired over.

SPECIFICATION

Mil Mi-24D 'Hind-D'
Rotor system: main rotor diameter 17.30 m (56 ft 9 in); tail rotor diameter 3.908 m (12 ft 10 in); main rotor disc area 235.00 m2 (2,529.52 sq ft); tail rotor disc area 11.99 m2 (129.12 sq ft)
Wing: span 6.536 m (21 ft 5.5 in)
Fuselage and tail: length overall, rotors turning 19.79 m (64 ft 11 in) and fuselage 17.51 m (57 ft 5.5 in) excluding rotors and gun; height overall 6.50 m (21 ft 4 in) with rotors turning and 4.44 m (14 ft 6.75 in) to top of rotor head; stabiliser span 3.27 m (10 ft 9 in); wheel track 3.03 m (9 ft 11.5 in); wheel base 4.39 m (14 ft 5 in)
Powerplant: two Klimov (Isotov) TV3-117 Series III turboshafts each rated at 1640 kW (2,200 shp)
Weights: empty 8400 kg (18,519 lb); normal take-off 11000 kg (24,250 lb); maximum take-off 12500 kg (27,557 lb)
Fuel and load: internal fuel 1500 kg (3,307 lb) or 2130 litres (563 US gal) plus provision for 1000 kg (2,205 lb) or 850 litres (225 US gal) of auxiliary fuel in a cabin tank; external fuel (instead of internal auxiliary tank) up to 1200 kg (2,646 lb) in four 500-litre (132-US gal) drop tanks; maximum ordnance 2400 kg (5,291 lb)
Speed: maximum level speed 'clean' at optimum altitude 310 km/h (168 kt; 192 mph); maximum cruising speed at optimum altitude 260 km/h (140 kt; 162 mph)
Range: 750 km (405 nm; 466 miles) with internal fuel; combat radius 160 km (86 nm; 99 miles) with maximum military load, or 250 km (135 nm; 155 miles) with two drop tanks, or 288 km (155 nm; 179 miles) with four drop tanks
Performance: maximum rate of climb at sea level 750 m (2,461 ft) per minute; service ceiling 4500 m (14,765 ft); hovering ceiling 2200 m (7,220 ft) out of ground effect

OPERATORS

Afghanistan: 60 Mi-24s currently operational; 'Hind-As', '-Ds', '-Es' and '-Fs' (some of them export Mi-25/-35 variants) served with the 332nd CHR at Jurum, the 375th CHR at Mazar-e-Sharif and the 377th CHR at Kabul. They now serve with unknown units supporting varying factions
Algeria: about 30 Mi-24s operational, including 'Hind-A', '-D' and possibly 'Hind-E' models
Angola: about 30 Mi-24s operational, including 'Hind-E' and '-F' models
Armenia: 13 Mi-24s operational
Azerbaijan: less than 10 'Hinds' in service
Bulgaria: 45 Mi-24s operational with CHRs at Stara Zagora and Targoviste
Byelorussia: 80 Hinds operational with OVPs at Pruzhany, Luninets and Borovtsy
Croatia: seen at Pula – believed to be ex-Ukranian
Cuba: at least 12 Mi-24s operational
Czech Republic: 20 'Hind-Ds' with the 51st VRP at Prostejov and 20 Mi-24Vs with 11th VRP at Line
Ethiopia: 11 survivors, probably fled after the fall of the Mengistu regime
Germany: operated Mi-24s with the following units: 20 Mi-24Ds with KHG-3 at Cottbus, 12 Mi-24Vs and 18 Mi-24Ds with KHG-5 at Basepohl, these units transferring briefly to the Luftwaffe after reunification
Hungary: 'Hinds' serve with the Bakony combat helicopter wing at Szentkirályszabadja, eight Mi-24Ds and eight Mi-24Vs with 1 CHS 'Phoenix', and 16 Mi-24D Mods with 2 CHS 'Falcon'
India: No. 125 HU at Pathankot has Mi-25 'Hind-Ds', while Mi-35 'Hind-Es' are operated by No. 116 HU (base unknown) and No. 104 HU at Pathankot
Iraq: at least 40 Mi-24s operational, including Hind-Ds' and possibly 'Hind-Es' and '-Fs'
Kazakhstan: in service with the 486th OVP at Ucharal
North Korea: at least 50 Mi-24s operational
Krygyzstan: some Mi-24s at Frunze
Laos: unconfirmed operator of eight 'Hind-Ds' (Mi-25s?)
Libya: 26 Mi-24s operational, including 'Hind-As', '-Ds' and possibly '-Es'
Mozambique: 15 'Hinds' in service
Nicaragua: six Mi-25s operational
Pakistan: some Afghani defectors evaluated
Peru: 24 Mi-25s operational
Russia: in service with the following units in East Germany, which all returned to Russia during 1991-

Mil Mi-24D 'Hind-D' and Mi-24V 'Hind-E'

The Mi-24DU is a little-known trainer version of the Mi-24D, with full dual controls permanently installed, and with no nose-mounted gun turret.

1994: 172nd VP from Parchum, 178th OVP from Borstel, 225th OVP at Allstedt, 336th OVP at Nohra, 337th OVP at Mahlwinkel, 439th OVP from Parchum, 440th OVP from Borstel, 485th OVP from Brandi, 486th OVP from Altes Lager, and 487th OVP from Gross-Dolln. The 55th OVP from Bagisz in Poland returned to Krasnodar in 1992. Many other Mi-24 units already served in Russia

Syria: over 50 Mi-24s in service, including Mi-25s and Mi-35s

United States: the US Army has at least one ex-Libyan 'Hind-D' and possibly also some captured Iraqi and ex-East German Mi-24s for evaluation

Vietnam: received 'Hind-As' which may be wfu

Yemen: delivered to South Yemen c. 1981, and absorbed by the unified Yemeni armed forces on the

merger of the two countries

Slovakia: eight Mi-24Ds, one Mi-24DU and 10 Mi-24Vs serve with the 4th Vrtulnikovy Pluk at Presov

Poland: 16 Hind-Ds' with 49 PSB at Proszcz-Gdansk and 16 Mi-24Vs with 56 PSB at Howrozclaw

Ukraine: 270 'Hinds' operational with 111 CHS and 119th OVP at Brody, 287th OVP at Rankhovka, 513th OVP at Berdichev, 441st OVP at Korosten, 442nd OVP at Zhovtnevoe, 335th OVP at Kalinov, and 488th OVP at Vapnyovka. Handfuls of 'Hind-Gs' serve with other Ukranian units

OVP – Independent Combat Helicopter Regiment
CHS/R – Combat Helicopter Squadron/Regiment
HU – Helicopter Unit

Mil Mi-24P 'Hind-F'

The development of the **Mil Mi-24P** was spurred by combat experience in Afghanistan. The 12.7-mm machine-gun had proved ineffective against some targets, but the use of rockets or guided missile was deemed wasteful. The obvious answer was a larger-calibre cannon. Interim solutions included a variety of podded cannon for carriage underwing, and the little-known **Mil Mi-24VP**, a 'Hind-E' with a twin-barrelled GSh-23L in its nose turret, may have dated from this time. The GSh-23L proved too big for the 'Hind's' turret mechanism, and ammunition stowage was also a problem, dropping to 300 rounds or less from the 1,470 carried by the 'Hind-D' and 'Hind-E' for their 12.7-mm machine-guns.

A better solution was to delete the nose turret altogether, and to rigidly mount a GSh-30-2 twin-barrelled 30-mm cannon, with 750 rounds of ammunition, on the star-

board side of the forward fuselage of a basic 'Hind-E'. This modification resulted in the Mil Mi-24P **'Hind-F'**. The new aircraft is often deployed in mixed regiments alongside Mi-24V 'Hind-Es', and the two types can usefully operate in concert.

Export versions of the 'Hind-F' are designated **Mil Mi-25P** and **Mil Mi-35P**. These are believed to have been supplied to **Angola** and **Iraq**.

SPECIFICATION

Mil Mi-24P 'Hind-F'
generally similar to the Mil Mi-24D 'Hind-D' except in the following particulars:
Fuselage and tail: overall length 19.19 m (62 ft 11.5 in)
Powerplant: two Klimov (Isotov) TV3-117 Series III turboshafts each rated at 1545 kW (2,072 shp)

Weights: empty 8550 kg (18,849 lb); normal take-off 11200 kg (24,691 lb); maximum take-off 11800 kg (26,014 lb)
Fuel and load: maximum ordnance 2400 kg (5,291 lb)
Speed: maximum level speed 'clean' at optimum altitude 335 km/h (180 kt; 208 mph); maximum cruising speed at optimum altitude 270 km/h (145 kt; 168 mph); economical cruising speed at optimum altitude 217 km/h (117 kt; 135 mph)
Range: ferry range 1200 km (648 nm; 746 miles) with

auxiliary fuel; range 500 km (270 nm; 310 miles) with internal fuel
Performance: hovering ceiling 1500 m (4,920 ft) out of ground effect

The Mi-24P has a twin-barrelled 30-mm cannon fixed to the starboard side of the forward fuselage to give heavier firepower. This colourful example wears Luftwaffe markings.

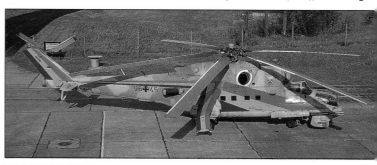

Mil Mi-24RCh 'Hind-G' and Mi-24K 'Hind-G2'

At least two 'Hind' reconnaissance variants have been produced for **Russia**, each carrying out different tasks over the battlefield. The first model to be identified by NATO was the **Mil Mi-24RCh** (OKB **Mi-24RKR**) **'Hind-G'**, which was seen in press and TV reports during the aftermath of the Chernobyl disaster. Equipped with 'clutching hand' devices at the bottom of the wing's vertical endplates in place of missile launch rails, and with no missile guidance pod or laser/electro-optical pods under the nose, the aircraft's role was correctly assumed to be 'connected with radiation sampling'. In fact, the aircraft is deployed in small numbers throughout the former Soviet armed forces, and is charged with NBC reconnaissance, picking up soil samples to ascertain the spread of fallout and of chemical and bacteriological agents. The aircraft is also fitted with a rearward-firing marker flare dispenser mounted on the tailskid, and has an unusual cylindrical device projecting down from the port side of the forward fuselage. The aircraft retains its undernose 12.7-mm gun turret, and sometimes carries rocket pods, although fuel tanks and box-like pods are also carried.

The second reconnaissance Mil Mi-24 version is the **Mil Mi-24K 'Hind-G2'**, used for fire correction. This is based on the airframe of the Mi-24RCh, but with a large, bulky camera housing under the nose, offset to starboard, in place of the laser/electro-optical package fitted to most late-model 'Hinds'. The housing clearly includes a moving section, presumably allowing the camera lens to be 'pointed'. 'Hind-G2' also has a square-shaped camera window set into the starboard side of the fuselage, where the lower half of the starboard cabin door would be, had the door not been faired over.

At least one Mil Mi-24V has been modified for environmental and ecological monitoring, and was displayed at an international 'Exhibition for Ecology and Resources' at Nizhny Novgorod. It featured a large, box-like pod on the starboard outer pylon, reportedly developed by the Polet Scientific Production Association and the Scientific Research Radiophysics Institute. This aircraft also has a tongue-like flat 'board' projecting ahead of the front cockpit from the position where the top of the gun turret would have been (if fitted). This device may or may not be retractable, and its purpose is unknown. Other one-off research helicopters based on the Mi-24RC hvae been identified.

Below: About half the front-line Russian army aviation independent helicopter regiments include single mixed flights of two Mi-24RKRs and two Mi-24Ks in each of their three constituent squadrons. More of these specialised aircraft serve with units attached directly to fronts and to manoeuvre groups.

Above: The Mi-24K is a dedicated artillery fire-correction helicopter, equipped with a huge oblique camera in the cabin. A smaller electro-optical or video device replaces the usual Mi-24D/V EO package.

Mil Mi-26 'Halo'

The **Mil Mi-26 'Halo'** was designed as a replacement for the Mil Mi-6, but was intended to offer 50-100 per cent greater capability. Designed around a cabin broadly equivalent to that of the Lockheed C-130 Hercules, the Mil Mi-26 is the world's most powerful helicopter. A prototype was first flown on 14 December 1977, and squadron-strength military evaluations began in 1983, with full service entry in 1985.

Although dimensionally slightly smaller than the Mil Mi-6, and with a 3-m (9.8-ft) smaller rotor diameter, the Mil Mi-26 uses advanced gearbox design and makes extensive use of composites and advanced aluminium-lithium alloys to save weight, resulting in an empty weight less than 1000 kg (2,204 lb) greater than the Mi-6. Its two D-136 turboshaftss are more than twice as powerful as those fitted to the 'Hook', and its advanced eight-bladed rotor allows it to lift almost twice the payload.

In addition to its crew of five, the Mil Mi-26's fusealge can accommodate up to 80 fully-equipped troops or 60 stretchers. There is a permanent four-seat passenger compartment aft of the flight deck, but the main hold can be reconfigured for passenger transport, air ambulance or freight duties.

This Mil Mi-26 belongs to India's No. 126 Helicopter Unit, the ironically named 'Feather-weights', which is based at Chandigarh. Ten were delivered to the unit.

Loading of the 'Halo' is achieved using a downward-hinged lower door, with an integral folding ramp, and the two clamshell upper doors. Two 2500-kg (5,511-lb) capacity electric overhead hoists and a 500-kg (1,102-lb) capacity winch are provided for freight handling, together with roller conveyors in the floor.

While command post versions of 'Halo' are expected, only one sub-variant has so far been announced: the **Mi-26TZ** tanker. An advanced transport version, with uprated engines and composite rotor blades, is also believed to be under development. A Russian air force Mil Mi-26 observed clandestinely at Mil's Moscow airfield during 1992 was described as having a nose-mounted gun (or possibly an inflight-refuelling probe).

The basic Mil Mi-26 is operated by both Aeroflot and the **Russian air force**, and has been exported to **India** (serving with No. 126 Helicopter Unit at Chandigarh). Some may also serve with **Ukrainian** armed forces, although this cannot be confirmed.

SPECIFICATION

Mil Mi-26 'Halo-A'
Rotor system: main rotor diameter 32.00 m (105 ft 9 in); tail rotor diameter 7.61 m (24 ft 11.5 in); main rotor disc area 804.25 m² (8,657.13 sq ft); tail rotor disc area 45.48 m² (489.60 sq ft)
Fuselage and tail: length overall, rotors turning 40.025 m (131 ft 3.75 in) and fuselage 33.727 m (110 ft 8 in) excluding tail rotor; height overall 8.145 m

(26 ft 8.25 in) to top of rotor head; wheel track 7.17 m (23 ft 6.25 in); wheel base 8.95 m (29 ft 4.5 in)
Powerplant: two ZMDB 'Progress' (Lotarev) D-136 turboshafts each rated at 8380 kW (11,240 shp)
Weights: empty 28200 kg (62,170 lb); normal take-off 49600 kg (109,347 lb); maximum take-off 56000 kg (123,457 lb)
Fuel and load: internal fuel 12000 litres (3,170 US gal); external fuel none; maximum payload 20000 kg (44,092 lb)
Speed: maximum level speed at optimum altitude 295 km/h (159 kt; 183 mph); normal cruising speed at optimum altitude 255 km/h (137 kt; 158 mph)
Range: ferry range 2000 km (1,080 nm; 1,240 miles) with auxiliary fuel; range 800 km (432 nm; 497 miles) with standard fuel
Performance: service ceiling 4600 m (15,090 ft); hovering ceiling 1800 m (5,905 ft) out of ground effect

Mil Mi-28 'Havoc'

Despite its reported defeat by the Kamov Ka-50 'Hokum', Mil claims to have received an order for the **Mil Mi-28** from the **Russian armed forces**, and continues to market the aircraft actively. The **'Havoc'** is of conventional 'helicopter gunship' configuration, with an undernose cannon and stepped armoured cockpits accommodating pilot (rear) and gunner (forward). The first of three Mil Mi-28 prototypes made its maiden flight on 10 November 1982.

A conventional three-bladed tail rotor was abandoned and replaced on the second and third prototypes by a 'scissors'-type tail rotor, with two independent two-bladed rotors on the same shaft. These are set at approximately 35° to each other and form a narrow X shape. The prototypes also had different exhaust suppressors.

The Mil Mi-28 is armed with a single-barrelled 2A42 30-mm cannon under the nose, with twin 150-round ammunition boxes co-mounted to traverse, elevate and depress with the gun itself, reducing the likelihood of jamming. The gun traverses through 110° on each side of the centreline, elevates to 13° and depresses through 40°. Two rates of fire are available for the gun: 300 rpm for air-to-ground use, and 900 rpm for air-to-air.

A total of four pylons is mounted under the stub wings. Each hardpoint can carry 480 kg (1,058 lb), typically consisting of four tube-launched AT-6 'Spiral' missiles or a variety of rocket pods. These can be loaded using a hand crank and built-in winch. The wingtip houses a chaff/flare dispenser.

The cockpit is covered by flat, non-glint panels of armoured glass, and is protected by titanium and ceramic armour. Vital components are heavily protected and duplicated, and shielded by less important items. In the event of a catastrophic hit, the crew are protected by energy-absorbing seats, which can withstand a 12 m (40 ft) per second crash landing. An emergency escape system is installed which blows off the doors and inflates air bladders on the fuselage sides. The crew members roll over these before pulling their parachute ripcords.

A hatch in the port side, aft of the wing, gives access to the avionics compartment and to an area large enough to accommodate two or three people (in some discomfort). This is intended to allow an Mi-28 to pick up the crew of another downed helicopter. The production **Mil Mi-28N** will feature FLIR and LLLTV in the nose, on each side of the laser rangefinder/designa-

tor turret, and will have an NVG-compatible cockpit. Above this is a radome for missile illumination/guidance. A transport derivative of the Mi-28, apparently designated **Mi-40**, is said to be under development.

SPECIFICATION

Mil Mi-28 'Havoc-A'
Rotor system: main rotor diameter 17.20 m (56 ft 5 in); tail rotor diameter 3.84 m (12 ft 7.25 in); main rotor disc area 232.35 m² (2,501.10 sq ft); tail rotor disc area 11.58 m² (124.66 sq ft)
Wing: span 4.87 m (16 ft 0 in)
Fuselage and tail: length overall, rotors turning 19.15 m (62 ft 10 in) and fuselage 16.85 m (55 ft 3.5 in); wheel track 2.29 m (7 ft 6.25 in); wheel base 11.00 m (36 ft 1 in)

The Mi-28 is of broadly conventional configuration, with stepped tandem cockpits for pilot and WSO/gunner.

Powerplant: two Klimov (Isotov) TV3-117 turboshafts each rated at 1640 kW (2,200 shp)
Weights: empty 7000 kg (15,432 lb); maximum take-off 10400 kg (22,928 lb)
Fuel and load: internal fuel about 1900 litres (502 US gal); maximum ordnance about 1920 kg (4,233 lb)
Speed: maximum level speed 'clean' at optimum altitude 300 km/h (162 kt; 186 mph); maximum cruising speed at optimum altitude 270 km/h (146 kt; 168 mph)
Range: 470 km (253 nm; 292 miles) with standard fuel; endurance 2 hours 0 minutes
Performance: service ceiling 5800 m (19,025 ft); hovering ceiling 3600 m (11,810 ft) out of ground effect

Mil Mi-34 'Hermit'

The **Mil Mi-34 'Hermit'** was designed as an Mi-1/Mi-2 replacement, both as a civil light helicopter and, more importantly, as a military trainer and liaison aircraft. It has seating for two pilots, with space behind for a bench seat for two passengers or for cargo. The first Soviet helicopter capable of executing a loop or roll, the Mil Mi-34 was flown initially during 1986. It is sparsely equipped and has unboosted mechanical controls, but incorporates some use of composites in the rotor and tail rotor.

The **Mil Mi-34V** or **Mi-34VAZ**, built by the VAZ motor car works at Togliatigrad, is a twin-engined version of the 'Hermit' and is powered by two 164-kW (220-hp) VAZ-430 twin-chamber rotary engines. A prototype flew during 1993. The Mi-34VAZ also features a totally new rotor head designed around a carbon-fibre star plate and giving very good control response. The new

variant offers improved range, endurance and performance characteristics.

SPECIFICATION

Mil Mi-34 'Hermit'
Rotor system: main rotor diameter 10.00 m (32 ft 9.75 in); tail rotor diameter 1.48 m (4 ft 10.25 in); main rotor disc area 78.54 m² (845.42 sq ft); tail rotor disc area 1.72 m² (18.51 sq ft)
Fuselage and tail: length of fuselage 8.71 m (28 ft 7 in); skid track 2.06 m (6 ft 9.25 in)
Powerplant: one VMKB (Vedeneyev) M-14V-26 nine-cylinder air-cooled radial engine rated at 242 kW (325 hp)
Weights: normal take-off 1080 kg (2,381 lb) for aerobatic use or 1200 kg (2,646 lb) for normal use; maximum take-off 1350 kg (2,976 lb)
Fuel and load: internal fuel 120 kg (265 lb); external fuel none

Speed: maximum level speed at optimum altitude 210 km/h (113 kt; 130 mph); maximum cruising speed at optimum altitude 180 km/h (97 kt; 112 mph); economical cruising speed at optimum altitude 160 km/h (86 kt; 99 mph)
Range: 450 km (243 nm; 280 miles) with a 90-kg (198-lb) payload or 180 km (97 nm; 112 miles) with a

The basic Mi-34 shows enormous potential as a training and light utility/liaison helicopter.

165-kg (353-lb) payload
Performance: service ceiling 4500 m (14,765 ft); hovering ceiling 1500 m (4,920 ft) in ground effect

323

Mil Mi-38

The **Mil Mi-38** was conceived as a replacement for the Mil Mi-8 and Mil Mi-17 in Aeroflot and Soviet air force/army service. Of similar configuration to the EH.101, but powered by a pair of 1753-kW (2,350-shp) Klimov TV7-117V turboshafts, the Mil Mi-38 was shown in model form at the 1989 Paris air show and in mock-up form at the 1992 Mosaero show at Zhukhovskii. Fuel is carried in bag-type tanks below the cabin floor, and auxiliary external tanks may also be provided. Seating up to 32 passengers or accommodating up to 5000 kg (11,020 lb) of cargo, the Mil Mi-38 will be cleared for single-pilot operation in the cargo role. Provision is to be made for running the aircraft on liquid gas instead of kerosene.

A first flight was once expected in 1993, with production provisionally scheduled to begin during 1996, but these dates have apparently 'slipped'. The sophisticated new helicopter has a six-bladed main rotor, with non-linear twist and swept tips, a delta 3-type (narrow X) tail rotor like that of the Mil Mi-28 and AH-64, FBW controls and EFIS instruments with five colour CRTs, and makes extensive use of composites and lightweight aluminium-lithium alloys. The aircraft has an entrance door at the front of the cabin to port, with a hatch in the floor, below the rotor drive shaft, for airdropping or underslung loads. This can be replaced by a camera window for survey work. Large clamshell doors are provided at the rear of the cabin, with an integral remotely controlled, hydraulically actuated loading ramp. A roller-conveyor and a powered 'travelling crane' hoist are provided to improve cargo handling.

Various advanced avionics systems will be available as customer options, together with sensors for weighing the cargo and finding the centre of gravity. A closed circuit TV system will be installed for monitoring cargo loading and underslung loads, and there may be a low-cost version of the helicopter with Mi-8-style electromechanical instrumentation.

SPECIFICATION

Mil Mi-38
Rotor system: main rotor diameter 21.10 m (69 ft 2.75 in); tail rotor diameter 3.84 m (12 ft 7.25 in); main rotor disc area 349.67 m² (3,763.91 sq ft); tail rotor disc area 11.58 m² (124.66 sq ft)
Fuselage and tail: length of fuselage 19.70 m (64 ft 7.5 in); stabiliser span 3.60 m (11 ft 9.75 in); wheel track 3.30 m (10 ft 10 in); wheel base 6.61 m (21 ft 8.25 in)
Powerplant: two Klimov (Isotov) TV7-117V turboshafts each flat-rated at 1753 kW (2,350 shp)
Weights: normal take-off 13460 kg (29,674 lb); maximum take-off 14500 kg (31,966 lb)
Fuel and load: external fuel none; maximum payload 5000 kg (11,023 lb)
Speed: maximum level speed 'clean' at optimum altitude 275 km/h (148 kt; 171 mph); maximum cruising speed at optimum altitude 250 km/h (135 kt; 155 mph)
Range: range 1300 km (700 nm; 808 miles) with a 1800-kg (3,968-kg) payload, or 800 km (430 nm; 497 miles) with a 3500-kg (7,716-lb) payload, or 530 km (286 nm; 329 miles) with a 4500-kg (9,921-lb) payload or 325 km (175 nm; 202 miles) with a 5000-kg (11,023 lb) payload
Performance: service ceiling 6500 m (21,325 ft); hovering ceiling 2500 m (8,200 ft) out of ground effect

---

Mitsubishi F-1

Mitsubishi Jukogyo Kabushiki Kaish
5-1, Marunouchi 2-chome, Chiyoda-ku
Tokyo 100, Japa

Following the successful development of its **T-2** supersonic twin-turbofan two-seat advanced trainer (described separately), Mitsubishi proceeded with a close-support fighter version, designated **F-1**, and tasked primarily with anti-shipping missions. The second and third T-2 prototypes were modified to single-seat configuration, the first such conversion making its maiden flight on 3 June 1975. After a year's evaluation by the **JASDF**'s Air Proving Wing at Gifu, the F-1 was accepted for service and ordered into production as Japan's first indigenous supersonic fighter. The first production F-1 made its maiden flight on 16 June 1977.

Dimensionally, the single-seater is similar to the T-2, but the space behind the pilot's (front) cockpit of the trainer has been replaced by a 'solid' fairing which contains an avionics compartment with a Mitsubishi Electric J/AWG-1 fire-control system and bombing computer, Ferranti 6TNJ-F INS and a radar warning and homing sub-system (the sensors of which are located at the top of the fin). The F-1 retains the T-2's Lear Siegler 5010BL attitude and heading reference system, but introduces a strike camera system. The principal anti-shipping weapon is the indigenously developed Mitsubishi ASM-1 (Type 80) solid-propellant missile with active radar terminal seeker, compatible with the J/ASQ-1 FCS. From 1982, a Mitsubishi J/AWG-12 air-to-air and air-to-ground radar replaced the J/AWG-11 search and ranging radar in the nose for compatibility with the ASM-1. The J/AWG-12 operates in conjunction with the retained Mitsubishi Electric (Thomson-CSF) HUD.

A total of 77 F-1s was produced for the JASDF, the last aircraft being delivered in March 1987. Original plans were for the production of about 160 aircraft but, as a result of budgetary constraints, procurement was halted at the 77th aircraft. The F-1 entered service in April 1978, replacing elderly F-86 Sabres with 3 Hikotai of 3 Kokudan at Misawa. Further units comprise 8 Hikotai (also of 3 Kokudan at Misawa) and 6 Hikotai of 8 Kokudan at Tsuiki.

As a result of delays to the FS-X fighter programme, the F-1s are expected to remain in service until at least 1999/2000, and are undergoing a service life extension programme that extends airframe life from 3,500 to 4,000 hours.

WEAPON OPTIONS

The F-1 retains the T-2's single JM61 Vulcan 20-mm rotary cannon in the lower port side of the nose. The F-1 is equipped with four underwing stores stations and a centreline fuselage hardpoint. Two radar-guided ASM-1s may be carried on the inboard wing pylons.

The 4.0-m (13 ft 1.5-in) long medium-range missile has a launch weight of 610 kg (1,348 lb) and a range of 50 km (27 nm; 31 miles). The longer-ranged ASM-2 (Type 88) IIR-guided missile is planned to enter service in 1995, carried by P-3 Orion maritime patrol aircraft and JASDF fighters, including the F-1. Development of this 150-km range missile began in 1987, with flight trials commencing in 1990. In the air combat role the principal weapon is the AIM-9L Sidewinder produced under licence by Mitsubishi. The AIM-9L was first tested with an F-1 in 1986 and issued to units in late 1987. Four of these may be carried on the outboard wing pylons and on the wingtip stations. Further stores options comprise bombs of 500 lb (227 kg) or 750 lb (340 kg) and rocket pods such as the 19 x 70-mm JLAU-3A, 7 x 70-mm RL-7 and 4 x 125-mm RL-4. Three auxiliary fuel tanks can also be carried under the fuselage and wings for long-range missions.

SPECIFICATION

Mitsubishi F-1
Wing: span 7.88 m (25 ft 10.25 in); aspect ratio 2.87; area 21.17 m² (227.88 sq ft)

The F-1 serves with three squadrons, mainly in the anti-shipping role. The tan and green camouflage seen here has been replaced on some aircraft by various toned-down colour schemes.

Fuselage and tail: length 17.86 m (58 ft 7 in) including probe; height 4.39 m (14 ft 5 in); tailplane span 4.33 m (14 ft 2.5 in); wheel track 2.82 m (9 ft 3 in); wheel base 5.72 m (18 ft 9 in)
Powerplant: two Ishikawajima-Harima TF40-IHI-801 (Rolls-Royce/Turboméca Adour Mk 801A) turbofans each rated at 5,115 lb st (22.75 kN) dry and 7,305 lb st (32.49 kN) with afterburning
Weights: operating empty 6358 kg (14,017 lb); normal take-off 12800 kg (28,219 lb); maximum take-off 13700 kg (30,203 lb)
Fuel and load: internal fuel 3823 litres (1,010 US gal); external fuel up to three 821-litre (217-US gal) drop tanks; maximum ordnance 6,000 lb (2722 kg)
Speed: maximum level speed 'clean' at 36,000 ft (10975 m) 917 kt (1,056 mph) 1700 km/h)
Range: ferry range 1,402 nm (1,616 miles; 2600 km); combat radius 189 nm (218 miles; 350 km) on a lo-lo-hi attack mission with eight 500-lb (227-kg) bombs, or 300 nm (345 miles; 555 km) on a hi-lo-hi attack mission with two anti-ship missiles and two drop tanks
Performance: maximum rate of climb at sea level 35,000 ft (10670 m) per minute; service ceiling 50,000 ft (15240 m); take-off run 4,200 ft (1280 m) at maximum take-off weight

Mitsubishi F-1

Mitsubishi/McDonnell Douglas RF/F-4EJ Kai Phantom II

The **McDonnell Douglas F-4E Phantom II** was selected by the **JASDF** as a replacement for the F-86 and F-104 in the air defence role. Designated **F-4EJ**, Japan's variant is optimised for the air defence role, with the bombing computer deleted and without inflight-refuelling capability (although this feature was later retrofitted). Many items of avionics equipment were of Japanese design, including an indigenous RWR. In a bid to save money, Japan's aircraft were delivered with unslatted wings and stabilators. Four F-4EJs were built by McDonnell Douglas, followed by 11 kits which were assembled by Mitsubishi, before Mitsubishi manufactured a further 125. The last of these was also the very last Phantom built. The designation **EF-4EJ** has been applied (perhaps unofficially) to some Japanese Phantoms used in an ECM role with underwing AN/ALQ-6 jammer pods.

Ninety-six of the 125 surviving F-4EJs are being extensively upgraded and modernised for service into the next century under the designation **F-4EJ Kai**. Airframe life is being extended from 3,000 to 5,000 hours and the aircraft is being fitted with an all-new avionics suite. The original Westinghouse APQ-120 radar is replaced by the same company's APG-66J, with much improved look-down/shoot-down capability.

The aircraft also has a new central computer, a Kaiser HUD, a Hazeltine APZ-79A IFF, a licence-built Litton LN-39 INS and indigenous J/APR-6 RWRs. The F-4EJ Kai can be identified by its distinctive twin RWR fairings on the fin and wingtip, by a taller blade antenna for the AC-164 UHF and by small conducting strips on the radome.

The F-4EJ Kai is compatible with the ASM-1 anti-ship missile, and some may be used in the maritime strike role. Three 22-aircraft squadrons will be retained. Of the remaining 29 F-4EJs, 12 will be retired and 17 adapted for the reconnaissance role.

Mitsubishi F-4EJ Kai

Japan's 14 dedicated **RF-4E** reconnaissance Phantoms are often wrongly identified as RF-4EJs, but were built by McDonnell. They are now being upgraded to Kai standard with a Texas Instruments AN/APQ-172 radar, a new INS, an IR reconnaissance system, digital cockpit displays and new defensive avionics. It is unclear as to whether the **RF-4E Kai** designation will be officially applied to these aircraft after conversion.

After conversion, the **RF-4EJ** designation is applied to 17 very different recce-tasked aircraft which are being modified from F-4EJ fighter airframes. These gain digital avionics (including RWRs and taller UHF antenna) but retain their APQ-120 radar and gun, carrying a variety of podded sensors, including the Thomson-CSF ASTAC, a Raphael-based SLAR and a LOROP pod. The RF-4EJs wear

the same three-tone camouflage as the original RF-4Es, serving alongside them with the 501st Hikotai at Hyakuri.

SPECIFICATION

Mitsubishi (McDonnell Douglas) RF-4E
generally similar to the McDonnell Douglas RF-4C Phantom II except in the following particulars:
Powerplant: two General Electric J79-GE-17A turbojets each rated at 11,810 lb st (52.53 kN) dry and 17,900 lb st (79.62 kN) with afterburning
Fuel and load: internal fuel 12,290 lb (5575 kg); external fuel up to 8,830 lb (4005 kg) in one 600-US gal (2271-litre) and two 370-US gal (1401-litre) drop tanks; maximum ordnance none
Speed: maximum level speed 'clean' at 36,000 ft (10975 m) 1,290 kt (1,485 mph; 2390 km/h)

The F-4EJ Kai can be distinguished from unconverted Japanese Phantoms by its new blade antennas and double RWR antenna fairings on the wingtips and fin trailing edge. Internally, the differences are more marked.

Mitsubishi/McDonnell Douglas **F-15J/DJ Eagle**

The **Mitsubishi F-15J/DJ Eagle** is the principal air superiority fighter operated by the **Nihon Koku Jietai**, or **JASDF**. Japanese pilots evaluated the F-15A/B at Edwards AFB, CA, in 1975, and in April 1978 Mitsubishi was selected as the prime contractor for Japanese F-15J/DJ Eagles. These differ from US F-15C/D Eagles only in the deletion of sensitive items of ECM, radar warning, and nuclear delivery equipment. The AN/ALQ-135 is replaced by indigenous J/ALQ-8 and the AN/ALR-56 RHAWS is replaced by J/APR-4. The aircraft

is also fitted with a datalink compatible with the Japanese GCI network.

The first two F-15Js and 12 F-15DJs were manufactured by McDonnell Douglas under Project Peace Eagle. The first Japanese aircraft, a single-seater, flew at St Louis on 4 June 1980. These were followed by eight F-15DJs delivered as knocked-down kits for assembly by Mitsubishi. Subsequent Japanese Eagles have been assembled in Japan from largely indigenously manufactured sub-assemblies and equipment. Mitsubishi is responsible for forward and cen-

tre fuselage sections, with Kawasaki making wings and tails. Further manufacturers include Shinmaywa (drop tanks), Sumitomo (landing gear), Fuji (landing gear doors) and Nippi (missile pylons and launchers). IHI produces the F100 engines under licence.

The Rinji F-15 Hikotai (Temporary F-15 Squadron) received the first operational Eagles at Nyutabaru in December 1981. A year later, this conversion unit was given permanent status as No. 202 Hikotai. Initial plans for the JASDF to operate 123 Eagles in five 18-aircraft squadrons have been

enlarged, and total F-15J/DJ procurement for seven 22-aircraft front-line squadrons is now to be 191 aircraft, including 173 locally built. These equip Nos 201 and 203 Hikotai of the Northern Air Defence Force's 2nd Kokudan at Chitose, No. 303 Hikotai of the Central Air Defence Force's 6th Kokudan at Komatsu, Nos 204 and 305 Hikotai of the Central ADF's 7th Kokudan at Hyakuri, and No. 202 Hikotai (the OCU) of the 5th Kokudan at Nyutabaru, and the 8th Kokudan's 304 Hikotai at Tsuiki. The 5th and 8th Kokudan form part of the Western Air Defence Force, which also controls the six-aircraft Hiko Kyodotai, a dedicated aggressor unit flying six F-15DJs, which wear two-tone camouflage schemes.

Mitsubishi/Lockheed (General Dynamics) **FS-X**

Japan's search for a replacement for the Mitsubishi F-1 support fighter ended in October 1987 with the selection of a developed version of the Lockheed (General Dynamics) F-16C. Identified as the **FS-X** at present, but likely to acquire the service designation **F-2**, the new close-support fighter will differ from the F-16C in several important respects. The FS-X will feature a 41-cm (16-in) aft fuselage extension, a larger wing of all-composites, co-cured

construction to be designed and produced in Japan, a larger tailplane, a lengthened nose to accommodate Mitsubishi Electrics (MELCO) phased-array radar, and a full FBW system. The FS-X will be powered by the 29,000-lb st (129-kN) General Electric F110-GE-129 turbofan assembled in Japan by IHI, with Mitsubishi responsible for airframe assembly using components contributed by Kawasaki and Fuji. With AAMs (Sidewinder or Mitsubishi AAM-3) mounted

at the wingtips, the FS-X will have six wing stores pylons – including two 'plumbed' for long-range tanks – and provision for various weaponry, including the Mitsubishi ASM-2 (Type 88) anti-shipping missile currently under development. The ASM-2 is a long-range ASM with an imaging infra-red (IIR) seeker for terminal guidance and a range of approximately 150 km (81 nm; 93 miles). Fixed armament on the FS-X will comprise a single 20-mm cannon.

The FS-X programme has suffered delays and cost escalation since it was first announced, and may undergo further changes to schedule or production quantities. The first of four prototypes, including one two-seat **TFS-X** conversion trainer, is expected to fly by mid-1995, followed by production orders in time for service entry in 1999. The JASDF has a requirement for up to 130 aircraft, including some two-seat TFS-Xs, to replace the F-1s currently serving in Nos 3, 6 and 8 Hikotais. However, due to slippage in the FS-X timescale, two squadrons of the upgraded F-4EJ Kai may be used as interim F-1 replacements.

Mitsubishi/Sikorsky **SH-60J Seahawk**

The **SH-60J** is a dedicated ASW helicopter produced under licence by Mitsubishi. Closely based on the SH-60B Seahawk, it is designed to replace the HSS-2B (a licence-built Sea King) in service with the **JMSDF** and is fitted with indigenous Japanese avionics. These include an HQS-103

sonar, HPS-104 search radar and HLR-108 ESM, plus indigenous displays, datalink, flight management system and ring-laser gyro/attitude and heading reference system. Imported systems include a Texas Instruments AN/ASQ-81D2(V) MAD, a General Instruments AN/ALR-66(VE) RWR and an

Edmac AN/ARR-75 sonobuoy receiver.

The first two **XSH-60J** prototypes were built by Sikorsky but were delivered 'green', to be reassembled and fitted out by Mitsubishi. Following the first flight on 31 August 1987, the XSH-60Js were subsequently evaluated by the 51st Air Develop-

ment Kokutai of the JMSDF at Atsugi, this process being completed in early 1991. A total of 56 production SH-60Js (designated **S-70B-3** by Sikorsky) has been ordered. The first production aircraft made its maiden flight on 10 May 1991 and was delivered three months later.

SPECIFICATION

Mitsubishi-Sikorsky SH-60J
generally similar to the Sikorsky S-70B (SH-60B Seahawk) except in the following particulars:
Powerplant: two Ishikawajima-Harima (General Electric) T700-IHI-401C turboshafts each rated at 1,900 shp (1417 kW)

A JMSDF SH-60J is seen in flight. The SH-60J is a Mitsubishi-built variant of the SH-60B with Japanese avionics, including search radar, sonar and ESM.

Mitsubishi-Sikorsky SH-60J Seahawk

Mitsubishi/Sikorsky UH-60J

The **Mitsubishi-Sikorsky UH-60J** is intended to replace Kawasaki-Vertol KV-107IIA5s with the Air Rescue Wing of the **JASDF** and Mitsubishi-Sikorsky S-61As serving with **JMSDF** rescue units. Designated **S-70A-12** by Sikorsky, the UH-60J is a dedicated SAR version of the **Sikorsky UH-60L** helicopter (described separately) with increased internal fuel capacity and indigenous avionics, notably a nose-mounted radar. The aircraft has a Sikorsky-integrated self-contained navigation system, a turret-mounted FLIR and bubble windows in the sides of the cabin.

The first two aircraft were manufactured by Sikorsky, and were followed by a further two supplied in kit form for licence-assembly by Mitsubishi. Total requirements are 46 for the JASDF and 18 for the JMSDF. The first Mitsubishi-built UH-60J was delivered on 28 February 1991 and UH-60Js became operational with the JMSDF in March 1992. Three units are planned ultimately, serving six bases at Atsugi, Hachinoe, Kanoya, Azuki, Shimofusa and Tokoshima. With the JASDF, UH-60Js will be based at Iruma, with detachments as required.

The UH-60J is replacing the KV-107 in the SAR role with both the JMSDF and the JASDF. The aircraft is a rescue-optimised UH-60L derivative, with indigenous search radar and a turret-mounted FLIR. Mitsubishi is manufacturing 22 of the 28 currently on order, and assembled the third and fourth aircraft delivered from components supplied by Sikorsky. The eventual requirement for the UH-60J will be for 64 aircraft.

SPECIFICATION

Mitsubishi/Sikorsky UH-60J
generally similar to the Sikorsky S-70A (UH-60L Black Hawk) except in the following particulars:
Powerplant: two Ishikawajima-Harima (General Electric) T700-IHI-701A turboshafts each rated at 1,723 shp (1285 kW) in JASDF helicopters or, for JMSDF aircraft, two Ishikawajima-Harima (General Electric) T700-IHI-401C turboshafts each rated at 1,940 shp (1447 kW) for take-off and 1,662 shp (1239 kW) for continuous running

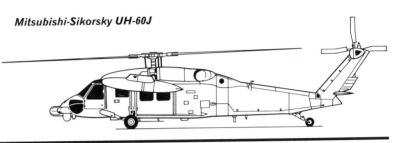
Mitsubishi-Sikorsky UH-60J

Mitsubishi MU-2

In 1959, Mitsubishi initiated design of a light twin-turboprop STOL utility transport designated **MU-2**. The aircraft emerged as a compact high-wing monoplane with a circular-section fuselage seating seven to nine passengers, and with wingtip tanks as standard. Designed primarily to serve as a light business transport, the majority of the 831 built were sold to civilian customers in this role. First flown on 14 September 1963, the Astazou-engined **MU-2A** prototype and initial production Garrett-engined **MU-2B** were fitted with pressurised fuselages for commercial use. The civil **MU-2G** was based on the MU-2B, but featured a 1.9-m (6.2-ft) fuselage stretch seating nine to 11 passengers, larger vertical tail, external undercarriage fairings to provide greater internal cabin volume, and uprated engines. Military sales of the MU-2 were limited to Japanese forces as a result of a policy towards the export of defence material. A total of 53 MU-2s was delivered to the **JASDF** and **JGSDF**, the majority of which remain in service.

Two MU-2 versions were ordered by the JGSDF as the sole fixed-wing assets for the liaison and photo-reconnaissance role. These comprised four **MU-2Cs**, an unpressurised variant of the basic MU-2B (first flown on 11 May 1967), and 16 **MU-2Ks**, developed from the **MU-2F**, but fitted with uprated turboprops for higher cruising speed. The wingtip tanks on the first MU-2C were removed in favour of an additional fuel tank carried aft of the cabin. Military equipment included one vertical and one swing-type oblique camera for reconnaissance, and the provision for side-looking radar, underwing stores (bombs and rockets), and two 12.7-mm (0.5-in) machineguns. Both versions received the service designation **LR-1**. Seventeen remain in service, assigned to the HQ Aviation Squadron of each Air Command (at Okadama, Kasuminome, Takayubaru, Tachikawa and Yao), HQ Flight of 1 Helicopter Brigade at Kisarazu

and the Air Training School at Utsonomiya.

To serve in the search and rescue role, the JASDF began to acquire MU-2s concurrently. The air force designation **MU-2S** was applied to a version with the Mitsubishi designation **MU-2E**. First flown on 15 August 1967, this unpressurised variant introduced extensive additional navigation and communications equipment, Doppler search radar in an extended 'thimble' nose radome, bulged observation windows in the fuselage sides below the wing and a port-side sliding entry door for dropping rafts. The wingtip tanks were enlarged to increase maximum fuel capacity to 1389 litres (367 US gal) and maximum take-off weight to 4560 kg (10,053 lb). Delivery of a batch of 27 began in December 1967, with a further two aircraft in 1987 after the Mitsubishi production line had closed. They remain in service with the Air Rescue Wing at Iruma, plus detachments. The **MU-2J** was based on the MU-2G, but introduced

more powerful TPE331-6-251M engines giving a cruising speed of 600 km/h (324 kt; 373 mph). Following a maiden flight on 31 January 1975, four MU-2Js were delivered to the Hiko Tenkentai (Flight Check Group) of the JASDF at Iruma in 1975-79 for navaid calibration duty.

SPECIFICATION

Mitsubishi MU-2C
Wing: span 39 ft 2 in (11.94 m) with tip tanks; aspect ratio 7.71; area 178.15 sq ft (16.55 m²)
Fuselage and tail: length 33 ft 3 in (10.13 m); height 12 ft 11 in (3.94 m); tailplane span 15 ft 9 in (4.80 m); wheel track 7 ft 9 in (2.36 m); wheel base 14 ft 10 in (4.52 m)
Powerplant: two Garrett TPE331-6-251M turboprops each rated at 724 ehp (540 kW)
Weights: empty equipped 5,920 lb (2685 kg); maximum take-off 9,920 lb (4500 kg)
Fuel and load: internal fuel 366 US gal (1387 litres); external fuel none
Speed: maximum cruising speed at 15,000 ft (4575 m) 318 kt (367 mph; 590 km/h); economical cruising speed at 25,000 ft (7620 m) 270 kt (311 mph; 500 km/h)

Mitsubishi MU-2

Range: 1,460 nm (1,681 miles; 2706 km)
Performance: maximum rate of climb at sea level 3,100 ft (945 m) per minute; service ceiling 33,200 ft (10110 m); take-off distance to 50 ft (15 m) 1,705 ft (520 m) at maximum take-off weight; landing distance from 50 ft (15 m) 1,495 ft (455 m) at normal landing weight

This MU-2J is one of those operated in the calibration role by the Hiko Tenkentai. Others serve in the SAR and liaison roles.

Mitsubishi T-2

In a fine exercise of farsighted ergonomics, Japan's first excursion into supersonic military aircraft design was a two-seat combat trainer which would, it was argued, double as an aircraft in which **JASDF** pilots

could be trained for the F-104J and F-4EJ combat aircraft, and which would provide design experience for a subsequent indigenous supersonic fighter. In the event, the **Mitsubishi T-2** itself proved readily adaptable to become that fighter, the **F-1** (described separately).

First flown on 20 July 1971 as the **XT-2**, the trainer superficially resembles the F-4

but features shoulder-mounted wings and fixed-geometry lateral air inlets (with blow-in doors) for the pair of Rolls-Royce/Turboméca Adour afterburning turbofans, mounted side-by-side in the lower rear fuselage. All components of the tricycle landing gear retract into the fuselage. The instructor and pupil pilot are accommodated in tandem under separate canopy seats and are

provided with Daiseru-built Weber ES-7J zero-zero ejection seats. Wing and tailplane incorporate marked anhedral, and roll control is effected by differential spoilers forward of the wide-span trailing-edge flaps.

Fixed armament comprises an internal JM61 Vulcan 20-mm multi-barrelled cannon in the lower port side of the nose, and external stores can be mounted on one centreline and four underwing hardpoints, while provision is made to mount AIM-9L Sidewinder AAMs on the wingtip stations. Avionics systems include Mitsubishi Electric J/AWG-11 search and ranging radar in the nose, Mitsubishi Electric (Thomson-CSF) head-up display, Mitsubishi Electric J/ARC-51 UHF, Nippon Electric J/ARN-53 TACAN, Tokyo Communication J/APX-101 SIF/IFF and Lear Siegler 501OBL AHRS.

The T-2 entered service in 1976 and joined the 4th Air Wing at Mitsushima, replacing North American F-86s, and has proved a popular and efficient aircraft, now obviously demonstrating the benefits of commonality with the F-1 fighter. One T-2 has been extensively modified for the Technical R&D Institute of the Japan Defence Agency as the **T-2CCV** control-configured vehicle (CCV). It features triplex digital fly-by-wire and computer control, vertical and horizontal canard surfaces, and is fitted with test equipment in the rear cockpit. The T-2CCV was first flown on 9 August 1983.

Total production orders amounted to 90 aircraft, of which 28 are T-2 advanced trainers and 62 are **T-2A** combat trainers, all of

which have been completed. The Adour engines are licence-built by Ishikawajima-Harima under the designation TF40-IHI-801A. Ninety-four T-2s were built, including two which were converted to serve as F-1 development aircraft. Eighty-eight were delivered to 21 and 22 Hikotais of the 4th Kokudan at Hamamatsu, and six were later reallocated to the 'Blue Impulse' formation display team.

SPECIFICATION

Mitsubishi T-2
Wing: span 7.88 m (25 ft 10.25 in); aspect ratio 3.0; area 21.17 m² (227.88 sq ft)
Fuselage and tail: length 17.86 m (58 ft 7 in) including probe; height 4.39 m (14 ft 5 in); tailplane span 4.33 m (14 ft 2.5 in); wheel track 2.82 m (9 ft 3 in); wheel base 5.72 m (18 ft 9 in)
Powerplant: two Ishikawajima-Harima TF40-IHI-801A (Rolls-Royce/Turboméca Adour Mk 801A) turbofans each rated at 5,115 lb st (22.75 kN) dry and 7,305 lb st (32.49 kN) with afterburning
Weights: operating empty 6307 kg (13,905 lb); normal take-off 9805 kg (21,616 lb); maximum take-off

12800 kg (28,219 lb)
Fuel and load: internal fuel 3823 litres (1,010 US gal); external fuel up to three 821-litre (217-US gal) drop tanks; maximum ordnance about 2000 kg (4,409 lb)
Speed: maximum level speed 'clean' at 36,000 ft (10975 m) 917 kt (1,056 mph; 1700 km/h)
Range: ferry range 1,400 nm (1,611 miles; 2593 km)
Performance: maximum rate of climb at sea level 35,000 ft (10670 m) per minute; service ceiling

The Mitsubishi T-2 combat trainers of the 'Blue Impulse' aerobatic team have a secondary air defence war role. Here one of the team's aircraft is seen taking off with underwing fuel tanks and wingtip-mounted AIM-9 air-to-air missiles.

50,000 ft (15240 m); take-off run 2,000 ft (610 m) at normal take-off weight

---

Morane-Saulnier **MS.760 Paris**

Developed as one of the first light aircraft to use jet engine power, the **MS.760 Paris** first flew on 29 July 1954 and was built primarily as a communications/liaison aircraft and advanced trainer for military use. The Paris is a low-wing monoplane powered by a pair of Marboré turbojets mounted side-by-side in the fuselage and exhausting under the tail. The tricycle undercarriage uses relatively short components, facilitating access to the cabin door on the port side of the fuselage forward of the wing. The Paris seats four in two side-by-side pairs. The **Armée de l'Air** retains up to 50 in its inventory, the principal units flying the type being 41e and 43e Escadres de Transport et d'Entraînement and ET 2/65 'Rambouillet', all as part of CoTAM. The Aéronavale also retains eight MS.760s in 57e Escadrille at Landivisiau for continuation

training, target simulation and liaison duties.

In **Argentina**, where FAMA assembled 48 Paris for the air force, about half that number remain in the hands of Escuadrónes II and III within IV Brigada Aérea at El Plumerillo, Mendoza, operating in the light strike/armed trainer role. Built as **MS.760A Paris I**s, with 3.91-kN (880-lb st) Turboméca Marboré IC turbojets, they have been upgraded to **MS.760B Paris II** standard with 4.71-kN (1,058-lb st) Marboré VIs. This version also introduced wingtip tanks.

SPECIFICATION

Morane-Saulnier MS.760B Paris II
Wing: span 10.15 m (33 ft 3.6 in); aspect ratio 5.72; area 18.00 m² (193.76 sq ft)
Fuselage and tail: length 10.24 m (33 ft 7.1 in);

This MS.760 Paris is used in the liaison role by Groupement d'Instruction 01/312 at Salon-de-Provence.

height 2.60 m (8 ft 6.4 in)
Powerplant: two Turboméca Marboré VI turbojets each rated at 4.71 kN (1,058 lb st) dry
Weights: empty equipped 2067 kg (4,557 lb); maximum take-off 3920 kg (8,642 lb)
Fuel and load: external fuel none; maximum ordnance 100 kg (220 lb)
Speed: maximum level speed 'clean' at 7620 m (25,000 ft) 695 km/h (375 kt; 432 mph)

Range: ferry range 1740 km (939 nm; 1,081 miles)
Performance: maximum rate of climb at sea level 750 m (2,461 ft) per minute; service ceiling 12000 m (39370 ft)

Argentina's ageing MS.760s continue to provide faithful service in the liaison, light strike and trainer roles.

Left: Escadrille de Servitude 57 uses a handful of MS.760s alongside Falcon 10MERs in the liaison and target roles.

Avions Mudry et Cie,
Aérodrome de Bernay, BP 214, F-27300,
Bernay, France

Mudry **CAP 10/CAP 10B**

Aderivative of the **Piel Emeraude** lightplane, the **Mudry CAP 10** two-seat light elementary/aerobatic trainer was developed initially for the **Armée de l'Air**, which has received some 56 from total production of more than 250. The CAP 10 was first flown in August 1968. The **CAP 10B** version features a larger rudder and a ventral fin. CAP 10s and 10Bs serve at the Ecole de l'Air (GE 312) at Salon-de-Provence to give *ab initio* pilot training and at the Ecole de Formation Initiale du Personnel Navigant (307 EFIPN) at Avord for navigator selection training. The Aéronavale also has eight CAP 10s with Escadrille de Servitude 51 at Rochefort/Soubise for screening/grading multi-engine pilots. Twenty CAP 10s acquired by **Mexico** are used at the Colegio del Aire, Zapopan, for aerobatic training.

SPECIFICATION

Mudry CAP 10B
Wing: span 8.06 m (26 ft 5.25 in); aspect ratio 6.0; area 10.85 m² (116.79 sq ft)
Fuselage and tail: length 7.16 m (23 ft 6 in); height 2.55 m (8 ft 4.5 in); tailplane span 2.90 m (9 ft 6 in); wheel track 2.06 m (6 ft 9 in)
Powerplant: one Textron Lycoming AEIO-360-B2F flat-four air-cooled piston engine rated at 180 hp (134 kW)
Weights: empty equipped 550 kg (1,213 lb); normal take-off 760 kg (1,675 lb) for aerobatics; maximum take-off 830 kg (1,829 lb)
Fuel and load: internal fuel 108 kg (238 lb); external fuel none; maximum ordnance none
Speed: never exceed speed 340 km/h (183 kt; 211 mph); maximum level speed 'clean' at sea level

270 km/h (146 kt; 168 mph); maximum cruising speed at optimum altitude 250 km/h (135 kt; 155 mph)
Range: 1000 km (539 nm; 621 miles)
Performance: maximum rate of climb at sea level 480 m (1,575 ft) per minute; service ceiling 5000 m (16,405 ft); take-off run 350 m (1,149 ft) at maximum

take-off weight; take-off distance to 15 m (50 ft) 450 m (1,477 ft) at maximum take-off weight; landing distance from 15 m (50 ft) 600 m (1,968 ft) at normal landing weight; landing run 300 m (984 ft) at normal landing weight
***g* limits:** -4.5 to +6

The Mudry CAP 10s of Escadrille de Servitude 51 at Rochefort/Soubise are used for grading and screening potential Aéronavale pilot trainees.

Mudry CAP 230

After producing single-seat aerobatic versions of the CAP 10 as the **CAP 20** and **CAP 21**, Mudry received a 1984 order for the **CAP 230**, for use by the **Royal Moroccan air force's** 'Green March' aerobatic team. The CAP 230 was derived from the CAP 21 (also used by the 'Green March') but with a more powerful flat-six AEIO-540 engine, greater g limits and higher weight. The CAP 230 flew in prototype form on 8 October 1985. Four CAP 230s were supplied to the 'Green March' and four to the French 'Equipe de Voltige de **l'Armée de l'Air**', of GE 312, Salon-de-Provence (which previously flew the CAP 20). Two were built for civil use before production switched to the **CAP 231**.

SPECIFICATION

Mudry CAP 230
Wing: span 8.08 m (26 ft 6 in); aspect ratio 7.0; area 9.66 m² (103.98 sq ft)

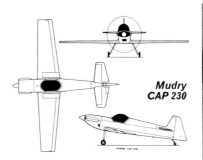

Mudry CAP 230

Fuselage and tail: length 6.75 m (22 ft 1.75 in); height 1.80 m (5 ft 11 in)
Powerplant: one Textron Lycoming AEIO-540-L1 flat-six air-cooled piston engine rated at 300 hp (224 kW)
Weights: empty 630 kg (1,389 lb); maximum take-off (aerobatic) 730 kg (1,609 lb); maximum take-off (normal) 820 kg (1,808 lb)
Fuel and load: external fuel none; ordnance none
Speed: never exceed speed 400 km/h (215 kt;

248 mph); maximum level speed 'clean' at sea level 340 km/h (183 kt; 211 mph); maximum cruising speed at optimum altitude and 75 per cent power 290 km/h (156 kt; 180 mph)
Range: 750 km (405 nm; 466 miles)
Performance: maximum rate of climb at sea level 1020 m (3,346 ft) per minute
g limits: -10 to +10

The single-seat CAP 230 is used by the 'Equipe de Voltige' aerobatic team, the second display unit of the Equipes de Présentation de l'Armée de l'Air (the first being the 'Patrouille de France'), and for instructor's flying at the Ecole de l'Air at Salon-de-Provence.

Myasishchev M-4 'Bison'

Myasishchev Design Bureau, 140160 Zhukovskii, Moscow Region, Russia.

Designed as a long-range strategic bomber, the 'Bison' was always handicapped by its inability to meet a totally unrealistic requirement: that it be capable of attacking targets in North America, which was impossible using the Soviet technology of the time. Myasishchev himself believed that the requirement could only be met by using turboprop engines, or by building a 250-tonne bomber with eight AM-3 engines. Wisely, he produced a superb medium-range bomber with four of these engines, but the political leadership was unhappy with the aircraft (which couldn't reach the American homeland) and production was limited to about 200 aircraft (despite the fact that it was a better medium bomber than the contemporary Tu-16 'Badger', which was built in much larger numbers). One limiting factor was the size of the bomb bay, which was limited in extent because it lay between the main units of the bicycle undercarriage.

There were three basic sub-variants of the aircraft, most of which were quickly

This 'Bison-A' is one of those still based at Zhukhovskii, and is probably used by the OKB in support of the VM-T Atlant programme, and may even be a candidate for conversion.

converted as tankers or reconnaissance platforms. The basic **M-4 'Bison-A'** was a strategic nuclear bomber version powered by four 85.32-kN (19,180-lb) Mikulin AM-3D turbojets in the wingroots (the prototype having podded, underslung engines) and had a short glazed nose and dihedral tailplanes. It could carry its 9000-kg (19,840-lb) warload over a range of about 8100 km (4,384 nm/5,032 miles). An inflight-refuelling probe could be fitted above the nose, but was not normally carried. The relocation of the engines from underslung pods necessitated the addition of small wingtip pods for the undercarriage outriggers, which had previously been housed in the outer engine nacelles. Production aircraft had two overwing fences, located well outboard. A handful of M-4s remain in use, primarily for training and perhaps as tankers.

The **3M** ('**Bison-B'**) was powered by the more powerful 107.9-kN (24,250-lb) VD-7 turbojet and introduced an inflight-refuelling probe above the lengthened nose, which had a large radome covering much of the underside, in turn necessitating provision of an undernose visual bomb-aiming gondola. Dihedral was removed from the tailplanes and a third (more prominent) fence was added above the wing, which featured a slightly increased span (from 50.526 m/165 ft 9¼ in to 53.14 m/174 ft

4¼ in). Range was increased to 12000 km (7,457 miles), still some 1500 km (932 miles) less than the Tu-95, and 3000 km (1,864 miles) less than the Tu-95M. The final variant was the **3MD**, which was powered by 93.20-kN (20,944-lb st) VD-7B engines. This had a completely new nose profile, with a refuelling probe at the tip, and an undernose radome for the 'Puff Ball' radar. This was given the NATO reporting name '**Bison-C'**. A related record-breaking aircraft known as the **M-201** or **M-3M** was powered by 127.49-kN (28,660-lb) VD-15B turbojets.

'Bison' tankers bear the Russian designation **3MS-2** and are mainly converted '**Bison-B**s'. These are believed to have been re-engined with the 93.20-kN (20,944-

A tanker-configured 'Bison-B' clearly shows this variant's extended nose, undernose visual bomb-aiming gondola and non-dihedral tailplane.

lb st) RD-3M-500A turbojet. They refuel probe-equipped receiver aircraft using a centreline hose-drogue unit mounted in the former bomb bay. Carrying up to 40 tonnes of fuel, the 3MS-2 can transfer fuel at up to 2250 litres (495 Imp gal) per minute and has a maximum endurance of 12 hours and 15 minutes. Some sources suggested that the 'Bison' had been entirely withdrawn from Soviet/CIS service, and there was a massive, and heavily publicised, scrapping of air-

The VM-T Atlant can carry outsized loads above its fuselage. It is seen here carrying a space shuttle fuel tank, landing after a display at the Moscow Aeroshow.

craft during the late 1980s. Certainly some 20 'Bison-B' and 'Bison-C' airframes were dismantled as part of the superpower strategic arms reduction programme, but at least a handful of **Russian** tankers remained in use, notably with a regiment based at Engels, long after this. Others still fly from Zhukhovskii, and perhaps from Ryazan. Il-78M 'Mainstays' used during the Gulf War were reportedly refuelled by 'Bison' tankers, and pairs of the big Myasishchev bomber/tankers have flown at recent air displays in the Soviet Union.

Also still active is a pair of 'Bison-Bs' converted to serve as the carriers of outsize loads. Designated **VM-T** and known as **Atlant**, these aircraft carry their cargoes (mainly components from the Soviet space programme, including the Buran shuttle orbiter) on their backs. To correct airflow problems over the tail and subsequently improve stability when carrying outsized loads, the M-4's conventional single tailfin has been replaced by a pair of endplate fins on a new dihedral tailplane.

SPECIFICATION

Myasishchev 3MS-2 'Bison-B'
Wing: span 53.14 m (174 ft 4 in); estimated aspect ratio 7.96; estimated area 320.00 m² (3,444.56 sq ft)
Fuselage and tail: length 51.7 m (169 ft 7½ in);
estimated height 14.10 m (46 ft 3 in); estimated tailplane span 15.00 m (49 ft 2.5 in)
Powerplant: four MNPK 'Soyuz' (Mikulin) RD-3M-500A turbojets each rated at 93.20 kN (20,944 lb st)
Weights: empty 75740 kg (166,975 lb); normal take-off 192000 kg (423,280 lb)
Payload: 24000 kg (52,910 lb)
Speed: estimated maximum level speed 'clean' at 11000 m (36,090 ft) 998 km/h (538 kt; 620 mph)
Range: 12400 km (6,712 nm; 7,705 miles)
Performance: estimated service ceiling 13700 m (44,950 ft)

Myasishchev **M-17 Stratosfera and M-55 Geophysica 'Mystic'**

Little is known about the origins of the 'Mystic', which probably began as a military high-altitude reconnaissance platform, despite its much-publicised recent history as a simple record breaker and ecological protection/earth resources survey aircraft. It was probably intended as a direct replacement for the Yak-25 'Mandrake'. The aircraft first came to the attention of the West during 1982, when a satellite photographed one at Zhukhovskii, which the West still referred to as Ramenskoye after the nearby town. The provisional reporting name **'RAM-M'** was allocated. Two of the original **M-17**s were built, each powered by a 68.6-kN (15,430-lb) Rybinsk RD-36-51V turbojet, reportedly developed from the Kuznetsov NK-144 engines of the Tu-144 'Charger'or the VD-7s of the M-50 'Bounder'. The first aircraft has been retired to the museum at Monino, while the second has made a series of flights monitoring pollution and examining the ozone layer. The M-17 is known as the **Stratosfera**.

A twin-engined derivative, the **M-55**, may have been developed because of short-comings in the original M-17 design. The **'Mystic-B'** has a slightly shorter-span wing than the original aircraft, and is powered by a pair of 49-kN (11,025-lb) Perm/Soloviev PS-30-V12 engines, derived from the powerplant of the MiG-31 'Foxhound'. The aircraft has a lengthened fuselage, accommodating a large sensor bay aft of the nosewheel bay. The M-55 Geophysica can carry a larger payload (up to 1500 kg/ 3,307 lb) and has a longer endurance (seven hours) than the M-17. The sensor package is believed to contain both optical and infra-red sensors (and possibly radar), including an A-84 camera, which covers an area 120 km (75 miles) wide from its operational height of 20000 m (65,600 ft). Development continues, reportedly under a Russian air force contract, and two pre-series aircraft are under construction.

SPECIFICATION

Myasishchev M-17 Stratosfera 'Mystic-A'
Wing: span 40.70 m (133 ft 6.5 in)
Fuselage and tail: length 21.20 m (69 ft 6.5 in); height 5.25 m (17 ft 3 in); wheel track 6.65 m (21 ft 10 in); wheel base 5.60 m (18 ft 4.5 in)
Powerplant: one RKBM (Novikov) RD-36-51V turbojet rated at 68.65 kN (15,432 lb st)
Weights: maximum take-off 19950 kg (43,981 lb)
Fuel and load: external fuel none
Range: endurance 2 hours 30 minutes
Performance: service ceiling 20000 m (65,615 ft)

Known mainly as a record-breaker and earth resources survey platform, the M-55 was almost certainly originally designed to meet a Soviet air forces requirement for a high-altitude reconnaissance aircraft, with U-2-type performance.

National Aerospace Laboratory (Kawasaki) **Asuka**

Using the airframe of the **Kawasaki C-1** transport (described separately), the Japanese National Aerospace Laboratory developed this highly-modified experimental STOL transport to explore the potential of upper surface blowing (USB) and other systems to achieve STOL performance. The C-1's two pylon-mounted JT8D engines were replaced by four indigenously-developed high-bypass ratio turbofans mounted in nacelles far ahead of the wing leading edges. The wings incorporate leading-edge and aileron BLC control systems. The fuselage and landing gear received structural strengthening, and a digital stability and control augmentation system was introduced. In this form, the **Asuka** first flew on 28 October 1985, and in its first STOL landing, on 23 March 1988, the prototype required a ground run of only 439 m (1,440 ft). The primary research programme was completed in 1989.

SPECIFICATION

NAL (Kawasaki) Asuka
Wing: span 30.60 m (100 ft 4.75 in); aspect ratio 7.8; area 120.50 m² (1,297.09 sq ft)
Fuselage and tail: length 33.154 m (108 ft 9.25 in); height 10.175 m (33 ft 4.5 in); tailplane span 11.30 m (37 ft 1 in); wheel track 4.40 m (14 ft 5.25 in); wheel base 9.33 m (30 ft 7.75 in)
Powerplant: four MITI/NAL FJR710/600S turbofans each rated at 10,582 lb st (47.07 kN)
Weights: normal take-off 38700 kg (85,320 lb) for short take-off; maximum take-off 45000 kg (99,210 lb) for conventional take-off
Fuel and load: internal fuel 12628 kg (27,840 lb); external fuel none

Speed: never exceed speed 320 kt (368 mph; 593 km/h); maximum cruising speed at optimum altitude 260 kt (299 mph; 482 km/h)
Range: range 720 nm (829 miles; 1334 km)

Performance: service ceiling 28,000 ft (8535 m); STOL take-off distance to 50 ft (15 m) 2,700 ft (853 m) at normal take-off weight; STOL landing distance from 50 ft (15 m) 2,800 ft (853 m) at normal landing weight

The Asuka is a Kawasaki C-1 with four turbofan engines and flap blowing over the upper surfaces.

NAMC YS-11

The Nihon Aeroplane Manufacturing Company (NAMC) was formed specifically to produc the YS-11 transport. As a collaborative project, it involved the following grouping of Japanes aerospace companies: Fuji, Kawasaki, Mitsubishi, Nippi, Shinmaywa and Show

The only airliner of indigenous design to achieve production in Japan, the **NAMC YS-11** was conceived in 1957 as a medium-range transport. Development of the aircraft was carried out as a collaborative project involving Fuji, Kawasaki, Mitsubishi, Nippi, Shinmaywa and Showa – this grouping was eventually named the Nihon Aeroplane Manufacturing Company (NAMC). The first of two prototype YS-11s made its maiden flight on 30 August 1962.

Production batches of the commercial **YS-11A**, all with Dart 542 turboprops, fell into several series, starting with the **Series 100**. The **Series 200** had increased gross weight, the **Series 300** and **Series 400** were similar but for mixed traffic and all-cargo operation, respectively, and the **Series 500** and **600** were Series 200 and 100 equivalents with further gross weight increases. Passenger accommodation varied between 48 and 70. Production ended in 1974 after 182 aircraft, most being delivered to commercial operators.

Of the commercial examples, six **Series 220**s were acquired from Olympic Airways in 1980 by the **Hellenic air force**, and the surviving five aircraft are in service as personnel transports with 356 'Iraklis' Mira, a tactical transport unit within the 112ª Ptérix Mahis (Combat Wing) at Elefsina. One example is also used to calibrate radar and instrument landing systems.

A total of 23 YS-11s was procured by the **JMSDF** (13) and **JASDF** (10) in a number of sub-variants. The JASDF acquired two **Series 103**s and two **Series 105**s as **YS-11P** VIP personnel transports in 1965/66, a **Series 305** as **YS-11PC** personnel/cargo transport in 1968 and four **Series 402**s as **YS-11C** freighters in 1969/70.

The YS-11E is a dedicated ECM/EW training aircraft, festooned with antenna fairings and a huge chaff dispenser aft of the wingroot. Two are in service.

One of the latter was converted to the **YS-11NT** navigational trainer in 1977, and a **Series 213** was acquired in 1971 as **YS-11FC** for flight check duties; this is currently based at Iruma. Finally, three further Series 402s were acquired in 1971, of which two were heavily modified in 1976/79 as **YS-11E** ECM trainers and the other became the **YS-11E(EL)** in 1982 for Elint duty. Further modification programmes in the late 1980s were to result in one YS-11 receiving the ALQ-7 jamming system and being re-engined with T64 turboprops to carry the increased weight of avionics, a further two being fitted with Litton avionics for calibration duties, three serving as VIP transports, and another three undertaking Elint missions with J/ALR-2 systems. YS-11Es serve with the Electronic Warfare Training Unit at Iruma. Originally equipping three transport units, Support Command's reconfigured YS-11s currently serve with 402 Hikotai at Iruma and 403 Hikotai at Miho.

JMSDF operation of the YS-11 began in 1970 with a **Series 112** and a **Series 113** as **YS-11M** transports, joined in 1971/73 by two **Series 404**s **YS-11M-A**, all serving with 61st Kokutai at Atsugi. The mixed-complement transports feature accommodation for 48 personnel and incorporate a cargo compartment at the rear of the fuselage, with a freight loading door on the port side. Four **Series 206**s and two **Series 624**s, delivered 1970-74, serve

as **YS-11T-A** ASW crew trainers in 205th Kyoiku Kokutai of the Shimofusa Air Training Group. The YS-11Ts are equipped with a maritime search radar in a belly-mounted radome.

SPECIFICATION

NAMC YS-11A-300

Wing: span 32.00 m (104 ft 11.75 in); aspect ratio 10.8; area 94.80 m² (1,020.45 sq ft)
Fuselage and tail: length 26.30 m (86 ft 3.5 in); height 8.98 m (29 ft 5.5 in); tailplane span 12.00 m (38 ft 2.5 in); wheel track 8.60 m (28 ft 2.5 in); wheel base 9.52 m (31 ft 2.5 in)
Powerplant: two Rolls-Royce Dart RDa.10/1 Mk 542-10K turboprops each rated at 3,060 ehp (2282 ekW)

Weights: operating empty 15810 kg (34,854 lb); maximum take-off 24500 kg (54,012 lb)
Fuel and load: internal fuel 7270 litres (1,921 US gal); external fuel none; maximum payload 6190 kg (13,646 lb)
Speed: maximum cruising speed at 15,000 ft (4570 m) 253 kt (291 mph; 469 km/h); economical cruising speed at 20,000 ft (6095 m) 244 kt (281 mph; 452 km/h)
Range: 1,735 nm (1,998 miles; 3215 km) with maximum fuel or 588 nm (677 miles; 1090 km) with maximum payload
Performance: maximum rate of climb at sea level 1,220 ft (372 m) per minute; service ceiling 22,900 ft (6980 m); take-off distance to 35 ft (10.7 m) 3,650 ft (1113 m) at maximum take-off weight; landing distance from 50 ft (15 m) 2,170 ft (661 m) at maximum landing weight

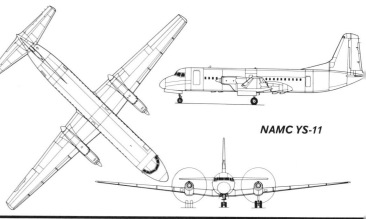

The YS-11E(EL) dedicated Elint aircraft is of similar appearance to the YS-11E ECM trainer. The former aircraft wears a more warlike grey camouflage.

NAMC YS-11

Nanchang (NAMC) CJ-6A

Serving the air force of the **People's Republic of China** as its standard basic trainer, the **CJ-6** piston-engined aircraft was developed at Shenyang in 1956-58 as a successor for the CJ-5 (itself a licence-built version of the Yak-18). Retaining the latter's overall configuration, it introduced a fully retractable undercarriage, with the main legs folding inwards into the wing centre-section and the nosewheel retracting aft into the forward fuselage. The outer wing panels introduced marked dihedral. The cockpit features tandem seating beneath a long 'glasshouse' canopy. The first prototype of the CJ-6, flown on 27 August 1958, was fitted with a 108-kW (145-hp) Mikulin M-11ER engine, with which it proved to be underpowered. The CJ-6 was later modified with an Ivchenko

AI-14R engine and first flew in this form on 18 July 1960. The **CJ-6A**, which became the standard production version from 1965, introduced an uprated HS6A engine. Ten armed **CJ-6B**s were built in 1964-66.

Production of the CJ-6A (the 'Westernised' designation of which is **PT-6A**) has totalled more than 1,800, and batches of the Nanchang trainer have been exported to several nations in the Chinese ambit including **Albania, Bangladesh, Cambodia, North Korea, Tanzania** and **Zambia**.

SPECIFICATION

Nanchang CJ-6A/PT-6A

Wing: span 10.18 m (33 ft 4.75 in)
Fuselage and tail: length 8.46 m (27 ft 9 in); height

3.25 m (10 ft 8 in)
Powerplant: one Zhuzhou (SMPMC) Huosai-6A (Ivchenko/Vedeneyev AI-14RF) nine-cylinder air-cooled radial engine rated at 213 kW (285 hp)
Weights: empty equipped 1172 kg (2,584 lb); maximum take-off 1419 kg (3,128 lb)
Fuel and load: internal fuel 110 kg (243 lb); external fuel none; ordnance none

Speed: maximum level speed 'clean' at optimum altitude 297 km/h (160 kt; 185 mph)
Range: endurance 3 hours 54 minutes
Performance: maximum rate of climb at sea level 380 m (1,248 ft) per minute; service ceiling 6250 m (20,500 ft); take-off run 280 m (920 ft) at maximum take-off weight; landing run 350 m (1,150 ft) at normal landing weight

The Chinese-built Nanchang BT-6 serves as the standard primary training aircraft of the Bangladesh air force, with No. 11 Squadron at Jessore. Twelve were delivered.

Nanchang Q-5/A-5 'Fantan'

The **Nanchang Q-5 'Fantan'** is a dedicated attack aircraft loosely based on the airframe of the Chinese-built MiG-19 or J-6. Development of the aircraft began in August 1958 to meet a **People's Liberation Army** requirement. The Nanchang Aircraft Factory had been established in

May 1951, and had been considerably rebuilt with Soviet assistance during the 1950s, but had always specialised in the production of propeller-driven aircraft. When development of the Q-5 attack aircraft was assigned to the factory, Nanchang therefore had much to learn. Shenyang helped with

initial design and mock-up construction, and the factory began licence-production of a small batch of MiG-19Ps and MiG-19PMs.

It would be easy to overstate the relationship of the Q-5 to the MiG-19, the new aircraft actually sharing only the rear fuselage and main undercarriage of the latter with a new, stretched fuselage, area-ruled to reduce transonic drag. The fuselage also accommodated a 4.00-m (13-ft) long internal weapons bay, with two adjacent fuselage

pylons. The new fuselage had a conica nose, giving an improved view forward and downward and providing a potential loca tion for an attack radar (which never mater alised). The Q-5 was also given wings o greater area and less sweep to give more lift and better turn performance. The tail plane was increased in size to improve lon gitudinal stability. This also necessitated the provision of lateral air intakes. The nose wheel was redesigned to rotate through 90°

s it retracted, allowing it to lie flat in the underside of the fuselage.

Internal armament of the Q-5 comprises two 23-mm cannon (downgraded from the MiG-19's 30-mm NR-30 cannon) each with 00 rounds. Tandem pairs of pylons are each capable of carrying a 250-kg (551-lb) bomb. The inboard underwing pylons are used for carriage of lighter stores such as practice bombs and rocket pods. The central underwing pylons can carry 760-litre (201-US gal) fuel tanks or a 500-kg (1,102-lb) bomb. The outboard hardpoints can carry 400-litre (106-US gal) tanks or a variety of bombs or air-to-air missiles.

Prototype construction began in May 1960, but was abandoned during the political turmoil of the early 1960s and reinstated by stages, first as a 'spare time venture', then resumed full-time in 1963 because of the progress made. The prototype finally made its maiden flight on 4 June 1965, but extensive modifications proved necessary to solve problems encountered with the hydraulics, brakes, fuel and weapons systems. Two new prototypes flew in October 1969 and the type was ordered into production as the Q-5.

There is a dedicated nuclear weapons-carrier version of the Q-5, but little is known about this aircraft, which may retain its internal bomb bay. It carries a single 5- to 20-kT weapon. China's 13th nuclear test in 1970 was of a weapon lofted by a Q-5.

An extended-range variant, the **Q-5I**, was certificated in 1983. This had a fuel tank in place of the internal weapons bay, a modified landing gear and relocated brake chute fairing at the base of the fin. Two additional underfuselage hardpoints were provided. A new rocket-powered Type I ejection seat was fitted (allowing ejections above 260 m/850 ft and 348 km/h/188 kt), as was a new short-range SSB radio. The aircraft was powered by the new Series 6 Wopen WP6 engine. Together, these modifications brought about a 130-m (425-ft) reduction in landing run, a 500-kg (1,102-lb) increase in warload, and a 35 per cent increase in low-level radius of action (or a 26 per cent increase in normal range). Some Q-5Is were modified to serve as missile-carriers with the **PLA navy**, and some of these aircraft may have been fitted with Doppler-type nose radar. C-801 ASMs and torpedoes could also be carried.

The **Q-5IA**, certificated for production in 1985, was fitted with an additional underwing hardpoint and introduced pressure refuelling, a new gun/bomb sighting system and new defensive avionics. The **Q-5II** received a radar warning receiver but was otherwise similar. The **A-5C** was an export version of the Q-5IA for **Pakistan**, and actually entered production before the domestic variant. The Chinese designation **Q-5III** applies to this version. Avionics were substantially improved, and compatibility with various Western weapons (including the AIM-9 Sidewinder) was provided. The aircraft was also fitted with a Martin-Baker Mk 10L ejection seat.

Production of the Q-5 continues, and over 1,000 are believed to have been delivered. **North Korea** took delivery of 40 Q-5IAs, while Pakistan received 52 A-5Cs between January 1983 and January 1984. **Bangladesh** took delivery of a further 20 similar aircraft. Pakistan paid $2.6 million for each of its A-5Cs, this low purchase price being offset by low airframe (600 hours) and engine (200 hours) TBO figures. Pakistan now undertakes all of its own A-5C servicing and overhauls at Kamra's repair and overhaul facility. Recent reports suggest that RWRs are being fitted to these aircraft as they go through Kamra.

Before the Tiananmen Square massacre in June 1989, there were a number of programmes to upgrade Chinese combat aircraft with Western avionics and/or equipment, several of these involving the Q-5. Britain's Flight Refuelling Ltd was involved in a project to design inflight-refuelling probes for the aircraft, and two competing upgrades were designed to meet a Chinese requirement. The **A-5K Kong Yun** (Cloud) was designed in association with Thompson-CSF with a TMV630 laser rangefinder. Development began in June 1987, and yielded a flying prototype on 17 September 1988, but the project was abandoned in 1990. The **A-5M** programme was launched in August 1986, in association with Aeritalia, which added an AMX-style avionics system. This included a Pointer 2500 ranging radar, LN-39 INS, Alenia HUD 35, and new IFF and RWR equipment. An extra underwing pylon was added (bringing the total to four per side) and compatibility with the PL-5 AAM was also incorporated. The prototype was powered by 36.78-kN (8,267-lb st) Wopen WP-6A engines and made its maiden flight on 30 August 1988, but was written off on 17 October. A second prototype flew on 8 March 1989 and development was completed on 19 February 1991.

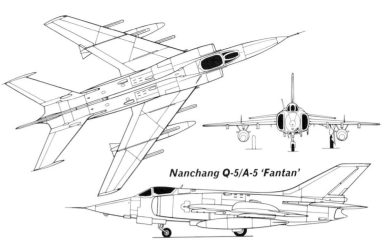

Nanchang Q-5/A-5 'Fantan'

SPECIFICATION

Nanchang Q-5IA 'Fantan'

Wing: span 9.68 m (31 ft 9 in); aspect ratio 3.37; area 27.95 m² (300.86 sq ft)

Fuselage and tail: length 15.65 m (51 ft 4.25 in) including probe; height 4.333 m (14 ft 2.75 in); wheel track 4.40 m (14 ft 5.25 in); wheel base 4.01 m (13 ft 2 in)

Powerplant: two Liming (LM) (previously Shenyang) Wopen-6A turbojets each rated at 29.42 kN (6,614 lb st) dry and 36.78 kN (8,267 lb st) with afterburning

Weights: empty 6375 kg (14,054 lb); normal take-off 9486 kg (20,913 lb); maximum take-off 11830 kg (26,080 lb)

Fuel and load: internal fuel 2827 kg (6,232 lb); external fuel up to 1178 kg (2,597 lb) in two 760- or 400-litre (201- or 106-US gal) drop tanks; maximum ordnance 2000 kg (4,409 lb)

Speed: maximum level speed at 11000 m (36,000 ft) Mach 1.12 (1190 km/h; 643 kt; 740 mph); maximum speed at sea level 1210 km/h (653 kt; 752 mph)

Range: combat radius with maximum external stores, afterburners off lo-lo-lo 400 km (216 nm; 248 miles), hi-lo-hi 600 km (324 nm; 373 miles); range at 11000 m (36,000 ft) with maximum internal/external fuel, afterburners off nearly 2000 km (1,080 nm; 1,243 miles)

Performance: maximum rate of climb at 5000 m (16,400 ft) 4980-6180 m (16,340-20,275 ft) per minute; service ceiling 15850 m (52,000 ft), take-off run 1250 m (4,100 ft); landing run 1060 m (3,480 ft)

Right: A pair of No. 8 Squadron, Bangladesh Defence Force Air Wing, Nanchang A-5s, armed with tiny Chinese rocket pods, executes a tidy break. A-5s also equip No. 21 Squadron at Dhaka.

Below: The A-5 equips three squadrons of the Pakistan air force, Nos 16 and 26 of No. 36 (Tactical Attack) Wing at Peshawar, and No. 7, the conversion unit, at Masroor.

Neico **Lancair 320**

Neico Aviation was based at Santa Paula in Cal;ifornia. Lancair aircraft are now produced by Lancair International, based at Redmond, Oregon. The Pacific Aeronautical Inc. is based at 25 First Avenue, Mactan Export Processing Zone, Lapu Lapu City 6015, Republic of the Philippines

The **Neico Lancair** family has been available to home-builders in kit form for some years, the side-by-side two-seater proving to be popular on account of its modern looks and high performance, the latter thanks to streamlined design and retractable tricycle undercarriage. A single **Lancair 320** was supplied to **Bolivia** for evaluation by the air force as a primary trainer, while Pacific Aeronautical Inc. (formerly Advanced Composite Technology) in the Philippines has developed the **ACT Apache I** for use in a similar role. **Zaïre** reportedly ordered 30 for its air force training requirements, but the status of the Apache programme is in some doubt.

Neiva **C-42/L-42 Regente**

Sociedade Constructora Aeronautica Neiva Ltda. was established on October 1953. The company was acquired by EMBRAER in 1975, which took charge of the latter's light plane manufacturing programme

More than half of 120 Regentes built by Neiva between 1961 and 1971 remain in service with the **Brazilian air force**, distributed through a number of squadrons for communications duties, and equipping one of the squadrons of 8° Grupo de Aviaco at Santa Cruz. The **Neiva Regente 360C** prototype was first flown on 7 September 1961. The Regente is a four-seat high-wing monoplane with fixed tricycle undercarriage and was the first of that company's light aircraft designs to feature all-metal construction. The single-spar wing incorporated semi-Fowler flaps and semi-Fowler ailerons.

For communications duties, the FAeB ordered 80 Regentes, initially with the designation **U-42**, later changed to **C-42**. The first of these flew in 1965 and deliveries were completed in 1968. Seating four, the C-42 was powered by the 180-hp (156-kW) Lycoming O-360-A1D flat-four piston engine. To serve more specifically in the liaison and AOP role, the **L-42** was developed in 1967, differing from the C-42 in having only three seats, a cut-down rear fuselage to improve the all-round view (compensation for the reduced keel area being provided by a dorsal fin extension) and a more powerful IO-360 flat-six piston engine. Following the first flight of a **YL-42** prototype in October 1967, 40 were delivered from June 1969.

Having previously built copies of the Piper Cub, the U-42 Regente was Neiva's first original design.

The three-seat L-42 Regente was a development of the U-42 which entered production in 1968.

NH Industries **NH 90**

NH Industries sarl, Le Quatuor, Batiment C, 42 Route de Galice F-13082 Aix en Provence France

In 1985 five European nations signed a Memorandum of Understanding covering a 'NATO helicopter for the '90s', designated **NH 90**. The United Kingdom dropped out of the programme in 1987, leaving France, Germany, Italy and the Netherlands in the project. Participating companies are Eurocopter France (43 per cent of the workshare), Agusta (26 per cent), Eurocopter Deutschland (24 per cent) and Fokker (seven per cent). Stated requirements are 220 for France, 214 for Italy, 272 for Germany and 20 for the Netherlands. A first flight is expected in 1995, with deliveries commencing in 1999.

Two versions are planned, the **NFH 90** (NATO Frigate Helicopter) with 360° search radar under the cabin and ASW equipment, and the **TTH 90** (Tactical Transport Helicopter) for assault transport, rescue, EW and VIP transport duties. The NH 90 exhibits a classic configuration, with a two-man flight deck and a cabin for either ASW equipment and one sensor operator or 20 fully-equipped troops. Power is to be provided by two of either the Rolls-Royce Turboméca/Piaggio/MTU RTM332 or General Electric/Alfa Romeo T700 turboshafts.

The first set of NH 90 rotor blades was handed over by NH Industries on 20 May

The NH 90 is planned in two versions. Seen in preliminary model form, they are (top) the NFH NATO Frigate Helicopter, and (below) the TTH Tactical Transport Helicopter. Estimated service requirements are for 192 NFHs and 554 TTHs. The first example is now heading towards roll-out in 1995.

1994, at La Corneuve. The blades mark the first use of new manufacturing techniques in such an item, as extensive use of CAD/CAM-originated resin components has been made, using the Catia 3-D design system.

SPECIFICATION

NH Industries NH 90 (provisional)
Rotor system: main rotor diameter 16.30 m (53 ft 5.5 in); tail rotor diameter 3.20 m (10 ft 6 in); main rotor disc area 213.82 m² (2,301.17 sq ft); tail rotor disc area 8.04 m² (86.57 sq ft)
Fuselage and tail: length overall, rotors turning 19.38 m (63 ft 7 in), fuselage 16.81 m (55 ft 1.75 in) and with main rotor blades and tail folded 13.50 m (44 ft 1.5 in); height overall 5.422 m (17 ft 9.5 in) with tail rotor turning, and 4.10 m (13 ft 5.5 in) with main rotor blades and tail folded; wheel track 3.20 m

(10 ft 6 in); wheel base 6.18 m (20 ft 3.25 in)
Powerplant: two Rolls-Royce/Turboméca/MTU (with Piaggio) RTM 322-01/02 turboshafts each rated at 1599.5 kW (2,145 shp) or two General Electric (with Alfa Romeo) T700-GE-401X turboshafts each rated at 2,400 shp (1789 kW)

Weights: empty 5700 kg (12,566 lb); maximum take-off 9100 kg (20,062 lb)
Fuel and load: internal fuel 1900 kg (4,189 lb); maximum payload more than 2000 kg (4,409 lb)
Range: operational radius 60 nm (69 miles; 111 km) for a 3-hour patrol; endurance 5 hours 30 minutes

Nord Aviation (Aérospatiale) **N 2501 Noratlas**

SNCAN (formed from a merger between Caudron and Amiot) later became Nord. The latter company itself merged with Sud Aviation to form Aérospatiale, in 1970

Designed as a military transport for service with the Armée de l'Air, the **Nord N 2501 Noratlas** transport first flew with the intended Hercules engines on November 1950. It adopted the same configuration as the Fairchild C-82 Packet – namely a high wing, twin engines and twin tailbooms – and can accommodate 45 troops, 36 fully-equipped paratroops, or 18 stretchers and medical attendants. The Noratlas entered service with the Armée de l'Air in 1951 (in **N 2501F** guise) and also served with the Luftwaffe, which received 186 **N 2501D**s. A few examples of this once widely-used tactical transport remain in service in some of the ex-French territories in Africa, having been supplied from surplus stocks after their retirement from both European air forces. Now nearing the end of their airframe lives, a total of 10 aircraft survives in service with the **Congo Republic**, **Djibouti**, **Niger** and **Rwanda**.

SPECIFICATION

Nord Aviation (Aérospatiale) N 2501 Noratlas
Wing: span 32.50 m (106 ft 7.5 in); aspect ratio 10.44; area 101.20 m² (1,089.34 sq ft)
Fuselage and tail: length 21.96 m (72 ft 0.6 in); height 6.00 m (19 ft 8.2 in)
Powerplant: two SNECMA-built Bristol Hercules Mk 738/739 14-cylinder air-cooled radial piston engines each rated at 2,040 hp (1521 kW)

Weights: empty equipped 13075 kg (28,825 lb); normal take-off 21000 kg (46,296 lb); maximum take-off 21700 kg (47,840 lb)
Load: maximum payload 7400 kg (16,314 lb)
Speed: maximum level speed 'clean' at 3050 m (10,000 ft) 440 km/h (237 kt; 273 mph); cruising speed at 1500 m (4,920 ft) 323 km/h (175 kt; 201 mph)
Range: 2500 km (1,349 nm; 1,553 miles) with a 4550-kg (10,031-lb) payload
Performance: maximum rate of climb at sea level 375 m (1,230 ft) per minute; service ceiling 7500 m (24,605 ft)

North American **T-6 Texan**

North American Aviation, founded in 1928, merged with the Rockwell-Standard Corporation, in 1967, becoming the North American Rockwell Corporation. This company became Rockwell International in 1973.

The **North American T-6** two-seat advanced trainer, officially named **Texan**, is better remembered by Commonwealth pilots as the **Harvard**. Similar to the USAAF's North American BC-1A basic combat trainer, the T-6 was introduced in 1938 and eventually replaced the BC-1A. Total T-6 production, which ended at the close of World War II, amounted to more than 16,000 in the US, while many more were manufactured under licence-production programmes throughout the Commonwealth.

The T-6 is an all-metal low-wing monoplane with retractable tailwheel landing gear. The pilot and instructor sat in tandem enclosed cockpits, the low sill of which gave an excellent view. Complete dual flight and engine controls are fitted in each cockpit. The powerful and reliable Pratt & Whitney Wasp air-cooled radial engine gave a sprightly performance, and the forgiving but responsive flying controls combined to make the T-6 an ideal training aircraft. Its distinctive rasping noise, not heard by the occupants, was caused by the high tip-speed of the direct-drive propeller.

The primary role of the T-6 as an armed trainer also made it suitable for light ground attack/COIN duties. Because of this, and its strong construction, reliability and ease of flying, the T-6 continued to be used for many years throughout the world.

Today the **South African Air Force** is the only major user, with over 100 Harvards

The South African Air Force was forced to retain substantial numbers of T-6 Harvards as its primary trainer well into the 1990s. Their replacement will come in the form of locally-assembled Pilatus PC-7 Mk IIs. While some aircraft have been disposed of, chiefly to civilian 'warbird' operators, the South Africans are being careful to dispose of their Harvards in a controlled fashion so as not to flood the market and depress the type's market value.

still flying with the Central Flying School at Langebaanweg. These were due for retirement in 1994, but their replacement has proceeded more slowly than expected. The Harvard's successor will be the Pilatus PC-7 Mk II, and small numbers of the SAAF's substantial T-6 fleet are being disposed of to civilian customers, but gradually, so as not to undermine their market value. Even when the type is finally replaced as the air force's primary trainer, 25 will reportedly be retained as a memorial to the wartime Empire flying programme, hosted by South Africa. Other military users include **Chile**, the **Dominican Republic**, **Portugal** and **Uruguay**, which each operates a pair of Texans. The **United Kingdom** has two Harvards at ETPS, Boscombe Down, as camera chase and training aircraft.

SPECIFICATION

North American T-6 Texan
Wing: span 42 ft 0.25 in (12.81 m); aspect ratio 6.96; area 253.70 sq ft (23.57 m²)
Fuselage and tail: length 29 ft 6 in (8.99 m); height 11 ft 9 in (3.58 m)
Powerplant: one Pratt & Whitney R-1340-AN-1 Wasp nine-cylinder air-cooled radial piston engine rated at 550 hp (410 kW)

Weights: empty equipped 4,158 lb (1886 kg); maximum take-off 5,300 lb (2404 kg)
Fuel and load: internal fuel 110 US gal (416 litres); external fuel none
Speed: maximum level speed 'clean' at 5,000 ft (1525 m) 178 kt (205 mph; 330 km/h); cruising speed at optimum altitude 148 kt (170 mph; 272 km/h)
Range: range 651 nm (750 miles; 1207 km)
Performance: maximum rate of climb at sea level 1,350 ft (411 m) per minute; service ceiling 21,500 ft (6555 m)

North American **T-28 Trojan**

Designed as a potential replacement for the successful T-6 Texan/Harvard family of trainers, the **T-28** was first flown on 26 September 1949 and entered production as a combined basic and primary trainer. The T-28 retained the T-6's basic trainer configuration, but introduced tricycle undercarriage and an 800-hp (597-kW) Wright R-1300-1A radial piston engine driving a two-bladed variable-pitch propeller. It was produced for the USAF (1,194 **T-28A**s) and the US Navy and Marine Corps, comprising 489 **T-28B Trojans** with more powerful 1,425-hp (1063-kW) Wright R-1820 engines driving three-bladed propellers, and 299 **T-28C**s with arrester hook and strengthened airframe to withstand carrier landings. Both these versions served until the 1970s. Production totalled 1,984 and numerous examples were delivered to foreign air forces through MAP and other arrangements.

In the early 1960s, subsequent conversion programmes produced the **T-28D** variant as a heavily-armed counter-insurgency aircraft. Several hundred surplus T-28As were modified by North American and Fairchild with R-1820 engines, three-bladed propellers, crew armour protection and six underwing stores hardpoints. T-28Ds served with US air commando squadrons as part of early American involvement in Vietnam, being fitted to carry podded 0.5-in (12.7-mm) machine-guns, 500-lb (227-kg) bombs, rockets and napalm weapons. Dissatisfaction with their performance led to transfer of 100 aircraft to the air forces of South Vietnam and the Philippines. A similar

programme in 1960-61 by Sud Aviation in France produced 245 **Fennec** conversions of the T-28A for the Armée de l'Air. These saw widespread service in the light-attack role in Algeria. Surplus Fennecs were sold to Morocco, Honduras and the Argentine navy (modified with arrester hooks).

T-28Ds remain in service as weapons/COIN trainers in the **Dominican Republic** (six Trojans were withdrawn from service and two were subsequently restored to use by 1988) and the **Philippines**, which originally received 60 **AT-28D** aircraft up to the mid-1970s. Although frequently unserviceable, they participated in some ground-attack missions, including coup attempts in 1987 and 1989 (in which several were destroyed). Several examples remain in service with the 16 AS and 18 AS, 15th Strike Wing at Sangley Point. The **Uruguayan navy** operates four Fennecs that previously served with the **Argentine navy**, and that have been further modified in Uruguay to have 1,525-hp (1138-kW) Wright R-1820-82WA engines from S-2A Trackers.

T-28s were retired from Philippine air force service in the mid-1980s, only to return to duty on COIN missions (in 1985) until 1992. The aircraft below are armed with underwing guns, bombs and 81-mm cluster grenades.

SPECIFICATION

North American T-28D Trojan
Wing: span 40 ft 1 in (12.22 m); aspect ratio 6.0; area 268.00 sq ft (24.90 m²)
Fuselage and tail: length 33 ft 0 in (10.06 m); height 12 ft 8 in (3.86 m)
Powerplant: one Wright R-1820-86 Cyclone 14-cylinder air-cooled radial piston engine rated at 1,425 hp (1063 kW)

Weights: empty equipped 6,424 lb (2914 kg); maximum take-off 8,500 lb (3856 kg)
Fuel and load: external fuel none; maximum ordnance 1,200 lb (544 kg)
Speed: maximum level speed 'clean' at 10,000 ft

(3050 m) 298 kt (343 mph; 552 km/h)
Range: ferry range 921 nm (1,060 miles; 1706 km)
Performance: maximum rate of climb at sea level 3,540 ft (1079 m) per minute; service ceiling 35,500 ft (10820 m)

Northrop **B-2 Spirit**

Northrop Corporation, B-2 Division 8900 East Washington Boulevard, Pico Rivera California 90660-3737, USA

The **Northrop B-2** flying wing was developed in great secrecy as a stealthy, or radar-evading, strategic bomber for the Cold War mission of attacking Soviet strategic targets with nuclear bombs and stand-off weapons. The B-2 began as a 'black' programme, known in its infancy as **Project Senior C. J.** and later as the **ATB**

(Advanced Technology Bomber). In its early days, US Air Force leaders believed that the service's top priority was the B-1B bomber, and only a handful even knew of the B-2 project. To the latter group, the B-1B was an 'interim' weapon awaiting the B-2; at the height of the Cold War, the USAF expected to procure no fewer than 132.

Drawing heavily on its previous flying wing designs, Northrop was aided extensively by Boeing, Vought and General Electric, using a three-dimensional computer-aided design and manufacturing system to create the B-2's unique 'blended wing/double-W' shape. More than 100,000 radar cross-section images of B-2 models and

components were analysed to assess their stealth properties, followed by 550,000 hours of wind tunnel tests. Nine hundred new manufacturing processes had to be developed for the programme, including rugged, high-temperature composite materials, ultra-sonic cutting machinery, automated tooling via the 3D database and laser

Left: The B-2's blended wing design necessitates a unique control surface layout. From the wingtip moving inboard are a drag rudder/spoiler and then an elevon running along the same hingeline. Two more elevons are located on the next trailing edge section. These move in unison, but can function as separate units. Above and behind the articulated centrebody ('beaver tail') is an instrumentation drogue carried by all the test aircraft.

Below: As this aircraft rolls onto finals for runway 22 at Edwards AFB, its auxiliary intake doors above the engines are clearly visible. In the distance at the dry lakebed site can be seen the secret North Base facility. Even during the early stages of the test programme, the B-2 was rolled smoothly to an angle of 45°. With spoilers deployed it maintains a touch-down pitch angle of only 7°, and with only moderate braking can come to a stop within 4,000 ft (1220 m). The B-2 has 50 per cent better fuel efficiency than the B-1B, and it requires less than half the latter's refuelling support to carry out a strike mission.

sheraography inspection. Northrop is responsible for building the forward sections and the cockpit, and Boeing builds the aft centre and outboard sections, while Vought produces the mid-fuselage sections and aluminium, titanium and composite parts.

Graphite/epoxy composites are extensively used on the B-2, to provide a radar-absorbent honeycomb structure. To reduce infra-red signature, the four General Electric F118-GE-110 turbofans exhaust through V-shaped outlets set back and above the trailing edges to hide these heat sources from the ground. Chloro-flourosulphonic acid is injected into the exhaust plume to suppress the formation of contrails. The B-2's swept (33°) leading edge and saw-tooth trailing edge configuration trap radar energy. Further low-observables (LO) measures include 'S'-curved engine intakes and stealthy dielectric panels covering the AN/APQ-181 J-band radar that hides its antenna from reflecting hostile radar waves while allowing it to function normally. The cockpit is equipped for two, with upward-firing Douglas/Weber ACES II ejection seats, and there is room for a third crew member. The pilot has charge of the mission computer, which handles target tasking (or retasking in flight). Navigation and weapons delivery is the responsibility of the WSO, in the right-hand seat. The two primary positions have four multi-function, colour displays. The aircraft has a quadruply-redundant digital fly-by-wire system, actuating movable surfaces on the wing trailing edges, which combine aileron, elevator and flap functions and occupy 15 per cent of the wing area. A beaver tail acts as a pitch-axis trimming surface and, along with the elevons, helps in gust alleviation.

To verify targets at the last moment, the B-2 will briefly turn on its AN/APQ-181, spotlighting only a small area, and then attack. Since 1987 the unit has been under test in a specially modified USADF C-135 and, although radar is installed on some

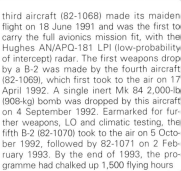

of the prototype B-2s, all radar testing has been done on the C-135. The B-2 will be equipped with an electronic warfare system, comprising the IBM Federal Systems AN/APR-50 (ZSR-63) RWR and the secret ZSR-62 defensive aids system.

The B-2 was originally envisaged as a high-level penetrator but, by the time its design was frozen in 1983, a low-level role had been assumed. Modifications needed to adapt the original ATB design to this new role included moving the cockpit and engine inlets, adding inboard elevons (resulting in the distinctive 'double-W' planform), modifying the leading edge and making substantial internal changes, including new bulkheads. In a surprise move, the USAF released an artist's impression of the aircraft, which had previously been shrouded in total secrecy, in April 1988. Six prototypes (five for the USAF) were funded in 1982. The first (82-1066) was rolled out at USAF Plant 42, Palmdale, on 22 November 1988. Northrop carefully managed the ceremony to

hide details of the aircraft's wing design and the 500 assembled guests had only a limited front view of the B-2 from ground level. An enterprising photographer discovered that Northrop had not blocked off the airspace above the plant, and obtained the first complete photographs of the aircraft after a quick sortie in a Cessna.

The B-2's first flight took place on 17 July 1990 (originally planned for 1987), when this aircraft (also referred to as AV-1/Air Vehicle One) was delivered to the USAF at Edwards AFB, to begin the test programme. The final date had been delayed from 15 July by a fuel system malfunction, and had been preceded by a series of high-speed taxi runs on 13 July, when the nose wheel was lifted briefly. AV-1 was joined by 82-1067 on 19 October 1990. A test schedule of 3,600 hours was set out, commencing with 16 flights (67 hours) of airworthiness and handling trials. Completed in mid-June 1990, these flights also included the first air-to-air refuelling, with a KC-10A, on 8 November 1989. Block 2 testing began in October 1990, investigating the LO characteristics of the 'real thing'. These flights provided the first signs that all was not as advertised with the stealthy B-2, and subsequent flights were halted while modifications were carried out on 82-1066. Stealth testing continued into 1993, while 82-1067 was engaged on further performance and load trials. The

third aircraft (82-1068) made its maiden flight on 18 June 1991 and was the first to carry the full avionics mission fit, with the Hughes AN/APQ-181 LPI (low-probability of intercept) radar, which first took to the air on 17 April 1992. The first weapons drop by a B-2 was made by the fourth aircraft (82-1069), which first took to the air on 17 April 1992. A single inert Mk 84 2,000-lb (908-kg) bomb was dropped by this aircraft on 4 September 1992. Earmarked for further weapons, LO and climatic testing, the fifth B-2 (82-1070) took to the air on 5 October 1992, followed by 82-1071 on 2 February 1993. By the end of 1993, the programme had chalked up 1,500 flying hours

In July 1991 deficiencies were revealed in the B-2's stealth profile. It has been admitted that the aircraft can be detected by some high-powered, land-based, early warning radars. Russian claims that the bomber is vulnerable to its new-generation SAM systems, such as the S-300PMU (SA-10/A 'Grumble') and S-300V-9M83/82 (SA-12A/B 'Gladiator'/'Giant'), have not been commented on. The USAF is implementing a 'set of treatments' to some leading edges and flying surfaces to reduce the aircraft's signature across a range of frequencies.

Problems with the B-2's performance have not aided it in the battle for funding on Capitol Hill. The original target was for a fleet of 133 airframes, including prototype, but by 1991 this had been cut back to 76 aircraft. After the original six aircraft, ordered in 1982, three more were funded while the B-2 was still a 'black' project. In 1989 money was allocated for a further three followed by two in 1990 and two in 1991. Congress then froze acquisition at 16 (15

The 509th BW's first B-2, 'Spirit of Missouri', carries its 'tail markings' on the undercarriage doors, ACC badge on the starboard fuselage and wing insignia to port.

for the USAF). The USAF claims it cannot provide effective operational capability with less than 20 aircraft, and five more were subsequently approved by 1993. This approval came with the caveat that the type's LO problems must be rectified before any production occurs. Unit costs per aircraft (flyaway) have risen to $2,220 million. Original 1987 estimates for a 75-aircraft programme stood at $64,700 million (in total), although it is not beyond the bounds of possibility that some of the huge budget dedicated to the B-2 has been spent on other 'black' projects. The FY1995 budget included $793 million for support equipment and provision for the closure of the production line.

The first aircraft for the USAF (88-0329/'WM', 'Spirit of Missouri') was delivered to the 509th BW at Whiteman AFB, MO, on 17 December 1993, exactly 90 years to the day after the Wright Brothers' first flight. This was the eighth production B-2 (AV-8), the first aircraft to production standard, which preceded AV-7 into the air. AV-7 was still undergoing extensive electromagnetic and emission-control tests, but along with the other aircraft involved in the flight test programme it will be delivered to the USAF by 1997. AV-9 made its maiden flight on 24 January 1994. The 509th BW will be divided into two squadrons, the 393rd and 750th BS. Each will be operational with eight B-2s in 1996/97. Both AV-8 and AV-9 are Block 10 standard aircraft, incorporating many of the stealth improvements which resulted from the test programme. These will subsequently be modified to the definitive Block 30 standard (see Weapon Options, below), once the whole fleet is operational in 1997.

One of the less critical problems with the B-2 is the lack of vertical surfaces on which to apply 'tailcodes'. As a result, the main undercarriage doors now carry the base code, FY serial and, on 88-0329 at least, the legends 'Spirit of Missouri' and 'Follow Us'.

WEAPON OPTIONS

The B-2 is built around two large side-by-side weapons bays in its lower centrebody. In front of each bay are small spoiler panels which drop down to produce vortices, ensuring clean weapons release. Rotary launchers in both bomb bays can accommodate a theoretical bomb load of 75,000 lb (34020 kg) but, under the US national war fighting SIOP (Single Integrated Operational Plan), any nuclear load would be limited to 20,000 lb (9072 kg). While the B-2 can carry 80 Mk 82 500-lb (227-kg) bombs, it is too valuable to be used as a 'bomb truck'. Its strength, in a conventional role, will lie in its ability to deliver up to 16 smart weapons over a wide area, in a single pass, to 30-ft (10-m) accuracy. The five prototypes destined for the USAF, along with AV-7, -8 and -9, have been completed to Block 10 standard. This qualifies them to carry 16 B83 freefall nuclear bombs or 16 Mk 84 2,000-lb (908-kg) conventional bombs. For stand-off strategic missions, the B-2 can carry 16 AGM-69 SRAM II or AGM-129A cruise missiles. The intermediate production standard, Block 20, will add B61 nuclear capability (a maximum of 16) or up to 36 CBU-87, -89, -97 and -98 conventional munitions with a limited conventional PGM (precision-guided munitions) capability from 1997. This will entail adding two new weapons still under development. The first of these is the AGM-137 TSSAM (Tri-Service Stand-off Attack Missile), a stealthy, subsonic cruise missile with a range of 375 miles (600 km) and a payload of IR- and acoustically-guided sub-munitions. Eight AGM-137s would be carried, four on each rotary launcher. The second new weapon is the GPS-aided JDAM (Joint Direct Attack Munition). Fitted to a Mk 82, Mk 84 or BLU-109 weapon, JDAM will provide highly accurate targeting guidance through the aircraft's navigation system and an onboard INS.

Eventually it will be an all-weather, autonomous weapon with a programmable fuse. The two final production B-2s will be completed to full Block 30 standard. They will be fully PGM-capable, in addition to carrying 80 Mk 82 500-lb (227-kg), or 36 Mk 117 750-lb (340-kg) GP bombs or 80 Mk 62 aerial mines. Block 30 B-2s will boast fully operational offensive and operational avionics and an improved SAR.

SPECIFICATION

Northrop B-2A Spirit
Wing: span 172 ft 0 in (52.43 m); aspect ratio more than 5.92; area more than 5,000.00 sq ft (464.50 m²)
Fuselage and tail: length 69 ft 0 in (21.03 m); height 17 ft 0 in (5.18 m); wheel track 40 ft 0 in (12.20 m)
Powerplant: four General Electric F118-GE-110 non-afterburning turbofans each rated at 19,000 lb st (84.52 kN)
Weights: empty between 100,000 and 110,000 lb (45360 and 49900 kg); normal take-off 371,330 lb (168433 kg); maximum take-off 400,000 lb (181437 kg)
Fuel and load: internal fuel between 180,000 and 200,000 lb (81650 and 90720 kg); external fuel none; maximum ordnance 50,000 lb (22680 kg)
Speed: maximum level speed at high altitude about 416 kt (475 mph; 764 km/h)
Range: more than 10,000 nm (11,515 miles; 18532 km) with one flight refuelling; range with a 37,300-lb (169219-kg) warload comprising eight SRAMs and eight B83 bombs 6,300 nm (7,255 miles; 11675 km) with internal fuel on a hi-hi-hi mission or 4,400 nm (5,067 miles; 8154 km) on a hi-lo-hi mission with 1,000 nm (1,152 miles; 1853 km) at low level; range with a 24,000-lb (10886-kg) warload comprising eight SRAMs and eight B61 bombs 6,600 nm (7,600 miles; 12231 km) with internal fuel on a hi-hi-hi mission or 4,500 nm (5,182 miles; 8339 km) with internal fuel on a hi-lo-hi mission
Performance: service ceiling 50,000 ft (15240 m)

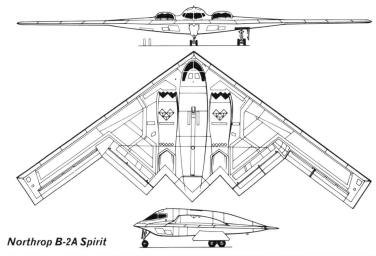

Northrop B-2A Spirit

The B-2's wingspan of 172 ft (52.43 m), is larger even than that of the KC-10A tanker. Its maximum internal fuel load of 200,000 lb (90720 kg) is sufficient for a mission of 7,500 miles (12000 km). With refuelling support, the Spirit's reach is global.

Northrop F-5 Freedom Fighter

Northrop Corporation, Aircraft Division
One Northrop Avenue, Hawthorne
California 90250, USA

In 1954 the US government initiated a study for a simple, lightweight fighter to be supplied to friendly nations via the Military Assistance Program. Northrop submitted its **N-156** proposal; in 1956 the USAF showed interest in a derivative supersonic trainer (the **T-38**, described separately) that was developed in parallel with the private-venture **N-156C**, which flew on 30 July 1959.

In April 1962 the US Secretary of Defense approved USAF selection of the N-156C as the required 'FX' fighter. This was designated **F-5**, and the **F-5A** prototype flew in May 1963. The two-seat **F-5B** fighter/trainer actually entered service ahead of the F-5A. Deliveries began on 30 April 1964 to the 4441st Combat Crew Training Squadron at Williams AFB. The first F-5As followed four months later, in August 1964.

The airframe incorporated new structural and aerodynamic features. These included leading-edge and trailing-edge flaps, area-ruled fuselage with two airbrakes on the undersurface, and in some versions manoeuvring flaps. Rocket-powered ejection seats were provided. The primary interception weapons comprised two nose-mounted 20-mm M39 guns, and two AIM-9 Sidewinder missiles on wingtip launchers. One underfuselage and four underwing pylons permitted the carriage of nearly 6,000 lb (2720 kg) of weapons, including a wide variety of bombs and rockets.

To evaluate the combat potential of the F-5A, 12 (later 18) aircraft were deployed to South East Asia in October 1965, under the codename Project Skoshi Tiger. The aircraft were diverted from the MAP and provided with a refuelling probe, armour, jettisonable pylons, additional avionics and camouflage.

In Canada, licence production was undertaken by Canadair for the **CF-5A/D** versions of the F-5A/B (Canadian Armed Forces designation **CF-116**) and for versions designated **NF-5A/B** for the Royal Netherlands air force. Both Canadian and Dutch versions are described separately. Some CF-5As can be fitted with a Vinten 70-mm camera nose and are then designated **CF-5A(R)**. The CF-5As can also be fitted with refuelling probes, but neither these nor the reconnaissance nose can be carried by the two-seat CF-5Ds. CASA-built Spanish versions are known in Spain's Ejercito del Aire as the **C.9** and **CE.9**, respectively, or as the **SF-5** and **SRF-5**. The **RF-5A** reconnaissance version is equipped with four KS-92A cameras mounted in the nose. Venezuela operates a mix of single- and two-seat F-5s known locally as **VF-5A** and **VF-5B**s.

Upgrades

The F-5, in all its versions, is a prime target for systems upgrades, and several companies are offering improvement packages. Simple system changes could include the addition of Westinghouse's AN/APG-66T multi-target track-while-scan radar (developed for the F-16A, now in trials for USN F-5s), or the General Electric AN/APG-67 multi-mode fire control radar (developed originally for the F-20 and now used by the AIDC Ching-Kuo), or Emerson's AN/APG-69 look-down/shoot-down radar.

Northrop invested heavily in the F-20 Tigershark (see F-5E entry) as an F-5 successor. When this project failed to attract sales, the manufacturer began to translate its F-20 experience into improved F-5 systems. As its chosen F-5A upgrade, Northrop offers APG-66 radar and an F-16-compatible cockpit with one or two Bendix multi-function, monochrome or colour displays (MFDs), Mason Electric HOTAS (Hands-On Throttle And Stick) controls, Honeywell laser-ring INS, Allied Signal air data and mission computer, Teac video recorder, new weapons control systems and a GEC Avionics wide-angle HUD. To fit new systems into the nose one M39 cannon has been removed, the bulkhead has been moved aft and the APG-66 antenna reduced in size. A new ejection seat, the Martin-Baker Mk 10LF, can also be fitted. Owing to the cost of the complete upgrade (approximately $4.5 million), prospective customers can choose which items they require from a list of options. While the F-5E is a more suitable recipient for upgrading, the **Turkish air force**'s F-5As are potential candidates (in a deal involving CASA and Allied Signal). A further option involves structural work, such as rewinging and fitting a new tail.

Thirteen **Canadian air force** CF-5As and 33 CF-5Ds (CF-116A/D) are being upgraded by **Bristol Aerospace**, to act as lead-in trainers for the CF-188 Hornet. New avionics items include a GEC Avionics HUD/WAC and air data computer, Litton ring-laser INS, AN/ARC-164 radios, Honeywell radar altimeter, Ferranti video camera and a remodelled HOTAS cockpit. The CF-5s are also having their wings and tails reskinned, a steel longeron fitted (replacing the original aluminium unit) and new landing gear. The first 'prototype' flew on 14 July 1991, upgraded CF-116s entered service with 419 Sqn in early 1992, and the programme is scheduled for completion in 1995. Bristol Aerospace was contracted in 1991 to overhaul 23 **Spanish air force** SF-5Bs, extending their useful lives as weapons trainers. They will also receive new IFF and RWR. So concerned was Northrop at Bristol Aerospace's gains in the upgrade market that they took the Canadian company to court, alleging 'infringement of their intellectual property' and specifically|infringement of the Northrop licence to support the Canadian air force's F-5s. The two companies settled out of court in May 1994, with Bristol paying an undisclosed sum to Northrop. Furthermore, the two signed a teaming agreement for any further work on F-5E/Fs.

Bristol Aerospace has also now teamed with **Eidetics International** (USA) to offer the **Tiger 2000** F-5A/B upgrade. Having zero-timed the airframe, Bristol will add substantial LERXes and an automatic manoeuvre flap system to the wing. Eidetics will integrate a redesigned cockpit with two MFDs, TACAN, ILS and HSI, along with new RWR and chaff/flare dispensers.

A structural overhaul for the **Venezuelan air force**'s VF-5As and sole VF-5B is being undertaken by **Singapore Aerospace**, which is also heavily involved in upgrading the Singapore air force's F-5E fleet. Venezuela withdrew its surviving 13 CF-5As and sole CF-5D (F-5B) in May 1990 due to fatigue problems. The first phase of a refurbishment programme commenced in May 1991, when one CF-5A (VF-5A) and one CF-5D (VF-5B) were dispatched to Singapore Aerospace, returning to service in May 1993. In the meantime, six former Netherlands air force F-5s (five NF-5As and one NF-5B) were acquired and refurbished, entering service in February 1992. The remaining Canadair-built aircraft are being rotated through Singapore Aerospace's facility at Paya Lebar.

Norway is another F-16 operator which relies on its F-5s as lead-in fighter trainers. **Vought Sierra Research Division** has been contracted to implement the **Tiger PAWS** (Programme for Avionics and Weapons Systems Improvements) for the Royal Norwegian air force. Beginning in late 1993, seven F-5As and eight F-5Bs were to be fitted with GEC Avionics HUD/WAC (compatible with Block 40 F-16C/Ds), MIL-STD-1553 digital databus, GEC Miniature Standard Air Data Computer, Litton AN-93 laser ring INS, new AoA sensors, colour video camera/recorder, and HOTAS controls. Norway was the first customer for a Sierra Industries upgrade, and the first aircraft was originally due to be handed over in May 1992. As the project grew in scope, the flight test programme stretched to hundreds of flights and, by November 1993, two of the first three F-5s were involved in weapons trials at Eglin AFB. All were handed over to the Norwegian air force the following month.

OPERATORS

Brazil: 80 CF-5A/Ds (including stored aircraft) – 14° GAvCa, 1° Esq 'Pampa', Canoas
Canada: 23 CF-5A (CF-116A), 14 CF-5D (CF-116D) – No. 419 Sqn, CFB Cold Lake
Greece: two squadrons of NF/F-5A and

Above: Surrounded by T-2D Buckeyes, this is one of the ex-KLu NF-5Bs refurbished for service with the Fuerza Aérea Venezolana. A small number of F-5A/Bs serve alongside Dassault Mirage III/5s (upgraded to Mirage 50EV standard), and F-16As.

Left: The Philippines has four AIM-9B-armed F-5As and a single F-5B operational. The 6th TFS moved to Mactan, from Basa, after the Mt Pinatubo eruption.

NF/F-5Bs, RF-5s reroled
   – 343 Mira, Thessaloniki; 349 Mira, Larissa
Morocco: 10 F-5A, two F-5B, one RF-5A
Norway: seven F-5A, eight F-5B – Skvadron 336, Rygge
Philippines: four F-5A, three F-5B
   – 6th TFS, 5th TFW, Mactan
Saudi Arabia: 15 F-5B – 3 Sqn, Taif; 16 Sqn, Tabuk
South Korea: F-5A, F-5B – 1st FW (OCU), Kwangju
Spain: 23 SF-5B – Esc 231/232, Ala 23, Talavera
Thailand: F-5A, F-5B
Turkey: three squadrons of CF/NF/F-5As,
   F-5Bs, RF-5A reroled
   – 133 Filo (3 Ana Jet Üs), Eskisehir
   – 151 and 152 Filos (5 Ana Jet Üs), Merzifon
Venezuela: 14 CF-5A, three CF-5D, six NF-5A
   – Escuadrón de Caza No. 36, Base
   Aérea Teniente Vicente Landaeta,
   Barquisimeto
Yemen: four F-5B

SPECIFICATION

Northrop F-5A Freedom Fighter
Wing: span 25 ft 3 in (7.70 m) without tip tanks and
25 ft 10 in (7.87 m) with tip tanks; aspect ratio 6.35;
area 170.00 sq ft (15.79 m2)
Fuselage and tail: length 47 ft 2 in (14.38 m); height
13 ft 2 in (4.01 m); tailplane span 14 ft 1 in (4.28 m);
wheel track 11 ft 0 in (3.35 m); wheel base 15 ft 4 in
(4.67 m)
Powerplant: two General Electric J85-GE-13 each
turbojets rated at 2,720 lb st (12.10 kN) dry and
4,080 lb st (18.15 kN) with afterburning
Weights: empty equipped 8,085 lb (3667 kg);
maximum take-off 20,677 lb (9379 kg)
Fuel and load: internal fuel 583 US gal (2207 litres)
plus provision for 100 US gal (378.5 litres) in two tip
tanks; external fuel up to three 150-US gal (568-litre)
drop tanks; maximum ordnance 4,400 lb (1996 kg)
Speed: maximum level speed 'clean' at 36,000 ft

Turkey received huge numbers of F-5s. An original MAP consignment of 75 F-5As, 20 RF-5As and 13 F-5Bs was joined by 32 ex-Norwegian F/RF-5As, four ex-USAF and two former Taiwanese F-5Bs, and 60 former Dutch NF-5A/Bs. Upgraded aircraft will serve with three squadrons beyond the year 2000.

(10975 m) 802 kt (924 mph; 1487 km/h); cruising speed
at 36,000 ft (10975 m) 556 kt (640 mph; 1030 km/h)
Range: ferry range 1,400 nm (1,612 miles; 2594 km);
combat radius 485 nm (558 miles; 989 km) on a hi-lo-hi
attack mission with two 530-lb (240-kg) bombs and
maximum fuel, or 170 nm (196 miles; 315 km) on a
hi-lo-hi attack mission with maximum warload
Performance: maximum rate of climb at sea level
28,700 ft (8748 m) per minute; service ceiling 50,500
ft (15390 m); take-off run 2,650 ft (808 m) at 13,677 lb
(6203 kg) with two AIM-9 Sidewinder AAMs; take-off
distance to 50 ft (15 m) 3,650 ft (1113 m) at 13,677 lb
(6203 kg); landing distance from 50 ft (15 m) 3,900 ft
(1189 m) at 9,843 lb (4464 kg) with brake chute

The aptly named Tiger PAWS (Programme for Weapons and Systems Improvements) upgrade currently being applied to all surviving Norwegian F-5As and F-5Bs (15 in total) ensures that the elderly aircraft will continue to have productive lives as lead-in trainers for the air force's F-16 fleet.

Northrop F-5E/F Tiger II

The **Northrop F-5E/F Tiger** is in widespread service around the world, having
been developed from the manufacturer's
earlier F-5A/B Freedom Fighter in response
to a 1969 requirement for an International
Fighter Aircraft to be sold to US allies.
Selection of the Northrop design took place
in November 1970. Development of the
F-5E/F resulted from the August 1969 Nixon
Doctrine which called upon US allies to
shoulder the burden of their defence, and
provided the justification for 'Vietnamisa-
tion' of, and US withdrawal from, the South
East Asia war. During the same period, the
US was assisting the Shah of Iran in a massive modernisation of military forces. It was
anticipated from the beginning that the first
three customers for the IFA would be Iran,
South Korea and South Vietnam.

A lightweight fighter with both air-to-air
and air-to-ground capability, the single-seat
F-5E is armed with two M39A2 20-mm
cannon with 20-mm rounds, and typically
carries two wingtip-mounted AIM-9 Sidewinder AAMs. The F-5E takes advantage of
features developed for earlier F-5A/B aircraft, including two-position nosewheel gear
which enables the aircraft to assume a
higher angle of attack for take-off, as well as
provision for JATO and an arrester hook.
The **F-5F** tandem two-seat trainer had its
fuselage lengthened by 3 ft 4 in (1.02 m)
but retained the combat capabilities of the
single-seater, although one cannon was
deleted. First flight of an F-5F took place
on 25 September 1974.

The first F-5E was flown on 11 August
1972. Initial deliveries of the F-5E were

made to the US Air Force's 425th Tactical
Fighter Squadron in early 1973, although the
USAF's sole purpose at the time was to
prepare the aircraft for foreign users. Some
1,300 F-5E/Fs were later supplied to 20 air
forces. The F-5E was also assembled under
licence in Taiwan and South Korea. The variant supplied to Saudi Arabia differed from
other F-5Es in having a Litton LN-33 inertial
navigation system which improved navigation and bombing accuracy. The **RF-5E**
(described separately) was a proposed reconnaissance variant equipped with four
KS-121A 70-mm framing cameras in a modified nose section.

Korean F-5s assembled by Korean Airlines, at Pusan, are referred to by the air
force as Chegoong Ho (Air Master), while
Taiwanese aircraft assembled by AIDC are
known locally as Chung Cheng.

The considerably upgraded **F-20 Tigershark** (originally designated **F-5G**) was
developed as an updated Tiger for service

in the 1980s and 1990s, but was rendered
superfluous by the availability of F-16As for
export. Recently, existing F-5 customers
have embarked on ambitious upgrade programmes to improve their aircraft, sometimes to the extent that the aircraft will
become *de facto* F-20s.

Upgrades

The F-5 is a prime candidate for upgrading. Twelve **Chilean** F-5Es and two F-5Fs,
for example, are being reworked by **IAI**'s
Bedek division with HOTAS controls, monochrome MFDs, a new El-Op HUD, MIL-STD-

Chile's air defence-tasked F-5Es are undergoing a far-reaching upgrade in the hands of IAI and ENAER, becoming F-5E Plus Tigre IIIs. The tiger motif of Grupo 7 was adopted on aircraft fins in 1989, and the orange stripes signify an aggressor combat training F-5.

Northrop F-5E/F Tiger II

Switzerland's Sidewinder-armed F-5Es will lose their air defence role with the arrival of the air force's F/A-18 Hornets. Adopting a ground attack role, they will be armed with AGM-65 Maverick ASMs.

Left: Singapore's 10 F-5Fs supplement its F-5Es in the ground attack role, in addition to undertaking training duties with No. 144 Sqn, at RSAF Paya Lebar.

1553 digital databus and air data computer, a new INS and the Elta EL/M-2032B multi-mode radar originally developed for the Lavi. The aircraft will also have an integrated self-defence system with 360° RWR coverage, active jammers and chaff/flare dispensers. Two underwing Rafael Python III AAMs are available as a weapons option, complementing smaller wingtip AIM-9 Sidewinders. The first two **F-5E Plus Tiger III**s (or **Tigre III** in Chile) were converted in Israel, flying for the first time post-rebuild on 8 July 1993. The rest will undergo conversion in Chile by ENAER, with Israeli assistance. IAI expects to market its F-5 upgrades to several other customers, and can also offer add-on refuelling probes, helmet-mounted sights and new ejection seats. A further South American customer for an F-5E upgrade is **Brazil**, which plans to equip its aircraft with the indigenous Tecnasa/SMA SCP-01 radar and the OMI/Alenia HUD as fitted to its AMX fleet. Brazilian F-5s had already received upgrade kits from the US with refuelling probes for use with KC-130s.

More ambitiously, Taiwan is considering upgrading its Tigers to **F-5E-SX** configuration with a J101 engine (or the F125X used by the indigenous Ching-Kuo) and a new radar, possibly the APG-67-based Sky Dragon. AIM-120 missiles would be carried.

OPERATORS

The F-5E/F Tiger belatedly acquired a role in the US as an aggressor trainer and about 100 served in this role in the **US Air Force** until the late 1980s. The **US Navy**, which uses the term 'adversary' for this DACT mission, also acquired a small number of F-5E/Fs, the few remaining examples of which were concentrated by mid-1994 in just three US Navy and **US Marine** squadrons: VFA-127 'Cylons' at NAS Fallon, NV, VF-45 'Blackbirds' at NAS Key West, FL, and VMFT-401 'Snipers' at MCAS Yuma, AZ. All of these squadrons are in the process of adopting the F/A-18 Hornet. Non-US operators of the F-5E/F comprise:
Bahrain: eight F-5Es and four F-5Fs ordered by Bahrain Amiri Air Force in 1985. Delivered by 1987, these aircraft are now based at Sitra.
Brazil: between 1975 and 1976, 36 F-5Es were

delivered (along with six F-5Bs) to the Força Aérea Brasiliera/Brazilian air force. Brazil then received 23 refurbished F-5Es from US stocks, along with three refurbished F-5Fs, between 1988 and 1989. All in service with 1° and 2° Esq, 1° GAvCa, at Santa Cruz and 1° Esq, 14° GAvCa, at Canoas
Chile: twelve (of 15 ordered) F-5Es and three F-5Fs, delivered to Fuerza Aérea de Chile/Chilean air force during 1976 despite arms embargo imposed that year. Offered for sale to Brazil in 1986, owing to low serviceability, but now undergoing Tigre III upgrade. In service with Grupo 7, Ala 1, 1Brigada, at Cerro Mereno, Antofagasta
Honduras: requested F-5E/Fs from 1982 to 1984. Ten refurbished F-5Es and two F-5Fs delivered to Fuerza Aérea Hondurena/Honduran air force between December 1987 and April 1989 to intercept 'arms flights to Nicaragua'. Operational with Escuadrilla de Caza, La Ceiba
Indonesia: by mid-1980, 12 F-5Es and four F-5Fs delivered to Tentara Nasional Indonesia – Angkatan Udara/Indonesian armed forces – air force. Surviving 10 F-5Es operational in air defence role (along with F-5Fs), at Madiun-Ishwayudi
Iran: Imperial Iranian Air Force acquired 166 F-5Es before fall of Shah, in February 1979. Small number of ex-Ethiopian F-5s believed obtained in 1986. Operational strength of Islamic Republic of Iran Air Force is estimated at 30-60 aircraft
Jordan: beginning 1975, 61 F-5Es and 12 F-5Fs delivered to Royal Jordanian Air Force. Operational with Nos 9 and 17 Sqns, air base H-5. Sought to acquire F-20 Tigershark as replacement in mid-1980s
Kenya: the '82 Air Force acquired 10 F-5Es and four F-5Fs between 1978 and 1982. Survivors remain operational at Nanyuki (Liakiapia)
Malaysia: between 1981 and 1985, 17 F-5Es delivered to Tentara Udara Diraja Malaysia/Royal Malaysian air force. Four ex-Thai F-5s acquired in 1982. Two RF-5E Tigereye delivered in 1983. Plans for 16 further F-5E/Fs abandoned in 1982. Aircraft

operational with Nos 11 'Cobra' and 12 'Tiger' Sqns, Butterworth
Mexico: between August and November 1984, 10 F-5Es and two F-5Fs delivered to Fuerza Aérea Mexicana/Mexican air force. All F-5Fs and nine F-5Es remain in service with Escuadrón de Defensa 401, 1 Grupo Aéreo, Santa Lucia
Morocco: Morocco's Force Royale Aérienne/Al Quwaat al Jawwiya al Malakiya received 16 F-5Es and four F-5Fs between 1981 and 1983. Followed by 10 ex-USAF F-5Es from October 1989, after overhaul in UK. Moroccan F-5s fitted with air-to-air refuelling probes, for use with KC-130s and converted 707 tanker. Several F-5s claimed shot down by Polisario guerrillas in operations over disputed Western Sahara. Aircraft believed based at Kenitra
Saudi Arabia: Royal Saudi Air Force/Al Quwaat al Jawwiya al Sa'udiya signed for 30 F-5Es in 1971, with a further 40 F-5Es and 20 F-5Fs ordered in 1974. Joined by four additional F-5Fs in 1976. Saudi Tigers armed with AGM-65 Maverick ASMs, AGM-45 Shrike ARMs, GBU-10/12 LGBs or Mk 20 CBUs. Aircraft also equipped with refuelling probes, Litton inertial navigation/attack systems, AN/ALQ-101/119/171 ECM pods, AN/ALE-46 RWR. Final F-5 deliveries, beginning in 1985, comprised 10 RF-5Es, plus attrition replacements in the form of four F-5Es and one F-5. Aircraft based at Taif, with Nos 3, 15 and 17 Sqns
Singapore: Republic of Singapore Air Force ordered 18 F-5s and three F-5Fs in 1979. Six F-5Es and three F-5Fs added in December 1987. Finally, five F-5Es assembled by Northrop from spares stock, and delivered to Singapore in 1989. Six F-5Es upgraded to RF-5E standard by Singapore Aerospace with FLIR and IRLS. Aircraft in service with No. 144 'Lynx' Sqn, Paya Lebar and No. 149 'Shirkah' Sqn, Tengah
South Korea: some (up to 19) F-5E escapees from South Vietnam air force, in 1974 joined by 126 US-supplied F-5Es and 20 F-5Fs. Between 1982 and 1986, 48 locally-assembled F-5Es and 20 F-5Fs delivered to Hankook Kong Goon (Republic of Korea air force). Aircraft in service with 115, 122 and 123 FS of the 1st Fighter Wing at Kwangju, and 102, 103 and 111 FS of the 10th Fighter Wing at Suwon
Sudan: the Sudanese Air Force/Silkakh al Jawwiya as Sudaniya received two F-5Fs and two F-5Es (from an order for 10) underwritten by Saudi Arabia between 1982 and 1984. One F-5E lost one week after arrival and remainder of order cancelled due to lack of funding
Switzerland: Swiss Air Force and Anti-Aircraft Command/Kommando der Flieger- und Fliegerabwhertruppen took delivery of 66 F-5Es and six F-5Fs under Peace Alps programme beginning in

These F-5Es of the RoCAF's 455th TFW wear the markings of No. 23 'Tsi Ching' Squadron – 'Tsi Ching' meaning that the aircraft were paid for by the Taiwanese people.

1978. First 13 F-5Es and all F-5Fs completed by Northrop, while remainder assembled by FFA, at Emmen. FFA also received 50 per cent off-set for follow-on order of 32 F-5Es and six F-5Fs, ordered in 1981 and delivered by 1985. Aircraft fitted with Dalmo Victor RWR, but addition of conformaL AN/ALQ-171 ECM pods cancelled. Aircraft in service with Fliegerstaffel 1 and 11, Flugwaffen Brigade 31, at Dübendorf; Fliegerstaffel 1 and 6, Fliegerregiment 1, at Turtmann and Sion; Fliegerstaffel 8, 13 and 18, Fliegerregiment 2, at Meiringen and Payerne; Fliegerstaffel 11, 16 and 19, Fliegerregiment 3, at Alpnach and Stans/Buochs

Taiwan: from 1973, 162 F-5Es and 21 F-5Fs initially assembled by AIDC, for Republic of China air Force/Chung-Kuo Kung Chuan, . Followed by 80 F-5Es and 35 F-5Fs delivered by 1986. Final batch of 30 F-5Es and 30 F-5Fs ordered in 1982. Aircraft later fitted with Litton ALR-46(V)3 RWR, Northrop AVQ-27 target designators, Tracor ALE-40(V)7 chaff/flare dispensers, with provision for AGM-65 ASMs and GBU-10 LGBs. Systems and radar upgrade now under consideration. Operational squadrons comprise 1,3, 9 Sqns (433rd TFW) at Tainan; 21,22, 23 Sqns (455th TFW) at Chia Yi; 17, 26, 27 Sqns (410st Tactical Combined Wing) at Taoyuan; 44, 45, 46 Sqns (737th TFW) at Taitung; and 14,15,16 Sqns (828th TFW) at Hualien

Thailand: first Tiger orders for the Royal Thai Air Force comprised 17 F-5Es and three F-5Fs in 1976. Beginning January 1981, second batch of 17 F-5Es and three F-5Fs delivered to form second squadron. Twenty aircraft upgraded from 1989 with Litton LN-39 INS, Texas Instruments AN/ALR-46 RWR, Tracor ALE-40 chaff/flare dispensers and GEC HUD/WAC. HUD and INS fitted to further 18 aircraft. GPU-5/A gun pods acquired for F-5s along with MATRA Durandal runway penetration bombs. Anti-shipping missile being sought. F-5 fleet augmented in late 1988 through addition of 10 ex-USAF F-5Es. Aircraft in service with No. 102 Sqn, No. 1 Wing, Korat and No. 103 Sqn, No. 4 Wing, Takhli

Tunisia: four F-5Fs delivered to Republic of Tunisia air force/Al Quwaat al Jawwiya al Jumhuriyah al Tunisiyah in 1981. Followed by eight F-5Es between 1984 and 1985. Five ex-USAF F-5Es added in 1989

Yemen: twelve F-5Es acquired, via Saudi Arabia, by Yemen Arab Republic air force (North Yemen) in 1979. Aircraft supported by Taiwanese technicians, and based at Sana'a. Current status unknown

SPECIFICATION

Northrop F-5E Tiger II

Wing: span 26 ft 8 in (8.13 m) without tip-mounted AAMs and 27 ft 11.875 in (8.53 m) with tip-mounted AAMs; aspect ratio 3.82; area 186.00 sq ft (17.28 m²)

Fuselage and tail: length 47 ft 4.75 in (14.45 m) including probe; height 13 ft 4.5 in (4.08 m); tailplane span 14 ft 1.5 in (4.31 m); wheel track 12 ft 5.5 in (3.80 m); wheel base 16 ft 11.5 in (5.17 m)

Powerplant: two General Electric J85-GE-21B turbojets each rated at 3,500 lb st (15.5 kN) dry and 5,000 lb (22.2 kN) with afterburning

Weights: empty 9,558 lb (4349 kg); maximum take-off 24,664 lb (11187 kg)

Fuel and load: internal fuel 677 US gal (2563 litres); external fuel up to three 275-US gal (1040-litre) drop tanks; maximum ordnance 7,000 lb (3175 kg)

Speed: maximum level speed 'clean' at 36,000 ft (10975 m) 917 kt (1,056 mph; 1700 km/h); cruising speed at 36,000 ft (10975 m) 562 kt (647 mph; 1041 km/h)

Range: ferry range 2,010 nm (2,314 miles; 3720 km) with empty tanks dropped or 1,715 nm (1,974 miles; 3175 km) with empty tanks retained; combat radius 760 nm (875 miles; 1405 km) with two AIM-9 AAMs

Performance: maximum rate of climb at sea level 34,300 ft (10455 m) per minute; service ceiling 51,800 ft (15590 m); take-off run 2,000 ft (610 m) at 15,745 lb 7142 kg); take-off distance to 50 ft (15 m) 2,800 ft 853 m) at 15,745 lb (7142 kg); landing distance from 50 ft (15 m) 3,900 ft (1189 m) at 11,340 lb (5143 kg); landing run 2,450 ft (747 m) at 11,340 lb (5143 kg) with brake parachute

COCKPIT
The most radical advance offfered by the upgrade concerns modifications made to the cockpit. Inside the F-5E Plus III, the pilot has one of the most up-to-date digital displays available. Two MFDs (either colour or monochrome) are provided, cued by HOTAS controls, and an El-Op HUD. Centralised computing allows data from all the aircraft's systems to be integrated and presented on a single tactical situation display, a feature which is available to very few pilots at present.

RAFAEL PYTHON MISSILE
The hard-hitting Python 3 entered service with the IDF/AF in time to see action over the Bekaa valley in 1982, where it was credited with many kills. With a launch weight of 264 lb (120 kg), the missile is 9 ft 10 in (3.0 m) long and has a body diameter of 6.3 in (0.16 m). The warhead is a 24-lb (11-kg) HE fragmentation unit, with active radar-homing. The Python 3 is primarily IR-guided, but can be radar-slaved in scan or boresight modes.

Northrop F-5E Plus Tiger III

Blessed with good performance and excellent agility, the Northrop F-5E serves in sufficient numbers to warrant substantial upgrade options. The IAI package does not alter the airframe or engines, as these were deemed to be adequate. However, avionics and armament have been greatly improved to include a new and far more capable radar, a much revised state-of-the-art cockpit layout (with two MFDs), new air-to-air missiles and provision for laser-guided weapons.

SIDEWINDER
The F-5 was designed around the lightweight AIM-9 Sidewinder, and this aircraft carries two late-model AIM-9Ps. The 'Papa' is 10 ft 1 in (3.07 m) long and, with a launch weight of 120 lb (82 kg), is substantially lighter than the 264-lb (120-kg) Python 3.

RADAR
A development of the EL/M-2035, the Elta EL/M-2032 multi-mode, pulse-Doppler fire control radar has a detection range of 20 miles (33 km) in the air-to-air mode. Its ultra-low sidelobe planar array was specially tailored to meet the narrow confines of the F-5's nose.

MARKINGS
The first F-5 Plus Tigre stayed in its basic FACh scheme (though without any national insignia) throughout the test programme, with various IAI-applied markings superimposed, principally for the type's appearance at the 1993 Paris air show.

CANNON
The F-5E is fitted with two M39A2 20-mm cannon, with 280 rounds. During the F-5E Plus test programme, the guns were removed and replaced with telemetry equipment.

RWR
The Chilean Tigre IIIs are fitted with a 360° radar warning receiver system (probably the ENAER Caiquen III), with antennas on either side of the nose and tail. This system displays its threat information on the cockpit MFDs.

Northrop **RF-5E Tigereye**

The F-5E, delivered from May 1973, has been a significant export success (with deliveries exceeding 1,000 aircraft) to a diverse range of nations. As a result of its universal appeal, on 31 March 1978 the US government approved the production of a specialised tactical reconnaissance version of the Tiger II, designated **Northrop RF-5E**. First flown in January 1979, the prototype of the **Tigereye** made its international debut at the Paris air show of the same year, following a flight from Edwards AFB, CA. Aircraft performance is barely affected by the additional weight of reconnaissance, navigation and communications equipment carried, and the Tigereye has essentially the same dimensions and characteristics as the F-5E, except for its weight, which is marginally increased.

The RF-5E is most easily distinguished from the conventional F-5E by its forward fuselage, which is modified to accommodate reconnaissance equipment: the nose is extended by 8 in (20.3 cm), and a KS-87D1 camera is fitted in a forward nose compartment. This camera is used in addition to either of two easily interchangeable pallets, each with a different set of reconnaissance cameras/sensors, to permit a greater degree of diversity in the use of the aircraft. Pallet 1 consists of KA-95B and KA-56B panoramic cameras and an RS-71 OE infrared linescanner, and Pallet 2 has KA-56B and KA-93B6 panoramic cameras. Under development is a third pallet carrying a KS-147A camera for LOROP missions; other pallet configurations are available.

The pilot of the RF-5E also has available a number of advanced navigation and communications systems and an ISCS to reduce workload and allow more time to operate and monitor reconnaissance and communications equipment. Otherwise, the Tigereye has basically the same capabilities (including the carriage of armament) as the F-5E.

Many of the nations currently employing the various versions of the F-5 have expressed an interest in the RF-5E since its debut. The first production aircraft flew in December 1982, and was one of two aircraft comprising the first export order, to the **Royal Malaysian air force** (serving with No. 11 'Cobra' Squadron). An additional 10 Tigereyes have been delivered to **Saudi Arabia** for No. 17 Squadron at Tabuk. In a three-year programme which began during 1990, six **Singapore air force** F-5Es were converted to RF-5E configuration by Singapore Aerospace, with assistance from Northrop.

SPECIFICATION

Northrop RF-5E Tigereye
Wing: span 26 ft 8 in (8.13 m) without tip-mounted AAMs and 27 ft 11.875 in (8.53 m) with tip-mounted AAMs; aspect ratio 3.82; area 186.0 sq ft (17.28 m²)
Fuselage and tail: length 48 ft 0.75 in (14.65 m); height 13 ft 4.5 in (4.08 m); tailplane span 14 ft 1.5 in (4.31 m); wheel track 12 ft 5.5 in (3.80 m); wheel base 16 ft 11.5 in (5.17 m)
Powerplant: two General Electric J85-GE-21B turbojets each rated at 3,500 lb st (15.5 kN) dry and

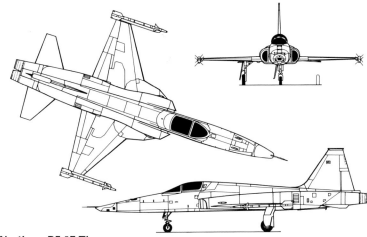

Northrop RF-5E Tigereye

5,000 lb (22.2 kN) with afterburning
Weights: empty 9,750 lb (4423 kg); maximum take-off 24,675 lb (11192 kg)
Fuel and load: internal fuel 677 US gal (2563 litres); external fuel up to three 275-US gal (1040-litre) drop tanks; maximum ordnance 7,000 lb (3175 kg), generally not carried
Speed: maximum level speed 'clean' at 36,000 ft (10975 m) 940 kt (1,082 mph; 1741 km/h)
Range: combat radius with one drop tank and two AIM-9 Sidewinder AAMs 250 nm (287 miles; 463 km) on a lo-lo-lo mission, or 410 nm (471 miles; 759 km) on a hi-lo-hi mission, or 365 nm (420 miles; 676 km) on a

hi-lo-lo-hi mission, or 495 nm (569 miles; 916 km) on a hi-hi-hi mission; combat radius with three drop tanks and two AIM-9 Sidewinder AAMs 365 nm (420 miles; 676 km) on a lo-lo-lo mission, or 560 nm (644 miles; 1037 km) on a hi-lo-hi mission, or 520 nm (598 miles; 963 km) on a hi-lo-lo-hi mission, or 630 nm (725 miles; 1166 km) on a hi-hi-hi mission

The reconnaissance-configured RF-5E is particular to Saudi Arabia, Malaysia and Singapore. This RMAF No. 11 Sqn RF-5E is seen in formation with two No. 11 Sqn F-5Es.

Northrop **T-38 Talon**

The **Northrop T-38 Talon** remains the USAF's standard advanced jet trainer. The first supersonic aircraft to be designed from the outset specifically as a trainer, the T-38 is of conventional design with two J85 engines mounted side-by-side, small span wings and a slender, area-ruled fuselage. The instructor sits behind and 10 in (25 cm) higher than the student.

Developed as the **N-156T** proposal, the first of three service-test **YT-38**s flew on 10 April 1959, powered by two non-afterburning YJ-85-GE-5 turbojets each rated at 2,100 lb st (9.41 kN). The first production T-38 was powered by two afterburning J85s each rated at 3,600 lb st (16.01 kN). The USAF ordered the T-38 into production in 1959 and the first **T-38A** became operational on 17 March 1961. Excluding prototype and pre-production aircraft, a total of 1,139 T-38s was manufactured, and although

In keeping with its other resident aircraft, the 9th Wing, at Beale AFB, have begun to repaint its T-38s in an overall black scheme.

the aircraft served primarily with the USAF, it was also sold to West Germany.

The first Talon went to the 3510th Flying Training Wing at Randolph AFB, TX, part of the USAF's Air Training Command. This organisation, which has been renamed Air Training and Education Command, remains the principal T-38A operator. In 1966, 46 T-38As were acquired by West Germany and they are still flown in standard USAF markings to train German pilots at Sheppard AFB, TX. NASA employs **T-38A(N)** variants as astronaut hacks; these differ in having heated intake lips and VHF radio. A small number of T-38As, **QT-38A** drones and **DT-38A** drone controllers served with the

US Navy. The USAF's 'Thunderbirds' flight demonstration team flew the T-38A during 1978-84. Several are used as chase aircraft at Air Force test establishments.

An early T-38A was fitted with hardpoints for ordnance to test the concept of a lead-in fighter trainer (LIFT) to provide a transition to high-performance warplanes such as the F-15 Eagle. A total of 132 aircraft was rebuilt

as **T-38B LIFT** aircraft, often referred to by the unofficial designation **AT-38B**. The AT-38B had a centreline station for a SUU-20/A rocket/practice bomb carrier, practice bomb rack, or an SUU-11 7.62-mm Minigun pod. LIFT training was carried out by the 479th Tactical Training Wing at Holloman AFB, NM, before being replaced in 1989 by an abbreviated syllabus called basic

Left: With the arrival of the Força Aérea Portugesa's first F-16s, the days of its 'fighter' T-38s are finally at an end. The Talons will serve as pure trainers.

Turkey's advanced fast-jet training needs are fulfilled entirely by the survivors of 30 T-38s, and a new batch of 40 ex-USAF T-38s delivered in 1993.

fighter training (BFT), which has since been dispersed among other ATC Talon squadrons. Other early weapons-related applications included use as aggressor aircraft.

From 1961 to 1993, every USAF pilot, even those assigned to transport types, could boast of having flown at least one high-performance aircraft – the T-38A, as a result of universal pilot training (UPT). This contrasts with the US Navy, which funnels student aviators through 'pipelines' and uses fast jet trainers only for a few. The USAF is now changing this system, partly to prolong the service life of its T-38As. Under specialised undergraduate pilot training (SUPT), student pilots destined for multi-engine aircraft will forfeit any T-38A experience to fly the Beech T-1A Jayhawk. Only pilots destined for reconnaissance, attack and fighter types will continue to fly the T-38.

T-38s were assigned at SAC bases for several years to perform Accelerated Co-pilot Enrichment (ACE). This programme is now known as CPT (Companion Trainer Program). On 1 January 1993 the CPT detachments were transferred to the reconstituted host wings, joining either ACC or AMC and acquiring the colour scheme of the aircraft of the host wing. For example, CPT T-38s at ACC B-1 and B-52 bases have changed from white to bomber grey. With no suitable replacement in sight, the 700

T-38As remaining are scheduled to be retired between 2010 and 2015.

The T-38 was exported only to two countries, each receiving aircraft from surplus USAF stocks. Eight of the Portugal's 12 T-38s were equipped with AIM-9 AAMS to fulfil the role of the Força Aérea Portugesa's primary interceptor, pending delivery of F-16s. Turkey's 30 T-38s are operated as part of Air Training Command.

Taiwan is leasing 40 from the USAF for three years to maintain supersonic pilot proficiency pending delivery of the first F-16s in 1997. The RoCAF previously operated 28 T-38s in the 1970s when F-5Es were urgently diverted to the South Vietnamese air force. At present, Taiwanese pilots undertake training on the T-38A with the 435th FS/49th FW at Holloman AFB, NM.

OPERATORS

Portugal: six T-38As delivered to Força Aérea Portugesa/Portuguese air force from late 1977 to supplement air defence F-86F Sabres. Equipped with AIM-9 Sidewinders and joined by another six aircraft in 1981. Eight T-38s now undertake 'Fighter Pilots' Complementary Instruction' and secondary air defence pending delivery of F-16s, with Esquadra 103, at Beja.
Taiwan: 40 aircraft to be leased from 1994-1997 to cover supersonic fighter availability shortfall

Turkey: 30 former USAF T-38s delivered to the Türk Hava Kuvvetleri/Turkish air force in 1979. A further batch of 40 was delivered in 1993, allowing retirement of T-33s from the training role. Aircraft operate as part of Häva Okullari Komuntanligi (Air Training Command), with 121 Filo, 2 Ana Üs, Cigli.

United States
Air Combat Command (ACC)
8th Air Force: 5th BW, Minot AFB, ND; 7th Wing Dyess AFB, TX; 28th BW, Ellsworth AFB, SD; 509th BW, Whiteman AFB, MO
9th Air Force: 4th Wing, Seymour Johnson AFB, NC
12th Air Force: 9th RW, Beale AFB, CA; 49th FW, Holloman AFB (433rd/435th FS), NM; 55th Wing, Offutt AFB, NE; 366th Wing, Mountain Home AFB, ID
Air Education and Training Command (AETC)
19th Air Force: 12th FTW, Randolph AFB, TX; 14th FTW, Columbus AFB, MI; 47th FTW, Laughlin AFB, TX; 64th FTW, Reese AFB, TX; 71st FTW Vance AFB, OK; 80th FTW, Sheppard AFB, TX; 82nd Training Wing, Sheppard AFB, TX (GT-38A and GAT-38B ground instructional airframes)
Air Mobility Command (AMC)
22nd ARW, McConnell AFB, KS; 43rd ARW, Malmstrom AFB, MT
Air Force Materiel Command (AFMC)
Air Force Flight Test Center/445th TS/412th TW, Edwards AFB, CA (includes Test Pilot School); Sacramento ALC/337th TS, McClellan AFB, CA; 586th TS/46th TG, Holloman AFB, NM

NASA: 31 T-38As are in service based at Ames, Langley, Dryden and Johnson Centers for astronaut proficiency and fast transport duties. Majority at Johnson (Ellington AFB)

SPECIFICATION

Northrop T-38A Talon
Wing: span 25 ft 3 in (7.70 m); aspect ratio 3.75; area 170.00 sq ft (15.79 m²)
Fuselage and tail: length 46 ft 4.5 in (14.14 m); height 12 ft 10.5 in (3.92 m); tailplane span 14 ft 1.5 in (4.31 m); wheel track 11 ft 0 in (3.35 m); wheel base 16 ft 11.5 in (5.17 m)
Powerplant: two General Electric J85-GE-5 turbojets each rated at 2,680 lb st (11.92 kN) dry and 3,850 lb st (17.13 kN) with afterburning
Weights: empty 7,174 lb (3254 kg); maximum take-off 12,050 lb (5465 kg)
Fuel and load: internal fuel 583 US gal (2206 litres); external fuel none; ordnance none
Speed: maximum level speed at 36,000 ft (10975 m) 745 kt (858 mph; 1381 km/h); maximum cruising speed at 40,000 ft (12190 m) 502 kt (578 mph; 930 km/h)
Range: ferry range 950 nm (1,094 miles; 1761 km); typical range 747 nm (860 miles; 1384 km)
Performance: maximum rate of climb at sea level 33,600 ft (10241 m) per minute; service ceiling 53,600 ft (16335 m); take-off run 2,500 ft (762 m) at maximum take-off weight; landing distance 3,000 ft (914 m) at maximum landing weight

---

Northrop (or Lockheed?) TR-3A

The existence of the **TR-3A** stealthy reconnaissance aircraft was first reported in mid-1991, at which time several were believed to be in USAF service alongside F-117A covert strike fighters. No official confirmation of the TR-3A's existence has been given. Of all-wing configuration, the single-seat TR-3A is believed to have a span of about 64 ft (19.50 m) and a length of 42 ft (12.80 m), with two engines in the 12,000-lb st (53.38-kN) class such as General Electric F404s. A somewhat smaller

prototype of similar construction was said to have flown in 1981 as the **Tactical High-Altitude Penetrator** (THAP), after Northrop had lost out to Lockheed in the Have Blue programme that produced the F-117A. The TR-3A is reportedly known as the **Black Manta**, and perhaps 20 to 30 may have been built for high-altitude reconnaissance as a stealthy replacement for the U-2R. The TR-3 was allegedly developed by Northrop alongside the F-117 at Groom Lake (Area 51, or simply 'the Box'). This team was

kept separate from Lockheed personnel at the same location and both designs were hidden from each other. Reportedly nicknamed 'Shamu' by its creators, aircraft answering the TR-3's description (slightly larger and faster than the Night Hawk) have been seen flying with F-117s near Tonopah, Edwards AFB and the Tehachapi Mountains.

Mention of the type was first made in a report by the Federation of American Scientists, and after Operation Desert Storm questions were raised regarding certain examples of target designation film supposedly taken through an F-117A's FLIR, which seemed to have come from a second orbiting aircraft.

The existence of a range of 'black' aircraft operating from Groom Lake and Papoose Lake, Nevada, has long been convincingly proposed, but little tangible evidence has appeared. What may be the first pictures of a TR-3 were taken during Operation Roving Sands 93 at Roswell, New Mexico. The aircraft was filmed in the air at dusk, revealing a flat-bottomed, V-shaped craft with a discontinuous trailing edge. It was also (perhaps) monitored arriving during the night at Holloman on 18 March 1993. At that time, an obviously sensitive aircraft that had made a precautionary landing (with another chase aircraft) was referred to over base radio as '806' and 'the STF'.

Pakistan Aeronautical Complex
Kamra, District Attock
Pakistan

PAC (AMF/Saab) Mushshak

After taking delivery from Sweden in 1974/75 of 28 **Saab MFI-17** light aircraft, Pakistan established an assembly line at Risalpur in an army workshop to build a further 92, delivered in kit form. Named **Mushshak** (Urdu for 'proficient'), the aircraft entered service with both the **Pakistan air force** and **army**, in training and liaison roles. The Aircraft Manufacturing Factory (AMF) was formed in 1983 to handle the Mushshak activity and transferred to Kamra, where more than 120 have since been built under licence, including 25 for the **Iranian air force** (Revolutionary Guards). The AMF developed an uprated version of the Mushshak, named **Shahbaz**, a prototype of which was first flown in July 1987 powered by a 210-hp (157-kW) Teledyne Continental TIO-360-MB turbo-supercharged engine. One further example was later completed.

SPECIFICATION

PAC (AMF) Mushshak
generally similar to the Saab MFI-17 Supporter except in the following particulars:
Fuel and load: maximum ordnance 300 kg (661 lb)
Speed: never exceed speed 365 km/h (197 kt; 227 mph); maximum level speed 'clean' at sea level 238 km/h (128 kt; 148 mph); cruising speed at sea level 210 km/h (113 kt; 130 mph)
Range: endurance 5 hours 10 minutes
Performance: maximum rate of climb at sea level 312 m (1,024 ft) per minute; climb to 1830 m (6,000 ft) in 7 minutes 30 seconds; service ceiling 4800 m (15,750 ft); take-off run 150 m (493 ft) at normal utility take-off weight; take-off distance to 15 m (50 ft) 305 m (1,000 ft) at normal utility take-off weight; landing distance from 15 m (50 ft) 350 m (1,149 ft) at normal utility landing weight; landing run 140 m (460 ft) at

normal utility landing weight
g limits: -3 to +6 aerobatic, or -2.7 to +5.4 normal utility or -2.4 to +4.8 maximum take-off weight

Iran's Pasdaran (Revolutionary Guards) obtained 25 PAC Mushshaks to establish their first aviation unit in 1991.

Pacific Aerospace (Aerospace/NZAI) CT-4 Airtrainer

Pacific Aerospace Corporatio
Private Bag HN 3027, Hamilton Airpo
Hamilton, New Zealan

Serving the air forces of three nations in its design role of primary trainer, the **Airtrainer** can trace its origins back to a two-seat light aircraft designed in 1953 by Henry Millicer, then the chief aerodynamicist of the Australian Government Aircraft Factories. Winner of a competition organised by the Royal Aero Club in Britain, this design entered production in Australia as the **Victa Airtourer** for civil use. After the sale of design rights to AESL in New Zealand, the latter company was reorganised as NZAI and continued development and production of the Airtourer. Modifications to suit the same basic aircraft to the military training role were introduced, including a structure restressed for limits of +6/-3 g and aerobatic manoeuvres. Named the Airtrainer, the prototype of this **CT-4** version flew on 23 February 1972. Features included side-by-side seating for pupil and instructor, a one-piece canopy hinged at the rear to open upwards, and provision for 13-Imp gal (59-litre) wingtip fuel tanks.

Orders for Airtrainers were announced during 1972 by both the **Royal Australian Air Force** (for 37) and the **Royal Thai air force**. Australia eventually also received 14 embargoed **CT-4A**s built for the (illegal) Rhodesian regime, and 47 remained in service for primary training (nicknamed 'Plastic Parrots') at No. 1 FTS, Point Cook, until mid-1992. The Thai order totalled 24 aircraft, all for use at the Kamphaeng San Flying Training School. Eighteen of this original batch are currently being rewinged by the RTAF, with PAC assistance to extend their service life. An additional six aircraft were ordered

The RNZAF is the last major user of the CT-4 Airtrainer. The Airtrainers provide basic training for pilots who then progress to the Aermacchi M.B.339. The 'Red Checkers' display team (right) is made up from CFS instructors. Often flying simply as a synchronised pair, up to six CT-4s have displayed under the team's banner.

from Pacific Aerospace in 1992. The final Airtrainer purchase was by the **Royal New Zealand Air Force**, which operates 19 **CT-4B**s (with higher gross weight). The RNZAF also had four **AESL T6/24 Airtourer**s at the CFS until their retirement in 1993. The remaining 18 CT-4Bs serve with the Pilot Training School, North Island. One Victa Airtourer acquired secondhand formed the sole equipment of the **Tonga air force** (formed in 1986) in 1994. One further CT-4, which served with Bangladesh, has now been retired.

Ownership of design rights in Airtourer passed to Pacific Aerospace Corp. in 1982 and, on 21 January 1991, PAC flew a prototype **CT-4C Turbine Airtrainer** with a 420-shp (313-kW) Allison 250-B17D turboprop, this being a conversion of a damaged

RNZAF CT-4B airframe. A derivative of the CT-4C has been proposed with a retractable undercarriage as the **CT-4CR**, and PAC also unsuccessfully submitted a version of the original Airtourer for the USAF EFS requirement, as the **CT-4E**.

SPECIFICATION

Pacific Aerospace (Aerospace) Airtrainer CT-4A
Wing: span 26 ft 0 in (7.92 m); aspect ratio 5.25; area 129.00 sq ft (11.98 m²)
Fuselage and tail: length 23 ft 2 in (7.06 m); height 8 ft 6 in (2.59 m); tailplane span 11 ft 10 in (3.61 m); wheel track 9 ft 9 in (2.97 m); wheel base 5 ft 7.375 in (1.71 m)
Powerplant: one Rolls-Royce (Continental) IO-360-H flat-six air-cooled piston engine rated at 210 hp (157 kW)

Weights: basic empty 1,460 lb (662 kg); empty equipped 1,490 lb (675 kg); maximum take-off 2,400 l (1089 kg)
Fuel and load: internal fuel 54 US gal (204.5 litres); external fuel none; ordnance none
Speed: never exceed speed 230 kt (265 mph; 426 km/h) maximum level speed 'clean' at 10,000 ft (3050 m) 142 kt (163 mph; 262 km/h) and at sea level 155 kt (178 mph; 286 km/h); cruising speed at 10,000 ft (3050 m) 125 kt (144 mph; 232 km/h)
Range: ferry range 708 nm (815 miles; 1311 km); typical range 596 nm (686 miles; 1104 km)
Performance: maximum rate of climb at sea level 1,350 ft (411 m) per minute; climb to 10,000 ft (3050 m in 11 minutes 40 seconds; service ceiling 17,900 ft (5455 m); take-off run 733 ft (224 m) at MTOW; take-off distance to 50 ft (15 m) 1,237 ft (377 m) at MTOW landing distance from 50 ft (15 m) 1,100 ft (335 m) at normal landing weight; landing run 510 ft (155 m)

Panavia Tornado IDS

As the most advanced tactical interdictor/strike (IDS) aircraft produced in Europe, the **Panavia Tornado** obviates NATO's lack of weapons standardisation by carrying almost every relevant air-launched armament in the inventory. It achieves this task at high subsonic speeds, masked from detection by automatic, all-weather terrain following, and protected from air and surface threats by a range of active and passive self-defence aids. Meeting a challenging specification issued in the late 1960s, the Tornado's intended roles were interdiction, counter-air operations against airfields,

battlefield interdiction, close air support, reconnaissance, maritime attack and point interception. An all-weather air superiority derivative, the **Tornado ADV** (described separately), was developed independently for UK requirements. Specific reconnaissance versions are also separately described. The three nations commissioning the Tornado are represented in prime contractor Panavia by their national aircraft industries, currently British Aerospace, DASA (Germany) and Alenia (Italy), which have programme shares of 42.5, 42.5 and 15 per cent, respectively. Assembly lines

have been established in all three countries, with manufacture for third parties being undertaken by the firm achieving the sale.

The Tornado is of modest overall dimensions and is powered by a pair of Turbo Union RB.199 reheated turbofans which are, like the majority of the avionics, a product of international collaboration. The shoulder-mounted, continuously variable-geometry wing incorporates full-span double-slotted flaperons, full-span leading-edge slats and upper surface spoilers/lift dumpers. A Krueger flap is located forward of each wing glove vane. The wing high-lift devices confer good field performance and, coupled with bucket-type thrust-reversers, allow the aircraft to land on short, perhaps damaged, lengths of runway and taxiway.

The Tornado's nav/attack system com prises a Texas Instruments multi-mode fo ward-looking, ground-mapping, terrain-fo lowing radar, Ferranti digital INS (DINS) an combined radar/map display, Decca 7 Doppler radar system, GEC Ferranti lase rangefinder and marked target seeker in a undernose fairing (RAF aircraft only) an Alenia radio/radar altimeter. The aircraft flight control system primarily comprises triply-redundant command stability augmer

The JP 233 area denial weapon was first used by RAF Tornados against Iraqi airfields, with a warload of 30 57-lb (26-kg) SG357 cratering bomblets and 215 5.5-lb (2.5-kg) HB876 mines.

tation system (CSAS) using fly-by-wire and autostabilisation, and an autopilot/flight director (APFD). Coupled with the nav/ attack system, these allow the aircraft to fly with high stability and near-sonic speed at 200 ft (61 m) above ground level in all weathers. Over known flat surfaces, such as southern Iraq during the 1991 Gulf War, altitude can be further reduced by reliance on the radar altimeter alone. With a high wing loading to minimise low-altitude gust response, the aircraft is a stable weapons platform and is both fast and comparatively comfortable for its crew when flying through the dense, low-level air. The reliable DINS, updated by periodic radar fixes, makes possible a single-pass attack of pinpoint accuracy in all weathers. The Tornado was also the first combat aircraft designed with a fly-by-wire control system, but was preceded into service by the similarly-controlled Lockheed (GD) F-16 Fighting Falcon. Fixed armament comprises two 27-mm IWKA-Mauser cannon on each side of the lower fuselage with 180 rounds per gun. Weapons and other stores are carried on a total of seven hardpoints: one centreline pylon, two fuselage shoulder pylons and two swivelling pylons under each wing. The inboard wing pylons are fitted with mountings for self-defence missiles.

At the peak of its strength, the Luftwaffe had five Tornado strike wings. This JBG 38 aircraft, based at Jever, carries an MW-1 weapons dispenser, the German equivalent to JP 233. Underwing are a BOZ-101 chaff/flare pod (port) and a Cerebrus ECM pod (port). The Tornado wears the lizard scheme adopted from 1983.

Tornado development

Design of the Tornado, initially known as the Multi-Role Combat Aircraft (**MRCA**), was initiated in 1968. The first of nine prototype and six pre-series Tornados flew on 14 August 1974, followed by the initial production aircraft on 10 July 1979. Six procurement batches covered by the original trinational agreement included 640 IDS aircraft, while a further 57 were added in Batch 7, as were four pre-series examples notionally refurbished to production standard. Aircraft of Batches 1-3 have 14,840-lb st (66.0-kN) RB.199 Mk 101 powerplants; the remainder have 16,075-lb st (71.5-kN) Mk 103s, although 100 RAF Mk 101 engines have been upgraded in service. RAF Tornados also have fin fuel tanks of 121-Imp gal (551-litre) capacity, augmenting a standard capacity of 1,285 Imp gal (5842 litres), and are cleared with the **F.Mk 3**'s 495-Imp gal (2250-litre) underwing drop tanks. Italy and Germany use only 220- or 330-Imp gal (1000- or 1500-litre) tanks, two

Right: Five Muharraq-based Tornados formate on a No. 55 Sqn Victor tanker.

Below: Operation Desert Storm marked the combat debut of the TIALD pod. Two prototype examples were rushed to the Gulf and were shared by at least six Tornados.

of which can also be installed beneath the fuselage of all variants. All IDS operators have some fully combat-capable dual-control Tornados for conversion and continuation training. In RAF service these 'twin-stickers' are given the (little-used) designation **GR.Mk 1(T)**. Production batches 6 and 7 incorporate MIL-STD 1553B digital databus, upgraded radar warning equipment and active ECM, improved missile control unit and integration of AGM-88 HARM missile.

RAF **Tornado GR.Mk 1**s include those based at Cottesmore, where the Trinational Tornado Training Establishment uses aircraft from all three European nations for type conversion, weapons instruction being at individual units in each country. Deliveries to TTTE began in July 1980, followed by formation of the first operational squadron (No. IX) in June 1982. Orders have totalled 164 standard GR.Mk 1s, 50 (plus one refurbished pre-series) dual-control aircraft, and 14 new-build **GR.Mk 1A** reconnaissance aircraft (described separately), although 16 Batch 3/5 machines were retrofitted with Mk 103 engines and recce equipment under the same designation.

In 1993-94, two squadrons (Nos 12 and 617, at RAF Lossiemouth) began to receive a maritime attack tasking with BAe Sea Eagle anti-ship missiles and 'buddy' refuelling pods under the designation Tornado **GR.Mk 1B**, to replace the RAF's ageing Buccaneers. Ten aircraft (including seven twin-stickers) were modified to accept 15 Sargent-Fletcher 28-300 pods (purchased from the Marineflieger) during the Gulf War, and these may become the first GR.Mk 1Bs.

A mid-life update later in the 1990s will raise aircraft to Tornado **GR.Mk 4** standard. This was to have provided the Tornado with a GEC Spartan terrain-referenced navigation

Panavia Tornado IDS

suite (cancelled in early 1993), new Ferranti HUD, updated weapon control system, colour head-down display, improved electronic warfare suite and a FLIR (cancelled in 1993). P15 served as a GR.Mk 4 development aircraft, flying for the first time in its new configuration in late 1993. Further downscaling of the upgrade was caused by constant Treasury opposition which threatened to cancel the project entirely, until the final decision to go ahead was announced under the 'Front Line First' study in July 1994. The resulting update will provide for a digital map display, GPS navigation, pilot's MFD, improved weapons systems, new HUD, video recorder and undernose FLIR. The GR.Mk 4 will be TIALD-capable. BAe will undertake the work on 80 aircraft between 1996 and 2000, with an option on a further 62 upgrades between 2000 and 2002. Service entry is slated for February 1998.

A peak of 11 squadrons was achieved in 1990 – eight in RAF Germany (II, IX, 14, XV, 16, 17, 20 and 31) and three in the UK (13, 27 and 617) – of which two were assigned to reconnaissance, but the 1994 position was to be eight: four in Germany (IX, 14, 17 and 31) and four in the UK, the latter comprising two recce (II and 13) and two maritime (12 and 617) squadrons.

In Germany, the Luftwaffe acquired 212 Tornado IDS, including two refurbished and 55 dual-control; the navy acquired 112, of which 12 are 'two-stick'. Luftwaffe aircraft were assigned to four fighter-bomber wings and one training wing, while the Marineflieger fielded two maritime attack units. One of these naval squadrons (MFG 1) has been disbanded and its aircraft transferred to the Luftwaffe to re-equip reconnaissance units AkG 51 and 52, which were formerly RF-4E operators. Over the course of a year 40 aircraft were transferred to a new unit, AG 51, which has adopted the badge and traditions of AkG 52. Established in January 1994, AG 51 undertakes a Baltic reconnaissance role identical to that of MFG 1. These aircraft will be initially equipped with (only nine) MBB/Aeritalia pods housing two Zeiss cameras and a Texas Instruments RS-710 IRLS, inherited from the Marineflieger. This makes them less capable than the Phantoms which they replaced, but development of a new DASA system, to enter service in 1998, is underway. Nine remaining HARM-capable Marineflieger Tornados have joined MFG 2.

In association with Italy, Germany is pursuing a Mid-Life Improvement plan. A step-by-step programme, it will involve integrat-

ing a new main computer with software and weapons systems, with a view to adding a FLIR, GPS navigation and improved ECM capabilities in the future. The German-developed electronic combat reconnaissance variant is described separately.

Italy received 100 Tornado IDS, including one refurbished and 12 dual-control. Three squadrons formed in 1983-84 and a fourth converted in 1993. This latter unit (102° Gruppo) will have a dual reconnaissance/attack role using podded Martin-Marietta ATARS (Advanced Tactical Air Reconnaissance System), and 155° Gruppo is already equipped with an MBB/Aeritalia podded recce system. Maritime attack is the responsibility of the Kormoran-equipped 156° Grupo. Italian plans for an update programme are comparable to those of Germany.

The sole IDS export contract covers 48 (including 14 dual-control and six reconnaissance) delivered to Nos 7 (replacing F-5Es) and 66 Sqns of the Royal Saudi air force from 1986. The follow-on 1993 Al-Yamamah II contract covered an additional purchase of 48 IDS-configured aircraft. Originally to be split between IDS and ADV variants, this order, confirmed in June 1993, will comprise virtually all IDS Tornados, with a small number of reconnaissance-capable examples. The last six of the first batch were already completed to GR.Mk 1A standard.

RAF, Italian and Saudi Tornados received

their combat debut in the 1991 Gulf War. One AMI and six RAF Tornados were lost in combat, the latter primarily due to AAA when employed on anti-airfield missions. The war also marked the operational debut of TIALD and ALARM. After closure of the German assembly line in January 1992, the UK remained the sole manufacturing source, delivering its last aircraft (an F.Mk 3) in 1993. Orders totalled 697 IDS, 35 ECR and 197 ADV interceptors. In mid-1994, the UK government was considering leasing GR.Mk 1s to the United Arab Emirates.

WEAPONS OPTIONS

The Tornado's fixed armament comprises a pair of 27-mm IWKA-Mauser cannon, with 180 rounds per gun. Most NATO standard weapons can be carried, on Sandall Mace ejector rails in the case of RAF aircraft and MWCS racks on German and Italian examples.

Weapons specific to RAF Tornados include the 950-lb (431-kg) WE177B nuclear bomb (remaining in the inventory until 2007), JP233 airfield-denial weapon, 1,000-lb (454-kg) freefall, retarded and Paveway II LGBs and (from 1991) BAe ALARM anti-radar missile and Marconi TIALD IR/laser designator pod. Defensive aids for the RAF include Bofors BOZ-107 chaff/flare dispenser pod, Marconi Sky Shadow jamming pod, two AIM-9L AAMs and internal Marconi RHWR radar warning receiver (replacing original Elettronica unit, which remains in Italian and German service). Aircraft tasked with replacing the Buccaneer in the maritime role will be equipped with the BAe Sea Eagle anti-shipping missile. Sea Eagle integration will be a two-stage process, with an interim fit providing for the carriage of two missiles and two underwing fuel tanks, or four underwing missiles. The full standard will provide for a further Sea Eagle-compatible station on the centreline, allowing five to be carried, or three missiles and two underwing tanks, or four missiles and a centreline fuel tank.

The GEC-Marconi Dynamics Lancelot PGM was offered in competition with the Paveway III in response to the Staff Requirement (Air) 1242 for a low-level stand-off bomb for the GR.Mks 1 and 4. Go-ahead for the purchase of Paveway III LGBs was approved in July 1994. Derived from the Al Hakim family of PGMs developed for the United Arab Emirates, the rocket-boosted 900-lb (408-kg) Lancelot can be fitted with mid-course guidance to provide a stand-off range of up to 10 miles (20 km) and carry a penetration or blast warhead. The first sightings of this class of weapon have been under an SAOEU Tornado GR.Mk 1. A variant known as Centaur is being offered for SR(A) 1236 for a conventional stand-off missile for the RAF.

Above: Still bearing traces of its Marineflieger past, this Tornado wears the panther badge of Luftwaffe reconnaissance unit AG 51 (formerly the badge of AkG 52).

Below: British Aerospace first flew their Tornado GR.Mk 4 demonstrator in May 1993, from the Warton factory. Note the new undernose sensor housings.

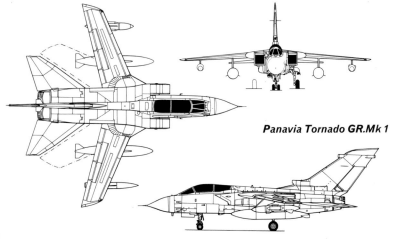

Panavia Tornado GR.Mk 1

Luftwaffe aircraft are armed with US-supplied B61 nuclear bombs, plus the MW-1 bomblet-dispensing system, AGM-65 and AGM-88 HARM. Self-defence is provided by Bofors BOZ-101 ECM pods, AIM-9Ls and Telefunken Systemtechnik Cerebrus II, III or IV jamming pods. Under development is the Franco-German APACHE stand-off missile, intended for Eurofighter and the Tornado. Flight tests commenced in April 1994. APACHE could be offered to the RAF for SR(A) 1236. The Luftwaffe is also seeking to to add further PGM capability to the Tornado

Naval weapons are the MBB Kormoran anti-ship missile, backed by AGM-88 and the BL755 cluster-bomb, plus SFC 28-300 'buddy' pods. While all German aircraft are AGM-88-capable, only the Luftwaffe's ECR version would use it on an 'offensive' role. Marineflieger aircraft, in contrast, train with HARM as one of their main anti-shipping weapons.

Italian Tornado weapons and equipment are largely the same as for German aircraft: B61, MW-1, AGM-65, AGM-88, Kormoran, Bofors BOZ-102, AIM-9L and Cerberus. AMI Tornados can also carry JP233, 1,000-lb bombs, ALARM, AIM-9L and Sea Eagle, plus RAF-type defensive pods. The AMI also purchased 1,700 IAI Griffin LGB systems in November 1993.

OPERATORS

Royal Air Force
No. 2 Sqn: RAF Marham (GR.Mk 1A)

No. 9 Sqn: RAF Brüggen (tasked with ALARM)
No. 12 Sqn: RAF Lossiemouth (GR.Mk 1B)
No. 13 Sqn: RAF Marham (GR.Mk 1A)
No. 14 Sqn: RAF Brüggen (tasked with TIALD)
No. 15(R) Sqn: RAF Lossiemouth (TWU)
No. 17 Sqn: RAF Brüggen
No. 31 Sqn: RAF Brüggen
No. 617 Sqn: RAF Lossiemouth (GR.Mk 1B)
Strike/Attack Operational Evaluation Unit: RAF Boscombe Down (GR.Mk 1/1A)
Tri-national Tornado Training Establishment: RAF Cottesmore, comprising 'A', 'B' and 'C' Squadrons for conversion of RAF, Luftwaffe and AMI crews, and 'S' (Standards) Squadron for instructor training
Aircraft & Armament Evaluation Establishment: RAF Boscombe Down (two GR.Mk 1 leased from BAe)
Defence Research Agency: RAF Boscombe Down (GR.Mk 1)

Luftwaffe
JBG 31 'Boelke': Norvenich
JBG 32: Lechfeld (ECR)
JBG 33: Büchel
JBG 34: Memmingen
JBG 38 'Friesland': Jever
AG 51 'Immelmann': Schleswig/Jagel
Tslw 1: Kaufbeuren

Marineflieger
MFG 2: Schleswig/Jagel

Aeronautica Militare Italia
6⁰ Stormo: 102⁰ and 154⁰ Gruppi, Brescia-Ghedi
36⁰ Stormo: 156⁰ Stormo, Gioia de Colle
50⁰ Stormo: 155⁰ Stormo, Piacenza/San Damiano
Reparto Sperimentale di Volo: Pratica di Mare

Royal Saudi Air Force
No. 7 Sqn: Taif
No. 66 Sqn: Dhahran

SPECIFICATION

Panavia Tornado GR.Mk 1
Wing: span 45 ft 7.5 in (13.91 m) minimum sweep (25°) and 28 ft 2.5 in (8.60 m) maximum sweep (67°); aspect ratio 7.73 spread and 2.96 swept; area 286.33 sq ft (26.60 m²)
Fuselage and tail: length 54 ft 10.25 in (16.72 m); height 19 ft 6.25 in (5.95 m); tailplane span 22 ft 3.5 in (6.80 m); wheel track 10 ft 2 in (3.10 m); wheel base 20 ft 4 in (6.20 m)
Powerplant: two Turbo-Union RB.199-34R Mk 101 turbofans each rated at 8,475 lb st (37.70 kN) dry and 14,840 lb st (66.01 kN) with afterburning or, in later aircraft, Turbo-Union RB.199-34R Mk 103 turbofans each rated at 8,650 lb st (38.48 kN) dry and 16,075 lb st (71.50 kN) with afterburning
Weights: basic empty about 30,620 lb (13890 kg); operating empty 31,065 lb (14091 kg); normal take-off 45,000 lb (20411 kg); maximum take-off about 61,620 lb (27951 kg)
Fuel and load: internal fuel 11,221 lb (5090 kg); external fuel up to 13,200 lb (5988 kg) in two 2250-litre (396-US gal) and two 1500-litre (396-US gal) or four 1500-litre (396-US gal) drop tanks; nominal maximum ordnance more than 9000 kg (19,841 lb)
Speed: limiting Mach No. Mach 1.4 with LRMTS, M1.3 with intakes deactivated (all RAF aircraft); limiting IAS 1482 km/h (800 kt; 921 mph); maximum level speed 'clean' at 36,000 ft (10975 m) 1,262 kt (1,453 mph; 2338 km/h)
Range: ferry range about 2,100 nm (2,420 miles; 3890 km) with four drop tanks; combat radius 750 nm (863 miles; 1390 km) on a typical hi-lo-hi attack mission with a heavy warload
Performance: climb to 30,000 ft (9145 m) in less than 2 minutes 0 seconds from brakes-off; service ceiling more than 50,000 ft (15240 m); take-off run less than 900 m (2,953 ft) at maximum take-off weight; landing run 370 m (1,214 ft) at maximum landing weight
g limits: +7.5
Panavia Tornado IDS
generally similar to the Panavia Tornado GR.Mk 1 except in the following particulars:
Powerplant: two Turbo-Union RB.199-34R Mk 101 turbofans each rated at 8,700 lb st (38.70 kN) dry and 14,840 lb st (66.01 kN) with afterburning or, in later aircraft, Turbo-Union RB.199-34R Mk 103 each rated at 9,100 lb st (40.48 kN) dry and 16,075 lb st (71.50 kN) with afterburning
Fuel and load: internal fuel 10,251 lb (4650 kg)

Panavia Tornado ADV

Developed from the Tornado IDS inter-dictor for wholly British requirements, the **Tornado ADV (Air Defence Variant)** was optimised for long-range interception. The primary missions were the protection of NATO's northern and western approaches, and long-range air defence of UK maritime forces. As envisaged by Air Staff Requirement 395, the aircraft was to loiter for long periods far from base before undertaking a low-level dash in any weather to shoot down missile-launching Soviet bombers at beyond visual range. Having demonstrated 920 mph (1480 km/h) at 2,000 ft (610 m), the Tornado is faster than most potential adversaries, but reliance on turbofan engines leaves it deficient in speed at medium altitude. Agility and close-in fighting capability were not important considerations for destroying bombers at long range. However, the position changed in the mid-1980s when it became apparent that the manoeu-vrable Sukhoi Su-27 'Flanker' long-range fighter might act as a bomber escort, and it shifted yet again with evaporation of the Soviet strategic threat in the early 1990s. Seen to be at a disadvantage for the limited or 'policing' type of warfare which the RAF now expects to be its future combatant role, the Tornado ADV is earmarked for early replacement by a more agile aircraft.

Design of the ADV was based around the carriage of four underfuselage BAe Sky Flash radar-homing AAMs, resulting in a 4-ft 5½-in (1.36-m) longer airframe which provides extra fuel space and increases internal capacity to 1,571 Imp gal (7143 litres). Only the port 27-mm cannon is retained, but the refuelling probe is housed internally, unlike the IDS's detachable bolt-on unit, and only inboard wing pylons are fitted. Each can carry a 495-Imp gal (2250-litre) drop tank and either one or two AIM-9L Sidewinder heat-seeking AAMs on additional launch rails. Avionics differ considerably from the IDS, having little need for extremely accurate ground position, but a second GEC-Ferranti FIN1010 inertial platform is added in all except the first 18 aircraft.

The intercept radar is the GEC-Marconi AI.Mk 24 Foxhunter, a multi-mode, track-while-scan, pulse-Doppler unit. Requirements called for Tornado radar to be capable of detecting targets at more than 115 miles (185 km) and tracking 20 while continuing to scan. The subject of serious development problems, Foxhunter almost suf-

A former Phantom operator, No. 29 Sqn was the first RAF unit to receive the F.Mk 3 after the OCU. Assigned to SACLANT for maritime air defence, it is also tasked with an 'out of area' role.

During Operation Desert Storm, Royal Saudi air force Tornado F.Mk 3s maintained constant CAPs alongside their RAF counterparts. The only air-to-air kills scored by the air force fell to an F-15C.

Panavia Tornado ADV

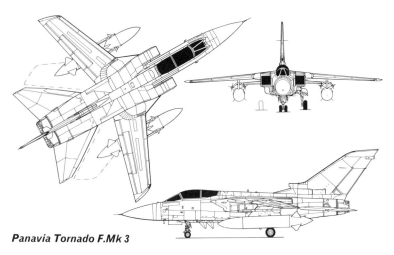

Panavia Tornado F.Mk 3

fered cancellation before being brought to a minimally acceptable standard (known as 'AA') early in 1989, this representing two-thirds of what was initially demanded. Further upgrading to 'AB' configuration, meeting the full specification, is due in the mid-1990s. Another delayed feature, automatic wing sweep, was developed to configure the aircraft optimally for any throttle setting, but is not employed at squadron level.

In 1976, it was revealed that 165 of the 385 Tornados earmarked for the UK would be ADVs. Of these, three emerged as non-operational prototypes and 18 as interim standard **Tornado F.Mk 2**s. The remainder are manufactured as Tornado **F.Mk 3**s, the current definitive production version. A

maiden flight by the first of the three ADV prototypes took place at BAe's Warton plant on 27 October 1979 and was followed by the first F.Mk 2 on 5 March 1984. Mk 2s, including eight with dual controls, were from Batch 4 and fitted with RB.199 Mk 103 powerplants of 16,075 lb st (38.5 kN), provision for only two Sidewinders, and a single FIN1010 INS. These early aircraft initially flew with ballast in place of delayed radars (the so-called 'Blue Circle' radar) and served only with No. 229 OCU at Coningsby for training. The last was replaced in January 1988. Plans for their conversion to near Mk 3 standard (apart from engines) as **F.Mk 2A**s have not been implemented and appear increasingly unlikely. One of the F.Mk 2s is currently operated by the DRA at Boscombe

Down as the **Tornado TIARA** (Tornado Integrated Avionics Research Aircraft). This is a testbed for next-generation fighter avionics including HOTAS controls, helmet-mounted sights and a holographic HUD.

The first Tornado F.Mk 3 flew on 20 November 1985, manufacture following of 144, including 38 with dual controls but fully combat-capable. A cancelled Omani order for eight was transferred to the RAF. Initial training was undertaken by No. 229 OCU, officially established at RAF Coningsby on 1 May 1985 (unofficially on 1 November 1984). This unit employed 16 F.Mk 2s, joined by its first F.Mk 3 on 28 July 1986. Delays in the training programme, and non-delivery of the radar, forced No. 229 OCU to declare itself to SACEUR as a combat-capable unit, and it adopted the identity of No. 65 (Reserve) Sqn as a result. This stayed the case until 1992, when the unit became No. 56(R) Sqn after the retirement of No. 56 Sqn's Phantoms. The first front-line unit was former Phantom-operator No. 29 Sqn, which became operational on 1 November 1987. It was followed by No. 5 Sqn (1 May 1988), No. 11 Sqn (1 November 1988), No. 23 Sqn (1 August 1989), No. 25 Sqn (1 January 1990), No. 43 Sqn (1 July 1990) and, finally, No. 111 Sqn (31 December 1990). Cut-backs in the 'Options for Change' defence review call for a reduction in the RAF's fighter force that saw No. 23 Sqn disband on 26 February 1994, to be followed by No. 25 Sqn.

F.Mk 3 improvements

The F.Mk 3 is fitted with an extended afterburner which increases the fuselage length by 14 in (36 cm). Other changes are provision for four, not two, Sidewinders, addition of a second INS, and incorporation of a spin prevention and incidence limitation system (SPILS) for 'carefree handling'. An upgrade, known as 'Stage 1+', was introduced on the production line early in 1989 and retrofitted throughout the fleet. Provisions include a new 'combat stick' with HOTAS controls, type AA Foxhunter radar, improvements to the Marconi Hermes radar homing and warning receiver, Have Quick UHF radios, radar-absorbent coating on the fin and wing leading edges, five per cent combat boost switch for engines, AIM-9M capability, and flare dispensers below the rear fuselage (briefly AN/ALE-40, but Vinten VICON 78 from 1991). The planned Stage 2, in the mid-1990s, will be concerned mainly with a further radar upgrade. JTIDS integration for the F.Mk 3 fleet is currently being undertaken by aircraft at RAF Coningsby.

Saudi Arabian Tornado ADVs were produced to RAF Stage 1 standard and, in fact, diverted from MoD contracts to speed delivery (the RAF gaining replacement machines built later). The total of 24 includes six with dual controls. Deliveries began to Nos 29 and 34 Squadrons in February 1989 and all had been received by early 1991, when RAF and RSAF Tornado interceptors participated in the Gulf War without seeing aerial combat.

A mix of No. 5 and No. 29 Sqn aircraft,

which were changing places for armament camp at Akrotiri, were dispatched from Cyprus to Dhahran on 29 August 1990, becoming No. 5 (Composite) Sqn. Six F.Mk 3s replaced the No. 29 Sqn examples in September 1990, establishing a new unit, No. 11(C) Sqn. A further six aircraft relieved the remaining No. 5 Sqn Tornados, and No. 11(C) Sqn was increased to war strength through the addition of six more F.Mk 3s on 22 September 1990. This Dhahran detachment was retitled No. 43(C) Sqn on 1 December 1990, until it flew its last operational sortie on 8 March 1991. The Tornados returned to the UK during the following week.

The drawdown in RAF strength has released sufficient airframes to equip a new Tornado F.Mk 3 operator. To act as a stop-gap measure pending delivery of its Eurofighter EFA 2000s, the Italian air force is undertaking a five-year lease (with a five-year extension option) of 24 aircraft. After six months of negotiations, against rival US bids of secondhand F-15s and F-16s, an agreement was signed on 17 November 1993 for a no-cost lease to supplement the AMI's existing F-104S ASA Starfighters. The Tornado's Sky Flash missiles may be replaced by Selenia Aspide AAMs in Italian service, and the F.Mk 3s will be operated by 12º Grupo, 36º Stormo, at Gioia de Colle and 18º Stormo, 37º Stormo, at Trapani/Bergi. Acquisition of the F.Mk 3s was eased by Italy's existing Tornado maintenance capability and the relative ease with which its Foxhunter radar can be adapted to use the Aspide missile (as opposed to the F-15 or F-16). However, as the AMI has no trained backseaters available, the aircraft will be crewed by pilots in both seats. The first 12 aircraft will be delivered to Gioia de Colle in early 1995, followed by the second batch two years later. Initial training will be undertaken by No. 56(R) Sqn, at RAF Coningsby.

The final production ADV Tornado was an F.Mk 3, ZH559, delivered to No. 56(R) Squadron on 24 March 1993.

WEAPONS OPTIONS

The Tornado F.Mk 3 retains only one (port side) of the 27-mm IWKA-Mauser cannon fitted to the IDS/GR.Mk 1 version. Its main armament is four BAe Sky Flash semi-active radar-homing AAMs, carried semi-recessed under the fuselage on Frazer-Nash ejector rails. RAF weapons have an MSDS monopulse, continuous wave seeker head, operating in the J-band, a 66-lb (30-kg) HE warhead and an effective range of 29 miles (49 km). Backing up the Sky Flash are up to four AIM-9L Sidewinders, carried in pairs on shoulder pylons above the main inboard hardpoints. The F.Mk 3 has only one pair of wing hardpoints, unlike the IDS/GR.Mk 1. Self-defence capability is provided by a Bofors Phimat chaff dispenser (starboard outer Sidewinder pylon). Future weapons fits will include four AIM-120 AMRAAMs or BAe Active Sky Flash, along with up to four new-generation short-range AAMs.

OPERATORS

Royal Air Force
No. 5 Sqn: RAF Coningsby
No. 11 Sqn: RAF Leeming

Left: The Tornado F.Mk 3 boasts a clean airframe and powerful engines, making it one of the best-performing fighters in the world.

Right: This Tornado bears the black eagle insignia of No. 11 Sqn. Based at Leeming, its aircraft are among those being fitted with JTIDS datalinks.

No. 25 Sqn: RAF Leeming
No. 29 Sqn: RAF Coningsby
No. 43 Sqn: RAF Leuchers
No. 56(R) Sqn: RAF Coningsby
No. 111 Sqn: RAF Leuchers
No. 1435 Flt: RAF Mount Pleasant, Falkland Islands

Under Operation Grapple, a detachment of Tornado Mk 3s drawn from the Leeming wing is currently stationed at Gioia del Colle, Italy. The Tornados are tasked with air support of UN operations in Bosnia.

Tornado F.Mk 3 Operational Evaluation Unit:
RAF Coningsby

Aircraft & Armament Evaluation Establishment:
RAF Boscombe Down (F.Mk 2/3)
DRA Boscombe Down: (F.Mk 2 TIARA)

Royal Saudi Air Force
No. 29 Sqn: Dhahran
No. 34 Sqn: Dhahran

SPECIFICATION

Panavia Tornado F.Mk 3
Wing: span 45 ft 7.5 in (13.91 m) spread and 28 ft 2.5 in (8.60 m) swept; aspect ratio about 7.73 spread and

2.96 swept; area 286.33 sq ft (26.60 m²)
Fuselage and tail: length 61 ft 3.5 in (18.68 m); height 19 ft 6.25 in (5.95 m); tailplane span 22 ft 3.5 in (6.80 m); wheel track 10 ft 2 in (3.10 m)
Powerplant: two Turbo-Union RB.199-34R Mk 104 turbofans each rated at 9,100 lb st (40.48 kN) dry and 16,520 lb st (73.48 kN) with afterburning
Weights: operating empty 31,970 lb (14502 kg); maximum take-off 61,700 lb (27986 kg)
Fuel and load: internal fuel 12,544 lb (5690 kg); external fuel up to 12,800 lb (5806 kg) in two 2250-litre (396-US gal) and two 1500-litre (396-US gal) or four 1500-litre (396-US gal) drop tanks; maximum ordnance 18,740 lb (8500 kg)

Speed: maximum level speed 'clean' at 36,000 ft (10975 m) 1,262 kt (1,453 mph; 2338 km/h)
Range: combat radius more than 300 nm (345 miles; 556 km) supersonic or more than 1,000 nm (1,151 miles; 1,852 km) subsonic; endurance 2 hours 0 minutes on a CAP at between 300- and 400-nm (345- and 460-mile; 555- and 740-km) radius
Performance: operational ceiling about 70,000 ft (21335 m); take-off run 2,500 ft (762 m) with normal fuel and weapon loads, or 5,000 ft (1524 m) in ferry configuration; take-off distance to 50 ft (15 m) less than 3,000 ft (915 m) at normal take-off weight; landing distance from 50 ft (15 m) about 2,000 ft (609 m) 1,215 ft (370 m) with thrust reversal

---

Panavia Tornado ECR and GR.Mk 1A

Although Marineflieger and (initially) AMI Tornado reconnaissance needs were met with a simple multi-sensor pod, the **Luftwaffe** and **RAF** have opted for more involved conversion. The German system is the more complex, as it includes a SEAD Suppression of Enemy Air Defences) capability and so warrants the designation **Tornado ECR** (Electronic Combat and Reconnaissance). The first of two converted prototypes flew on 18 August 1988, while deliveries of 35 new-build ECRs from Batch 7 production began on 21 May 1990 and were completed on 28 January 1992. These were issued to two squadrons within two wings (JBGs 32 and 38), and are the only Tornados so far fitted with Mk 105 RB.199 turbofans.

Operational equipment includes a Texas Instruments ELS (Emitter Location System) with antennas in the wing glove and in the forward fuselage, and two underfuselage AGM-88 HARM missiles. Data is handled by a MIL STD 1553B databus and threat information is displayed on two dedicated screens in the WSO's cockpit. The pilot's standard combined electronic display and map can access the same information, as a back-up. The ELS allows the aircraft to plot and identify threat radars and, while it was designed for use against ground targets, it also has a limited capability against airborne radars (though without IFF). Its area coverage, unlike the USAF's F-4G's, is not 360°, and the ECR is blind to signals from the rear. Luftwaffe tactics call for two aircraft to operate in a racetrack pattern to overcome this deficiency. The ECR also relies on a pre-programmed library of radar signals, loaded on to the ELS prior to each sortie. The current system is not reprogrammable in flight, or indeed on the flight line, and so is unable to respond to unexpected threats. The Luftwaffe claims that its (and NATO's) Sigint resource is more than adequate.

The crew can elect to attack a target independently or transmit target information to another aircraft via the ODIN (Operational Data INterface) datalink, carried in the forward fuselage. The ECR retains all the terrain-following capability of the standard IDS, so can carry out its mission at high speed, low level and in all weathers – unlike the medium-altitude F-4G. The ECR will release the Luftwaffe and other NATO air forces from reliance on USAF SEAD assets, such as the elderly 'Wild Weasel' F-4Gs, and can sweep an area or escort a strike as required.

Reconnaissance features are a Honeywell/Sondertechnik horizon-to-horizon IR linescan (or IIS – Imaging Infra-red System) in a blister under the forward fuselage, and Zeiss FLIR immediately ahead. The IIS is a film-based system that can relay a video image to the WSO, or transmit to a ground station via the ODIN link. Its information can be merged on the cockpit displays with data

from the ELS to produce a graphic image of an active threat area.

The ECR retains the Cerberus jamming pod, BOZ-101 chaff/flare dispenser and AIM-9L self-defence AAMs of the German Tornado IDS, but both internal cannon are deleted. Protracted delays with the emitter locater system led to the aircraft operating at a reduced level of capability, but production ELS sets began to be delivered from April 1993. After protracted indecision, Italy elected to produce 16 of its own ECRs by conversion of existing aircraft, which are to retain their original engines. The prototype **Tornado ITECR**, converted by Alenia at Turin, first flew in July 1992, the type being scheduled to achieve IOC in 1995. While the ECR provides a considerable reconnaissance asset to the Luftwaffe, the service is committed to acquiring 40 dedicated reconnaissance Tornados in a conversion programme of former Marineflieger aircraft announced in early 1994.

While ECR Tornados were originally delivered to two squadrons, the Luftwaffe has consolidated its SEAD force with one unit. On 1 July 1994, JBG 32, based at Lechfield, was declared operational as the sole ECR squadron. It operated a mix of ECR and IDS aircraft until October 1994, when all the ECRs delivered to JBG 38 were swapped for JBG 32's remaining IDS Tornados. JBG 38, based a Jever, then reverted to a standard Tornado IDS unit.

The surplus of German Tornados has opened the possibility of supplying 24 ECRs to the Republic of Korea. An MoU has been signed for the Korean requirement which had previously been for new-build aircraft. The current availability of airframes makes the deal far more likely.

RAF reconnaissance

RAF Tornado **GR.Mk 1A**s have no specific defence-suppression capability, but may revert to a secondary attack role with all weapons except WE177B nuclear bombs and internal cannon. They were the first reconnaissance aircraft to dispense completely with traditional film and rely entirely on video. A Vinten 4000 infra-red linescan is

Panavia Tornado ECR

mounted in a blister fairing beneath the forward fuselage, giving 180° coverage. Since details near the horizon are indistinct on its wide-angle presentation, a BAe SLIR (Side-Looking IR) sensor with a 10° field is mounted in each side of the fuselage to cover this area. The system is optimised for ultra-low-level operations under cover of darkness, requires no illumination, and is self-stabilising up to an aircraft banking angle of 30°. The navigator is able to produce a tape of the most important aspects of the mission for immediate analysis after landing, but sensors are allowed to run during the whole time the aircraft is over hostile territory. The first of 16 conversions from GR.Mk 1 standard flew on 11 July 1985, while 14 new-build Mk 1As were delivered from 13 October 1989. Operating squadrons are Nos II and 13.

The housing for the Tornado GR.Mk 1A's Vinten 4000 IR linescan is visible behind the nose gear, under the fuselage, on this No. II Sqn example.

SPECIFICATION

Panavia Tornado ECR
generally similar to the Panavia Tornado GR.Mk 1 except in the following particulars:
Powerplant: two Turbo-Union RB.199-34R Mk 101 turbofans each rated at 8,700 lb st (38.70 kN) dry and 14,840 lb st (66.01 kN) with afterburning or, in later aircraft, Turbo-Union RB.199-34R Mk 103 turbofans each rated at 9,100 lb st (40.48 kN) dry and 16,075 lb st (71.50 kN) with afterburning
Fuel and load: internal fuel 10,251 lb (4650 kg)

JBG 32 is now the Luftwaffe's sole Tornado ECR unit, providing a powerful SEAD asset courtesy of its AGM-88-armed aircraft.

Piaggio **P.166**

Industrie Aeronautiche e Meccaniche Rinaldo Piaggio SpA
Via Cibrario 4, I-16154 Genova Sestri,
Genoa, Italy

First flown on 26 November 1957, the **Piaggio P.166** twin-engined utility transport was a direct evolution of the earlier, smaller P.136 amphibian that was of similar configuration and had flown for the first time on 29 August 1948. Features of the design were the high-mounted gull wing, pusher engines and wingtip fuel tanks. Powered by two 340-hp (254-kW) Lycoming GSO-480-B1C6 flat-six piston engines, the early production **P.166AL1**s were for commercial use, but were matched in most de-tails by the more numerous **P.166ML1**s, 51 of which were built by Piaggio for the **Italian air force**. With an additional cockpit door, stronger cabin floor, standard seating for eight passengers and larger main loading door, the **P.166M** was widely dispersed in the communications role, and about half continue to be so used by various of the 600-series Squadriglia Collegiamento (communication flights) attached to each major base.

On 3 July 1976, Piaggio flew the prototype of a turboprop version of the P.166, identified as the **P.166-DL3** and similar in most respects other than the powerplant to the P.166M. Production of this version included four for **Somalia**, used in a quasi-military role by the Ministries of Defence and of Transport. Six P.166DL3s for the Italian air force are equipped with a vertically-mounted Zeiss camera in the cabin to serve in the aerial survey role with 303° Gruppo di Volo Autonomo at Guidonia, Rome, to supplement the **P.166M/APH** variant used previously for similar duties.

Between 1988 and 1990, delivery was made of variants for maritime and ecological patrols (Sorveglianza Ecologica e Marittima) flown by the **Italian navy** on behalf of the Ministry of Merchant Marine's Capitanerie di Porto (Coast Guard). These **P.166-DL3SEM**s carry Bendix RDR 1500 radar with a radome under the nose, FLIR, and have provision for two 177- or 284-litre (46.8- or 75-US gal) underwing fuel tanks, as the wingtip containers are used for sensors and equipment.

They equip four aircraft flights at Guidonia, Catania, Fontanarossa and Pescara. Ten similar P.166-DL3SEMs were purchased in 1991/92 by the Italian Guardia di Finanza (Customs Service).

Included in the fleet of 303° Gruppo, at Guidonia, are six 'sharp-nosed' P.166DL-3s, equipped for photo-survey duties with vertical Zeiss cameras in their fuselages.

SPECIFICATION

Piaggio P.166-DL3
Wing: span 13.51 m (44 ft 4 in) without tip tanks or 14.69 m (48 ft 2.5 in) with tip tanks; aspect ratio 7.3; area 26.56 m2 (285.90 sq ft)
Fuselage and tail: length 11.88 m (39 ft 0 in); height 5.00 m (16 ft 5 in); tailplane span 5.10 m (16 ft 9 in)
Powerplant: two Textron Lycoming LTP101-700 turboprops each flat-rated at 600 shp (448 kW)
Weights: empty equipped 2650 kg (5,842 lb); maximum take-off 4300 kg (9,480 lb)

Fuel and load: internal fuel 1139 kg (2,511 lb); external fuel none; maximum payload 1073 kg (2,365 lb)
Speed: never exceed speed 220 kt (253 mph; 407 km/h); maximum level speed 'clean' at 10,000 ft (3050 m) 215 kt (248 mph; 400 km/h); economical cruising speed at 12,000 ft (3660 m) 162 kt mph; 300 km/h)
Range: 1,125 nm (1,295 miles; 2084 km) with max fuel or 750 nm (864 miles; 1390 km) with payload
Performance: maximum rate of climb at sea level 2,200 ft (671 m) per minute; service ceiling 28,000 ft (8535 m); take-off distance to 50 ft (15 m) 2,180 ft (665 m) at maximum take-off weight; landing distance from 50 ft (15 m) 1,500 ft (457 m) at maximum landing weight

Piaggio **P.180 Avanti**

At the 1983 NBAA convention in Dallas, Texas, Piaggio announced the birth of a new twin turboprop-powered business aircraft. Design work on the **P.180 Avanti** had begun at Piaggio's Genoa headquarters in 1979. Seating six to 10 passengers, it was a radical departure from anything the company had previously produced.

The major design feature of the aircraft is its use of three lifting surfaces. The main wing is fitted above the mid-set position in the fuselage, with the main spar running behind the passenger cabin. Its straight leading edge is broken only by the engine nacelle inlets and the wing has a slight dihedral of 2°. The T-tail and elevator act as the second lifting surface, in addition to being orthodox control surfaces. The foreplane, however, is not a simple canard, but provides a positive lift component in addition to that produced by the wing. This in turn allows the wing to be reduced in size, decreasing overall weight and drag. The engines specified were Pratt & Whitney Canada PT6A-66A turboprops, each driving a five-bladed Hartzell fully-feathering reversible-pitch propeller with spinner. The engines are mounted in composite-material nacelles. The Avanti makes considerable use of composites. Carbon-fibre and a graphite/epoxy mix represent about 10 per cent of the aircraft's weight. Wings and tail sections are produced by Piaggio at Genoa,

while the forward fuselage is the responsibility of Piaggio Aviation in Wichita. Final assembly is completed in Italy.

The cockpit is fitted with a Collins EFIS system, comprising three CRTs, and Collins navigation and weather radar systems are standard. The aircraft is certified for single-pilot operations. In 1983 Gates Learjet became a partner in the project, but withdrew for economic reasons in January 1986. All the tooling and the forward fuselages of the three pre-production Avantis which were on the line at Wichita were transferred to Italy. Assembly of the first P.180 began on Piaggio's Finale Ligne plant in 1986 and the first flight was made on 23 September 1986 (I-PJAV). The Avanti was certified in Italy in March 1990, and in May 1990 the first production aircraft was rolled out. The final hurdle of US certification was passed in October 1990 and the first customer delivery took place the following September. By early 1994, despite or perhaps because of its radical appearance and advanced design, only 27 Avantis had been built for its (intended) civilian market.

The Avanti has gained its only military order from the **Italian air force**, which ordered six aircraft for delivery in two batches. The first P.180s entered service, in 1993, with 313° Grupo Autonomo, at Guidonia, 636ª Squadriglia Collegiamento, at Gioia and 653ª Squadriglia Collegiamento, at

Cameri/Novara. The remaining three AMI Avantis will be delivered in 1994.

SPECIFICATION

Piaggio P.180 Avanti
Wing: span 14.03 m (46 ft in); wing aspect ratio 12.30; foreplane aspect ratio 5.05; area, gross 16.00 m2 (172.22 sq ft)
Fuselage and tail: length 14.41 m (47 ft 3½ in); height 3.94 m (12 ft 11 in); tailplane span 4.25 m (13 ft 11½ in); wheel track 2.84 m (9 ft 4 in)
Powerplant: two 1,485-shp (1107-kW) Pratt & Whitney PT6A-66 turboprops

All of the Italian air force's intended complement of six Avantis had entered service by the end of 1994, a welcome addition to the type's halting sales.

Weights: empty, stripped 3384 kg (7,460 lb); maximum take-off 5080 kg (11,200 lb)
Speed: maximum operating Mach number Mach 0.67 maximum level speed 482 km/h (455 mph)
Range: at 11890 m (39,000ft), with reserves 3187 km (1,980 miles)
Performance: maximum rate of climb at sea level 875 m (2,870 ft) per minute; service ceiling 12500 m (41,000 ft) take-off to 15 m (50 ft) at sea level 864 m (2,835 ft)

Piaggio-Douglas **PD-808**

Originally known as the **Vespa-Jet**, the PD-808 was essentially designed by Douglas Aircraft Co. in the US as the subject of a joint programme with Piaggio, the latter being responsible for marketing. Failing to attract orders in the corporate market at which it was aimed, the PD-808 was bought only by the **Italian air force**, which contracted for 22 in 1965. The prototype PD-808 flew on 29 August 1964 and production was in four versions: staff transport/communications with nine seats, VIP transport seating six, electronic warfare (guerra elettronica, **GE**) and airways/navaid checking (radiomisure, **RM**).

Almost all of the PD-808s remain in service, but most of the 12 transports are progressively being converted to the GE or RM mission. Five **PD-808TA** transports

are shared by 306° Gruppo TS and 92° Gruppo TS in 31° Stormo 'Carmelo Raiti' at Ciampini. The special-purpose aircraft are based at Pratica di Mare and flown by 14° Stormo 'Sergis Sartof', whose 8° Gruppo uses seven of the RM version, and 71° Gruppo which flies eight GE models.

14° Stormo, AMI, uses its ECM-configured PD-808GEs for NATO EW training. Its aircraft are now adopting an overall grey scheme.

SPECIFICATION

Piaggio-Douglas PD-808
Wing: span 37 ft 6 in (11.43 m) without tip tanks and 43 ft 3.5 in (13.20 m) with tip tanks; aspect ratio 6.25; area 225.00 sq ft (20.90 m2)
Fuselage and tail: length 42 ft 2 in (12.85 m); height 15 ft 9 in (4.80 m); tailplane span 17 ft 9.5 in (5.43 m); wheel track 12 ft 0.75 in (3.68 m); wheel base 14 ft 9 in (4.50 m)

Powerplant: two Piaggio (Rolls-Royce/Bristol Siddeley) Viper Mk 526 turbojets each rated at 3,350 lb st (14.90 kN)
Weights: empty equipped 4830 kg (10,648 lb); maximum take-off 8165 kg (18,000 lb)
Fuel and load: internal fuel 985 US gal (3727 litres); external fuel none; maximum payload 1,600 lb (726 kg)
Speed: maximum level speed 'clean' at 19,500 ft (5945 m) 460 kt (530 mph; 852 km/h); maximum cruising speed at 36,100 ft (11000 m) 432 kt (497 mph;

800 km/h); economical cruising speed at 41,000 ft (12500 m) 390 kt (449 mph; 722 km/h)
Range: 1,105 nm (1,272 miles; 2048 km)
Performance: maximum rate of climb at sea level 5,415 ft (1650 m) per minute; service ceiling 45,000 ft (13715 m); take-off run 2,905 ft (885 m) at maximum take-off weight; take-off distance to 50 ft (15 m) 3,350 ft (1020 m) at maximum take-off weight; landing distance from 50 ft (15 m) 3,800 ft (1158 m) at normal landing weight

Pilatus P-3

Pilatus Flugzeugwerke AG
CH-6370 Stans
Switzerland

Developed for the Swiss air force in the early 1950s as a replacement for the North American T-6, the **Pilatus P-3** has been in service as a primary trainer since 1955. Production totalled 72 for the **Swiss air force** and six for the **Brazilian navy**. The latter are no longer in service, but the Piloten Rekrutenschule 42 and 242 at Magadino retain a few, while others previously used for student pilot training are now distributed around operational bases for liaison and refresher flying tasks. The P-3 has been largely replaced in Swiss service by the Pilatus PC-7 Turbo Trainer.

SPECIFICATION

Pilatus P-3
Wing: span 10.40 m (34 ft 1.4 in); aspect ratio 6.56; area 16.50 m² (177.61 sq ft)
Fuselage and tail: length 8.75 m (28 ft 8.5 in); height 3.05 m (10 ft 0 in)
Powerplant: one Textron Lycoming GO-435-C2A piston engine rated at 260 hp (194 kW)
Weights: empty equipped 1110 kg (2,447 lb); maximum take-off 1500 kg (3,307 lb)
Fuel and load: external fuel none; maximum ordnance about 150 kg (331 lb)

Sizeable numbers of P-3s remain in Swiss air force service as squadron and base liaison aircraft.

Speed: maximum speed at 2000 m (6,560 ft) 167 kt (192 mph; 310 km/h); maximum cruising speed at optimum altitude 149 kt (171 mph; 275 km/h); economical cruising speed 137 kt (158 mph; 255 km/h)

Range: 405 nm (466 miles; 750 km)
Performance: maximum rate of climb at sea level 1,380 ft (421 m) per minute; service ceiling 18,000 ft (5485 m)

Pilatus PC-6 Porter/Turbo Porter

One of the most successful aircraft in its class, the **Pilatus PC-6 Porter** STOL utility transport has been produced in both piston-engined and turboprop versions. Design requirements were for a strong, reliable airframe, excellent STOL performance, good low-speed handling and excellent load-carrying capability. With seating for seven, the high-wing PC-6 first flew on 4 May 1959 with a supercharged Lycoming GSO-480-B1A6 piston engine rated at 253 kW (340 shp). A total of 50 or so Porters was built, before production changed to a turboprop-powered variant. With accommodation for up to nine passengers and a double loading door to facilitate cargo loading, the **PC-6/A-H1 Turbo Porter** first flew on 2 May 1961, powered by a 390-kW (523-shp) Turboméca Astazou IIE engine.

Subsequent production has encompassed several variants, mostly distinguished by versions of the Astazou engine (**PC-6/A**), Pratt & Whitney Canada PT6A (**PC-6/B**) or Garret TPE331 (**PC-6/C**) turboprops. A total of over 500 PC-6s of all versions has been built, including 90 manufactured under licence by Fairchild in the US (as **Heli-Porters**). Twenty-five armed PC-6/Cs were produced for COIN duties in Vietnam as the **Fairchild AU-23A Peacemaker** (described separately). The majority of the

considerable number of PC-6s sold for military use in the communications, liaison or reconnaissance roles have been the **B2-H2** version, with seating for 11 passengers. The current **PC-6/B2-H4** production variant features turned-up wingtips, enlarged dorsal fin, and minor structural and undercarriage improvements to increase payload by 570 kg (1,257 lb).

Principal users of the Turbo Porter include the **Australian army** (No. 173 GS Squadron) and **Switzerland**'s Leichte-fliegerstaffel 7, a light transport squadron manned by the militia. Other operators include the military air arms in **Angola**, **Argentina** (navy), **Austria**, **Bolivia**, **Chad**, **Colombia** (operated by the para-military airline SATENA), **Dubai**, **Ecuador**, **Indonesia**, **Iran**, **Myanmar**, **Oman**, **Peru** (operated by the para-military airline TANS), **Sudan** and the former **Yugoslavia**. The **US Army** bought two Turbo Porters to operate in Berlin, with the designation **UV-20A** and name **Chiricahua**. The **French army** ordered five PC-6/B2-H4s in 1992 for use as transport/paradrop aircraft.

The PC-6 is ideally suited to operations in mountainous Austria, and some have even been modified for fire-fighting tasks.

Fuel and load: internal fuel 508 kg (1,120 lb); external fuel up to 392 kg (864 lb) in two 245-litre (65-US gal) underwing auxiliary tanks; maximum payload 1130 kg (2,491 lb) with reduced internal fuel, 1062 kg (2,341 lb) with maximum internal fuel and 571 kg (1,259 lb) with maximum internal and external fuel
Speed: never exceed speed 151 kt (174 mph; 280 km/h; economical cruising speed at 10,000 ft (3050 m) 115 kt (132 mph; 213 km/h)
Range: ferry range 870 nm (1,002 miles; 1612 km) with auxiliary fuel; range 500 nm (576 miles; 926 km) with maximum internal fuel or 394 nm (453 miles; 730 km) with maximum payload
Performance: maximum rate of climb at sea level 941 ft (287 m) per minute; maximum operating altitude 25,000 ft (7620 m); take-off run 646 ft (197 m) at maximum take-off weight; landing run 417 ft (127 m) at normal landing weight
g limits: -1.5 to +3.72

SPECIFICATION

Pilatus PC-6/B2-H4 Turbo-Porter
Wing: span 15.87 m (52 ft 0.75 in); aspect ratio 8.4; area 30.15 m² (324.54 sq ft)
Fuselage and tail: length 11.00 m (36 ft 1 in); height 3.20 m (10 ft 6 in) tail down; elevator span 5.12 m (16 ft 9.5 in); wheel track 3.00 m (9 ft 10 in); wheel base 7.87 m (25 ft 10 in)
Powerplant: one 680-shp (507-kW) Pratt & Whitney Canada PT6A-27 turboprop flat-rated at 550 shp (410 kW)
Weights: empty equipped 1270 kg (2,800 lb); maximum take-off 2800 kg (6,173 lb) on wheels or 2699 kg (5,732 lb) on skis

Pilatus PC-7 Turbo Trainer

Although the **Pilatus PC-7** directly derives from the early 1950s piston-powered Pilatus P-3 (the prototype of which was re-engined with a 550-shp (410-kW) Pratt & Whitney Canada PT6A-20 turboprop to fly as HB-HON in April 1966), little of the original design is now retained in the definitive **Turbo Trainer**. After a forced landing through fuel mismanagement during initial flight development, the project was shelved until 1973, when one of SAFAAC's P-3 trainers (from 73 originally built) was bailed by Pilatus for similar modification with a 650-shp (484.9-kW) PT6A-25 flat-rated to 550 shp (410.3 kW). Registered HB-HOZ (later A-901 with SAFAAC), this first flew on 12 May 1975, but then underwent major structural changes to take full advantage of the extra power.

In conjunction with Dornier, Pilatus designed a completely new low-fatigue one-piece wing with leading-edge integral tanks ahead of the single mainspar, while retaining the P-3's original span, planform and 15-12 per cent NACA 64A laminar-flow section. Dornier also helped design an entirely new electrically-actuated undercarriage, replacing the P-3's oil-damped coil-spring shock absorbers with Do 27/28-type oleo-pneumatic legs, to meet a 57 per cent increase in maximum take-off weight. Flight development with these modifications in the second prototype also resulted in aerodynamic changes to the rear fuselage and tail, includ-

ing adding a tailcone and small ventral fin, and extending the fuselage aft of the tailplane, to which was added strakes on the inner leading edges for unlimited spin clearance. The tailplane was shortened, allowing its elevators to become externally horn-balanced.

These and other changes, including the clear-vision moulded bubble canopy for the non-pressurised cockpit, were all embodied in the first production PC-7 (HB-HAO), which made its initial flight on 18 August 1978 at Stans. First deliveries were to the **Myanmar air force**, as launch customer, following FAA civil certification in early 1979. With the Beech T-34C then its sole production competitor, the PC-7 achieved growing export success, supplemented in June 1981 after a year-long evaluation of two examples, plus the second prototype, by a **Swiss air force** order for 40 to equip the two *Fliegerschulen* at Magadino. For weapons training, six underwing hardpoints can accommodate external stores of up to 2,293 lb (1040 kg), and PC-7s are believed to have been used operationally by both sides in the Iran/Iraq war.

Between 1983 and 1984, 44 PC-7s replaced the Bulldog in Malaysian air force service. This is one of the nine aircraft flown by the 'Tamin Sari' ('Magic Sword') aerobatic display team, based at Alor Setar.

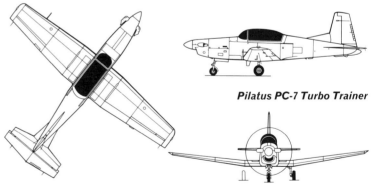

Pilatus PC-7 Turbo Trainer

Pilatus PC-7 Turbo Trainer

The Swiss air force's Fliegerschule I Teil is based at Magadino, in the Ticino region near Italy. It flies PC-7s as basic and advanced instrument trainers.

France's civil/military Centre d'Essais en Vol (CEV) flight test establishment flies five PC-7s among a wide variety of jet, prop and rotary types for general trials duties.

In 1985, Pilatus offered an optional installation of twin Martin-Baker CH.Mk 15A ejection seats, to provide an escape envelope from ground level/60 kt to 32,000 ft (9753 m)/300 kt, with **Iran** as first retrofit customer. Nearly 500 PC-7s had been sold by early 1994 to mostly military customers, including **Abu Dhabi** (24), **Angola** (18), **Austria** (16), **Bolivia** (36), **Myanmar** (17), **Chad** (two), **Chile** (10), **France** CEV (five), **Guatemala** (12), **Iran** (35), **Iraq** (52), **Malaysia** (44), **Mexico** (75), **Netherlands** (10), **Nigeria** (seven), **Switzerland** (40), and **Surinam** (two). Planned orders for 60 **PC-7 Mk 2**s, equipped with a higher-powered flat-rated PT6A with a four-bladed propeller and Martin-Baker ejection seats, were reported in late 1992 for the South African air force, for a total cost of some SwFr200 million. These were to be delivered from July 1994, with 55 per cent South African industrial participation, including local assembly, to replace the SAAF's veteran Harvard trainers. Interest in six PC-7s was also reported from Uruguay.

SPECIFICATION

Pilatus PC-7 Turbo Trainer
Wing: span 10.40 m (34 ft 1 in); aspect ratio 6.5; area 16.60 m² (178.69 sq ft)

Fuselage and tail: length 9.78 m (32 ft 1 in); height 3.21 m (10 ft 6 in); tailplane span 3.40 m (11 ft 2 in); wheel track 2.60 m (8 ft 6 in); wheel base 2.32 m (7 ft 7 in)
Powerplant: one 650-shp (485-kW) Pratt & Whitney Canada PT6A-25A turboprop flat-rated at 550 shp (410 kW)
Weights: basic empty 1330 kg (2,932 lb); normal take-off 1900 kg (4,188 lb) for aerobatics; maximum take-off 2700 kg (5,952 lb)
Fuel and load: internal fuel 474 litres (125 US gal); external fuel up to two 240- or 152-litre (63.5- or 40-US gal) drop tanks; maximum ordnance 1040 kg (2,293 lb)
Speed: never exceed speed 270 kt (311 mph; 500 km/h); maximum cruising speed at 20,000 ft (6095 m) 222 kt (256 mph; 412 km/h); economical cruising speed at 20,000 ft (6095 m) 171 kt (197 mph; 317 km/h)
Range: ferry range 1,420 nm (1,634 miles; 2630 km) with drop tanks; range 647 nm (746 miles; 1200 km); endurance 4 hours 22 minutes
Performance: maximum rate of climb at sea level 2,150 ft (655 m) per minute; climb to 16,400 ft (5000 m) in 9 minutes 0 seconds; service ceiling 33,000 ft (10060 m); take-off run 780 m (2,560 ft) at maximum take-off weight; take-off distance to 50 ft (15 m) 1180 m (3,870 ft) at maximum take-off weight; landing distance from 50 ft (15 m) 800 m (2,625 ft) at maximum landing weight; landing run 505 m (1,655 ft) at maximum landing weight
g limits: -3 to +6 at normal take-off weight or -2.25 to +4.5 at maximum take-off weight

---

Pilatus **PC-9**

The Royal Thai air force ordered 20 PC-9s in 1992, followed by a further 10, replacing RFB Fantrainers.

When rumours of a 'big brother' to the Pilatus PC-7 (described separately) began to circulate in 1983, it was thought to have a Garret engine, but when the prototype **Pilatus PC-9** made its first flight on 7 May 1984 it was powered by a Pratt & Whitney Canada PT6A-62. There is only 10 per cent commonality between the PC-7 and PC-9. The latter is similar, but recognisable by its larger canopy, stepped tandem cockpits with ejection seats, ventral airbrake and four-bladed prop. Development began in 1982, and flight testing of many features and components was carried out using a PC-7 testbed before the construction was initiated of two pre-production prototypes.

The PC-9 was one of four shortlisted contenders to meet the RAF's AST.412 requirement for a Jet Provost replacement, eventually losing to the Shorts-modified EMBRAER Tucano, amid some acrimony and accusations of a 'political' decision. By the time that the PC-9 was certificated on 19 September 1985 (three months ahead of schedule), the RAF competition had taken place, but Pilatus had retained its AST.412 marketing link with BAe. This was a strong factor in securing the initial PC-9 production order, announced only a week later, for 30 aircraft for the **Royal Saudi air force**.

Pilatus then switched its marketing effort to **Australia**, offering offset package deals on both the PC-7 and PC-9 to the Australian government as alternatives to the ailing Wamira programme for an RAAF trainer. The decision this time went in favour of the PC-9, which was co-produced by Hawker de Havilland in Australia under the designation **PC-9/A**. Australian PC-9s are equipped with Bendix EFIS, and PC-7-style low-pressure tyres. Two Swiss-built aircraft were delivered in 1987, and 17 more were supplied in kit form. The remaining 48 aircraft are being built by Hawker de Havilland.

A German target-towing version, designated **PC-9B**, is operated by Holstenair on behalf of the **Luftwaffe**. This is equipped with two Southwest RM-24 winches on inboard pylons, with the targets stowed aft of the winch, and sufficient fuel for a 3-hour 20-minute mission. Other PC-9 operators include the air forces of **Cyprus**, **Myanmar**, **Thailand** and **Switzerland**. Approximately 150 PC-9s had been sold by mid-1994.

The announcement, in 1993, of a buy of 20 'TX-Io' trainers for the **Republic of Korea air force** was hit by controversy. The Korean PC-9s were to act as lead-in trainers for the BAe Hawk, but the air force wished them to be weapons-capable. Swiss law forbade such an 'arms' export and the deal stalled in a debate over whether Pilatus had ever confirmed the PC-9 could be fitted with hardpoints or not. In July 1994, South Korea shelved plans to acquire PC-9s after the contract expired, and chose instead to develop the rival Daewoo KTX-1 turboprop trainer. This, and other controversial deals, led Pilatus to announce that it was considering moving PC-7/-9 assembly to the Britten-Norman plant in the UK to circumvent current and pending Swiss legislation.

In conjunction with Beechcraft, Pilatus is offering the **PC-9 Mk 2** as a JPATS contender. This differs substantially from the PC-9, with a 70 per cent redesign, including a strengthened fuselage and pressurised cockpit. New digital avionics include GPS, MLS, collision avoidance system and provision for a HUD. An engineering testbed aircraft flew first, followed on 23 December 1992 by the first Beechcraft-assembled aircraft, at Wichita. After the final JPATS RFP was issued in May 1994, the first week-long flight tests of the PC-9 Mk II began in July 1994 at Wright-Patterson AFB, Ohio.

SPECIFICATION

Pilatus PC-9
Wing: span 10.124 m (33 ft 2.5 in); aspect ratio 6.3; area 16.29 m² (175.35 sq ft)
Fuselage and tail: length 10.175 m (33 ft 4.75 in); height 3.26 m (10 ft 8.33 in); wheel track 2.54 m (8 ft 4 in)
Powerplant: one 1,150-shp (857-kW) Pratt & Whitney Canada PT6A-62 turboprop flat-rated at 950 shp (708 kW)
Weights: basic empty 1685 kg (3,715 lb); normal take-off 2250 kg (4,960 lb) for aerobatics; maximum take-off 3200 kg (7,055 lb)
Fuel and load: internal fuel 535 litres (141.3 US gal); external fuel up to two 248- or 154-litre (65.5- or 40.7-US gal) drop tanks; maximum ordnance 1040 kg (2,293 lb)

This is the first Beech-built PC-9 Mk II. With the end of JPATS flight tests in October 1994, a final decision will be made in February 1995.

Pilatus PC-9

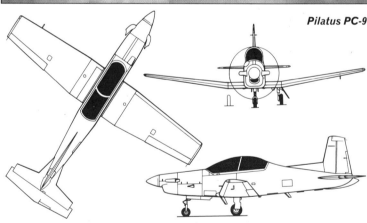

Speed: maximum level speed 'clean' at 20,000 ft (6095 m) 300 kt (345 mph; 556 km/h) and at sea level 270 kt (311 mph; 500 km/h)
Range: range 887 nm (1,020 miles; 1642 km); endurance two 1-hour missions
Performance: maximum rate of climb at sea level 4,090 ft (1247 m) per minute; service ceiling 38,000 ft (11580 m); take-off run 227 m (745 ft) at normal take-off weight; take-off distance to 50 ft (15 m) 440 m (1,444 ft) at normal take-off weight; landing distance from 50 ft (15 m) 530 m (1,739 ft) at normal landing weight
g limits: -3.5 to +7 at normal take-off weight or -2.25 to +4.5 at maximum take-off weight

Pilatus Britten-Norman **BN-2B Islander/Defender**

Pilatus Britten-Norman Ltd
Bembridge, Isle of Wight PO35 5PR
United Kingdom

The **Britten-Norman Islander** was developed as a rugged and versatile twin-engined feederliner to replace aircraft like the de Havilland Rapide, but has confounded all expectations by becoming one of the most widely built aircraft of its class and a *de facto* Dakota replacement. By 1994, orders for all variants exceeded 1,200.

The prototype first flew on 13 June 1965, powered by 210-hp (157-kW) Rolls-Royce/Continental IO-360B engines. The production aircraft gained 4 ft (1.2 m) extra wing-span and Lycoming O-540 engines (both modifications being flown on the original prototype on 17 December 1965). The first production prototype was flown on 20 August 1966, and deliveries began one year later. By mid-1967 orders stood at over 200, and production was transferred to the British Hovercraft Corporation to meet the expanding order book. In addition, Islanders were built by Romania's IRMA, the first of an initial 215 such aircraft making its maiden flight on 4 August 1969. Romanian production continues, and has almost reached 500.

Despite its healthy order book, Britten-Norman ran into financial difficulties and was acquired by the Fairey Group on 31 August 1972. The company's lack of 'in-house' production capacity was eased by the establishment of a third production line at Fairey SA's factory at Gosselies, Belgium. In September 1979, Britten-Norman (Bembridge) Ltd and the production hardware at Gosselies was acquired by Pilatus. During 1974, production of the Islander began in the Philippines Aircraft Development Corporation, which eventually built 55, and assembled 67 from kits supplied by PBN.

The basic **BN-2** was succeeded on the production line by the improved **BN-2A** in June 1969, and then by the further improved **BN-2B**. Some improvements were introduced within the sub-variants, including an optional extended nose which gave 28 cu ft (0.79 m³) of baggage space, extended raked wingtips, and different engine options, from the 260-hp (194-kW) IO-540-E4C5 (with or without Rajay turbo-superchargers) to the 300-hp (224-kW) IO-540-K1B5 or the turbo-supercharged 300-hp (225-kW) TSIO-540E.

Unarmed Islanders have been delivered to several military customers, including **Ciskei**, **Haiti**, **Indonesia**, **Iraq**, **Israel**, **Qatar**, **Somalia**, **Turkey**, **Venezuela**, **Zaïre** and **Zimbabwe**, while a dedicated military derivative, named **Defender**, has been more widely exported. This has underwing hardpoints allowing the carriage of

Twenty-three PADC-assembled BN-2A Islanders were delivered to the Philippine air force between 1976 and 1981.

NATO pylons, stressed for loads of 450 kg (992 lb) (outboard) and 700 kg (1,543 lb) (inboard). These allow the aircraft to carry a variety of payloads, including 60-US gal (227-litre) external tanks and a variety of bombs, rockets, gun pods, wire-guided missiles, recce flares and anti-personnel mines. Defenders have been delivered to **Abu Dhabi**, **Belgium**, **Belize**, **Botswana**, **Ghana**, **Guyana**, **Hong Kong**, **Jamaica**, **Malagasy**, **Malawi**, **Mauritania**, **Mexico** (Presidential Flight), **Oman**, **Panama**, **Qatar**, **Rwanda**, **Seychelles** and **Surinam**.

The **Maritime Defender** is a dedicated naval variant, optimised for coastal patrol, fisheries protection, and search and rescue. A modified nose accommodates a Bendix-King RDR-1400 search radar, and the crew comprises two pilots, a radar operator and two observers. The aircraft is offered with a variety of enhanced avionics suites, and can carry loudspeakers, searchlights, FLIR, flares, dinghy packs or weapons on its underwing pylons. Maritime Defenders have been delivered to **Cyprus**, the **Indian Navy** (in addition to some non-radar Defenders), **Pakistan** and the **Philippines**.

PBN subsequently introduced a turbine-powered variant as the **BN-2T**. Powered by two Allison 250-B17C turboprops flat-rated at 320 shp (298 kW), the prototype first flew on 2 August 1980. The militarised equivalent of the BN-2T is named **Turbine Defender** and examples are operated by **Belgium** (Gendarmerie), **Botswana**, **Ghana**, and **Morocco**. A **Turbine Islander** with a sliding para-door is operated by the **British army**'s parachute association. The Turbine Islander has spawned a number of specialised military Pilatus Britten-Norman Ltd versions (described separately).

A maritime turbine derivative was the **ASW/ASV Islander**, flown in demonstrator form (G-OPBN) in time for the 1984 Hanover air show. A production version could have featured 360° radar, FLIR, sonobuoy processing and a MAD. Sea Skua missiles or Stingray torpedoes were offered as weapons options. The demonstrator was eventually purchased by the **Royal Navy** for underwater weapons trials.

An enhanced turbine derivative is the **BN-2T2 Defender 4000**, based on the long-span Trislander-winged and up-engined AEW Defender, enabling the aircraft to lift 1,500 lb (680 kg) greater weight and provide 50 per cent extra internal fuel capacity.

SPECIFICATION

Pilatus Britten-Norman BN-2B Defender

Wing: span 49 ft 0 in (14.94 m) with standard tips or 53 ft 0 in (16.15 m) with ferry tips; aspect ratio 7.39 with standard tips or 8.34 with ferry tips; area 325.00 sq ft (30.19 m²) with standard tips or 337.00 sq ft (31.31 m²) with ferry tips

Fuselage and tail: length 35 ft 7.75 in (10.86 m); height 13 ft 8.75 in (4.18 m); tailplane span 15 ft 4 in (4.67 m); wheel track 11 ft 10 in (3.61 m); wheel base 13 ft 1.25 in (3.99 m)

Powerplant: two Textron Lycoming IO-540-K1B5 flat-six piston engines each rated at 300 hp (224 kW)

Weights: empty equipped 4,244 lb (1925 kg); maximum take-off 6,600 lb (2993 kg)

Fuel and load: internal fuel 780 lb (354 kg) plus 510 lb (231 kg) in optional ferry tips; external fuel up to two 50-Imp gal (60-US gal; 227-litre) drop tanks; maximum ordnance 2,000 lb (907 kg)

Speed: never exceed speed 183 kt (211 mph; 339 km/h); maximum level speed 'clean' at sea level 151 kt (173 mph; 280 km/h); maximum cruising speed at 7,000 ft (2135 m) 142 kt (164 mph; 264 km/h); economical cruising speed at 12,000 ft (3660 m) 132 kt (152 mph; 245 km/h)

Range: ferry range 1,496 nm (1,723 miles; 2773 km) with auxiliary fuel; range 1,061 nm (1,221 miles; 1965 km) with optional fuel or 613 nm (706 miles; 1136 km) with standard fuel

Performance: maximum rate of climb at sea level 1,130 ft (344 m) per minute; service ceiling 17,200 ft (5240 m); take-off run 866 ft (264 m) at maximum take-off weight; take-off distance to 50 ft (15 m) 1,155 ft (352 m) at maximum take-off weight; landing distance from 50 ft (15 m) 980 ft (299 m)

Indian Naval Air Squadron 550 operates six radar-nosed Maritime Defenders that replaced de Havilland Doves as surveillance and training aircraft.

Pilatus Britten-Norman **Turbine Islander/Defender special versions**

The Islander/Defender's versatility and load-carrying capability has led to its adoption for a variety of roles. The first such specialised variant was the **CASTOR Islander** (later **ASTOR**). This was used as a testbed for the Corps Airborne Stand-Off Radar, developed to fulfil a UK Ministry of Defence requirement for a 'big picture' battlefield surveillance aircraft. Two separate competing platforms were evaluated, one based on the modified Thorn EMI Searchwater radar (CASTOR-C) carried by a Canberra, and the other based on a new Ferranti I-band radar (CASTOR-I). This was originally to have been helicopter-mounted, but was instead fitted on a Turbine Islander acquired for army evaluation. The Canberra began flight trials in 1982, but the Islander did not fly until 12 May 1984, and then only with a ballasted nose radome. This was flat-bot-

tomed and circular in plan view, and required a 12-in (30-cm) extension to the nosewheel leg and the fitting of Trislander mainwheel units. In 1988 the ASTOR Islander was fitted with a Thorn-EMI Skymaster radar in a bulbous spherical nose radome, continuing low-level ASTOR trials and evaluating interoperability with the Grumman E-8 J-STARS. At the end of the project definition stage, due to be completed in 1994, a development and initial production contract was to be awarded. The decision, made late in 1993, not to do so means that firms will be invited to tender on a revised specification, further setting back CASTOR's planned service date of 2003.

In association with Motorola and Thorn-EMI, PBN have further developed the **MASTOR** (Multi-role Airborne STand-off Radar) platform, which integrates the Thorn-

EMI Searchwater 2 radar with mobile ground stations based on those built by Motorola for the E-8 J-STARS. MASTOR's bulbous nose radome (similar to that of the MSSA) houses the MTI-capable radar, and the aircraft also has provision for a FLIR and LLLTV.

The Thorn-EMI Skymaster radar also formed the heart of the private-venture **AEW/MR Islander** demonstrator (G-TEMI), which could be used with pulse-Doppler processing to acquire and track airborne targets in the AEW role or, using a non-coherent, frequency-agile mode, could detect small surface targets, even in high sea states. A second radar operator's console (by comparison with the ASTOR aircraft) increased operational flexibility. A synthetic aperture mode was partly developed (aiming to give high-resolution video mapping) and the border surveillance role was

examined. The potential for fitting ESM, IFF and datalinks was also explored.

The AEW demonstrator was eventually converted to serve as the prototype **MSSA** (Multi-Sensor Surveillance Aircraft), being rolled out in its new guise at Baltimore on 10 September 1992. The MSSA is being developed in association with Westinghouse to provide a simple, low-cost, off-the-shelf surveillance, drug interdiction and border/fisheries patrol platform. The MSSA is equipped with an integrated sensor system which includes an AN/APG-66 radar with a 360° rotating antenna, WF-360 FLIR, GPS, LTN-92 ring-laser gyro INS and a real time video datalink. The demonstrator was leased to the **US Navy** for trials in 1992, and offered to the **British army** for use in Bosnia later that same year. **Turkey** has purchased one MSSA, with an option on

three, and the company hopes for an order for 12 from the US Air National Guard. In July 1993 the sale of three MSSAs was announced to an 'undisclosed Far Eastern nation', for delivery in 1994.

The **Internal Security Islander** has been supplied to the **Netherlands** and **Cyprus** police forces and is equipped with Bendix/King RDR 1400C radar, a Racal R-NAV2 navigation system, and underwing hardpoints for fuel tanks, weapons, camera pods, thermal imagers or FLIR sensors. The **British army**'s seven **Islander AL.Mk 1**s are similarly equipped, without radar, but with R-NAV2, Doppler 91, Mk 32 Decca navigator receiver and underwing hardpoints for a variety of sensors. They may be equipped to carry cameras and/or IRLS equipment in

When the CASTOR Islander first flew in May 1984, it was fitted with this flat-bottomed radome. It later received a lengthened undercarriage and a larger, bulbous radome.

the fuselage, which seems to have bulges (camera ports) in the belly. Even less is known about the **RAF**'s **Islander CC.Mk 2** and **CC.Mk 2A**, operated by RAF Northolt's Station Flight (not No. 32 Squadron), which are said to be equipped for mapping duties. The CC.Mk 2A aircraft (ZF573) was at one time a PBN demonstrator and retains the capability to fire torpedoes. Both aircraft are fully airways equipped and have Bendix/King weather radar in the nose.

The MSSA is based on the airframe of the AEW Islander and carries a Westinghouse APG-66SR radar with 360° coverage, FLIR and laser-ring gyro navigation system and INS.

SPECIFICATION

Pilatus Britten-Norman BN-2T Turbine Defender generally similar to the Pilatus Britten-Norman BN-2B Defender except in the following particulars:
Fuselage and tail: length 35 ft 7.75 in (10.86 m) with standard nose or 36 ft 3.75 in (11.07 m) with weather radar nose
Powerplant: two 400-shp (298-kW) Allison 250-B17C turboprops each flat-rated at 320 shp (238.5 kW)
Weights: empty equipped 4,220 lb (1914 kg);

maximum take-off 7,000 lb (3175 kg)
Fuel and load: internal fuel 1,191 lb (540 kg) plus 51 lb (231 kg) in optional ferry tips; external fuel up to two 50-Imp gal (60-US gal; 227-litre) drop tanks; maximum ordnance 2,000 lb (907 kg)
Speed: maximum cruising speed at 10,000 ft (3050 m) 170 kt (196 mph; 315 km/h); economical cruising speed at 5,000 ft (1525 m) 142 kt (164 mph; 263 km/h)
Range: 728 nm (838 miles; 1349 km)
Performance: maximum rate of climb at sea level 1,050 ft (320 m) per minute; service ceiling more than 25,000 ft (7620 m); take-off run 837 ft (255 m) at maximum take-off weight; take-off distance to 50 ft (15 m) 1,250 ft (381 m) at maximum take-off weight; landing distance from 50 ft (15 m) 1,115 ft (340 m) at normal landing weight; landing run 747 ft (228 m) at normal landing weight

Piper **PA-18 Super Cub**

*Piper Aircraft Corporation
2926 Piper Drive, PO Box 1328, Vero Beach
Florida 32960, USA*

Descended from the famed J-3C Cub and wartime L-4 Grasshopper, the **Piper PA-18 Super Cub** was the last of the Pipers to retain the classic high-wing, tailwheel configuration. Production against US government contracts totalled many hundreds for US Army and Mutual Defense Aid Programs under **L-18** and **L-21** designations. A handful now remain in service, with the final operators comprising the **Belgian air force**, providing five (of six originally supplied) **L-21B** glider tugs for the cadet force; the Israeli air force with over 15 for basic flying training; the **Uganda army air force**, which received 16 from Israel in the 1960s (although the serviceability of these aircraft is questionable); the **Uruguayan air force**, with two in its Escuadrilla de Enlaces (communications flight) at Durazno; and the **Uruguayan navy**, with a single example.

Uruguay is one of the very few military Super Cub operators remaining, with a handful in air force and navy service.

SPECIFICATION

Piper PA-18 Standard Super Cub 150
Wing: span 35 ft 2.5 in (10.73 m); aspect ratio 7.0; area 178.50 sq ft (16.58 m²)
Fuselage and tail: length 22 ft 7 in (6.88 m); height 6 ft 8.5 in (2.02 m); tailplane span 10 ft 6 in (3.20 m); wheel track 6 ft 0.5 in (1.84 m)
Powerplant: one Textron Lycoming (Continental) O-320 flat-four piston engine rated at 150 hp (112 kW)
Weights: empty equipped 946 lb (429 kg); maximum take-off 1,750 lb (794 kg)
Fuel and load: internal fuel 36 US gal (136 litres); external fuel none; maximum ordnance none
Speed: never exceed speed 133 kt (153 mph; 246 km/h);

maximum cruising speed 113 kt (130 mph; 208 km/h)
Range: 399 nm (460 miles; 735 km)
Performance: maximum rate of climb at sea level 960 ft (293 m) per minute; service ceiling 19,000 ft

(5795 m); take-off run 200 ft (61 m) at maximum take-off weight; take-off distance to 50 ft (15 m) 500 ft (153 m) at maximum take-off weight; landing distance from 50 ft (15 m) 725 ft (221 m) at normal landing weight

Piper **PA-23 Apache/Aztec**

Piper's first twin-engined aircraft, the **PA-23 Apache**, actually originated as the **Twin Stinson** prototype, flown before Piper acquired the Stinson division of Convair in November 1948. From 1953, Piper built 2,047 PA-23 Apache twins and 4,929 of the improved **PA-23 Aztec**, which was distinguished by a swept fin and rudder. Small numbers have reached military service over the years, mostly in the liaison/ light transport role, and a few Aztecs are still used in this role. In particular, the **Spanish air force** has six (local designation **E.19**) used for refresher training by Esc 423 at Getafe. The PA-23 is also operated by the air arms of **Cameroon** (two), **Costa Rica** (one), **Madagascar** (one) and **Mexico** (one). Some examples may still be operated by **Uganda**. The US Navy acquired 20 Aztecs as **UO-1**s for logistic support; later redesignated **U-11A**s, these have been replaced by Beech UC-12s.

To the Ejercito del Aire Español, the Piper PA-23-250 Aztec is the E.19. The six Aztecs serve alongside Beech Barons, providing refresher flying training.

SPECIFICATION

Piper PA-23-250 Aztec D
Wing: span 37 ft 2.5 in (11.34 m); aspect ratio 6.67; area 207.56 sq ft (19.28 m²)
Fuselage and tail: length 30 ft 2.625 in (9.21 m); height 10 ft 4 in (3.15 m); tailplane span 12 ft 6 in (3.81 m); wheel track 11 ft 4 in (3.45 m); wheel base 7 ft 6 in (2.29 m)
Powerplant: two Textron Lycoming IO-540-C4B5 flat-six piston engines each rated at 250 hp (186 kW)
Weights: empty 2,933 lb (1330 kg); maximum take-off 5,200 lb (2359 kg)
Fuel and load: internal fuel 144 US gal (544 litres); external fuel none

Speed: maximum level speed 'clean' at optimum altitude 188 kt (216 mph; 348 km/h); normal cruising speed at 4,000 ft (1220 m) 182 kt (210 mph; 338 km/h); economical cruising speed at 6,400 ft (1950 m) 177 kt (204 mph; 328 km/h)
Range: 720 nm (830 miles; 1338 km) at maximum cruising speed or 1,050 nm (1,210 miles; 1947 km) at economical cruising speed

Performance: maximum rate of climb at sea level 1,490 ft (454 m) per minute; absolute ceiling 21,100 ft (6430 m); take-off run 820 ft (250 m) at maximum take-off weight; take-off distance to 50 ft (15 m) 1,250 ft (381 m) at maximum take-off weight; landing distance from 50 ft (15 m) 1,250 ft (381 m) at normal landing weight; landing run 850 ft (259 m) at normal landing weight

Piper PA-28/-32 Cherokee/Arrow/Dakota/Cherokee Six

First flown on 10 January 1960, the PA-28 Cherokee succeeded the high-wing Cub series as Piper's principal single-engined lightplane, production totalling 29,285 in a number of variants to which the names **Cruiser, Flite Liner, Cadet, Challenger, Archer, Charger, Pathfinder** and **Dakota** were progressively applied.

A number of PA-28 four-seat cabin monoplanes were sold to military operators. Remaining users include the **Chilean air force**, which has 16 **PA-28-236 Dakota**s assembled by ENAER, used as instrument trainers and for SAR/liaison duties at various bases, and **Argentina**'s quasi-military

National Civil Aviation Institute, which has 10 Dakotas and four **PA-28-201 Arrow IV**s (assembled by Chincul) for training at Moron AFB. Four Arrow IVs are used by the KuljLv (Transport Squadron) of the **Finnish air force**, and five **Arrow II**s are distributed between the three operational squadrons Hav LLv 11, 21 and 31, the Air Academy and the HQ Flight. Five earlier **PA-28-140 Cherokee** trainers remain in service in **Tanzania**. Also in use are a few examples of the six-seat **PA-32 Cherokee Six**, flown for liaison and communications in the **Colombian air force**, **Costa Rican Police Security Air Section, Tanzanian air force** and **Turkish army**.

SPECIFICATION

Piper PA-28RT-201 Arrow IV
Wing: span 35 ft 5 in (10.80 m); aspect ratio 7.39; area 170.00 sq ft (15.79 m2)
Fuselage and tail: length 27 ft 0 in (8.23 m); height wheel track 10 ft 5.5 in (3.19 m); wheel base 7 ft 10.25 in (2.39 m)
Powerplant: one Textron Lycoming IO-360-C1C6 flat-four piston engine rated at 200 hp (149 kW)
Weights: empty 1,636 lb (742 kg); maximum take-off 2.750 ft (1247 kg)
Fuel and load: internal fuel 77 US gal (291 litres); external fuel none
Speed: never exceed speed 186 kt (214 mph; 344 km/h);

maximum level speed 'clean' at 14,000 ft (4625 m) 178 kt (205 mph; 330 km/h) and at sea level 149 kt (172 mph; 276 km/h); maximum cruising speed at optimum altitude 143 kt (165 mph; 265 km/h); economical cruising speed at optimum altitude 128 kt (147 mph; 237 km/h)
Range: 934 nm (1,076 miles; 1733 km)
Performance: maximum rate of climb at sea level 831 ft (253 m) per minute; service ceiling 16,200 ft (4940 m); take-off run 1,025 ft (312 m) at maximum take-off weight; take-off distance to 50 ft (15 m) 1,600 ft (488 m) at maximum take-off weight; landing distance from 50 ft (15 m) 1,625 ft (465 m) at normal landing weight; landing run 615 ft (187 m) at normal landing weight

The Finnish air force operates Piper PA-28R and T-tailed PA-28RT-201 Turbo Arrow IVs as primary training and liaison aircraft, based at Kauhava.

The long-nosed PA-32 Cherokee Six is a rare sight in military service, but the Colombian air force operates a single example, at Barranquilla.

Piper PA-31/T Navajo/Navajo Chieftain/Cheyenne

The six/eight-seat **Piper Navajo** was introduced in 1965, powered by 300-hp (224-kW) Lycoming IO-540-M engines. Developments introduced the **PA-31P Pressurised Navajo** with turbocharged engines, **PA-31-350 Navajo Chieftain** with a 2-ft (0.61-m) stretch and counter-rotating props, and the **PA-31T Cheyenne** with 500-shp (373-kW) Pratt & Whitney PT6A-11s. The principal military user is the **Aéronavale**, with 12 for transport (2S and 3S), crew ferrying (Escadrille de Réception et de Convoyage) and navigator/flight engineer training (56S). The **Finnish air force** operates seven Chieftains with transport

and communications flights, and Britain's **MoD (PE)** has four Navajo Chieftains to support A&AEE and Test & Evaluation Establishment operations. Two modified **Cheyenne II**s are operated by the **Mauritanian Islamic Republic Air Wing** for coastal patrols. One or two Navajo, Chieftain and Cheyenne twins are in service with the air arms of **Argentina, Bolivia, Chile, Colombia, Dominica, Honduras, Israel, Kenya, Nigeria, Panama, Peru, Spain** (designated **E.18** for the single PA-31P and **E.18B** for two PA-31Ts) and **Syria** (two Navajos operated for survey duties with civil registrations).

SPECIFICATION:

Piper PA-31-300 Navajo
Wing: span 40 ft 8 in (12.40 m); aspect ratio 7.23; area 229.00 sq ft (21.27 m2)
Fuselage and tail: length 32 ft 7.5 in (9.94 m); height 13 ft 0 in (3.96 m); tailplane span 18 ft 1.5 in (5.52 m); wheel track 13 ft 9 in (4.19 m)
Powerplant: two Textron Lycoming IO-540-M flat-six piston engines each rated at 300 hp (224 kW)
Weights: empty 3,744 lb (1698 kg); maximum take-off 6,200 lb (2812 kg)
Fuel and load: internal fuel 190 US gal (719 litres); external fuel none

Speed: maximum level speed 'clean' at sea level 197 kt (227 mph; 365 km/h); maximum cruising speed at 6,400 ft (1950 m) 185 kt (213 mph; 343 km/h); economical cruising speed at 14,600 ft (4450 m) 171 kt (197 mph; 317 km/h)
Range: range 1,107 kt (1,275 miles; 2052 km) at maximum cruising speed or 1,346 nm (1,550 miles; 2494 km) at economical cruising speed
Performance: maximum rate of climb 1,670 ft (509 m) per minute; service ceiling 16,600 ft (5060 m); take-off run 1,010 ft (308 m) at maximum take-off weight; take-off distance to 50 ft (15 m) 2,130 ft (646 m) at maximum take-off weight; landing distance from 50 ft (15 m) 2150 ft (655 m) at normal landing weight; landing run 1,725 ft (526 m) at normal landing weight

The Royal Air Force's quartet of PA-31-350 Navajo Chieftains is operated by the A&AEE at Boscombe Down, and T&TE at Llanbedr or West Freugh.

The more refined PA-31T Cheyenne is one of several types in service with Escuadrón de Transporte 214 of the Colombian air force.

Piper PA-34 Seneca/PA-44 Seminole

The six/seven-seat **PA-34 Seneca** was essentially a twin-engined PA-32. Piper then developed the **PA-34 Seneca II** with Continental TSIO-360-E engines, plus Bendix RDR-160 radar. Senecas have achieved limited military use and the major user is the **Brazilian air force**, which purchased 12 EMBRAER-manufactured **EMB-810C Seneca II**s (**U-7**s), followed by 20 **U-7A**s incorporating Robertson STOL modifications. Other operators of the Seneca are **Argentina**'s National Civil Aviation Institute with three (assembled by Chincul), **Colombia, Costa Rica** and **Pakistan** (No. 41 Sqn at Chaklala). **Colombia** also operates a single **PA-44 Seminole**, which is in effect a twin-engined T-tailed PA-28R and is generally similar to the Seneca.

SPECIFICATION

Piper PA-34 Seneca II
Wing: span 38 ft 10.75 in (11.85 m); aspect ratio 7.4; area 208.70 sq ft (19.39 m2)
Fuselage and tail: length 28 ft 7.5 in (8.73 m); height 9 ft 10.75 in (3.02 m); tailplane span 13 ft 6.75 in (4.14 m); wheel track 11 ft 1.25 in (3.38 m)
Powerplant: two Teledyne Continental TSIO-360-E flat-four turbocharged piston engines each rated at 200 hp (149 kW)
Weights: empty 2,857 lb (1296 kg); maximum take-off 4,570 lb (2073 kg)
Fuel and load: internal fuel 558 lb (253 kg) plus provision for 180 lb (82 kg) of auxiliary fuel in two 15-US gal (57-litre) wing tanks; external fuel none
Speed: maximum level speed 'clean' at 12,000 ft

(3660 m) 195 kt (225 mph; 361 km/h); maximum cruising speed at 20,000 ft (6100 m) and 75 per cent power 190 kt (219 mph; 352 km/h)
Range: with standard fuel and 45 minute reserves 546 nm (629 miles; 1012 km)

Performance: maximum rate of climb at sea level 1,340 ft (408 m) per minute; certificated ceiling 25,000 ft (7620 m); take-off run 900 ft (274 m) at maximum take-off weight; take-off run to 50 ft (15 m) 1,240 ft (378 m) at maximum take-off weight

This is a U-7A in service with 2ᵃ ELO (naval co-operation squadron) of the Brazilian air force.

Piper PA-38-112 Tomahawk

Last of the primary trainers to bear the Piper name, the **PA-38-112 Tomahawk** was designed specifically for pilot training and was certified in December 1977. Production totalled 2,531 when the last Tomahawk was delivered in 1982. The Tomahawk is a cantilever low-wing monoplane with fixed, wide-track tricycle undercarriage, and a T-tail (the prototype originally flew in low-tailed configuration). The roomy cabin seats two, side-by-side, with good all-round view and dual controls standard. Piper offered several Special Training Packages

with different instruments fit, and introduced the **Tomahawk II** in 1981 with minor equipment changes. The **Indonesian naval air arm** (TNI-AL) is the sole military customer, having acquired five Tomahawks to serve in Skwadron Udara 400 at Surabaya.

SPECIFICATION

Piper PA-38-112 Tomahawk II
Wing: span 34 ft 0 in (10.36 m); aspect ratio 9.27; area 124.70 sq ft (11.59 m2)
Fuselage and tail: length 23 ft 1.25 in (7.04 m); height 9 ft 0.75 in (2.76 m); tailplane span 10 ft 6 in (3.20 m); wheel track 10 ft 0 in (3.05 m); wheel base 4 ft 9 in (1.45 m)
Powerplant: one Textron Lycoming O-235-L2C flat-four piston engine rated at 112 hp (83.5 kW)
Weights: empty 1,128 lb (512 kg); maximum take-off 1,670 lb (757 kg)
Fuel and load: internal fuel 32 US gal (121 litres); external fuel none; maximum ordnance none
Speed: never exceed speed 138 kt (159 mph; 256 km/h); maximum level speed 'clean' at sea level 109 kt

(126 mph; 202 km/h); maximum cruising speed at 7,100 ft (2165 m) 108 kt (124 mph; 200 km/h); economical cruising speed at 10,500 ft (3200 m) 100 kt (115 mph; 185 km/h)
Range: 468 nm (539 miles; 867 km)
Performance: maximum rate of climb at sea level 718 ft (219 m) per minute; service ceiling 13,000 ft (3960 m); take-off run 820 ft (250 m) at maximum take-off weight; take-off distance to 50 ft (15 m) 1,460 ft (445 m) at maximum take-off weight; landing distance from 50 ft (15 m) 1,544 ft (471 m) at normal landing weight; landing run 707 ft (215 m) at normal landing weight

Promavia Jet Squalus F1300 NGT

Promavia SA
Chaussée de Fleurus 181, B-6041 Gosselies-Aéroport
Belgium

Plans to launch production of the **Promavia Jet Squalus** in Portugal (by OGMA) to meet the needs of the Portuguese air force and other agencies were put into abeyance in 1991, leaving this basic jet trainer with no customers to date. Based on designs by Stelio Frati as an extension of his **F400 Cobra** prototype flown in Italy in 1960, the Jet Squalus (Shark) prototype was built by General Avia in Milan by arrangement with Promavia SA and with financial aid from the Belgian government, and first flew on 30 April 1987.

The Jet Squalus was designed to cover all stages of flying training, comprising *ab initio*, primary, basic and part of the advanced syllabus. The low-wing configuration features side-mounted intakes and side-by-side seating in Martin-Baker Mk 11 lightweight ejection seats, and design work has been completed to provide a pressurised cockpit if required. The prototype flew on 30 April 1987, powered by a TFE109-1 turbofan rated at 1,330 lb st (5.92 kN), and a second prototype was prepared for testing in 1991 with an uprated TFE109-3 and provision for external stores on four wing stations for weapons training or light tactical missions.

As part of its marketing effort, Promavia has proposed use of the Jet Squalus in an

AWS 'air ward system' in four versions: maritime surveillance/search and rescue (**AWS-MS/SAR**) with SLAR and VHF-FM com radio; photo-reconnaissance (**AWS-R**) with VLF/Omega R/Nav; weapons training and armed patrol (**AWS-W**); and target-towing (**AWS-TT**). The derived **ATTA 3000**, with an EFIS-cockpit and stepped tandem seats, was offered, unsuccessfully, to the US Air Force and US Navy as a JPATS contender. An agreement to transfer manufacturing to Saskatoon in Canada (pending its potential selection as a T-33 replacement for the Canadian air force) has been superseded by an agreement with Russian aerospace giant Mikoyan, despite the latter organisation already having several other trainer projects under development.

SPECIFICATION

Promavia Jet Squalus F1300 NGT
Wing: span 9.04 m (29 ft 8 in); aspect ratio 6.0; area 13.58 m2 (146.17 sq ft)
Fuselage and tail: length 9.36 m (30 ft 8.5 in); height 3.60 m (11 ft 9.75 in); tailplane span 3.80 m (12 ft 5.5 in); wheel track 3.59 m (11 ft 9.25 in); wheel base 3.58 m (11 ft 9 in)
Powerplant: one Garrett TFE109-3 turbofan rated at

1,600 lb st (7.12 kN)
Weights: empty equipped 1400 kg (3,086 lb); normal take-off 2100 kg (4,630 lb) for aerobatics; maximum take-off 2400 kg (5,291 lb)
Fuel and load: internal fuel 720 litres (190 US gal); external fuel none; maximum ordnance 600 kg (1,323 lb)
Speed: (with TFE109-1 engine) never exceed speed 345 kt (397 mph; 638 km/h); maximum level speed 'clean' at 14,000 ft (4265 m) 280 kt (322 mph; 519 km/h); cruising speed at optimum altitude 260 kt (299 mph; 482 km/h)
Range: (with TFE109-1 engine) ferry range 1,000 nm (1,152 miles; 1854 km)
Performance: (with TFE109-1 engine) maximum rate

Only two Jet Squalus have been completed since the first prototype flew in 1987. The design has competed for military and civil (airline) trainer orders, but so far to no avail.

of climb at sea level 2,500 ft (762 m) per minute; service ceiling 37,000 ft (11275 m); take-off run 1,100 ft (335 m); take-off distance to 50 ft (15 m) 1,300 ft (396 m) landing distance from 50 ft (15 m) 1,400 ft (427 m) landing run 1,200 ft (366 m)
g **limits:** -3.5 to +7 for aerobatics or +2.8 sustained at 10,000 ft (3050 m)

PZL Mielec M-18 Dromader

WSK-PZL Mielec
ul.Ludowego Wojska Polskiego 3
PL-39-300 Mielec, Poland

The **PZL Mielec M-18 Dromader** (Dromedary) was developed with the co-operation of Rockwell International and incorporates some components from the Thrush Commander S-2R. The M-18 is a low-wing, single-seat agricultural aircraft with fixed tailwheel undercarriage and is powered by a 746-kW (1,000-hp) PZL-Kalisz (licence-built Shvetsov) ASz-621R nine-cylinder supercharged air-cooled radial engine. In its original form, the M-18 first flew in Poland on 27 August 1976, and more than 600 have been built, including some developed as two-seat **M-18A** versions, primarily for export. Attrition of the fleet of Grumman Ag-Cats used for crop spraying by 359 Mira of the **Greek air force** led to the selection in 1983 of the

Dromader, a batch of 30 being ordered to augment the Ag-Cats. Based at Dekelia, and detached locally, the Dromaders are used also in the fire-fighting role, for which appropriate systems are available.

The PZL M-18 Dromader was chiefly built for export and is in widespread civil use, not only in Eastern Europe but also in such unlikely places as Chile, China, Morocco, Nicaragua, Swaziland and Venezuela. In military service, it is confined to the 30 aircraft purchased by the Greek air force, 29 of which are still active. This Elliniki Aeroporia (Greek air force) example displays the dromadary logo worn by most M-18s.

PZL I-22 Iryda

Just as it had preferred to procure its own trainer (the TS-11 Iskra) rather than take up the Czech L-29 adopted by every other Warsaw Pact nation, **Poland** opted to design an indigenous trainer rather than follow the overall Warsaw Pact line and adopt the L-29's successor, the L-39 Albatros.

The **PZL I-22 Iryda** (Iridium) was designed by Warsaw's Instytut Lotnictwa to succeed both the TS-11 and the LiM-6 (a Polish-built MiG-17 derivative used for advanced, tactical pilot training). About 50

are required to equip the Aviation Academy at Deblin, and the 45 LPSz-B at Babimost. Others will serve with front-line units as communications aircraft, for instrument and spin training and for standardisation. The I-22 will be able to train fast-jet pilots for air combat, ground attack and reconnaissance, and is designed to have a measure of night/all-weather capability.

Engineers from various research institutes formed a team under the leadership of Dr Eng Alfred Baron. The Warsaw team was responsible for initial design, and collaborated with WSK-Mielec for production and some flight test work. The prototype made its maiden flight on 5 March 1985,

but was lost in a crash on 31 January 1987. Four more prototypes were built and all were in flight test by late 1991, when an initial order for nine pre-production aircraft was announced at the Poznan air show.

Very similar in configuration to the Dassault-Breguet/Dornier Alpha Jet, the I-22 is a high-wing monoplane of typical light alloy construction. The wing, of laminar-flow aerofoil section, has 20° sweepback on the leading edge and incorporates conventional ailerons and single-slotted flaps at the trailing edge. The fuselage, of semi-monocoque construction, includes a door-type airbrake in each side of the upper rear surface, and has one non-afterburning turbojet engine

pod-mounted on each lower side of its central structure. The tandem-seat accommodation is pressurised and air conditioned and the instructor's rear seat is elevated by 40 cm (15.75 in) to provide a good forward view. Both crew members have rocket-powered ejection seats that can be operated at zero altitude and at speeds exceeding 81 kt (150 km/h; 93 mph). Full blind flying instrumentation is standard, and avionics can include VHF, UHF, ADF marker beacon receiver, radar altimeter radio compass and/or other equipment to individual customer requirements.

The main hydraulic system operates the undercarriage, flaps, airbrake, tailplane incidence, brake chute deployment and braking. Emergency undercarriage and flap extension is pneumatic, as is canopy opening. Engine bleed air is used for air conditioning, *g* suit operation, canopy demisting and de-icing of the engine intakes.

The I-22's light attack capability has been evaluated by the second prototype, which carries a 23-mm twin-barrelled cannon pod with 200 rounds on the underfuselage centreline. The aircraft's four underwing pylons are each stressed to a maximum loading of 500 kg (1,102 lb); in addition, the inboard pair is 'plumbed' for the optional carriage of 380-litre (83.6-Imp gal) drop tanks.

The Iryda can carry a maximum external stores load of 1200 kg (2,646 lb), and can also fulfil the light close-support task. The airframe is rugged and robust, and is designed to be quickly and easily repaired and resistant to battle damage. It is already stressed for the carriage of greater external loads, and for the fitting of more powerful engines than the PZL-5 (formerly SO-3W22) turbojets presently used.

The first two standard (PZL-5-powered) I-22s (serialled 103 and 105) were delivered to the air force on 24 October 1992, although problems with winterisation trials delayed full service clearance until November. These were followed by three further aircraft by early 1994, all of which are in service at the Deblin air academy. Four K-15-powered I-22M92s are due to be delivered by the end of 1994 and some reports suggest that at least one of these will be fitted with improved Sagem avionics. The PZL-5 engines are acknowledged as being inadequate for some roles, and Mielec is examining the possibilities of fitting a number of alternative powerplants, including the indigenous 17.69-kN (3,968-lb st) D-18A or K-15, and foreign engines. The first K-15-engined aircraft (SP-PWD, the fourth prototype), designated **I-22M92**, first flew on 22 December 1992. PZL next flew the 3,370-lb (15-kN) thrust Rolls-Royce Viper 545-powered **I-22M93V** (again SP-PWD) on 24 April 1994. The M93 is seen primarily as an export version, with new Sagem avionics (including INS, HUD, HOTAS and colour MFDs), and first flew with the new equip-

ment on 24 May 1994. K-15-powered upgraded aircraft are designated **I-22M93**.

Dedicated combat versions have also been proposed. The two-seat **M-95** reconnaissance/close-support version features a new supercritical wing, 30-mm integral cannon, reprofiled nose and tail, and eight underwing hardpoints. It would be fitted with foreign engines such as the Rolls-Royce Viper, General Electric J85 or Larzac 04P20. A similar single-seat fighter/attack version, fitted with wingtip missile rails, is designated **M-97S**. A second single-seat variant, the **M-97MS**, resembles the M-97S but is a simplified version, lacking a ventral gunpack and some avionics systems. It is likely that all these versions would be powered, at least initially, by 3,968-lb (17.65-kN) D-18A engines. Developed to compete with the now-defunct Skorpion, the **M-99 Orkan** single-seat battlefield support aircraft features a larger wing (with tip-mounted missile rails), larger engines and a forward fuselage section similar to that of the M-97MS.

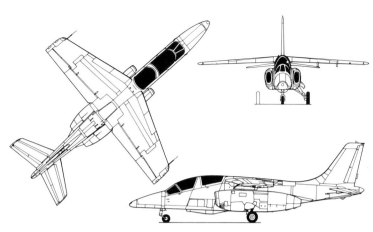

PZL I-22 Iryda

SPECIFICATION

PZL I-22 Iryda
Wing: span 9.60 m (31 ft 6 in); aspect ratio 4.6; area 19.92 m² (214.42 sq ft)
Fuselage and tail: length 13.22 m (43 ft 4.5 in); height 4.30 m (14 ft 1.25 in); tailplane span 4.90 m (16 ft 1 in); wheel track 2.71 m (8 ft 10.75 in); wheel base 4.92 m (16 ft 1.75 in)
Powerplant: two PZL Rzeszow PZL-5 SO-3W22 turbojets each rated at 10.79 kN (2,425 lb st)
Weights: empty 4700 kg (10,361 lb); normal take-off 6650 kg (14,660 lb); maximum take-off 6900 kg (15,512 lb)
Fuel and load: internal fuel 1974 kg (4,352 lb); external fuel up to 600 kg (1,323 lb) in two 400-litre (106-US gal) drop tanks; maximum ordnance 1200 kg (2,646 lb)
Speed: maximum level speed 'clean' at 5000 m (16,405 ft) 840 km/h (453 kt; 522 mph); maximum cruising speed at 5000 m (16,405 ft) 720 km/h (389 kt; 447 mph); economical cruising speed at 5000 m (16,405 ft) 570 km/h (308 kt; 354 mph)
Range: ferry range 900 km (485 nm; 559 miles); range 420 km (226 nm; 261 miles) with maximum ordnance
Performance: maximum rate of climb at sea level 1500 m (4,921 ft) per minute; service ceiling 11000 m

(36,090 ft); take-off run 785 m (2,575 ft) at normal take-off weight; take-off distance to 15 m (50 ft) 1260 m (4,135 ft) at normal take-off weight; landing distance from 15 m (50 ft) 1375 m (4,512 ft) at normal landing weight with brake chute; landing run 750 m (2,461 ft) at normal landing weight with brake chute
g limits: -4 to +8

While the Iryda has spent a long time under development, the first PZL-5-engined examples are now entering service at the Polish air force academy in Deblin. These will soon be joined by higher-powered I-22M92s.

PZL Mielec **TS-11 Iskra**

The **PZL Mielec TS-11 Iskra** (Spark) was designed to meet a Warsaw Pact specification for a jet-powered basic and advanced trainer. The prototype made its maiden flight on 5 February 1960. It lost an evaluation against the Czech Aero L-29, after which the latter aircraft was selected for production for the USSR and most of its clients. Poland, with its own aircraft industry to support, chose to develop the Iskra for its own use, and the aircraft entered quantity production in 1963. The first Iskra was formally handed over to the **Polish air force** in March 1963, and the type entered service in 1964.

A mid-wing monoplane of all-metal construction, the TS-11 has a pod-and-boom type fuselage structure, adopted to raise the tail unit well clear of the efflux of the turbojet engine, mounted within the fuselage aft of the cockpit. The instructor and pupil are in tandem on lightweight ejection seats, the instructor's (rear) seat being slightly raised, and both positions are enclosed by a one-piece canopy which is hinged at its rear edge and is jettisonable. The retractable tricycle landing gear has a pneumatic emergency extension system, and underwing hardpoints allow for the carriage of training weapons. Fully aerobatic, the Iskra is stressed to g limits of +8/-4.

The early production Iskra was powered initially by the Polish-designed H-10 turbojet

The Indian Air Force's Air Academy at Hakimpet (formerly the Fighter Training Wing) is the only TS-11 operator outside its native Poland. The oldest of these Iskras are approaching their 20th anniversary. Competition among Western manufacturers, particularly BAe and Dassault, to replace them is now hotting up.

of 7.65 kN (1,720 lb) thrust, pending availability of the intended 9.81-kN (2,205-lb) thrust SO-1 turbojet designed by the Instytut Lotnictwa and manufactured by WSK-PZL Rzeszow; from the late 1960s, the SO-1 was often replaced by the improved SO-3 of similar thrust rating.

There have been a confusing number of sub-variants, including the **Iskra-Bis A** with two underwing hardpoints and the **Iskra-Bis B** with four. A single-seat reconnaissance version was designated **Iskra-Bis C** and first flew in June 1972, but was not built in large numbers. At one time the single-seat prototype was known as the **Iskra 200**. The **Iskra-Bis D** or **Iskra 200SB** was a two-seat trainer able to carry a wider range of weapons, and 50 of these were exported to **India** between October 1975 and June 1976 for advanced flying training (unarmed) with the Air Force Academy at Hakimpet. At least five have been

lost in spinning and engine-related (flame-out) accidents.

Production of the Iskra was halted in 1979, after about 500 Iskras had been built, then resumed in 1982. The only variant produced after 1982 was the **Iskra-Bis DF**. This was a dedicated reconnaissance trainer with an AFA-39 camera in each air intake fairing and one in the rear cockpit floor. The 23-mm cannon in the starboard forward fuselage was retained, along with its associated camera gun, and four underwing

pylons. Avionics include an RS6106 VHF, and ALR-1603 radio compass.

Six Iskra Bis DFs have been converted to **TS-11R** configuration with weather radar in a reshaped nose (and a display in the backseat) and three Russian AFA-39 cameras. These replaced ageing SBLim-2As (recce-configured Polish-built MiG-15UTIs) with the navy's 7th Regiment at Siemirowice. Iskras remain in Polish air force service with 58 LPSz at Deblin, 60 LPSz at Radom and 66 LPSz at Tomaszow Mazowieckie.

PZL TS-11 Iskra

SPECIFICATION

PZL Mielec TS-11 Iskra-bis B
Wing: span 10.06 m (33 ft 0 in); aspect ratio 5.71; area 17.50 m² (188.37 sq ft)
Fuselage and tail: length 11.17 m (36 ft 7.75 in); height 3.50 m (11 ft 5.5 in); tailplane span 3.84 m (12 ft 7.25 in); wheel track 3.48 m (11 ft 5 in); wheel base 3.44 m (11 ft 3.5 in)
Powerplant: one IL SO-3 turbojet rated at 9.81 kN (2,205 lb st)
Weights: empty 2560 kg (5,644 lb); normal take-off

3800 kg (8,377 lb); maximum take-off 3840 kg (8,465 lb)
Fuel and load: internal fuel 1200 litres (317 US gal); external fuel none; maximum ordnance 400 kg (882 lb)
Speed: never exceed speed 750 km/h (405 kt; 466 mph); maximum level speed 'clean' at 5000 m (16,405 ft) 720 km/h (414 kt; 477 mph); cruising speed at optimum altitude 600 km/h (324 kt; 373 mph)
Range: standard range 1250 km (674 nm; 776 miles)
Performance: maximum rate of climb at sea level 888 m (2,913 ft) per minute; climb to 6000 m (19,685 ft) in 9 minutes 36 seconds; service ceiling 11000 m (36,090 ft); take-off run 700 m (2,296 ft) at normal take-off weight; take-off distance to 15 m (50 ft) 1190 m (3,904 ft) at normal take-off weight; landing distance from 15 m (50 ft) 1110 m (3.642 ft) at normal landing weight; landing run 650 m (2,132 ft) at normal landing weight
g limits: -4 to +8

PZL Mielec (Antonov) **An-28 'Cash'**

The **An-28** was derived from the Antonov An-14 (described separately) and was originally known as the **An-14M**. The prototype retained little more than the basic configuration of the An-14 and similar high-lift devices, double-slotted flaps and single-slotted ailerons. The An-14M prototype made its maiden flight in September 1969; it had a retractable undercarriage, but this was felt to impose an unacceptable cost and weight penalty and subsequent aircraft had simpler non-retractable levered undercarriage units. Changes were sufficient for a new designation of An-28 to be allocated. Development was protracted and production was assigned to PZL Mielec in 1978, the first Polish-built aircraft making its maiden flight on 22 July 1984.

The An-28 has double the capacity of the earlier aircraft, accommodating two pilots and up to 17 passengers, or a 2000-kg (4,409-lb) payload. The cabin is fitted with an internal cargo-handling hoist of 500-kg (1,102-lb) capacity. The aircraft incorporates several novel stall-protection devices, including tailplane slats which improve high angle-of-attack handling and also prevent ice from collecting on the tailplanes themselves if the normal anti-icing system fails. If an engine fails, a spoiler automatically opens in front of the opposite aileron, reducing wing drop.

Most production has been for civilian customers, although three **An-28B1R Bryza**s have been delivered to the Polish air force for SAR duties. These feature improved avionics, GPS, Doppler nav, ventral SRN-441XA search radar, flares, dinghy and stretchers. The air force has a requirement for eight, and also operates a small number of transport An-28s.

SPECIFICATION

PZL Mielec (Antonov) An-28 'Cash'
Wing: span 22.063 m (72 ft 4.5 in); aspect ratio 12.25; area 39.72 m² (427.56 sq ft)
Fuselage and tail: length 13.10 m (42 ft 11.75 in); height 4.90 m (16 ft 1 in); tailplane span 5.14 m (16 ft 10.25 in); wheel track 3.405 m (11 ft 2 in); wheel base 4.354 m (14 ft 3.5 in)
Powerplant: two WSK-PZL Rzeszów (Glushenkov) TWD-10B turboprops each rated at 716 kW (960 shp)
Weights: empty equipped 3900 kg (8,598 lb); maximum take-off 6500 kg (14,330 lb)
Fuel and load: internal fuel 1529 kg (3,371 lb); external fuel none; maximum payload 2000 kg (4,409 lb)

Speed: never exceed speed 390 km/h (210 kt; 242 mph); maximum level speed 'clean' and maximum cruising speed at 3000 m (9,845 ft) 350 km/h (188 kt; 217 mph); economical cruising speed at 3000 m (9,845 ft) 335 km/h (181 kt; 208 mph)
Range: range 1365 km (736 nm; 848 miles) with a 1000-kg (2,205-lb) payload and maximum fuel, or 560 km (302 nm; 348 miles) with maximum payload
Performance: maximum rate of climb at sea level

500 m (1,640 ft) per minute; service ceiling more than 6000 m (19,685 ft); take-off run 260 m (853 ft) at maximum take-off weight; take-off distance to 10.7 m (35 ft) 360 m (1,180 ft) at maximum take-off weight; landing distance from 10.7 m (35 ft) 315 m (1,035 ft) at normal landing weight; landing run 170 m (558 ft) at normal landing weight
g limits: +3

Alongside its naval SAR-configured 'Bryzas', the Polish air force operates a small number of standard transport An-28s.

PZL Swidnik (Mil) **Mi-2 'Hoplite'**

PZL Swidnik SA ul.Przodowników Pracy 1, 21-045 Swidnik k/Lublina, Poland

The **PZL Swidnik Mi-2**, which has the NATO reporting name **'Hoplite'**, derives from the Soviet Mil Design Bureau, as indicated by the 'Mi-2' in its designation. At first intended as a replacement for the Mil Mi-1 and flown initially during September 1961, two prototypes were completed and flying before, in January 1964, an agreement was concluded with the Polish government under which PZL at Swidnik was given full responsibility for the development, manufacture and marketing of this helicopter. Following licence-production of 1,700 Mil-1 'Hare' Soviet helicopters built from 1955, the first Polish-built Mi-2 made its maiden flight on 4 November 1965, the first of over 5,000 built at the Swidnik factory.

Of conventional pod-and-boom configuration, with three-bladed main and two-bladed anti-torque tail rotors, the Mi-2 has twin-turbine powerplant mounted above the cabin, non-retractable tricycle landing gear, and a cabin that seats a pilot and up to eight passengers in an air-conditioned environment.

Seats are easily removable to permit the carriage of up to 700 kg (1,543 lb) of cargo and, in an ambulance role, the cabin can accommodate four stretchers and a medical attendant, or two stretchers and two seated casualties. For freight lifting, an external cargo hook of 800-kg (1,764-lb) capacity can be installed, this weight representing the Mi-2's maximum payload.

PZL not only licence-built the Mil Mi-2 but also embarked on an ambitious programme of development and modification to improve the basic helicopter and equip it for other roles. Dedicated air ambulance, agricultural, survey and TV relay versions were built, as well as a number of specific military variants.

Mil Mi-2Ts with dual controls serve as trainers, and **Mi-2R**s have a 120-kg (264-lb) capacity rescue winch, while more offensive variants include the **Mi-2US**, **Mi-2URN** and **Mi-2URP**. The Mi-2US sports a single NS-23KM cannon mounted on the port side of the cabin, below door and floor level, fed from an ammunition box in the cabin. This is aimed by the pilot, using a collimator-type PKV gunsight. It can also carry vestigial stub pylons for four 7.62-mm PK machine-guns.

Unarmed Mi-2s operate alongside Polish Mi-8/-17 units, while armed variants serve with the air force's two Mi-24 attack regiments.

Two more 7.62-mm machine-guns (each with 500 rounds) can be pintle-mounted in the rear windows.

The Mi-2URN was developed in 1973 and retains the NS-23 cannon, and carries two 57-mm Mars 2 rocket pods instead of the pylon-mounted machine-guns. The 1976-vintage Mi-2URP is similar, but carries up to four 9M14M Malyutka (AT-3 'Sagger') anti-tank missiles on its pylons. The **Mil Mi-2CH** is an unidentified military sub-type used by the Polish air force, while the **Mil Mi-2RM** is a naval variant. Improved **Mi-2B** versions are also available, with a revised electrical system and advanced navaids.

Some Warsaw Pact air forces may have used numerical designations for their Mi-2 sub-types. East Germany certainly used the designation **Variant 56** for one sub-type, **Variant 55** for the maritime version, and **Variant 51** for a reconnaissance sub-type. Designations for EW and artillery-spotting versions remain unknown.

In the late 1970s, PZL Swidnik, in conjunction with the Allison Division of General Motors in the USA, developed an export version of the Mil Mi-2 fitted with two Allison turboshaft engines. Given the names **Kania** or **Kitty Hawk**, they were generally similar to the PZL Swidnik Mi-2, being conversions of production airframes. The first (SP-PSA) was flown on 3 June 1979 and was intended, like the standard Mi-2, to fulfil a variety of roles. It could accommodate a pilot and a maximum of nine passengers or, alternatively, pilot and co-pilot plus eight passengers, and the cabin seats were removable to allow use in the agricultural or air ambulance roles. Reconfigured, it could carry up to 800 kg (1,764 lb) of cargo, some externally slung. The number ultimately converted (to the **Kania Model 1**) is believed

to have totalled four prototypes plus half a dozen definitive aircraft.

In August 1978, PZL Swidnik concluded an agreement with the Spitfire Helicopter Company of the US allowing them to market a modified version of the Kania as the **Spitfire Taurus**. This differed primarily from the Polish version by introducing uprated Allison 250-C28 turboshafts, each with a take-off rating of 373 kW (500 shp)

fed by a large common intake, and having revised nose contours and a ventral fin. The company has since gone out of business.

More than 5,250 Mil Mi-2s had been built by the time production was suspended in 1991, pending PZL's 1992 privatisation. Mi-2s (but no Kanias) have been exported to a number of military customers, and remain in service in **Bulgaria** (14), **Cuba** (two for liaison), **Czech** and **Slovak Republics**

(38), **Hungary** (31), **Nicaragua** (two), **Poland** (113), **Romania** (six), **CIS** (about 750) and **Syria** (20).

Ethiopia, Iraq, Lesotho, Libya and North Korea have been quoted as Mi-2 operators, but none is believed to operate the aircraft now. East Germany took delivery of 44, and the surviving 36 were handed over to the Luftwaffe on reunification but were not taken into service.

PZL Swidnik **W-3 Sokól**

Although developed from the Mil Mi-2, the **W-3 Sokól** (Falcon) is a new design, retaining the configuration of the Hoplite' but with larger overall dimensions and extensive aerodynamic and structural changes. The first of five prototypes made its maiden flight on 16 November 1979, and the second, incorporating further changes, on 6 May 1982. Production began in 1985.

The aircraft has a new four-bladed fully-articulated main rotor, with tapered tips and a pendular Saloman-type vibration absorber. Bladder tanks below the floor give a combined capacity of 1700 litres (374 Imp gal) and there is provision for a 1100-litre (242-Imp gal) auxiliary tank. The cabin accommodates 12 in three-abreast rows, with access via sliding doors on each side of the cabin.

The first batch of 50 was completed in 1991, and another batch of 20 is under construction. Military customers include **Myanmar** (12) and **Poland**. Operating units comprise the navy (six), the 47th Helicopter Training Regiment at Nowe Miasto (six), the 36th Special Air Transport Regiment at Warsaw/Okecie (one), and the Straz (a paramilitary fire brigade) at Bemow (three).

Four of the Polish navy's aircraft are designated **W-3R Anakonda**, with six flotation bags and a rescue winch. They have an extra window in the lower half of each flight deck door, and have a sealed watertight cabin. The type was evaluated against the Mi-14PS in 1989, resulting in a 1992 order for 25 aircraft. Those delivered so far (two W-3s and the W-3Rs) serve with the 18 Eskandra. The **W-3U-1 Alligator** is a proposed ASW version. The unflown **W-3 Sokól-Long** has engines uprated to 1,000 shp (746 kW), and a stretched cabin seating 14 fully-equipped troops. Development was discontinued in early 1993, but plans for an EW variant remain.

At least one W-3 has been flown with a

GSh-23L cannon pack mounted along the port lower fuselage, and with an undernose EO package similar to that of the Mi-24V 'Hind-E'. The AT-6 ATGM command guidance radome is mounted in the nose. Outriggers carry two 10-round 80-mm rocket pods and four AT-6 'Spiral' missile launch tubes. In April 1993, PZL received an export order for a similar armed version, the **W-3 Huzar**, with an undernose 20-mm low-recoil cannon (in an AH-64-type mounting) and with a stabilised roof-mounted TV/IR sight for the laser-guided Grot missile. Provision is made for a laser rangefinder and a helmet-mounted sight. Alternative weapons can include the 16-round Mars-2 rocket pod, ZR-8 four-round rocket packs or 9M32M Strzala (SA-7 'Grail') AAMs.

In conjunction with Denel's guided weapons subsidiary, Kentron, PZL offered an export Huzar variant with a weapons system based largely on that of the CSH-2 Rooivalk attack helicopter. Armament included the ZT-3 laser-guided ATM, a turreted 20-mm cannon, and rocket pods. However, the agreement was terminated in

mid-1994, and PZL is continuing to examine both Western and Russian ATGMs, such as the 9M120 Vikhr missile.

SPECIFICATION

PZL Swidnik W-3 Sokól
Rotor System: rotor diameter 15.70m (51 ft 6 in); rotor disc area 193.6 m² (2,083.8 sq ft)
Fuselage and tail: length, fuselage 14.21 m (46 ft 7½ in); height, to top of rotor head 4.12 m (13 ft 6¼ in); wheel track 3.40 m (1 ft 2 in)
Powerplant: two WSK-PZL Rzeszów TWD-10W turboshafts, rated at 671-kW (900-shp) for take-off
Weights: minimum basic empty 3300 kg (7,275 lb); normal take-off 6400 kg (14,110 lb)
Fuel and load: maximum payload 2100 kg (4,630 lb)
Speed: never exceed speed 145 kt (270km/h; 167 mph); maximum cruising speed 127 kt (235 km/h; 146 mph)
Range: with auxiliary fuel, no reserves 661 nm (1225 km/761 miles)
Performance: service ceiling 4650 m (15,250 ft); hovering ceiling, in ground effect 2500 m (8,200 ft), out of ground effect 660 m (2,165 ft); maximum rate of climb, at sea level 492 m (1,615 ft) per minute

Left: The W-3 Sokól entered service with the Straz unit of the Polish Ministry of the Interior, near Warsaw.

Right: The sole Bendix-King avionics-equipped W-3SP Anakonda Special began tests in mid-1993 at Bemowo.

PZL Warszawa-Okecie **PZL-104 Wilga**

PZL Warszawa-Okecie
Aleja Krakowska 110/114,
PL-00-971 Warsaw, Poland

The original **PZL 104 Wilga** (Thrush) prototype, powered by a 134-kW (180-hp) Narkiewicz WN-6 flat-six piston engine, first flew on 24 April 1962. It was intended to replace the Polish-built Yak-12 and its **PZL-101 Gawron** development. A cantilever high-wing monoplane with fixed tailwheel gear and an enclosed cabin, it was followed by the **Wilga 2P** and **Wilga CP**, powered by the 138-kW (185-hp) Narkiewicz WN-6RB2 and 168-kW (220-hp) Continental O-470-13A or O-470-L flat-six engines, respectively. The PZL 104 was offered initially in versions equipped for use as a four-seat passenger-carrying or liaison aircraft; for club flying, glider towing or parachuting; for agricultural use with a 500-litre (110-Imp gal) hopper for dust or liquid application; and as an air ambulance carrying pilot, doctor, two stretcher patients and medical equipment.

Following construction of a number of prototypes, the type entered production initially as the **Wilga 3A** club aircraft and the **Wilga 3S** air ambulance. In 1967 the design was revised with better cabin accommodation and improved landing gear, production beginning in 1968 of the **Wilga 35** which, powered by a 194-kW (260-hp) Ivchenko AI-14R engine, had flown for the

first time on 28 July 1967, and of the **Wilga 32** with a 172-kW (230-hp) Continental O-470-K flown on 12 September 1967. This last version was built under licence in Indonesia as the **Lipnur Gelatik 32** (Rice Bird), with a Continental O-470-R engine of similar output.

Developments of the Wilga 35 have included the multi-purpose Wilga 35M fitted with a 261-kW (360-hp) M-14P radial engine, flown in prototype form in 1990. A similar version, meeting US FAR Part 23 requirements, is designated the **Wilga 80**. The first of these flew on 30 May 1979. A more radical redesign, originally identified as the **Wilga 88**, has become the **PZL 105 Flamingo**. The Wilga 35 and revised 80 remained in production in 1993, by which time PZL had sold around 900 examples to countries around the world.

In an emergency, many civilian Wilgas would be impressed by the military and flown by reservists in the liaison, artillery-spotting, special forces insertion and even light attack roles. Some 15 Wilgas are also permanently on Polish air force charge, operating in the liaison role. Other military Wilgas serve in **Russia**, **Mongolia**, **Egypt** (10), and **Indonesia** (army and air force, totalling 24 Wilga 32s).

SPECIFICATION

PZL Warszawa PZL-104 Wilga 35
Wing: span 11.12 m (36 ft 5.75 in); aspect ratio 8.0; area 15.50 m² (166.85 sq ft)
Fuselage and tail: length 8.10 m (26 ft 6.75 in); height 2.96 m (9 ft 8.5 in); tailplane span 3.70 m (12 ft 1.75 in); wheel track 2.75 m (9 ft 0.75 in)
Powerplant: one PZL (Ivchenko) AI-14RA flat-six piston engine rated at 260 hp (194 kW)
Weights: empty equipped 870 kg (1,918 lb); maximum take-off 1300 kg (2,866 lb)
Fuel and load: internal fuel 195 litres (51.5 US gal); external fuel none
Speed: never exceed speed 279 km/h (150 kt; 173

mph); maximum cruising speed at optimum altitude 157 km/h (84 kt; 97 mph)
Range: 510 km (275 nm; 317 miles)
Performance: maximum rate of climb at sea level 276 m (905 ft) per minute; climb to 1000 m (3,280 ft) in 3 minutes 0 seconds; service ceiling 4040 m (13,250 ft); take-off run 121 m (397 ft) at maximum take-off weight on a grass runway

PZL Warszawa PZL-104 Wilga 80
generally similar to the PZL Warszawa PZL-104 Wilga 35 except in the following particulars:
Wing: span 11.13 m (36 ft 6.25 in)
Fuselage and tail: length 8.03 m (26 ft 4.25 in)
Powerplant: one PZL (Ivchenko) AI-14RA-KAF rated at 260 hp (194 kW)

The PZL-104 became the first aircraft to be licence-built in Indonesia when 10 were initially assembled by Lipnur, as the Gelatik, for the army.

PZL Warszawa-Okecie PZL-130/T Orlik/Turbo Orlik

The **PZL-130 Orlik** (Spotted Eaglet) primary and basic trainer was designed as the airframe component of an overall training system which also included a simulator and an electronic diagnosis system. A team under Andrzej Frydrychewicz began detail design of this tandem two-seat trainer in the autumn of 1983.

Of all-metal construction, the **PZL-130 Orlik** was a low-wing monoplane, the wing incorporating single-slotted trailing-edge flaps and Frise-type ailerons; the tricycle landing gear is retracted and lowered pneumatically, and powerplant consisted of a Vedeneyev M-14Pm radial engine driving a constant-speed propeller. Both wing and tail unit leading edges had provision for the installation of an anti-icing system, if required. Access to the cockpit was via the sideways-hinged one-piece canopy (jettisonable in flight), the pupil being seated forward and the instructor aft on electrically adjustable seats, with the instructor's raised slightly. Full dual controls were standard, as was heating and ventilation for the cockpit.

The Orlik represents the airborne component of what is known as the 'System 130', which includes the PZL-130 Profesor flight simulator from which the student gains initial familiarisation before taking to the air in the Orlik. The remaining component of System 130 is the PZL-130 Inspektor, intended to ensure maximum utilisation of the Orlik fleet by providing automatic diagnosis of engine and system faults. One other advanced feature of the Orlik is the use of easily-changed modular displays and instruments in the cockpits; this feature is intended to allow use of the aircraft as a flying simulator for a variety of aircraft. The Orlik is intended to serve for the full spectrum of civil and military training, ranging from preselection to aerobatics, and including air combat, air gunnery, ground attack and reconnaissance.

Construction of four airframes – one for static testing plus three flying prototypes – began in 1982, and the first aircraft (SP-PCA) flew on 12 October 1983, followed quickly by the second. However, the third aircraft did not fly until January 1985, and the two pre-production machines which followed did not take to the air until February 1988, owing to serious delays in deliveries of the 246-kW (330-hp) Vedeneyev M14PM nine-cylinder Soviet powerplant. By that time PZL was seriously looking for another engine, and one contender was the company-produced but less powerful Kalisz K8-AA, which took the underpowered second pre-production aircraft ('006') into the air in March 1988. Although testing continued over the next two years, and included an evaluation by the Polish air force, the piston-engined Orlik was abandoned in 1990.

Turboprop power

In 1984, while still awaiting supplies of the Vedeneyev M14PM engine, PZL commenced development of a turboprop-powered Orlik. Accordingly, SP-PCC, the third airframe (of six original piston-engined aircraft, one a static test airframe) was re-engined with a Pratt & Whitney PT6A-25A engine and reregistered SP-RCC. It made its maiden flight in this configuration on 13 July 1986, but was lost in a crash in January 1987. A seventh Orlik was flown with a 750-shp (560-kW) Motorlet M601E as the **PZL-130TM**, and an eighth (SP-WCA) with a 550-shp (415-kW) PT6A-25A as the **PZL-130T**. The ninth was built with a PT6A-62 as the **PZL-130TP**, and two more aircraft were built during 1991 with M601E and PT6A engines.

The Polish air force production trainer, the **PZL-130TB**, was derived from the PZL-130TM, and is powered by an M601E engine, although the fully aerobatic M601T is also available as an option. The wing is

increased in span and in incidence, lowering the nose in normal cruising flight. The ventral fin is redesigned, and double-slotted trailing-edge flaps are provided. The cockpit is closely related to that of the Su-22, and is covered by a canopy of revised shape. The prototype was rolled out in May 1991, and first flew on 18 September. The aircraft is fitted with East European avionics and indigenous LFK-K1 zero-70 (0 ft altitude, minimum 70 kt forward speed) ejection seats. Six underwing hardpoints are provided (inboard and centre stressed for loads of up to 160 kg/353 lb, outboard to 80 kg/176 lb) for bombs, Zeus 7.62-mm gun pods, 57-mm or 80-mm rocket pods, or even Strela IR-homing AAMs. Forty-eight have been ordered for the Polish air force.

Three similar versions are available for export, all equipped with Western avionics (to customer specification) and powered by Western engines. The **PZL-130TC** is the most potent, with a 950-shp (708-kW) Pratt & Whitney Canada PT6A-62 engine, Bendix King avionics and a Martin-Baker ejection seat, while the 750-shp (559-kW) PT6A-25C-powered **PZL-130TD** is equipped identically. The PZL-130TC first flew in early June 1993, after a delay reportedly due to the refusal of PZL test pilots to fly it on account of the new high-powered engine. The PZL-130TD followed in November of that year. The **PZL-130TE** is a proposed 'economy' export version, with no ejection seats, limited avionics and a 550-shp (410-kW) PT6A-25A engine. No export orders have yet been placed, although the aircraft has reportedly been evaluated by Israel and South Africa.

In late 1993, PZL applied for the Turbo-Orlik to be certified in the USA, and distributed by Illinois-based Cadmus (already PZL's general aviation distributor for North America). The PZL-130TC was the chosen version, but this variant was then grounded (in Poland) in October 1993, setting back the

flight test programme significantly. At firs this was believed to be the fault of th PT6A-62 engine, but PZL later admitted tha financial constraints on the leased turbo props largely had forced them to halt flying.

By mid-1994, nine PZL-130TBs had bee delivered to the Polish air force's 45 LED a Radom and 60 LPSz at Deblin. A further 1 aircraft are due to be delivered by the end c the year, and 15 pilots trained. Aircraft seri 009, the prototype PZL-130TB, has bee converted to a version similar to the PZL 130TC with new avionics and ejection seats designated **PZL-130TC1**, and it has bee suggested that similar improved version will comprise a portion of the air force's 4£ aircraft order.

SPECIFICATION

PZL Warszawa PZL-130TB Turbo Orlik
Wing: span 9.00 m (29 ft 6¼ in); aspect ratio 6.23; area 13 m² (139.93 sq ft)
Fuselage and tail: length 9.00 m (29 ft 6¼ in); heigh 3.53 m (11 ft 7 in); tailplane span 3.50 m (11 ft 5¾ in); wheel track 3.10 m (10 ft 2 in); wheel base 2.90 m (9 ft 6 in)
Powerplant: one Motorlet M601E turboprop, rated a 750 kW (560 hp)
Weights: empty equipped 1600 kg (3, 527 lb); norma take-off 2000 kg (4,409 lb) for aerobatics; maximum take-off 2700 kg (5,952 lb)
Fuel and load: internal fuel 504 litres (142.7 US gal), external fuel 340 litres (90 US gal)
Speed: maximum level speed 'clean' at optimum altitude 501 km/h (270 kt; 311 mph)
Range: with maximum fuel 970 km (523 nm; 602 miles)
Performance: maximum rate of climb at sea level 798 m (2,620 ft) per minute; service ceiling, TC only 10,060 m (33,000 ft); take-off run 222 m (729 ft) at normal take-off weight
g limits: -3 to +6 at normal take-off weight or -1.76 t +4.4 at maximum take-off weight

Left: Initial production Orliks for the Polish air force are powered by the Motorlet M601E.

Right: The PZL-130TC has been re-engined with a PT6A-62. At first, test pilots refused to fly with this radically new engine.

PZL Warszawa-Okecie PZL-230F Skorpion

The **PZL-230F** was designed to meet a Polish air force requirement for a small, agile battlefield attack (SABA) aircraft. Development began in 1987, when the aircraft was envisaged as being powered by a pair of turbojet engines. These were soon replaced by twin pusher Pratt & Whitney Canada PT6A-67A turboprops, and then replaced again by unspecified turbofans (possibly two 5,225-lb st/23.24-kN Pratt & Whitney Canada PW305s) mounted further apart. This engine configuration was demonstrated in the full-scale mock-up that was rolled out on 23 December 1992.

The mock-up differed in many ways from previous artist's impressions of the aircraft, with a higher-set cockpit and canard foreplanes, and twin inward-canted tailfins in place of the original single fin. The basic philosophy behind the **Skorpion** was to produce a highly manoeuvrable but relatively slow (600-650 km/h; 350-400 mph) aircraft,

capable of evading SAMs and of carrying a 2000-kg (4,409-lb) warload on its eight underwing weapons pylons. A fixed gun was also envisaged, perhaps a 25-mm GAU-12. PZL planned for a first flight in 1996, with deliveries following in 2000.

Development of the Skorpion was terminated in June 1994. A more likely SABA candidate is a single-seat attack version of the I-22 Iryda (described separately), but in September 1993 PZL unveiled a second advanced contender in the form of the **PZL Kobra**, powered by a pair of thrust-vectoring Polish-built D-18 turbofan engines.

A full-size wooden mock-up of the PZL-230F Skorpion was unveiled at the Okecie plant in early 1993. The canard-equipped, double-delta design is intended to carry a podded GAU-8 30-mm cannon.

Reims Aviation-Cessna **F406 Caravan II**

Reims Aviation SA
Aérodrome de Reims Prunay, BP 1745
F-51062 Reims, France

Although Reims Aviation had built over 6,350 Cessna-designed aircraft by 1992, the US firm sold its 49 per cent interest in the French associate early in 1989. The sole aircraft in production at Reims in the early 1990s was the jointly-developed **F406 Caravan II** and its fisheries-protection counterpart with Ferranti Seaspray radar, the **Vigilant**. The aircraft is basically turbine-powered **Cessna Titan**, itself derived from the **Cessna 402** twin-turbo-prop light business and 12/14-seat utility transport. Two **F406 Vigilant**s have been delivered to the Scottish Fisheries Protection Agency. Para-military users include the French customs service, which has four equipped with Crouzet Nadir navigation computer, and Bendix RDR 1500 radar with 360° scan in an underbelly radome.

Military operations are restricted to two target-towing aircraft operated by **French Army Light Aviation** (ALAT) for anti-aircraft artillery training, which were delivered

to the Peloton d'Avions (Aeroplane Platoon) of 3 Groupe d'Hélicoptères Légers (3 Light Helicopter Group) at Rennes in May/June 1987. The target gear, which includes 7 km (4.35 miles) of cable, may be quickly exchanged for nine passenger seats. Normally towing sleeve targets, the aircraft are regularly used over the ranges at Biscarosse and Toulon, and have also flown at Cherbourg, Veule-les-Roses, Mailly, Suippes, Canjuers and Baumholder (Germany).

Nearly 100 F406s have been built by Reims Aviation, which is 100 per cent French-owned. This is one of two target-tug versions operated by the ALAT.

SPECIFICATION

Reims-Cessna F 406 Caravan II
Wing: span 15.08 m (49 ft 5.75 in); aspect ratio 9.7; area 23.50 m² (252.96 sq ft)
Fuselage and tail: length 11.89 m (39 ft 0 in); height 4.01 m (13 ft 2 in); tailplane span 5.87 m (19 ft 3 in); wheel track 4.28 m (14 ft 0.5 in); wheel base 3.81 m (12 ft 5.875 in)
Powerplant: two Pratt & Whitney Canada PT6A-112

turboprops each rated at 500 shp (373 kW)
Weights: empty equipped 2460 kg (5,423 lb); maximum take-off 4468 kg (9,850 lb)
Fuel and load: internal fuel 1444 kg (3,183 lb); external fuel none; maximum payload 1563 kg (3,446 lb)
Speed: maximum operating speed 464 km/h (229 kt 263 mph); economical cruising speed at optimum altitude 370 km/h (200 kt; 230 mph)

Range: 2135 km (1,153 nm; 1,327 miles)
Performance: maximum rate of climb at sea level 564 m (1,850 ft) per minute; service ceiling 9145 m (30,000 ft); take-off run 526 m (1,725 ft) at maximum take-off weight; take-off distance to 15 m (50 ft) 803 m (2,635 ft) at maximum take-off weight; landing distance from 15 m (50 ft) 674 m (2,212 ft) at normal landing weight without propeller reversal

---

RFB **Fantrainer and Ranger 2000**

Rhein-Flugzeugbau GmbH
Flugplatz (PO Box 408), D-4050 Mönchengladbach 1
Germany

The **RFB Fantrainer** is a two-seat primary and basic trainer and is a product of the Rhein Flugzeugbau company (which has successively been a subsidiary of VFW-Fokker, MBB and now ABS International). The configuration of the Fantrainer is unusual, with propulsion provided by an integral ducted fan, i.e. a small-diameter pusher propeller rotating in a shroud to provide thrust efficiently and allow for an aerodynamically clean airframe design. After this concept had been proved with the two-seat side-by-side **Fanliner** flown late in 1973, RFB obtained German Ministry of Defence backing for two prototypes of the **AWI-2 Fantrainer**. These featured tandem seating and the first, flown on 27 October 1977, was powered by two 150-hp (112-kW) Audi NSU EA 871-L Wankel rotary engines. A 420-shp (313-kW) Allison 250-C20B turboshaft was used in the second prototype, flown on 31 May 1978.

Production versions of the Fantrainer were of similar configurations to the prototypes, and were launched in August 1982 when the **Royal Thai air force** ordered 47. Thirty-one of these were to be **Fantrainer 400**s and 16 **Fantrainer 600**s, with one of each completed in Germany and the balance supplied in kit form for assembly in Thailand by the RTAF. Changes from the second prototype included a 15-cm (6-

in) fuselage stretch, an enlarged canopy for improved all-round vision, relocation of the air intakes above the wings and an improved fan reduction gearbox allowing full utilisation of engine thrust. The Fantrainer 600 is fitted with a 485-kW (650-shp) Allison 250-C30 turboshaft with consequent increases in weight and performance. In addition, metal wings were designed for manufacture in Thailand in place of the composite structure of the original aircraft.

The first Fantrainer 600 flew in Germany on 12 August 1984 and deliveries to Thailand began in October 1984. However, a setback in plans to fit the locally-assembled wings to German-supplied fuselage kits delayed until 1986 the roll-out of the first indigenously-assembled aircraft. Service use of the Fantrainer 600 began in January 1987 and all 16 serve with the Flying Training School/ No. 402 Sqn at Kamphong Son. Despite delivery of all German kits by late 1987, the programme has progressed only slowly. Assembly of the Fantrainer 400s was to be completed by the end of 1991. Thai air force dissatisfaction with the type has led to their rapid replacement with Aero L-39s, among others.

In association with Rockwell, RFB (under the auspices of DASA) has entered the **Rockwell/DASA Ranger 2000** for the USAF/USN JPATS competition. Launched in

May 1991, the first of two prototypes (D-FANA) flew from Manching on 15 January 1993. The Ranger 2000 is powered by a 3,190-lb (14.19-kN) Pratt & Whitney Canada JT15D-5C turbofan. Production aircraft will be assembled by Rockwell in the USA, while programme costs will be shared 50-50 between the two partners.

SPECIFICATION

RFB Fantrainer 400
Wing: span 9.74 m (31 ft 11.5 in); aspect ratio 6.8; area 14.00 m² (150.70 sq ft)
Fuselage and tail: length 9.48 m (31 ft 1.25 in) including probe and 9.20 m (30 ft 2.25 in) excluding probe; height 3.16 m (10 ft 4.5 in); tailplane span 3.59

The second prototype Ranger 2000 was lost in a crash, and a replacement is now under construction. German type approval was gained in June 1994, with the first prototype.

m (11 ft 9.5 in); wheel track 1.94 m (6 ft 4.25 in); wheel base 3.89 m (12 ft 9 in)
Powerplant: one Allison 250-C20B turboshaft rated at 420 shp (313 kW)
Weights: empty equipped 1114 kg (2,456 lb); normal take-off 1600 kg (3,527 lb) for aerobatics; maximum take-off 1800 kg (3,968 lb)
Fuel and load: internal fuel 384 kg (847 lb); external fuel none; maximum ordnance none
Speed: never exceed speed 250 kt (288 mph; 463 km/h); maximum level speed 'clean' at 10,000 ft (3050 m) 200 kt (23 mph; 370 km/h); cruising speed at 10,000 ft (3050 m) 175 kt (201 mph; 325 km/h)
Range: 640 nm (737 miles; 1186 km); endurance 4 hours 36 minutes
Performance: maximum rate of climb at sea level 1,550 ft (472 m) per minute; service ceiling 20,000 ft (6096 m)

Robin **HR.100**

Avions Pierre Robin's first all-metal light-plane, the four/five-seat **HR.100** low-wing monoplane, made its maiden flight on 3 April 1969. In November 1972, Robin introduced the **HR.100/285**, which was the first model in the Robin range to feature retractable tricycle landing gear. A batch of 20 generally similar **R.100/250TR**s was acquired in 1975 for service in the liaison and communications roles with the **Centre**

d'Essais en Vol at Istres, where 13 remain. The HR-100 was also certificated by the CEV on behalf of the **Aéronavale** for training duties at Brétigny. A further two HR-100 lightplanes are currently operated for communications tasks by the Direction des Constructions et Armes Navales, based at Hyères and Cuers.

SPECIFICATION

Robin HR 100/250TR
Wing: span 9.08 m (29 ft 2.5 in); aspect ratio 5.36;

area 15.20 m² (163.62 sq ft)
Fuselage and tail: length 7.59 m (24 ft 10.75 in); height 2.71 m (8 ft 10.75 in); tailplane span 3.20 m (10 ft 10 in); wheel track 3.225 m (10 ft 7 in); wheel base 2.16 m (7 ft 1 in)
Powerplant: one Textron Lycoming IO-540-C4B5 flat-six air-cooled piston engine rated at 250 hp (186 kW)
Weights: empty equipped 840 kg (1,852 lb); maximum take-off 1400 kg (3,086 lb)
Fuel and load: internal fuel 440 litres (116.25 US gal); external fuel none; maximum ordnance none
Speed: never exceed speed 360 km/h (194 kt; 223 mph); maximum level speed 'clean' at sea level 315 km/h (170 kt; 196 mph); maximum cruising speed at 2135 m

(7,005 ft) 297 km/h (161 kt; 185 mph); economical cruising speed at 3050 m (10,000 ft) 285 km/h (154 kt; 177 mph)
Range: ferry range 2344 km (1,264 nm; 1,456 miles); range 2130 km (1,149 nm; 1,323 miles)
Performance: maximum rate of climb at sea level 324 m (1,065 ft) per minute; service ceiling 5700 m (18,700 ft); take-off run about 325 m (1,066 ft) at maximum take-off weight; take-off distance to 15 m (50 ft) about 600 m (1,970 ft) at maximum take-off weight; landing distance from 15 m (50 ft) about 660 m (2,166 ft) at normal landing weight; landing run about 350 m (1.150 ft) at normal landing weight

---

Robinson **R22**

Robinson Helicopter Company
24747 Crenshaw Boulevard, Torrance
California 90505, USA

Development of the **Robinson R22** two-seat light helicopter began in 1973, with particular emphasis on efficiency, low noise and minimum maintenance. The R22 seats two side-by-side and is equipped with full dual controls. Since the first flight of the prototype on 28 August 1975, over 2,000 examples have been delivered, primarily for

commercial use. The improved **R22 Alpha** permitted a 31.5-kg (70-lb) increase in gross weight and was certificated in October 1983. From the 501st aircraft onwards, the standard production version has been the **R22 Beta**, which introduced various detail improvements. In March 1992, the **Turkish army** became the first military user of the

R22, when 10 Betas were acquired for service at the army's Aviation Training Centre in Ankara, where they operate alongside Enstrom TH-28s. A further 40 have been ordered by **Argentina**, including 10 **R22M Mariners**. These are equipped with floats and ground wheels, and are chiefly intended for the Buenos Aires Police.

SPECIFICATION

Robinson Model R22 Beta
Rotor system: main rotor diameter 25 ft 2 in (7.67 m); tail rotor diameter 3 ft 6 in (1.07 m); main rotor disc area 497.44 sq ft (46.21 m²); tail rotor disc area 9.63 sq ft (0.89 m²)

Robinson R-22

Fuselage and tail: length overall, rotors turning 28 ft 9 in (8.76 m) and fuselage 20 ft 8 in (6.30 m); height overall 8 ft 9 in (2.67 m) to top of rotor head; skid track 6 ft 4 in (1.93 m)
Powerplant: one 160-hp (119-kW) Textron Lycoming O-320-B2C flat-four piston engine derated to 131 hp (97.5 kW)
Weights: empty 824 lb (374 kg); maximum take-off 1,370 lb (621 kg)
Fuel and load: internal fuel 115 lb (52 kg) plus provision for 63 lb (28.6 kg) of auxiliary fuel; external fuel none

Speed: never exceed speed 102 kt (118 mph; 190 km/h); maximum level speed at optimum altitude 97 kt (112 mph; 180 km/h); normal cruising speed at 8,000 ft (2440 m) 96 kt (110 mph; 177 km/h); economical cruising speed at optimum altitude 82.5 kt (95 mph; 153 km/h)
Range: range 320 nm (368 miles; 592 km) with auxiliary fuel and maximum payload
Performance: maximum rate of climb at sea level 1,200 ft (366 m) per minute; service ceiling 14,000 ft (4265 m); hovering ceiling 6,970 ft (2125 m) in ground effect

Turkish Army Aviation ha a large rotary-winged flee gathered from severa sources. In 1992, 10 R22 Betas were obtained fo. training.

Rockwell **B-1 Lancer**

Rockwell International Corporatio
2201 North Douglas Street, PO Box 425
Seal Beach. California 90740-8350, US

To provide an important component of the United States' 'Triad' nuclear deterrent, studies initiated in 1962 led, in 1965, to the **USAF**'s Advanced Manned Strategic Aircraft (AMSA) requirement for a low-altitude penetration bomber. Suffering a protracted gestation, today's **Rockwell B-1B Lancer** traces its origins via the AMSA back to the **B-1A**, the winning contender in a competition for a new strategic bomber involving North American, Rockwell, General Dynamics and Boeing. Selected for further development in June 1970, the first of four B-1A prototypes made its maiden flight from Palmdale, CA, on 23 December 1974.

At that time, SAC hoped for 250 to replace ageing B-52s. Congressional opposition and a new administration culminated in its downfall, President Carter announcing in June 1977 that testing of the four prototypes would continue only as a form of 'insurance'. At the same time, he confirmed that production would be shelved.

By 1981, the political climate (and the President) had changed again and the new occupant of the White House took a much more hard-line attitude towards the Soviet Union. An immediate beneficiary was SAC, which was informed in September 1981 that it would at last receive the long-overdue new bomber, but in reduced numbers – exactly 100 derivative B-1Bs, outwardly generally similar to the fourth B-1A prototype.

The B-1B has a blended low-wing/body configuration with variable geometry on the outer panels. The structure utilises a mixture of aluminium and diffusion bonded titanium alloy construction, with some components manufactured from GRP. The fuselage structure is strengthened to resist nuclear blast overpressure. Aft of the titanium wing pivots are overwing fairings blended into the wing trailing edges and the engine nacelles. Four General Electric F101 turbofans are mounted in pairs beneath and aft of the fixed centre-section of the wing. The nacelles are close to the CoG for optimum stability in low-altitude turbulence. The wing itself incorporates full-span seven-segment leading-edge slats and six-segment, single-

slotted trailing-edge flaps. No ailerons are provided, roll control being effected by four-segment airbrakes/spoilers on each outer wing. All flying controls are operated by an electro-hydraulic system, with the exception of the two outboard spoilers on each wing, which are fly-by-wire. High-lift devices were incorporated to ensure that the B-1 could take-off more rapidly than the B-52, and to be able to deploy quickly in times of crisis to more austere forward operating bases. Small moveable composite vanes with 30° anhedral are located below and forward of the cockpit. These sense lateral and vertical motion in turbulent flight and provide both yaw and pitch damping. The B-1B is fitted with a nose-mounted refuelling receptacle.

B-1B modifications

The absolute performance of the B-1B has been downgraded compared to the B-1A, due primarily to reasons of cost. Major airframe improvements were introduced, including strengthened landing gear, a moveable bulkhead in the forward weapons bay to allow for the carriage of a diverse range of different-sized weapons, optional weapons bay fuel tanks for increased range, and external underfuselage stores stations for additional fuel or weapons. The reduction in the B-1A's high-level supersonic (Mach 2.5) dash capability led to the replacement of the variable engine inlets with those incorporating a fixed inlet geometry. The low-altitude, high-speed penetration role against sophisticated air defence systems was to be carried out using electronic jamming equipment, IR countermeasures, radar location and warning systems, and application of 'low observables' technology.

Careful attention to intake geometry resulted in the compressor face being hidden from radar, much use also being made of

RAM on key components. Perhaps the be evidence of success in reducing the ele tronic 'footprint' of the Lancer is provided b the fact that its radar cross-section is least an order of magnitude smaller tha that of a B-52, yet the B-1B is only margi ally smaller and is of comparable weight.

The four-man crew of the B-1B consis of pilot, co-pilot, offensive systems operat (OSO) and defensive systems operato (DSO). The pilot and co-pilot are accomm dated side by side, as are the OSO and DS who occupy a compartment at the rear the cockpit. All four crew are seated o Weber ACES II ejection seats with zero-zer capability. These replace the original B-1A crew escape capsule. The FBW and electro mechanical flight control systems are co nected to the pilot and co-pilot, with com mon reversionary links in event of failure The OSO functions mainly as a navigato being tasked with guiding the B-1B to it target and ensuring that its weaponry released at the optimum moment. All win dows can be fitted with PLZT (zirconiur titanate) radiation glare shields.

The offensive avionics systems was th main responsibility of Boeing. The primar system is the Westinghouse AN/APQ-16 multi-mode offensive radar system (derive from the F-16's AN/APG-66), which include a low-observable phased-array antenna fo low-altitude terrain following and accurat navigation. Other navigation systems in clude a high-accuracy INS and a Honeywe ASN-121 radar altimeter. The Honeywe offensive display sets comprise three MFD with two for the OSO (one showing threa on alphanumeric labels and one for tabu lated threat information) and one for th defensive systems operator.

The latter is concerned with counterin external threats and monitors the much troubled Eaton AN/ALQ-161 system, whic forms the core of the Lancer's continuousl upgradable defensive capability. The syster comprises an AN/ALQ-161A radio frequenc surveillance/ECM system, tail warning func

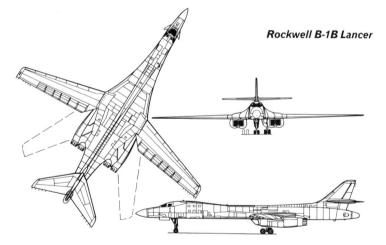

Rockwell B-1B Lancer

After a lengthy trials period, the B-1B is finally qualified to carry a maximum conventional load of 84 Mk 82 500-lb bombs.

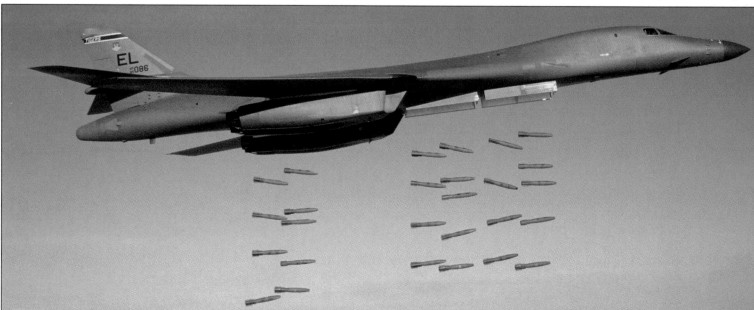

The B-1B fleet has adopted a new look, with tailcodes and an overall grey scheme. This 319th BW Lancer is based at Grand Forks.

...on, AN/ASQ-184 defensive management system and an expendable countermeasures system (chaff and flares). The system can detect, locate and classify signals from hostile emitters transmitting simultaneously via a number of receivers situated around the airframe in order to provide full 360° coverage. It is also able to establish priority in dealing with those threats and automatically initiates countermeasures via a large number of Northrop jamming transmitters and Raytheon phased array antennas.

The first production B-1B (82-0001) flew on 18 October 1984. Deliveries began on 27 July 1985 at Offutt AFB, Nebraska, with SAC achieving IOC exactly one year later, thereafter rapidly building up four bomb wings. The first 29 B-1Bs were assigned to the 96th BW at Dyess, Texas, excluding the ninth example, which was delivered to Edwards for test duties. Subsequent units to form comprised the 28th Wing at Ellsworth, SD, the 319th Wing at Grand Forks, ND, and the 384th Wing at McConnell, Kansas. 74-0160, a B-1A, is employed at Lowry, CO, as a ground instruction trainer.

Since then, the career of the B-1B has been coloured by controversy and interrupted by frequent lengthy grounding orders, and several highly-publicised losses. Problems were caused by false-alarms from the computerised self-diagnostic systems, non-functioning TFR, and repeated failure of the AN/ALQ-161 ECM system. Engine problems were also a significant factor in the type's grounding, and perhaps some of the losses. One of the more recent periods of enforced inactivity prevented the B-1B from playing any part in Desert Storm operations. However, the Lancer was still (nominally) fulfilling SAC's 'alert' nuclear role.

Under the FY1994 budget, $49 million has been allocated for R&D, while another $161 million has been set aside for modifications and components. So much money has been spent on the AN/ALQ-161 system that no funds have been released for FY1994.

Future plans for the fleet include the addition of GPS, a MIL-STD-1760 databus, ECM improvements and advanced weapons capability. A six-month operational readiness assessment began in June 1994, which the USAF hopes will break Congressional opposition to further funding. The USAF seeks to prove it can maintain a 75 per cent readiness level, in contrast to the current figure of only 55 per cent, which it blames on a poorly funded spares resource. The 28th Wing will be provided with a full complement of spares and crews to participate in deployments and exercises, thus further downgrading the 7th Wing and 384th BG. A report on the success of this endeavour is due to be presented by 1 March 1995. A positive result would ease release of the $2.7 billion required to upgrade the fleet's conventional capabilities, in addition to $830 million for full spares support.

WEAPON OPTIONS

Thus far, the Lancer has been primarily concerned with strategic applications. The B-1B is fitted with three internal weapons bays, comprising a 31-ft 3-in (9.53-m) long double bay forward of the wing carry-through structure and a single 15-ft (4.57-m) bay aft, with hydraulically actuated doors. Weapons include B61 and B83 thermonuclear bombs up to a maximum payload of 75,000 lb (34020 kg). Alternatively, the internal ordnance bays may contain three racks or SRAM launchers, for up to 24 AGM-69A short-range attack missiles (SRAM-As), 12 B-28 or 28 700-lb (318-kg) B-61, or 2,400-lb (1089-kg) B-83 freefall nuclear bombs. The B-1B also has the capacity to carry eight

AGM-86B ALCMs (with subsequent modifications to the forward double bomb bay using the moveable bulkhead) on a common strategic rotary launcher (CSRL), although cruise missiles have never been carried in routine operations.

Future strategic weapons options will include advanced PGMs, such as the AGM-129 Advanced Cruise Missile, AGM-137 Tri-service Stand-off Attack Missile (TSSAM), Joint Direct Attack Munition (JDAM), and Joint Stand-off Weapon (JSOW).

In the conventional role, the B-1B is potentially able to carry a maximum of 84 500-lb (227-kg) Mk 82 bombs or 500-lb (227-kg) Mk 36 mines internally. It is probably also compatible with the AGM-86C ALCM that is armed with a 1,000-lb (454-kg) blast-fragmentation warhead in place of the AGM-86B's nuclear warhead. The six underfuselage stores stations could carry an additional 12 ALCMs, or additional conventional stores for a maximum total load of 134,000 lb (60782 kg).

The B-1B's conventional weapons potential is being comprehensively upgraded, following the withdrawal of the B-52G. The Lancer will ultimately acquire the ability to utilise 'smart' PGMs such as the AGM-84 Harpoon anti-ship missile and, in time, the AGM-142 Popeye stand-off missile. This is a 3,300-lb (1497-kg) conventional stand-off missile developed by Rafael, and procured under the 'Have Nap' programme. Other missions might include interdiction of sea lanes through the use of air-delivered mines.

OPERATORS

Ninety-five B-1Bs remain in service with the USAF.
Air Combat Command (ACC)
7th Wing – Dyess AFB, TX ('DY')
28th Bomb Wing – Ellsworth AFB, SD ('EL')

319th Bomb Group – Grand Forks AFB, ND ('GF'), disbanding in 1994
366th Wing – Ellsworth AFB, SD ('MO')
384th Bomb Group – McConnell AFB, OZ ('OZ'), disbanding in late 1994. Aircraft assigned to the 184th Bomber Group of the Kansas ANG

Air Force Materiel Command (AFMC)
412th Test Wing – Edwards AFB, CA ('ED')

SPECIFICATION

Rockwell B-1B Lancer
Wing: span 136 ft 8.5 in (41.67 m) minimum sweep (15°) and 78 ft 2.5 in (23.84 m) maximum sweep (67° 30'); aspect ratio about 9.58 fully spread and 3.14 fully swept; area approximately 1,950.00 sq ft (181.16 m^2)
Fuselage and tail: length 147 ft 0 in (44.81 m); height 34 ft 10 in (10.36 m); tailplane span 44 ft 10 in (13.67 m; wheel track 14 ft 6 in (4.42 m)
Powerplant: four General Electric F101-GE-102 turbofans each rated at 14,600 lb st (64.94 kN) dry and 30,780 lb st (136.92 kN) with afterburning
Weights: empty equipped 192,000 lb (87091 kg); maximum take-off 477,000 lb (216365 kg)
Fuel and load: internal fuel 195,000 lb (88450 kg); external fuel none; maximum ordnance 75,000 lb (34019 kg) carried internally and 59,000 lb (26762 kg) carried externally
Speed: maximum level speed 'clean' at high altitude about Mach 1.25 or 715 kt (823 mph; 1324 km/h); penetration speed at about 200 ft (61 m) more than 521 kt (600 mph; 965 km/h)
Range: range about 6,475 nm (7,455 miles; 12000 km) with standard fuel
Performance: service ceiling more than 50,000 ft (15240 m)

Rockwell International OV-10 Bronco

In the early 1960s, the **US Marine Corps** recognised its need for a purpose-built COIN aircraft and drew up the specification for what it identified as a LARA (Light Armed Reconnaissance Airplane) with additional observation and FAC roles. Procurement was initiated by a design competition, with North American's **NA-300** proposal being selected as the winner in August 1964. The initial contract covered seven

YOV-10A prototypes, the first flying on 16 July 1965 powered by two 492-kW (660-shp) Garrett T76 turboprops.

Testing revealed some shortcomings that were rectified by a 3.05-m (10-ft) increase in wingspan, and the introduction of an uprated version of the T76 engine in nacelles that were moved outboard slightly to reduce engine noise in the cabin. The increased span was premiered on a proto-

Rockwell OV-10A Bronco

type first flown on 15 August 1966, and the seventh prototype was given alternative Pratt & Whitney Canada T74 engines (military designation for the PT6A turboprop) for comparative evaluation.

The resultant **Rockwell OV-10 Bronco** is of distinctive configuration with a shoulder-mounted constant-chord wing, and twin booms extending aft from the engine nacelles to terminate in vertical tail surfaces that are linked by a fixed-incidence

The Venezuelan air force received 18 surplus USAF OV-10As (seen here), which serve alongside 11 OV-10Es, from Maracaibo. The OV-10s are also detached to the Colombian border for COIN operations.

tailplane with inset elevator. A slender pod-type fuselage accommodates the crew of two in tandem under a large canopy with excellent all-round view. The fuselage pod could accommodate two stretchers and a medical attendant, or up to five paratroops.

The OV-10 was armed with four fixed 7.62-mm (0.3-in) M60C machine-guns (each with 500 rounds), comprising two in each sponson. Four 600-lb (272-kg) underwing hardpoints were located on sponsons projecting from the fuselage sides, with a 1,200-lb (544-kg) centreline hardpoint and two underwing stations. Weapons available for use included napalm, slick and retarded Mk 82 500-lb (227-kg) bombs, unguided 2.75-in or 5-in rockets, machine-gun and cannon pods, flares and smoke tanks.

Procurement of the initial **OV-10A** covered 114 aircraft for the US Marine Corps, the first of them flown on 6 August 1967. This service used the type for forward air

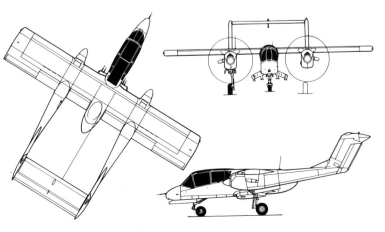

control and helicopter escort, in addition to the intended role of light armed reconnaissance. VMO-2 was the first unit to deploy, to Vietnam in July 1968, and the Bronco served with the Marines, Navy and Air Force. It soon demonstrated its superior performance against other FAC platforms. USMC OV-10As are fast disappearing, but continue to serve with HMT-303, VMO-1, VMO-2 and VMO-4. The USAF acquired 157 OV-10As, primarily for forward air control, but with a secondary limited ground support role in the absence of tactical fighters. USAF OV-10As have been retired, although some were transferred to the USMC.

Six generally similar **OV-10B** aircraft were supplied to West Germany for use as target tugs, followed by 12 higher-performance **OV-10B(Z)** aircraft with a 2,950-lb (13.12-kN) thrust General Electric J85-GE-4 turbojet pylon-mounted above the wing.

These aircraft are no longer in service.

Rockwell developed several production versions generally similar to the OV-10A. Thirty-two **OV-10C**s were delivered to the **Royal Thai air force** in 1971-74, of which 24 remain with No. 411 Squadron at Chiang Mai and No. 711 Squadron at Surat Thani. A further order for six was apparently not undertaken. The **OV-10E** (16 built – 11 remaining) serves with the **Venezuelan air force**. Venezuela also had taken delivery of 18 former USAF OV-10As by April 1991, and both versions serve with Escuadrón 151 'Geronimos', and 152 'Zorros', of Grupo 15, based at Base Aérea General En Jefe Rafael Urdaneta, Maracaibo, Zulia. The FAV undertakes detachments for COIN operations to the Colombian border (when they are usually armed with a single underwing rocket pod and flare pod). Three OV-10s were reported as shot down during

the attempted coup in late 1992. The **OV-10F** (16 built – 12 remaining) is currently operated at Baucau by Skwadron Udara 3 of the **Indonesian air force**. In 1981 the **Moroccan air force** took delivery of six refurbished, former USMC OV-10As for COIN operations. The (three) survivors are based at Ménara.

Additional deliveries of surplus USMC OV-10As include 24 to the **Philippine air force**. These were supplied to serve with the 15th Air Strike Wing at Sangley Point.

SPECIFICATION

Rockwell OV-10A Bronco
Wing: span 40 ft 0 in (12.19 m); aspect ratio 5.5; area 291.00 sq ft (27.03 m²)
Fuselage and tail: length 41 ft 7 in (12.67 m); height 15 ft 2 in (4.62 m); tailplane span 14 ft 7 in (4.45 m;

wheel track 14 ft 10 in (4.52 m)
Powerplant: two Garrett T76-G-416/417 turboprops each rated at 715 ehp (533 ekW)
Weights: empty equipped 6,969 lb (3161 kg); normal take-off 9,908 lb (4494 kg); maximum take-off 14,444 lb (6552 kg)
Fuel and load: internal fuel 578 US gal (976 litres); external fuel up to one 150-US gal (568-litre) drop tank; maximum ordnance 3,600 lb (1633 kg)
Speed: maximum level speed 'clean' at sea level 244 kt (281 mph; 452 km/h)
Range: ferry range 1,240 nm (1,428 miles; 2298 km) with drop tank; combat radius 198 nm (228 miles; 367 km) with maximum warload and no loiter
Performance: maximum rate of climb at sea level 2,650 ft (808 m) per minute; service ceiling 24,000 ft (7315 m); take-off run 740 ft (226 m) at normal take-off weight; take-off distance to 50 ft (15 m) 2,408 ft at maximum take-off weight; landing distance from 50 ft (15 m) 1,220 ft (372 m) at normal landing weight; landing run 740 ft (226 m) at normal landing weight

Rockwell International **OV-10D Bronco**

A suitably equipped OV-10 seemed ideal to fulfil a night FAC and strike designation role in the light of the **USAF**'s Vietnam experience. While the OV-10A was effective, it could not stop the infiltration of men and supplies at night. In the early 1970s, 15 OV-10As were modified under the USAF's Pave Nail programme. Specialised equipment given to these aircraft included a combined laser rangefinder/target illuminator, a LORAN receiver and a LORAN co-ordinate converter. After the withdrawal from Vietnam, these Pave Nail OV-10s reverted to standard configuration.

The **USN** had been slightly ahead of the USAF in considering the OV-10A for such a task, and in 1970 two Navy OV-10As were converted as **Rockwell YOV-10D NOGS** (Night Observation/Gunship System) prototypes with enhanced night and all-weather capability. They were equipped with an undernose turret in an extended nose carrying a FLIR and laser target designator, a rear underfuselage turret to mount a 20-mm can-

non, and two underwing pylons carrying extra stores. By the time evaluation was complete, the US had withdrawn its forces from Vietnam, but in 1974 the US Navy contracted Rockwell to establish and test an **OV-10D** production configuration. This resulted in 17 of the **USMC** OV-10As being converted as OV-10Ds for a **NOS** (Night Observation Surveillance) role, all of them being redelivered during 1979-80.

They are equipped with a Texas Instruments AN/AAS-37 pod that incorporates a FLIR sensor, laser target designator and automatic video tracker, and can be armed with an M197 20-mm three-barrelled cannon with 1,500 rounds (in place of the OV-10A's conventional armament), which can be directed by the AAS-37 system. These OV-10Ds also have uprated engines with IR-suppressing exhaust ducts, LW-3B zero-zero ejection seats, AN/APR-39 RWR and additional underwing pylons suitable for weapons (the OV-10D introduced AIM-9 capability) or auxiliary fuel. The OV-10D saw

active service during Operation Desert Storm, with two lost in combat. Fourteen survivors, plus 23 OV-10As, were to have been upgraded to a common **OV-10D+** standard, with structural strengthening to permit carrier operations plus upgraded avionics, navigation and weapons systems. The programme should have been completed by late 1993, but the final withdrawal of the type was brought forward to FY1994. VMO-1 and -2 disbanded on 20 May and 31 July 1993, respectively. VMO-4, the last (USMC Reserve) unit, followed in March 1994. It has been mooted that surplus aircraft will be passed on to South Korea.

SPECIFICATION

Rockwell OV-10D Bronco
generally similar to the OV-10A Bronco except in the following particulars:
Fuselage and tail: length 44 ft 0 in (13.41 m)
Powerplant: two Garrett T76-G-420/421 turboprops each rated at 1,040 ehp (776 kW)
Weights: empty equipped 6,893 lb (3127 kg)
Speed: maximum level speed 'clean' at sea level 250 kt (288 mph; 463 km/h)
Range: combat radius 265 nm (305 miles; 491 km) with maximum warload and no loiter
Performance: maximum rate of climb at sea level at 12,443 lb (5644 kg) 2,665 ft (812 m) per minute; service ceiling 30,000 ft (9145 m); take-off run 1,110 ft (338 m) at 13,284 lb (6025 kg); landing run 800 ft (244 m) at maximum landing weight

Rockwell OV-10D Bronco

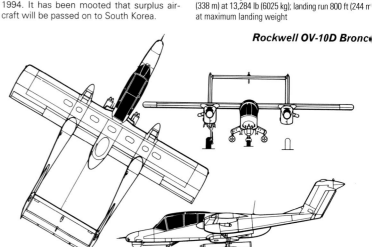

Formerly based at New River, alongside the FMFLant helicopter fleet, VMO-1 flew its OV-10Ds on observation and FAC missions.

Rockwell **T-2 Buckeye**

In 1956 the **US Navy** identified a requirement for a jet trainer which would be suitable to take the pupil, after completion of the *ab initio* phase, through all the more advanced stages, including bombing, gunnery and fighter tactics, to the point of carrier qualification. Competitive procurement was contested by a number of US manufacturers but North American Aviation, which incorporated in its **NA-249** design proposal proven features from in-production aircraft (the FJ-1 Fury and T-28 Trojan), was selected and contracted in late 1946 to build six pre-production **YT2J-1** aircraft for evaluation; there was no prototype as such.

The first of the pre-production aircraft, flown initially on 31 January 1958, was of mid-wing configuration, accommodating pupil and instructor in tandem on LS-1 ejection seats. The instructor's seat, at the rear,

was raised to provide a good view forward. The design provided a robust landing gear, powered controls, large trailing-edge flaps, an airbrake on each side of the fuselage and a retractable sting-type arrester hook, all hydraulically actuated. The YT2J-1 and initial production **T2J-1** (designated **T-2A** from 1962) was powered by a single 3,400-lb (15.12-kN) thrust Westinghouse J34-WE-48 turbojet within the fuselage. Named **Buckeye** before entering service in July 1959, the T2J-1 initially equipped BTG-7, later named VT-7, based at NAS Meridian. T2J-1 (T-2A) production totalled 201 aircraft.

The first of two YT2J-2 test aircraft (T2J-1 conversions) was flown on 30 August 1962 with two 3,000-lb (13.34-kN) thrust Pratt & Whitney J60-P-6 turbojets. This version was selected to supersede the T-2A, the first of 97 production **T-2B** aircraft being

The US Navy trains 2,000 pilots and naval flight officers per year and, until the T-45 is fully in service, will continue to rely on the T-2Cs for most of its training needs. Unlike the USAF, it is only the prospective jet pilots who train on Buckeyes, such as these TW-6/VT-4 examples.

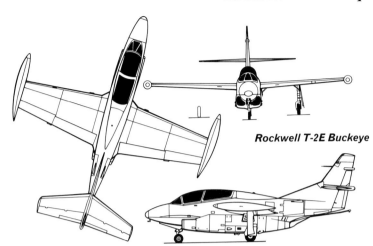

Rockwell T-2E Buckeye

flown on 21 May 1965 and entering service with Training Squadron VT-4 at NAS Pensacola in December 1965. Following evaluation of a T-2B converted to **YT-2C** configuration with two General Electric J85-GE-4 engines, 231 aircraft designated **T-2C** were built for the US Navy Air Training Command, the first production example being flown initially on 10 December 1968. At a later date, small numbers of T-2B and T-2C aircraft were converted as drone directors under the respective designations **DT-2B** and **DT-2C**. In 1982, 17 US Navy T-2Bs were removed from storage and refurbished, 15 of them later entering service to supplement T-2Cs that currently remain active.

The US Navy also procured two T-2 trainer variants (basically similar to the T-2C) on behalf of the **Venezuelan** and **Greek** air forces. The FAV received 12 **T-2D** trainers in 1973, plus an additonal 12 weapons-capable aircraft in 1976. The 19 surviving aircraft comprise 10 weapons-capable T-2Ds and nine trainers, equipping the Grupo Aéreo de Entrenamiento, based at Boca Del Rio, Maracay. Some T-2Ds flew with rebel forces during the 1992 coup

attempt. The Greek air force relies for advanced training on the 36 surviving **T-2E**s of 362 'Nestor' Mira and 363 'Danaos' Mira, of 120 Ptérix, based at Kalamata.

The T-2C is the only current variant in service with the US Navy, flying with VT-4 and VT-26 at Pensacola, FL, VT-19 at Meridian, MS, VT-23 at Kingsville, TX, and VT-26 at Chase Field, TX, in the training role. A small number served with aggressor units VF-43 at Oceana, VA, and VF-126 at Miramar, CA, for spin-training, and the Naval Test Pilot's School at Patuxent River, MD.

SPECIFICATION

Rockwell T-2C Buckeye

Wing: span 38 ft 1.5 in (11.62 m) with tip tanks; aspect ratio 5.7; area 255.00 sq ft (23.69 m²)
Fuselage and tail: length 38 ft 3.5 in (11.67 m); height 14 ft 9.5 in (4.51 m); tailplane span 17 ft 11 in (5.46 m); wheel track 18 ft 6 in (5.64 m)
Powerplant: two General Electric J85-GE-4 turbojets each rated at 2,950 lb st (13.1 kN)
Weights: empty 8,115 lb (3680 kg); maximum take-off 13,179 lb (5977 kg)

Fuel and load: internal fuel 691 US gal (2616 litres); external fuel none; maximum ordnance 640 lb (290 kg)
Speed: maximum level speed 'clean' at 25,000 ft (7620 m) 469 kt (540 mph; 840 km/h)

Range: range 909 nm (1,047 miles; 1685 km)
Performance: maximum rate of climb at sea level 6,200 ft (1890 m) per minute; service ceiling 40,415 ft (12320 m)

Rockwell **Commander twins**

Shrike Commander was the final name used by Rockwell for the piston-engined light business twin originated in 1948 by Aero Design and Engineering (later Aero Commander). With engines of varying power, the aircraft were identified as **Aero Commander 500**, **Commander 560**, **Commander 680** and – with a lengthened fuselage – **Commander 680FL**. The name Shrike Commander applied to the seven-seat **Models 500V** and **500S**, built until 1979, and the 11-seat **Model 680FL** became the **Grand Commander**.

Commander twins have entered military service in the liaison and aerial survey roles. The **Argentinian** armed forces are the principal operators of the type, with a 12-strong fleet of **Model 500U**s used by the air force for medevac service and a single

Commander 560 for army transport duties. The **Mexican air force** uses 15 Model 500s for light transport and photographic reconnaissance. Other users of the Model 500 include the **Royal Bahamas Defence Force**, **Benin** armed forces and **Burkina Faso air force**. The long-fuselage Model 680FL serves with the armies of **Greece** and **Indonesia**, and a single Aero Commander 680 in **Dominica**.

SPECIFICATION

Rockwell Shrike Commander

Wing: span 49 ft 0.5 in (14.95 m); aspect ratio 9.45; area 255.00 sq ft (23.69 m²)
Fuselage and tail: length 36 ft 9.75 in (11.22 m); height 14 ft 6 in (4.42 m); tailplane span 16 ft 9 in

Thirteen of the 15 Aero Commander 500s that have been delivered to the air force of Argentina (SADEN) still serve in support of regional commands and HQs.

(5.10 m); wheel track 12 ft 11 in (3.95 m
Powerplant: two Textron Lycoming IO-540-E1B5 flat-six piston engines each rated at 290 hp (216 kW)
Weights: empty equipped 4,608 lb (2090 kg); maximum take-off 6,750 lb (3062 kg)
Fuel and load: internal fuel 156 US gal (590 litres); external fuel none
Speed: maximum level speed 'clean' at sea level 187 kt

(215 mph; 346 km/h); maximum cruising speed at 9,000 ft (2745 m) 176 kt (203 mph; 326 km/h)
Range: range 936 nm (1,078 miles; 1735 km)
Performance: maximum rate of climb at sea level 1,340 ft (408 m) per minute; service ceiling 19,000 ft (5915 m); take-off distance to 50 ft (15 m) 1,915 ft (584 m) at maximum take-off weight; landing distance from 50 ft (15 m) 2,235 ft (681 m) at normal landing weight

Rockwell **Turbo Commander**

The early success of the Aero Commander 500/560 series had indicated a worthwhile market for a larger-capacity, higher-speed derivative. In its initial form, the Commander Model 680FL (Grand Commander) was first flown on 29 December 1962, incorporating a 1.88-m (6-ft 2-in) fuselage stretch to seat pilot and co-pilot on a separate flight deck, and from four to nine passengers according to cabin layout. A pressurised development with turboprops was flown by Aero Commander (then a division of Rockwell Standard) as the **Turbo Commander 690**, on 31 December 1964. Successive variants were built by Rockwell until February 1981, when the production line was sold to Gulfstream American and the name was changed to the **Gulfstream/Jetprop 840, 900, 980** or **1000**, depending on engine power and gross weight.

Military users of the Turbo Commander

in its various manifestations include the **Colombian air force** (one Turbo Commander 680V), the **Honduran air force** (one Gulfstream 1000), the **Iranian air force** (four Turbo Commander 681/Bs), **army** (five Turbo Commanders 690/As) and **navy** (four Turbo Commander 690/As), the **Mexican air force** (one Turbo Commander 690B, one Gulfstream 980, three Gulfstream 1000s) and **navy** (two Gulfstream 1000s), the **Pakistan army** (two Gulfstream 840s), the **Royal Thai air force** (one Turbo Commander 690A for survey duties), and the **Turkish air force** (one Turbo Commander 690A).

SPECIFICATION

Rockwell Turbo Commander 690B

Wing: span 46 ft 8 in (14.22 m); aspect ratio 8.19;

A sizeable number of Rockwell's sleek Turbo Commander family are in military service. This is one of the Pakistan army's two Gulfstream 840s.

area 266.00 sq ft (24.71 m²)
Fuselage and tail: length 42 ft 11.75 in (13.10 m); height 14 ft 11.5 in (4.56 m); tailplane span 19 ft 9.25 in (6.03 m); wheel track 15 ft 5 in (4.70 m)
Powerplant: two Garrett TPE331-5-521K turboprops each rated at 700 ehp (522 ekW)
Weights: empty 5,910 lb (2681 kg); maximum take-off 10,250 lb (4649 kg)
Fuel and load: internal fuel 384 US gal (1453 litres); external fuel none
Speed: maximum level speed 'clean' at 12,000 ft

(3660 m) 285 kt (328 mph; 528 km/h); economical cruising speed at 25,000 ft (7620 m) 231 kt (266 mph; 428 km/h)
Range: range 1,360 nm (1,567 miles; 2522 km) with maximum fuel and a 1,817-lb (824-kg) payload, or 701 nm (808 miles; 1300 km) with maximum payload
Performance: maximum rate of climb at sea level 2,849 ft (868 m) per minute; service ceiling 32,900 ft (10030 m); take-off run 1,434 ft (437 m) at maximum take-off weight; take-off distance to 50 ft (15 m) 2,216 ft (675 m) at maximum take-off weight

Rockwell/Deutsche Aerospace (MBB) **X-31A**

Flying under the programme title **EFM (Enhanced Fighter Maneuverability)**, the **X-31A** is an experimental aircraft intended to evaluate advanced aerodynamic and propulsive systems with the aim of increasing fighter agility, widening the flight

envelope and conferring an ability to point the nose 'off axis' to increase firing opportunities for boresighted or forward hemisphere weapons. The X-31A explores that area of the envelope which lies beyond the conventional 'stall barrier', and investigates

the tactical applications. The project will also help the development of requirements for future fighters, and will itself demonstrate and validate methods of producing low-cost prototypes. MBB has already proposed using flight control software developed for the X-31A as the basis of a new flight control system for the Eurofighter EFA, demonstrating the potential spin-offs from this remarkable programme. The use of advanced aerodynamics and flight control surfaces, combined with the use of engine thrust as a flight control in its own right, are the central key to avoiding departure and to manoeuvring successfully at very low airspeeds and very high angles of attack.

OPERATORS

Flygvapnet (The Swedish air force)

Northern Air Command
F21 Luleå/Kallax
1 Spaningsflygdivisionen (Urban röd) – SF/SH 37

Southern Air Command
F10 Angleholm (forming with AJS 37)

SPECIFICATION

Saab SF 37 Viggen
generally similar to the Saab AJ 37 Viggen except in
the following particulars
Weights: maximum take-off 17000 kg (37,478 lb)

Saab SF 37 Viggen

This SF 37 (Spanings Foto, photo reconnaissance)
Viggen wears the markings of Bråvalla Flygflottilj F13,
formerly based at Norköping, which disbanded in June
1994. The wing's first squadron (1 Spaning-
flygdivisionen) flew both the SF and SH 37 (Spanings
Havsövervakning, coastal surveillance) variants. With
the advent of the AJS 37 programme, SF 37s (and SH
37s) are being allocated to the 'attack' Viggen units
around Sweden.

WING
The wing incorporates hydraulically
actuated two-section elevons on the
trailing edge. The leading edge has
compound sweep, and is extended
forward on the outer sections, outboard
of the prominent bullet fairings which
accommodate an RWR antenna.

UNIT MARKINGS
All camouflaged Flygvapnet
aircraft carry their wing
number in yellow on the
forward fuselage, along with a
two-digit individual
identification code, in red, on
the tailfin. In reconnaissance
squadrons, even numbers were
reserved for the SF 37s, while
the SH 37s had odd numbers.
Whenever possible, these two
digits coincided with the last
two of the aircraft's serial.
Most Viggens now carry wing
badges on the fin, while some
carry individual squadron
badges elsewhere.

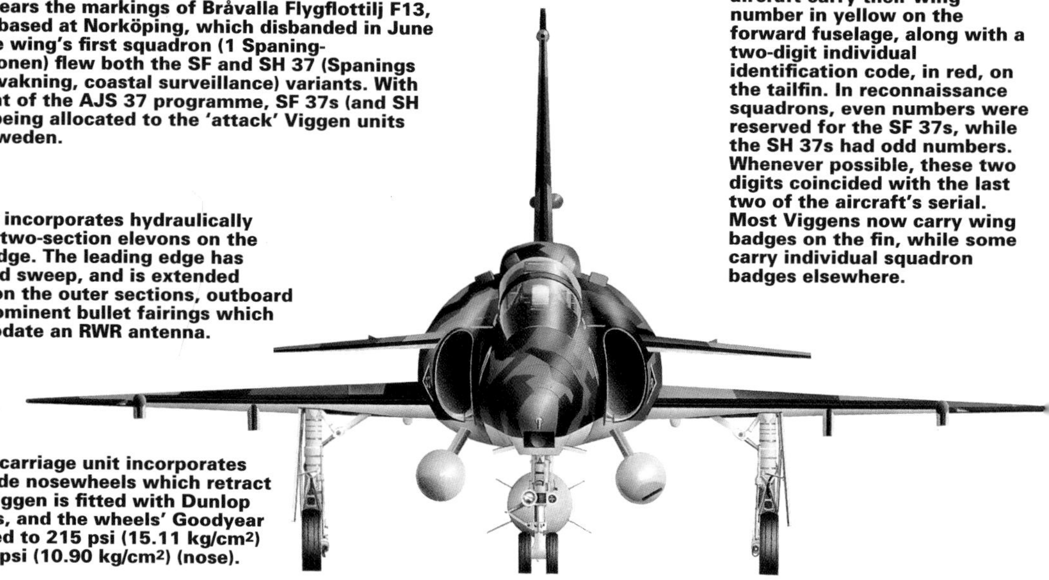

NOSE GEAR
The nose undercarriage unit incorporates
twin, side-by-side nosewheels which retract
forward. The Viggen is fitted with Dunlop
anti-skid brakes, and the wheels' Goodyear
tyres are inflated to 215 psi (15.11 kg/cm²)
(main) and 155 psi (10.90 kg/cm²) (nose).

WINDSCREEN
The Viggen's hardened, wraparound
single-piece windscreen provides not
only excellent visibility, but also
protection against birdstrikes.

CAMOUFLAGE
Apart from the majority of JA 37s, all
Viggens wear a unique four-colour
camouflage, often referred to as the
'splinter' scheme. The Flygvapen refers to
it as the 'fields and meadows' camouflage,
and it convincingly hides the aircraft at
their forest dispersal bases and in their
low-level operational environment. The
undersides remain grey, but when seen
from above the straight-edged pattern
conceals the overall aircraft shape.

FOLDING TAILFIN
One of the Viggen's more unusual
features is its folding fin. The
aircraft's rudder is of metal-bonded
honeycomb construction, and the
entire unit folds to port to facilitate
storage in underground and small
hardened shelters.

MAIN UNDERCARRIAGE
The thinness of the wing dictated the use of
tandem mainwheels, the incidental advantages
of which include better energy absorption on
landing and lower snow resistance when
taxiing. The oleos are shortened during
retraction. Built by Motala Verkstad, the
undercarriage can withstand sink rates
of up to 5 m (16 ft) per second, allowing
steep approaches and no-flare landings.

CAMERA NOSE
The SF 37 dispenses with radar and instead
carries a battery of cameras comprising three
fanned 120-mm SKA 24C, one vertical
VKA 702 infra-red and vertical
SKA 24, two 600-mm SKA 31,
and a 57-mm SKA 24 units.

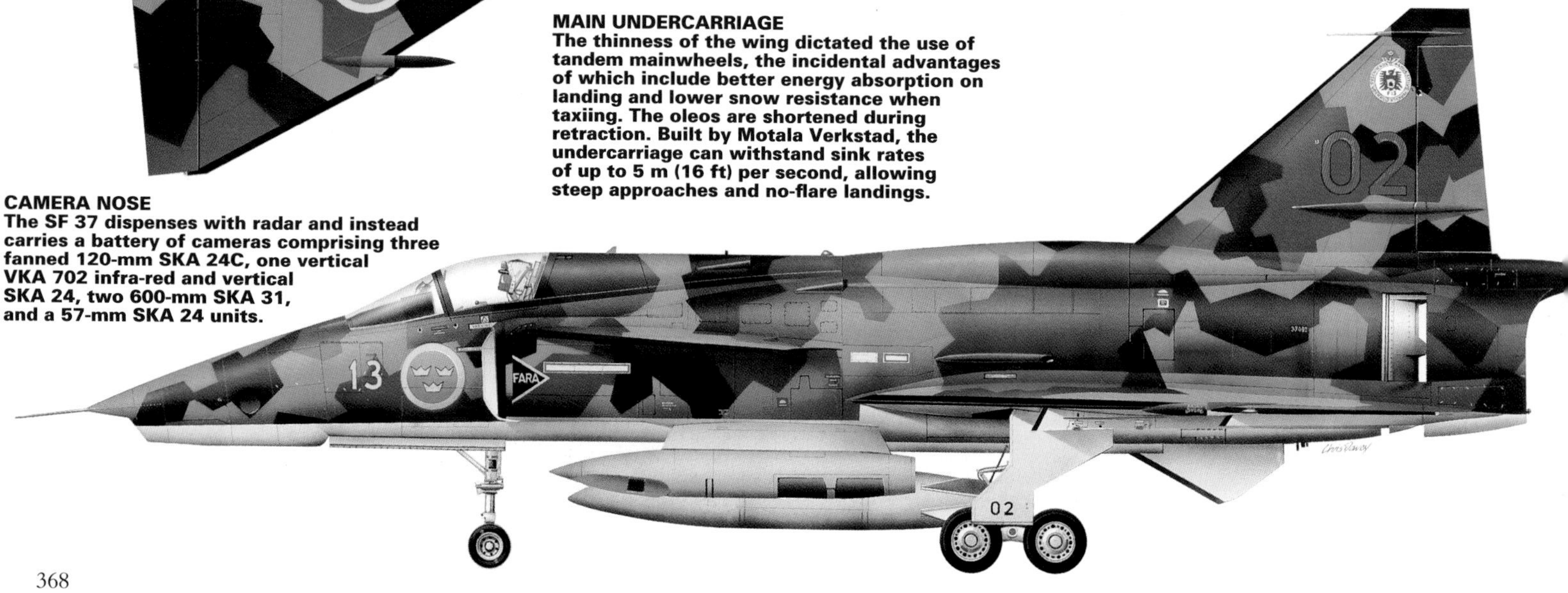

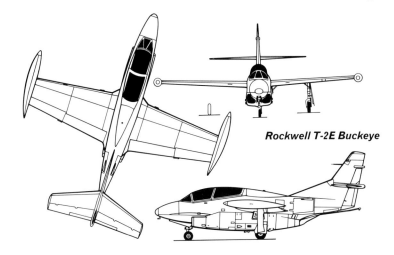

Rockwell T-2E Buckeye

flown on 21 May 1965 and entering service with Training Squadron VT-4 at NAS Pensacola in December 1965. Following evaluation of a T-2B converted to **YT-2C** configuration with two General Electric J85-GE-4 engines, 231 aircraft designated **T-2C** were built for the US Navy Air Training Command, the first production example being flown initially on 10 December 1968. At a later date, small numbers of T-2B and T-2C aircraft were converted as drone directors under the respective designations **DT-2B** and **DT-2C**. In 1982, 17 US Navy T-2Bs were removed from storage and refurbished, 15 of them later entering service to supplement T-2Cs that currently remain active.

The US Navy also procured two T-2 trainer variants (basically similar to the T-2C) on behalf of the **Venezuelan** and **Greek** air forces. The FAV received 12 **T-2D** trainers in 1973, plus an additonal 12 weapons-capable aircraft in 1976. The 19 surviving aircraft comprise 10 weapons-capable T-2Ds and nine trainers, equipping the Grupo Aéreo de Entrenamiento, based at Boca Del Rio, Maracay. Some T-2Ds flew with rebel forces during the 1992 coup

attempt. The Greek air force relies for advanced training on the 36 surviving **T-2E**s of 362 'Nestor' Mira and 363 'Danaos' Mira, of 120 Ptérix, based at Kalamata.

The T-2C is the only current variant in service with the US Navy, flying with VT-4 and VT-26 at Pensacola, FL, VT-19 at Meridian, MS, VT-23 at Kingsville, TX, and VT-26 at Chase Field, TX, in the training role. A small number served with aggressor units VF-43 at Oceana, VA, and VF-126 at Miramar, CA, for spin-training, and the Naval Test Pilot's School at Patuxent River, MD.

SPECIFICATION

Rockwell T-2C Buckeye

Wing: span 38 ft 1.5 in (11.62 m) with tip tanks; aspect ratio 5.7; area 255.00 sq ft (23.69 m2)
Fuselage and tail: length 38 ft 3.5 in (11.67 m); height 14 ft 9.5 in (4.51 m); tailplane span 17 ft 11 in (5.46 m); wheel track 18 ft 6 in (5.64 m)
Powerplant: two General Electric J85-GE-4 turbojets each rated at 2,950 lb st (13.1 kN)
Weights: empty 8,115 lb (3680 kg); maximum take-off 13,179 lb (5977 kg)

Fuel and load: internal fuel 691 US gal (2616 litres); external fuel none; maximum ordnance 640 lb (290 kg)
Speed: maximum level speed 'clean' at 25,000 ft (7620 m) 469 kt (540 mph; 840 km/h)

Range: range 909 nm (1,047 miles; 1685 km)
Performance: maximum rate of climb at sea level 6,200 ft (1890 m) per minute; service ceiling 40,415 ft (12320 m)

Rockwell **Commander twins**

Shrike Commander was the final name used by Rockwell for the piston-engined light business twin originated in 1948 by Aero Design and Engineering (later Aero Commander). With engines of varying power, the aircraft were identified as **Aero Commander 500**, **Commander 560**, **Commander 680** and – with a lengthened fuselage – **Commander 680FL**. The name Shrike Commander applied to the seven-seat **Models 500V** and **500S**, built until 1979, and the 11-seat **Model 680FL** became the **Grand Commander**.

Commander twins have entered military service in the liaison and aerial survey roles. The **Argentinian** armed forces are the principal operators of the type, with a 12-strong fleet of **Model 500U**s used by the air force for medevac service and a single

Commander 560 for army transport duties. The **Mexican air force** uses 15 Model 500s for light transport and photographic reconnaissance. Other users of the Model 500 include the **Royal Bahamas Defence Force**, **Benin** armed forces and **Burkina Faso air force**. The long-fuselage Model 680FL serves with the armies of **Greece** and **Indonesia**, and a single Aero Commander 680 in **Dominica**.

SPECIFICATION

Rockwell Shrike Commander

Wing: span 49 ft 0.5 in (14.95 m); aspect ratio 9.45; area 255.00 sq ft (23.69 m2)
Fuselage and tail: length 36 ft 9.75 in (11.22 m); height 14 ft 6 in (4.42 m); tailplane span 16 ft 9 in

Thirteen of the 15 Aero Commander 500s that have been delivered to the air force of Argentina (SADEN) still serve in support of regional commands and HQs.

(5.10 m); wheel track 12 ft 11 in (3.95 m
Powerplant: two Textron Lycoming IO-540-E1B5 flat-six piston engines each rated at 290 hp (216 kW)
Weights: empty equipped 4,608 lb (2090 kg); maximum take-off 6,750 lb (3062 kg)
Fuel and load: internal fuel 156 US gal (590 litres); external fuel none
Speed: maximum level speed 'clean' at sea level 187 kt

(215 mph; 346 km/h); maximum cruising speed at 9,000 ft (2745 m) 176 kt (203 mph; 326 km/h)
Range: range 936 nm (1,078 miles; 1735 km)
Performance: maximum rate of climb at sea level 1,340 ft (408 m) per minute; service ceiling 19,000 ft (5915 m); take-off distance to 50 ft (15 m) 1,915 ft (584 m) at maximum take-off weight; landing distance from 50 ft (15 m) 2,235 ft (681 m) at normal landing weight

Rockwell **Turbo Commander**

The early success of the Aero Commander 500/560 series had indicated a worthwhile market for a larger-capacity, higher-speed derivative. In its initial form, the Commander Model 680FL (Grand Commander) was first flown on 29 December 1962, incorporating a 1.88-m (6-ft 2-in) fuselage stretch to seat pilot and co-pilot on a separate flight deck, and from four to nine passengers according to cabin layout. A pressurised development with turboprops was flown by Aero Commander (then a division of Rockwell Standard) as the **Turbo Commander 690**, on 31 December 1964. Successive variants were built by Rockwell until February 1981, when the production line was sold to Gulfstream American and the name was changed to the **Gulfstream/Jetprop 840, 900, 980** or **1000**, depending on engine power and gross weight.

Military users of the Turbo Commander

in its various manifestations include the **Colombian air force** (one Turbo Commander 680V), the **Honduran air force** (one Gulfstream 1000), the **Iranian air force** (four Turbo Commander 681/Bs), **army** (five Turbo Commanders 690/As) and **navy** (four Turbo Commander 690/As), the **Mexican air force** (one Turbo Commander 690B, one Gulfstream 980, three Gulfstream 1000s) and **navy** (two Gulfstream 1000s), the **Pakistan army** (two Gulfstream 840s), the **Royal Thai air force** (one Turbo Commander 690A for survey duties), and the **Turkish air force** (one Turbo Commander 690A).

SPECIFICATION

Rockwell Turbo Commander 690B

Wing: span 46 ft 8 in (14.22 m); aspect ratio 8.19;

A sizeable number of Rockwell's sleek Turbo Commander family are in military service. This is one of the Pakistan army's two Gulfstream 840s.

area 266.00 sq ft (24.71 m2)
Fuselage and tail: length 42 ft 11.75 in (13.10 m); height 14 ft 11.5 in (4.56 m); tailplane span 19 ft 9.25 in (6.03 m); wheel track 15 ft 5 in (4.70 m)
Powerplant: two Garrett TPE331-5-521K turboprops each rated at 700 ehp (522 ekW)
Weights: empty 5,910 lb (2681 kg); maximum take-off 10,250 lb (4649 kg)
Fuel and load: internal fuel 384 US gal (1453 litres); external fuel none
Speed: maximum level speed 'clean' at 12,000 ft

(3660 m) 285 kt (328 mph; 528 km/h); economical cruising speed at 25,000 ft (7620 m) 231 kt (266 mph; 428 km/h)
Range: range 1,360 nm (1,567 miles; 2522 km) with maximum fuel and a 1,817-lb (824-kg) payload, or 701 nm (808 miles; 1300 km) with maximum payload
Performance: maximum rate of climb at sea level 2,849 ft (868 m) per minute; service ceiling 32,900 ft (10030 m); take-off run 1,434 ft (437 m) at maximum take-off weight; take-off distance to 50 ft (15 m) 2,216 ft (675 m) at maximum take-off weight

Rockwell/Deutsche Aerospace (MBB) **X-31A**

Flying under the programme title **EFM (Enhanced Fighter Maneuverability)**, the **X-31A** is an experimental aircraft intended to evaluate advanced aerodynamic and propulsive systems with the aim of increasing fighter agility, widening the flight

envelope and conferring an ability to point the nose 'off axis' to increase firing opportunities for boresighted or forward hemisphere weapons. The X-31A explores that area of the envelope which lies beyond the conventional 'stall barrier', and investigates

the tactical applications. The project will also help the development of requirements for future fighters, and will itself demonstrate and validate methods of producing low-cost prototypes. MBB has already proposed using flight control software developed

oped for the X-31A as the basis of a new flight control system for the Eurofighter EFA, demonstrating the potential spin-offs from this remarkable programme. The use of advanced aerodynamics and flight control surfaces, combined with the use of engine thrust as a flight control in its own right, are the central key to avoiding departure and to manoeuvring successfully at very low airspeeds and very high angles of attack.

Rockwell/Deutsche Aerospace (MBB) X-31A

MBB began work in 1977 on the project, and was joined by Rockwell in 1983. Rockwell's HiMAT RPV and MBB's TKF-90 study (a progenitor of the Eurofighter) provided useful data for the X-31, development of which was covered by a joint US/German MoU in 1986. Funding for two prototypes was provided in August 1988. Rockwell was responsible for the configuration and aerodynamics of the X-31, and assembled the aircraft, the first of which (BuNo. 164584) made its maiden flight on 11 October 1990. The second (BuNo. 164585) followed on 19 January 1991. MBB built major sub-assemblies for the aircraft (including the wings), and designed the flight control system and thrust vectoring system. The programme is managed by DARPA (acting through the US Naval Air Systems Command) and the German Ministry of Defence.

The X-31 has a cranked delta wing incorporating twist, a single fin and powered canard foreplanes, all control surfaces being actuated by a fly-by-wire flight control system. Many sub-systems were taken from existing aircraft types to minimise costs. On 14 February 1991, the first aircraft flew with a three-paddle thrust vectoring system fitted, these units deflecting the exhaust by up to 10°. A four-phase 'pure research' programme has not prevented the aircraft from being used in simulated air combat against (for example) US Navy F/A-18s, in which its unique capabilities have enabled it to gain the upper hand.

The X-31's sole purpose is to investigate low-speed, high angle-of-attack handling. From its current arrangement with thrust vectoring paddles, the aircraft will progress to a fully-tailless configuration in 1995. Already the X-31A has demonstrated a dramatic post-stall hammerhead called the 'Herbst manoeuvre'.

SPECIFICATION

Rockwell/Deutsche Aerospace (MBB) X-31A
Wing: span 23 ft 10 in (7.26 m); aspect ratio 2.51; area 226.30 sq ft (21.02 m²); canard foreplane span 8 ft 8 in (2.64 m); aspect ratio 3.18; canard foreplane area 23.60 sq ft (2.19 m²)
Fuselage and tail: length 48 ft 8.5 in (14.85 m) including probe and 43 ft 4 in (13.21 m) excluding probe; height 14 ft 7 in (4.44 m)
Powerplant: one afterburning General Electric F404-GE-400 turbofan rated at 16,000 lb st (71.17 kN)
Weights: empty equipped 11,410 lb (5175 kg); normal take-off 14,600 lb (6622 kg); maximum take-off 15,935 lb (7228 kg)
Fuel and load: internal fuel 4,136 kg (1876 kg); external fuel none; ordnance none
Speed: never exceed speed and maximum level speed 'clean' between sea level and 28,000 ft (8535 m) 1,485 kt (1,710 mph) 2752 km/h) and between 28,000 and 40,000 ft (8535 and 12190 m) Mach 1.3
Performance: maximum rate of climb at sea level 43,000 ft (13106 m) per minute; maximum operating altitude 40,000 ft (12190 m); take-off run 1,500 ft (457 m) at maximum take-off weight; take-off distance to 50 ft (15 m) 2,700 ft (823 m) at maximum take-off weight; landing distance from 50 ft (15 m) 3,700 ft (1128 m) at maximum landing weight; landing run 2,700 ft (823 m) at maximum landing weight
g limits: -4 to +9

Rockwell (Lockheed) AC-130U Spectre

The **AC-130U** is a **Lockheed C-130H Hercules** converted by Rockwell into a third-generation **Spectre** gunship for the **US Air Force**'s Special Operations Command's 16th Special Operations Squadron at Hurlburt Field, FL. Painted gunship grey in service, the AC-130U is powered by four 4,900-shp (3655-ekW) Allison T56-A-15 turboprop engines and has a crew of 13. It has a performance that is generally similar to that of the C-130H transport.

To engage ground targets in a pylon turn, the AC-130U retains the single L-60 40-mm Bofors cannon and M102 105-mm howitzer of earlier Spectre gunships. A single 25-mm GAU-12 cannon with 3,000 rounds replaces the AC-130H's two M61 cannons. The new cannon is fitted on a trainable mount, with an autonomous ammunition-handling and feed system (firing rate 1,800 shots/minute) and a stand-off range of 12,000 ft (3657 m). The AC-130U's sensors include a Hughes AN/APQ-180 main fire control radar (a derivative of the APG-70 developed for the F-15E), Texas Instruments AAQ-117 FLIR, Ball Aerospace All-Active Low-Light-Level TV with laser target designator and rangefinder (mounted in a turret under the fuselage with a 360° field of view), and Rockwell ALQ-172 jammer and expendable countermeasures package. The four IBM IP-102 mission computers are linked by a 1553B databus. Navigation is greatly facilitated by a combined INS and GPS/Navstar. Fully all-weather capable, the AC-130U is able to engage two target simultaneously.

The first AC-130U, the sole full-scale development aircraft in the series (scheduled to become an operational aircraft at a later date), made its initial flight on 20 December 1990 and entered testing at Edwards AFB, CA, in September 1991. By January 1993, one FSD and five operational AC-130Us had been completed, and delivery of the first operational aircraft to Hurlburt Field was made, after further FSD work, in June 1994.

The USAF plans to acquire 13 AC-130U models, one of these being a replacement for an AC-130H lost in the Gulf War. The AC-130H Spectre will then be transferred to the Air Force Reserve, replacing its current, surviving elderly AC-130As.

Thirteen AC-130Us will be modified from standard C-130H Hercules, becoming the USAF Special Operations Command's next-generation gunship. While its armament may appear deficient when compared to the AC-130H or AC-130A, the new Spectre's targeting systems promise unrivalled accuracy. To carry out its designated fire support, interdiction, escort, armed surveillance or air base defence missions, the AC-130U also comes equipped with INS, GPS, pilot's HUD and Spectra ceramic armour. The eight AC-130Hs in service with the 16th SOS will be replaced by AC-130Us from 1994, and already its enthusiastic crews have dubbed their new mount the 'U-Boat'.

Rogerson Hiller VS-1100/M Hornet and UH-12E

*Rogerson Hiller Corporation
2140 West 18th St, Port Angeles
Washington 98362, USA*

Demonstrated in 1985, the **Rogerson RH-1100M** prototype is a multi-mission military derivative of the **Hiller RH-1100** five-seat utility helicopter. This was derived from the original **Hiller OH-5A** observation helicopter built to the US Army's LOH (Light Observation Helicopter) specification in 1963 but produced as a refined development only for commercial and foreign customers as the **Fairchild (Hiller) FH-1100**. These are described under the Fairchild-Hiller heading. Production totalled 246 and ended in 1974, with design rights subsequently acquired by Rogerson Aircraft. The **RH-1100M** offers a variety of armament options on fuselage-side pylons, including four TOW anti-armour missiles or a pair of rocket pods or machine-guns, and provision for autopilot, FLIR anti-missile warning systems, AAM system capability, and a chin- or roof-mounted sight.

Rogerson Hiller also resumed production, in the early 1990s, of the Hiller FH-1100 as the **RH-1100C** and seven-seat **RH-110S**. These proved unsuccessful in the civil market, and the company's attention turned to the US Army's NTH (New Training Helicopter) competition, for which a design based on the Hiller UH-12E was resurrected. Rogerson Hiller began building the civil **UH-12E Hauler** in 1992, and from it developed the Soloy/Allison 250-C20B-powered **UH-12ET** for the NTH requirement. The US Army selected Bell's Model 206 Jet Ranger derivative, the TH-57 Creek, as its NTH winner, as opposed to the archaic-looking UH-12ET. Thus far, customers for the basic UH-12E have been purely civilian, including crop-spraying aircraft ordered by the Indian government and several similar examples delivered to Taiwan and Hungary.

SPECIFICATION

Rogerson Hiller RH-1100M Hornet
Rotor system: main rotor diameter 35 ft 5 in (10.80 m); tail rotor diameter 6 ft 0 in (1.83 m); main rotor disc area 985.16 sq ft (91.52 m²); tail rotor disc area 28.27 sq ft (2.63 m²)
Fuselage and tail: length overall, rotors turning 41 ft 4 in (12.60 m) and fuselage 29 ft 9.5 in (9.08 m); height overall 9 ft 2 in (2.79 m) to top of rotor head; skid track 7 ft 2¾ in (2.20 m)
Powerplant: one Allison 250-C20R turboshaft rated at 450 shp (336 kW)
Weights: empty 1,710 lb (776 kg); maximum take-off 3,500 lb (1588 kg)
Fuel and load: internal fuel 459 lb (208 kg); external fuel none; maximum payload 1,500 lb (680 kg)
Speed: maximum level speed 'clean' at sea level 116 kt (134 mph; 216 km/h); maximum cruising speed at 5,000 ft (1525 m) 116 kt (134 mph; 216 km/h)
Range: range 341 nm (393 miles; 632 km)
Performance: maximum rate of climb at sea level 1,790 ft (546 m) per minute; service ceiling 19,000 ft (5790 m); hovering ceiling 11,000 ft (4990 m) in ground effect and 6,700 ft (2040 m) out of ground effect

Saab 32 Lansen

The transonic Avon-engined two-seat **Saab 32 Lansen** was operational with front-line squadrons of the **Flygvapen** (Swedish air force) until late 1979, when the last two S 32C squadrons disbanded in F11 (Recce). The Lansen was originally built from 1953-60 for attack (287 **A 32A**s), all-weather/night-fighting (120 **J 32B**s) and photo reconnaissance (45 **S 32C**s).

Lansens still operate in electronic warfare, aggressor and target-towing roles with F16M (Målflygdivision – MFD) detachment at Malmen, Linköping. This unit flies 25 Lansens, in three forms. Its chief equipment is 13 **J 32E** ECM-configured versions, which the squadron flies in its primary role as an EW aggressor training unit for the Swedish air force, army and naval units. In

their ECM role, the Lansens can carry nose-mounted G24 jammers covering L-, S- and C- (NATO D-, E- & F- and G- & H-) bands for use against ground- and ship-based radars. Other integral equipment includes Mera VHF and UHF radio jammers and Ingeborg homing receivers. The J 32E can also carry Adrian S- and C- band, and Petrus X- (NATO I- and lower-J band) underwing jamming pods, in addition to two Bofors BOZ3 chaff dispensers

The J 32E is a conversion of the two-seat J 32B all-weather fighter, which was replaced by the J35 Draken in 1969. MFD still retains three J 32Bs as crew trainers. The third Lansen variant remaining in use is the **J 32D** target tug. Five J 32Ds, with yellow Dayglo patches, are uses to tow VM-6

aerial targets and occasionally act as radar targets themselves. Some target tugs were operated by a civil contractor, Swedair, but these have now been reabsorbed by the

Flygvapen. For approximately seven months of the year, two J 32Ds are based at Fällfors air base, in northern Sweden, supporting air-to-air gunnery training.

The Lansen was the first supersonic Swedish aircraft, and a prototype exceeded Mach 1 as early as 1952. This is one of F16M's remaining ECM J 32Es.

Saab 35 Draken

In 1949 the Swedish **Flygvapen** drew up an ambitious requirement for a new fighter to replace the Saab J 29, calling for a performance 50 per cent better than that of fighters then entering service with other nations. After extensive flight-testing on the seven-tenths scale **Saab 210**, three full-scale **Saab 35 Draken** prototypes with the distinctive double-delta wing followed. The first flew on 25 October 1955. The rest of the structure was largely conventional, apart from the wing configuration which was fitted with powered controls for each movable surface. These were operated by two tandem hydraulic jacks fed by separate hydraulic systems. Other novel features included a raked ejection seat (of indigenous design) which increased pilot tolerance to g forces. The prototypes were each powered by an imported Rolls-Royce Avon turbojet, but initial production **J 35A**s featured the licence-built Svenska Flygmotor (later Volvo Flygmotor) RM6B with a more efficient afterburner developed by the Swedes.

Air-defence J 35A Drakens first equipped Flygflottilj 13 (F13) at Norköping in March 1960. The subsequent air-defence **J 35B** variant had a lengthened rear fuselage and introduced twin retractable tailwheels intended primarily to permit more effective aerodynamic braking during the landing run; most J 35As were later modified to this configuration. The next air-defence version was the **J 35D**, featuring the more powerful RM6C engine plus more advanced radar and equipment. The final air-defence variant for the Flygvapen was the **J 35F**, developed from the J 35D. The J 35F introduced more capable radar and collision-course fire control, deleted one 30-mm cannon and introduced licence-built Hughes Falcon AAMs and, in the **J 35F-II**, a Hughes IR sensor. The J 35F also introduced a new, more bulged canopy, an improved autopilot and a ground-air datalink. Fuel capacity was increased to 880 Imp gal (400 litres), making the J 35F a much longer-ranged fighter than its precursors. A new afterburner further improved performance. One other variant for the Swedish air force was the reconnaissance **S 35E**, based on the J 35D, with the radar nose replaced by a pressurised nose section housing five cameras as standard.

All of these variants have now been retired, although 64 (or 66, according to some sources) J 35Fs were converted to **J 35J** standard. These continue to serve with the Flygvapen's F10 at Angelholm. The J 35J modification added extra armament capability in the form of two additional pylons under the engine intake ducts. The J 35J also gained improvements to the radar, IR sensor, IFF, cockpit and avionics.

A two-seat trainer version, designated **Sk 35C**, made its maiden flight on 30 December 1959. Initially a new-build development of the J 35A, but later including also

J 35A conversions, the Sk 35C seated pupil and instructor in tandem in a modified forward fuselage that provided the additional rear position for the instructor without any increase in fuselage length. In Flygvapnet service, the Sk 35C initially equipped the Draken OCU that was based at Uppsala. A handful remain active today with F10 at Angelholm to provide training and standardisation for J 35J pilots.

In the mid-1960s, Saab began work on export versions of the Draken. The **J 35H** offered and demonstrated to Switzerland was stillborn, but more successful was a development of the J 35F that incorporated structural strengthening for the carriage of loads up to a maximum of 4500 kg (9,921 lb) and had increased internal and external fuel capacity. Designated **Saab 35X**, this soon proved of interest to the **Danish air force**, which ordered a total of 46 during 1968/69. This included the basic **A 35XD** fighter-bomber (Danish designation **F-35** – 20 built); a basically similar **RF-5** reconnaissance/fighter version that differs by having the camera nose of the S 35E Draken but retaining wing cannon (20 built); and **TF-35** (**Sk 35XD**) trainer similar to the Swedish Sk 35C but retaining one wing cannon. Denmark's Drakens were extensively modified during the mid-1980s, receiving a Lear-Siegler nav/attack computer, a Singer-Kearfott INS, a Marconi Series 900 HUD and a Ferranti LRMTS in a reprofiled nose. Esk 725 disbanded on 1 January 1992, passing on some of its F-35s to Esk. 729. This, the last Danish Draken unit, disbanded at Karup on 31 December 1993.

Finland was the second export customer, ordering 12 Saab 35Xs in 1970 for assembly by Valmet Oy. Six Swedish air force J 35Bs (designated **J 35S**, with radar removed) were first leased for training purposes and then purchased in 1975, becoming **J 35BS**. Finland has also procured 24 J 35Fs and Sk 35Cs from Sweden, the first five being redesignated **J 35FS** and the trainers becoming **J 35CS**. They currently equip Nos 11 and 21 squadrons, based at Rovaniemi and Tampere, repspectively.

The final Draken customer was **Austria**, whose air force was directed to purchase 24 surplus Swedish J 35Ds in 1985. The Swedish aircraft were selected instead of ex-Saudi Lightnings offered by BAe. The aircraft are fitted with J 35F-style bulged canopies, but apparently retained J 35D avionics and radar. Redesignated **J 35Ö**, the first Drakens were handed over in June 1987 and, after training in Sweden, the aircraft were ferried to Austria during 1988 and 1989. They equip No. 1 Staffel (Blau) and No. 2 Staffel (Rot), of the Fliegerregiment II's Überwachungsgeschwader, at Graz-Thalerhof. These aircraft have a podded reconnaissance system and acquired AIM-9P-3s in January 1994.

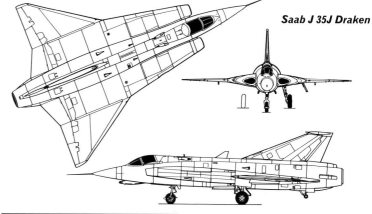

Saab J 35J Draken

SPECIFICATION

Saab J 35J Draken

Wing: span 9.40 m (30 ft 10 in); aspect ratio 1.77; area 49.20 m² (529.60 sq ft)

Fuselage and tail: length 15.35 m (50 ft 4 in); height 3.89 m (12 ft 9 in); wheel track 2.70 m (8 ft 10½ in)

Powerplant: one Volvo Flygmotor RM6C turbojet (licence-built Rolls-Royce Avon Series 300 turbojet fitted with a Swedish-designed afterburner) rated at 12,790 lb st (56.89 kN) dry and 17,650 lb st (78.51 kN) with afterburning

Weights: empty 8250 kg (18,188 lb); normal take-off 11400 kg (25,132 lb); maximum take-off 12270 kg (27,050 lb) interceptor. 15000 kg (33,069 lb) attack

Fuel and load: internal fuel 4000 litres (1,057 US gal); external fuel up to 5000 litres (1,321 US gal) in

1275-litre (280-US gal) and 500-litre (132-US gal) drop tanks; maximum ordnance 2900 kg (6,393 lb)

Speed: maximum level speed 'clean' at 36,000 ft (10975 m) more than 1,147 kt (1,321 mph; 2126 km/h) and at 300 ft (90 m) 793 kt (913 mph; 1469 km/h)

Range: ferry range 1,533 nm (1,765 miles; 2840 km); combat radius 304 nm (350 miles; 564 km) on a hi-lo-hi attack mission with internal fuel or 388 nm (477 miles; 720 km) on a hi-lo-hi attack mission with two 1,000-lb (454-kg) bombs and two drop tanks

Performance: maximum rate of climb at sea level 34,450 ft (10500 m) per minute with afterburning; service ceiling 65,600 ft (19995 m); take-off run 650 m (2,133 ft) at 11400 kg (25,132 lb) with afterburning; take-off distance to 50 ft (15 m) 960 m (3,150 ft) at normal take-off weight with afterburning or 1550 m (5,085 ft) at maximum attack mission take-off weight; landing run 530 m (1,739 ft) at 8800 kg (19,400 lb)

Above: Swedish J 35Js of F10 are adopting this two-tone grey scheme as they pass through overhaul.

Below: Austrian J 35Ös have been more active recently, owing to the nearby war in former Yugoslavia.

Saab AJ 37 Viggen

In the early 1960s, when seeking a multi-role J 32 replacement, Saab began studies of a relatively low-cost single-seat single-engined type capable of supersonic flight at low altitude and Mach 2 at height, but able to take off and land in 500 m (1,640 ft). This was necessary to operate from the SAF's STRIL 60 integrated air defence system and BASE 90 concept dispersed airstrips, comprising lengths of roadway 800 x 9 m (2,625 x 29.5 ft) in size. For good short-field performance, Saab pioneered the use of flap-equipped canard foreplanes with a delta-wing configuration in its new **System 37**, allowing over 50 per cent more lift than conventional delta types, in conjunction with an integral thrust-reverser for the RM8 turbofan.

For reliability, this powerplant was based on the 14,771-lb st (65.7-kN) commercial Pratt & Whitney JT8D-22 turbofan, developed and built by Svenska (later Volvo) Flygmotor for supersonic flight, and with a Swedish afterburner providing over 70 per cent thrust increase to around 26,014 lb (115.7 kN) for take-off. An autoland technique (again pioneered by Saab) for minimum distance involved automatic approach speed control and selection of reverse thrust in a no-flare touchdown with compression of the 16.4 ft (5 m) per second oleos of the tandem mainwheels. The initial **AJ 37** attack aircraft, soon named **Viggen** (Thunderbolt), incorporated many other features novel for its time, including a Saab CK-37 miniaturised digital air data and nav/attack computer, SRA head-up display for primary flight data, and a Cutler-Hammer AIL microwave beam landing guidance system. A rocket-boosted Saab ejection seat provided zero-zero escape capabilities.

Built with extensive bonded alloy honeycomb structures, the first of seven prototypes made its initial flight on 8 February 1967, followed by the second aircraft on 21

September of the same year and the third on 29 March 1968. On 5 April 1968, the Swedish government authorised the air force to order 175 AJ/SF/SH 37s for delivery from 1971, and by April 1969 all six single-seat prototypes were flying, the last fully representative of the initial production attack variants. The first of these became airborne on 23 February 1971, deliveries starting soon afterwards in June to F7 at Satenas to replace A 32A Lansens; four attack squadrons became operational with AJ 37s by mid-1975. Seven of the Flygvapen's nine attack squadrons were scheduled to re-equip with AJ 37s, and the 109 aircraft built of this variant eventually equipped two squadrons each in F6, F7 and F15 at Karlsborg, Satenas and Söderhamn after F7's third squadron disbanded. The second unit at Söderhamn is the AJ 37 OCU, equipped jointly with two-seat Sk 37 Viggen trainers for type conversion. F6 disbanded at Karlsborg/Vastagota on 30 June 1994, while F15 will re-organise to declare two full AJ 37 squadrons (instead of the current 1½), using former F6 aircraft. AJ 37s are currently being upgraded to **AJS 37** standard (see separate entry), extending their useful life into the next century.

WEAPON OPTIONS

AJ 37 primary armament is the fire-and-forget Saab RB 15F anti-ship missile or Rb 75 TV-guided (AGM-65) Maverick ASMs on two to four underwing or three fuselage weapons pylons. Older weapons such as the the Saab Rb 04E anti-ship missile, and Rb 05A ASM are used largely for training. For their secondary interception role, the early Viggens carried licence-built Rb 27/28 Hughes AIM-4 Falcon or Rb 24 AIM-9B/J Sidewinder AAMs. Today Viggens are more likely to carry the AIM-9L version, designated Rb 74. With no built-in gun, the AJ 37 could carry underwing

pods containing 30-mm ADEN cannon as an alternative to four 2.95-in (7.5-cm) Bofors M57 or 5.3-in (13.5-cm) M70 six-round rocket pods, or up to five tonnes (11,023 lb) of conventional FFV 120-, 250-, 500- or 600-kg bombs or M71 Virgo retarded bombs. Fire control is via an Ericsson PS-37A X-band monopulse radar with a large-diameter cassegrain antenna.

OPERATORS

Flygvapnet (The Swedish air force)

Middle Air Command
F15 Söderhamn
1 Attackflygdivisionen (Olle röd)
2 Attackflygdivisionen (Olle blaü- OCU)

Southern Air Command
F10 Angelholm (forming one squadron with AJS 37)

First Fighter Bomber Air Command
F7 Satenas/Skaraborgs (introducing JAS 39)
1 Attackflygdivisionen (Gustav röd)
2 Attackflygdivisionen (Gustav blaü)

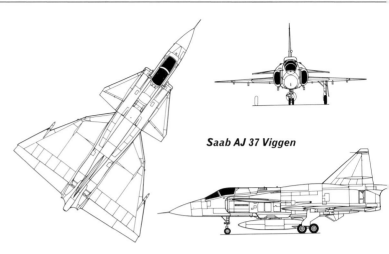

Saab AJ 37 Viggen

SPECIFICATION

Saab AJ 37 Viggen
Wing: span 10.60 m (34 ft 9.25 in); aspect ratio 2.45; area 46.00 m2 (495.16 sq ft); canard foreplane span 5.45 m (17 ft 10.5 in); canard foreplane area 6.20 m2 (66.74 sq ft)
Fuselage and tail: length 16.30 m (53 ft 5.75 in) including probe; height 5.80 m (19 ft 0.25 in); wheel track 4.76 m (15 ft 7.5 in); wheel base 5.60 m (18 ft 4.5 in)
Powerplant: one Volvo Flygmotor RM8A turbofan (Pratt & Whitney JT8D-22 turbofan with Swedish-designed afterburner and thrust reverser) rated at 14,770 lb st (65.70 kN) dry and 26,015 lb st (115.72 kN) with afterburning
Weights: empty equipped about 11800 kg (26,014 lb); normal take-off 15000 kg (33,069 lb); maximum take-off 20500 kg (45,194 lb)
Fuel and load: internal fuel about 5700 litres (1,506 US gal); maximum ordnance 6000 kg (13,228 lb)
Speed: maximum level speed 'clean' at 11000 m (36,090 ft) more than 2125 km/h (1,146 kt; 1,320 mph)
Range: combat radius more than 1000 km (539 nm; 621 miles) on a hi-lo-hi attack mission, or more than 500 km (270 nm; 311 miles) on a lo-lo-lo attack mission
Performance: climb to 10000 m (32,810 ft) from brakes-off in less than 1 minute 40 seconds with afterburning; service ceiling about 18300 m (60,040 ft); take-off run about 400 m (1,312 ft); landing run about 500 m (1,640 ft) at normal landing weight

The AJ 37 'attack' Viggen is a potent weapon, made even more so by its wartime operation from concealed roadway strips hidden in Sweden's densely wooded landscape. The AJS 37 upgrade now underway will result in a truly multi-role Viggen.

Saab JA 37 Viggen

For its dedicated interception role, with a secondary ground-attack capability, Saab developed the **JA 37 Viggen**. Although little changed externally from the attack variant, the interceptor introduces some fundamental changes under the skin, with avionics, armament, engine and structural modifications. The JA 37's primary sensor is the Ericsson PS-46/A medium-PRF multi-mode X-band pulse-Doppler look-down/shoot-down radar, which has four air-to-air modes and a look-down range in excess of 48 km (30 miles). New avionics include an upgraded and higher-capacity Singer-Kearfott SKC-2037 central digital computer and KT-70L INS, Decca Doppler Type 72 nav

radar, Garrett AiResearch LD-5 digital air data computer, Saab-Honeywell SA07 digital AFCS, Svenska Radio integrated electronic display system, and an SRA HUD. The RM8B turbofan is uprated by Volvo to develop 16,600 lb (73.84 kN) maximum dry thrust and 28,109 lb (125 kN) with afterburning. This extra power allows the JA 37 to fly at Mach 1.2 at low altitude, and exceed Mach 2 at higher altitudes. Airframe changes include a wing restressed for a higher load factor, a fuselage stretch of 10 cm (4 in) ahead of the wing to accommodate the modified powerplant, a 10-cm (4-in) fin extension to that of the Sk 37 trainer, and four instead of three elevator actuators

under each wing. Radar trials, designed to intercept from east or west low-flying high-speed targets, such as cruise missiles, began in 1973 in a Lansen testbed aircraft that had made 87 test flights by late 1974.

Four AJ 37 prototypes were modified to JA 37 standard for the development programme, the first making its initial flight on 27 September 1974, a few days after SAF orders for the first 30 production Viggen interceptors. A fifth JA 37 prototype, which initially flew in 1975, was built to pre-production standards, the first series aircraft following on 4 November 1977.

In March 1980, the Swedish government authorised a third batch of 59 JA 37s, increasing overall production of this variant to 149 and the Viggen total to its final figure of 330. JA 37s were planned to replace Flygvapnet's J 35 Drakens in the 1978-85 period

and to arm at least eight of the 10 Draken air defence squadrons at that time. Those re-equipped eventually comprised two *divisionen* (squadrons) each of F4, F16 and F21 at Ostersund, Uppsala and Lulea, and one *divisionen* each in F13 and F17 at Norköping and Ronneby. As part of the overall reduction in Swedish wings, F13 was disbanded on 30 June 1994, and the JA 37s of its single squadron, 2 Jaktflygdivisionen (Martin blä), were dispersed among other units.

A specially-equipped Viggen interceptor, the **Saab 37E Eurofighter**, was put forward as a possible alternative to the multinational European Fighter Group in 1975. Despite their many advanced features and excellent all-round performance, no Viggens have ever achieved any export sales, mostly because of Sweden's rigidly non-aligned political policies during the Cold War.

By mid-1994 most of Sweden's 'fighter' Viggen force had adopted this two-tone air superiority grey scheme, with high-visibility Dayglo orange codes on the tail and above the wings. These two-digit codes are usually (though not always) the last two numbers of the aircraft's full (five-digit) serial. Radio callsigns are allocated to the Flygvapen's four JA 37 Viggen wings (and all Swedish armed forces flying units) according to the wing number's position in the Swedish (phonetic) alphabet; thus, F21 uses the name 'Urban', F4 'David', and so forth. Each wing is divided into two or more squadrons (divisionen), always in the order red, blue and yellow.

WEAPON OPTIONS

The JA 37 introduces an integral high-velocity 30-mm Oerlikon KCA revolver cannon (offset to port) with 150 rounds mounted in a ventral pack, and aimed by a new radar-based weapons sight. JA 37 primary armament comprises up to six AAMs. Standard BVR weapon is the medium-range, semi-active radar-guided, all-weather BAeD Rb 71 Sky Flash. Rb 74 (AIM-9L) IR-homing Sidewinders are fielded for short-range work. Seven to nine weapons pylons similar to those on the AJ 37 accommodate up to 13,000 lb (5897 kg) of external stores. These include four pods each containing six Bofors 5.3-in (13.-5cm) rockets for air-to-surface use.

OPERATORS

Flygvapnet (The Swedish air force)
Northern Air Command
F4 Ostersund/Froson
1 Jaktflygdivisionen (David röd)
2 Jaktflygdivisionen (David blä)
F21 Luleä/Kallax
2 Jaktflygdivisionen (Urban blä)
3 Jaktflygdivisionen (Urban gul)

Middle Air Command
F16 Uppsala
1 Jaktflygdivisionen (Petter röd)
2 Jaktflygdivisionen (Petter blä)

Southern Air Command
F17 Ronneby/Belkinge
1 Jaktflygdivisionen (Quintus röd)
2 Jaktflygdivisionen (Quintus blä)

SPECIFICATION

Saab JA 37 Viggen
generally similar to the AJ 37 Viggen except for the following particulars:
Fuselage and tail: length 16.40 m (53 ft 9.75 in) including probe; height 5.90 m (19 ft 4.25 in); wheel base 5.69 m (18 ft 8 in)

Powerplant: one Volvo Flygmotor RM8B turbofan (Pratt & Whitney JT8D-22 with Swedish-designed afterburner and thrust reverser) rated at 16,200 lb st (72.06 kN) maximum military dry and 28,110 lb st (125.04 kN) with afterburning
Weights: normal take-off 15000 kg (33,069 lb); maximum take-off 17000 kg (37,478 lb) interceptor, or 20500 kg (45,194 lb) attack
Speed: maximum level speed 'clean' at 10975 m (36,000 ft) more than 2126 km/h (1,147 kt; 1,321 mph)
Performance: climb to 32,800 ft (10000 m) in less than 1 minute 40 seconds from brakes-off with afterburning; service ceiling about 60,000 ft (18290 m); take-off run about 400 m (1,312 ft) at typical take-off weight; landing run about 500 m (1,640 ft) at normal landing weight

Saab SF 37/SH 37 Viggen

Designed as an S 35E Draken replacement, the **SF 37** adaptation of the AJ 37 is equipped for all-weather day and night overland reconnaissance with low- and high-altitude film cameras giving complete horizon-to-horizon lateral coverage, plus a VKA 702 infra-red camera recording thermal images in place of the nose radar. Twin ventral pods also house night cameras and illumination equipment, the photoflash system operating with light just outside the visible wavelengths. A Red Baron IR line-scan system, with the standard active and passive underwing ECM pods, may also be carried, but the SF 37 has no attack capability and armament is normally confined only to defensive Rb 74 (AIM-9L) AAMs. All nine cameras have automatic exposure control and image motion compensation controlled by the aircraft's central computer.

First flight of the prototype SF 37 was on 21 May 1973, and deliveries began to the SAF in early 1977. The last of 28 SF 37s built was handed over for delivery to F21 at Lulea in northern Sweden on 7 February 1980, thereby ending AJ 37 series production. SF 37s also equip additional single reconnaissance squadrons in F13 at Norköping in the south-east and F17 at Ronneby in the south. In addition, they operate in conjunction with specially-equipped 'S 37 Intelligence Platoons', comprising mobile evaluation centres with briefing, processing, evaluation and interpretation facilities.

The **SH 37** was modified from the AJ 37 as a successor to the Saab S 32C Lansen for all-weather sea surveillance and patrol, with secondary maritime strike capability, and fitted with modified radar, plus ventral night reconnaissance and SKA 24D 600-mm lens long-range camera pods. Underwing ECM pods are also normally carried, as well as AAMs on the outboard wing stations. Both the SF and SH 37s normally operate with a ventral fuselage drop tank. F13 at Norköping formed the first SH 37 squadron in late 1976, and the 27 Viggens of this type built between 1977 and 1979 served alongside the SF 37s to equip the three mixed reconnaissance squadrons in F13, F17 and F21. F13 disbanded on 30 June 1994, and F17 has also relinquished its reconnaissance role, though SF 37s remained at Ronneby in mid-1994. F10, and other units, are currently receiving the first AJS 37 Viggens, the combined attack/reconnaissance version (described seperately). Reconnaissance Viggens will benefit chiefly from improved (air-to-air) armament capability in the AJS 37 programme, and they are currently being distributed throughout the Flygvapen's AJ 37 units.

F13 was an SF 37 (Spanings Foto, or photo reconnaissance) operator until its 1994 disbandment. Some of its aircraft were transferred to F21, currently the sole SF/SH 37 unit.

Right: The SH 37 maritime radar-reconnaissance Viggen closely resembles the AJ 37. Only its podded cameras and LOROP betray its mission.

OPERATORS

Flygvapnet (The Swedish air force)

Northern Air Command
F21 Luleå/Kallax
1 Spaningsflygdivisionen (Urban röd) – SF/SH 37

Southern Air Command
F10 Angleholm (forming with AJS 37)

SPECIFICATION

Saab SF 37 Viggen
generally similar to the Saab AJ 37 Viggen except in the following particulars
Weights: maximum take-off 17000 kg (37,478 lb)

Saab SF 37 Viggen

This SF 37 (Spanings Foto, photo reconnaissance) Viggen wears the markings of Bråvalla Flygflottilj F13, formerly based at Norköping, which disbanded in June 1994. The wing's first squadron (1 Spaning-flygdivisionen) flew both the SF and SH 37 (Spanings Havsövervakning, coastal surveillance) variants. With the advent of the AJS 37 programme, SF 37s (and SH 37s) are being allocated to the 'attack' Viggen units around Sweden.

WING
The wing incorporates hydraulically actuated two-section elevons on the trailing edge. The leading edge has compound sweep, and is extended forward on the outer sections, outboard of the prominent bullet fairings which accommodate an RWR antenna.

NOSE GEAR
The nose undercarriage unit incorporates twin, side-by-side nosewheels which retract forward. The Viggen is fitted with Dunlop anti-skid brakes, and the wheels' Goodyear tyres are inflated to 215 psi (15.11 kg/cm²) (main) and 155 psi (10.90 kg/cm²) (nose).

WINDSCREEN
The Viggen's hardened, wraparound single-piece windscreen provides not only excellent visibility, but also protection against birdstrikes.

UNIT MARKINGS
All camouflaged Flygvapnet aircraft carry their wing number in yellow on the forward fuselage, along with a two-digit individual identification code, in red, on the tailfin. In reconnaissance squadrons, even numbers were reserved for the SF 37s, while the SH 37s had odd numbers. Whenever possible, these two digits coincided with the last two of the aircraft's serial. Most Viggens now carry wing badges on the fin, while some carry individual squadron badges elsewhere.

CAMOUFLAGE
Apart from the majority of JA 37s, all Viggens wear a unique four-colour camouflage, often referred to as the 'splinter' scheme. The Flygvapen refers to it as the 'fields and meadows' camouflage, and it convincingly hides the aircraft at their forest dispersal bases and in their low-level operational environment. The undersides remain grey, but when seen from above the straight-edged pattern conceals the overall aircraft shape.

FOLDING TAILFIN
One of the Viggen's more unusual features is its folding fin. The aircraft's rudder is of metal-bonded honeycomb construction, and the entire unit folds to port to facilitate storage in underground and small hardened shelters.

MAIN UNDERCARRIAGE
The thinness of the wing dictated the use of tandem mainwheels, the incidental advantages of which include better energy absorption on landing and lower snow resistance when taxiing. The oleos are shortened during retraction. Built by Motala Verkstad, the undercarriage can withstand sink rates of up to 5 m (16 ft) per second, allowing steep approaches and no-flare landings.

CAMERA NOSE
The SF 37 dispenses with radar and instead carries a battery of cameras comprising three fanned 120-mm SKA 24C, one vertical VKA 702 infra-red and vertical SKA 24, two 600-mm SKA 31, and a 57-mm SKA 24 units.

Saab Sk 37 Viggen

With the Viggen fulfilling its role as the Flygvapen's primary combat aircraft system, there was a pressing need for a trainer version. The **Sk 37 Viggen** (Skol, or School) tandem two-seat trainer was developed simultaneously with the AJ 37. This variant is somewhat unusual in having two separate cockpits for pilot and instructor. The stepped rear instructor's cockpit is fitted with a bulged canopy and twin lateral periscopes, replacing some electronics and a forward fuel tank. Fuel capacity was partially restored by a permanently-mounted ventral fuel tank (although a centreline tank is also invariably carried). Other changes include a 10-cm (4-in) taller fin to restore stability after modification with the deeper forward fuselage. Because of its height, even the standard AJ 37 fin can be folded on the ground to allow clearance for the

SAF's cavern-based hangars. Despite its radome, the Sk 37 has no radar and, therefore, no radar navigation capability (and limited operational capability), having to rely on Doppler and DME. The first Sk 37 was the seventh Viggen prototype and initially flew on 2 July 1970. Sk 37 deliveries started to F7 in June 1972, and 15 of just 17 trainers built equip the Viggen OCU part of F15 at Söderhamn, alongside AJ 37s.

Hålsingge Flygflottilj F15 currently fields '1½' squadrons, as 2 Attackflygdivisionen/ Typingflyingskola (Olle blä) flies both AJ and Sk 37s. The wing's first squadron (1 Attack-flygdivisionen, Olle röt) flies AJ 37s also, but the Sk 37s train Viggen pilots for all versions, even the JA 37. F15 is due to absorb some of the former F6 AJ 37s, and will ultimately possess two full attack squadrons, in addition to the OCU *divisionen*.

The small number of Sk 37s have been heavily utilised throughout their lives, restricting operations today to essential training only.

Saab AJS 37 Viggen

Modification of Viggens to **AJS 37** standard, plus approval for the Swedish government's proposals to disband one and a half Viggen squadrons, were among the Swedish Parliamentary Defence Committee recommendations adopted in June 1992. This SEK300 million ($50 million) upgrade proposed by Saab in mid-1991 involves 115 surviving AJ, SF and SH 37s, and will combine their various specialised systems, plus enhanced computer power from a multi-processor/databus, to produce the multi-role AJS 37 Viggen. This will use some of the JAS 39 Gripen's weapon systems, including the Saab Rb 15F anti-ship missile, BK/DWS sub-munitions dispenser, various advanced AAMs,

and the JAS 39's planned reconnaissance and ECM pods, for which Ericsson and MBB have been competing. Modified AJS 37s started to re-equip four Flygvapnet squadrons in 1993, being allocated to units on completion of conversion rather than forming dedicated AJS 37 units. All but the former SF 37s (which retain their camera nose) will be fitted with the SH 37's radar.

There will be no external differences to distinguish upgraded aircraft, which will in fact be completed to slightly differing standards depending on the original airframe (AJ, SF or SH 37). The SF and SH 37 will benefit chiefly from improved armament options, particularly the ability to carry additional air-to-air missiles.

The last production AJ 37 Viggen was also one of the first AJS 37 conversions to be completed. Older weapons, such as these Rb 05 ASMs, will be now be replaced by the JAS 39's Rb 15 ASMs and DWS 39 sub-munitions dispensers.

Saab JAS 39 Gripen

By early 1980, with Viggen deliveries continuing apace, it was clear that if Sweden was to maintain its status as a military airframe manufacturer, and its policy of operating only indigenous combat aircraft, work on a successor to the Saab Viggen would have to begin soon. Strict government control dictated an aircraft design that would cost only 60-65 per cent more than the Saab 37, and be only half the weight. Its primary role would be as a fighter interceptor, with an important, but secondary, attack mission. It was to be a fully multi-role aircraft, in marked contrast to the mission-specific Viggen family. It was also hoped that this new aircraft would provide a replacement for the ageing Sk 60 trainer fleet.

After IG JAS submitted its initial proposal in June 1981, over seven years passed before the prototype made its maiden flight.

The JAS Industry Group was formed by Saab, Volvo Flygmotor, Ericsson and FFV, and their bid to develop the new aircraft was accepted by the Swedish government. Following the cancellation of the Saab 38 (B3LA) light-attack/advanced trainer project in February 1979, Saab began development of preliminary designs for a single-seat, single-engined, fly-by-wire, delta-winged aircraft, with an all-flying canard. Thirty per cent of its eight-tonne final weight was to be of composite materials.

The proven General Electric F404J turbofan was chosen as the powerplant. Volvo Flygmotor would share assembly and testing of the engine, designated RM12, with the American manufacturer. The RM12 had a dry rating of 12,150 lb (54.05 kN), or 17,800 lb (79.18 kN) with a new Volvo/GE afterburner, to give the Gripen all-altitude supersonic performance with only fixed rectangular intakes.

Unlike the Viggen, the Gripen lacks a thrust reverser. It gains its short-field performance from its large, all-moving canard foreplanes, which can be rotated downwards through almost 90° to assist ground-braking in conjunction with the rear-fuselage lateral airbrakes. These are augmented by saw-toothed leading-edge flaps and linked with the four drooping elevon control surfaces through the full-authority triplex digital FBW system with an analog back-up. As a control-configured vehicle for extra agility, the Gripen is claimed by Saab to be the first inherently unstable canard production fighter and features 40 computers interlinked via three MIL STD 1553B databuses.

Ericsson was tasked with developing a new multi-mode, pulse-Doppler, X-band PS-046 (later PS-05) radar, while FFV developed the nav/attack systems. The HOTAS cockpit would have three Ericsson EP-17 multi-function cockpit displays and a wide-angle holographic HUD, and it was planned to integrate a FLIR system with the radar and avionics. A Martin-Baker S10LS zero-zero ejection seat replaces Saab systems used in all previous Flygvapnet combat jets.

Contracts between FMV (Defence Materiel Administration), the Swedish defence procurement agency and IG JAS for the newly designated **JAS 39** were signed in June 1982. These contracts (worth SEK11.5 billion, then $1.87 billion) covered the development of five prototypes and an initial production run of 30 aircraft. Options for a further 110 aircraft were also undertaken. In June 1984, the Riksdag (Swedish parliament) gave the go-ahead to this JAS (Jakt, Attak, Spanning: fighter,

The Gripen relies far more heavily on aerodynamic braking than its predecessors, using its all-moving canards for short stops.

Saab JAS 39 Gripen

The Gripen's initial task will be to replace the Flygvapen's 'first-generation' Viggens, the attack AJ 37s. The smaller JAS 39 will carry the same weapons, including the Rb 15F AShM and Rb 75 Maverick.

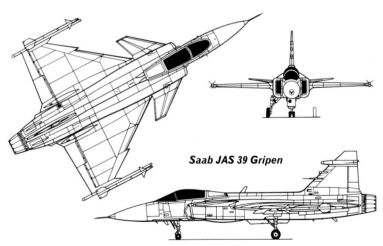

Saab JAS 39 Gripen

attack, reconnaissance) project as an affordable answer to the Flygvapen's need for a third-generation combat aircraft. New facilities were built by Saab at Linköping to cope with the demand. By now the name **Gripen** (Griffin) had been adopted. The projected requirement was for 350 aircraft, with the first in service by 1992, rather than 1990 as originally hoped .

Engine tests began in 1984, and five test rigs had accumulated over 800 running hours by June 1985. A full-size mock-up was completed by early 1986, differing from the initial conceptual drawings by being a more stocky and box-like design, while still retaining its small size. The first flight was planned for 1986, but problems with the software for the complex fly-by-wire system (developed by Lear-Siegler, now GEC Astronics) caused this date to be set back progressively. The project was also troubled by rising costs, which threatened its cancellation by parliament. Finally, the aircraft was rolled out at Linköping on 26 April 1987 (Saab's 50th anniversary). The first JAS 39 (39-1) flew for a total of 51 minutes on 9 December 1988, in the hands of Stig Holmstrom. From then, the aircraft's performance helped it to survive a critical funding review in January of the following year, when the threat of an off-the-shelf purchase, instead of the Gripen, finally subsided.

A major set-back was suffered on the sixth flight, when a failure of the flight control system caused the crash of the first aircraft on 2 February 1989. The pilot, Lars Rådeström, was unhurt but for a broken arm. Major software corrections were undertaken in the United States by Calspan, with a modified T-33. This caused another 15 months' delay before the second prototype flew on 4 May 1990, putting the programme some three years behind schedule, though the JAS 39 returned to flying status in May. After two investigations, the FMV underlined its commitment to the JAS 39, and ultimately the government compensated Saab for its loss. Problems were also encountered with the RM12, which suffered from 'thrust-droop', and cracks in the compressor blades, but these, too, were soon rectified. The new PS-05/A radar was tested in a modified Viggen (until the end of

1991), and both air and ground tests proved encouraging, if time-consuming. A study for a projected two seat **JAS 39B** aircraft was begun in 1989, while the single-seat programme continued with the second aircraft (39-2) flying on 4 May 1990. This was followed by 39-4 (with the first full avionics fit on 20 December 1990, 39-3 (the first with full radar and avionics fit) on 25 March 1991 and 39-5 on 23 October 1991.

Flight tests (costed at only $2,500 per hour) soon revealed that aerodynamic drag and induced drag, in clean configuration were 10 per cent lower than expected. Any engine thrust anomalies had been ironed out, and airfield performance was above the specification. In freeflow, the canards are the primary brakes, deployed from a landing speed of 220 km/h (136 mph). Gripens have repeatedly demonstrated their ability to operate from a standard Base 90 runway, i.e. a hardened road-strip, typically 800 m x 9 m (2600 ft x 30 ft). The JAS 39 has been flown to a load of 9g and the static test airframe has been subjected to 230 per cent of the limit load before failure (design requirement was for 180 per cent only). In October 1991, Saab submitted its costing proposal for the **JAS 39B** operational trainer and the follow-on Batch 2 order for 110 single-seat aircraft. By January 1992 the flight test programme had reached 300 flights, and that year was joined by the first production aircraft (39-101) allocated after the crash of the prototype. Problems were encountered with the APU and the environmental control systems. A possible replacement APU has been mooted to overcome the current units high failure rate.

June 1992 saw the final go-ahead for the Batch 2 aircraft and the JAS 39B, for an adjusted cost of SEK18 billion ($3 billion). To be tasked primarily with conversion and tactical training, the JAS 39B operational trainer will have a performance equivalent to that of the single-seater but involves a 40 per cent change from that type, including a 65.5-cm (25.8-in) fuselage stretch. The rear cockpit is the same as the front, barring a HUD, but HUD imagery can be monitored on one of the displays. By mid-1994, the prototype (39-800) was taking shape at Linköping, along with 39-801 and a fatigue test airframe. Ejection seat sled tests commenced in the US in July 1993 and are progressing. First flight is planned for 1996 with deliveries in 1988.

A milestone in the test programme was reached on 21 April 1993, when the 1,000th test flight took place. The four prototypes were joined by the first production Gripen (39-101) on 4 March 1993, when it made its maiden flight, piloted by Lars Rådeström. The second production example (39-102) became the first to be handed over to the Flygvapen, at Linkoping on 8 June 1993, being delivered to F7 at Satenas the same day. On 18 August, 39-101 was lost in a dramatic crash during an air display over Stockholm, and the pilot (Lars Rådeström again) ejected. Saab later announced that the accident was caused by "the flight control system's high amplification of stick commands in combination with large, rapid stick movements by the pilot. This led to the stability margin being exceeded, and the aircraft entered a stall." A contributing factor

39-102, the second production Gripen, was formally handed over to the Swedish air force in June 1993 when it was escorted from Linköping to its future home of Satenas by a pair of F7 AJ 37s.

or was the late display of the STYRSÄK (flight attitude) warning, giving the pilot too little time to react. Flying was suspended until 29 December 1993, after the fitting of updated flight control software.

By mid-1994, after nearly 1,300 flights, the remaining Gripens had completed 60 per cent of the total flight test programme, verifying 80 per cent of their contractual obligations. Weapons tests have included Rb 74 (AIM-9L) firings at 6g, Rb 75 (AGM-65) firings at 3g and successful separations from DWS 39, Rb 15 and external tanks. Flying was briefly suspended between 14 January and 15 February 1994, after Volvo identified blade failure in an RM12 low-pressure fan, caused by defective fuel injectors leading to uneven fuel flow and vibration. With deliveries resumed, 15 engines have so far been delivered.

By mid-1994, Gripens 39-105 to -113 are in check-out or final assembly. Saab expects to deliver 140 aircraft between 1993 and 2002, in addition to 14 JAS 39Bs. These aircraft will replace eight squadrons of AJ 37 Viggens, but there will then be a need to replace the younger JA 37 aircraft in the air defence role. A total Gripen purchase of 300 aircraft is likely, for an overall programme cost of SEK57.8 billion ($7.8 billion). Ten were planned to be delivered to the Flygvapen by the end of 1994 (though this is likely to be reduced to five, as so far only 39-104 and -105 have been handed over), and they will remain at Linköping, not Satenas. The first squadron (F7's 2 divisionen) will begin conversion by October 1995, and already Saab has a modification programme in hand to recall the initial 30 Batch 1 aircraft and update their software to Batch 2 standard. These will feature a PP12 processor for the EP17 MFDs, replacing the current EP1 and EP2 units which are twice the size and weight.

With a planned production rate of 20 to 30 aircraft a year, Saab is also working hard to sell the Gripen abroad, in a marked reversal of former policy. At Farnborough in 1992, Swedish Defence Minister Anders Bjoerck revealed SAF plans for a so-called upgraded 'Turbo Gripen', or **JAS 39C**, for a third production batch. This would have an uprated RM12 turbofan, Ericsson D80E computers and more weapons, for both potential export and for further Flygvapnet deliveries to replace the last of some 350 Viggens. Finland's fighter evaluation prior to its 1992 F/A-18 order included over 250 Gripen sorties by two Finnish test pilots, while in the same year Defence Minister Bjorck discussed possible **JAS 39X** (export) purchases.

WEAPON OPTIONS

Basic armament for all roles includes an integral 27-mm Mauser BK27 cannon under the port centre fuselage and two wingtip-mounted Rb 74 (AIM-9L) or other IR-homing AAMs, supplemented by four underwing and a ventral weapons pylons for external stores. These include medium-range active-radar AAMs, ASMs, Saab Rb 15F anti-ship missiles, DWS 39 or other cluster-bomb dispensers,

conventional or retarded bombs, air-to-surface rockets, fuel tanks or FLIR, reconnaissance and electronic warfare pods. In August 1994 the FMV announced a buy of 100 Hughes AIM-120 AMRAAMs to serve as an interim BVR missile for the JAS 39 force. This purchase, much smaller than the 500 expected, was made in favour of the MATRA Mica or BAe Active Sky Flash. However, it leaves the way open for the future acquisition of a more advanced long-range weapon, such as the S225X missile under development with BAe (already a close Saab partner), Thomson-CSF and GEC-Marconi.

SPECIFICATION

Saab JAS 39A Gripen
Wing: span 8.00 m (26 ft 3 in)
Fuselage and tail: length 14.10 m (46 ft 3 in); height 4.70 m (15 ft 5 in); wheel track 2.60 m (8 ft 6½ in); wheel base 5.30 m (17 ft 4¾ in)
Powerplant: one Volvo Flygmotor RM12 turbofan (General Electric F404-GE-400) rated at 12,140 lb st (54.00 kN) dry and 18,100 lb (80.51 kN) with afterburning
Weights: operating empty 6622 kg (14,599 lb); normal take-off about 8000 kg (17,637 lb); maximum take-off 12473 kg (27,498 lb)
Fuel and load: internal fuel 2268 kg (5,000 lb); maximum ordnance 6500 kg (14,330 lb)
Speed: maximum level speed 'clean' at 36,000 ft (10975 m) 1,147 kt (1,321 mph); 2126 km/h)
g limits: +9

Below: Gripen 39-101, the first production aircraft, joined the surviving four prototypes in the test programme after the loss of 39-1. 39-102 wears what will probably be the standard scheme for service aircraft, despite their attack role.

Above: In addition to Sidewinders, this Gripen (39-2) carries a dummy DWS 39 for separation tests. Two camera pods are carried, to starboard and on the centreline.

Below: The same aircraft is seen here with a less advanced, but equally effective, load of Bofors rocket pods. It, too, carries an all-aspect test camera pod.

Saab 105

Developed as a private venture, the **Saab 105** is a trainer and light ground-attack aircraft that is also capable of other roles, including reconnaissance, liaison and executive transport (for which the side-by-side ejection seats can be replaced by four fixed seats). The first of two prototypes flew on 29 June 1963, and the following year the Saab 105 was ordered into production for the Swedish air force, the first of 150 flying on 27 August 1965.

Designated **Sk 60**, the Saab 105 is powered by two Turboméca Aubisque turbofans and entered service in the spring of 1966 with F5, the Flygvapen Basic Flying Training School at Ljungbyhed, in southern Sweden. Most were later given armament hardpoints, gunsights and associated equipment. Variants include the **Sk 60B** with light attack capability, and the **Sk 60C**, which is equipped for photographic reconnaissance with a Fairchild KB-18 camera in the nose, yet retains a ground-attack capability. The Sk 60A and Sk 60B are virtually identical, though no Sk 60A ever carries underwing pylons. However, while all aircaft carry (F5)

codes on the nose, Sk 60B codes are higher to avoid a dielectric panel on the nosecone. The **Sk 60D** is a special crew trainer, while the **Sk 60E** is a four-seat liaison variant.

Over 100 Sk 60A/B/Cs remain in service, primarily in the training role, with four squadrons of F5 and with 5 divisionen (Petter Swarz) of F16, based at Uppsala. The latter unit also supports the Royal Air Cadet School. Every Sk 60 wears the unit identifier of F5, regardless of where it is based, as all aircraft are distributed from a central maintenance pool. All basic flying training is undertaken at the GFU (Basic Flying Training School) at Ljungbyhed, while weapons

qualification is the responsibility of the Uppsala-based GTU. This unit has a complement of 16-18 aircraft, and in time of war would act as an autonomous *Lätt Attackenheter* (Light Attack unit), along with a second unit drawn from F5 proper.

Three Sk 60Ds and 16 Sk 60Es remain in service, small numbers being assigned to the *Sambandsflygrupp* of each tactical wing. These aircraft are assigned to liaison and instrument check ride duties.

Between 1988 and 1991, the Sk 60 fleet underwent a programme of structural modifications that increased the aircrafts's g limits from 4.5 to 6 and added new ejection

Saab 105

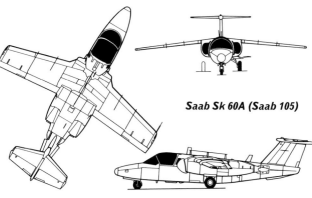

Saab Sk 60A (Saab 105)

Above: The Saab 105Ös of Austria's 1 Staffel, Jagdbombergeschwader, Fliegerregiment III, wear a fin badge depicting a cartoon tiger on a red '1', with a blue background encircled by a green laurel wreath.

Below: Designated Sk 60 in Flygvapnet service, the Saab 105 is fulfils a number of roles from light transport to light attack. It is also the mount of the national aerobatic team, 'Team 60', comprising six Sk 60s drawn from F5.

seats and rewinging, therbey extending their working lives to 2000. In a programme costing SEK900 million, 115 aircraft (with an option on another 20) will be further upgraded from 1995 to extend their service to 2010 and beyond. Two contracts cover design and modification of a single Sk 60, spares supply and engine maintenance for the first 10 years of operation. Chief among the improvements planned is re-engining

with 1,900-lb (8.45-kN) Williams Rolls FJ44 two-shaft turbofans. This will dramatically improve their overall and single-engine performance, in addition to appreciably reducing running costs, and aircaft noise. A first flight is planned for spring 1995, to be followed by nine conversions in 1996. From then, the bulk of the modifications will be carried out in the workshops of the Air Force Flight Academy, at Ljungbyhed, until their completion in 1998.

The **Saab 105XT** development, powered by J85 turbojets, first flew on 29 April 1967. Fuel capacity was increased to 2050 litres (451 Imp gal), two 500-litre (110-Imp gal) underwing drop tanks also being available. In addition to enhanced performance, the 105XT had improved avionics, and a strengthened wing allows the underwing load to be increased to 2000 kg (4,409 lb). This version can perform interception and target-towing roles. IR-guided missiles such as Sidewinder are carried for day interceptor duties. Forty aircraft designated **Saab 105Ö** were built for the **Austrian air force**. These aircraft were the country's only air defence assets for a period, pending delivery of Saab Drakens. Thirty survivors currently fly with Fliegerregiment III at Hörsching, employed on ground attack and reconnaissance duties. Two squadrons are identified by colour, 1 Staffel being 'gelb' and 2 Staffel 'grün'. The latter unit undertakes the reconnaissance mission with

large underwing camera pods, and provides aircraft for advanced and weapons training. A handful have had their ejection seats removed to be reconfigured as four-seat liaison aircraft.

SPECIFICATION

Saab 105 (Sk 60B)
Wing: span 9.50 m (31 ft 2 in); aspect ratio 5.54; area 16.30 m2 (175.46 sq ft)
Fuselage and tail: length 10.50 m (34 ft 5 in); height 2.70 m (8 ft 10 in); wheel track 2.00 m (6 ft 7 in); wheel base 3.90 m (12 ft 9.5 in)
Powerplant: two Turboméca Aubisque turbofans each rated at 7.29 kN (1,638 lb st)
Weights: basic empty 2510 kg (5,534 lb); normal take off 4050 kg (8,929 lb); maximum take-off 4500 kg (9,921 lb)
Fuel and load: internal fuel 1400 litres (370 US gal); external fuel none; maximum ordnance 700 kg (1,543 lb)
Speed: maximum level speed 'clean' at 6000 m (19,685 ft) 765 km/h (413 kt; 475 mph) and at sea level 720 km/h (388 kt; 447 mph); maximum cruising speed at 6000 m (19,685 ft) 685 km/h (370 kt; 426 mph)
Range: ferry range 1780 km (960 nm; 1,106 miles); standard range 1400 km (756 nm; 870 miles)
Performance: maximum rate of climb at sea level 1050 m (3,445 ft) per minute; climb to 9000 m (29,530 ft) in 15 minutes; service ceiling 12000 m (39,370 ft); take-off run 610 m (2,000 ft) at 4000 kg (8,818 lb); take-off distance to 15 m (50 ft) 940 m (3,084 ft) at 4000 kg (8,818 lb); landing distance from 15 m (50 ft) 880 m (2,887 ft); landing run 550 m (1,804 ft)

Saab **MFI-15 Safari and MFI-17 Supporter**

In 1967 Saab began the design of a two/three-seat lightplane for training and other utility duties, based largely on the **MFI-9 Minicom** two-seat lightplane. Six armed **MFI-9B**s (flown by mercenary pilots) were used by the Biafran air force during the four-year civil war. In 1968 construction began of a **Saab MFI-15** prototype (SE-301) that first flew on 11 July 1969. A monoplane of all-metal construction with a conventional tail unit, it had fixed tricycle (or optional tail-wheel) landing gear, a 119-kW (160-hp) Avco Lycoming IO-320-B2 flat-four piston engine, and a braced, shoulder-mounted wing incorporating unusual limited forward

sweep. Beneath an upward-hinged canopy were two side-by-side seats, with space behind them for baggage or an optional rear-facing third seat. Dual controls were standard, with provision for IFR instrumentation and a radio. Early tests led to the adoption of a T-tail layout (with an all-moving tail-plane) reducing the risk of damage by debris and a new uprated Lycoming engine. The modified prototype resumed flying on 26 February 1971, entering production as the **Safari**. Most were sold for civil use, but some were delivered to military customers. The first two production examples were sold in 1973 to **Sierra Leone** for pilot train-

ing, and subsequently sold in 1978. **Norway** ordered an initial batch of 16 in 1981 for basic training as replacements for ageing Saab Safirs. Attrition replacements of three and four were received in 1982-83 and 1987, respectively. The 19 surviving MFI-15s are used for pilot screening at Vaernes.

In early 1972, the second Safari was modified with six hardpoints for up to 300 kg (661 lb) of ordnance including rockets, two twin-machine gun pods, or six Bantam wire-guided ATMs. First flown as the **MFI-17** on 6 July 1972, the type was named **Supporter** when offered for sale to air arms. When Saab ended manufacture in the late 1970s, the combined Safari/Supporter production total was approximately 250, including a small number for military use. **Denmark** received 32 Supporters (designated **T-17**) in 1976, primarily for pilot training. Nine were supplied to the army for artillery-spotting, observation and liaison, and the remainder went to the air force for pilot training at the Flyveskolen at Avnø (where they are also used to initially train army pilots) and for liaison duties. **Pakistan** received a substantial number of Supporters from 1974-75, the majority of which were manufactured locally under licence as the PAC Mushshak (described separately).

The remaining customer was the **Zambian air force**, which received 20 MFI-17s in 1977-78 for both COIN and training duties.

SPECIFICATION

Saab MFI-17 Supporter
Wing: span 8.85 m (29 ft 0.5 in); aspect ratio 6.58; area 11.90 m2 (128.09 sq ft)
Fuselage and tail: length 7.00 m (22 ft 11.5 in); height 2.60 m (8 ft 6.5 in); tailplane span 2.80 m (9 ft 2.25 in); wheel track 2.30 m (7 ft 6.5 in); wheel base 1.59 m (5 ft 2.25 in)
Powerplant: one Textron Lycoming IO-360-A1B6 flat-four piston engine rated at 200 hp (149 kW)
Weights: empty equipped 646 kg (1,424 lb); normal take-off 1125 kg (2,480 lb); maximum take-off 1200 kg (2,646 lb)
Fuel and load: internal fuel 190 litres (50.2 US gal); external fuel none; maximum ordnance 150 kg (330 lb)
Speed: maximum level speed 'clean' at sea level 236 km/h (127 kt; 146 mph); cruising speed at optimum altitude 208 km/h (112 kt; 129 mph)
Performance: maximum rate of climb at sea level 246 m (807 ft) per minute; service ceiling 4100 m (13,450 ft); take-off run 205 m (673 ft) at normal take-off weight; take-off distance to 15 m (50 ft) 385 m (1,263 ft) at normal take-off weight; landing distance from 15 m (50 ft) 390 m (1,280 ft) at normal landing weight
g limits: -3 to +6 lightly-loaded aerobatic or -1.76 to +4.4 utility

The Kongelige Danske Flyvevaaben's (Danish air force) Saab Supporters are still very active in their training and liasion roles. The Flyveskolen aircraft operate from Avnø, on the island of København, while others are attached to the transport unit, Esk 721 based at Vaerløse. Army MFI-17s fly from Kompagni, alongside Fennecs and Hughes 500s.

Saab 91 Safir

The **Saab-91 Safir** was a three-seat cabin monoplane of cantilever low-wing configuration which had retractable tricycle landing gear and was powered by a 130-hp (97-kW) de Havilland Gipsy Major 1C inline engine. Following the first flight of the prototype in 1945, successful testing led to the first production version, the **Saab-91A**, which differed by having the more powerful de Havilland Gipsy Major 10 engine. Interest in this aircraft by the **Swedish air force** as a primary trainer led to a prototype powered by a 190-hp (142-kW) Avco Lycoming O-435-A flat-six engine, first flown on 18 January 1949. This was adopted by the Flygvapen as a standard trainer as the **Sk 50**, built by Saab with the same powerplant as the **Saab-91B**. It could be equipped to carry guns, practice bombs or rockets, and served also with the air forces of Ethiopia and Norway. For training, this version was also adopted by a number of European airlines. The **Saab-91C**, first flown in September 1953, differed from its predecessors by having four seats. The final production version was the **Saab-91D**, which introduced a number of improvements, including a new Avco Lycoming O-360-A1A engine, disc brakes and other advanced equipment that offered weight saving. Twenty-four Saab-91Ds were sold to the **Austrian air force**. When production ended, a total of 323 Safirs had been built.

Austria's last 15 Safirs served with the Ubungsstaffel of the Pilotenschule at Zeltweg, students then progressing to the PC-7. These veterans were retired in 1992. Safirs can still be found in Flygvapen markings, but the type is no longer on charge with the air force. Retired from their final role as liasion aircraft, Sk 50s have been disposed of to base flying club. Many retain full camouflage and markings with roundels, but are now civil registered.

Saab 340

The **Saab 340** 37-seat regional transport was originally developed in partnership with Fairchild and first flew on 25 January 1983. It has been a wholly Swedish programme since November 1985. By June 1994, 355 aircraft were in service. The original **340A** has been replaced by the **340B** featuring General Electric CT7-9B turboprops for improved 'hot-and-high' performance, higher weights, increased tailplane span and improved payload/range capability.

To date, only one example has been sold to a military customer. This aircraft is a Saab 340B (c/n 170) purchased for the Swedish air force. Delivered in February 1990 under the military designation **Tp 100** and serialled '10001', it is based at Stockholm-Tullinge with the Royal Flight. A current development of the Saab 340 holds the promise of significant future orders. In early 1993, Sweden chose the Saab 340B as an airborne early warning platform, carrying an Ericsson Erieye side-looking radar in a canoe fairing above the fuselage. Erieye is a long-range, S-band, pulse-Doppler radar which

The Flygvapen's Royal Flight operates a single VIP-configured Saab 340B, with the air force designation Tp 100.

uses a phased array antenna housed in a 9-m (29-ft 6-in) fairing and weighing some 900 kg (1,984 lb). The radar has a detection range of over 300 km (186 miles) against small airborne targets, from a cruising altitude of 8000 m (26,000 ft). The aircraft has been dubbed the Saab **340AEW&C**, as it also has a command and control role with one or more command consoles in the cabin, along with IFF/SSR interrogators, ESM capability, INS and GPS navigation systems and secure voice and datalinks. The prototype first flew, without the radar antenna, on 17 January 1994, and with the antenna on 1 July. It was fitted out by Hunting Ltd in the UK (as are all Saab 340s) before returning to Sweden for flight tests and delivery to the Flygvapen in early 1995. Several other nations have shown interest, including Australia.

This retouched picture illustrates the final configuration of the Swedish air force's Saab 340AEW&C.

Sabreliner Corp. (North American/Rockwell) Sabreliner/T-39 Sabre

Sabreliner Corportaion
6161 Aviation Drive, St Louis
Missouri 63134, USA

In 1956, when the **USAF** announced it sought a small jet transport and training aircraft on an off-the-shelf basis, North American Aviation (NAA) had such a design, which was renamed as the **N.A.246 Sabreliner**. The prototype (N4060K) was rolled out at the manufacturer's Inglewood plant on 8 May 1956, and made its maiden flight on 16 September at Palmdale. As the only aircraft to actually fly (despite competition from eight other manufacturers), North American had presented the USAF with a *fait accompli*, and was notified that the Sabreliner had won the UTX competition.

The USAF placed an initial order for seven aircraft, designated **T-39A** (**N.A.265**). These were fitted with 13.35-kN (3,000-lb) Pratt & Whitney J60-P-3 engines. While the T-39As took shape, the USAF decided the type would make a suitable radar trainer for its F-105Ds. Consequently, the sixth T-39A was converted to **T-39B** (**N.A.265-20**) standard. On 15 January 1960 a follow-on order for 35 aircraft was placed, the first four of which would be T-39Bs. The first T-39A flew on 30 June 1960, operational deliveries commenced on 4 June 1962, and the last of 143 T-39As was delivered in late 1963. T-39Bs had slightly larger noses to house the F-105's R-14 radar and APN-131 Doppler. Lastly came three **T-39F** 'Teeny Weeny Weasels', which were As modified to train F-105G 'Wild Weasel' crews.

In 1961 the **US Navy** began to order the **T3J-1**, a navalised T-39B equipped with Magnavox APQ-94 radar, to train pilots and RIOs for its Crusaders and Phantoms. In November 1962, before this version had actually flown, the USAF and USN designation system was brought into line and the T3J-1 became the **T-39D** (**N.A.265-30**). Forty-two were delivered to the Navy by November 1964.

North American offered civil versions as the Pratt & Whitney JT12A-8-powered **Sabreliner 40**, and later stretched it to become the 10-seat **Sabreliner 60**. On 22 September 1967, NAA merged with the Rockwell-Standard Corporation to become the North American Rockwell Corp. and this later evolved into the Sabreliner Division of Rockwell International. The USN next ordered seven Sabreliner 40s in the form of **CT-39E**s (briefly **VT-39E**) in May 1967 for fleet support with TACAN and less-plush interiors. An order for the Sabreliner 60 was placed in September 1971. The first two were also designated **CT-39E**, until the **CT-39G** title was applied, and 10 were acquired for the Navy and **Marine Corps**.

For the civil market, Rockwell later developed the enlarged **Sabreliner 70** in 1970 with 'stand-up cabin' (later renamed **Sabre 75**), the General Electric CF700D-2-powered **Sabre 80** in 1972 (later renamed **Sabre 75A**) and finally, in 1976, the Garrett TFE731-3-powered **Sabre 65**. The Sabre 65 featured a supercritical wing developed by the Reisbeck Corp. By the early 1980s the company's financial position was far from secure and only the Sabre 65 remained in production. On 1 January 1982 production at El Segundo ceased, and the plant's lease expired on that day. There followed a hiatus of over a year until July 1983, when Rockwell finally sold the production rights for the aircraft to the St Louis-based Sabreliner Corporation.

In 1987 Sabreliner was awarded a five-year contract to support USAF and USN T-39s, and also completed a SLEP on 10 USAF aircraft, delivered in 1988. Sabreliner's most recent activities include the Undergraduate Naval Flight Officer (UNFO) programme at NAS Pensacola. The UNFO contract covers the training of of US Navy RIOs in 17 modified **T-39N** radar trainers, all converted by Sabreliner from civil Sabre 40s from 1991. With the exception of one **NT-39B** in service with the 412th TW, Edwards AFB, the T-39 is virtually out of service with the USAF. In addition to the UNFO aircraft, the USN operates two CT-39Es and five CT-39Gs (attached to VR-40, CFSLW and the Dept of the Navy). These serve alongside the USMC's six CT-39Gs (attached to two Station Operations and Engineering Squadrons, and the HQ unit).

Other military users include **Argentina** (two Sabre 75As operated by the army and air force), **Ecuador** (two Sabreliner 40/As, two Sabre 60s and one Sabre 75 operated by the Ministerio de Defence Nacional), **Mexico** (two Sabre 60s operated by the army and navy) and **Sweden** (two Sabreliner 40s, operated as testbeds under the local designation **Tp 86**).

Above: Perhaps the last active Sabre in the USAF inventory is this NT-39B (seen here with underslung jamming pod) flown by the 453rd TS, 412th TW.

Right: Sweden also uses its two Sabreliner 40s (Tp 86s) as test aircraft. Recently they have been involved in the first successful tests of a synthetic airborne radar system that can detect buried objects.

Scaled Composites (Rutan Model 151) ARES

Scaled Composites Incorporated
Hangar 78, Mojave Airport, Mojave
California 93501, USA

The **Agile Response Effective Support (ARES)** aircraft was designed by Burt Rutan and built by his Scaled Composites company over the period 1985-1990. First flying on 19 February 1990, it closely matches a US Army proposal for a Low Cost Battlefield Attack Aircraft (LCBAA) drawn up in 1981, and is claimed to be of interest to developing countries as well as more advanced nations.

The prototype **Rutan Model 151** (N151SC) is essentially a proof-of-concept vehicle and features an unusual fuselage configuration, comprising an engine intake to port and a gun to starboard. The 25-mm five-barrelled GAU-12/U cannon is installed in a 'focused depression' in the lower forward fuselage to shield the cockpit canopy from the blast, and so that the gun blast impinges on the forward fuselage and counteracts recoil. The JT15D turbofan is offset 8° to port of the centreline and is served by a similarly offset circular intake to avoid ingesting gases from the gun; the jetpipe is curved to align the efflux along the fuselage axis. Both features contribute to low radar reflectivity by shielding the compressor and turbine. Twin booms carrying fins and rudders shield jet efflux from IR detection. For

agility, the wing layout uses compound sweep angles of 50° (inner wing) and 15° (outer panels), with canard foreplanes swept forward at 10° – with built-in aerodynamic AoA protection .The structure is primarily composite, comprising carbon-fibre/epoxy over foam/PVC. The pilot sits on an SIIS-3ER ejection seat. Provision is made for the carriage of two AIM-9L Sidewinder or four AIM-92 Stinger AAMs on external hardpoints. ARES completed live cannon firing tests in 1991, with USAF funding, and since then it has continued in flight test. A two-seat trainer variant is also planned.

SPECIFICATION

Scaled Composites (Rutan Model 151) ARES
Wing: span 35 ft 0 in (10.67 m); aspect ratio 6.5; area 188.30 sq ft (17.49 m²); canard foreplane span 19 ft 2 in (5.84 m) canard foreplane area 34.30 sq ft (3.19 m²)
Fuselage and tail: length 25 ft 5¼ in (8.97 m); height 9 ft 10 in (3.00 m)
Powerplant: one Pratt & Whitney JT15D-5 turbofan rated at 2,950 lb st (13.12 kN)
Weights: empty unarmed 2,884 lb (1308 kg); normal take-off unarmed 4,804 lb (2179 kg); maximum take-off 6,100 lb (2767 kg)

The Scaled Composites (Rutan) ARES has adopted a novel engine intake layout to avoid the problem of gun gas ingestion.

Fuel and load: internal fuel 1,700 lb (771 kg); external fuel none
Speed: never exceed speed Mach 0.65; maximum level speed 'clean' at 35,000 ft (10670 m) 375 kt (432 mph; 695 km/h); (demonstrated) up to 305 kts IAS (351 mph;

656 km/h) in level flight; 405 kts TAS (466 mph; 750 km/h) at 7620 m (25,000 ft)
Range: (demonstrated) more than 1,000 nm (1,150 miles; 1850 km) flown on internal fuel at 7,620 m (25,000 ft)

Scheibe SF 25B/C Falke/Venture T.Mk

Schiebe Flugzeugbau Gmbh
August-Pfalz-Strasse 23, Postfach 1829
8060 Dachau, Germany

Examples of the **Scheibe SF 25B/C Falke** powered glider are operated by the air arms of **Singapore** and **Pakistan**, primarily for recreational and training duties. The Falke is a side-by-side two-seat motor glider, intended for training and with dual controls as standard. The two-piece cantilever wooden wing is fitted with airbrakes,

while the fuselage is fabric-covered welded steel tube. The undercarriage comprises a single main wheel, a steerable tailwheel and spring outrigger stabilising wheels under each wing. The Falke is powered by a 45-hp (33.6-kW) Stamo MS 1500 four-stroke horizontally-opposed engine. Five civil-registered **SF 25B**s equip the para-military

Junior Flying Club which the Singapore defence ministry operates at Seletar. This organisation has the 'shadow' designation of No. 151 Squadron in the RSAF.

The **SF 25C** is an improved version of the SF 25B, differing primarily by having a more powerful 60-hp (44.7-kW) Limbach SL 1700 EA modified Volkswagen automobile

engine. Four SF 25Cs provide for recreational flying at the Pakistan Air Force College at Sargodha. In 1970, the SF 25C was the basis for licence-production in the UK of 40 **Slingsby T.61E Venture T.Mk 2** trainers for the Air Cadet Force, replacement of which by the Grob G 109 Vigilant T.Mk 1 is now complete.

Schleicher Vanguard and Valiant T.Mk 1

Alexander Achleicher Segel-Flugzeugbau
6416 Poppenhausen/Wasserkuppe
Germany

Examples of the **Schleicher ASK-21** high-performance single-seat glider and of the **ASW-19** two-seat sailplane serve in the United Kingdom with the **Air Cadet**

Force, providing opportunities for more advanced flying by members of the Air Training Corps and Combined Cadet Force who have previously learned to fly on the

Grob Viking T.Mk 1. Five ASW-19 two-seaters were acquired and given the name **Valiant T.Mk 1**, while 10 ASK-21s became **Vanguard T.Mk 1**s. Both types

serve at the Air Cadet Central Gliding School at RAF Syerston, and Vanguards were also used to equip No. 618 Volunteer Gliding School at West Malling.

Schweizer (Hughes) Model 200/269/300

Schweizer Aircraft Corporation
PO Box 147, Elmira
New York 14902, USA

The Hughes Aircraft Company began specialising in helicopters in 1948, and its second design proved one of the most successful light helicopters ever. The first of two **Model 269** two-seat prototypes flew in October 1956 and, refined and re-engineered for production, became the **Model 269A**. Five were acquired by the **US Army** in 1958 for trials at Fort Rucker as observation helicopters, under the designation **YHO-2-HU**. The Model 269A had a

lightweight fuselage that accommodated its two crew members and the 180-hp (134-kW) Lycoming HIO-360-A1A powerplant. With a fully-articulated three-bladed main rotor, the Model 269A had a two-bladed anti-torque tail rotor (to port) and an upward-canted stabiliser to starboard. It was designated **Model 200** for civil customers.

Experience with the YHO-2-HU eventually led to an order in 1964 for a new primary trainer. A military version of the Model

269C was chosen, itself an improved version of the two-seat dual-control Model 269A, powered by a 180-hp (134-kW) Avco Lycoming HIO-360-B1A flat-four piston engine. An initial batch of 20 **TH-55A Osage**s was ordered, but total procurement eventually reached 792 by the time deliveries ceased in March 1969.

The TH-55A was supplied to **Spain** for training duties under the local designation **HE.20** (17 delivered), and to **Sweden** as the **Hkp 5B** (16 delivered). Model 269As were supplied to **Brazil** (16), while TH-55s were delivered to **Nigeria** (15), **Algeria** (six), and **Haiti** (two). **Colombia** took eight Model 300Cs and six TH-55s. Thirty Model 300Cs were acquired by **Iraq** for crop-spraying, but were actually used for training military helicopter pilots. In **Japan**, Kawasaki assembled 38 of the **TH-55J** variant which was almost identical to the TH-55A. The **Model 269B** was a similar three-seater (designated **Model 300** for civilian customers), and the **Model 300C** is a further improved derivative, which first flew in August 1969 offering a 45 per cent

increase in payload. It is powered by a 225-hp (168-kW) HIO-360-D1A derated to 190 hp (142 kW). Hughes became a subsidiary of McDonnell Douglas on 6 January 1984, and was renamed McDonnell Douglas Helicopters on 27 August 1985, but production of the Model 300C had already been transferred to Schweizer in July 1983. The Model 300C was also built under licence by Breda Nardi in Italy as the **NH-300C**. Schweizer bought up the entire programme in November 1986, by which time Hughes production of all models had reached 2,800.

The first Schweizer-built helicopter, a Model 300C, flew in June 1984, followed by several new variants. These have included the **TH-300C** dual-control military trainer, the **Model 300C Sky Knight** police variant with armoured seats and searchlight, and even the **Model 300QC** with a lengthened tailboom and a 75 per cent reduction in noise level.

Schweizer has delivered 30 Model 300Cs to the US Army (following a $4.9 million order in late 1985). Thirty TH-300Cs were delivered to **Turkey** during 1982/1983 and two batches (each of 24 TH-55Cs) went to the **Royal Thai army** in 1986, augmenting the survivors of 23 ex-US Army TH-55As. The type remains in service with Algeria (six Model 269), Colombia (six TH-55, seven Model 300C), Greece (26 **ND300C**),

In Spanish air force service the Hughes 269 is referred to as the HE.20 and serves in several different sub-types with basic traing unit Esc 782 of Ala 78, based at Granada.

Japan (33 TH-55J with the **JGSDF**), Nigeria (14 Model 300C), Sweden (26 with the army), Thailand (68), Turkey (30), the US Army and possibly Iraq.

SPECIFICATION

Schweizer (Hughes) Model 300C
Rotor system: main rotor diameter 26 ft 10 in (8.18 m); tail rotor diameter 4 ft 3 in (1.30 m); main rotor disc area 565.51 sq ft (52.54 m2); tail rotor disc area 14.19 sq ft (1.32 m2)
Fuselage and tail: length overall, rotors turning 30 ft 10 in (9.40 m); height overall 8 ft 8.675 in (2.66 m) to top of rotor head; skid track 6 ft 6.5 in (1.99 m)
Powerplant: one 225-hp (168-kW) Textron Lycoming HIO-360-D1A flat-four piston engine derated to 190 hp (142 kW)
Weights: empty 1,046 lb (474 kg);normal take-off 2,050 lb (930 kg); maximum take-off 2,150 lb (975 kg)
Fuel and load: internal fuel 49 US gal (185.5 litres); external fuel none
Speed: never exceed speed at sea level 91 kt (105 mph; 169 km/h); maximum cruising speed at optimum altitude 82.5 kt (95 mph; 153 km/h); economical

cruising speed at 4,000 ft (1220 m) 67 kt (77 mph; 124 km/h)
Range: 195 nm (224 miles; 360 km); endurance 3 hours 24 minutes
Performance: maximum rate of climb at sea level 750 ft (229 m) per minute; service ceiling 10,200 ft (3110 m); hovering ceiling 5,900 ft (1800 m) in ground effect and 2,750 ft (840 m) out of ground effect

The Schweizer/ Hughes 300 is the Turkish army's principal training helicopter, rival Enstrom TH-28s and Robinson R22s having proved surprisingly unpopular.

Schweizer **Model 330**

A turboshaft-engined derivative of the Model 300 was flown by Schweizer during June 1988 as the **Model 330**. This was intended for commercial customers and to meet the US Army's NTH (New Training Helicopter) requirement. This allows the use of cheaper, more common turbine fuel (Avtur rather than Avgas) and gives much improved 'hot-and-high' performance. Increased power to the tail rotor also improves hover crosswind limits. The aircraft has three sets of flying controls and the student pilot seats can be moved to

allow one student to observe the other being given instruction. The tailplane is enlarged and features endplate fins, in addition to a large new dorsal fin. The Model 330 was unsuccessful in the NTH competition, losing out to the Bell 206 derivative.

As the TH-330, Schweizer offered its turbine-powered Model 330 for the US Army NTH competition, which was eventually won by the Bell TH-57 Creek. The 330 has chalked up some civilian sales, however.

Schweizer **TG-7A (SGM 2-37)**

First flown on 21 September 1982, the SGM 2-37 motorised glider was developed to meet a **USAF** requirement for such a craft to be used at the Air Force Academy for 'motivational' flight training on a voluntary basis up to solo standard. The Academy previously used sailplanes that required a a powered aircraft to tow them aloft. The SGM-2-37 is a low-wing glider which combines the wings of the Schweizer **SGS 1-36** single-seat sailplane with the rear of the earlier **SGS2-32** and the powerplant module of a Piper Tomahawk. Two side-by-side seats are provided beneath a sliding canopy and the SGM 2-37 has a fixed tailwheel-type undercarriage. Designated **TG-7A** in the DoD glider category,

the SGM 2-37 was first ordered with FY81 funds and a total of 12 has entered service with the 94th Air Training Squadron at the Academy at Colorado Springs. The TG-7A enables up to 1,200 cadets each year to make their first solo flights. The first aircraft was delivered in 1984, but early in its service life two were lost in crashes. To check the TG-7A's tendency to stall and 'depart', locally-designed leading-edge fillets (cuffs) were added after the second crash.

SPECIFICATION

Schweizer TG-7A
Wing: span 59 ft 6 in (18.14 m); aspect ratio 18.1;

area 195.71 sq ft (18.18 m2)
Fuselage and tail: length 27 ft 5 in (8.36 m); height 7 ft 9.5 in (2.37 m); wheel track 9 ft 2 in (2.79 m); wheel base 18 ft 10 in (5.74 m)
Powerplant: one Textron Lycoming O-235-L2C flat-four piston engine rated at 112 hp (83 kW)
Weights: empty 1,260 lb (572 kg); maximum take-off 1,850 lb (839 kg)
Fuel and load: internal fuel in port wing 15.5 US gal (59 litres) plus provision in starboard wing for 15.5 US gal (59 litres) of auxiliary fuel; external fuel none
Speed: maximum cruising speed at 7,500 ft (2285 m) 99 kt (114 mph; 183 km/h); economical cruising speed at optimum altitude 81 kt (95 mph; 153 km/h); maximum smooth-air gliding speed 116 kt (133 mph; 214 km/h); maximum rough-air gliding speed 88 kt (101 mph; 162 km/h)
Range: ferry range 520 nm (598 miles; 963 km) with auxiliary fuel; range 213 nm (246 miles; 396 km) with standard fuel
Performance: maximum rate of climb at sea level

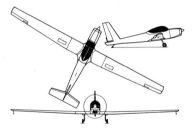

Schweizer TG-7A

1,075 ft (328 m) per minute; service ceiling more than 24,000 ft (7315 m); best glide ratio 22; minimum gliding sink rate 3.7 ft (1.13 m) per second; take-off run 500 ft (152 m) at maximum take-off weight; landing distance from 50 ft (15 m) 1,266 ft (386 m) at normal landing weight; landing run 654 ft (200 m) at normal landing weight

Schweizer **RG-8A Condor (SA 2-37A)**

In continuation of the investigation into quiet surveillance and special missions aircraft begun with the Lockheed QT-I (a modified Schweizer SGS 2-32 sailplane), the **US Army** backed the development by Schweizer of a variant of the **TG-7A** (SGM 2-37) motorised glider (described separately). The **SA 2-37A** introduced increased wingspan with aerodynamic changes to improve stall characteristics, a bulged, upward-opening canopy for enhanced visibility and a 65-cu ft (1.84-m3) payload bay

behind the cockpit to carry various palletised sensors or cameras. The SA 2-37A featured a much more powerful engine, fitted with mufflers (a long exhaust on each

side of the cowling) and driving an advanced McCauley three-bladed constant-speed low-noise propeller. The engine can be run at very low rpm, since only 52 hp (38.8 kW) is

required to maintain height, giving a very low acoustic signature. Internal fuel capacity was trebled, with mission duration reported to run as long as eight hours. To fit it for the covert surveillance role, the **RG-8A** is painted in low-visibility grey and can be equipped with a Hughes AN/AAQ-16 thermal imaging system, Texas Instruments

In stark contrast to their high-visibility red and white siblings, US Coast Guard RG-8As wear toned-down insignia over gunship grey.

Schweizer RG-8A Condor (SA 2-37A)

AAQ-15 FLIR, secure communications equipment, IR sensors, low-light TV and other payloads. The pilots' seats are armoured and the cockpit is NVG-compatible. Full IFR capability is provided, permitting operation around the clock, and other avionics equipment allegedly includes Litton INS as well as a Bendix/King avionics suite.

First flying in prototype form in 1986, an initial batch of two was procured by the US Army. Following the loss of one of the original pair, a replacement was obtained. The two survivors were subsequently passed to the **US Coast Guard** to be operated out

of Opa Locka, FL, on long-endurance drug interdiction sorties. The RG-8As usually operating singly, flying a search pattern with a track of some 500 miles (805 km). One RG-8A has been used by the **CIA** as a data relay platform for reconnaissance drones flying over Bosnia.

SPECIFICATION

Schweizer RG-8A Condor
Wing: span 61 ft 6 in (18.745 m); aspect ratio 18.97; area 199.40 sq ft (18.52 m2)

Fuselage and tail: length, fuselage 27 ft 9 in (8.46 m); height 7 ft 9 in (2.36 m) tail down; wheel track 9 ft 2 in (2.79 m); wheel base 19 ft 8 in (5.99 m)
Powerplant: one Textron Lycoming IO-540-W3A5D flat-six piston engine rated at 235 hp (175 kW)
Weights: empty 2,025 lb (918 kg); maximum take-off 3,500 lb (1587 kg)
Fuel and load: internal fuel 52 US gal (196.8 litres) plus provision for 15 US gal (57 litres) of auxiliary fuel; external fuel none; maximum mission payload 750 lb (340 kg)
Speed: maximum cruising speed at 5,000 ft (1525 m) 138 kt (159 mph; 256 km/h); economical cruising speed at 5,000 ft (1525 m) 129 kt (148 mph; 239 km/h)

Range: endurance more than 8 hours
Performance: maximum rate of climb at sea level 960 ft (292 m) per minute; service ceiling 18,000 ft (5490 m); take-off run 1,270 ft (387 m) at maximum take-off weight from a paved runway or 1,750 ft (533 m) at maximum take-off weight from a grass runway; take-off distance to 50 ft (15 m) 2,010 ft (612 m) at maximum take-off weight from a paved runway or 2,490 ft (759 m) at maximum take-off weight from a grass runway; landing distance from 50 ft (15 m) 2,230 ft (680 m) at normal landing weight on a paved runway or 2,400 ft (732 m) at normal landing weight on a grass runway
g limits: -3.3 to +6.6

Schweizer X-26A (SGS 2-32)

A pair of two-seat SGS 2-32 sailplanes continues to serve with the **US Naval Test Pilot's School** at Patuxent River, MD. Five of these aircraft have been acquired since 1968, initially to give experience of yaw/roll coupling and other handling characteristics common to aircraft with high aspect ratio wings. Designated **X-26A**, they are essentially civilian gliders in military guise. Two 100-hp (74.6-kW) **X-26B**s were also delivered to the NTPS, these having been previously in US Army hands as **Lockheed QT-2PC (Quiet Thruster)** low-noise surveillance aircraft. Based on the SGS 2-32 airframe, there is modified seating for two in tandem. The X-26Bs were withdrawn from use during 1973.

SPECIFICATION

Schweizer X-26A
Wing: span 57 ft 1 in (17.40 m); aspect ratio 18.13; area 180.00 sq ft (16.70 m2)
Fuselage and tail: length 26 ft 9 in (8.15 m); height 9 ft 3 in (2.82 m); tailplane span 10 ft 6 in (3.20 m)
Weights: empty 857 lb (389 kg); maximum take-off 1,430 lb (649 kg)
Fuel and load: internal fuel none
Speed: maximum tow speed 96 kt (110 mph; 177 km/h); maximum gliding speed 137 kt (158 mph; 254 km/h)
Performance: service ceiling 18,500 ft (5640 m); best glide ratio 34:1 at 51 kt (59 mph; 95 km/h); minimum sinking speed 2.38 ft (0.72 m) per second at 43 kt (50 mph; 80 km/h)

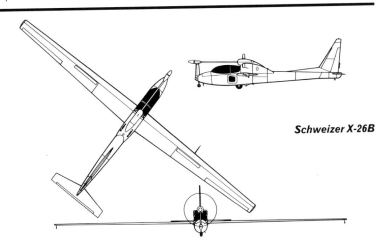

Schweizer X-26B

SEPECAT **Jaguar GR.Mk 1/T.Mk 2**

British Aerospace Defence Ltd
Warton Aerodrome, Preston
Lancashire PR4 1AX, UK

Produced to meet a joint Anglo-French specification in 1965 for a dual-role aircraft (advanced/operational trainer and tactical support), the **SEPECAT Jaguar** was transformed into a potent fighter-bomber and gained some success in the export field, as described separately. Breguet (now part of Dassault) and the British Aircraft Corporation's Warton Division (later BAe Warton) were chosen to participate, the joint company being registered in France to reflect Breguet's design leadership. It was titled SEPECAT – Société Européenne de Production de l'Avion d'Ecole de Combat et d'Appui Tactique (European Production Company for the Combat Training and Tactical Support Aircraft) – and formed in May 1966. The Jaguar was the first Anglo-French combat aircraft and the first RAF aircraft designed completely in metric units. The RAF intended to use its aircraft exclusively as advanced trainers, whereas French inter-

est lay in a ground-attack aircraft with STOL performance. Eventually, both the RAF and Armée de l'Air abandoned the combat training role and used the aircraft for strike and attack in single-seat form, merely retaining a handful of two-place machines for pilot conversion duties.

Designed from the outset for close support and daytime interdiction, the Jaguar has a configuration and wing loading optimised for ease of weapon-carrying and stability as a weapon platform at low altitude. Power is provided by two Rolls-Royce/Turboméca Adour reheated turbofans that were the subject of an associated joint development programme. Engine thrust originally lagged behind progressive increases in aircraft weight, leaving the Jaguar noticeably underpowered in hot climates, although this short-coming was eventually remedied in RAF and export aircraft. Low-speed handling is improved by

double-slotted flaps along the entire wing trailing edge, ailerons being omitted in favour of outer wing spoilers.

The first of eight Jaguar prototypes was actually a French two-seat aircraft and made its maiden flight on 8 September 1968, the remaining aircraft of this batch soon displaying the significant differences between UK and French versions. Each air force agreed to buy 200 Jaguars, the RAF split being 165 single-seat and 35 two-seat machines, the former designated **Jaguar S** (for 'Strike') by the manufacturers and **GR.Mk 1** by the RAF. GR.Mk 1s are immediately recognisable by their chisel-shaped noses and fin-top pods, respectively housing a Ferranti ARI23231 LRMTS (Laser Ranger and Marked Target Seeker) and Marconi ARI18223 radar warning receiver. Internally, the GR.Mk 1 had a Marconi-GEC 920ATC NAVWASS (Navigation and Weapon-Aiming Sub-System) projecting relevant route and targeting

information on the pilot's HUD and driving a look-down moving-map display. As built, RAF aircraft had an empty weight of 7390 kg (16,292 lb) and were powered by Mk 102 engines of 32.5 kN (7,305 lb st).

The first British aircraft was a single -seat Jaguar (the S-06 prototype XW560), which initially flew on 12 October 1969. Delivered between 1973 and 1978, RAF Jaguar GR.Mk 1s served four nuclear strike squadrons at Brüggen, Germany (Nos 14, 17, 20 and 31), a recce squadron (No. II) at Laarbruch, Germany, and the Coltishall Wing of Nos 6, 41 (recce) and 54 Squadrons, all three based tasked with conventional support of NATO forces anywhere within Europe. Despite its lack of radar, a navigator and air defence capability,

The No. 6(C) Sqn Jaguars involved in Operation Grapple armed support flights over Bosnia have adopted this effective overall grey scheme.

he Jaguar marked a quantum improvement ver the F-4 Phantoms it replaced, giving a enuine ability to find pinpoint targets and ttack them with a hitherto unknown degree of accuracy. All-weather operation was ot degraded, and the new aircraft proved much more difficult to intercept due to its igh speed at very low level. The aircraft lso introduced an oft-practised capability f operating from motorway strips, and an npractised rough-field capability. The aguar is equipped with anti-skid Messier-lispano undercarriage (each gear unit having win low-pressure tyres) and a 5.5-m (18-ft .5-in) diameter brake parachute housed in ne fuselage tailcone. Replacement a decade later by Panavia Tornados was comparatively rapid, but cast no aspersions on the aguar's capability in the conventional role. Reconnaissance aircraft carry a centreline od containing a fan of five cameras, plus n infra-red linescan, although this was augmented in 1991 by a Vinten VICON 18 long-ange optical pod.

The **Jaguar B** two-seat training variant eatures a 0.9-m (2-ft 11-in) fuselage stretch o accommodate a second seat, which is aised by 59.1 cm (15 in). The aircraft were uilt with the full navigation and attack vionics suite but have limited combat capaility, since they lack lasers, inflight-refu-lling probes or radar warning receivers, and ave only the port cannon fitted. The first British Jaguar B flew as the B-08 prototype XW566) on 30 August 1970. Britain assigned 35 Jaguar Bs to training duties. Designated **T.Mk 2**, they were delivered to No. 29 OCU at Lossiemouth for pilot conversion and to each squadron as continuation rainers. A total of 14 T.Mk 2s was upgraded vith the more capable FIN1064 nav/attack init, becoming **T.Mk 2A**s, and also gaining Mk 104 engines. In addition, three extra .Mk 2s were bought for the Empire Test Pilots' School (two) and Royal Aircraft Establishment (now Defence Research Agency). All UK Jaguars are fitted with Martin-Baker Mk 10 zero-zero ejection seats.

Only the Coltishall Wing remains active. ts aircraft were upgraded in 1978-84 with 35.1-kN (7,900 lb-st) Adour Mk 104 engines, nd raised further from December 1983 to **GR.Mk 1A** standard by replacement of NAVWASS with the considerably more accurate Ferranti FIN1064 inertial navigation system. Although FIN1064 is 50 kg (110 lb) ighter, aircraft weight increased through ther modifications to 7700 kg (16,976 lb), gainst a take-off weight of 15500 kg 34,172 lb).

Further changes introduced from 1982 ncluded addition of AN/ALE-40 flare dis-ensers in a scabbed fitting under the engine nacelles, Philips-MATRA Phimat flare ods and Westinghouse AN/ALQ-101(V)-10 amming pods. Both Phimat and ALQ-101 re interchangeable with AIM-9G (later -9L) Sidewinder AAMs.

For the 1991 Gulf War, radar warners vere uprated to Sky Guardian 200 standard, nd CBU-87 medium-altitude releasable luster bombs and CRV-7 rockets were add-d to the usual armoury of BL755 low-level CBUs, 540-lb (245-kg) and 1,000-lb (454-kg) ombs carried on a fuselage centreline and our underwing hardpoints. Self-defence vas improved by the addition of overwing Sidewinder pylons, obviating the previous either/or' situation. Another Jaguar upgrade vith higher-powered engines and night-vision systems has been abandoned for rea-sons of cost, despite the aircraft being des-ined to serve into the 21st century. Mk 1A conversions total 75, of which most remain.

Twelve Coltishall-based Jaguars were mong the first British forces deployed in October 1990 for Operation Granby. The air-craft were based at Thumrait, Oman, and Muharraq, Bahrain, and were assigned bat-lefield air interdiction missions on tactical argets, mainly in Kuwait. They flew a total

The RAF's Jaguar record in the Gulf was outstanding, with several aircraft chalking up over 40 missions. Twelve aircaft flown by 22 pilots operated the 'JagDet' from Muharraq, Bahrain. Initially armed with BL755 cluster bombs, the Jaguars later adopted CRV-7 rocket pods.

of 618 sorties, including 31 reconnaissance missions, and incurred no combat losses. After the Gulf War, Jaguars flew Operation Warden missions over northern Iraq until their replacement by Harrier GR.Mk 7s in April 1993. In mid-1994, a detachment of up to 12 aircraft is based at Gioia del Colle for Operation Grapple, supporting the UN mission in Bosnia.

OPERATORS

Royal Air Force

No. 6 Sqn: (GR.Mk 1A/T.Mk 2A) – RAF Coltishall
No. 41 Sqn: (GR.Mk 1A/T.Mk 2A) – RAF Coltishall
No. 54 Sqn: (GR.Mk 1A/T.Mk 2A) – RAF Coltishall
No. 16(R) Sqn: (GR.Mk 1A/T.Mk 2A)
– Operational Conversion Unit, RAF Lossiemouth

Operation Grapple, Jaguar Detachment
No. 6 (Composite) Sqn: Gioia de Colle, Italy

Strike/Attack Operational Evaluation Unit
– A&AEE, RAF Boscombe Down (T.Mk 2A)
Aircraft & Armament Evaluation Establishment
– RAF Boscombe Down (GR.Mk 1A)
Empire Test Pilots' School
– RAF Boscombe Down (T.Mk 2A)
Defence Research Agency
– RAF Boscombe Down (GR.Mk 1A/T.Mk 2)

SPECIFICATION

SEPECAT Jaguar S (Jaguar GR.Mk 1A)
Wing: span 8.69 m (28 ft 6 in); aspect ratio 3.13; area 24.18 m² (260.27 sq ft)
Fuselage and tail: length 16.83 m (55 ft 2.5 in) including probe and 15.52 m (50 ft 11 in) excluding probe; height 4.89 m (16 ft 0.5 in); wheel track 2.41 m (7 ft 11 in); wheel base 5.69 m (18 ft 8 in)
Powerplant: two Rolls-Royce/Turboméca Adour Mk 104 turbofans each rated at 5,320 lb st (23.66 kN) dry and 8,040 lb st (35.75 kN) with afterburning
Weights: empty equipped 7700 kg (16,975 lb); normal take-off 10954 kg (24,149 lb); maximum take-off 15700 kg (34,612 lb)
Fuel and load: internal fuel 3337 kg (7,357 lb); external fuel up to 2844 kg (6,270 lb) in three 1200-litre (317-US gal) drop tanks; maximum ordnance 4,536 kg (10,000lb)
Speed: maximum level speed 'clean' at 36,000 ft (10975 m) 917 kt (1,056 mph; 1699 km/h) and at sea level 729 kt (840 mph; 1350 km/h)
Range: ferry range 1,902 nm (2,190 miles; 3524 km) with drop tanks; combat radius 460 nm (530 miles; 852 km) on a hi-lo-hi attack mission with internal fuel, or 290 nm (334 miles; 537 km) on a lo-lo-lo attack mission with internal fuel, or 760 nm (875 miles;

1408 km) on a hi-lo-hi attack mission with drop tanks, or 495 nm (570 miles; 917 km) on a lo-lo-lo attack mission with drop tanks
Performance: climb to 9145 m (30,000ft) in 1 minute 30 seconds; service ceiling 14000 m (45,930 ft); take-off run 565 m (1,854 ft) 'clean' or 880 m (2,887 ft) with four 1,000-lb (454-kg) bombs, or 1,250 m (4,101 ft) with eight 1,000-lb (454-kg) bombs; take-off distance to 50 ft (15 m) 940 m (3,084 ft) at typical take-off weight; landing distance from 50 ft (15 m) 785 m (2,575 ft) at typical landing weight; landing run 470 m (1,542 ft) at typical landing weight with brake chute
g limit: +8.6 at typical weight or +12 ultimate

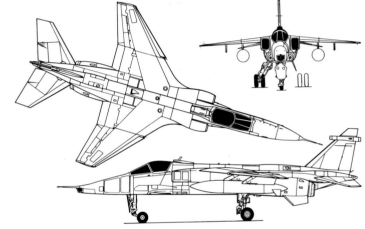

SEPECAT Jaguar GR.Mk 1A (Jaguar T.Mk 2A lower side view)

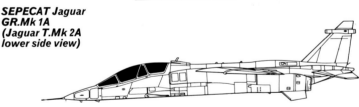

No. 41 Sqn is one of two Jaguar recce units, with a wartime ACE NATO Mobile Force base at Tromsø in Norway. This aircraft carries an EMI optical/IRLS pod.

SEPECAT Jaguar B (Jaguar T.Mk 2A)
generally similar to the SEPECAT Jaguar S (Jaguar GR.Mk 1A) except in the following particulars:
Fuselage and tail: length 17.53 m (57 ft 6¼ in) including probe and 16.42 m (53 ft 10½ in) excluding probe; wheel track 2.40 m (7 ft 10½ in); wheel base 5.67 m (18 ft 7¼ in)

SEPECAT Jaguar A/E

France elected to procure 200 Jaguars for the **Armée de l'Air**, eventually purchasing 160 single-seat and 40 two-seat aircraft. Compared with their British equivalent, French single-seat **Jaguar A**s (for 'Appui', or attack) have a generally less capable standard of avionics fit, but remain effective strike aircraft. Like RAF GR.Mk 1s, they have a retractable refuelling probe and two internal 30-mm cannon (DEFA 553 in place of ADEN). The off-the-shelf avionics include a CSF31 weapon-aiming computer, SFIM 250-1 twin-gyro platform, Decca RDN72 Doppler and a Crouzet 90 navigation computer. There has been no avionics upgrade, although the second half of aircraft procured had a Thomson-CSF TAV-38 laser ranger under the nose and an improved version of CFTH RWR, and the last 30 are able to carry a nose-mounted Thomson-CSF ATLIS laser designator, introduced in 1980. An OMERA 40 panoramic camera was installed beneath the nose of the 113th and subsequent Jaguar As and retrofitted, while a few carry an RP36 drop tank fitted with a fan of three cameras. With the temporary exception of the first 10 production aircraft, Armée de l'Air Jaguars were fitted with and retain Mk 102 engines.

France's 40 tandem-seat **Jaguar E**s (for 'Ecole', or school) are issued only at squadron level, rather than to a single OCU. They lack a full nav/attack avionics fit, but those from No. 27 were fitted on the production line with a fixed refuelling probe to provide limited tanker training (the A's retractable probe being in a different position). Some 25 Es remain in service.

The first Jaguar to fly was a French Jaguar E prototype, E-01, on 8 September 1968, and was followed on 23 March 1969 by the first flight of the prototype Jaguar A (A-03). The **Jaguar M** carrier-based strike fighter was flown in prototype form (M-05) on 14 November 1969. This retained the original short fin configuration and intake splitter plates, but had a much-modifed

undercarriage comprising single-wheel main units and twin-nosewheels on an extended leg, a 5.5*g* arrester hook (as opposed to the land-based variant's 2*g*) and laser range-finder as standard. The promising Jaguar M completed deck landing trials before falling victim to escalating costs and hostility from Dassault (which was marketing its Super Etendard). It was subsequently cancelled.

Initial deliveries of the Jaguar A were made to the Armée de l'Air from January 1972, and EC 1/7 'Provence' became the first unit to equip with the type, at St Dizier in June 1973. With deliveries completed in December 1981, Jaguars went on to equip nine squadrons, four each in 7 and 11 Escadres (Wings) and one element of 3E. Two nuclear-strike squadrons of 7E were tasked with delivering AN52 25-kT nuclear bombs (these bombs were withdrawn in September 1991), the others concentrating on tactical attack in Europe and in those African countries that have defence agreements with France.

The range of French Jaguar weapons is considerable and includes the laser-guided BGL 1,000-lb (454-kg) bomb and AS30L laser-guided missile; Aérospatiale AS37 Martel anti-radar missiles; 125-, 250- and 400-kg (275-, 551- and 882-lb) bombs; MATRA Belouga cluster-bombs; MATRA F1 (36 x 68 mm) and R3 (4 x 100 mm) rocket pods; Thomson-Brandt BAP-100 anti-runway and BAT-120 area-denial bomblets; and MATRA Magic infra-red AAMs. Thirty Jaguars have been fitted with an ATLIS (Automatic Tracking and Laser Illumination System) comprising a Martin-Marietta pod on the fuselage centreline, to give self-designation capability for the BGLs and AS30L missiles. System integration was the responsibility of Thomson-CSF. In the offensive jamming role, the Thomson-CSF CT51J pod can be used as an alternative to the Thomson-CSF Barracuda or Dassault Barax. Chaff/flare pods are either the Philips-MATRA Phimat or Bofors BOZ-103,

although an 18-shot Lacroix flare unit may be fitted in the braking parachute housing. The Jaguar may also be fitted with an Alkan LL 5020 conformal pod which contains chaff and flare dispensers under the wingroot.

Armée de l'Air Jaguars have seen action in Mauritania, Chad and the Gulf. During the latter conflict, a total of 28 Jaguars flew 615 sorties (three fewer than the RAF's 12 Jaguars). By mid-1994, France was operating some 85 Jaguar As within five squadrons.

OPERATORS

Armée de l'Air

7ᵉ Escadre de Chasse
Base Aérienne 113 'Commandant Antoine de Saint-Expuéry', St Dizier/Robinson

Escadron de Chasse 1/7 'Provence'
1ᵉ Escadrille (SPA 15)
2ᵉ Escadrille (SPA 77)

Escadron de Chasse 2/7 'Argonne'
1ᵉ Escadrille (SPA 31)
2ᵉ Escadrille (SPA 48)

Escadron de Chasse 3/7 'Languedoc'
1ᵉ Escadrille (3C-1)
2ᵉ Escadrille (SPA 38)

11ᵉ Escadre de Chasse
Base Aérienne 136 'Colonel Georges Phelut', Toul/Rosières

Escadron de Chasse 2/11 'Vosges'
1ᵉ Escadrille (SPA 91)
2ᵉ Escadrille (SPA 97)

Escadron de Chasse 3/11 'Corse'
1ᵉ Escadrille (SPA 88)
2ᵉ Escadrille (SPA 69)

Centre d'Instruction Tactique 339
– Base Aérienne 116 'Lt Col Papin', Luxeuil/St Sauveur
Centre d'Expériences Aériennes Militaires (CEAM)
– Base Aérienne 118, 'Capt K. W. Rozanoff', Mont-de-Marsan
Centre d'Essais en Vol (CEV)
– Brétigny-sur-Orge

SPECIFICATION

SEPECAT Jaguar A
Wing: span 8.69 m (28 ft 6 in); aspect ratio 3.13; area 24.18 m² (260.27 sq ft)
Fuselage and tail: length 16.83 m (55 ft 2½ in) including probe and 15.52 m (50 ft 11 in) excluding probe; height 4.89 m (16 ft 0½ in); wheel track 2.41 m (7 ft 11 in); wheel base 5.69 m (18 ft 8 in)
Powerplant: two Rolls-Royce/Turboméca Adour Mk 102 turbofans each rated at 5,115 lb st (22.75 kN dry and 7,305 lb st (32.49 kN) with afterburning
Weights: empty equipped 7000 kg (15,432 lb); normal take-off 10954 kg (24,149 lb); maximum take-off 15700 kg (34,612 lb)
Fuel and load: internal fuel 3337 kg (7,357 lb); external fuel up to 2844 kg (6,270 lb) in three 1200-litre (317-US gal) drop tanks; maximum ordnance 4536 kg (10,000 lb)
Speed: maximum level speed 'clean' at 36,000 ft (10975 m) 917 kt (1,056 mph; 1699 km/h) and at sea level 729 kt (840 mph; 1350 km/h)
Range: ferry range 1,902 nm (2,190 miles; 3524 km) with drop tanks; combat radius 460 nm (530 miles; 852 km) on a hi-lo-hi attack mission with internal fuel or 290 nm (334 miles; 537 km) on a lo-lo-lo attack mission with internal fuel, or 760 nm (875 miles; 1408 km) on a hi-lo-hi attack mission with drop tanks or 495 nm (570 miles; 917 km) on a lo-lo-lo attack mission with drop tanks
Performance: climb to 9145 m (30,000ft) in 1 minute 30 seconds; service ceiling 14000 m (45,930 ft); take-off run 565 m (1,854 ft) 'clean' or 880 m (2,887 ft) with four 1,000-lb (454-kg) bombs, or 1,250 m (4,101 ft) with eight 1,000-lb (454-kg) bombs; take-off distance to 50 ft (15 m) 940 m (3,084 ft) at typical take-off weight; landing distance from 50 ft (15 m) 785 m (2,575 ft) at typical landing weight; landing run 470 m (1,542 ft) at typical landing weight with brake chute
g **limit:** +8.6 at typical weight or +12 ultimate

SEPECAT Jaguar E
generally similar to the SEPECAT Jaguar A except in the following particulars:
Fuselage and tail: length 17.53 m (57 ft 6¼ in) including probe and 16.42 m (53 ft 10½ in) excluding probe; wheel track 2.40 m (7 ft 10.5 in); wheel base 5.67 m (18 ft 7¼ in)

SEPECAT Jaguar A (Jaguar E upper side view)

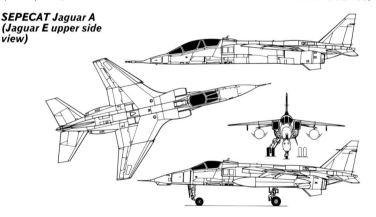

Above: French aircraft wearing desert camouflage carry small, toned-down markings. Serials are prefixed 'E' for two-seat, and 'A' for single-seat Jaguars.

Left: During Operation Daguet, the French codename for operations during the Gulf War, a force of 28 Jaguars, drawn from EC 11 (with pilots from that unit and EC 7), was based at Al Ahsa, in Saudi Arabia. Missions were flown from 17 January 1991 to 27 February. This aircraft carries laser-guided AS30L ASMs with an ATLIS designation pod on the centreline.

SEPECAT Jaguar International

All export Jaguars have been based on the Jaguar B/S airframe, and all orders have been secured by BAC or BAe, since Dassault has always preferred to market wholly French types, where an order results in 100 per cent of the work. Thus, the Jaguar has frequently competed against the Mirage.

Serious marketing of the Jaguar began in 1974, when BAC revealed details of export orders from undisclosed customers (Ecuador and Oman). Several days later an RAF aircraft (actually the first production S) appeared at the Farnborough show with **Jaguar International** titles and a mocked-up radar nose, surrounded by weaponry appropriate to an export aircraft. This aircraft was subsequently fitted with Adour Mk 104 RT-172-26 engines with 27 per cent higher thrust than the original Mk 102s, effectively becoming the prototype Jaguar International.

The designation **Jaguar K** had originally been reserved for export variants based on the **Jaguar S** and **Jaguar B**, but this was never used, each export customer receiving its own specific two-letter designator. The first production Jaguar International was an Ecuadorean two-seater, correctly known as a **Jaguar EB**, and it first flew on 19 August 1976. The Ecuadorean single-seat variant is designated **Jaguar ES**. Ecuador's 12 aircraft (including two EBs) were delivered during 1977, replacing Meteor FR.Mk 9s, and the seven survivors (including one EB) were augmented by three refurbished RAF aircraft during 1991.

Oman began to receive its Jaguar Internationals during March 1977, taking delivery of an initial batch of 12 aircraft (10 **Jaguar OS** and two **Jaguar OB** trainers), these wearing national markings in red and white. A second batch, of similar composition but with blue markings, was delivered during 1983. The two-seaters in the second batch are unique in having fin-mounted antennas for ARI18223 RWR and French-style, nose-mounted, fixed inflight-refuelling probes. All of the second-batch aircraft were powered by 8,400-lb st (37-kN) RT-172-58 Adour Mk 811 turbofans. Oman's original 24 aircraft were augmented by an ex-RAF T.Mk 2 previously loaned to India, and an ex-RAF single-seater. These were delivered in 1982 and 1986, respectively. Originally using overwing Magic AAMs, Oman's Jaguars switched to AIM-9P4 Sidewinders carried

on the outboard underwing pylons. Between 1986 and 1989, the 21 survivors were upgraded with FIN1064 nav/attack systems in place of their original GEC 920ATC NAVWASS computers, bringing them up to RAF GR.Mk 1A standard.

The biggest Jaguar operator today is India, which took delivery of an eventual 116, plus 18 on loan from the RAF (returned by 1984). These equip five squadrons, with one more unit being due to form. The loaned RAF aircraft were used for training and to form the first squadron, No. 14, while the second batch of aircraft, comprising 35 **Jaguar IS** and five **Jaguar IT** trainers, was undergoing assembly by HAL, from BAe kits. These aircraft were powered by 8,040-lb (35.75-kN) Adour 804s and were fitted with NAVWASS.

India's third batch consisted of 35 Jaguar ISs and 10 Jaguar ITs, assembled by HAL from kits which contained progressively fewer large UK-built sub-assemblies under Phases II-VI. These aircraft were fitted with a locally integrated DARIN (Display Attack and Ranging Inertial Navigation) system, with a Sea Harrier-type GEC Type 1301 HUDWAS, a GEC Ferranti COMED 2054 combined map and electronic display, as used on the F/A-18, and a SAGEM ULISS 82 INS. These aircraft were also powered by the more powerful Adour Mk 811.

Artist's impressions of radar-equipped Jaguar Internationals were released by BAe during the 1970s, and the Agave radar was actually flown in the nose of a modified fuel tank, slung beneath a French two-seat Jaguar. This was intended both for air-to-surface and air-to-air use and would probably have been adopted by the Aéronavale's carrierborne Jaguar M had it entered production. For anti-shipping duties with the Indian Air Force, BAe designed and HAL built the **Jaguar IM** with the same Agave radar (as used in the Super Etendard) replacing the nose-mounted LRMTS. The prototype made its maiden flight during November 1985. Eight were delivered to equip No. 6 Squadron's A Flight at Poona, and are armed with the BAe Sea Eagle missile, operating alongside Canberras in the anti-shipping role.

These aircraft were drawn from Batch Three and Batch Four. The latter had originally been intended to cover full licence-production of 56 Jaguars, and then to fulfil the

remainder of the original IAF requirement for 160 aircraft. In the end, it covered the assembly of 31 more Jaguar ISs supplied in kit form. From Batch Three, all Indian Jaguars have indigenously-designed IFF, ADF, radar, V/UHF radios and HF SSB, and locally built Martin-Baker I9B ejection seats, RWRs, hydraulic and fuel systems. Indian Jaguars have provision for the distinctive Jaguar International overwing launch rails which are used to carry MATRA Magic AAMs. Armament can include BL755 cluster bombs, MATRA Durandal runway-cratering weapons and MATRA F4 rocket pods.

The final export customer was Nigeria, which took delivery of 13 **Jaguar SN**s and five two-seat **Jaguar BN**s during 1984. The 10 surviving SNs and four BNs face retirement as an economy measure. BAE is attempting during 1994 to acquire them for possible resale to Oman.

OPERATORS

Ecuador – Fuerza Aérea Ecuatoriana
Escuadrón de Combate 2111
Grupo 211, Ala de Combate 21, Base Aérea Militar Taura, Guayaquil

India – Indian Air Force
No. 5 Sqn 'Tuskers': Ambala
No. 6 Sqn (A Flight) 'Dragons': Poona (Jaguar M)
No. 14 Sqn 'Bulls': Poona
No.16 Sqn 'Cobras': Gorakhpur
Aircraft and Systems Testing Establishment
Bangalore

Nigeria – Nigerian Air Force
One Squadron, Makurdi

Oman – Royal Air Force of Oman
No. 8 Sqn: Masirah
No. 20 Sqn: Masirah

SPECIFICATION

SEPECAT Jaguar International
Wing: span 8.69 m (28 ft 6 in); aspect ratio 3.13; area 24.18 m² (260.27 sq ft)
Fuselage and tail: length 16.83 m (55 ft 2½ in) including probe and 15.52 m (50 ft 11 in) excluding probe; height 4.89 m (16 ft 0.5 in); wheel track 2.41 m (7 ft 11 in); wheel base 5.69 m (18 ft 8 in)
Powerplant: two Rolls-Royce/Turboméca Adour Mk 804 turbofans each rated at 5,320 lb st (23.66 kN) dry and 8,040 lb st (35.75 kN) with afterburning, or Adour Mk 811 turbofans each rated at 5,520 lb st (24.55 kN) dry and 8,400 lb st (37.36 kN) with afterburning
Weights: empty equipped 7700 kg (16,975 lb); normal take-off 10954 kg (24,149 lb); maximum take-off 15700 kg (34,612 lb)
Fuel and load: internal fuel 3337 kg (7,357 lb); external fuel up to 2844 kg (6,270 lb) in three 1200-litre (317-US gal) drop tanks; maximum ordnance 4763 kg (10,500lb)
Speed: maximum level speed 'clean' at 36,000 ft (10975 m) 917 kt (1,056 mph; 1699 km/h) and at sea level 729 kt (840 mph; 1350 km/h)
Range: ferry range 1,902 nm (2,190 miles; 3524 km) with drop tanks; combat radius 460 nm (530 miles; 852 km) on a hi-lo-hi attack mission with internal fuel, or 290 nm (334 miles; 537 km) on a lo-lo-lo attack mission with internal fuel, or 760 nm (875 miles; 1408 km) on a hi-lo-hi attack mission with drop tanks, or 495 nm (570 miles; 917 km) on a lo-lo-lo attack mission with drop tanks
Performance: climb to 9145 m (30,000ft) in 1 minute 30 seconds; service ceiling 14000 m (45,930 ft); take-off run 565 m (1,854 ft) 'clean' or 880 m (2,887 ft) with four 1,000-lb (454-kg) bombs, or 1,250 m (4,101 ft) with eight 1,000-lb (454-kg) bombs; take-off distance to 50 ft (15 m) 940 m (3,084 ft) at typical take-off weight; landing distance from 50 ft (15 m) 785 m (2,575 ft) at typical landing weight; landing run 470 m (1,542 ft) at typical landing weight with brake chute
g limit: +8.6 at typical weight or +12 ultimate

Below: India has eight distinctive Jaguar IMs for maritime strike. These aircraft are equipped with Agave radar and Sea Eagle AShMs.

Right: All Jaguar International operators fly two-seat aircraft. This Omani example has a refuelling probe and a fintop ARI18223 RWR.

Seyedo Shohada Zafar 300

Defence Industries, Seyedo Shohada Project
Km 5, Qom Road, Kashan
Iran

The **Zafar 300** is a locally-developed conversion of a Bell 206A JetRanger engineered in **Iran** by Akbar Akhundzadeh as the **Seyedo Shohada** project of the Defence Industries. For use as a two-seat light attack helicopter but also applicable to agricultural duties, the Zafar 300 retains the main and tail rotor systems of the JetRanger, with some changes to the control system. The forward fuselage has a modified profile with flat side windows, tandem seating for two with individual doors, and

incorporates an outer shell of reinforced glass-fibre. The front seat is occupied by the gunner, who controls a multi-barrelled cannon located under the nose, and a seven-round rocket launcher on each side of the fuselage to the rear of the pilot's position.

Design began in March 1987 and the Zafar 300 prototype was first flown on 31 January 1989. It is equipped for VFR/VMC flights only. More comprehensive avionics and instrumentation may be fitted to any future conversions of JetRangers, of which

the Islamic Republic of Iran army aviation force has a substantial number remaining from 184 AB 206B-1s purchased from the Agusta licence-production line in Italy.

SPECIFICATION

Seyedo Shohada Zafar 300
Rotor system: main rotor diameter 35 ft 4 in (10.77 m); tail rotor diameter 5 ft 2 in (1.575 m); main rotor disc area 980.51 sq ft (91.09 m2); tail rotor disc area

20.97 sq ft (1.95 m2)
Fuselage and tail: length overall, rotors turning 39 ft 7.5 in (12.075 m); height overall 9 ft 6.75 in (2.915 m)
Powerplant: one Allison 250-C18 turboshaft rated at 317 shp (236 kW)
Weights: empty 758 kg (1,671 lb); maximum take-off 1300 kg (2,866 lb)
Fuel and load: internal fuel 270 litres (71.3 US gal); external fuel none
Speed: never exceed speed at sea level 130 kt (149 mph; 240 km/h)
Range: endurance 3 hours with 20 minute reserves

Shaanxi Y-8/Y-8MPA

Shaanxi Aircraft Company
PO Box 34, Chengdu, Shaanxi 723213
People's Republic of China

The **Yunshuji 8** (Transport aircraft number 8) is a reverse-engineered unlicensed copy of the **Antonov An-12 'Cub'** (described separately). The task of designing and developing the aircraft was initially given to the Xian Aircraft Company, which built and subsequently flew the first prototype on 25 December 1974. Production was transferred to the Shaanxi Aircraft Company in 1972, and their first aircraft flew on 29 December 1975. From the start, the Chinese-built 'Cub' could be distinguished by its longer nose glazing, which is similar to that fitted to the Chinese-built 'Badger'. The prototypes and initial aircraft were simply designated **Y-8** and were quickly replaced on the production line by a number of specialised types.

The **Y-8A** is a dedicated helicopter-carrier, optimised for transporting **China**'s Sikorsky S-70 Black Hawks to more remote areas. Internal cabin height was increased by deleting the internal gantry and travelling cranes/hoists. A civilian passenger/freighter version is designated **Y-8B**, while a fully pressurised version (all other versions are, like An-12s, only partly pressurised), the **Y-8C**, was developed in collaboration with Lockheed. Intended for civil and military customers, the aircraft has a redesigned cargo door, a longer hold (with no fuselage stretch), and various new systems. Two prototypes are flying.

The **Y-8D** is a dedicated military export version, one pair of which was bought by both **Sri Lanka** and **Sudan**; **Myanmar**

has also ordered the type. Sri Lankan aircraft have reportedly been converted for use as bombers, but one Y-8 was lost soon after delivery. The **Y-8E** is a drone-carrier, developed to replace elderly Tupolev Tu-4 'Bulls' used in the same role. The forward pressurised cabin accommodates a drone-controller's console, and two drones can be carried on trapezes under the wings. The **Y-8F** is a uniquely Chinese aircraft, a dedicated livestock carrier with cages for 350 goats or sheep.

Other versions are under development, including an inflight-refuelling tanker and an AEW platform (GEC Marconi are collaborating on the latter programme). A prototype of the **Y-8X** (previously known as the **Y-8MPA**) is flying. This has a Litton (Canada) AN/APS-504(V)3 search radar under the nose, in a new, deepened drum-like radome, and Western INS, ADF, DME, and other avionics. The aircraft also carries optical and infra-red cameras, an IR detection system and sonobuoys.

SPECIFICATION

Shaanxi Y-8C
Wing: span 38.00 m (124 ft 8 in); aspect ratio 11.85; area 121.86 m2 (1,311.73 sq ft)
Fuselage and tail: length 34.02 m (111 ft 7.5 in); height 11.16 m (36 ft 7.5 in); tailplane span 12.196 m (40 ft 0.25 in); wheel track 4.92 m (16 ft 1.75 in); wheel base 9.58 m (31 ft 5 in)
Powerplant: four Zhuzhou (SMPMC) Wojiang-6

(Ivchyenko AI-20K) turboprops each rated at 3,169 ekW (4,250 ehp)
Weights: empty equipped 35500 kg (78,263 lb); maximum take-off 61000 kg (134,480 lb)
Fuel and load: internal fuel 22909 kg (50,505 lb); external fuel none; maximum payload 20000 kg (44,092 lb)
Speed: maximum level speed 'clean' at 7000 m (22,965 ft) 662 km/h (357 kt; 411 mph); maximum cruising speed at 8000 m (26,250 ft) 550 km/h (297 kt; 342 mph); economical cruising speed at 8000 m (26,250 ft) 530 km/h (286 kt; 329 mph)
Range: 5615 km (3,030 nm; 3,489 miles) with maximum fuel or 1273 km (687 nm; 791 miles) with maximum payload; endurance 11 hours 7 minutes

The Y-8 is an unlicensed copy of the An-12. Whereas Antonov has rolled out the An-70, no such Chinese developments have occurred, and Shaanxi continues to produce 40-year old technology.

Performance: maximum rate of climb at sea level 473 m (1,552 ft) per minute; service ceiling 34,120 ft (10400 m); take-off run 1,230 m (4,035 ft) at maximum take-off weight; take-off distance to 50 ft (15 m) 3,007 m (9,866 ft) at maximum take-off weight; landing distance from 50 ft (15 m) 2174 m (7,133 ft) at normal landing weight; landing run 1100 m (3,609 ft) at normal landing weight

Shenyang J-5/F-5

Shenyang Aircraft Corporation
PO Box 328, Shenyang, Liaoning 110034
People's Republic of China

The **Shenyang J-5** was **China**'s first indigenously-built fighter, 'J-2' having been a Western designation erroneously applied to Soviet-built MiG-15, and the J-4 designation being wrongly applied to MiG-17s from the same source. It has often been reported that China built the MiG-15 and MiG-15UTI, but this was never the case. The J-5 was the real Chinese designation for a Chinese-built copy of the MiG-17F. Unlike later 'Chinese MiG copies'

the J-5 was produced with close Soviet collaboration. The Shaanxi Aircraft Company itself was largely designed and constructed by the Soviets, and J-5 production followed a carefully planned, four-phase programme under which local workers learned each major production process, starting with mere assembly of Soviet-built sub-assemblies and ending with manufacture of about 48 per cent of each aircraft.

The first J-5 made its maiden flight on 19

July 1956, and in September was cleared for mass production. Seventeen were completed in 1956, with 142 following in 1957, 429 in 1958 and 179 in 1959, bringing the total to 767. Production then switched to the J-6 (MiG-19). The introduction of the aircraft was a tremendous morale booster to industry and air force alike, and allowed the Chinese to shoot down a number of Taiwanese 'intruders', including two F-84Gs, six F-86s and an F-100 in 1958, an RB-57 in 1957, and an F-4 in 1967. J-5s are believed to remain in service with the People's Liberation Army Air Force. The type was exported, under the designation F-5, to **Albania** (where about 11 remain in service), and to **North Korea**, **Sudan** and **Tanzania**, where handfuls may remain active.

Later derivatives of the MiG-17F were developed and constructed by Chengdu (described separately) under the **JJ-5/FT-5** heading.

While in its day it was an impressive fighter, the Chinese J-5 MiG-17 copy (export designation F-5) is now little more than a museum piece. However, circumstances have forced the Albanian air force to retain its services.

SPECIFICATION

Shenyang J-5/F-5 'Fresco'
Wing: span 9.63 m (31 ft 7 in); aspect ratio 4.1; area 22.60 m2 (243.27 sq ft)
Fuselage and tail: length 11.36 m (37 ft 3.25 in); height 3.80 m (12 ft 5.5 in
Powerplant: one Liming (LM) Wopen-5 (Klimov VK-1F) turbojet rated at 29.50 kN (5,732 lb st) dry and 33.14 kN (7,451 lb st) with afterburning
Weights: maximum take-off 6075 kg (13,393 lb)
Fuel and load: internal fuel 1155 kg (2,546 lb); external fuel up to 655 kg (1,444 lb) in two 400- or 240-litre (106- or 63-US gal) drop tanks; maximum ordnance 500 kg (1,102 lb)
Speed: maximum level speed 'clean' at 3000 m (9,845 ft) 1145 km/h (617 kt; 711 mph) or at 10000 m (32,810 ft) 1071 km/h (578 kt; 666 mph)
Range: ferry range 1980 km (1,068 nm; 1,230 miles) with drop tanks; combat radius 700 km (378 nm; 435 miles) on a hi-lo-hi attack mission with two 250-kg (551-lb) bombs and two drop tanks
Performance: maximum rate of climb at sea level 3900 m (12,795 ft) per minute; climb to 5000 m (16,405 ft) in 2 minutes 36 seconds at dry thrust or 1 minute 48 seconds at afterburning thrust; service ceiling 15000 m (49,215 ft) at dry thrust and 16600 m (54,460 ft) at afterburning thrust; take-off run 590 m (1,936 ft) at normal take-off weight; landing run 850 m (2,789 ft) at normal landing weight

Shenyang J-6/F-6

China began assessment of the supersonic MiG-19 during the late 1950s. It was selected for production under the second Five Year Plan. Design drawings were supplied to the Shenyang Aircraft Factory, which produced their own production tooling and design documentation for a copy of the basic **MiG-19P** all-weather interceptor under the designation **J-6**. The first Chinese-assembled aircraft made its maiden flight on 17 December 1958, and the first Chinese-built aircraft followed on 30 September 1959.

Licence-production of the MiG-19 and **MiG-19PM** was also assigned to the Nanchang Aircraft Factory, laying the foundations for later production of the **Q-5** (described separately). Seven MiG-19Ps were built, the first flying on 28 September 1959. Five MiG-19PMs were assembled from Soviet kits, and another 19 were built at the factory, these apparently being designated **J-6B**. Unfortunately, the turbulence of the 'Great Leap Forward' destroyed the carefully built-up quality control procedures instituted during the first Five Year Plan, and between 1958 and 1960 not one J-6 from Shenyang or Nanchang was accepted by the **PLA air force**. Many were scrapped after failing post-production inspections, and others had to be rebuilt before delivery.

The programme to build the MiG-19 began again in 1961 using Soviet-supplied drawings and technical documents, after having completely rebuilt the production tooling. Production was of the basic **MiG-19S 'Farmer-C'** day fighter, rather than the radar-equipped MiG-19P, although small numbers of the latter, and the MiG-19PM, may also have been constructed. The first 'second batch' J-6 flew in December 1961.

The aircraft was recertificated in December 1963, and began to enter service in significant numbers in 1964-65. The period between 1963 and 1966 was one of relative stability, and high morale, high quality, sensible production targets and a logical engineering approach prevailed. All this was swept away in the Cultural Revolution, in which political dogma replaced planning, and a period turbulence once more affected the industry. The effect on the J-6 programme was devastating, and provoked a restoration of investment, proper inspection, quality control and workers' education.

By 1973, the prevailing situation had improved sufficiently for the development of new variants. The most important of these was the **JJ-6** trainer, but this was accompanied by the **JZ-6**. Handfuls of J-6s had been built for medium-level and low-level recce duties from 1967, under the JZ-6 designation, and three more were modified for high-altitude reconnaissance between 1971 and 1975. A requirement for an entirely new JZ-6 was issued in January 1976, and construction of a prototype/demonstrator began in April. This used optical and infra-red sensors.

Frequently misidentified as the **J-6Xin**, and attributed to have an indigenous all-weather radar in a 'needle-nose radome' intake centrebody, the **J-6III** was actually a high-speed day fighter whose sharp, conical, needle nose served as a variable shock-cone. Development of the new variant began in 1969, and a prototype flew on 6 August 1969. The J-6III was a very different looking aircraft, with short-span, cropped wings and increased-chord ailerons and flaps. The aircraft was powered by uprated WP6A turbojets. The J-6III proved to be faster, faster climbing and tighter turning than the basic J-6, but was plagued by handling and quality control problems. 'Hundreds' had to be returned to the factory and rebuilt during a four-year programme.

The more modest **J-6C** was more successful, differing from the basic J-6/MiG-19S in having a relocated brake-chute fairing at the base of the trailing edge of the tailfin, below the rudder.

Guizhou was responsible for the final variant, the all-weather **J-6A**, which may also have been designated **J-6IV**. This was based on the J-6C airframe, but introduced all-weather radar and compatibility with the PL-2 missile. By comparison with the original all-weather J-6s (based on the MiG-19P and MiG-19PM), the J-6A/J-6IV had slightly recontoured radomes, with a larger and more bulbous 'upper lip' and a more pointed and conical centrebody. It is unknown whether the aircraft retains cannon in the wingroots or under the fuselage.

The 1950s-vintage J-6 was produced into the 1980s, by which time approximately 3,000 had been built. It was exported in substantial quantities to **Albania, Bangladesh, Egypt, Iran, Iraq, North Korea, Pakistan, Somalia, Tanzania,** **Vietnam** and **Zambia**, most of which continue to operate the type in small numbers. It remains in service in larger numbers with the Air Force of the People's Liberation Army, with which service it is numerically the most important type, fulfilling both attack and fighter roles.

Pakistan purchased two batches of 60 **F-6**s after the 1971 conflict with India, and even in late 1994 the type remained in service with No. 15 Sqn at Kamra, No. 19 (OCU) Sqn at Mianwali and Nos 17 and 23 Sqns at Samungli. The massive overhaul facility at Kamra kept the aircraft viable through frequent overhauls, and by incorporating many modifications, including AIM-9 Sidewinder compatibility, Martin-Baker ejection seats and various new avionics systems, probably including most of those fitted to upgraded Nanchang A-5s (though not the RWRs). Pakistani F-6s are also configured to carry a huge semi-conformal bathtub external fuel tank below the belly. Some aircraft were passed to Bangladesh, where the type remains in use with No. 25 (OCU) Sqn as an advanced/tactical trainer.

SPECIFICATION

Shenyang J-6/F-6 'Farmer'
Wing: span 9.20 m (30 ft 2¼ in); aspect ratio 3.24; area 25.00 m2 (269.11 sq ft)
Fuselage and tail: length 14.90 m (48 ft 10½ in) including probe and 12.60 m (41 ft 4 in) excluding probe; height 3.88 m (12 ft 8¾ in); tailplane span 5.00 m (16 ft 4¾ in); wheel track 4.15 m (13 ft 7½ in)
Powerplant: two Liming (LM) Wopen-6 (Tumanskii R-9BF-811) turbojets each rated at 5,730 lb st (25.49 kN) dry and 7,165 lb st (31.87 kN) with afterburning
Weights: nominal empty 5760 kg (12,698 lb); normal take-off 7545 kg (16,634 lb); maximum take-off about 10000 kg (22,046 lb)
Fuel and load: internal fuel 1687 kg (3,719 lb); external fuel up to two 1140-litre (301-US gal) or 760-litre (201-US gal) drop tanks; maximum ordnance 500 kg (1,102 lb)
Speed: never exceed speed at 35,000 ft (10670 m) 1700 km/h (917 kt; 1,056 mph); maximum level speed 'clean' at 36,000 ft (10975 m) 1540 km/h (831 kt; 957 mph); cruising speed at optimum altitude 950 km/h (512 kt; 590 mph)
Range: ferry range 2200 km (1,187 nm; 1,366 miles) with two 760-litre (201-US gal) drop tanks; normal range at 46,000 ft (14020 m) 1390 km (750 nm; 863 miles); combat radius 685 km (370 nm; 426 miles) with two 760-litre (201-US gal) drop tanks
Performance: maximum rate of climb at sea level more than 9145 m (30,000 ft) per minute; service ceiling 58,725 ft (17900 m); take-off run about 670 m (2,198 ft) with afterburning; take-off distance to 80 ft (25 m) 1525 m (5,003 ft) with afterburning; landing distance from 80 ft (25 m) 1980 m (6,496 ft) without brake chute; landing run 600 m (1,969 ft) with brake chute

Shenyang J-6/F-6 'Farmer'

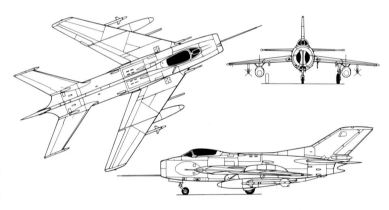

Above: Still the AFPLA's most numerically important type, this J-6 is one of several Communist aircraft to defect to Taiwan over the years.

Below: Pakistan operates J-6s in two-tone grey and natural metal schemes, but this No. 19 Sqn example wears an all-white finish.

Right: The Bangladesh Defence Force Air Wing has now only a single J-6 (F-6) unit: No. 25 Sqn (OCU) 'The Trendsetters', based at Jessore.

Below: While deficient in range, the J-6 remains a useful ground attack aircraft. This Pakistan Fiza'ya aircraft carries a pair of rocket pods.

Shenyang JJ-6

Another manifestation of the restoration of stability for the aircraft industry was the production by Shenyang of the **JJ-6** two-seat trainer, which first flew on 6 November 1970, but the certification of which was delayed until December 1973. A two-seat MiG-19UTI was built in small numbers by Mikoyan, but the type never entered service, conversion from the MiG-15UTI not being judged to be a problem. By the 1970s, however, flight safety considerations had assumed greater importance, and China felt that a trainer with handling characteristics similar to the J-6 was essential. This view was reinforced by significant export orders.

The Chinese two-seat trainer owes little to the Russian original. The fuselage is stretched by some 84 cm (33 in) ahead of the wing, and the wingroot-mounted NR-23 cannon are deleted to make room for extra fuel, restoring fuel capacity to within 150 litres (33 Imp gal) of the single-seater. A single cannon is usually retained below the fuselage. Two ventral fins are added below the rear fuselage to maintain stability.

The JJ-6 is based on the airframe of the later J-6C with the relocated brake-chute fairing, tubeless tyres, and disc brakes on the main undercarriage units. The type also has nosewheel braking, and various new avionics systems.

Production of the JJ-6 totalled 634 examples, and many were exported under the designation **FT-6** to serve as conversion and continuation trainers for the F-6 and A-5. In **Pakistan**, surviving FT-6s have been extensively upgraded (to the same standards as that nation's F-6 fighters) with Martin-Baker Mk 10L rocket-powered ejection seats. The zero-zero capability offered by this seat is a quantum leap from the 260 m (853 ft)/350 km/h (218 mph) minima of the original Shenyang seat. Using the 'lower-slung' Martin-Baker seat, pilots whose height exceeds 1.73 m (5 ft 8 in) can at last wear a proper flying helmet. JJ-6 trainers also remain in service in **Bangladesh**, **China** and **North Korea**.

SPECIFICATION

Shenyang/Tianjin JJ-6/FT-6
Wing: span 9.20 m (30 ft 2.25 in); aspect ratio 3.24; area 25.00 m² (269.11 sq ft)
Fuselage and tail: length 13.44 m (44 ft 1 in) excluding probe; height 3.88 m (12 ft 8¾ in); tailplane span 5.00 m (16 ft 4¾ in); wheel track 4.15 m (13 ft 7½ in)
Powerplant: two Liming (LM) Wopen-6 (Tumanskii R-9BF-811) turbojets each rated at 25.50 kN (5,732 lb st) dry and 31.88 kN (7,167 lb st) with afterburning
Fuel and load: internal fuel about 2000 litres (528 US gal); external fuel up to two 1140- or 760-litre (301- or 201-US gal) drop tanks; maximum ordnance 500 kg (1,102 lb)
Speed: never exceed speed at 10670 m (35,000 ft) 1700 km/h (917 kt; 1,056 mph); maximum level speed 'clean' at 11000 m (36,090 ft) 1540 km/h (831 kt; 957 mph) and at sea level 1340 km/h (723 kt; 832 mph); cruising speed at optimum altitude 950 km/h (512 kt; 590 mph)
Range: ferry range 2200 km (1,186 nm; 1,366 miles); standard range 1390 km (749 nm; 863 miles); combat radius 685 km (370 nm; 426 miles) on a typical hi-lo-hi mission with two drop tanks
Performance: maximum rate of climb at sea level more than 9145 m (30,000 ft) per minute with afterburning; service ceiling 17900 m (58,725 ft); take-off run about 670 m (2,200 ft) at maximum take-off weight with afterburning; take-off distance to 25 m (82 ft) 1525 m (5,000 ft) at maximum take-off weight with afterburning; landing distance from 25 m (82 ft) 1700 m (5,580 ft) at normal landing weight with brake chute; landing run 600 m (1,970 ft) at normal landing weight with brake chute
g limit: +8

With the MiG-19-derived J-6 as China's most significant warplane, the JJ-6 conversion trainer fulfils an important function.

Shenyang J-8 and J-8I 'Finback-A'

The **J-8** originated from a **PLA** requirement for a fighter with performance and combat capability superior to that of the MiG-21. Shenyang's decision to use twin engines, and the company's long association with the 'tailed delta' MiG-21-type configuration, ensured that the new aircraft looked like a scaled-up MiG-21; as such, it bore an astonishing resemblance to Mikoyan's Ye-152A 'Flipper'. The requirement was proposed in 1964, and development was in full swing by 1965.

The two prototypes were completed in July 1968, at the height of the Cultural Revolution but, remarkably, the flight test programme went ahead, albeit at a slow pace. The first J-8 made its maiden flight on 5 July 1969, and certification followed 10 years later. Engine shutdowns, high temperatures in the rear fuselage and transonic vibration were the only problems. These were quickly solved, and the 10-year gap before certification was almost entirely due to political interference and disruption to the factory by the repression of many of its key workers.

The original J-8 had a small ranging radar in the intake centrebody, and retained the single-piece forward-hinging canopy of the original J-7. The aircraft was armed with a single 30-mm cannon and up to four underwing PL-2 air-to-air missiles. Any production was very limited.

The **J-8I** was designed as an all-weather fighter derivative of the basic J-8, and featured a new Type 204 Sichuan SR-4 radar in an enlarged intake centrebody. The 30-mm cannon was replaced by a twin-barrelled 23-mm 23-III cannon, and provision was made for four rocket pods as an optional alternative to the PL-2 missiles. The J-8I retained the same 59-kN (13,450-lb st) WP-7B engines as the basic J-8 (also used in the Chengdu F-7M) but introduced some aerodynamic refinements, with small fences above the wing, revised wingtips and relocated airbrakes. The aircraft also introduced a two-piece canopy, with an upward-hinging rear transparency and a fixed windscreen. This marked the replacement of the highly unpopular Type I ejection seat with the Type II, which was more reliable and which could be used at ground level at speeds in excess of 140 kt (160 mph; 259 km/h).

Prototype assembly was completed in May 1980, but the aircraft burned out during its first engine run after a fuel or hydraulic pipe fractured due to resonance. The second prototype was hurriedly completed and made the type's maiden flight on 24 April 1981. Certification was granted in July 1985. J-8 and J-8I production totalled about 100 aircraft, and some of the original J-8s are said to have been converted to the later standard.

SPECIFICATION

Shenyang J-8 I 'Finback-A'
generally similar to the Shenyang J-8 II 'Finback-B' except in the following particulars:
Powerplant: two Liyang (LMC) Wopen-7B turbojets each rated at 43.15 kN (9,700 lb st) and 59.82 kN (13,448 lb st) with afterburning
Range: combat radius 800 km (497 miles)
Performance: maximum rate of climb at sea level 12000 m (39,370 ft) per minute; service ceiling 18000 m (59,050 ft)

Above: This line-up probably shows most of the original J-8Is, believed to have been used only for trials duties.

Left: The J-8I carries an air intercept radar in its conical intake centrebody.

Shenyang J-8II 'Finback-B'

Although the J-8I marked a great improvement over the original 'Finback', there was clearly scope for a more radical redesign. This led to the development of the **J-8II 'Finback-B'**, which was given the go-ahead in May 1981. The new variant had relocated lateral air intakes to feed its 69-kN (15,430-lb st) WP-13B turbojets, leaving the nose free for a radar antenna of the largest possible diameter. The engine intakes bear a striking similarity to those of the MiG-23 'Flogger', which should come as no surprise, since some of Egypt's MiG-23s were shipped to **China** in exchange for J-7 deliveries. The original aircraft's twin ventral strakes were replaced by a MiG-23-style folding fin. Seventy per cent of the airframe was changed by comparison with the original J-8, as were 30 per cent of the contractor-supplied parts.

The operational requirement for the new variant was approved in September 1980. The extensive use of CAD/CAM reduced design and development time to the minimum, the first of four prototypes flying on 12 June 1984. There has been small-scale batch production of the J-8II, but the type may not have entered service. An export version, designated **F-8B**, is powered by a pair of WP-13B turbojets and introduces a pulse-Doppler look-down radar and digital avionics, with a HUD and two HDDs.

On 5 August 1987 Grumman received a $501.8 million contract to design, develop and test an avionics upgrade for the J-8II under the Foreign Military Sales Program. Sponsored by the USAF's Aeronautical Systems Division, the contract covered installation of the new avionics package in two J-8II airframes supplied by China, and the provision of 50 shipsets for local installation, with development to be completed by February 1991 and delivery of the modification kits to be completed by January 1995. The new avionics package included a modified Westinghouse AN/APG-66 radar, with a constant wave illuminator to give compatibility with semi-active radar homing missiles like the AIM-7 Sparrow. The aircraft would also receive a modern HUD, a US ejection seat and a Litton LN39 INS, plus a bubble canopy and frameless wraparound windscreen. The massacre in Tiananmen Square in June 1989 led to an immediate halt on work on the project, and the expulsion of many of the Chinese engineers. Development restarted, but flight test and kit delivery would have required a change in State Department policy; with deliveries unlikely, China pulled out of the project, leading to its cancellation.

The cancellation of the Peace Pearl upgrade may have killed off the J-8. The PLAAF has taken delivery of Su-27 'Flankers', and seems more likely to purchase further examples, and perhaps MiG-29s, than to procure an indigenous alternative lacking sophisticated modern avionics and which represents an 'F-4-generation' aircraft.

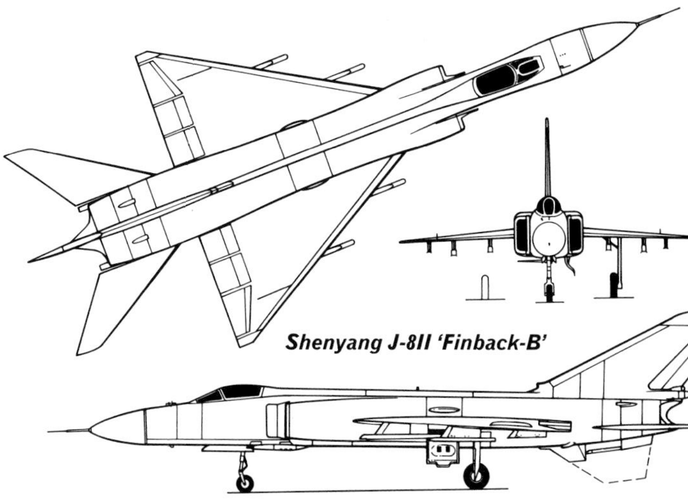

Shenyang J-8II 'Finback-B'

SPECIFICATION

Shenyang J-8 II/F-8B 'Finback-B'
Wing: span 9.34 m (30 ft 7.875 in); aspect ratio 2.1; area 42.20 m² (454.25 sq ft)
Fuselage and tail: length 21.59 m (70 ft 10 in) including probe; height 5.41 m (17 ft 9 in); wheel track 3.74 m (12 ft 3¼ in); wheel base 7.34 m (24 ft 0¾ in)
Powerplant: two Liyang (LMC) Wopen-13A II turbojets each rated at 9,590 lb (42.66 kN) dry and 14,815 lb (65.90 kN) with afterburning
Weights: empty 9820 kg (21,649 lb); normal take-off 14300 kg (31,526 lb); maximum take-off 17800 kg (39,242 lb)
Fuel and load: internal fuel about 5400 litres (1,426 US gal); external fuel up to three drop tanks
Speed: maximum level speed 'clean' at 36,000 ft (10975 m) 2338 km/h (1,262 kt; 1,453 mph)
Range: ferry range 2200 km (1,187 nm; 1,367 miles) with drop tanks; combat radius 800 km (432 kt; 497 miles)
Performance: maximum rate of climb at sea level 12000 m (39,370 ft) per minute; service ceiling 20200 m (66,275 ft); take-off run 670 m (2,198 ft) at maximum take-off weight with afterburning; landing run 1000 m (3,280 ft) with brake chute
g limits: +4.83 in a sustained turn at Mach 0.9 at 16,400 ft (5000 m)

Development of the J-8 was halted by the Tiananmen Square massacre, which left development aircaft embargoed in the USA. Since then, China has opted to buy Su-27 'Flankers' from Russia.

Shijiazhuang (SAP) Y-5

Shijiazhuang Aircraft Plant
PO Box 164, Shijiazhuang, Hebei 050062
People's Republic of China

Manufactured under Soviet licence, the Antonov An-2 general-purpose biplane was built in China for 30 years for both civil and military tasks. The first Chinese-produced An-2 was flown on 7 December 1957 as the **Y-5**, a total of 727 aircraft of this type being built at Nanchang, of which 384 were either for military use or for export. Production terminated at Nanchang in 1968, but was resumed in 1970 at Shijiazhuang (SAP), where an additional 221 were built before manufacture ended in 1986.

Extensively employed for utility tasks by the Chinese armed forces, the Y-5 was widely exported. A major recipient was the **Korean People's Army Air Force**, this North Korean service having received in excess of 160 aircraft of this type from Nanchang and Shijiazhuang production. For a number of years, the North Korean Y-5s were used for nocturnal missions over South Korea, flying at extremely low altitudes and sometimes depositing agents and saboteurs.

In 1989 the type again entered production as the **Y-5B**, a specially modified agricultural version.

SPECIFICATION

Shijiazhuang Y-5N
generally similar to the PZL Mielec (Antonov) An-2T Antek 'Colt' except in the following particulars:
Powerplant: one SMPMC (Zhuzhou) Huosai-5 (Shvetsov ASh-62IR) radial piston engine rated at 986 hp (735.5 kW)

ShinMaywa Industries US-1 (SS-2A)

ShinMaywa Industries Ltd
Nippon Building, 6-2, Otemachi 2-chome, Chiyoda-ku
Tokyo 100, Japan

Following the 1989 retirement of PS-1 patrol aircraft, the related **US-1** remains in military service in **Japan**. Fourteen were procured to serve with the 71st Kokutai of the JMSDF at Iwakuni and Atsugi, in the SAR role. The US-1 first flew on 16 October 1974 (from water) and on 3 December 1974 (from land). With a crew of nine, the US-1 has provision for 20 seated survivors or 12 stretchers. Experiments have also been made with one aircraft converted for the fire-fighting role by means of a tank system developed by Comair in Canada. All remaining aircraft have been converted to **US-1A** standard with the replacement of original T64-IHI-10 engines by more powerful -10J versions.

In 1992 Shin Meiwa (known as Kawanishi until 1949) was renamed ShinMaywa Industries and the US-1 production line was surprisingly reopened to meet an order for a 14th aircraft for the JMSDF. Another US-1A was approved in the FY 1993 budget, and more examples may yet follow.

SPECIFICATION

ShinMaywa Industries US-1A
Wing: span 108 ft 9 in (33.15 m); aspect ratio 8.1; area 1,462.00 sq ft (135.82 m²)
Fuselage and tail: length 109 ft 9¼ in (33.46 m); height 32 ft 7¾ in (9.95 m); tailplane span 40 ft 8½ in (12.36 m); wheel track 11 ft 8¼ in (3.56 m); wheel base 27 ft 4 in (8.33 m)
Powerplant: four Ishikawajima-built General Electric T64-IHI-10J turboprops each rated at 3,493 ehp (2605 ekW) and, powering the boundary layer control system, one Ishikawajima-built General Electric T58-IHI-10-M2 turboshaft rated at 1,360 shp (1014 kW)
Weights: manufacturer's empty 23300 kg (51,367 lb); empty equipped 25500 kg (56,217 lb); normal take-off 43000 kg (94,797 lb) from water; maximum take-off 45000 kg (99,206 lb) from land
Fuel and load: internal fuel 22489 litres (5,941 US gal); external fuel none
Speed: maximum level speed at 10,000 ft (3050 m) 282 kt (325 mph; 522 km/h); cruising speed at 1,000 ft (3050 m) 230 kt (265 mph; 426 km/h)
Range: 2,060 nm (2,372 miles; 3817 km)
Performance: maximum rate of climb at sea level 1,600 ft (488 m) per minute; service ceiling 23,600 ft (7195 m); take-off run 1,820 ft (555 m) at normal take-off weight on water; take-off distance to 50 ft (15 m) 2,150 ft (655 m) at maximum take-off weight on land; landing distance from 50 ft (15 m) 2,655 ft (809 m) at normal landing weight on land with propeller reversal; landing run 720 ft (219 m) at normal landing weight on water without propeller reversal

In a surprising move, the US-1 re-entered production in 1992, and further deliveries are pending.

ShinMaywa Industries (Learjet) U-36A

Four **Learjet 36A** twin-jets were converted by Shin Meiwa (renamed in 1992 as ShinMaywa) to serve as fleet training support aircraft for the JMSDF, with the designation **U-36A**. Extensive modifications allow these aircraft to tow targets and fly anti-ship missile simulation and ECM missions. Large wingtip pods house an HWQ-1T missile seeker simulator, AN/ALQ-6 jammer and cameras. A long-range ocean surveillance radar is fitted, with a large underbelly radome housing the scanning aerial, and the U-36A also carries AN/ALE-43 chaff dis-

penser and a high-speed sleeve target with scoring equipment. The U-36A operates at higher weights than the Learjet 36A, and has expanded underwing stores capability.

SPECIFICATION

ShinMaywa Industries (Learjet) U-36A
generally similar to the Learjet 35A except in the following particulars:
Fuel and load: internal fuel 1,110 US gal (4202 litres); external fuel none

The JASDF's U-36s are flown by the 81st Kokutai at Iwakuni, and in addition to ECM duties are used as target tugs – hence the orange colour scheme.

Shorts SC-7 Skyvan

Short Brothers PLC
PO Box 241, Airport Road, Belfast BT3 9DZ
Northern Ireland

Of notably utilitarian appearance, the **Shorts Skyvan** began life in piston-engined form (first flown 17 January 1963, with Continental engines) but acquired Astazou II turboprops (flown 2 October 1963) before production began for both military and civil use. The principal military variant is the **Skyvan 3M**, flown early in 1970 and subsequently purchased by about 20 air forces. In military guise, the Skyvan 3M can accommodate 22 equipped troops, 16 paratroops (dropped through the rear loading ramp), 12 stretchers or a variety of cargo.

Among the first, and still the largest, military user is the **Royal Air Force of Oman** (formerly the Sultan of Oman Air Force), which bought 16 for operation by No. 2 Squadron. **Ghana** and **Singapore** each bought six, used for both transport and SAR/coastal patrol duties by, respectively, No. 1 Squadron at Takoradi and No. 121 Squadron at Changi. Other users, mostly with two aircraft each, are **Austria, Botsawana, Ciskei, Guyana, Mauritania, Mexico, Nepal,** and **(North) Yemen**.

SPECIFICATION

Shorts SC.7 Skyvan Series 3M
Wing: span 64 ft 11 in (19.79 m); aspect ratio 11.0; area 373.00 sq ft (34.65 m²)
Fuselage and tail: length 40 ft 1 in (12.21 m) with standard nose or 41 ft 4 in (12.60 m) with weather radar nose; height 15 ft 1 in (4.60 m); tailplane span 17 ft 4 in (5.28 m); wheel track 13 ft 10 in (4.21 m); wheel base 14 ft 10 in (4.52 m)
Powerplant: two Garrett TPE331-2-201A turboprops each rated at 715 shp (533 kW)
Weights: operating empty 7,400 lb (3356 kg) in utility configuration, or 7,620 lb (3456 kg) in freighter configuration, or 8,330 lb (3778 kg) in trooping configuration; normal take-off 13,700 lb (6214 kg); maximum take-off 14,500 lb (6577 kg)
Fuel and load: internal fuel 2,320 lb (1052 kg) plus provision for 800 lb (363 kg) of auxiliary fuel; external fuel none; maximum payload 5,200 lb (2358 kg) standard or 6,000 lb (2722 kg) overload
Speed: never exceed speed 217 kt (250 mph; 402 km/h); maximum cruising speed at 10,000 ft (3050 m) 175 kt (202 mph; 324 km/h); economical cruising speed at

The Royal Nepalese Army Air Corps (which gained autonomy from the air force in 1979) operates a mix of fixed- and rotary-winged types that includes three Shorts Skyvan 3s, based at Tribhuvan.

10,000 ft (3050 m) 150 kt (173 mph; 278 km/h)
Range: 582 nm (670 miles; 1075 km) with maximum fuel or 208 nm (240 miles; 386 km) with a 5,000-lb (2268-kg) payload
Performance: maximum rate of climb at sea level 1,530 ft (466 m) per minute; service ceiling 22,000 ft

(6705 m); take-off run 780 ft (238 m) at maximum take-off weight; take-off distance to 50 ft (15 m) 1,260 ft (384 m) at maximum take-off weight; landing distance from 50 ft (15 m) 1,395 ft (425 m) at maximum landing weight; landing run 695 ft (212 m) at maximum landing weight

---

Shorts 330/C-23 Sherpa

Developed from the Skyvan light transport, the **Shorts 330** was a regional airliner which could also be reconfigured for transport tasks. Its box-like fuselage offered exceptional load-carrying capacity for the aircraft's size, and the high-lift wing and powerful engines provided good STOL performance. Cargo versions were configured with a full-width rear loading ramp. The **Thai army** operates two aircraft designated **Shorts 330UTT** in the transport role.

The major military customer was the **US Air Force**, which bought 18 **C-23As** for its EDSA (European Distribution System Aircraft) requirement, these being used to shuttle spare parts between the USAFE maintenance and distribution centres and the front-line bases. Based with the 10th MAS at Zweibrücken AB, Germany, the C-23As served from November 1984 until 31 October 1990, when the EDSA programme was ended.

Four C-23As remained in USAF hands at Edwards AFB, where they served the 6510th Test Wing (now 412th TW) for the USAF Test Pilots' School. Eight were diverted to the US Forestry Service, and six were transferred to the **Army National**

This Connecticut AVCRAD C-23B (note the cabin windows) is a US Army-operated Sherpa and sports Desert Storm nose art.

Guard, which also ordered 10 more new-build **C-23Bs**, distinguished by their cabin windows.

It is believed that four 330s are in Army service. The Army fleet flies utility transport missions on behalf of the Army's maintenance organisation, single aircraft being assigned to the STARCs (State Area Commands) of Alabama, California, Connecticut, Mississippi, Oregon, Puerto Rico and Utah. At least three are assigned to the Missouri AVCRAD, and six more were delivered during 1992. At least one of the Army C-23s is reputed to have a special mission, perhaps involving electronic reconnaissance, and was seen on service during the Gulf War.

Under the designation **C-23B+**, 20 modified **Shorts 360** commuter airliners (with an option on 10) are to be acquired by the US Army National Guard. These aircraft, bought back by Shorts, will be converted to (twin-tailed) C-23 standard through the addition of new tail sections, along with new

avionics, in a programme to be undertaken at the West Virginia Air Center. The first conversion began in January 1994, and deliveries are due to be completed by 1996.

SPECIFICATION

Shorts C-23A Sherpa
Wing: span 74 ft 8 in (22.76 m); aspect ratio 12.2; area 453.00 sq ft (42.08 m²)
Fuselage and tail: length 58 ft 0½ in (17.69 m); height 16 ft 3 in (4.95 m); tailplane span 18 ft 7¾ in (5.68 m)
Powerplant: two Pratt & Whitney Canada T101-CP-100 (PT6A-45R) turboprops each rated at 1,198 shp (893 kW)
Weights: empty equipped 14,727 lb (6680 kg);

maximum take-off 25,500 lb (11566 kg)
Fuel and load: internal fuel 4,480 lb (2032 kg); external fuel none; maximum payload 7,100 lb (3221 kg)
Speed: maximum cruising speed at 10,000 ft (3050 m) at 21,000 lb (9526 kg) 190 kt (218 mph; 352 km/h); economical cruising speed at 10,000 ft (3050 m) at 21,000 lb (9526 kg) 157 kt (181 mph; 291 km/h)
Range: 669 nm (770 miles; 1239 km) with 5,000-lb (2268-kg) payload or 195 nm (225 miles; 362 km) with 7,000-lb (3,175-kg) payload
Performance: maximum rate of climb at sea level 1,180 ft (360 m) per minute; service ceiling 20,000 ft (6095 m); take-off distance 1,840 ft (561 m) at maximum take-off weight; take-off distance to 50 ft (15 m) 2,610 ft (796 m) at maximum take-off weight; landing distance from 50 ft (15 m) 1,900 ft (579 m) at maximum landing weight

---

Shorts Tucano

In 1985 the **RAF** selected the **Tucano** as its new *ab initio* trainer following an international competition that had involved the Pilatus PC-9, the Hunting Turbo-Firecracker and the AAC/Westland A 20. Based on an original design by EMBRAER of Brazil, the turboprop-powered Tucano offered by

Shorts promised economy and a performance not far short of that of the Jet Provost T.Mk 5, the main type it would replace in RAF service. As the first tandem-seat non-jet trainer to be ordered for the RAF since the Chipmunk, the Tucano reflects a current trend back to a more 'traditional' seating arrangement for pupil and instructor.

Considerable modification was undertaken to tailor the basic airframe to British

requirements, including substituting a Garrett turboprop in place of the original Pratt & Whitney PT6A – which significantly improved the rate of climb – and reprofiling the cockpit to provide commonality with the BAe Hawk. EMBRAER flew a Garrett-engined prototype in Brazil in February 1986 and delivered this to Shorts in Belfast as a pattern aircraft, the first **Tucano T.Mk 1** making its maiden flight on 30 December that year. The total RAF production order

covered 130 aircraft, first delivery to the Central Flying School at Scampton taking place in June 1988. The balance of the RAF order was completed in 1993. Tucanos equip No. 1 FTS at Linton-on-Ouse, No. 3 FTS at Cranwell, and No. 6 FTS at Finningley, with others at Scampton with the CFS.

By opting to train embryo fast-jet pilots on a turboprop aircraft, the RAF gained considerably. Economically a better proposition than a jet type, the Tucano is less demanding from the viewpoint of student pilots in the earliest stages of flight training. To extend the Tucano's capability in both military training and counter-insurgency roles, Shorts conducted a series of Tucano weapon trials in the spring of 1991 using twin FNNH machine-gun pods, the FNNH heavy MG and rocket launcher and the LAIJ32 seven-round rocket launcher, plus bombs up to 250 kg (551 lb). Customers for the armed export Tucano have been **Kuwait** (**T.Mk 52**), which took delivery of the last of 16 aircraft in 1991 (though they remained in the UK pending reformation of the KAF and formation of their operating unit, No. 19 Sqn), and **Kenya** (**T.Mk 51**), which received the last of 12 in June 1991.

This Tucano T.Mk 1 wears the blue band of No. 3 FTS, at Cranwell. The modified (frameless) canopy was one of the design changes specified by the RAF.

SPECIFICATION

Shorts Tucano T.Mk 1
Wing: span 37 ft 0 in (11.28 m); aspect ratio 6.58; area 208.00 sq ft (19.33 m2)
Fuselage and tail: length 32 ft 4¼ in (9.86 m); height

11 ft 1¾ in (3.40 m); tailplane span 13 ft 3½ in (4.66 m); wheel track 12 ft 4 in (3.76 m); wheel base 19 ft 4½ in (3.16 m)
Powerplant: one Garrett TPE331-12B turboprop rated at 1,100 shp (820 kW)
Weights: basic empty 4,872 lb (2210 kg); normal take-off 5,952 lb (2700 kg) for aerobatics; maximum take-off 6,470 lb (2935 kg)
Fuel and load: internal fuel 1,202 lb (545 kg); external fuel up to two 71-Imp gal (85.3-US gal; 323-litre) drop tanks; ordnance none
Speed: never exceed speed 330 kt (380 mph; 611 km/h); maximum level speed 'clean' and maximum cruising speed at 10,000 ft (3050 m) 277 kt (319 mph; 513 km/h) and at sea level 269 kt (310 mph; 498 km/h); economical cruising speed at 20,000 ft (6095 m) 220 kt (253 mph; 407 km/h)
Range: ferry range 1,790 nm (2,061 miles; 3317 km) with drop tanks; range 954 nm (1,099 miles; 1767 km)

with internal fuel; endurance 5 hours 12 minutes
Performance: maximum rate of climb at sea level 3,270 ft (997 m) per minute; service ceiling 34,000 ft (10365 m); take-off run 1,190 ft (363 m) at normal take-off weight; take-off distance to 50 ft (15 m) 1,930 ft

(590 m) at normal take-off weight; landing distance from 50 ft (15 m) 2,050 ft (625 m) at normal landing weight; landing run 1,180 ft (360 m) at normal landing weight
g limits: -3.3 to +6.5

SIAI-Marchetti **S.208M**

Agusta SpA Rome Works (Siai-Marchetti)
Via della Vasca Navale 79/81
I-00146 Rome, Italy

Based on the S.205 four-seat touring aircraft, the first post-war production aircraft of SIAI-Marchetti, the **S.208** was developed in 1967 with more power, retractable gear and five seats. The **Italian air force** acquired 45 in the **S.208M** version (with jettisonable cabin door) and these continue to be used for liaison duties and as glider tugs. A couple of the Italian aircraft

were passed to the **Tunisian air force** to serve in the communications role.

SPECIFICATION

SIAI-Marchetti S.208M
Wing: span 10.86 m (35 ft 7.5 in); aspect ratio 7.33; area 16.09 m2 (173.20 sq ft)

Fuselage and tail: length 8.00 m (26 ft 3 in); height 2.89 m (9 ft 5¾ in); tailplane span 3.42 m (11 ft 2½ in); wheel track 3.55 m (11 ft 8 in); wheel base 1.90 m (6 ft 2¾ in)
Powerplant: one Textron Lycoming O-540-E4A5 flat-six piston engine rated at 260 hp (194 kW)
Weights: empty equipped 780 kg (1,720 lb); maximum take-off 1350 kg (2,976 lb)
Fuel and load: internal fuel 215 litres (56.8 US gal)

plus provision for 231 litres (61 US gal) of auxiliary fuel in two wingtip tanks; external fuel none
Speed: maximum level speed 'clean' at sea level 320 km/h (173 kt; 199 mph); cruising speed at optimum altitude 300 km/h (162 kt; 187 mph)
Range: ferry range 2000 km (1,079 nm; 1,243 miles) with optional fuel; range 1200 km (648 nm; 746 miles) with internal fuel
Performance: service ceiling 5400 m (17,715 ft)

SIAI-Marchetti **SF.260/TP**

Designed by Stello Frati, the three-seat **SF.260** was put into production by SIAI Marchetti after prototypes had been built and flown by Aviamilano (as the **F.250** and **F.260**). The SF.260 was soon marketed in military guise as the **SF.260M** and **SF.260W**, the latter named **Warrior** and having a strengthened airframe and underwing hardpoints for the ground attack role. Production has totalled well over 850, including dedicated variants for the civil market (**SF.260A, B, C** and **D**).

The SF.260M was first flown on 10 October 1970 and is equipped to provide basic and instrument flying. First flown in May 1972, the SF.260W has two or four pylons with a combined capacity for 300 kg (661 lb), and is suitable for light COIN duty and armament training. A turboprop version of the SF.260M/W, the **TP** model, first flew in July 1980, the prototype being a converted airframe. Apart from changes ahead of the firewall to accommodate the Allison 250-B17D turboprop, differences from the piston-engined version were limited to the fuel feed system and a changed rudder trim tab. Production of the SF.260TP is reported to exceed 60.

for use by No. 2 Squadron at Gwelo. In 1994-1995 the Philippine air force will take delivery of 19 SF.260TPs to replace existing SF.260Ms.

OPERATORS

Specific customer variants of the SF.260 are identified by a letter suffix added to the basic 'M' or 'W' designation. Among these are the **SF.260 MB**, Burma; **MP**, Philippines; **MS**, Singapore; **MT**, Thailand; **MC**, Zaïre; and **MZ**, Zambia. Warrior designations included **SF.260 WD**, Dubai; **WE**, Ireland (Eire); **WL**, Libya; **WP**, Philippines; **WS**, Somalia; **WT**, Tunisia; and **WC**, Zimbabwe (local name is **Genet**). Aircraft for the Italian air force are designated **SF.260AM** and a batch ordered by the Turkish air force in 1989 for co-production and local assembly are **SF.260Ds** (a civil designation); 39 remain active. Small numbers of SF.260WLs were transferred to Chad and to Nicaragua by Libya, where a local assembly/production centre was established with Italian help to supplement 110 aircraft delivered from Italy. Other users of SF.260Ms include Belgium, Brunei, Burkino-Faso and Burundi.

Customers for the SF.260TP include the Burundi army aviation, Dubai air wing, Ethiopian air force, Haitian air corps and Sri Lanka air force. Ethiopian and Sri Lankan aircraft have seen service in the armed light COIN role but are often used, like the others, for basic training. In addition, the air force of Zimbabwe has 10 SF.260TP that were, uniquely, locally converted from piston-engined SF.260WC Genet armed trainers

SPECIFICATION

SIAI-Marchetti SF.260W Warrior
Wing: span 8.35 m (27 ft 4¾ in) over tip tanks; aspect ratio 6.3; area 10.10 m2 (108.72 sq ft)
Fuselage and tail: length 7.10 m (23 ft 3½ in); height 2.41 m (7 ft 11 in); elevator span 3.01 m (9 ft 10½ in); wheel track 2.27 m (7 ft 5½ in); wheel base 1.66 m (5 ft 5¼ in)
Powerplant: one Textron Lycoming O-540-E4A5 flat-six piston engine rated at 260 hp (194 kW)
Weights: empty equipped 830 kg (1,830 lb); normal take-off about 1140 kg (2,513 lb); maximum take-off

1300 kg (2,866 lb)
Fuel and load: internal fuel 169 kg (372.5 lb); external fuel up to 114 kg (251.5 lb) in two 80-litre (21-US gal) drop tanks; maximum ordnance 300 kg (661 lb)
Speed: maximum level speed 'clean' at sea level 165 kt (190 mph; 305 km/h); cruising speed at 5,000 ft (1525 m) 152 kt (175 mph; 281 km/h)
Range: ferry range 925 nm (1,066 miles; 1716 km); combat radius 300 nm (345 miles; 556 km) on a single-seat hi-lo-hi attack mission, or 250 nm (287 miles; 463 km) on a single-seat attack mission with two 5-minute loiters over separate en-route target areas
Performance: maximum rate of climb at sea level 1,250 ft (381 m) per minute; climb to 7,550 ft (2300 m) in 10 minutes 20 seconds; service ceiling 14,700 ft (4480 m); take-off distance to 50 ft (15 m) 825 m (2,707 ft) at maximum take-off weight
g limits: -2.2 to +4.4 without external stores

The Sri Lankan air force has a single SF.260 unit, No. 1 Flying Training Wing at Anuradhapur. This is one of its eight SF.260TPs, with rockets.

SIAI-Marchetti **SM 1019**

Eighty of these FAC and liaison aircraft were built for the **Italian army** between 1972 and 1979, after SIAI-Marchetti had fitted turboprop engines in two remanufactured Cessna O-1s to serve as prototypes; these were first flown on 24 May 1969 and on 18 February 1971 as **SM 1019** and **SM 1019A**. The production **SM 1019E1** was largely redesigned in Italy but retained the O-1's basic configuration. Seating two in tandem, the SM 1019 intro-

duced hardpoints for external loads of up to 227 kg (500 lb) that could include gun pods, rockets and bombs. Most remain in service, including some with the **air force**, which handles *ab initio* training of army pilots.

SPECIFICATION

SIAI-Marchetti SM.1019EI
Wing: span 10.97 m (36 ft 0 in); aspect ratio 7.44;

area 16.16 m2 (173.95 sq ft)
Fuselage and tail: length 8.52 m (27 ft 11½ in) tail up; height 2.86 m (9 ft 4½ in) tail down; tailplane span 3.42 m (11 ft 2¾ in); wheel track 2.29 m (7 ft 7¼ in); wheel base 6.23 m (20 ft 5¼ in)
Powerplant: one Allison 250-B17 turboprop rated at 400 shp (298 kW)
Weights: empty equipped 690 kg (1,521 lb); operating empty 730 kg (1,609 lb); normal take-off 1300 kg (2,866 lb); maximum take-off 1450 kg (3,196 lb)
Fuel and load: internal fuel 320 litres (84 US gal); external fuel none; ordnance none
Speed: never exceed speed 169 kt (194 mph; 313 km/h); maximum cruising speed at 8,200 ft (2500 m) 162 kt (186 mph; 300 km/h); economical cruising speed at

8,200 ft (2500 m) 152 kt (175 mph; 281 km/h)
Range: ferry range 730 nm (840 miles; 1352 km) with auxiliary fuel; range 610 nm (702 miles; 1130 km) with standard fuel; endurance 8 hours 45 minutes with auxiliary fuel or 7 hours 20 minutes with standard fuel
Performance: maximum rate of climb at sea level 1,810 ft (551 m) per minute; service ceiling 25,000 ft (7620 m); take-off run 218 ft (716 m) at maximum take-off weight; take-off distance to 50 ft (15 m) 1,185 m (361 m) at maximum take-off weight; landing distance from 50 ft (15 m) 992 ft (281 m) at maximum landing weight; landing run 443 ft (135 m) at maximum landing weight

Sikorsky (Orlando Helicopter Airways) S-55/H-19

In 1964 Orlando Helicopter Airways Inc., (OHA) of Florida, was founded to support and, in some cases, restart production of Sikorsky helicopters no longer built by the parent company. In addition to a huge spares resource, Orlando Helicopters held

the FAA type certificates for all **Sikorsky H-19** and civilian **S-55** models, until the company stopped trading in 1993. Several S-55 versions were developed by the firm. The majority of these were aimed at the civil market for applications including VIP transport, aerial advertising, crop spraying and logging or construction work.

Seeking to obtain drone helicopters simulating the Mil Mi-24P 'Hind-F' assault helicopter, the US Army Missile Command in Huntsville, Alabama, latched on to a proposal from OHA to modify H-19/S-55s into realistic 'Hind' Look-Alike drones with similar size, appearance, radar return and infrared emissions.

When flown by a live pilot, the H-19 'Hind' is flown from the original cockpit, behind the simulated 'intakes' for the Isotov turboshafts.

OHA designed a new nose section, with simulated cockpits for the weapons operator in front and the pilot aft and above, and added stub wings with external store pylons. The simulated cockpits were empty (except, if desired, for the addition of mannequins to give a more realistic appearance), the 'Hind' Look-Alike being flown by a pilot in a cockpit hidden above and behind the simulated twin intakes for the absent Isotov TV3-117 turboshaft engines. All aircraft retained the 597-kW (800-hp) Lycoming-built Wright R-1300-30 radial. The first two aircraft retained the original three-bladed rotor of the S-55/H-19. However, like subsequent drones, they were later fitted with a new five-bladed main rotor.

To simulate more realistically the operating characteristics of the 'Hind', the Look-Alikes were fitted, after completion of initial trials, with infra-red equipment, duplicating

the exhaust of the Mi-24s, and with IR and RF jammers having capabilities similar to those in Russian service. Two of the 'Hind' Look-Alike helicopters have been retained as trainers, whereas the other 13 have been fitted by Sperry Defense Systems with full radio controls. Still man-rated, the 13 drones are being expended in missile trials at the White Sands Missile Range.

A second, more aggressive military version was marketed by OHA as the armed **OHA-AT-55 Defender**, design of which began in 1990. Re-engined with a Garrett TPE331-3 turboshaft or a Wright R-1330-3 radial, the Defender also features a stub wing with pylons capable of carrying up to 500 kg (227 lb) of weapons, and a five-bladed rotor. Capable of carrying up to 10 fully-equipped troops, the Defender could also be fitted out to accommodate six stretchers and two attendants.

Sikorsky S-58/H-34 Choctaw

Sikorsky Aircraft, Division of United Technologies Corporation, 6900 Main Street, Stratford, Connecticut 06601-1381, USA

Developed initially for the US Navy in the anti-submarine role, the **S-58** first flew on 20 September 1954 and was produced in military and civil versions as a general transport helicopter, carrying up to 18 troops in military **CH-34 Choctaw** configuration. In its original form with an R-1820-84 piston engine it is now out of service, but small numbers of the twin-turbine **S-58T** conversion remain in use.

Sikorsky flew the first re-engined S-58T on 19 August 1970, powered by the 1,800-shp (1343-kW) Pratt & Whitney PT6T-3 Twin Pac paired turboshaft. The manufacturer produced nearly 150 conversions or kits for local programmes before selling S-58T rights to California Helicopters International in 1981.

Twelve S-58Ts are used by No. 201 Squadron of the **Royal Thai air force** at Lop Buri, and a similar number are flown by Logistics Command of the **Indonesian air force** (TNI-AU). Two are maintained by the Presidential Aircraft Squadron in

Argentina, but three supplied to South Korea have been retired. The **Uruguayan navy** exchanged two of its **CH-34J**s for three refurbished **Westland Wessex 60**s (described separately). The latter were overhauled by Hi-Lift Helicopters International, Florida. The company began to develop the S-58 design by converting an ex-RTAF S-58T with a new cockpit and forward fuselage section, similar in profile to the Sikorsky S-76. This **Viking** project had been temporarily shelved in July 1994.

SPECIFICATION

Sikorsky S-58 (CH-34A Choctaw)
Rotor system: main rotor diameter 56 ft 0 in (17.07 m); tail rotor diameter 9 ft 6 in (2.90 m); main rotor disc area 2,463.01 sq ft (228.81 m²); tail rotor disc area 70.88 sq ft (6.58 m²)
Fuselage and tail: length overall, rotors turning 56 ft 8.25 in (17.27 m) and fuselage 46 ft 9 in (14.25 m); height overall 15 ft 11 in (4.85 m) and 14 ft 3.5 in

(4.36 m) to top of rotor head; wheel track 14 ft 0 in (4.27 m); wheel base 28 ft 3 in (8.75 m)
Powerplant: one Wright R-1820-84B/D Cyclone radial piston engine rated at 1,525 hp (1137 kW)
Weights: empty equipped 7,750 lb (3515 kg); normal take-off 13,000 lb (5897 kg); maximum take-off 14,000 lb (6350 kg)
Fuel and load: internal fuel 306.5 US gal (1159 litres) plus provision for 150 US gal (568 litres) of auxiliary

fuel in an external tank; external fuel none
Speed: maximum level speed at sea level 106 kt (122 mph; 196 km/h); maximum cruising speed at optimum altitude 84 kt (97 mph; 156 km/h)
Range: 215 nm (247 miles; 397 km) with standard fuel
Performance: maximum rate of climb at sea level 1,100 ft (335 m) per minute; service ceiling 9,500 ft (2895 m); hovering ceiling 4,900 ft (1490 m) in ground effect and 2,400 ft (730 m) out of ground effect

The Royal Thai air force flies 18 S-58Ts converted from CH-34C Choctaws. They are operated by No. 201 Sqn at Lop Buri on heli-support duties.

Sikorsky S-61/SH-3 Sea King

US Navy experience with the Sikorsky S-58 highlighted the shortcomings of operating hunter/killer pairs of helicopters in the anti-submarine role, so in 1957 Sikorsky was awarded a contract to combine the two functions in a single airframe. The resulting S-61 prototype, designated **YHSS-2 Sea King**, made its first flight on 11 March 1959. Production aircraft were known as the **HSS-2** until 1962, when redesignation resulted in the Sea King becoming the **SH-3A**.

The new helicopter featured two General Electric T58 turboshafts above the main cabin, driving a five-bladed rotor. The rugged fuselage had a two-man cockpit, a cabin with two sensor operators and their ASW equipment, a boat hull for amphibious operations (rarely practised) and outrigger floats which also housed the main undercarriage. As a 'hunter', the SH-3A's primary sensors were a Bendix AQS-10 dipping sonar and a Ryan APN-130 search radar; in the 'killer' role, it could carry a pair of torpedoes or depth charges. Mounted over the sliding starboard-side cabin door was a SAR rescue winch.

Two hundred and forty-five SH-3As were built, followed by a prototype and 73 production **SH-3D**s, these introducing uprated T58-GE-10 engines, AQS-13A sonar and APN-182 radar. One hundred and three SH-3As and two SH-3Ds were converted to **SH-3G** standard to act as general-purpose rescue platforms and transports. The modification involved removing the ASW equipment and installing 15 canvas seats and long-range fuel tanks.

A decision to retire dedicated ASW carriers in the early 1970s dictated the

next Sea King version, the **SH-3H**. These had to perform not only the inner-zone ASW mission, but also plane-guard, surface surveillance and surface targeting missions within the all-purpose carrier air wing. One hundred and sixteen of the earlier three variants were converted to the new standard. This comprised installation of AQS-13B sonar, Canadian Marconi LN66HP radar, chaff dispensers and ASQ-81 towed MAD bird, the latter housed in the starboard undercarriage sponson. Subsequently, ESM equipment and the radar were deleted, the weight saved being expended on a modern tactical navigation suite and improved sonobuoy and sonar processing capability.

In US Navy service, the SH-3H was deployed in six-aircraft squadron detachments on each carrier. It has now largely been replaced by the Sikorsky SH-60F Ocean Hawk, and by mid-1994 it served only with HS-1, 11 and 75 at NAS Jacksonville, FL, for Atlantic Fleet support, and

with HS-12 (NAS Atsugi, Japan), and HS-85 (NAS Alameda, CA) with the Pacific Fleet. Others are spread around disparate test and utility units. The remaining SH-3Gs are primarily operated by HC-1 at North Island and HC-2 at NAS Norfolk, VA (with detachments at Naples and Bahrain), and with a few composite units, base flights, etc. The **UH-3A** and **VH-3A** were utility transport conversions of the SH-3A, and some examples remain in Navy service, while the **HH-3A** was a SAR conversion. The US Marine Corps continues to operate the **VH-3D** with the executive transport flight of HMX-1 at MCAS Quantico, these fulfilling Presidential transport duties.

OPERATORS

Sikorsky licensed the Sea King to a number of companies. Agusta in **Italy** and Westland in the **United Kingdom** both developed the aircraft further, and their variants are described separately. In Japan,

Left: The veteran SH-3H has carried out the vital ASW task for many years from US Navy carriers. The type's retirement is long overdue and it is now giving way to the more capable SH-60F. However, a few SH-3Hs remain in service.

Right: The Spanish navy took delivery of former US Navy SH-3Ds. Some have been progressively upgraded to SH-3G and, finally, SH-3H standard. The ASW variants will receive further modernisation in the form of new sonar and radar.

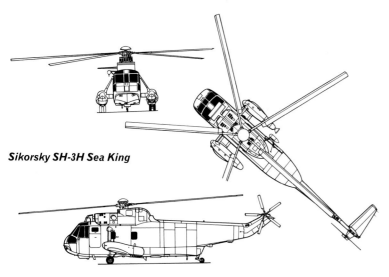

Sikorsky SH-3H Sea King

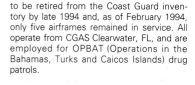

Mitsubishi built the S-61 for the **Japanese Maritime Self-Defence Force**, producing 55 **HSS-2**s (SH-3A – now all withdrawn), 29 **HSS-2A**s (SH-3D) and 83 **HSS-2B**s (SH-3H). These serve with 101, 121 and 122 Kokutai at Tateyama, 123 and 124 Kokutai at Ohmura, the Ohmura and Ominato base squadrons and 211 Kokutai at Kanoya for training. Sikorsky-built **S-61A**, **S-61A-1** and **S-61AH** helicopters serve with the JMSDF for SAR duties.

United Aircraft of Canada assembled 37 **CHSS-2**s, after the supply of four US-built aircraft for the Canadian forces. Most were upgraded to **CH-124A** standard. Eight CH-124As subsequently received a package of modifications for service in 1990/91 during Operation Friction. The ASW gear was removed and a 'Gulf Mods' package was installed. This included a FLIR turret, chaff and flare dispensers, and provision for a machine-gun in the door. The

modified aircraft were initially designated **CH-124C**, but later reverted to the CH-124A designator. Many of the modifications have been retained (now known as 'surveillance mods') and are used during anti-smuggling patrols. The **CH-124B** designation was to have been assigned to six modified Sea Kings which were to have served as lead-in trainers to the cancelled EH.101. These were equipped with HELTAS (Helicopter Towed Array Support) and updated mission systems.

Further export orders were received from **Argentina** (which bought five **S-61D-4**s, similar to the SH-3D, supplemented by Agusta-built ASH-3Hs), **Brazil** (six SH-3Ds purchased for 1° Esquadrão de Helicopteros Anti-Submarinos) and **Denmark** (eight remaining of nine **S-61A-5**s bought for long-range SAR work without ASW equipment with Eskadrille 722 at Vaerløse). **Malaysia** purchased 40 **S-61A-4**

Nuri transports for the air force. Thirty-four survivors have been upgraded by LAS and Aerospace Industries of Malaysia with new radar and Doppler; these serve with No. 3 Sqn at Butterworth, No. 5 Sqn at Labuan, No. 10 Sqn at Subang and 2 FTS at Keluang. A total of 18 SH-3A/D/Gs was transferred from the US Navy to **Spain**'s Arma Aérea de la Armada. Eight of these have been progressively upgraded to SH-3H standard for ASW work with Escuadrilla 005 at Rota. Three SH-3Ds were converted under a 1984 contract with Thorn-EMI Searchwater radar to perform the AEW role. Preliminary plans have been approved for the purchase of six Sea Kings by the **Royal Thai navy**. These are to be operated from its new aircraft-carrier under construction in Spain, and are to be joined by an additional eight SH-3s.

SPECIFICATION

Sikorsky S-61 (SH-3H Sea King)
Rotor system: main rotor diameter 62 ft 0 in (18.90 m); tail rotor diameter 10 ft 7 in (3.23 m); main rotor disc area 3,019.0 sq ft (280.47 m²); tail rotor disc area 87.97 sq ft (8.17 m²)
Fuselage and tail: length overall, rotors turning 72 ft 8 in (22.15 m), fuselage 54 ft 9 in (16.69 m), and with

The Brazilian navy received six SH-3Ds from 1970 for coastal patrol, marines support and carrier-based ASW duties. The Sea Kings fly with HS-1 from São Pedro de Aldeia. This example is armed with an AM39 Exocet anti-ship missile.

tail pylon folded 47 ft 3 in (14.40 m); height overall 16 ft 10 in (5.13 m) and to top of rotor head 15 ft 6 in (4.72 m); wheel track 13 ft 0 in (3.96 m); wheel base 23 ft 1.5 in (7.18 m)
Powerplant: two General Electric T58-GE-10 turboshafts each rated at 1,400 shp (1044 kW)
Weights: empty 12,350 lb (5601 kg); maximum take-off 21,000 lb (9526 kg)
Fuel and load: internal fuel 840 US gal (3180 litres); external fuel none; maximum ordnance 840 lb (381 kg)
Speed: maximum level speed 'clean' at optimum altitude 144 kt (166 mph; 267 km/h); economical cruising speed 118 kt (136 mph; 219 km/h)
Range: 542 nm (625 miles; 1005 km)
Performance: maximum rate of climb at sea level 2,200 ft (670 m) per minute; service ceiling 14,700 ft (4480 m); hovering ceiling 10,500 ft (3200 m) in ground effect and 8,200 ft (2500 m) out of ground effect

Sikorsky **S-61/HH-3 Pelican**

US Air Force interest in the S-61 as a transport resulted in several airframes being used to support the East Coast 'Texas Tower' radar platforms. In turn, this led to a specific requirement for a long-range tactical transport, which was answered by a reworked Sea King known as the **S-61R**, or **CH-3C**. This was a radically revised variant, retaining the boat hull but with a redesigned rear fuselage incorporating a rear loading ramp. The undercarriage floats gave way to sponsons and the tailwheel was replaced by a nosewheel.

Sikorsky built 75 CH-3Cs, most of which were re-engined with T58-GE-5 engines to become **CH-3E**s, this variant also accounting for 45 new-build airframes. Several CH-3C/Es joined six new-build aircraft

as **HH-3E** rescue platforms with IFR probes as the renowned 'Jolly Green Giants' of Vietnam fame. These are virtually out of service, and many been replaced on rescue and SOF units by the HH/MH-60G Pave Hawk. Until as late as the end of 1992, HH-3Es could be found with the 33rd Rescue Squadron at Kadena, Japan.

Another US S-61R operator is the Coast Guard, which bought 40 **HH-3F Pelican**s from 1968 for SAR duties. Essentially similar to the HH-3E, they lack armour protection and other combat-related equipment, but have a search radar in a nose radome offset to port, and are internally configured for the carriage of up to 15 stretchers. The Coast Guard also purchased at least nine surplus CH-3Es and HH-3Es to augment its

MRR (medium-range recovery) fleet. Some were used as spares for the flying fleet and five were brought up to HH-3F standard.

Sikorsky HH-60J Jayhawks have now entirely supplanted the HH-3F in the MRR role, although the Pelicans' amphibious landing capability, endurance and sheer lifting ability will be missed. The type is scheduled

Five HH-3Fs remain in service with the US Coast Guard. This example is fitted with a FLIR turret and a powerful searchlight for anti-drug patrols.

to be retired from the Coast Guard inventory by late 1994 and, as of February 1994, only five airframes remained in service. All operate from CGAS Clearwater, FL, and are employed for OPBAT (Operations in the Bahamas, Turks and Caicos Islands) drug patrols.

Sikorsky **S-65 Sea Stallion/CH-53**

Answering a US Marine Corps requirement to replace its Sikorsky CH-37 heavylift helicopters, the prototype **S-65** was first flown on 14 October 1964, entering service in September 1965. One hundred and forty-one of the first production model, the **CH-53A**, were built but none remains in US service. The last examples served with USMC training and reserve units, but were retired in July 1993.

Powered by two T64 engines mounted either side of the upper fuselage, driving the transmission proven by the CH-54 Tarhe, the CH-53 featured a large boxlike cabin with a rear loading ramp and forward side doors. The main undercarriage retracted into sponsons slung low on the fuselage sides, and in most respects the helicopter was conventional. It was big,

however, and on delivery to the war zone in Vietnam quickly established a reputation for carrying outstanding loads either internally or from its cargo hook. Known as the **Sea Stallion**, the CH-53A was to become the USMC's principal heavylift helicopter, a position it has held ever since through updated variants.

The major current variant of the first-generation Stallions is the **CH-53D**, of which 124 were built with uprated engines, automatic blade folding and revised interior for more troop accommodation. Many of these are still in Marine service, flying with the following Marine Air Groups (MAGs): MAG 26 at New River, NC (HMM-362, HMT-204); MAG 16 at Tustin, CA (HMH-363, HMH-462); MAG 24 at Kanehoe Bay, HI (HMH-463); and the USMC reserve unit MAG 41

at NAS Dallas, TX (HMH-777). Two **VH-53D** aircraft are assigned to VIP transportation unit HMX-1 at Quantico.

Sea Stallions have been involved in many

The USMC remains the principal user of twin-engined CH-53s. This war-weary CH-53D was deployed to Saudia Arabia for Desert Storm operations by HMH-462.

actions following the Vietnam War, notably Grenada, Panama, Lebanon and the Gulf. In the air assault role, the D model is configured for the carriage of 55 fully-equipped troops or 8,000 lb (3630 kg) of cargo internally. Owing to the CH-53's large size, and the availability of the CH-46, the Sea Stallion is usually used for the transportation of

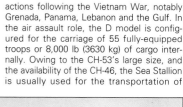

An IDF/AF S-65C-3 undertakes a maritime rescue using the starboard side door winch. The type has proved extremely useful during Israel's recent conflicts, and is being upgraded under the Yas'ur programme for continued service.

responsible for a major structural and systems upgrade programme, known as **CH-53 2000**, or **Yas'ur 2000** (Albatros 2000) to keep the aircraft serviceable into the next century. This will provide a new Elisra EW system, two multi-function cockpit displays, a new autopilot and a new mission computer. Seventy-two systems are upgraded, 42 are replaced and 24 are completely new. The first prototype made its maiden flight in May 1992 and was returned to service in early 1993.

West Germany was the major foreign user of the type, choosing the CH-53 to replace Piasecki H-21s and Sikorsky H-34s on army assault units. Beating off the CH-47 in competition, the **CH-53G** was first ordered in June 1968. Two Sikorsky-built aircraft were supplied, similar to the CH-53D. These were followed by 20 assembled from kits by a VFW-Fokker-led consortium, and then 90 built in Germany with a gradually decreasing number of US-made parts. Dornier supplied the rotor blades.

First flight of a German-assembled CH-53G occurred at Speyer on 11 October 1971, and the first example was put into operational service in March 1973 with Heeresfliegerregiment 35 at Mendig. This unit was joined by HFR 15 at Rheine/Bentlage, HFR 25 at Laupheim and the Heeresfliegerwaffenschule at Bückeberg. In 1993, 107 CH-53Gs were still in service with the Heeresflieger.

supplies and equipment rather than personnel. However, for rapid evacuation duties, the CH-53 is ideal, its internal volume being able to accommodate large numbers of evacuees in an emergency, and its good range reducing the time spent on refuelling between trips. For ferry purposes, the CH-53D can be fitted with up to five auxiliary tanks in the cabin.

Although the Marine Corps is the main user of the first-generation CH-53s, there have been others. A small number of ex-USMC CH-53As were transferred to the

US Air Force as **TH-53A**s, used by the 1550th FTS at Kirtland AFB, NM, for aircrew training for the MH-53 fleet. These replaced CH-53As borrowed from the USMC. US Air Force interest in the early variants led to purchase of the **HH-53B** and **HH-53C** rescue platforms, which introduced a refuelling probe and external tanks fitted to the undercarriage sponsons. The similar **CH-53C** lacked the probe, and was used for training, general transport duties and for the support of ground-based forward air control teams. Survivors

of the CH/HH-53B/C fleet were upgraded to **MH-53J** standard in the 1980s, and are described in a separate entry.

OPERATORS

Exports were restricted to **Austria**, **West Germany** and **Israel**. The Austrians purchased two **S-65C-2**s, also known as the **S-65Ö** and similar to the USAF's CH-53C. Ordered in March 1969 and delivered in 1970, the pair of heavylifters was purchased to assist relief agencies during disasters. Despite their suitability for role, the pair proved expensive to operate, and was sold to Israel in May 1981.

Israel received 33 **S-65C-3**s from 1969. These are fitted with a refuelling probe and are similar to the USAF's HH-53C. They have proved extremely useful in a variety of roles, including combat rescue and heavylift and, together with the two S-65C-2s from Austria, continue to provide the IDF/AF with its only heavylift capability. After the 1991 Gulf War, Israel was supplied with an additional 10 ex-USMC CH-53As. The Mata Helicopter Division of IAI is

The major S-65 export customer was the Heeresflieger (German army), which received licence-built CH-53Gs. This aircraft demonstrates its precise handling during a competition.

SPECIFICATION

Sikorsky S-65 (CH-53A Sea Stallion)
generally similar to the Sikorsky S-65 (RH-53D Sea Stallion) except in the following particulars:
Powerplant: two General Electric T64-GE-16 turboshafts each rated at 3,435 shp (2562 kW)
Weights: normal take-off 35,000 lb (15876 kg)
Fuel and load: internal fuel 630 US gal (2384 litres); maximum payload 8,000 lb (3629 kg) as an internal load or 13,000 lb (5897 kg) as an external load
Speed: maximum level speed 'clean' at sea level 169 kt (195 mph; 314 km/h); cruising speed at sea level 149 kt (172 mph; 277 km/h)
Range: 223 nm (257 miles; 413 km); endurance more than 4 hours
Performance: maximum rate of climb at sea level 2,240 ft (683 m) per minute; service ceiling 18,550 ft (5655 m)

Sikorsky **S-65/HH-53 and MH-53**

Development of the H-53 as a combat rescue/special operations helicopter in USAF service began with the loan of two CH-53As from the USMC in late 1966. These were followed by eight **HH-53B**s and 44 **HH-53C**s tailored to the rescue role with extra external tanks and a refuelling probe, and 20 **CH-53C**s used for general transport work. In late 1969, the Pave Low I LLLTV system was applied to one HH-53 to provide some measure of night capability.

A single HH-53B was converted to **YHH-53H Pave Low II** standard, which added a terrain-following radar in a nose radome, offset to port, and other night/ adverse-weather equipment. Subsequently, eight HH-53s and two CH-53Cs were upgraded to **HH-53H Pave Low III** standard, featuring an AN/APQ-158 TF radar, Marconi Doppler navigation, Litton INS, AAQ-10 FLIR in a turret under the nose fairing, map display system and numerous countermeasures. When a Spe-

cial Forces role was added under the Constant Green programme, the designation changed to **MH-53H**, one major change being the adoption of an NVG-compatible cockpit.

Under a programme beginning in 1986 and running for four years, 39 HH-53B/C/H and CH-53C airframes were all upgraded to the current **MH-53J Pave Low III Enhanced** standard. This features the full range of upgrades, including TFR, FLIR,

NVG, armour plating, mounts for 0.50-in (12.7-mm) machine-guns and/or 7.62-mm Miniguns, AN/ALQ-162 continuous-wave radar missile jammers, ALE-40 chaff/flare dispensers, ALQ-157 IR missile jammers, ALR-69 missile warning receivers, GPS, projected map display, IFR probe, external tanks, secure communications, undernose searchlight, starboard-side heavy-duty hoist with jungle penetrator and litter attachments, and 1,000 lb (454 kg) of titanium armour. Power is provided by the uprated T64-GE-415. Not all MH-53Js are identical, as those converted from the HH-53B retain strut bracing for the sponson tanks.

A UK-based 21st SOS MH-53J demonstrates some of its special operations/rescue equipment. The winch has a tree penetrator attached, with the winch litter beside it. Note the IRCM turret on the sponsons. A Block 1 upgrade programme adds a rotor fold facility, improved EW systems and a 45 per cent increase in payload capability.

Sikorsky MH-53J Pave Low III Enhanced

MH-53J deliveries commenced in 1987. Three tasks are assigned, the major one being support of Special Forces. Using inflight refuelling to increase range, the Pave Low uses its comprehensive avionics to penetrate hostile airspace covertly at very low level in all weathers to infiltrate or extract Special Forces teams and their equipment. Secondly, the aircraft flies the combat rescue mission to retrieve downed airmen from hostile territory, either alone at night or under the cover of support aircraft during the daytime. Lastly, the MH-53Js are made available to civilian rescue agencies during peacetime. The crew consists of two pilots and two pararescuemen (PJs), the latter acting as loadmasters, winchmen, medics and gunners, for the MH-53J has provision for three 7.62-mm Miniguns in the door/rear ramp positions.

MH-53Js inserted SEAL commandos during the invasion of Panama, and were heavily used in Desert Storm, notably in the 'Special Forces theme park' of the western Iraqi desert, where teams used sand rovers to locate 'Scud' missiles, sabotage air defence installations and other SOF activities.

Three units fly the MH-53J: the 20th SOS/16th SOW at Hurlburt Field, FL, 21st SOS/352nd SOG at RAF Alconbury, England, and the 31st SOS/353rd SOG at Osan AB, RoK. Additionally, the 16th SOW at Hurlburt Field may be supported by two **NCH-53**s for test duties. The 58th SOW (formerly the 542nd CTW) of Air Training and Education Command at Kirtland AFB, NM, trains aircrew for the active fleet using four MH-53Js and four **TH-53A**s. These are ex-USMC CH-53As which have been modified with T64-GE-416 engines, an IFR probe and some USAF systems, for use as basic qualification trainers. Another two CH-53As are scheduled for conversion.

The USAF has undertaken a series of upgrades, known collectively as the **Block 1** modifications, which it is envisaged will carry its MH-53J fleet viable until 2008-10. Most aircraft have already undergone a service life extension programme (SLEP), which is applied at the Navy's aviation depot at Pensacola, Florida. The SLEP modernises the

basic airframe structure, hydraulics and wiring. The structural modifications increase gross weight by 8,000 lb (3629 kg) to give an effective increase of 45 per cent in payload capability. In operational terms, the MH-53J can carry an additional 3,970 lb (1800 kg) of fuel, which can extend time between refuellings from three hours to five hours.

A further modification known as Shipboard Operations (SBO) was funded in light of the abortive rescue attempt in Iran in 1980, and aims to improve shipboard stowage by adding fully-automatic rotor blade and tail pylon folding. An additional benefit of this modification is that it greatly reduces the time taken to prepare the MH-53J for transport aboard a C-5 Galaxy. Thirty-three MH-53Js have been cycled through the SLEP, and it is expected that the remaining eight aircraft will have received this update by July 1995.

Further upgrades

A contract was awarded to IBM/Loral in November 1993 to integrate and test new avionics and systems on two MH-53Js. These include an Integrated Defensive Avionics System via a Mil Std 1553 databus (incorporating the AAR-47 missile plume detector and the ALQ-136 missile jammer) and a Multi-Mission Advanced Tactical Terminal (IDAS/MATT). The latter adds a receiver which can downlink threat information from a classified database known as Constant Source, and display this data on a cockpit digital map system.

The USAF will decide to apply IDAS/ MATT to the remaining 39 MH-53Js once flight testing has been accomplished.

SPECIFICATION

Sikorsky S-65 (MH-53J Pave Low III Enhanced)
Rotor system: main rotor diameter 72 ft 3 in (22.02 m); tail rotor diameter 16 ft 0 in (4.88 m); main rotor disc area 4,099.82 sq ft (380.87 m2); tail rotor disc area 201.06 sq ft (18.68 m2)
Fuselage and tail: length overall, rotors turning 88 ft 3 in (26.90 m) and fuselage 67 ft 2 in (20.47 m) excluding IFR probe; height overall 24 ft 11 in (7.60 m)

and to top of rotor head 17 ft 1.5 in (5.22 m); wheel track 13 ft 0 in (3.96 m); wheel base 27 ft 0 in (8.23 m)
Powerplant: two General Electric T64-GE-7A turboshafts each rated at 3,936 shp (2935 kW)
Weights: empty 23,569 lb (10691 kg); mission take-off 38,238 lb (17344 kg); maximum take-off 42,000 lb (19051 kg)
Fuel and load: internal fuel 630 US gal (2384 litres); external fuel up to two 450-US gal (1703-litre) drop

tanks; maximum payload 20,000 lb (9072 kg)
Speed: maximum level speed 'clean' at sea level 170 kt (196 mph; 315 km/h); cruising speed at optimum altitude 150 kt (173 mph; 278 km/h)
Range: 468 nm (540 miles; 868 km)
Performance: maximum rate of climb at sea level 2,070 ft (631 m) per minute; service ceiling 20,400 ft (6220 m); hovering ceiling 11,700 ft (3565 m) in ground effect and 6,500 ft (1980 m) out of ground effect

A 20th Special Operations Squadron MH-53J cruises just above the trees during a training mission. The installed avionics allow it to perform similar profiles at night, vital for covert infil/exfil missions into hostile territory.

Sikorsky **S-65/RH-53D**

From the 34th aircraft, all CH-53s were fitted with hardpoints for the towing of mine countermeasures equipment. However, the use of such equipment required a greater level of power than was generally available. Consequently, the US Navy re-engined 15 aircraft with the T64-GE-413 powerplant, and added rear-view mirrors on tube mounts either side of the nose. Designated **RH-53A**, these served with HM-12, but were subsequently demodified back to CH-53A status. Some Marine CH-53Ds have been used in the mine-hunting role.

Aiding this application was the adoption of the definitive **RH-53D** variant, which introduced T64-GE-415 engines of greater power and the option to mount a refuelling probe and sponson tanks. The mine countermeasures equipment is towed behind the aircraft from a heavy trapeze attached to the rear ramp and rear fuselage. Optional equipment includes various floating sleds to handle contact, acoustic and magentic mines. The SPU-1 Magnetic Orange Pipe system is used against shallow-water mines. Mines brought to the surface by the system are detonated by using a pair of door-mounted 0.50-in machine-guns. In addition to its primary role, the RH-53D can also be employed in the transport role.

RH-53Ds are being phased out of service as the more capable MH-53E (described separately) is introduced. Two US Navy

Reserve squadrons, HM-18 at Norfolk and HM-19 at Alameda, continue to fly the type, as do USMCR units HMH-769 and HMH-772 Det A. The former unit was reactivated at NAS Alameda, CA, in April 1993. The latter unit deployed some aircraft during the Gulf War. Unfortunately, the best-remembered use of the RH-53D was during the disastrous Eagle Claw operation to rescue US hostages from Iran. Eight helicopters set off but three dropped out and, of the five that arrived at the Desert One refuelling stop, one struck a Hercules and was destroyed. The remainder were left in the desert.

This proved to be fortuitous for **Iran**, which is the only foreign operator of the type. Six were delivered to an MCM unit at Kharg Island, but the US embargo following the taking of the hostages severely affected their serviceability. The Desert One debacle provided a source of spares for the Iranian fleet, but it is thought that only two are now in a serviceable state.

RH-53Ds were deployed to the Persian Gulf for mine-sweeping operations in 1987, and in 1991. During Desert Storm, a six-aircraft detachment from USMCR squadron HMH-772 operated from Al Jubail. RH-53Ds are now used for exercise support as aggressors.

SPECIFICATION

Sikorsky S-65 (RH-53D) Sea Stallion
Rotor system: main rotor diameter 72 ft 3 in (22.02 m); tail rotor diameter 16 ft 0 in (4.88 m); main rotor disc area 4,099.82 sq ft (380.87 m2); tail rotor disc area 201.06 sq ft (18.68 m2)
Fuselage and tail: length overall, rotors turning 88 ft 3 in (26.90 m) and fuselage 67 ft 2 in (20.47 m) without probe; height overall, rotors turning 24 ft 11 in (7.60 m) and to top of rotor head 17 ft 1.5 in (5.22 m); wheel track 13 ft 0 in (3.96 m); wheel base 27 ft 0 in (8.23 m)
Powerplant: two General Electric T64-GE-415 turboshafts each rated at 4,380 shp (3266 kW)

Weights: empty 22,444 lb (10180 kg); normal take-off 42,000 lb (19050 kg); maximum take-off 50,000 lb (22680 kg)
Fuel and load: internal fuel 622 US gal (2354 litres); external fuel up to two 550-US gal (2082-litre) drop tanks; ordnance none
Speed: maximum level speed 'clean' at sea level 170 kt (196 mph; 315 km/h); cruising speed at sea level 150 kt (173 mph; 278 km/h)
Range: 223 nm (257 miles; 413 km); endurance more than 4 hours
Performance: maximum rate of climb at sea level 2,100 ft (664 m) per minute; service ceiling 21,000 ft (6400 m); hovering ceiling 13,400 ft (4080 m) in ground effect and 6,500 ft (1980 m) out of ground effect

Sikorsky S-70A/UH-60 Black Hawk

As early as 1965, the US Army began to look for a replacement for the Bell UH-1 assault helicopter, but the needs of the Vietnam War continually delayed any serious attempts to provide a successor. The request for proposals for what became known as the UTTAS (utility tactical transport aircraft system) were not issued until January 1972. These called for a helicopter to carry the same squad-sized unit as the UH-1H, but with far better performance and crashworthiness. Sikorsky submitted its **S-70** design, designated **YUH-60A**, which first flew on 17 October 1974.

In configuration, the YUH-60A featured a broad, squat cabin with rearward-sliding doors, and had a two-pilot flight deck. The four-bladed rotor was driven by two T700-GE-700s mounted above the cabin, and the aircraft featured immensely strong undercarriage. The all-round survivability of the aircraft was exceptional, and in December 1976 Sikorsky was announced the winner of the competition after a long evaluation against Boeing Vertol's competing YUH-61 submission. The first production **UH-60A Black Hawk** flew on 17 October 1978, and the type entered service with the 101st Airborne Division in June 1979.

At once the Black Hawk demonstrated considerable advances over the Huey. The nominal load was two pilots, one crew chief/door gunner and 11 troops, but the cabin could take up to 20 if required. Heavy external loads could be carried from a cargo hook, and overall performance, notably under 'hot-and-high' conditions, was dramatically improved. Manoeuvrability and crashworthiness were also improved considerably.

Production UH-60As incorporated bulletproof fuel tanks and folding tails, the latter so that the helicopter could be air-transportable in Lockheed C-5s. Over the years several modifications have been introduced to the fleet, including the ESSS shoulder-mounted wings with four pylons for fuel or weapons, an optional medevac kit, winterisation kit, rescue hoist, pintle-mounted M134 Miniguns or 7.62-mm M60 machine-guns, wire strike protection, HIRSS to cool the exhaust and reduce vulnerability to heat-seeking missiles, and improved avionics and defensive countermeasures.

The US Army naturally took the major share of UH-60As, these being distributed (apart from the 101st) mainly to theatre forces in Europe and Korea before the re-equipment of CONUS units began. Under the Foreign Military Sales programme, one UH-60A was delivered to Bahrain and 10 to the Colombian air force, the latter for anti-drug operations. This role is also undertaken by 16 aircraft transferred to the US Customs Service. Equipped with large searchlights, they are informally known as 'Pot Hawks'. Two UH-60As were handed to the US Navy Test Pilot's School at Patuxent River, while another was transferred to the Philippine air force. Saudi Arabia received eight during Desert Shield. The US Army also uses **GUH-60A** ground instructional airframes and **JUH-60A** test machines.

Improved L model

As more equipment was added to the UH-60, so the weight grew and power margins were reduced. Accordingly, uprated versions were discussed, including the cancelled **UH-60B**. Sikorsky introduced the cheaper **UH-60L** on the production line, this featuring the uprated T700-GE-701C engine that restored the performance and allowed the helicopter to lift an HMMWV with TOW anti-tank installation. The first UH-60L flew on 22 March 1988; deliveries began in October 1989 and continue at a high rate today. The US Army expects to procure a total of at least 1,400 UH-60A/Ls, compared to the initial requirement for 2,262. Two UH-60Ls were transferred to Bahrain in 1991, and 100 essentially similar aircraft, designated **UH-60P**, are being supplied to the Republic of Korea army. The first was handed over by Sikorsky on 10 December 1990, the next 19 being assembled by Korean Air from kits. Subsequent production is handled in Korea.

For the medical evacuation role, the US Army is to acquire the **UH-60Q** to replace medevac-configured UH-60A/Ls in the 'Dustoff' role. Among the changes is the adoption of an external hoist rather than the swing-out, internally-stowed unit currently fitted, and an entirely new aeromedical interior. It will also have weather radar, FLIR and comprehensive defensive systems, plus a digital avionics suite similar to that of HH/MH-60 variants. A single proof-of-concept prototype was converted from a UH-60A and first flown in January 1993. It was delivered to the Tennessee Army National Guard in March 1993, and will be used to conduct a test and evaluation programme to determine what equipment and modifications will be selected for the definitive 'production' UH-60Q.

Based closely on late-model UH-60As are the **VH-60N** 'Presidential Hawks' used by the Marine Corps' HMX-1 based at MCAS Quantico, VA. Nine were supplied in November 1988, originally known as **VH-60A**s but redesignated a year later. They differ from late-production UH-60As by having SH-60B flight control system, cabin radio operator position, soundproofed VIP-configured cabin, avionics upgrades and hardening against the effects of electromagnetic pulse. Their primary task is trans-

The UH-60A Black Hawk was the initial production variant of the US Army's main assault helicopter. This example has ESSS pylons and wears the overall desert camouflage scheme applied for participation in Operation Desert Storm.

port of the President (with callsign 'Marine One') and his staff, both at home and on overseas trips.

OPERATORS

In addition to the aircraft under UH-60 designations mentioned above, there have been many exports under the **S-70A** designation. The **S-70A-1 Desert Hawk** was sold to **Saudi Arabia**, the purchase comprising 12 in utility transport configuration for the **Royal Saudi land forces**, one with a VIP interior and eight dedicated **S-70A-1L** medevac aircraft. Two **S-70A-5**s were supplied to the **Philippines**, and one **S-70A-9** to **Australia**. This preceded 38 more aircraft built locally by Hawker de Havilland. At first assigned to the **RAAF**, they were subsequently turned over to the **Australian army**. Further exports comprise three **S-70A-11**s to **Jordan** and one **S-70A-12** to **Japan**. This SAR-dedicated variant is fitted with a rescue winch, nose search radar and FLIR. Following the delivery of the first aircraft, Mitsubishi assembled two from kits and then built eight for the **JASDF** and 18 for the **JMSDF** under the designation **UH-60J**. This variant is described in greater detail in a separate entry. A single **S-70A-14** was supplied to **Brunei**, one **S-70A-16** to **Rolls-Royce** for use as a testbed for the Rolls-Royce/Turboméca RTM 332 engine, and 12 **S-70A-17**s to **Turkey** for the police and paramilitary police forces. The **S-70A-19** designation covered one aircraft assembled by **Westland** as the **WS-70** prior to potential UK production. Further exports have been made to **Egypt** (two **S-70A-21**s), **Mexico** (two **S-70A-24**s), **Morocco** (two **S-70A-26**s), and **Hong Kong** (two **S-70A-27**s). The latest customer is **Israel**, which received 10 surplus Black Hawks in July 1994 free of charge from the US drawdown inventory.

The **S-70C** designation ostensibly covers the civil versions of the Black Hawk, but 24 **S-70C-2** utility helicopters were delivered to the **People's Republic of China**, while the **Republic of China (Taiwan)** received 14 **S-70C**s for rescue duties with external hoist. **Brunei** has also received one S-70C.

SPECIFICATION

Sikorsky S-70A (UH-60A Black Hawk)
Powerplant: two General Electric T700-GE-700 turboshafts each rated at 1,560 shp (1151 kW) or, in export helicopters, two General Electric T700-GE-701A turboshafts each rated at 1,723 shp (1285 kW)
Rotor system: main rotor diameter 53 ft 8 in (16.36 m)

The UH-60L superseded the A model on the production line. It introduces more powerful engines, uprated transmissions and a refined gearbox to give much improved performance, especially in 'hot-and-high' conditions or with external loads. The HIRSS exhaust suppression system is fitted as standard.

Australia took delivery of both US-built S-70A-9s and Hawker de Havilland-manufactured examples. The Black Hawks served originally with the Royal Australian Air Force but were subsequently transferred in 1990 to the army.

tail rotor diameter 11 ft 0 in (3.35 m); main rotor disc area 2,262.03 sq ft (210.14 m²); tail rotor disc area 95.03 sq ft (8.83 m²)
Fuselage and tail: length overall, rotors turning 64 ft 10 in (19.76 m), fuselage 50 ft 0.75 in (15.26 m) and with rotors and tail pylon folded 41 ft 4 in (12.60 m); height overall 16 ft 10 in (5.13 m) with tail rotor turning, to top of rotor head 12 ft 4 in (3.76 m) and in air-transportable configuration 8 ft 9 in (2.67 m); stabiliser span 14 ft 4.5 in (4.38 m); wheel track 8 ft 10.5 in (2.705 m); wheel base 28 ft 11.75 in (8.83 m)
Weights: empty 11,284 lb (5118 kg); normal take-off 16,994 lb (7708 kg); maximum take-off 20,250 lb (9185 kg)
Fuel and load: internal fuel 360 US gal (1361 litres) plus provision for 370 US gal (1400 litres) of auxiliary fuel in two fuselage tanks; external fuel up to two 230-US gal (870-litre) and/or two 450-US gal (1703-litre) tanks; maximum payload 2,640 lb (1197 kg) carried internally or 8,000 lb (3629 kg) carried externally
Speed: maximum level speed 'clean' at sea level 160 kt (184 mph; 296 km/h); maximum cruising speed at 4,000 ft (1220 m) 145 kt (167 mph; 268 km/h); economical (single-engine) cruising speed at 4,000 ft (1220 m) 105 kt (121 mph; 195 km/h)
Range: ferry range 1,200 nm (1,382 miles; 2224 km) with four external auxiliary tanks; range 319 nm (368 miles; 592 km) with standard fuel; endurance 2 hours 18 minutes

Performance: maximum vertical rate of climb at 4,000 ft (1220 m) 411 ft (125 m) per minute; service ceiling 19,000 ft (5790 m); hovering ceiling 9,500 ft (2895 m) in ground effect and 10,400 ft (3170 m) out of ground effect

The Royal Saudi Land Forces initially received 13 S-70A-1 Desert Hawks (illustrated) configured for a variety of duties. These were later supplemented by eight US Army UH-60As transferred during the Gulf War, and eight S-70A-1L dedicated medevac helicopters.

Sikorsky **S-70A/EH-60**

As an ongoing part of its SEMA (special electronics mission aircraft) programme, the **US Army** fitted several Bell UH-1Hs with the ALQ-151 Quick Fix II direction-finding, intercept and communications jamming equipment, the resultant conversions being known as EH-1Xs. The volume and weight of the ALQ-151 installation – approximately 1,800 lb (815 kg) – proved too heavy for the Huey, so in 1980 Electronic Systems Laboratories was awarded a contract to fit improved Quick

Fix IIB equipment into a UH-60A. The resultant **YEH-60A** proved effective in trials of the battlefield jamming system, and the Army progressed to acquiring production examples. The Sikorsky/ESL team lost out to Tracor, which undertook the conversions at its Flight Systems division at Mojave, CA. The first **EH-60A** was delivered in July 1987. The model designation was subsequently changed to **EH-60C**.

EH-60Cs are readily identified by the two dipole antennas on either side of the tailboom, and the retractable whip aerial under the fuselage. One aircraft has been noted with revised tailboom antennas with a square, tubular aerial whose 'uprights' are located in approximately the same location as the normal vertical dipoles. A two-man operator station is in the main cabin, and the EH-60C has datalinks to downlink

information to ground units, or to interface with other SEMA aircraft. Originally 138 EH-60Cs were planned, but in the event only 66 were funded. The US Army is, however, seeking the necessary finance for a command and control version equipped with the ASC-15B(V)1 communications suite.

This close-up view of an EH-60C clearly shows the forward-hemisphere radar warning receiver antennas, the prominent dipole antennas mounted on the tailboom and the massive HIRSS engine exhausts.

The fuselage-mounted antennas immediately identify this Black Hawk as a Quick Fix EH-60C. Its retractable ventral whip antenna is fully deployed.

Sikorsky **S-70A/HH-60G and MH-60G Pave Hawk**

Procured as a replacement for the Sikorsky HH-3E, the H-60 underwent a confusing birth in USAF service. The original requirement was for the superbly-equipped **HH-60D Night Hawk** and, of 10 UH-60As bought by the USAF to support this programme, one aircraft was converted to serve as the prototype but without mission avionics. This plan was too

costly and was leavened by the adoption of a mix of D models with the **HH-60E**, which dispensed with many night/adverse-weather avionics. The HH-60D/E plan was then cancelled in favour of the **HH-60A** 'Rescue Hawk', which was pitched closer to the HH-60E in terms of fit. The HH-60D was redesignated to serve as a flying prototype, but this, too, was unable to find

funding, and the USAF adopted a three-phase procurement process.

Phase One consisted of upgrading the 10 existing USAF Black Hawks, plus nine more, to **UH-60A Credible Hawk** standard. These featured an inflight-refuelling probe, options for external tank pylons and additional cabin tanks. Pintle-mounted 0.50-in (12.7-mm) machine-guns were fit-

ted. The next two phases involve upgrading the existing Credible Hawks and new-build UH-60As to one of two standards, although both were initially designated **MH-60G Pave Hawk**.

Sikorsky delivers the UH-60As with only some Air Force equipment installed, consisting of folding stabilator, HIRSS, winterisation and wire-strike kits, rescue

Sikorsky S-70A/HH-60G and MH-60G Pave Hawk

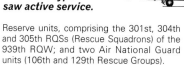

The USAF's MH-60G was developed as a dedicated combat rescue and SOF support helicopter. This 1st SOW example wears desert camouflage and white recognition stripes for Desert Storm, where the type saw active service.

Sikorsky HH-60G

hoist and NVG-compatible cockpit. Next, Sikorsky Support Services at Troy fits a refuelling probe, auxiliary cabin tanks and hardpoints for external tank carriage, and finally the mission avionics are installed at the Naval Air Depot at Pensacola, FL.

A total of 98 HH/MH-60 aircraft had been funded up to FY 1991, with a further five in the FY1992 budget. Sixteen aircraft are dedicated to the special operations role; 10 serve with the 16th SOW at Hurlburt Field/Eglin AFB, FL, and the remainder are operated by the 58th SOW at Kirtland, NM. All retain the MH-60G designation, and are fitted with a Bendix-King 1400C colour radar in a port-side nose radome, global positioning, Carousel INS, map display, Doppler, secure communications equipment and full countermeasures. Further SOF-dedicated equipment includes AAQ-16 FLIR under the

nose, pilot head-up display that projects on to one of the lenses of the NVG system, and numerous other improvements.

Eighty-two aircraft have been designated **HH-60G** since October 1991 to reinforce the combat rescue role they undertake. These aircraft have the basic Phase Two avionics, but funding for their updating with the Phase Three equipment (FLIR, HUD etc.) has not yet been forthcoming. HH-60Gs are usually seen with M60 or Minigun door weapons in place of the MH-60G's usual 0.50-in (12.7-mm) guns.

HH-60Gs are operated by three Air Combat Command wings: the 49th FW at Holloman, NM, the 57 Wing at Nellis (including the Combat Rescue School), NV, and the 35th Wing at NAS Keflavik, Iceland; and PACAF's 18th Wing at Kadena, Japan. They are also assigned to three Air Force

Reserve units, comprising the 301st, 304th and 305th RQSs (Rescue Squadrons) of the 939th RQW; and two Air National Guard units (106th and 129th Rescue Groups).

SPECIFICATION

Sikorsky S-70A (MH-60G Pave Hawk)
Rotor system: main rotor diameter 53 ft 8 in (16.36 m); tail rotor diameter 11 ft 0 in (3.35 m); main rotor disc area 2,262.03 sq ft (210.05 m²); tail rotor disc area 95.03 sq ft (8.83 m²)
Fuselage and tail: length overall, rotors turning 64 ft 10 in (19.76 m) and fuselage including retracted flight refuelling probe 57 ft 0.25 in (17.38 m); height overall, rotors turning 16 ft 10 in (5.13 m) and to top of rotor head 12 ft 4 in (3.76 m); stabiliser span 14 ft 4.5 in (4.38 m); wheel track 8 ft 10.5 in (2.705 m); wheel base 29 ft 0 in (8.84 m)

Powerplant: two General Electric T700-GE-700 turboshafts each rated at 1,622 shp (1210 kW)
Weights: maximum take-off 22,000 lb (9979 kg)
Fuel and load: internal fuel 360 US gal (1361 litres) plus provision for 117 US gal (443 litres) of auxiliary fuel; external fuel up to two 450- or 230-US gal (1703- or 871-litre) drop tanks; maximum payload 8,000 lb (3629 kg)
Speed: maximum level speed 'clean' at sea level about 160 kt (184 mph; 296 km/h); cruising speed at 4,000 ft (1220 m) 145 kt (167 mph; 268 km/h)
Range: ferry range about 1,200 nm (1,380 miles; 2220 km); operational radius about 520 nm (599 miles; 964 km) with two 450-US gal (1703-litre) drop tanks or about 347 nm (400 miles; 644 km) with two 230-US gal (871-litre) drop tanks; endurance 4 hours 51 minutes with maximum fuel
Performance: maximum vertical rate of climb at sea level more than 450 ft (137 m) per minute; service ceiling 19,000 ft (5790 m)

Sikorsky S-70A/MH-60K

Looking to expand its ability to support special operations forces, the US Army modified 30 UH-60A Black Hawks to **MH-60A** standard, with some special

equipment fitted, such as FLIR, extra nav/comms, auxiliary fuel tanks and Miniguns, intended for the covert infil/exfil mission. As much of the equipment was

fitted at unit level more by ingenuity than design, the aircraft are colloquially known as 'Velcro Hawks'. Initially serving with the 160th Special Operations Aviation Regiment at Fort Campbell, KY, the MH-60As now serve with the Oklahoma Army National Guard. Their place with the 160th SOAR was taken by a similar number of **MH-60L** 'Velcro Hawks', which are fitted with the same systems but are based on the more powerful UH-60L.

These are themselves to be replaced by the definitive US Army SOA variant, the **MH-60K**, which features a comprehensive range of night/adverse-weather low-level avionics, including APQ-174 terrain-following radar in a nose radome, AAQ-16B FLIR underneath, night vision imaging system

and moving map display. Other features are pintle-mounted 0.50-in machine-guns, stub wings for external fuel tanks, retractable refuelling probe, HIRSS exhaust suppressors, comprehensive communications and navigation gear, and an impressive array of defensive warning receivers and countermeasures. The aircraft can launch AIM-92A Stinger air-to-air missiles. The FLIR is being reworked under the AESOP (Airborne Electro-Optical Special Operational Payload) programme to allow it to act as a thermal-imaging sight for the launch of Hellfire missiles.

The first prototype MH-60K flew from the Stratford, Connecticut, plant on 10 August 1990 and was followed on 26 February 1992 by the first of 22 currently-funded production MH-60Ks. Deliveries began to the 1st Battalion of the 160th SOAR in June 1992. Thirty-eight additional MH-60Ks are believed to be included in a multi-year contract awarded in April 1992, and will eventually equip the 1/245th Avn, a special operations unit of the Oklahoma Army National Guard, plus an Army reserve special operations battalion.

Compared to the USAF's MH-60G, the US Army's special operations MH-60K is equipped from the outset with dedicated mission equipment and systems. Note the nose-mounted sensors (FLIR turret and radome for TFR), IFR probe and external tanks.

Sikorsky S-70B/SH-60B Seahawk

Navalising of the H-60 was performed by Sikorsky in response to the LAMPS (light airborne multi-purpose system) III requirement, which specified a helicopter to be used for providing an over-the-horizon search and strike capability for the latest

ASW frigates and destroyers, partnering the Kaman SH-2 Seasprite which served on earlier vessels. Sikorsky was awarded the development contract on the basis of its mock-up and proposal based on the Black Hawk in September 1977. Indeed, the

Army's decision to adopt the UH-60 was seen as a major factor in influencing the Navy to choose the **S-70B Seahawk**.

The first **YSH-60B** flew on 12 December 1979 to initiate a successful flight test programme. The first production **SH-60B** flew on 11 February 1983. Retaining some 83 per cent commonality with the UH-60A, the Seahawk nevertheless introduced some important features, including anti-corrosion treatment on airframe and T700-GE-401 engines, and RAST (recovery assist secure and traverse) gear for use during landing on

Although the Royal Australian Navy's initial S-70B-2s were received directly from Sikorsky, the third and subsequent Seahawks were locally assembled. Their mission-specific equipment includes a new MEL Super Searcher radar.

small platforms in heavy seas. Mission equipment consisted of an APS-124 360° search radar housed under the forward fuselage, a 25-tube sonobuoy launcher in the port side of the cabin, ASQ-81(V)2 towed MAD mounted on a pylon on the starboard rear fuselage, ALQ-142 ESM antennas in four box-like fairings, datalinks, secure communications and various onboard computers and processing units. A hoist is fitted for a secondary SAR role and the aircraft can be employed on utility transport missions.

A crew of three consists of a pilot, an airborne tactical officer/co-pilot and a sensor operator. The basic functions of the search are handled remotely by the parent vessel's combat information centre, although the final localisation of submarines using MAD and the prosecution of attacks is handled autonomously by the SH-60B crew. The standard weapon is the Mk 46 torpedo, of which two can be carried under stub pylons attached to the fuselage sides. Anti-ship capability is being added in the form of the

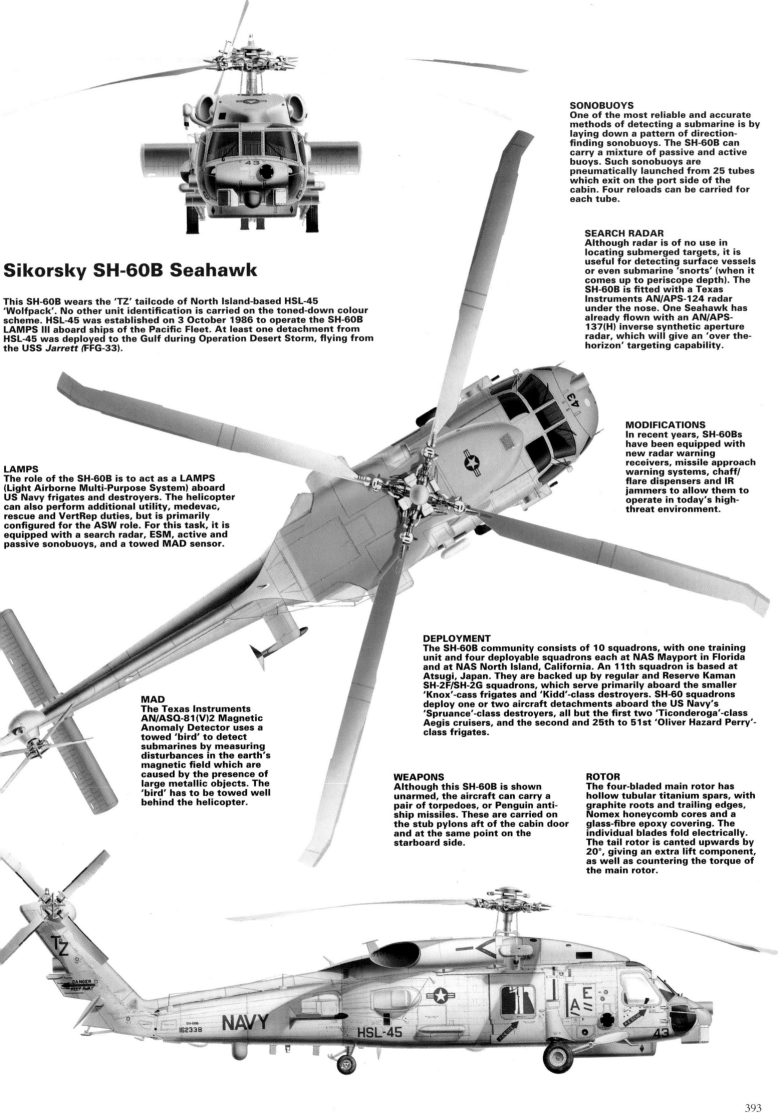

Sikorsky SH-60B Seahawk

This SH-60B wears the 'TZ' tailcode of North Island-based HSL-45 'Wolfpack'. No other unit identification is carried on the toned-down colour scheme. HSL-45 was established on 3 October 1986 to operate the SH-60B LAMPS III aboard ships of the Pacific Fleet. At least one detachment from HSL-45 was deployed to the Gulf during Operation Desert Storm, flying from the USS *Jarrett* (FFG-33).

SONOBUOYS
One of the most reliable and accurate methods of detecting a submarine is by laying down a pattern of direction-finding sonobuoys. The SH-60B can carry a mixture of passive and active buoys. Such sonobuoys are pneumatically launched from 25 tubes which exit on the port side of the cabin. Four reloads can be carried for each tube.

SEARCH RADAR
Although radar is of no use in locating submerged targets, it is useful for detecting surface vessels or even submarine 'snorts' (when it comes up to periscope depth). The SH-60B is fitted with a Texas Instruments AN/APS-124 radar under the nose. One Seahawk has already flown with an AN/APS-137(H) inverse synthetic aperture radar, which will give an 'over the-horizon' targeting capability.

MODIFICATIONS
In recent years, SH-60Bs have been equipped with new radar warning receivers, missile approach warning systems, chaff/flare dispensers and IR jammers to allow them to operate in today's high-threat environment.

LAMPS
The role of the SH-60B is to act as a LAMPS (Light Airborne Multi-Purpose System) aboard US Navy frigates and destroyers. The helicopter can also perform additional utility, medevac, rescue and VertRep duties, but is primarily configured for the ASW role. For this task, it is equipped with a search radar, ESM, active and passive sonobuoys, and a towed MAD sensor.

DEPLOYMENT
The SH-60B community consists of 10 squadrons, with one training unit and four deployable squadrons each at NAS Mayport in Florida and at NAS North Island, California. An 11th squadron is based at Atsugi, Japan. They are backed up by regular and Reserve Kaman SH-2F/SH-2G squadrons, which serve primarily aboard the smaller 'Knox'-cass frigates and 'Kidd'-class destroyers. SH-60 squadrons deploy one or two aircraft detachments aboard the US Navy's 'Spruance'-class destroyers, all but the first two 'Ticonderoga'-class Aegis cruisers, and the second and 25th to 51st 'Oliver Hazard Perry'-class frigates.

MAD
The Texas Instruments AN/ASQ-81(V)2 Magnetic Anomaly Detector uses a towed 'bird' to detect submarines by measuring disturbances in the earth's magnetic field which are caused by the presence of large metallic objects. The 'bird' has to be towed well behind the helicopter.

WEAPONS
Although this SH-60B is shown unarmed, the aircraft can carry a pair of torpedoes, or Penguin anti-ship missiles. These are carried on the stub pylons aft of the cabin door and at the same point on the starboard side.

ROTOR
The four-bladed main rotor has hollow tubular titanium spars, with graphite roots and trailing edges, Nomex honeycomb cores and a glass-fibre epoxy covering. The individual blades fold electrically. The tail rotor is canted upwards by 20°, giving an extra lift component, as well as countering the torque of the main rotor.

are built by Mitsubishi. **Greece** has purchased five **S-70B-6** aircraft for operation from its MEKO 200 frigates. These are SH-60B/F hybrids with Eaton AN/APS-143 (V)3 radar, Bendix AN/ASQ-18 (V)3 dipping sonar and Penguin missile capability. Deliveries are scheduled to start in 1995.

SPECIFICATION

Sikorsky S-70B (SH-60B Seahawk)
Rotor system: main rotor diameter 53 ft 8 in (16.36 m); tail rotor diameter 11 ft 0 in (3.35 m); main rotor disc area 2,262.03 sq ft (210.05 m); tail rotor disc area 95.03 sq ft (8.83 m²)
Fuselage and tail: length overall, rotors turning 64 ft 10 in (19.76 m), fuselage 50 ft 0.75 in (15.26 m), and with rotor and tail pylon folded 40 ft 11 in (12.47 m); height overall, rotor turnings 17 ft 0 in (5.18 m), to top of rotor head 11 ft 11 in (3.63 m), and with tail pylon folded 13 ft 3.25 in (4.04 m); stabiliser span 14 ft 4.5 in (4.38 m); wheel track 9 ft 2 in (2.79 m); wheel base 15 ft 10 in (4.83 m)
Powerplant: two General Electric T700-GE-401 turboshafts each rated at 1,690 shp (1260 kW) or, in helicopters delivered from 1988, two General Electric T700-GE-401C turboshafts each rated at 1,900 shp (1417 kW)
Weights: empty 13,648 lb (6191 kg) for the ASW mission; mission take-off 20,244 lb (9182 kg) for the ASW mission or 18,373 lb (8334 kg) for the ASST mission; maximum take-off 21,884 lb (9926 kg) for the utility mission
Fuel and load: internal fuel 590 US gal (2233 litres); external fuel up to 120-US gal (455-litre) drop tanks; maximum payload 8,000 lb (3629 kg)
Speed: dash speed at 5,000 ft (1525 m) 126 kt (145 mph; 234 km/h)
Range: operational radius 50 nm (57.5 miles; 92.5 km) for a 3-hour loiter, or 150 nm (173 miles; 278 km/h) for a 1-hour loiter
Performance: maximum vertical rate of climb at sea level 700 ft (213 m) per minute

The SH-60B is the US Navy's primary embarked H-60 variant, fulfilling the vital ASW role from frigates and destroyers. In a typical operational scene, a Seahawk of HSL-46 winds up to full power in anticipation of getting airborne from the USS Doyle, somewhere in the Indian Ocean.

AGM-119B Mod 7 Penguin missile, and pintle-mounted 0.50-in machine-guns are becoming increasingly common. One SH-60B has flown with Rolls-Royce Turboméca RTM 322 engines (this is described separately under the heading Westland WS-70), and another has been fitted with a GEC Sea Owl passive IR detection system.

During operations in the Gulf from 1987, 25 SH-60Bs received AN/ALQ-144 IR jammers, chaff/flare dispensers, AN/AAR-47 MAWS and a Texas Instruments AN/TAS-6A thermal imager. Seven aircraft were equipped with a Ford AN/AAS-38 FLIR pod.

US Navy requirements for the SH-60B are stated to be 260, of which about 150 have been delivered. These serve with US Navy squadrons HSL-40, 41, 42, 43, 44, 45,

46, 47, 48 and 49, homeported at NAS Mayport, FL, for Atlantic Fleet units, and NAS North Island, CA, for Pacific units. HSL-51 is forward-based at NAS Atsugi, Japan.

In the mid- to late 1990s, plans call for surviving SH-60Bs and SH-60Fs to be brought up to a common standard, known as **SH-60R**, which will give increased armaments options, improved defences and the combined sensor options of both variants.

OPERATORS

Export orders have come from **Spain**, which has bought 12 Seahawks under the designation **HS.23**. These differ from the SH-60B by having Bendix Oceanics AQS-13F dipping sonar. They are operated

from the main Armada air base at Rota, although deployments are made aboard 'Santa Maria'-class guided missile frigates. **Australia**'s **S-70B-2** aircraft combine features of both SH-60B and SH-60F (described separately) with RAN-specified equipment. This includes MEL Super Searcher X-band search radar in a new, smaller radome, CAE Electronics AQS-504 internally-mounted MAD system and other sonar processing equipment. The S-70B-2 also carries 25 SSQ-801 Barra sonobuoys and may later have provision for Sea Skua and Penguin Mk 2 Mod 7 anti-ship missiles. Eight were built by Sikorsky, and a further eight completed by ASTA in Australia from US-supplied kits. RAN S-70B-2s deployed to the Gulf were equipped with AN/AAQ-16 FLIR and AN/AAR-47 MAWS. **Japan** is procuring the indigenously-assembled **S-70B-3** for its Maritime Self-Defence Force to replace ageing Sikorsky HSS-2s. These are designated **SH-60J** in service and are described more fully in a separate entry. Two were supplied by Sikorsky, and fitted out by Mitsubishi with indigenous equipment as **YSH-60J**s. Subsequent aircraft, of which 47 have been funded from a requirement of 80,

Sikorsky **S-70B/SH-60F Ocean Hawk**

Anti-submarine work is also performed by the **SH-60F Ocean Hawk**, but this differs significantly from the SH-60B. Obtained to replace the elderly SH-3H

The SH-60F is designed for inner-zone ASW protection of the carrier battle group, using its sonar to detect enemy submarines, which it may then engage or leave to other assets. A cousin of the SH-60B, it differs in having a cleaner appearance, with the deletion of external ESM and MAD bird.

on aircraft-carrier decks, the SH-60F performs the **US Navy**'s CVW Inner Zone ASW mission, known informally as 'CV-helo'. In addition, it is required to have secondary missions of plane-guard rescue and general utility transport.

Although the airframe of the Ocean Hawk is similar to that of the Seahawk, the latter's LAMPS III system is completely removed, along with small vessel-related items such as the RAST. Instead, the mission equipment centres around the Bendix AQS-13F dipping sonar and improved detec-

tion systems such as FLIR and ESM. An extra weapon station on the port side allows the carriage of three torpedoes, usually the Mk 50 weapon. Its performance is generally similar to that of the SH-60B, although maximum take-off weight is now increased to 23,500 lb (10659 kg).

The first flight of an aircraft in SH-60F configuration took place on 19 March 1987, and its initial fleet deployment was made aboard USS Nimitz in 1991. The variant now serves with squadrons HS-2, 3, 4, 6, 8, 9, 10 and 15, these being shore-based at NAS North Island, CA, or NAS Jacksonville, FL. Options remain for fitting other sensors such as MAD and search radar, and increasing armament options. Along with SH-60Bs, this will bring surviving SH-60Fs up to a common **SH-60R** standard.

Taiwan has bought 10 similar aircraft designated **S-70C(M)-1 Thunderhawk**. Based closely on the SH-60F, they are fitted with Telephonics AN/APS-128C pulse compression radar, Bendix AN/AQS-18(V) dipping radar, and with fixed searchlights in the old ESM fairings, and new antennas for the Litton AN/ALR-606(V)2 ESM. They are being deployed aboard six 'Kwang Hua I'-class ('Oliver Hazard Perry'-class) guided missile frigates. The pseudo-civilian designation is in fact a political expedient to smooth relations between the US and the two Chinese republics.

Sikorsky **S-70B/HH-60H Rescue Hawk**

Closely based on the SH-60F Ocean Hawk, the **HH-60H Rescue Hawk** is the **US Navy**'s strike rescue/covert operations platform. Procurement of 45 examples is continuing, the first 18 being acquired for

two Reserve squadrons, HCS-4 at NAS Norfolk, VA, and HCS-5 at NAS Point Mugu, CA. The remainder are distributed among SH-60F-operating HS units at NAS North Island, CA, and NAS Jacksonville, FL, each

unit sending a mix of four Ocean Hawks and two Rescue Hawks as part of each carrier air wing.

The HH-60H is tailored to its primary role of recovery of downed aircrew. Whereas

the Navy had previously undertaken the role it called combat rescue, a reactive mission to retrieve crew, the HH-60H's role of strike rescue is intended as a proactive mission, with the Rescue Hawk an integral part of any mission planning. A requirement to recover a four-man crew 250 nm (287 miles; 463 km) from base was the primary goal behind the initial requirement. The sec-

Sikorsky S-70B/HH-60H Rescue Hawk

During Desert Storm, Minigun-armed HH-60Hs were based at Al Jouf, from where they were used for covert operations. Navy operations placed a greater emphasis on combat rescue and anti-terrorist support than the USAF's SOF helicopters.

Sikorsky HH-60H Rescue Hawk

ondary role of covert operations largely centres around the infil/exfil of SEAL commando teams. For this tasking the HH-60H has RAST gear to allow it to operate from vessels other than its parent aircraft-carrier.

The Rescue Hawk features a wide array of equipment suitable to its tasks. All avionics are concerned with self-protection and accurate navigation. HIRSS can be fitted to reduce the infra-red signature. The Rescue is fitted with door guns, initially 0.30-in (7.62-mm) M60s, but they are being replaced by GECAL 0.50-in (12.7-mm) machine-guns.

The first HH-60H flew on 17 August 1988 and deliveries to the first unit, HCS-5, com-

menced on 8 July 1989. The first fleet unit (HS-2) took HH-60Hs aboard USS *Nimitz* on 25 February 1991. HCS-4 and HCS-5 each sent two-aircraft detachments to Al Jouf for operations in Desert Storm. From their experience, the HH-60H is being upgraded with a turreted AAQ-16 FLIR, lengthened sponsons to house more defensive systems, and forward-firing armament, probably 2.75-in rocket pods and 0.50-in guns. Early aircraft are being retrofitted, while new aircraft will have the modifications fitted during production. At a later date, it is intended to fit provision for launching Maverick, Sidewinder or Sidearm missiles. Plans

exist to fit a Texas Instruments AN/APS-137(H) inverse synthetic aperture radar, if funds can be obtained.

SPECIFICATION

Sikorsky HH-60H Rescue Hawk
Rotor system: main rotor diameter 53 ft 8 in (16.36 m); tail rotor diameter 11 ft 0 in (3.35 m); main rotor disc area 2,262.03 sq ft (210.05 m2); tail rotor disc area 95.03 sq ft (8.83 m2)
Fuselage and tail: length overall, rotors turning 64 ft 10 in (19.76 m), fuselage 50 ft 0.75 in (15.26 m), and with rotor and tail pylon folded 41 ft 0.625 in (12.51 m); height overall with rotors turning 17 ft 0 in

(5.18 m), to top of rotor head 11 ft 11 in (3.63 m), and with tail pylon folded 13 ft 3.25 in (4.04 m); stabiliser span 14 ft 4.5 in (4.38 m); wheel track 9 ft 2 in (2.79 m); wheel base 15 ft 10 in (4.83 m)
Powerplant: two General Electric T700-GE-401C turboshafts each rated at 1,900 shp (1417 kW)
Weights: empty 13,480 lb (6114 kg)
Fuel and load: internal fuel 590 US gal (2233 litres); external fuel up to two 120-US gal (455-litre) drop tanks; maximum payload 8,000 lb (3629 kg)
Speed: dash speed at 5,000 ft (1525 m) 126 kt (145 mph; 234 km/h)
Range: operational radius 250 nm (288 miles; 463 km) on a SAR mission or 200 nm (230 miles; 370 km) on a a SEAL insertion/extraction mission

---

Sikorsky S-70B/HH-60J Jayhawk

Procured to replace HH-3Fs in US Coast Guard service, the **HH-60J Jayhawk** is essentially similar to the US Navy's HH-60H Rescue Hawk, but dispenses with combat equipment such as HIRSS and defensive avionics in favour of dedicated search equipment. Chief among these is a thimble radome on the nose housing a Bendix/King RDR-1300 search/weather radar, supported by a direction finder and ILS/VOR receiver. A 30-million candlepower searchlight can be fitted to the port fuel tank pylon, and the cockpit is NVG-compatible. Funding for a thermal imager is being sought. Whereas the HH-60H routinely carries two external fuel tanks, the HH-60J can carry an additional tank on the port pylon to meet Coast Guard range requirements, the asymmetric arrangement being dictated by the need to provide clearance for the rescue hoist on the starboard side. RAST gear can be fitted for operations

from Coast Guard cutters in the 'Hamilton' and 'Bear' classes.

A crew of four flies the Jayhawk, comprising two pilots, flight engineer/hoist operator and a rescue swimmer. With all three external tanks, the HH-60J can fly to 300 nm (345 miles/555 km) from base, remain on scene for 45 minutes and return with six survivors with a safe fuel margin. There is no emergency capability of alighting on the water, one retrograde step compared to its predecessor.

The first HH-60J flew on 8 August 1990, and Jayhawks were soon delivered to the USCG Aviation Technical Training Center at Elizabeth City, NC, and the Air Training Center at Mobile, AL. Jayhawks are now operational with Coast Guard Air Stations at Cape Cod, MA, Elizabeth City, NC, Clearwater, FL, Mobile, AL, Traverse City, MI, San Francisco, CA, Kodiak, AK, and Sitka, AK. The USCG is investigating the feasibility of

deploying Jayhawks regularly aboard surface vessels, and trials have been conducted aboard various medium- and heavy-

endurance USCG cutters. A total of 42 has been ordered, of which 37 aircraft had been delivered by February 1994. The US Coast Guard has a requirement for a further 33 to reinforce the numbers operating in the secondary role of the Jayhawk, namely that of drug interdiction.

The HH-60J is the US Coast Guard's standard MRR (medium-range recovery) platform, operating from shore bases. Plans exist to increase the Jayhawks' flexibility by regular deployments aboard USCG vessels.

Sikorsky S-76/H-76 Eagle

The eight/12-passenger **S-76** was developed by Sikorsky as a general-purpose twin-turbine helicopter. It first flew on 13 March 1977, powered by 650-shp (485-kW) Allison 250-C30 turboshafts, and was followed in production by the improved **S-76 Mark II**. The **S-76 Utility** is a more basic version of the S-76 Mk II and is of greater interest to military customers. The **AUH-76** armed utility derivative incorporates optional sliding doors, armour protection, defensive avionics and a wide range of weapon options, including gun and rocket pods, anti-armour missiles and associated targeting equipment. First flying on 22 June 1984, the current **S-76B** production variant features two 981-shp (732-kW) Pratt & Whitney PT6B-36A turboshafts. The **S-76A** and **S-76C**, flown on 18 May 1990, became available with 732-shp (539-kW) Turboméca Arriel 1S1 engines. A more specifically militarised S-76B variant is the **H-76 Eagle**, which offers a similar range of options to the AUH-76. Other features include door-mounted weapons, an uprated transmission and strengthened structural items.

OPERATORS

The **Philippine air force** was an early military user. Its order for 17 S-76 Utility aircraft comprises 12 AUH-76s for COIN, troop/logistic support and medevac duties and five S-76 Mk IIs – two for SAR and three passenger transports. The AUH-76s are armed with FN Herstal HMP 0.50-in (12.7-mm) machine-gun pods and other light weapons. The **Royal Jordanian air force** bought 18, of which four were for medevac duty in paramilitary service and 12 for SAR/general transport duty, with two others (later replaced by S-76Bs) for VIP use. Jordan transferred two of its S-76s to **Iraq** and four are reported to have gone to **Guatemala**. It has disposed of the remaining S-76s. In the VIP role, single examples are used by the **Chilean army**, the **Dubai air wing** and the **Honduras air force**. The **Royal Hong Kong Auxiliary Air Force** has six S-76As, of which three have an advanced equipment fit (including FLIR) for all-weather SAR and patrol, plus two S-76Cs for VIP transport. Eight **Spanish air force** S-76Cs are for IFR training, provided by Esc 783 at Granada, and **Japan** is to acquire up to 20 S-76Cs for SAR duty. More than 150 H-76 Eagles are to be produced locally for the **South Korean army**.

SPECIFICATION

Sikorsky H-76 Eagle
Rotor system: main rotor diameter 44 ft 0 in (13.41 m); tail rotor diameter 8 ft 0 in (2.44 m); main rotor disc area 1,520.53 sq ft (141.26 m2)
Fuselage and tail: length overall, rotors turning 52 ft 6 in (16.00 m) and fuselage 43 ft 4.5 in (13.22 m); height overall 14 ft 9.25 in (4.52 m) with tail rotor turning; stabiliser span 10 ft 4 in (3.15 m)
Powerplant: two Pratt & Whitney Canada PT6B-36 turboshafts each rated at 960 shp (716 kW) for take-off and 870 shp (649 kW) for continuous running
Weights: basic empty 5,610 lb (2545 kg); empty equipped

6,680 lb (3030 kg); maximum take-off 11,400 lb (5171 kg)
Fuel and load: internal fuel 262 US gal (993 litres)
Speed: never exceed speed 155 kt (178 mph; 287 km/h); maximum cruising speed at optimum altitude 145 kt (167 mph; 269 km/h); economical cruising speed at optimum altitude 131 kt (151 mph; 243 km/h)
Range: about 312 nm (359 miles; 578 km)
Performance: maximum rate of climb at sea level 1,500 ft (457 m) per minute; service ceiling 15,000 ft (4570 m); hovering ceiling 5,400 ft (1645 m) out of ground effect

The Spanish air force's eight S-76Cs (local designation HE.24) are used for rotary wing training by Esc 783.

Sikorsky S-80/CH-53E Super Stallion

Early generations of CH-53 had proved their ability to recover downed aircraft, but the process was marginal at best. This prompted the **USMC** to issue a specification for a heavylift helicopter with 1.8 times the lifting capacity of the CH-53A, but still small enough to operate from its amphibious assault vessels. Sikorsky, meanwhile, had been working to a similar goal, and came up with the elegant solution of adding a third T64 engine to the basic design. This

is mounted behind the rotor mast and is fed by an intake on the port side.

The new variant was assigned the company model number **S-80**, and the first **YCH-53E** prototype flew from Stratford on 1 March 1974, initially with a large tailfin and low-set tailplane. Power was provided by three T64-GE-415s driving a seven-bladed main rotor, via an uprated transmission. Twin-engined CH-53s have six rotor blades. The airframe itself was longer than

earlier CH-53s, enabling it to carry 55 troops and light vehicles easily, while the fuselage sponsons were lengthened to house more fuel, and external tank capability was provided from the outset. Following the destruction of the first prototype in a ground run, the second prototype resumed flying with a revised tail, the upright fin being canted 20° to port and fitted with a gull-wing tailplane cantilevered to starboard.

First of the pre-production **CH-53E**s flew on 8 December 1975, but it was not until February 1981 that the first USMC unit, HMH-464 (now HMM-464), achieved initial operating capability at MCAS New River, NC. Five more units have been equipped with the type (HMM-461 at New River, HMH-361, 465 and 466 at Tustin, CA, and HMT-302 at Tustin for training). The CH-53E is now a vital part of USMC amphibious operations, partnering the smaller CH-46 on assault missions. Thanks to its lifting capability, the CH-53E is primarily used to move materiel as opposed to personnel. In a typical composite squadron aboard an assault ship, four CH-53Es are assigned. The type was used widely in the Desert Storm conflict.

US Navy interest in the Sea Stallion lay in its use for supplying vessels from shore bases, the combination of lifting ability and range proving ideal for the task. Small numbers fly with HC-1 at NAS North Island, CA, HC-2 at NAS Norfolk, VA, and HC-4 at NAS Sigonella, Sicily, respectively supporting the Pacific, Atlantic and Mediterranean Fleets.

No foreign sales of the **S-80E** export

model have yet been made, and current US Navy and Marine Corps acquisitions stand at 142, although eventual requirements are for 177, with production ending in 1995.

SPECIFICATION

Sikorsky S-80 (CH-53E Super Stallion)
Rotor system: main rotor diameter 79 ft 0 in (24.08 m); tail rotor diameter 20 ft 0 in (6.10 m); main rotor disc area 4,901.67 sq ft (455.38 m2); tail rotor disc area 314.16 sq ft (29.19 m2)
Fuselage and tail: length overall, rotors turning 99 ft 0.5 in (30.19 m), fuselage 73 ft 4 in (22.35 m), and overall with rotor and tail pylon folded 60 ft 6 in (18.44 m); height overall, rotors turning 29 ft 5 in (8.97 m), to top of rotor head 17 ft 5.5 in (5.32 m), and overall with rotor and tail pylon folded 18 ft 7 in (5.66 m); wheel track 13 ft 0 in (3.96 m); wheel base 27 ft 3 in (8.31 m)
Powerplant: three General Electric T64-GE-416 turboshafts each rated at 4,380 shp (3266 kW) for 10 minutes, 4,145 shp (3091 kW) for 30 minutes and 3,696 shp (2756 kW) for continuous running
Weights: empty 33,338 lb (15072 kg); maximum take-off 69,750 lb (31640 kg) with an internal payload or 73,500 lb (33340 kg) with an external payload
Fuel and load: internal fuel 1,017 US gal (3849 litres); external fuel up to two 650-US gal (2461-litre) drop tanks; maximum payload 36,000 lb (16330 kg), or 30,000 lb (13607 kg) carried internally over a 100-nm (115-mile; 185-km) radius or 32,000 lb (14515 kg) carried externally over a 50-nm (57-mile; 92.5-km) radius
Speed: maximum level speed 'clean' at sea level 170 kt (196 mph; 315 km/h); cruising speed at sea level 150 kt (173 mph; 278 km/h)
Range: ferry range 1,120 nm (1,290 miles; 2075 km) without flight refuelling; operational radius 500 nm (575 miles; 925 km) with 20,000-lb (9072-kg) external payload or 50 nm (57.5 miles; 92.5 km) with 32,000-lb (14515-kg) external payload
Performance: maximum rate of climb at sea level with 25,000-lb (11340-kg) payload 2,500 ft (762 m) per minute; service ceiling 18,500 ft (5640 m); hovering ceiling 11,550 ft (3520 m) in ground effect and 9,500 ft (2895 m) out of ground effect

Above: The addition of a third powerplant dramatically improved the CH-53's lifting abilities. It is the USMC's primary heavylift type and is used by five operational units. Early problems during trials were rectified by a canted fin and a gull-wing tail.

The US Navy's CH-53Es provide heavylift and vertical delivery support of the Mediterranean, Pacific and Atlantic Fleets. HC-4 covers the European/Middle East theatre and is based at Sigonella, Italy.

Sikorsky S-80M/MH-53E Sea Dragon

Just as the CH-53E dramatically improved the assault capabilities of the Stallion, so the **MH-53E Sea Dragon** has increased the ability of the AMCM (airborne mine countermeasures) force. Utilising the basic airframe of the CH-53E, the MH-53E differs by having grossly enlarged fuselage sponsons housing fuel which allows the type to mine-sweep for four hours while operating 30 minutes from base. The refuelling probe can further extend time on station, and ferry tanks can be fitted internally. Mine-hunting equipment remains essentially that devel-

oped for the RH-53D, but with additional items such as the ALQ-160 acoustic countermeasures system, ALQ-166 magnetic mine hydrofoil sled and the Northrop ALARMS (airborne laser radar mine sensor), the latter housed in a 35-ft (10-m) internal container. The MH-53E also retains a secondary transport role, but this is little used due to the Navy's adoption of the CH-53E.

The first pre-production machine took to the air on 1 September 1983, following trials of a **YMH-53E** that initially lacked the enlarged sponsons. Deliveries began to the

US Navy in June 1986 and in April 1987 the type joined HM-14 at NAS Norfolk, VA, followed by HM-12 at the same base and HM-15 at NAS Alameda, CA. The total US Navy requirement is for 56 airframes and the formation of a fourth squadron.

One export customer has been found for the Sea Dragon, this being the **Japanese Maritime Self-Defence Force**, which has purchased 11 **S-80M-1** aircraft, essentially similar to the MH-53E but lacking the refuelling probe. After trials with 51 Kokutai at Atsugi, the S-80M entered service with

31 Kokutai at Iwakuni to replace KV-107-IIs in the AMCM role.

SPECIFICATION

Sikorsky S-80 (MH-53E Sea Dragon)
generally similar to the Sikorsky S-80 (CH-53E Super Stallion) except in the following particulars:
Weights: empty 36,336 lb (16482 kg); maximum take-off 69,750 lb (31640 kg) with an internal payload or 73,500 lb (33340 kg) with an external payload
Fuel and load: internal fuel 3,200 US gal (12113 litres) plus provision for 2,100 US gal (7949 litres) of auxiliary fuel in up to seven internal tanks; useful load for influence sweep mission 26,000 lb (11793 kg)

The latest mine-countermeasures S-80 variant offers greatly improved capability through its increased power and advanced avionics. Huge external sponsons and rear-view mirrors identify this mine-hunter as a Japanese S-80M-1. It lacks the refuelling probe associated with the US Navy's MH-53E.

Sikorsky MH-53E Sea Dragon

Sikorsky S-92

In 1992 Sikorsky unveiled a mock-up of its S-92 'Helibus', a growth derivative of the S-70 series aimed primarily at the civilian market. As currently marketed, the civil S-92C will combine a new conventional structure fuselage of increased dimensions, with a 6 ft x 6 ft (1.83 m x 1.83 m) cross-section, a cabin length of 19 ft 4 in (5.89 m), and accommodation for up to 22 passengers. It will also feature the SH-60B's 3,350-shp (2500-kW) transmission, a modified UH-60L main rotor head, and an improved main rotor

with graphite blade spar, broader-chord blades and anhedral blade tips. Power is to be provided by two 2,200-shp (1640-kW) General Electric CT-7 or Rolls-Royce Turboméca RTM 322 turboshafts. Crash-resistant fuel tanks will be incorporated in enlarged sponsons on the fuselage sides, and an optional loading ramp at the rear of the cabin will be available.

A military S-92M derivative is also being marketed, with refuelling probe, aft-loading ramp, automatic main rotor blade-fold and

tail-fold. Capable of carrying 18 to 24 troops, or 16 litter patients, on 200-nm (230-mile; 370-km) missions, the S-92M is initially aimed at satisfying anticipated USMC/USN requirements for medium-lift helicopters to replace Boeing CH-46E/UH-46Ds in the combat assault/vertical replenishment roles respectively. In the combat SAR role, the S-92M is being promoted as an alternative to the V-22 Osprey and is being proposed to replace Sikorsky MH-53Js in service with the USAF's AFSOC.

Powered by uprated General Electric T701-GE 401X engines, the S-92M will have a full range of 400 nm (460 miles; 740 km) and a cruising speed of 150 kt (173 mph; 278 km/h). Maximum take-off weight will be 22,000 lb (9980 kg) in the land assault mission, and 23,000 lb (10435 kg) in the amphibious assault role.

Development of the S-92 was delayed in 1993 due to the economic downturn. Sikorsky is currently looking for further international partners to launch the programme.

Singapore Aerospace A-4SU Super Skyhawk

Singapore Aerospace Ltd
540 Airport Road,
Paya Lebar, Singapore 1953

The A-4 Skyhawk first entered service with the Republic of Singapore Air Force in 1974. Some 40 former US Navy A-4Bs were removed from storage following a mid-1972 order from the RSAF. The first eight were refurbished by Lockheed to A-4S standard with over 100 modifications. These included installation of 8,400-lb st (37.36-kN) J65-W-20 turbojets, twin 30-mm ADEN cannon, new instrumentation and a Ferranti lightweight lead-computing weapon aiming system. The aircraft also featured unique overwing spoilers, and a brake parachute below the rear fuselage. The remaining 32 aircraft were refurbished in Singapore by January 1976. The upgraded aircraft entered service with Nos 142 'Gryphon' and 143 'Phoenix' Sqns, along with seven Skyhawks modified to TA-4S trainers with unique, separate tandem cockpits.

Singapore purchased 70 additional A-4Cs in 1980 and 16 more A-4Bs in 1983 from the same source, cannibalising many of them to provide spares, and converting 40 to A-4S-1 and 10 to TA-4S-1 configuration with spoilers, minor avionics modifications, rewiring and higher-rated wing hardpoints. The additional procurement allowed the formation of No. 145 'Hornet' Squadron. By 1984 the Singaporean government decided not to procure a new-generation fighter (for reasons of affordability), and elected instead to upgrade these modestly-equipped, elderly aircraft to A-4SU Super Skyhawk standard. An additional benefit of upgrading the aircraft indigenously was the boost it would give to Singapore's developing aerospace industry.

Phase One of this effort involved the replacement of the J65 turbojet with a non-afterburning variant of the General Electric F404-GE-100D turbofan that develops a maximum of 10,800 lb st (48.04 kN). The package also involved the associated structural hardening, modification of the engine intakes, redesigned mounts and installation of new engine ancillary systems. The work was carried out by SAe and was supervised by Grumman. The 27 per cent increase in thrust is claimed to provide a 15 per cent increase in maximum dash speed, 35 per cent faster climb rate, 40 per cent increase in level acceleration, a better sustained turn performance than the A-4M and substantial improvement in take-off performance and agility. The 34 per cent heavier F404 also features significantly improved specific fuel consumption and maintainability.

One prototype each of the single-seat A-4S and two-seat TA-4S was re-engined, the first of these taking to the air for the initially on 19 September 1986. Production-conversions of 40 A-4S-1s and eight TA-4S-1s were completed during 1989, with No. 143 squadron the first to achieve IOC (on 1 March 1989), followed by Nos 145 and 142. In 1990 six re-engined A-4S Skyhawks were displayed as the 'Black Knights' aerobatic team.

Delphi avionics upgrade

The completely separate Phase Two of the programme involved a comprehensive avionics modernisation developed by Ferranti Defence Systems of the UK (now part of GEC-Marconi). Named Delphi, it was applied by a joint RSAF/SAe team at the company's facility at RSAF Paya Lebar. It comprises a GEC-Ferranti Type 4510 raster/stroke HUD and MED 2067 head-down MFD; a Litton LN-93 ring-laser gyro INS; Bendix flight data recorder; and a mission computer complete with data transfer module for computerised mission planning. The aircraft have been rewired with the standard MIL 1553B databus. One of the factors governing the choice of Ferranti's

package was a refusal by the US government to allow American contractors to release computer system software codes to Singapore. All aspects of software development for the avionics package were reportedly developed indigenously.

Singapore declared its first A-4SU Super Skyhawk fighter unit, No. 145 Squadron, fully operational on 24 February 1992. Two further Super Skyhawk squadrons, Nos 142 and 143, are receiving aircraft as they are recycled through the modification package. The entire RSAF Skyhawk fleet is based at RASAF Tengah. The A-4SUs are fitted with LAU-10 and Alkan triple ejector racks, and can carry a wide range of ordnance including AGM-65B/E Maverick ASMs, Mk 82 bombs, CRV-7 rocket pods, AIM-9J AAMs, SUU-40/A flare dispensers, SNEB 68-mm rockets and SUU-23 20-mm gun pods.

Further modifications are being planned. These include the provision of 20 GEC Avionics Atlantic FLIR pods for all-weather navigation and weapons targeting, as well as laser rangefinders for air-to-ground ranging and targeting. The RSAF already has about 30 Martin-Marietta AN/AAS-35 Pave Penny laser spot tracker pods which may be installed on the A-4SUs.

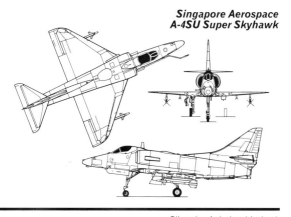

Arguably the most advanced A-4s in service anywhere today, the RSAF's A-4SU Super Skyhawks were declared operational with No. 145 Squadron in early 1992. These were the first to feature the Delphi avionics modernisation package, as well as F404 turbofan powerplants.

Singapore Aerospace A-4SU Super Skyhawk

Slingsby T67 Firefly

Slingsby Aviation Limited,
Ings Lane, Kirbymoorside,
North Yorkshire YO6 6EZ, United Kingdom.

After acquiring a licence for production in the UK of the Fournier RF-6B motorised glider (as the T67A Firefly), Slingsby developed an all-composite airframe for the T67B and subsequent variants of this two-seat, side-by-side aerobatic, training and sporting aircraft. Intended primarily for military use, the T67M featured an AEIO-320-D1B engine and, in its Mk II version, a one-piece upward-opening

canopy. The T67M200 was first flown on 16 May 1985 and introduced a 200-hp

(149-kW) AEIO-360-A1E engine and three-bladed propeller.

Slingsby T67 Firefly

The T-3A is steadily replacing ageing Cessna T-41A/C Mescaleros with the 557th FTS at the Air Force Academy in Colorado, and with AETC's 1st FTS at Hondo, Texas. This T-3A is shown at the roll-out ceremony at Kirbymoorside in late 1993.

Slingsby T67 Firefly

In 1991, Slingsby developed the more powerful **T67M260** with a 260-hp (195-kW) AETO-540-D4A5 flat-six engine to meet the USAF requirement for an Enhanced Flight Screener. The service will acquire 113 of these Fireflies with the designation **T-3A**. Hunting Aircraft Ltd has been contracted to provide elementary flying training (effectively for screening inexperienced trainee pilots) using **T67M-IIs**. These will replace ageing de Havilland Chipmunks and Scottish Aviation Bulldogs presently used by the EFTS at RAF Swinderby and by the RNEFTS at Topcliffe.

Four T67s are operated by the **Royal Hong Kong AAF**. Twelve similar **T67C3s** are used by Canadair to train pilots for the **Canadian Forces** at Portage la Prairie. Other users include civil schools in **Turkey**, the **Netherlands** and **Norway** that have some responsibilities for preliminary training and grading of military pilots. The **USAF**'s T-3As are replacing T-41A/Cs with the Air Force Academy, Colorado, and with a training squadron in Texas.

SPECIFICATION

Slingsby T67M Mk II Firefly
Wing: span 34 ft 9 in (10.59 m); aspect ratio 8.88; area 136.00 sq ft (12.63 m²)
Fuselage and tail: length 24 ft 0.25 in (7.32 m); height 7 ft 9 in (2.36 m); tailplane span 11 ft 1.75 in (3.40 m)
Powerplant: one Textron Lycoming AEIO-320-D1B four cylinder horizontally-opposed piston engine rated at 160 hp (119 kW)
Weights: empty equipped 1,450 lb (658 kg); maximum take-off 2,100 lb (952 kg)

Fuel and load: internal fuel 252 lb (114 kg)
Speed: maximum level speed 'clean' at sea level 136 kt (157 mph; 252 km/h); maximum cruising speed at 8,000 ft (2440 m) 127 kt (146 mph; 235 km/h)
Range: 529 nm (608 miles); endurance 5 hours 5 minutes at economical cruising speed
Performance: maximum rate of climb at sea level 1,100 ft (335 m) per minute; take-off distance to 50 ft (15 m) 1,319 ft (402 m) at MTOW; landing distance from 50 ft (15 m) 1,750 ft (533 m) at normal landing weight
g limits: -3 to +6

SOCATA (Aérospatiale) Rallye/Guerrier

SOCATA,
12 Rue Pasteur,
F-92150 Suresnes, France

In 1966 the SOCATA subsidiary of Aérospatiale took over production of the **Rallye** lightplane, which was first flown on 10 June 1959 as a Morane-Saulnier product. SOCATA also developed the **Rallye 235G Guerrier** for light attack, army support and weapons training. Based on the four-seat **Rallye 235GT Gabier**, it features a two-seat cabin with dual controls, provision for two further seats behind the pilots and a tailwheel undercarriage. It introduces four underwing hardpoints for twin 7.62-mm (0.3-in) gun pods, MATRA F22 rocket launchers each with six 68-mm (2.68-in) rockets, 50-kg (110-lb) bombs or battlefield illumination, surveillance or SAR equipment. It can also carry a stretcher or an underwing TV reconnaissance pod.

The major user is the French **Aéronavale**. Four Rallyes of 50S at Lanvéoc-Poulmic provide informal flying instruction to students of the Ecole Navale (Naval College). 51S at Rochefort/Soubise has 11 Rallyes to grade NCO students. Other Rallye operators include the Royal air force of **Morocco** (10), the **Moroccan Gendarmerie** (two) and **Libya** (eight). Single examples serve in **Chad**, **Djibouti**, the **Dominican Republic** and the **Seychelles**. Two Guerriers went to the **Rwandese army air corps** and four to the air force of **Senegambia**, which also bought four Rallyes as trainers.

The Aéronavale's Rallye lightplanes are used primarily to grade prospective students, and for general instruction for non-aircrew. Two variants are operated, the two-seat spinnable Rallye Club 100S and the three/four-seat Rallye Club 100ST.

SPECIFICATION

SOCATA Rallye 235 Guerrier
Wing: span 9.74 m (31 ft 11 in); aspect ratio 7.57; area 12.28 m² (132.19 sq ft)
Fuselage and tail: length 7.25 m (23 ft 9.5 in); height 2.80 m (9 ft 2.25 in); tailplane span 3.67 m (12 ft 0.5 in); wheel track 2.01 m (6 ft 6.5 in); wheel base 1.71 m (5 ft 7.25 in)

Powerplant: one Textron Lycoming O-540-B4B5 six-cylinder horizontally-opposed piston engine rated at 235 hp (175 kW)
Weights: empty 710 kg (1,565 lb); normal take-off 1200 kg (2,646 lb); maximum take-off 1350 kg (2,976 lb)
Fuel and load: internal fuel 282 litres (74.5 US gal); external fuel none; maximum ordnance 300 kg (661 lb)
Speed: maximum level speed 'clean' at sea level 275 km/h (148 kt; 171 mph); cruising speed at 1500 m (4,925 ft) 245 km/h (132 kt; 152 mph)
Range: ferry range 1300 km (701 nm; 807 miles); combat radius 515 km (278 nm; 320 miles) on an armed reconnaissance mission with two machine-gun pods, or 265 km (143 nm; 165 miles) on an armed reconnaissance mission with four rocket launchers
Performance: maximum rate of climb at sea level 300 m (984 ft) per minute; service ceiling 4500 m (14,760 ft); take-off run 150 m (492 ft) at maximum take-off weight; take-off distance to 15 m (50 ft) 305 m (1,000 ft) at maximum take-off weight; landing run 130m (427 ft) at normal landing weight

---

SOCATA (Aérospatiale) TBM700

First flown on 14 July 1988, the **SOCATA TBM700** was at first a joint project between Aérospatiale subsidiary SOCATA and Mooney in the US, but it is now an all-French programme. The **Armée de l'Air** became the first military user of the TBM700 when it took delivery in May 1992 of two of these seven-seat single-engined 'mini-airliners', from an unannounced order for six aircraft. The TBM700s have been acquired to serve with the Groupe Aérien d'Entraînement et de Liaison (GAEL) at Villacoublay, replacing veteran twin-jet MS 760 Paris communications aircraft in Escadron de Transport 2/65 'Rambouillet'. The Armée de l'Air has a requirement for up to 35 TBM700s for use in the vital, if unsung, liaison and light utility roles.

SPECIFICATION

SOCATA (Aérospatiale) TBM700
Wing: span 12.16 m (39 ft 10.75 in); aspect ratio 8.21; area 18.00 m² (193.75 sq ft)
Fuselage and tail: length 10.43 m (34 ft 2.5 in); height 3.99 m (13 ft 1 in)
Powerplant: one Pratt & Whitney Canada PT6A -64 turboprop rated at 522 kW (700 shp)
Weights: empty equipped 1826 kg (4,025 lb); maximum take-off and landing 2991 kg (6,595 lb)

The Armée de l'Air is currently the sole military operator of SOCATA TBM700 business aircraft. They are based at Villacoublay, near Paris, and are used for liaison duties.

Fuel and load: useable fuel 866 kg (1,910 lb); total baggage load 80 kg (176 lb)
Speed: maximum cruising speed at 7925 m (26,000 ft) 555 km/h (300 kt; 345 mph)
Range: at maximum speed with maximum payload and 45 min reserves 1,001 nm (1855 km; 1,152 miles); at long-range cruising speed with maximum fuel and no reserves 1,611 nm (2985 km; 1,855 miles)
Performance: maximum rate of climb at sea level and at all-up weight of 2500 kg (5,511 lb) 702 m (2,303 ft) per minute, certificated ceiling 9150 m (30,000 ft)

SOKO G-2A Galeb

First flown in May 1961, the **G-2A Galeb** (Seagull) was the first indigenous Yugoslav jet design to enter production. The Galeb is a conventional low-wing monoplane. The wing has strong points for two 100-kg (220-lb) bombs and up to six 57-mm (2.2-in) rockets. Two 12.7-mm machine-guns are fitted in the nose. A version of the trainer flew on 19 August 1970 with an uprated Viper 532 engine as the **Galeb 3**, this being in effect the prototype for the two-seat **TJ-1 Jastreb** (described separately). The Galeb entered service with the **Yugoslav air force** (JRV) in 1965, production of more than 120 being needed to meet the requirements of the Air Academy and the fighter and fighter ground-attack schools. In post-civil war Yugoslavia, Galebs were flying exclusively with the **Serbian air force**, equipping the 105th Fighter-Bomber Regiment at Kovin. The other major customer was **Libya**, which received 120 in two batches before production ended in 1985; six others went to **Zambia**.

The largest export recipient of the SOKO Jastreb was the Libyan air force. About 30 G-2As remain in service for counter-insurgency and training duties.

SPECIFICATION

SOKO G-2A Galeb
Wing: span 11.62 m (38 ft 1.5 in) with tip tanks; aspect ratio 5.55; area 19.43 m² (209.15 sq ft)
Fuselage and tail: length 10.34 m (33 ft 11 in); height 3.28 m (10 ft 9 in); tailplane span 4.27 m (14 ft 0 in)
Powerplant: one licence-built Rolls-Royce (Bristol Siddeley) Viper 11 Mk 22-6 turbojet rated at 2,500 lb st (11.12 kN) dry
Weights: empty equipped 2620 kg (5,776 lb); normal take-off typically 3828 kg (8,439 lb) with tip tanks; maximum take-off 4300 kg (9,480 lb)
Fuel and load: internal fuel 780 kg (1,720 lb); external fuel up to 340 kg (750 lb) in two jettisonable tip tanks; maximum ordnance 300 kg (661 lb)
Speed: maximum level speed 'clean' at 6200 m (20,340 ft) 812 km/h (439 kt; 505 mph) and at sea level 756 km/h (408 kt; 470 mph); maximum cruising speed at 6000 m (19,685 ft) 730 km/h (393 kt; 453 mph)
Range: ferry range 670 nm (772 miles; 1242 km) with tip tanks; endurance 2 hours 30 minutes
Performance: maximum rate of climb at sea level 1370 m (4,495 ft) per minute; climb to 6000 m (19,685 ft) in 5 minutes 30 seconds; service ceiling 12000 m (39,370 ft); take-off distance to 15 m (50 ft) 640 m (2,100 ft) at MTOW; landing distance from 15 m (50 ft) 710 m (2,329 ft) at normal landing weight
g limits: -4 to +8

SOKO G-4 Super Galeb

First flown on 17 July 1978, the **SOKO G-4 Super Galeb** is a two-seat advanced and tactical trainer of similar configuration to the BAe Hawk. The G-4 was developed during the 1970s as a replacement for the G-2A Galeb and T-33. Pre-production aircraft followed from late 1980 and full service use began in 1985, with G-4s replacing G-2As at the advanced flying training school at Titograd. Further deliveries allowed G-4s to supplant the earlier model at the **JRV**'s Air Academy at Zadar and a second training school at Pula. At least 30 Super Galebs now fly at each unit, from production of more than 136. Pilots are streamed following 60 hours in G-4s at Zadar. Ground-attack pilots go to Titograd and interceptor pilots go to Pula for a further 120 hours. The air academy has an aerobatic team (the 'Flying Stars'/'Letece Zvezde') equipped with six G-4s. Super Galebs also equip the 105th LBAP at Kovin, the 172nd LBAP at Golubovci, Macedonia, and the 252nd LBAE at Batajnica. Export sales are limited to six G-4s for the **Myanmar air force**.

When the Mostar factory was abandoned in May 1992, some G-4 airframes were left uncompleted. The production jigs were transferred to UTVA, although no evidence exists that production has restarted. An enhanced ground-attack capability is offered in the **G-4M**, which appeared in 1991 and can carry 1680 kg (3,704 lb) of ordnance. It features a new avionics system and new nav/attack equipment including HUD, INS, electronic sight and MFDs. Capable of covering the continuation phase of training for which two-seat versions of operational aircraft are frequently used, the

In an attempt to upgrade its forces in the face of stiffening guerrilla resistance, and in the face of international sanctions which have hindered arms procurement, the Myanmar air force became the first export customer for the Super Galeb, acquiring a quantity of these light attack aircraft/jet trainers from 1990.

G-4M is being used to replace Jastrebs in some ground-attack units.

WEAPON OPTIONS

For the ground attack role, the G-4 can carry a ventral 23-mm GSh-23L gun pod with 200 rounds and up to 1280 kg (2,822 lb) of ordnance on four hardpoints. These include a wide range of indigenously-developed weapons such as S-8-16 cluster bombs, KPT-150 expendable containers with anti-tank or anti-personnel bomblets, L-57-16MD 57-mm rocket pods, SN-3 carriers for 50-kg (110-lb) and 100-kg (221-lb) bombs, and 12.7-mm gun pods. The G-4M can carry both AGM-65B Maverick and AS-7 'Kerry' ASMs, KMGU cluster bombs and BL755 bombs. There is provision for wingtip missile rails that can mount K-13 (AA-2 'Atoll') or R-60 (AA-8 'Aphid') AAMs for self-defence and for a secondary point defence role.

SPECIFICATION

SOKO G-4 Super Galeb
Wing: span 9.88 m (32 ft 5 in); aspect ratio 5.0; area 19.50 m² (209.90 sq ft)
Fuselage and tail: length 12.25 m (40 ft 2.25 in) including probe; height 4.30 m (14 ft 1.25 in); tailplane span 3.97 m (13 ft 0.25 in); wheel track 3.49 m (11 ft 5.5 in); wheel base 4.15 m (13 ft 7.5 in)
Powerplant: one ORAO (Rolls-Royce/Bristol Siddeley) Viper Mk 632-46 turbojet rated at 4,000 lb st (17.79 kN)
Weights: empty equipped 3172 kg (6,993 lb); normal take-off 4708 kg (10,379 lb) as a trainer; maximum take-off 6300 kg (13,889 lb)
Fuel and load: internal fuel 1307 kg (2,881 lb); external fuel up to 575 kg (1,268 lb) in two 368.5-litre (97.3-US gal) drop tanks; maximum ordnance 1280 kg (2,822 lb)
Speed: maximum level speed 'clean' at 6000 m (19,685 ft) 920 km/h (491 kt; 565 mph); maximum cruising speed at 6000 m (19,685 ft) 845 km/h (456 kt; 525 mph)
Range: ferry range 1,349 nm (1,553 miles; 2500 km) with drop tanks; range 1,025 nm (1,180 miles, 1900 km) with internal fuel or 701 nm (807 miles; 1300 km) with cannon pack and four BL755 cluster bombs; combat radius 210 nm (242 miles; 389 km) on a lo-lo-lo attack with cannon pack and four BL755 cluster bombs, or 438 nm (504 miles; 812 km) on a hi-lo-hi attack with two BL755 cluster bombs and two drop tanks
Performance: maximum rate of climb at sea level 1860 m (6,100 ft) per minute; climb to 8000 m (26,245 ft) in 6 minutes; service ceiling 12850 m (42,160 ft); take-off run 572 m (1,877 ft) at normal take-off weight; landing distance from 15 m (50 ft) 1065 m (3,494 ft) at normal landing weight without brake chute or 690 m (2,264 ft) at normal landing weight with brake chute; landing run 815 m (2,674 ft) at normal landing weight
g limits: -4.2 to +8

SOKO J-1 Jastreb

Entering production in 1970, the single-seat **J-1 Jastreb** (Hawk) eventually equipped five wings of the **Yugoslav air force** (JRV) for ground-attack duties, for which it was armed with three 12.7-mm machine-guns in the nose and bombs or rocket pods on four wing hardpoints. Although the single-seat J-I (**J-21** in the JRV) has been progressively replaced by the Orao, about 40 J-21s remained in service as late as 1992, including a few for continuation training of reservist officers. In mid-1994, J-21s equipped the 92nd AB at Banja Luka, the 98th AB at Petrovac, and the 252nd LBAE at Batjnica.

Production of the Jastreb totalled 250-300, of which 30 were the **RJ-1** (**IJ-21** in the JRV) reconnaissance model with wingtip camera pods. A handful survive in service with the **Serbian air force**.

The production total also included 15 **JT-1** (**TJ-21**) two-seat training variants that closely resembled the Galeb basic jet trainer from which the Jastreb was origi-

Derived from the G-2 Galeb trainer, the single-seat J-1 (J-21 in Yugoslav service) Jastreb light attack aircraft has been used extensively during Yugoslavia's protracted civil war.

nally developed. The sole export customer was the **Zambian air force**, which received 20 **J-1E/RJ-1E** aircraft in 1971, about half of which may currently remain operational.

SPECIFICATION

SOKO J-1 Jastreb
Wing: span 10.56 m (34 ft 8 in) with tip tanks; aspect ratio 5.74; area 19.43 m² (209.14 sq ft)
Fuselage and tail: length 10.88 m (35 ft 8.5 in); height 3.64 m (11 ft 11.5 in); tailplane span 4.27 m (14 ft 0 in); wheel track 3.89 m (12 ft 9 in); wheel base 3.61 m (11 ft 10 in)
Powerplant: one licence-built Rolls-Royce (Bristol Siddeley) Viper Mk 531 turbojet rated at 3,000 lb st (13.32 kN)
Weights: empty equipped 2820 kg (6,217 lb); normal take-off 4666 kg (10,287 lb); maximum take-off 5100 kg (11,243 lb)
Fuel and load: internal fuel 440 kg (970 lb); external fuel up to two 275-litre (72.6-US gal) drop tanks; maximum ordnance 800 kg (1,764 lb)
Speed: maximum level speed 'clean' at 6000 m (19,685 ft) 820 km/h (442 kt; 510 mph); maximum cruising speed at 5000 m (16,405 ft) 740 km/h (399 kt; 460 mph)
Range: ferry range 820 nm (1520 km; 945 miles) with drop tanks
Performance: maximum rate of climb at sea level 1260 m (4.134 ft) per minute; service ceiling 12000 m (39,370 ft); take-off run 700 m (2,297 ft) at 3968 kg (8,748 lb); landing run 600 m (1,969 ft) at normal landing weight

---

SOKO J-20 Kraguj

After a 20-year period of service, SOKO's **J-20 Kraguj** lightweight close support aircraft was retired by the Yugoslav air force in 1990, a few survivors being then passed to the Slovenian national guard. These were, however, repossessed by the JRV before Slovenia broke away, in June 1991, from the former Yugoslavian confederation.

The single-seat Kraguj has a built-in armament of two 7.7-mm machine-guns and six wing hardpoints for bombs, rocket pods or other light weapon loads. Bosnian Serb militia have used the Kraguj in the civil war against the Moslem and Croat forces.

SPECIFICATION

SOKO J-20 Kraguj
Wing: span 10.64 m (34 ft 11 in); aspect ratio 6.66; area 17.00 m² (182.99 sq ft)
Fuselage and tail: length 7.93 m (26 ft 0.25 in); height 3.00 m (9 ft 10 in); tailplane span 3.04 m (10 ft 0 in)
Powerplant: one Textron Lycoming GSO-480-B1A6 piston engine rated at 340 hp (253.3 kW)
Weights: empty equipped 1130 kg (2,491 lb); maximum take-off 1624 kg (3,580 lb)
Fuel and load: internal fuel 240 litres (63.4 US gal)
Speed: maximum level speed 'clean' at 1500 m (4,920 ft) 295 km/h (159 kt; 183 mph); maximum cruising speed at 1500 m (4,920 ft) 280 km/h

This J-20 Kraguj displays some of the stores available for its close support role. The type remains in limited service with Bosnian Serb militia forces in 1994.

(151 kt; 174 mph)
Range: 432 nm (497 miles; 800 km)
Performance: maximum rate of climb at sea level 480 m (1,575 ft) per minute; take-off run 110 m (361 ft) at normal take-off weight; landing run 120 m (394 ft) at maximum landing weight

SOKO (Eurocopter) SA 342 Gazelle/Partizan

After taking delivery of 21 **SA 341H** Gazelles from Aérospatiale in 1972/1973, Yugoslavia obtained a licence for Gazelle production by SOKO at Mostar. Production of 132 SA 341Hs was followed by approximately the same number of **SA 342L**s, which is a military variant with higher weights. Known as **Partizan** in Yugoslavia, the Gazelles served principally with the **Yugoslav air force** (JRV) and in small numbers with the navy and army.

SOKO developed the armed **GAMA** model of the Gazelle for anti-tank duties. This can carry four AT-3 Maljutka missiles on twin rail assemblies on the pylons on either side of the fuselage, aimed by a roof-mounted sight. Between each pair of 'Saggers' can be carried an SA 7 Strela 2M AAM for anti-helicopter work. The anti-tank Gazelles are supplemented by the **HERA** version, which serves in the observation role. Typically, operational squadrons of Partizans fly four each of the GAMA, HERA and liaison versions.

Gazelles of the JRV participated in the various conflicts that followed the break-up of the Yugoslav federation. As a consequence of these activities, one SA 341H became the nucleus in June 1991 of the **Slovenian Territorial Defence Force**, and at least one was in the hands of the newly-formed **Croatian air force**. Most are concentrated with **Serb**ian forces.

SPECIFICATION

SOKO (Aérospatiale) SA 342L-1 GAMA
generally similar to the Aérospatiale SA 341L-1 Gazelle

SOKO assembled more than 250 Gazelles and has developed two distinct variants to serve in anti-tank (GAMA) and observation (HERA) duties.

SOKO/IAv Craiova J-22 Orao/IAR-93

The **SOKO/IAv Craiova J-22 Orao/IAR-93** is the product of an unlikely collaborative agreement between Yugoslavia and Romania. Both nations had a requirement for a lightweight but robust transonic close-support/ground-attack aircraft with secondary interceptor and reconnaissance capabilities, to enter service around 1977. Construction was allocated to two companies: Romania's CNIAR (now IAv Craiova) and SOKO in Yugoslavia.

The aircraft emerged with a configuration reminiscent of the larger SEPECAT Jaguar. It features a shoulder-mounted wing of similar planform and a similar sturdy undercarriage. SOKO had gained experience of building the Rolls-Royce Viper turbojet under licence for other military aircraft, and selected non-afterburning Turbomécanica/ORAO Viper Mk 632-41Rs as powerplants. These are mounted side-by-side in the rear fuselage and are each rated at 17.79 kN (4,000 lb st). Reheat was considered a desirable option for production aircraft, however.

Single-seat and two-seat prototypes were constructed in each country, and these made simultaneous first flights on 31 October 1974 and 29 January 1977 (two-seaters). Manufacture of pre-production batches of 15 aircraft then began in both countries, and the first of these made their maiden flights in late 1978.

Series production of the Romanian **IAR-93** followed in 1979, and of the Yugoslavian **J-22 Orao** (Eagle) in 1980. Continued non-availability of afterburners meant that the first 20 production aircraft in each country were delivered without reheat.

The first Romanian version of the aircraft was the non-afterburning **IAR-93A**, which made its maiden flight in 1981. CNIAR built 26 single-seaters and 10 two-seat trainers with an extended forward fuselage and sideways-opening canopies. The following **IAR-93B** variant first flew in 1985 and introduced afterburning Viper Mk 633-41 turbojets. It also featured wing leading-edge root extensions but lacked inboard wing fences. IAR-93Bs, and two-seat IAR-93As, lack ventral fins. Interestingly, single-seat IAR-93Bs feature a manually operated sideways-opening canopy, whereas all other single-seaters have an upward-hinging, electrically actuated canopy. Romania ordered 165 Oraos, including two-seaters.

Production variants

In Yugoslavia, the first production variant was the **Orao 1**, powered (like the IAR-93A and pre-series aircraft) by non-afterburning Vipers, as a result of the continuing problems with developing an afterburner. The lack of performance of these early production aircraft was such that they were allocated to the tactical reconnaissance role under the designation **IJ-22**. A handful of the batch of 20 aircraft appeared as two-seat trainers designated **NJ-22**. These aircraft still equip a photo reconnaissance *eskadrilla* based near Zagreb.

The Orao 1 was followed by the single-seat **Orao 2** or **J-22(M)**, with enlarged integral wing fuel tanks, and with increased capacity in two fuselage tanks. Afterburning Viper 633-41 engines made possible a small increase in payload. The Orao 2 also has a Thomson-CSF HUD. The prototype flew for the first time on 20 October 1983 and the new variant entered production in late 1984, but by mid-1985 there were 16 complete aircraft awaiting reheated engines. These eventually arrived and the aircraft began to enter service in 1986.

The two-seat Orao 1 proved to be somewhat underpowered and short-legged, and SOKO therefore designed a new two-seat trainer incorporating the more powerful engines and the increased-capacity wing tanks of the Orao 2. The first example of the new **Orao 2D**, or **NJ-22(M)**, made its maiden flight on 18 July 1986, and production 2Ds have been augmented by a conversion programme bringing all surviving Orao 1 two-seaters up to the same standard. Like the Orao 2, the 2D has the same wing LERXes as are fitted to the IAR-93B.

By 1994, the Orao 2 was operated by the following **Serbian air force** units: the 92nd Aviation Brigade (AB) at Banja Luka, the 98th AB at Petrovac and the 172 Fighter-Attack Squadron at Batajnica. In **Romania**, the IAR-93B was in service with the 67th Regiment at Craiova.

WEAPON OPTIONS

The IAR-93/Orao is equipped with two GSh-23L twin-barrelled 23-mm cannon mounted in the forward fuselage. The Orao 1 has five weapons pylons, one under the fuselage and two under the inner wings stressed to carry up to 500 kg (1,102 lb), and two outboard pylons for stores of up to 300 kg (660 lb). The outboard pylons of the Orao 2 are stressed for loads of up to 500 kg (1,102 lb), while the fuselage pylon on this variant can carry up to 800 kg (1,763 lb). Oraos can carry a range of stores including AGM-65 Maverick and Grom (an indigenous version of the AS-7 'Kerry') ASMs and Durandal penetration bombs.

SPECIFICATION

SOKO/CNIAR (now SOKO/Avioane) J-22 Orao
Wing: span 9.30 m (30 ft 6.25 in); aspect ratio 3.33; area 26.00 m² (279.87 sq ft)
Fuselage and tail: length 14.90 m (48 ft 10.625 in) including probe; height 4.52 m (14 ft 10 in); tailplane span 4.59 m (15 ft 0.75 in); wheel track 2.50 m (8 ft 2.5 in); wheel base 5.40 m (17 ft 8.5 in)
Powerplant: two Turbomécanica/ORAO-built Rolls-Royce Viper Mk 632-41R turbojets each rated at 4,000 lb st (17.79 kN) dry or, in most aircraft, two Turbomécanica/ORAO-built Rolls-Royce Viper Mk 633-41 each rated at 4,000 lb st (17.79 kN) dry and 5,000 lb st (22.24 kN) with afterburning
Weights: empty equipped 5500 kg (12,125 lb); normal take-off 8170 kg (18,012 lb); maximum take-off 11080 kg (24,427 lb)
Fuel and load: internal fuel 2430 kg (5,357 lb); external fuel up to 1500 kg (3,307 lb) in three 500-litre (132-US gal) drop tanks; maximum ordnance 2800 kg (6,173 lb)
Speed: maximum level speed 'clean' at 11000 m (36,090 ft) 1020 km/h (551 kt; 634 mph) and at sea level 1130 km/h (610 kt; 702 mph); maximum cruising speed at 11000 m (36,090 ft) 743 km/h (401 kt; 462 mph)
Range: ferry range 712 nm (820 miles; 1320 km) with two drop tanks; combat radius 282 km (324 nm; 522 miles) on a hi-lo-hi attack mission with four cluster bombs and one drop tank, or 248 nm (286 miles; 460 km) on a hi-lo-hi attack mission with four 500-kg (1,102-lb) air mines and one drop tank, or 200 nm (230 miles; 370 km) on a hi-lo-hi attack mission with eight 250-kg (551-lb) bombs and one drop tank
Performance: maximum rate of climb at sea level 5340 m (17,520 ft) per minute; climb to 6000 m (19,685 ft) in 1 minute 20 seconds; service ceiling 15000 m (49,210 ft); take-off run 880 m (2,888 ft) with four cluster bombs; take-off distance to 15 m (50 ft) 1255 m (4,118 ft) at normal take-off weight; landing distance from 15 m (50 ft) 1295 m (4,249 ft) at normal landing weight; landing run 755 m (2,477 ft) at normal landing weight without brake chute or 530 m (1,739 ft) at normal landing weight with brake chute
g limits: -4.2 to +8

This early IAR-93A (note wing fences and ventral fins) wears the original Romanian air force insignia. The IAR-93As were virtually identical to early J-22 Oraos, differing only in minor avionics items.

One of the 20 J-22 Orao 1s taxis in after a sortie, still trailing its brake chute. These aircraft were powered by non-afterburning Viper engines and have been relegated to reconnaissance duties with an eskadrilla near Zagreb. They are equipped with a centreline camera pod, as seen here.

The range and power shortcomings of the two-seat Orao 1 were rectified by the improved Orao 2 trainer. This Orao 1 two-seater has been brought up to Orao 2D standards with the extended leading edges of the Orao 2, and afterburning engines, but retaining the original four-fence outer wing.

Sperry/North American QF-86 Sabre

North American Aviation Inc., established in 1928, merged with the Rockwell-Standard Corporation in September 1967 to form the North American Rockwell Corporation

Undeniably one of the great warplanes of history, the **North American F-86 Sabre** is now used primarily as a drone by the **US Navy**. Surplus USAF/ANG **F-86H** aircraft provided the initial basis for conversion, but the only version in current use is the **QF-86F**, primarily ex-JASDF and -RoKAF aircraft converted to drone status under a programme managed by Sperry. Although Sabres are expended during live missile tests, the US Navy maintains sufficient stocks to keep the type in service for some years yet. The two operating units are at Point Mugu and China Lake in California, both part of the Naval Air Warfare Center/Weapons Division.

Elsewhere, Sabres are used as civilian 'warbirds' on the air show circuit, but a handful continue in use for military duties. **Corporate Jets Inc.** operates a pair of Orenda 14-engined Canadair-assembled

Sabre Mk 6s as target tugs from Decimomannu, Sardinia, operating occasionally from other NATO air bases. Grupo Aéreo de Caza 32 of the **Fuerza Aérea Boliviana** at Santa Cruz retains the F-86E, but these are seldom flown, pilots instead using the T-33 to maintain currency.

SPECIFICATION

Sperry (North American) QF-86F Sabre
Wing: span 38 ft 9.5 in (11.82 m); aspect ratio 4.8; area 313.40 sq ft (29.12 m2)
Fuselage and tail: length 37 ft 6 in (11.43 m); height 14 ft 8.75 in (4.49 m)
Powerplant: one General Electric J47-GE-27 turbojet rated at 5,970 lb st (26.56 kN)
Weights: empty 11,125 lb (5046 kg); normal take-off 15,198 lb (6893 kg)
Speed: maximum level speed 'clean' at sea level

589 kt (678 mph) 1091 km/h)
Performance: maximum rate of climb at sea level 9,800 ft (2987 m) per minute

A Corporate Jets Canadair-manufactured Sabre Mk 6 taxies out for a gunnery training hop, carrying an underwing target winch.

Sperry/Tracor/North American QF-100 Super Sabre

The **F-100** was a stalwart of the USAF for many years. A total of 340 was earmarked for conversion to drone status for use in air defence exercises and missile tests. The first 100 were **QF-100D**s converted by Sperry, but subsequent conversions, including some two-seat **QF-100F** aircraft, have been undertaken by **Tracor Flight Systems** at Mojave, CA. This total included ex-Turkish and ex-USAF aircraft.

QF-100s can be flown in piloted or pilotless ('nolo' – no live operator) mode, and many have been expended by the two **USAF** operating units (the 6585th TG at Holloman AFB, NM, and the 82nd Tactical Aerial Targets Squadron of the 475th Weapons Evaluation Group at Tyndall AFB). QF-106 and QF-4 drones are replacing the QF-100s.

SPECIFICATION

Sperry (North American) QF-100 Super Sabre
Wing: span 38 ft 9.5 in (11.82 m); aspect ratio 3.91; area 385.00 sq ft (35.77 m2)
Fuselage and tail: length excluding probe 47 ft

1.25 in (14.357 m); height 16 ft 2.67 in (4.945 m)
Powerplant: one Pratt & Whitney J57-P-21A turbojet rated at 11,700 lb st (52.04 kN) dry and 16,950 lb st (75.4 kN) with afterburning

Weights: mission take-off 31,000 lb (14062 kg)
Fuel and load: internal fuel 770 US gal (2915 litres); external fuel two 450-US gal (1703-litre) drop tanks
Speed: maximum level speed 'clean' at 36,000 ft

(10975 m) 750 kt (864 mph; 1390 km/h) and at sea level 669 kt (770 mph; 1239 km/h)
Range: typical range 521 nm (600 miles; 966 km); operational radius 120 nm (138 miles; 222 km) under radar control; endurance between 40 and 55 minutes
Performance: maximum rate of climb at sea level 16,550 ft (5045 m) per minute; service ceiling 50,000 ft (15240 m); minimum operating height 200 ft (60 m)

The 475th WEG at Tyndall 'flies' target drones on behalf of the AWDC, and in support of William Tell gunnery/missile competitions. QF-100s wear high-visibility orange wingtips, noses, tailfins and tailplanes, and are fitted with underwing pylons for chaff/flare dispensers and propane burners to increase IR signature.

Sukhoi Su-7 'Fitter-A/B'

Sukhoi Design Bureau Aviation Scientific-Industrial Complex,
23A Polikarpov Street,
Moscow 125284, Russia

From December 1949, the Sukhoi OKB was closed on the orders of Stalin to punish Sukhoi for the failure of a jet fighter prototype. Sukhoi and his team transferred to Tupolev, where they worked on their own projects until the death of Stalin, when permission was given to reopen the bureau. During his time at Tupolev, Sukhoi had worked on two configurations which he dubbed S (swept wing, 60-62° sweep) and T (delta wing, 57-60° sweep). All subsequent prototypes were numerically designated with an S- or T- prefix.

The first product of the reopened bureau was the **S-1**, prototype of the **Su-7**. This was designed as an air-to-air fighter, but the existence of the smaller, more agile MiG-21 prompted a redesign for the ground attack role. The resulting **S-2** was followed by a series of pre-production aircraft, culminating in the **S-22** which formed the basis of the production **Su-7B** (Bombardirovschkik, or fighter-bomber). Powered by a Lyul'ka AL-7 turbojet and with a variable shock cone in the pitot intake, the Su-7 was capable of speeds of up to Mach 1.6, but fuel consumption was excessive, and even with two underfuselage fuel tanks radius of action was unimpressive.

The Su-7B was armed with a pair of Nudelmann Richter NR-30 cannon in the wingroots, and had a retractable box con-

taining 32 spin-stabilised rockets in the belly. UV-8-32 rocket pods could be carried under each wing. The rocket box was deleted in the **Su-7BM** which followed, and which introduced the more powerful 99.12-kN (22,282-lb st) Lyul'ka AL-7F-1 engine. Underwing pylons were restressed for loads of up to 500 kg (1,102 lb) and were plumbed for the carriage of fuel tanks. The avionics were improved, and a pair of side-by-side cable ducts was added above the fuselage. The pitot probe gained yaw vanes and was moved from the top of the intake to a '10 o'clock' position. The designation

Su-7BMK was applied to an export version.

In order to improve rough-field capability, Sukhoi developed the **Su-7BKL**, which became the standard version in **VVS** service. This introduced provision for SPRD-110 assisted take-off rockets, a new brake chute fairing at the base of the tailfin which housed new twin brake parachutes, and also featured redesigned trailing-edge flaps. The undercarriage was redesigned, with a new low-pressure nosewheel which necessitated the provision of bulged nosewheel doors, and the addition of small skis on shock struts outboard of each mainwheel. These could

be extended to bear almost the full weight of the aircraft on soft ground, or retracted when operating from a hard surface.

Two-seat trainer versions were designated **Su-7U** and **Su-7UM** (based on the BM airframe) and received the NATO reporting name **'Moujik'**. Su-7BMs and Su-7Us remain in service in **Algeria** and perhaps in **Iraq**, and Su-7BKLs may serve in **North Korea**. In early 1994, the **Czech** and **Slovak Republics** still had a handful of Su-7s on charge, probably as ground instructional airframes.

In the former Soviet Union, a handful of Su-7s remain in service for test duties. This Su-7U was used as an ejection seat test aircraft, with the test seat (and an instrumented dummy) in the rear cockpit.

401

SPECIFICATION

Sukhoi Su-7BMK 'Fitter-A'
Wing: span 8.93 m (29 ft 3.5 in); aspect ratio 2.89; area 27.60 m² (297.09 sq ft)
Fuselage and tail: length 17.37 m (57 ft 0 in)

including probe; height 4.57 m (15 ft 0 in)
Powerplant: one NPO Saturn (Lyul'ka) AL-7F-1 turbojet rated at 68.65 kN (15,432 lb st) dry and 99.12 kN (22,282 lb st) with afterburning
Weights: empty equipped 8620 kg (19,004 lb); normal take-off 12000 kg (26,455 lb); maximum take-off 13500 kg (29,762 lb)

Fuel and load: internal fuel 2350 kg (5,181 lb); external fuel up to two 600-litre (158.5-US gal) and two 1800- or 900-litre (457.5- or 237.75-US gal) drop tanks; maximum ordnance 2500 kg (5,511 lb)
Speed: maximum level speed 'clean' at 11000 m (36,090 ft) 1700 km/h (916 kt; 1,055 mph) and at sea level 1350 km/h (729 kt; 840 mph)

Range: ferry range 1450 km (782 nm; 901 miles) with drop tanks; combat radius 345 km (186 nm; 214 miles) on a hi-lo-hi attack mission with a 1000-kg (2,205-lb) warload and two drop tanks
Performance: maximum rate of climb at sea level about 9120 m (29,920 ft) per minute; service ceiling 15150 m (49,705 ft); take-off run 880 m (2,887 ft)

Sukhoi **Su-15 'Flagon'**

The career of the **Sukhoi Su-15 'Flagon'** is drawing to a close, with only a handful of **PVO** regiments remaining active in Ukraine, Siberia and other remote regions. The type has been replaced by more modern interceptors, including the Su-27 and the MiG-31.

The Su-15 was of enormous importance, serving as the standard PVO interceptor at

bases across the length and breadth of the former USSR. When the Korean Airlines Boeing 747 (Flight KE007) was shot down in September 1983, after overflying the Kamchatka Peninsula, it was no surprise that the fighter involved was an Su-15.

Of similar configuration to the earlier Su-9 and Su-11, the Su-15 was a larger aircraft, powered by twin R-25 engines and

Sukhoi Su-15TM 'Flagon-F'

This Sukhoi Su-15UM 'Flagon-G' is one of those used by the LII Gromov Flight Research Centre at Zhukhovskii for test and trials work. A handful of two-seat 'Flagons' also remain in use to support the dwindling number of PVO Su-15 interceptors.

with a large search radar occupying the nose, necessitating the use of separate lateral air intakes on each side of the fuselage.

The prototype, designated **T-58**, first flew in 1961 in the hands of Vladimir Ilyushin, and was followed by a pre-production batch of similar aircraft, designated **Su-15** and allocated the reporting name **'Flagon-A'** by NATO. The reporting name **'Flagon-B'** was allocated to the **T-58VD**, a one-off STOL research aircraft with a redesigned wing having reduced span on the outer panels, and with three RD-36-35 lift jets in the fuselage. This made its maiden flight during 1966 and was demonstrated at Domodyedovo in July 1967. The **Su-15U** was a tandem two-seat trainer version of the basic fighter, with the instructor's cockpit in place of the No. 1 fuselage fuel tank and with separate upward-hinging canopies over the cockpits. This trainer variant was dubbed **'Flagon-C'** by NATO.

The first 'second-generation' Su-15 was the **Su-15M**, which introduced a new wing based on that of the T-58VD with extended ailerons, and a tailplane with reduced anhedral. This was called **'Flagon-D'** by NATO.

'Flagon-E', introduced in 1973, superseded the earlier variant. This was powered by a pair of R-13F-300 engines, and featured increased internal fuel capacity. To cope with the increased weight, the undercarriage was strengthened, and a new twin-wheel nose gear was introduced, with bulged doors. Extra underwing pylons allowed the carriage of up to four R-60s (AA-8 'Aphids') in addition to the K-8 (AA-3 'Anab') missiles on the outboard pylons. Alternatively, each underfuselage pylon was stressed for the UPK-23-250 cannon pod or

an external fuel tank.

The **Su-15TM 'Flagon-F'** introduced the Taifun radar, which required a shorter ogival radome in place of the conical radome fitted to earlier variants. It was powered by a pair of R-13F2-300 engines and entered service during 1974. The two-seat trainer version with Taifun radar and the new wing is designated **Su-15UM**, and has the reporting name **'Flagon-G'**.

Western speculation that the designation **Su-21** was applied to the later 'Flagons' has since proved incorrect.

In 1994 a confirmed Su-15 user is **Ukraine**, which has two units operational. These are the 62nd Fighter Aviation Regiment at Bel'bek and the 636th Fighter Aviation Regiment at Kramatorsk.

SPECIFICATION

Sukhoi Su-15TM 'Flagon-F'
Wing: span 10.53 m (34 ft 6.6 in); aspect ratio 3.08; wing area 36.00 m² (387.51 sq ft)
Fuselage and tail: length 20.50 m (67 ft 3.1 in); height 5.00 m (16 ft 5 in); tailplane span 6.10 m (20 ft 0.2 in)
Powerplant: two MNPK 'Soyuz' (Tumanskii) R-13F2-300 turbojets each rated at 40.21 kN (9,039 lb st) dry and 69.63 kN (15,653 lb st) with afterburning
Weights: empty 12250 kg (27,006 lb); normal take-off 18000 kg (39,683 lb); maximum take-off 20000 kg (44,092 lb)
Speed: maximum level speed 'clean' at 11000 m (36,090 ft) 2655 km/h (1,433 kt; 1,650 mph)
Range: ferry range 2250 km (1,214 nm; 1,398 miles) with drop tanks; combat radius 745 km (371 nm; 450 miles) on a hi-hi-hi interception mission
Performance: maximum rate of climb at sea level 13700 m (44,948 ft) per minute; service ceiling 20000 m (65,615 ft); take-off run about 460 m (1,509 ft) at MTOW

Sukhoi **Su-17/-20 'Fitter-C'**

While the original Su-7 'Fitter' was highly prized for its handling, robust and rugged airframe and outright performance, it proved deficient in range and short take-off/landing capability. It was decided to produce an improved version with a variable-geometry wing. Sukhoi used the same TSAGI-developed VG wing configuration as Tupolev used for the Tu-22M, with pivots outboard. This allowed the existing wing-mounted main undercarriage to be retained and minimised shifting of the centre of lift as the wing swept. Vladimir Ilyushin flew the **S-22I** (also known as the **Su-7IG**) for the first time on 2 August 1966, and it was publicly displayed at Domodyedovo in July 1967. The Su-7IG was assumed by many

Western observers to be a mere VG research aircraft, and not the effective prototype for a new swing-wing fighter-bomber, although it was allocated the NATO reporting name **'Fitter-B'**.

The Su-7IG (a converted Su-7BMK) was followed by two squadrons worth of pre-production **Su-17**s (with the OKB designation **S-32**). These had a longer forward fuselage based on that of the Su-7U and a large, bulged fuselage spine like the definitive **'Fitter-C'**, but retained the external cable ducts of the Su-7BM and BMK/BKL, and probably retained the same AL-7F-1 engine rated at 68.64 kN (15,432 lb st). The first series production variant was designated **Su-17M** (OKB designation **S-32M**)

and shared the same NATO reporting name of 'Fitter-C'. The Su-17M differed primarily in that it featured the 20 per cent more powerful (and more fuel efficient) AL-21F-3 engine rated at 110.32 kN (24,802 lb st), and introduced a new nav/attack system, which received inputs from twin nose-mounted pitot booms.

An AoA vane (located on the port side of the cockpit) helps the 'Fitter-C' to land some 62 mph (100 km/h) slower than the Su-7BMK, reducing the requirement for very heavy braking and allowing a single brake chute to replace the original Su-7's twin chutes. Nine hardpoints are provided: one on the centreline, tandem pairs on the fuselage 'shoulders' and pairs under the fixed inboard wing sections.

A handful of 'Fitter-Cs' were built for reconnaissance duties, with provision for mounting a variety of multi-sensor reconnaissance pods, under the designation **Su-17R** or **Su-20R**.

OPERATORS

'Fitter-Cs' remain in front-line service in Poland and, under the export designation **Su-20** (OKB designation **S-32MK**), were delivered to Afghanistan, Algeria, Angola, Egypt, Iraq, North Korea, Syria and Vietnam.

Initial deliveries to Poland of the variable-geometry 'Fitter' were of the Su-20 'Fitter-C' version, powered by the Lyul'ka AL-21 turbojet. Su-20s remain in service with a regiment based at Pila, in north-west Poland.

Two ex-Egyptian Su-20s were delivered to Germany in 1985 for evaluation. Soviet Su-17 'Fitter-Cs' have probably been retired.

SPECIFICATION

Sukhoi Su-17M 'Fitter-C'
Wing: span 13.80 m (45 ft 3 in) spread and 10.00 m (32 ft 10 in) swept; aspect ratio 4.8 spread and 2.7 swept; area about 40.00 m² (430.57 sq ft) and about 37.00 m² (398.28 sq ft) swept
Fuselage and tail: length 18.75 m (61 ft 6.25 in) including probes; height 5.00 m (16 ft 5 in)
Powerplant: one NPO Saturn (Lyul'ka) AL-21F-3 turbojet rated at 76.49 kN (17,196 lb st) dry and 110.32 kN (24,802 lb st) with afterburning, plus provision for two RATO units
Weights: normal take-off 16400 kg (36,155 lb); maximum take-off 19500 kg (42,989 lb)
Fuel and load: internal fuel 4550 litres (1,202 US gal); external fuel up to four 800-litre (211-US gal) drop tanks; maximum ordnance 4250 kg (9,369 lb) theoretical and 1000 kg (2,205 lb) practical when drop tanks are carried
Speed: maximum level speed 'clean' at 11000 m (36,090 ft) 2220 km/h (1,198 kt; 1,379 mph) and at sea level 1285 km/h (693 kt; 798 mph)
Range: 2300 km (1,240 nm; 1,430 miles) at high altitude or 1400 km (755 nm; 870 miles) at low altitude; combat radius 685 km (370 nm; 426 miles) on a hi-lo-hi attack mission with a 2000-kg (4,409-lb) warload, or 445 km (241 nm; 277 miles) on a lo-lo-lo attack mission with a 2000-kg (4,409-lb) warload
Performance: maximum rate of climb at sea level 13800 m (45,276 ft) per minute; service ceiling 15200 m (49,870 ft); take-off run 900 m (2,953 ft) at maximum take-off weight; landing run 950 m (3,117 ft) at maximum landing weight

Sukhoi Su-17M-2/-3/-22M-3 'Fitter-D/-F-/H/-J'

Known to the OKB as the **S-32M2**, the **Su-17M-2D 'Fitter-D'** entered production in 1974. Based on the airframe of the 'Fitter-C', it introduced a slightly lengthened, slightly drooping nose and a revised avionics suite. The Su-7's SRD-5M ranging radar was finally abandoned, and the intake centrebody was fixed in one position instead of being able to move in and out. This had little effect except on absolute Mach number attainable at high level. The conical centrebody now served as the location of a Klem laser rangefinder (which probably also functions as a marked target seeker). A fairing was added below the nose to accommodate the new Doppler and, according to some reports, a terrain-avoidance radar. The latter seems unlikely.

A slightly sanitised version, with a new dorsal fin fillet and possibly without a laser rangefinder, was built for export under the designation **Su-17M-2K** (or **S-32M-2K**). The **'Fitter-F'** was powered by a Tumanskii/Khatchaturov R-29BS-300 engine (as fitted to some MiG-23 variants) and thus required a slightly bulged, slightly shortened rear fuselage. Operators have included **Angola**, **Libya** and **Peru**.

The S-32M-2 was soon replaced by the **Su-22M-3**, which was based on the airframe of the two-seat **'Fitter-G'** trainer (described separately). The Su-22M-3 featured the same deepened forward fuselage and tall, squared-off tailfin and removable

Tyres stream clouds of smoke as an Su-22M-3 'Fitter-H' lands at Taszar, making a characteristically heavy, no-flare arrival. Hungarian 'Fitter-Hs' serve with the 3rd ('Bumble Bee') squadron of the Kapos wing.

ventral fin, but with two wingroot cannon and only a single cockpit. The deeper fuselage allowed the Doppler to be fitted internally, behind a flush dielectric panel, and the undernose fairing of the S-32M-2 was deleted. To improve self-defence capability, a dedicated AAM launch rail is added beneath each inner wing, between the two existing pylons, and this carries an R-60 (AA-8 'Aphid') or K-13 (AA-2 'Atoll') IR-homing AAM. Internal fuel capacity is considerably increased, and can be augmented by up to four external fuel tanks.

Designated **Su-17M-3** in service (NATO reporting name **'Fitter-H'**), the aircraft was delivered only to **Frontal Aviation**. The very similar **Su-22M-3K** (mostly fitted with the R-29BS engine) was exported to **Angola**, **Hungary**, **Libya**, **Peru** and both **Yemen** republics.

SPECIFICATION

Sukhoi Su-17M-2 'Fitter-D'
generally similar to the Sukhoi Su-17M 'Fitter-C'

Variable-geometry wings enable the Su-17's field performance to be kept within acceptable limits. Hungary's 12 'Fitter-Hs' replaced the earlier Su-7.

except in the following particulars:
Fuselage and tail: length 19.13 m (62 ft 9.2 in) including probes
Performance: take-off run 900 m (2,953 ft) at maximum take-off weight

---

Sukhoi Su-17UM-2 'Fitter-E' and Su-17/-22UM-3 'Fitter-G'

The first two-seat 'Fitter' trainer was the **Su-17UM-2D** (bureau designation **U-32**), given the reporting name **'Fitter-E'** by NATO. This was based on the airframe of the Su-17M-2D but with no increase in fuselage length. The fuselage was deepened and 'drooped' and the windscreen was moved forward, giving a better view forward and down. This location of the forward cockpit was to be retained on all subsequent single-seat variants. The port cannon was not fitted, but all avionics, including the laser rangefinder, were retained. The Su-17UM-2D was powered by the Lyul'ka AL-21F-3 engine, while export aircraft, designated **Su-17UM-2K**, used the R-29BS-300, as used in various 'Flogger' variants. The latter type was exported to **Afghanistan**, **Algeria**, **Angola**, **Iraq**, **Libya**, **Peru**, **Vietnam** and both **Yemen** republics.

The next two-seater (given the OKB designation **S-52**) was based on the tall-tailed airframe of the Su-17M-3. The **'Fitter-G'** did not retain full operational capability, having had some avionics items deleted, but is by far the fastest Su-17, being capable of reaching Mach 2.1, while single-seaters are limited to Mach 1.7. The instructor has a sophisticated system for simulating the workings of the weapons delivery system, and generating synthetic emergen-

This Sukhoi Su-17UM 'Fitter-G' was one of those based at Kunmanderas, east of Budapest, which housed a Soviet reconnaissance/EW regiment equipped with Su-24MR 'Fencer-Es' and Su-17M-4 'Fitter-Ks'. Like most single-seat 'Fitter' units, it had a handful of two-seaters on charge for conversion, continuation and instrument training. This aircraft carries ECM pods on its inboard underwing pylons, perhaps indicating an Elint or 'Wild Weasel' role. Long-range fuel tanks are carried outboard.

cies. Those for export customers were all designated **Su-22UM-3K**, those for Afghanistan, Czechoslovakia, East Germany, Hungary, and Poland retaining Lyul'ka engines, the others having the bulged rear fuselage and Tumanskii/Khatchaturov engines. Su-22UM-3Ks were exported to all 'Fitter-H', 'Fitter-J' and 'Fitter-K' operators includ-ing **Afghanistan**, **Angola**, **Czechoslovakia**, **East Germany**, **Hungary**, **Libya**, **Peru**, **Poland**, **Syria** and the **Yemen** republics.

Sukhoi Su-17M-4 and Su-22M-4 'Fitter-K'

Under the OKB designation **S-54**, a new 'Fitter' variant, with new avionics and compatibility with an even wider range of weapons, was developed for the Soviet air forces and for export. The **Su-22M-4 'Fitter-K'** is externally identifiable by a prominent ram-air inlet projecting forward from the finroot. This increases cooling airflow to the afterburner. Ram air inlets on the sides of the rear fuselage were enlarged and repositioned at the same time.

Since the aircraft was optimised for high speed at low level, with no requirement for high-level performance, the intake centrebody is fixed, and a removable ventral fin is fitted below the rear fuselage. (The latter feature has been retrofitted to some earlier 'Fitter-Hs' and 'Fitter-Js'.)

New avionics included a new CVM 20-22 mission computer and PrNK-54 navigation system (using the LORAN-equivalent RSDN and the TACAN-equivalent A-312), which reduced pilot workload and improved navigational and weapons delivery accuracy. Other avionics include a DISS-7 Doppler, a Klem-45 laser rangefinder, an ASP-17BC gunsight, an IKV-8 inertial platform, an ARK-22 radio compass, an SRO-2 IFF system, an SO-69 transponder and an SPO-15LE (Sirena) RWR.

WEAPON OPTIONS

In its primary ground attack role, the Su-22M-4 can carry a wide range of freefall bombs and podded and unpodded unguided rocket projectiles ranging in calibre from 57 mm to 330 mm. For precision attacks from stand-off range, the aircraft can carry a variety of air-to-surface missiles, including the radio command-guided or laser-homing, or anti-radiation Kh-25 (AS-10 'Karen' and AS-12 'Kegler') and Kh-29, and the Kh-58E (AS-11 'Kilter') anti-radar missile. When the latter is used, a box-like BA-58 Vjuga emission location system pod is carried on the centreline. Later Su-22M-4s have a TV display to allow the use of TV-guided missiles, and this can be retrofitted to earlier aircraft.

The new variant has the auxiliary underwing AAM pylon also seen on some 'Fitter-Hs', located between the two normal underwing pylons. This is normally used to carry an R-60 (AA-8 'Aphid') IR-homing air-to-air missile, but can also take a K-13 (AA-2 'Atoll'). To further improve self-defence capability, four 32-round upward-firing ASO chaff/flare dispensers can be scabbed on to either side of the tailfin, augmenting

This sharkmouthed 20th Guards Fighter-Bomber Regiment Su-17M-4 was based at Templin in the former East Germany until May 1994. It departed for Taganrog on the Black Sea and may possibly be reallocated to the AV-MF.

the two six-tube KDS-23 dispensers mounted flush with the dorsal spine.

For strafe attacks, the Su-22M-4's wingroot-mounted NR-30 30-mm cannon (each with 80 rounds) can be augmented by gun pods carried under the wings or fuselage. These can include the SPPU-22-01 (with 260 rounds), whose twin 23-mm barrels can be depressed, and which can be mounted facing forward or aft. The 'Fitter-K' can be used in the tactical reconnaissance role, carrying the same KKR

reconnaissance pod as has been applied to the 'Fitter-C' and 'Fitter-H'. This contains three optical cameras, flares and Elint modules, and is usually carried in association with the SPS ECM pod.

SPECIFICATION

Sukhoi Su-17M-4 'Fitter-K'
generally similar to the Sukhoi Su-17M 'Fitter-C' except in the following particulars:
Speed: maximum level speed 'clean' at sea level 1400 km/h (756 nm; 870 mph)
Range: combat radius 1150 km (621 nm; 715 miles) on a hi-lo-hi attack mission with a 2000-kg (4,409-lb) warload, or 700 km (378 nm; 435 miles) on a lo-lo-lo attack mission with a 2000-kg (4,409-lb) warload
Performance: service ceiling 15200 m (49,870 ft)

Afghanistan received a number of Su-22M-4s which were probably directly transferred from the Soviet Union. A disaffected pilot flew this 'Fitter-K' to Pakistan.

OPERATORS
'Fitter-Ks' are in widespread service with a number of air forces in the former Soviet Union. In Ukraine, about 130 serve with regiments at Ovruch and Limanskoye. Less than five aircraft each are operational with Azerbaijan and Byelorussia. More 'Fitter-Ks' are in service with Turkmenistan. The Su-22M-4 was exported to Poland, Czechoslovakia, the former East Germany and Afghanistan.

CAMOUFLAGE
Polish air force Su-22M-4s wear an effective green and brown colour scheme.

Sukhoi Su-22M-4 'Fitter-K'

This 'Fitter-K' wears the colourful markings of the Polskie Wojska Lotnicze (Polish air force). The 'Fitter-K' is the latest and most advanced 'Fitter', with much improved avionics and equipment. The aircraft appears to be fitted with the new K-36D seat, as used by the MiG-29 and Su-27.

DEFENSIVE ARMAMENT
Although its twin 30-mm cannon are primarily intended for strafing ground targets, they can be used against airborne targets ranging from enemy helicopters to opposing fighters. Additionally, the aircraft has the extra AAM pylons originally fitted to the Su-22M-3, carrying K-13 (AA 2 'Atoll'), R-60 (AA-8 'Aphid') and perhaps R-73 (AA-11 'Archer') IR homing AAMs.

SWING WINGS
Sukhoi adopted an outboard pivoting VG configuration (with a large wing glove and relatively small wing panels) to minimise the shift in aerodynamic centre as the wings sweep. It also allows fixed hardpoints to be mounted below the wing, and gives a suitably wide-track undercarriage.

WEAPON OPTIONS
The 'Fitter-K' retains eight dedicated weapons pylons, and these are used to carry a variety of stores, including the Type S-24 240-mm rocket, GSh-23L 23-mm cannon pods, UV-32-57 rocket pods, chemical weapons and the full range of 100-, 200-, 500- and even 1000-kg (220-, 440-, 1,102- or 2,204-lb) bombs, cluster, anti-runway, slick, retarded, incendiary or even tanks full of FAE or nuclear weapons.

ENGINE INSTALLATION
The 'Fitter-K' is powered by a Lyul'ka AL-21F-3 turbojet, but this is given increased cooling through a number of vents and intakes, most noticeably at the base of the fin.

Sukhoi **Su-24 'Fencer-A/-B/-C'**

The increasing efficiency of SAMs and interceptors led aircraft designers all over the world to the same conclusion. To penetrate enemy defences one would have to fly 'under the radar' at very low altitude, using terrain masking to hide from probing radars. The Sukhoi OKB was entrusted with the task of developing such a bomber as a replacement for the Ilyushin Il-28 and Yak-28 in Soviet service.

The requirement was extremely ambitious, calling for an aircraft with supersonic performance (even at low level), capable of day and night/adverse weather operation, and able to find and attack fixed and mobile targets with pinpoint accuracy using manual and automatic control modes. Furthermore, the aircraft was expected to be able to undertake a secondary photographic reconnaissance role, and to destroy enemy transport, liaison and observation aircraft using IR-homing AAMs or its built-in cannon. Mindful of the vulnerability of long fixed runways, the requirement also specified that the aircraft should be able to operate from unpaved airstrips of limited size.

The latter part of the requirement led Sukhoi to develop a delta-winged VTOL bomber, with separate cruise and lift engines. This was built as the **T-6-1** and first flew in June 1967. The wing was of compound leading-edge sweep, and was based on the planform used by the T-58VD. This aircraft proved unsuccessful, and planned participation at Domodyedovo was cancelled because of the aircraft's atrocious handling characteristics. The aircraft was later converted to STOL configuration, with the lift jets removed, and with downturned wingtips, prominent ventral fins and enormous new slotted flaps. The vertical tailfin was also shortened, cut off immediately above the top of the rudder. In its later configuration the aircraft proved more practical, and bore some resemblance to the British BAC TSR.Mk 2, but the large size of the wing gave a poor low-level ride. "It was like being dragged across a washboard," complained one Sukhoi test pilot.

The success of the S-22I (Su-17) and Mikoyan 23-11 pointed the way forward, which was to adopt a variable-geometry wing. This was applied to a second T-6 prototype (the **T-6-2IG**), retaining the same basic fuselage and equipment. The vertical fin was restored to its original height, and the main undercarriage doors were modified to serve as airbrakes. The removal of the heavy lift jets from the centre fuselage left space for extra fuel or weapons. The wing, like that of the broadly contemporary F-111, incorporated similar full-span leading-edge slats and double-slotted flaps. Ailerons are not fitted, the Su-24 being controlled in roll by the all-moving tailerons. The wing can be swept forward to 16° for take-off

and landing, giving an approach speed of 124 kt (230 km/h; 143 mph) and consequent good STOL capability. At the other extreme the wing can be swept fully back to 69° (compared to the F-111's 72½°), with intermediate settings of 35° and 45°. The aircraft made its maiden flight during May 1970 and may have been powered by a pair of AL-7F-1 turbojets. It was given the cover designation **Su-15M**, and mistranslation of this led to initial Western reports erroneously referring to the aircraft as the **Su-19**.

The production **Su-24 'Fencer-A'** was powered by a pair of Perm/Soloviev AL-21F-3 turbofans. These were originally fed by intakes with variable ramps, which allowed Mach 2.18 performance at high level. Because the Su-24 spends its entire life at low level, where such Mach numbers are impossible, the actuators have since been removed to save weight and reduce maintenance requirements. This disables the variable intakes and restricts top speed to about Mach 1.35, but has virtually no effect on low-level performance.

The Su-24 was designed around the Soviet Union's first integrated avionics system, with a bombsight, weapons control system and navigation complex linked by computer. This made possible major weight savings, but required huge advances in processing speed and capacity. The total system allowed fully automatic terrain-following flight and facilitated automatic attacks. The Su-24 was also the first Soviet aircraft to be equipped with the zero-zero Severin K-36D ejection seat, and also featured a command ejection system which could be actuated by either crew member. This

allowed the minimum time separation between ejections while still ensuring that seat collisions could not occur.

Relatively minor changes in equipment fit resulted in the allocation of new NATO reporting names, although the Soviet designation remained the same, and NATO's different variants were probably regarded in the USSR as a single sub-type, albeit with minor differences in equipment. The **'Fencer-B'** had a rear fuselage more closely following the jet pipes, by comparison with the 'boxed-in', slab-sided rear fuselage of the prototypes and 'Fencer-A'. It also introduced a cylindrical brake chute fairing below the base of the rudder.

'Fencer-C'

The **'Fencer-C'** is similar to the 'Fencer-B', and is distinguishable only by the triangular RWR fairings (similar to those fitted to the Su-24M 'Fencer-D') on the sides of the fin tip and on the engine intakes extending ahead of the wing leading edge. 'Fencer-Cs' were first noted in 1981. Contrary to early Western reports, apart from a handful of early '-As' all three sub-types have a small air intake at the base of the fin leading edge and the same kink in the tailfin leading edge higher up, which is level with the top of the rudder.

Because a control column can easily be fitted in front of the WSO, no dedicated dual-controlled trainer variant of the Su-24 has ever been developed.

It is believed that the Su-24 entered squadron service during 1974, and began to be deployed outside the USSR in 1979 when a regiment of 'Fencer-Bs' deployed to

Templin in East Germany for operational evaluation. In 1984 a regiment began operations over Afghanistan (flying from airfields in the USSR), participating in air strikes against rebel targets in the Panjshir Valley with freefall bombs and precision-guided missiles. During the 1980s, Su-24 bomber regiments were based in Germany (at Grossenhain, Templin and Brand), in Poland (at Zagan, Szprotawa and Krzywa), and in Hungary, with more regiments in the Western part of the USSR.

'Fencer-Bs' and 'Fencer-Cs' remain in widespread front-line use with the **Russian air force**, and with the air arms of a number of former Soviet states. One of three front-line Su-24 bomber regiments withdrawn from Poland in 1992 was equipped solely with these 'early models', for example.

Three Su-24 regiments were based in Poland until they were withdrawn in 1992/93. This Osla-based 'Fencer-B' carries white two-digit tactical codes.

WEAPON OPTIONS

The early 'Fencers' were armed with a single GSh-6-23M cannon in the starboard side of the lower fuselage, with the muzzle covered by an eyelid shutter. Ammunition was housed in a port underfuselage fairing. There are hardpoints for a centreline and two underfuselage pylons, with further pylons under the fixed inboard sections of the wing, and with swivelling pylons under the outboard panels. The aircraft could carry the freefall TN-1000 and TN-1200 nuclear bombs, and a variety of conventional freefall bombs and guided ASMs.

This Osla-based 'Fencer-B' Su-24 appears to have a non-standard nose sensor, with side-by-side pitots below the curved 'hockey stick'. It also seems to have an extra projection on the undernose sensor.

Sukhoi Su-24 'Fencer-C'

An underside view of a Poland-based 'Fencer-C' (note the intake-mounted triangular RWR fairing) shows no provision for built-in cameras or other optical or electro-optical sensors. There may, of course, be a SLAR in the forward fuselage, with an overpainted radome, or podded reconnaissance equipment may be carried. Alternatively, these aircraft may serve as the attack half of a 'Foxbat-F'/ 'Fencer-C' hunter/killer 'Wild Weasel' team.

SPECIFICATION

Sukhoi Su-24 'Fencer-C'
Wing: span 17.63 m (57 ft 10 in) spread and 10.36 m (34 ft 0 in) swept; estimated area 42.00 m2 (452.10 sq ft)
Fuselage and tail: length 24.53 m (80 ft 5.75 in)

including probe; wheel track 3.70 m (12 ft 1.5 in)
Powerplant: two NPO Saturn (Lyul'ka) AL-21F-3A turbojets each rated at 76.49 kN (17,196 lb st) dry and 110.32 kN (24,802 lb st) with afterburning thrust
Weights: estimated empty equipped 19000 kg (41,887 lb); normal take-off 36000 kg (79,365 lb); maximum take-off 39700 kg (87,522 lb)
Fuel and load: estimated internal fuel about 13000

litres (3,434 US gal); external fuel up to four 1250-litre (330-US gal) drop tanks; maximum ordnance 8000 kg (17,637 lb)
Speed: maximum level speed 'clean' at 11000 m (36,090 ft) 2320 km/h (1,251 kt; 1,441 mph) and at sea level 1470 km/h (793 kt; 913 mph)
Range: combat radius 1050 km (565 nm; 650 miles) on a hi-lo-hi attack mission with a 3000-kg (6,614-lb)

warload and two drop tanks, or 950 km (512 nm; 590 miles) on a lo-lo-hi attack mission with a 2500-kg (5,511-lb) warload, or more than 322 km (174 nm; 200 miles) on a lo-lo-lo attack mission with an 8000-kg (17,637-lb) warload
Performance: service ceiling 17500 m (57,415 ft); take-off run 1300 m (4,265 ft) at maximum take-off weight

Sukhoi Su-24M and Su-24MK 'Fencer-D'

Work on improving the Su-24's combat effectiveness began in 1975 (and continues today), eventually resulting in the **Su-24M 'Fencer-D'** which entered service in 1986. This introduced a retractable IFR probe above the nose, on the centreline immediately ahead of the windscreen, and the ability to carry a UPAZ-A buddy refuelling pod on the centreline. These modifications were intended to allow the Su-24 to carry a greater weapons load by taking off with partial fuel and topping up after take-off. The avionics suite was upgraded to allow the aircraft to carry a new generation of TV- and laser-guided weapons, to improve navigational and bombing accuracy, and to enhance survivability.

Most noticeably, the Su-24M received a new radar which is housed in a shortened, reshaped radome and tipped by a single simple pitot in place of the multiple fittings of the earlier variants. The Orion-A forward-looking attack radar is partnered by a Relief terrain-following radar. The latter is coupled to the SAU-6M1 AFCS, which allows fully

automatic terrain-following flight. Other elements of the PNS-24M sighting and navigation complex include the pilot's PPV HUD, the Kaira 24 laser and TV sighting system, the MIS-P/II inertial platform and the TsVU-10-058K digital computer.

The Kaira laser and TV designator/tracker gives compatibility with the newest Soviet ASMs, and is housed behind a glazed fairing on the centreline ahead of the gun and ammunition fairings. The Su-24M can also carry all of the weapons carried by the earlier 'Fencers'. Survivability is enhanced by the improved defensive aids, which include an SPO-15S RHAWS, an LO-82 missile launch warning system, an SPS-161 active ECM, and an APP-50 chaff/flare dispenser. SRZO IFF interrogator and SO-69 transponder are also incorporated.

Many 'Fencer-Ds' lack the large combined fences/underwing pylons which act as mountings for the chaff/flare dispensers, and such aircraft sometimes have chaff/flare launchers scabbed on above the rear fuselage, on each side of the tailfin. A hand-

ful of Su-24Ms in Soviet colours have been seen in this configuration, along with some (but definitely not all) export aircraft. Aircraft with these fences may qualify for the revised reporting name **'Fencer-D (Mod)'**. Export Su-24 'Fencer-Ds' are designated **Su-24MK**, and presumably have a downgraded avionics system, although reports that some Su-24MKs lack inflight-refuelling capability are believed to be erroneous.

OPERATORS

Su-24s were produced for Frontal Aviation and were assigned directly to Strategic Air Armies, and to Tactical Air Forces supporting fronts and regions. The break-up of the Soviet Union did not lead to a proliferation of new users, however, since Russia was careful to ensure that these advanced strike aircraft returned to Russia wherever possible. Current

operators of all 'Fencer' variants are as follows:
Russia: The Russian republic has some 480 bomber and 90 reconnaissance-tasked Su-24s. The 3rd BAP at Krzywa in Poland returned to Russia with its Su-24s, while the Su-24Ms of the 42nd Guards BAP at Zagan and the 89th BAP at Szprotawa returned to bases in the Eastern MD and near Kuban, respectively. East Germany-based Su-24s returned to Starokonstantinov in Ukraine and to a base in Russia (an unidentified unit formerly at Brand). In May 1992, Su-24MRs of the 164th Guards RAP moved from Kryzwa (Poland) to Staelewo near Smolensk. Germany-based 'Fencer-Es' of the 11 'Vitebski' RAP from Neu Welzow returned to Marinovka in Russia. Russia also has four Su-24MPs which were formerly with the 11th RAP.
Ukraine: The largest non-Russian operator is Ukraine, which has gained a large number (over 175) of attack-dedicated Su-24s. Units comprise the following BAPs: 7th BAP at Starokonstantinov (formerly at Grossenhain in East Germany), 727th BAP at Kanatovo, 69th BAP at Ovruch South-West, 806th BAP at Lutsk and 947th BAP at Dubno. Su-24MR units are the 511th RAP at Blagoyevo and the 48th RAP at Kolomyya. Eight Su-24MPs of the former 11th RAP are based with the 118th RAP at Chortkov

An Su-24M 'Fencer-D' takes off from Szprotawa in Poland. The manner in which the main gear doors can also act as airbrakes can be clearly seen. It carries a single rocket pod and a FAB-250 fragmentation bomb.

Sukhoi Su-24M 'Fencer-D'

An Su-24M rests on the flight line. The retractable inflight-refuelling probe is visible above the nose, immediately below the windscreen, and the Kaira laser and TV designator can be seen below the forward fuselage.

Azerbaijan: The Azeri republic also seized some 11 Su-24s when the USSR disintegrated. These are not believed to be in an airworthy condition.

Kazakhstan: Attack-tasked Su-24s serve with the 149th BAP at Nikolaevka, while reconnaisance Su-24s serve with the 39th RAP at Balkesh.

Export customers: Su-24MKs have been delivered to **Libya** (between six and 15 of the 18 ordered before relations cooled) and to **Iran** and **Iraq** (all 24 of the latter being absorbed into the Iranian air force after fleeing to Iran during Desert Storm), and 42 are believed to have been delivered to **Syria**. Both bomber and reconnaissance versions of the aircraft are being actively marketed.

SPECIFICATION

Sukhoi Su-24M 'Fencer-D'

Wing: span 17.63 m (57 ft 10 in) at 16° sweep and 10.36 m (34 ft 0 in) at 69° sweep; area 55.16 m² (593.75 sq ft) at 16° sweep and 51.00 m² (548.95 sq ft) at 69° sweep

Fuselage and tail: length 24.53 m (80 ft 5.75 in) including inflight-refuelling probe; height 6.19 m (20 ft 3 in);

Powerplant: two Perm/Soloviev (Lyul'ka) AL-21F-3A turbojets each rated at 109.83 kN (24,691 lb st) with afterburning thrust

Weights: empty equipped 22320 kg (49,206 lb); normal take-off 36000 kg ((79365 lb)); maximum take-off 39700 kg (87,522 lb)

Fuel and load: internal fuel 11,700 litres (2574 Imp gal); maximum combat load 8000 kg (17,637 lb); normal combat load 3000 kg (6614 lb)

Speed: maximum level speed 'clean' at 11000 m (36,089 ft) Mach 1.35 and at low-level 1320 km/h (712 kt; 820 mph); maximum level speed at low-level with six FAB-500 bombs 1200 km/h (648 kt; 746 mph)

Range: ferry range 2500 km (1349 nm; 1553 miles) with maximum internal and external fuel and 4270 km (2304 nm; 2653 miles) with one in-flight refuelling; lo-lo-lo radius with six FAB-500 bombs 410 km (221 nm; 255 miles) without external fuel and 560 km (302 nm; 348 miles)

Performance: service ceiling 11000 m (36090 ft); take-off run between 1300-1400 m 4265-4593 ft); landing distance 950 m (3117 ft) with brake parachute

Sukhoi **Su-24MR 'Fencer-E' and Su-24MP 'Fencer-F'**

The Su-24 airframe was a natural choice when it came to looking for a replacement for the Yak-28 'Brewer' in the tactical and maritime reconnaissance and tactical electronic warfare roles, since it combined long range and excellent performance with the ability to carry a reasonable payload. The resulting **Su-24MR** was designed for the primary role of tactical reconnaissance using internal and podded sensors of various types, able to transmit reconnaissance data from some sensors to a ground station in real time. The aircraft also has secondary civilian roles of ecological, environmental, agricultural and forestry monitoring, and can be used in emergency situations.

The 30-mm cannon and Kaira laser/TV system are deleted, allowing the installation of an AP-402 panoramic camera in the

The Su-24MP has an undernose fairing and 'hockey-stick' aerials under the intakes, and is assigned the reporting name 'Fencer-F'. Only a handful (about a dozen) of these EW aircraft were built.

underside of the nose and an A-100 forward/oblique camera mounted in the floor of the port air intake duct. Working on the AP-402 is remarkably easy, since it can be dropped down on cables, complete with its hatch and window, giving all-round access. The AP-402 camera has a 90.5-mm lens and produces an 80-mm x 250-mm frame, with a linear resolution of 0.2 m at a height of 400 m (1,312 ft). The camera can be used at altitudes from 150 - 2000 m (492 - 6,562 ft) and at speeds of 600 - 1320 km/h (373 - 820 mph). Coverage is equivalent to 10x altitude. At the cost of limited film capacity, the Kadr (picture) device can be used, which allows a cassette of processed film to be parachuted to the ground. The A-100 camera has a 100-mm lens and can be used at altitudes down to 50 m (164 ft), producing a 75-mm frame.

Located immediately behind the AP-402 is an Aist-M (Stork-M) TV reconnaissance camera, covering a swath of ground equivalent to 9x aircraft height. This can transmit pictures back to the ground station using the VPS-1 broadband radio channel. The air-

craft is also fitted with an RDS BO Shtik (Bayonet) synthetic aperture side-looking radar which has a moving target indicator mode and a high resolution (5-m) mapping mode. Radar maps thus produced can be recorded on film. The radar can cover an area 4 - 28 km (2.5 - 17 miles) out from the aircraft and has two large flush antennas,

The Su-24MR is a dedicated tactical reconnaissance model of the 'Fencer'. Emerging from overhaul at Novosibirsk, and still in primer finish, is this 'Fencer-E', complete with new fuselage chaff/flare dispensers.

one on each side of the nose, immediately ahead of the windscreen. Another onboard sensor is the Zima (Winter) IR reconnaissance system. This can detect temperature differences as low as 0.3°C (1.8°F) and scans a strip equivalent to 3.4x aircraft height. It can downlink directly to ground stations (which must be within line-of-sight

Sukhoi Su-25UB/UT/UTG 'Frogfoot-B'

Development of a two-seat trainer version of the Su-25 was not accorded a high priority, since the basic single-seater was simple to fly, with benign handling characteristics. **VVS** Su-25 regiments therefore used Czech Aero L-39s for training and standardisation, and also for FAC duties. These aircraft have still not been entirely replaced by two-seat Su-25Us.

Two prototype trainers were converted from unfinished Su-25s at Tbilisi, under the designations **T-8-UB1** and **T-8-UB2**, making their maiden flights during 1985. After acceptance trials, the first prototype was flown to Ulan Ude to serve as a pattern aircraft. Production of the definitive **Su-25UB 'Frogfoot-B'** began in 1987, all aircraft produced there being decorated with the factory's bear badge.

The Su-25UB has forward fuselage slightly lengthened to accommodate the new stepped cockpits. These are covered by separate canopies and are divided by a sealed, armoured windscreen which prevents both cockpits depressurising if only one loses its integrity. The instructor is provided with a retractable periscope to improve his view directly forward on approach or on the ground. The tailfin is increased in height to compensate for the greater 'keel' area forward. The trainer retains all operational equipment and is fully combat-capable, although the weight and drag of the

second cockpit, and the slight reduction in fuel capacity, have an impact on performance.

Production of the Su-25UB ended in December 1991, after five Soviet Su-25 regiments had received their aircraft. Production also included about 16 **Su-25UBK** trainers for **Bulgaria**, **Czechoslovakia**, **Iraq** and **North Korea**. These aircraft lacked chaff/flare dispensers and were fitted with downgraded avionics.

The Su-25UB has also formed the basis of three more Su-25 sub-variants. The first of these was the **Su-25UT**, later redesignated **Su-28**. The prototype was a converted Su-25UB, with all armament and weapons systems removed, and it made its maiden flight on 6 August 1985. The aircraft was intended as a successor to the Czech Aero L-29 and L-39 in the pilot training role in both air force and DOSAAF service. It retained only two underwing hardpoints, to carry fuel tanks.

One prototype was painted in DOSAAF colours and participated in the 1988 DOSAAF aerobatic competition, pilot Yevgeni Frolov gaining a creditable third place. Although it offered some advantages over the L-39 (whose airframe life is already running out) the aircraft was unable to attract an order.

The basic Su-25 two-seater also served as the basis for the **Su-25UTG**, a dedicated carrier training aircraft (the G in the

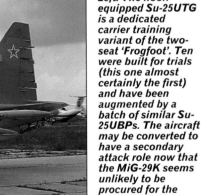

The Su-28 is a dedicated advanced trainer version of the Su-25UB. Whereas the heavier machine is fully armed and armoured and is used for conversion training, the Su-28's main role is intended to be advanced pilot training.

suffix stands for Gak, or hook) for pilots destined to serve aboard the *Kuznetsov* (formerly *Tbilisi*). Development work began in 1987, and the prototype made its maiden flight in that same year. The airframe and undercarriage were considerably strengthened, and a heavy-duty arrester hook was mounted below the tailcone.

At one stage it was reported that a pre-production batch of 10 aircraft had been ordered, and these were constructed at Ulan Ude during 1989-90. Only the first was used for trials aboard the *Kuznetsov* flown

by Igor V. Botintsev and Alexander V. Krutov. It was also used for training test pilots involved in the Su-27K programme. One of the remainder crashed, and five were left at Saki (to be integrated into the **Ukrainian** forces), leaving four to be transferred to Severomorsk on the Kola Peninsula. This location has taken over from Saki as the **AV-MF**'s development centre. In March 1993, Sukhoi claimed that 10 Su-25UBs were being converted to a similar standard under the designation **Su-25UBP** (P for Palubnyi, or shipborne).

Finally, the Su-25UB served as the basis for the **Su-25T**, described separately.

SPECIFICATION

Sukhoi Su-25UB 'Frogfoot-B'
generally similar to the Sukhoi Su-25K 'Frogfoot-A' except in the following particulars:
Fuselage and tail: height 5.20 m (17 ft 0.75 in)

Left: The hook-equipped Su-25UTG is a dedicated carrier training variant of the two-seat 'Frogfoot'. Ten were built for trials (this one almost certainly the first) and have been augmented by a batch of similar Su-25UBPs. The aircraft may be converted to have a secondary attack role now that the MiG-29K seems unlikely to be procured for the carrier Kuznetsov.

Below: Many Su-25UBs carry a bear badge on the nose. This is the emblem of the Ulan Ude factory which produced all two-seat Su-25s. This particular aircraft is armed with S-8 20-round 80-mm rocket pods. Plates on the wingtip fairings shield the pilot from the glare of the pop-down landing lights.

Sukhoi Su-24M 'Fencer-D'

An Su-24M rests on the flight line. The retractable inflight-refuelling probe is visible above the nose, immediately below the windscreen, and the Kaira laser and TV designator can be seen below the forward fuselage.

Azerbaijan: The Azeri republic also seized some 11 Su-24s when the USSR disintegrated. These are not believed to be in an airworthy condition.

Kazakhstan: Attack-tasked Su-24s serve with the 149th BAP at Nikolaevka, while reconnaissance Su-24s serve with the 39th RAP at Balkesh.

Export customers: Su-24MKs have been delivered to **Libya** (between six and 15 of the 18 ordered before relations cooled) and to **Iran** and **Iraq** (all 24 of the latter being absorbed into the Iranian air force after fleeing to Iran during Desert Storm), and 42 are believed to have been delivered to **Syria**. Both bomber and reconnaissance versions of the aircraft are being actively marketed.

SPECIFICATION

Sukhoi Su-24M 'Fencer-D'

Wing: span 17.63 m (57 ft 10 in) at 16° sweep and 10.36 m (34 ft 0 in) at 69° sweep; area 55.16 m² (593.75 sq ft) at 16° sweep and 51.00 m² (548.95 sq ft) at 69° sweep

Fuselage and tail: length 24.53 m (80 ft 5.75 in) including inflight-refuelling probe; height 6.19 m (20 ft 3 in);

Powerplant: two Perm/Soloviev (Lyul'ka) AL-21F-3A turbojets each rated at 109.83 kN (24,691 lb st) with afterburning thrust

Weights: empty equipped 22320 kg (49,206 lb); normal take-off 36000 kg ((79365 lb); maximum take-off 39700 kg (87,522 lb)

Fuel and load: internal fuel 11,700 litres (2574 Imp gal); maximum combat load 8000 kg (17,637 lb); normal combat load 3000 kg (6614 lb)

Speed: maximum level speed 'clean' at 11000 m (36,089 ft) Mach 1.35 and at low-level 1320 km/h (712 kt; 820 mph); maximum level speed at low-level with six FAB-500 bombs 1200 km/h (648 kt; 746 mph)

Range: ferry range 2500 km (1349 nm; 1553 miles) with maximum internal and external fuel and 4270 km (2304 nm; 2653 miles) with one in-flight refuelling; lo-lo-lo radius with six FAB-500 bombs 410 km (221 nm; 255 miles) without external fuel and 560 km (302 nm; 348 miles)

Performance: service ceiling 11000 m (36090 ft); take-off run between 1300-1400 m 4265-4593 ft); landing distance 950 m (3117 ft) with brake parachute

Sukhoi **Su-24MR 'Fencer-E'** and **Su-24MP 'Fencer-F'**

The Su-24 airframe was a natural choice when it came to looking for a replacement for the Yak-28 'Brewer' in the tactical and maritime reconnaissance and tactical electronic warfare roles, since it combined long range and excellent performance with the ability to carry a reasonable payload. The resulting **Su-24MR** was designed for the primary role of tactical reconnaissance using internal and podded sensors of various types, able to transmit reconnaissance data from some sensors to a ground station in real time. The aircraft also has secondary civilian roles of ecological, environmental, agricultural and forestry monitoring, and can be used in emergency situations.

The 30-mm cannon and Kaira laser/TV system are deleted, allowing the installation of an AP-402 panoramic camera in the

The Su-24MP has an undernose fairing and 'hockey-stick' aerials under the intakes, and is assigned the reporting name 'Fencer-F'. Only a handful (about a dozen) of these EW aircraft were built.

underside of the nose and an A-100 forward/oblique camera mounted in the floor of the port air intake duct. Working on the AP-402 is remarkably easy, since it can be dropped down on cables, complete with its hatch and window, giving all-round access. The AP-402 camera has a 90.5-mm lens and produces an 80-mm x 250-mm frame, with a linear resolution of 0.2 m at a height of 400 m (1,312 ft). The camera can be used at altitudes from 150 - 2000 m (492 - 6,562 ft) and at speeds of 600 - 1320 km/h (373 - 820 mph). Coverage is equivalent to 10x altitude. At the cost of limited film capacity, the Kadr (picture) device can be used, which allows a cassette of processed film to be parachuted to the ground. The A-100 camera has a 100-mm lens and can be used at altitudes down to 50 m (164 ft), producing a 75-mm frame.

Located immediately behind the AP-402 is an Aist-M (Stork-M) TV reconnaissance camera, covering a swath of ground equivalent to 9x aircraft height. This can transmit pictures back to the ground station using the VPS-1 broadband radio channel. The air-

craft is also fitted with an RDS BO Shtik (Bayonet) synthetic aperture side-looking radar which has a moving target indicator mode and a high resolution (5-m) mapping mode. Radar maps thus produced can be recorded on film. The radar can cover an area 4 - 28 km (2.5 - 17 miles) out from the aircraft and has two large flush antennas,

The Su-24MR is a dedicated tactical reconnaissance model of the 'Fencer'. Emerging from overhaul at Novosibirsk, and still in primer finish, is this 'Fencer-E', complete with new fuselage chaff/flare dispensers.

one on each side of the nose, immediately ahead of the windscreen. Another onboard sensor is the Zima (Winter) IR reconnaissance system. This can detect temperature differences as low as 0.3°C (1.8°F) and scans a strip equivalent to 3.4x aircraft height. It can downlink directly to ground stations (which must be within line-of-sight

Sukhoi Su-24MR 'Fencer-E' and Su-24MP 'Fencer-F'

Sukhoi Su-24MR 'Fencer-E'

One of the 11th Independent Reconnaissance Aviation Regiment's Su-24MR 'Fencer-Es' is seen leaving its base at Welzow in East Germany for its new home at Marinovka. The flush dielectric panels on the sides of the nose are clearly visible. Internal sensors are augmented by various pods.

range) using the VPS-1, or can record on film, using up to seven shades of grey. It is located in the starboard air intake duct.

Other reconnaissance sensors carried by the Su-24MR are podded, carried underwing or on the centreline. The largest of these is the 6-m (19.7-ft) long Shpil-2M (Needle-2M) laser reconnaissance pod which scans an area equivalent to 4x aircraft height. This can be used by day or night in VMC conditions, and offers outstanding resolution (0.25 m/0.82 ft). Data can be downlinked or recorded on film, which can be processed in flight. Alternatively the slab-sided Tanghazh Elint pod can be carried on the centreline. The final type of pod carried is the Efir-1M radiation detector, which contains two sensors, each with a 120° scanning angle. This can plot the extent of radioactive contamination on the

ground from an altitude of 500 m 1,640 ft), recording this on tape and transmitting data to ground stations. This much smaller pod (some 3 m/9.8 ft long) is normally carried on the starboard outboard underwing pylon, with a pair of R-60 AA-8 'Aphid' AAMs to port, and external 3000-litre (660-Imp gal) fuel tanks inboard.

Those sensors which can directly transmit data to a ground station feed the incredible Posrednik-1 data reception, processing and decoding complex, based in 12 lorries. Two of these are generator trucks and another is believed to be used for aircraft tracking. Data is transmitted via the VPS-1 broadband radio link to the receiver truck, which in turn feeds three processing laboratories for the TV, IR and laser sensors. Photographic films and radar/Elint tapes unloaded from the aircraft after it lands are

processed in three more trucks. Data from all six processing trucks are printed and copied in two more trucks for interpretation and distribution to the tasking authorities. The complex can decode and process data from a one-target mission in an average of 20 minutes from landing, and can process up to 18000 m (59,055 ft) of film and print up to 2000 photos in a 24-hour period.

The Su-24MR is fitted with a Relief terrain-avoidance radar, a radio altimeter, a DISS-7 Doppler, an MIS-P inertial platform, and an SBU Orbita-10-058R digital computer, as well as an RSBN-6S Shoran/ILS, an ARK-15M radio compass and other navaids. The Karpati integrated defence system includes SRO-15 Bereza RWRs, a MAK-UL missile launch warning receiver, Gerani-F active jammers (controlled by a Neon-F control unit) and Automat-F chaff/flare dispensers.

'Fencer-Es' have been seen with and without the distinctive combined fences/underwing pylons, and aft of the windscreen are externally almost indistinguishable from the 'Fencer-D' bomber. The most obvious external change is the provision of a larger-capacity, bulged heat exchanger to give increased cooling for the reconnaissance aircraft's many new black boxes.

Ukraine has two recce 'Fencer' units. These comprise the 511th RAP at Buyalik (Blagoyevo) with 24 aircraft and the 48th RAP at Kolomyya with 12 Su-24MRs. In **Russia**, two Su-24 reconnaissance regiments have been confirmed. In May 1992, Poland-based Su-24MRs of the 164th

Guards RAP moved from Kryzwa to Staelewo near Smolensk. Germany-based 'Fencer-Es' of the 11 'Vitebski' RAP from Neu Welzow returned to Marinovka. **Kazakhstan** operates some recconaissance-tasked 'Fencers' with the 39th RAP at Balkesh.

The **Su-24MP** (Modification Pastanovchik – Modification to Direct) is a similar-looking aircraft, and like the Su-24MR often has its nose painted white to resemble a standard Su-24M bomber. It can be distinguished from the earlier aircraft by a prominent fairing below the nose, behind the radome, and by the provision of swept-back 'hockey stick' antennas outboard of long shallow strakes on the bottom corners of the intakes, immediately ahead of the main-wheel bays. The pattern of flush dielectric antennas on the sides of the nose is also different, and the smaller 'Fencer-C/-D' heat exchanger is mounted above the fuselage.

The Su-24MP is designated **'Fencer-F'** by NATO, and is believed to have a primary electronic intelligence-gathering role. Before the demolition of the Berlin Wall, recce 'Fencer' units in Poland and Germany included both Su-24MRs and Su-24MPs, but the Su-24MPs were rapidly withdrawn, perhaps to avoid the attentions of spotters' cameras. It is believed that only 12 of these aircraft were built, and eight were retained by **Ukraine** after their withdrawal from Germany. The 11 RAP's MPs ended up at Chortkov with the 118th Independent Aviation Regiment, leaving **Russia** with only four aircraft and a need to retain its exhausted Yak-28 'Brewer-Es'.

SPECIFICATION

Sukhoi Su-24MR 'Fencer-E'
generally similar to the Sukhoi Su-24 'Fencer-D' except in the following particulars:
Weights: normal take-off 33325 kg (73,468 lb); maximum take-off 39700 kg (87,522 lb)
Speed: maximum low-level speed with reconnaissance pods and two R-60 AAMs 1200 km/h (648 kt; 746 mph)
Range: ferry range with one iflight refuelling 4360 km 2353 nm; 2709 miles); operating radius on a lo-lo-lo mission 410 km (221 nm; 255 miles) without fuel tanks and 560 km 302 nm; 348 miles) with external fuel tanks
Performance: take-off run 1100-1200 m (3609-3937 ft)
g limits: +6.5

Sukhoi Su-25 'Frogfoot-A'

Development of the **Su-25 'Frogfoot'** began during the late 1960s, when the Sukhoi OKB commenced studies of a jet *Shturmovik*, parallelling the US studies which resulted in the AX competition and the ensuing Northrop YA-9 and Fairchild YA-10 prototypes. Sukhoi, like the American firms, was heavily influenced by USAF experience in the Vietnam War, but all three firms reached different conclusions. Sukhoi believed that high speed was essential to ensure survivability over the battle-

field, and chose to use turbojet engines and relatively little armour, while the US designs were turbofan-powered, emphasising very high agility and heavy armour.

The design team, which was successively led by Oleg Samolovich, Yuri Ivashechkin and Vladimir Babak, eventually won the support of General A. N. Yefimov, air force Deputy C-in-C and himself a former Il-2 *Shturmovik* pilot, who in turn won the support of the ground forces commander, General Pavlovsky. In this unorthodox manner (by Soviet standards), Sukhoi eventually received funding for a prototype, designated **T-8**. This made its first flight at Zhukhovskii in the hands of Vladimir Ilyushin, Sukhoi's chief test pilot, on 22 February 1975. A second prototype followed, introducing a two-piece rudder, revised wing fences, wingtip pods and a taller tailfin. The **T-8-2** was also the first aircraft with a titanium-armoured cockpit, the first prototype having used steel of equivalent weight. Like the first aircraft, it had an SPPU-22-01 23-mm cannon pod in a gondola fairing below the starboard lower fuselage, and was powered by a pair of Tumanskii RD-9B turbojets, as used by the MiG-19. However, the after-

burners were removed, giving 27 kN (6,070 lb st) of thrust. The aircraft was spotted by a passing US satellite soon after its first flight, and was allocated the provisional reporting name 'Ram-J', indicating that it was the 10th new type spotted at what the West still called Ramenskoye.

The two T-8 prototypes were equipped with the weapons system of the Su-17M2 'Fitter-D', with ASP-PF gunsight, PBK-3 bombsight and Fone laser rangefinder. The second was re-engined with the R-95Sh (receiving the new designation **T-8-2D**) in March 1976, and the **T-8-1** was re-engined in 1978. The R-95Sh is a non-afterburning modified version of the MiG-21's R-13-300 turbojet and was capable of running on a variety of fuels. Weapons trials at Akhtubinsk had shown that the aircraft was underpowered and prone to compressor stalls when firing cannon or rockets. It was also felt that production could not be authorised while the aircraft used a powerplant which was out of production.

The new powerplant necessitated some changes, including the angling down of the engine nozzles and the incorporation of 5° dihedral on the tailplane, instead of the original 5° anhedral. With the new engine fitted, the two prototypes began state acceptance trials.

Further prototypes were built at Tbilisi, these having the production armament

Czechoslovak Su-25s equipped the 30th Close Air Support Regiment at Pardubice, whose aircraft wear the white horse badge of the city crest. This Su-25K also carries a fearsome sharkmouth on the nose.

of an AO-17 twin-barrelled 30-mm cannon and the weapons system of the Su-17M-3 'Fitter-H' with ASP-17 gunsight, and a Klen laser rangefinder. Series production was finally authorised, and the first and third prototypes were sent to Afghanistan for a combined series of operational and state acceptance trials (Operation Rhombus), alongside a handful of Yak-38 'Forgers' flying from Shindand. The trials lasted from 16 April to 5 June 1980, the two aircraft flying 30 state acceptance and 70 combat sorties. The first pre-production Su-25 introduced a number of changes, including modified tailplanes, enlarged air intakes, heavier, thicker cockpit armour and increased armour around critical components, including the oil tank. The fuel tanks were filled with reticulated foam and the control rods were formed from 40-mm diameter titanium rods, capable of withstanding a direct hit from a 12.7-mm shell. One prototype even tested a radar-absorbing material coating on the forward fuselage and leading edges, but this was not adopted.

Afghan deployment

Some sources suggest that the initial batch of aircraft retained the T-8 designation even in service, and that the designation Su-25 was applied to series production aircraft, whose main recognition feature was a small ram-air intake at the base of the tailfin leading edge. Whatever the designation, the early batch aircraft saw extensive service in Afghanistan, where the first 12 aircraft served with the 200th Guards Independent Attack Squadron at Shindand, pilots including the former Russian Federation Vice-President, then-Colonel Alexander Rutskoi, who became the most highly decorated pilot of the war. The 200th formed at Sital-Chai in Azerbaijan on 4 February 1981, receiving their Su-25s from April, and moving to Shindand on 18 June. This unit gave the Su-25 its *grach* (rook) nickname, and began the tradition of painting a rook onto the intake. The unit was later expanded to full regimental strength, as the 60th Independent Attack Regiment, and maintained a squadron-sized rotational deployment in Afghanistan. The Su-25 eventually flew some 60,000 combat sorties in Afghanistan, and 23 were lost.

Experience in Afghanistan led to a number of modifications, including bolt-on ASO-2V chaff/flare dispensers, an exhaust IR signature reduction system, a freon gas fire-extinguishing system, and a titanium plate between the engines, designed to prevent debris or fire from a damaged engine from damaging its neighbour. Other improvements adopted during the course of production included refinements to the wingtip speed-brakes, with two extra separately controlled forward-folding segments being added. Wingtip pods were also fitted with plate-like fins designed to prevent the pop-down landing lights from dazzling the pilot. Larger twin braking parachutes were also adopted.

During 1987, production aircraft were fitted with the more powerful R-195 engine, which was also fitted to all production 'Frogfoot' two-seaters. The new engine further improves the Su-25's ability to operate from austere forward airfields, and to support such operations a special set of support equipment has been developed which can be carried by the aircraft itself in four underwing pods. These contain test equipment, an electrical generator and starter unit, a fuel pump and protective covers and maintenance equipment. The engines can run on kerosene, diesel and petrol, if required.

Su-25 production at Tbilisi ended in 1989, after some 330 aircraft had been delivered. A handful of Su-25s have been modified to serve as target tugs, with gun removed and gun port faired over, with the laser removed and faired over, and with a TO-70 target winch and Kometa target mounted under the port inboard underwing pylon. These aircraft are designated **Su-25BM** (Buksir Misheni, or target tug).

WEAPON OPTIONS

Ten underwing hardpoints are provided, the outermost pair being smaller and more lightly stressed and used almost exclusively to carry R-60 (AA-8 'Aphid') AAMs for self-defence. External fuel tanks can be carried on the inboard pylons, and a second pair can be carried on the next-but-one pylon further outboard.

The Su-25 is equipped with an internal 30-mm AO-17A cannon in the port lower fuselage, with 250 rounds of ammunition. The nosewheel is offset about 11.5 cm (4½ in) to the right of the centreline to give greater clearance for the gun. The aircraft can carry a wide range of ordnance underwing, including unguided rockets ranging in calibre from 57 mm to 330 mm. ASMs include the Kh-23 (AS-7 'Kerry'), Kh-25 (AS-10 'Karen') and Kh-29 (AS-14 'Kedge').

When laser-guided weapons are carried, the Su-25 must carry an underwing laser illuminator since the onboard laser in the nose is insufficiently powerful to illuminate a target for long-range missiles, but is adequate for guiding laser-guided bombs. Various freefall and laser-guided bombs, cluster bombs, dispenser weapons and incendiary weapons can also be carried, along with a variety of cannon pods, including the SPPU-22, whose 23-mm cannon has barrels which can be depressed for strafing ground targets.

Sukhoi Su-25 'Frogfoot-A'

Sukhoi Su-25 'Frogfoot-A'

OPERATORS

The **Soviet air forces** had a peak strength of about 270 Su-25s. Known Su-25 operators were the 200th Guards OShAP in Afghanistan, and one squadron of the 234th Guards at Kubinka (which parents the 'Sky Hussars' aerobatic team) with other regiments in Turkmenistan and Byelorussia. Su-25s deployed to the Group of Soviet Forces in Germany operated in two direct-reporting units as part of the 16th Air Army. The break-up of the former Soviet Union has led to the Su-25 gaining new users.

The 357th OShAP was based at Brandis and returned to **Russia** in 1992. The 368th OShAP formerly at Demmin-Tutow is now based at Budyennovsk. At least three regiments in Georgia remain under Russian control, including the two units from the 16th Air Army. Some Su-25s (mainly UTGs and UBs) serve with naval units. **Ukraine** has a total of 35 Su-25s . The 452nd OShAP, based at Chorkov, has become part of that republic's air arm. Further 'Frogfoots' are based at Ovruch and at Saki, including some of the navalised Su-25UTGs. **Byelorussia** has 100 Su-25s based at Luninets. Su-25s from the 80th OShAP at Sital-Zhay defected to **Azerbaijan** and have been absorbed into the Azeri air force. Three have been shot down by Armenian forces, but five remain in service. **Georgia**, which is home to the Tbilisi plant which manufactures single-seat Su-25s, has less than five 'Frogfoots' on strength. More were lost in action to Abkhasian forces.

Export 'Frogfoots' are designated **Su-25K**. Thirty-six were delivered to **Czechoslovakia**, the first export customer, to equip the 34th Fighter-Bomber Division's 30th 'Ostravsky' Close Air Support Regiment . Some remained with the Czech Republic (still with the 30th at Pardubice) after division, 13 others going to Slovakia's 2 ZDLP at Piestany. **Bulgaria** took delivery of a further 36, these equipping a regiment at Bezmier. **Iraq** received 30 Su-25Ks, 20 of which were extant at the start of Operation Desert Storm. Several were destroyed on the ground or in air combat, and seven survivors fled to Iran. The last overseas customer was **North Korea**, which also received 36 aircraft. Czech and Bulgarian examples differ little from standard Russian Su-25s, but Iraqi and Korean aircraft may have downgraded avionics. Plans to transfer Su-25 production to **Poland** during 1977 were cancelled when the Polish air force rejected the aircraft. Some reports suggest that Su-25s were also exported to **Afghanistan** and **Angola**, and there have been recent reported sightings in both countries.

SPECIFICATION

Sukhoi Su-25K 'Frogfoot-A'
Wing: span 14.36 m (47 ft 1.4 in); aspect ratio 6.12; area 30.10 m² (324.00 sq ft)
Fuselage and tail: length 15.53 m (50 ft 11.5 in); height 4.80 m (15 ft 9 in)
Powerplant: two MNPK 'Soyuz' (Tumanskii) R-195 turbojets each rated at 44.13 kN (9,921 lb st) dry
Weights: empty equipped 9800 kg (21,605 lb); normal take-off 14600 kg (32,187 lb); maximum take-off 18600 kg (41,005 lb)
Fuel and load: internal fuel about 5000 kg (11,023 lb); maximum ordnance 4000 kg (8,818 lb)
Speed: maximum level speed 'clean' at sea level 950 km/h (513 kt; 590 mph)
Range: combat radius 495 km (267 nm; 308 miles) on a hi-lo-hi attack mission with a 4000-kg (8,818-lb) warload and two drop tanks
Performance: service ceiling 7000 m (22,965 ft); take-off run 600 m (1,969 ft) typical at maximum take-off weight or less than 1200 m (3,937 ft) at maximum take-off weight from an unpaved runway; landing run 600 m (1,969 ft) at normal landing weight without brake chutes or 400 m (1,312 ft) at normal landing weight with brake chutes

Regarded as a latter-day successor to the legendary Il-2 Shturmovik, the Su-25 saw use in Afghanistan. Still wearing the distinctive desert-type camouflage applied for operations in Afghanistan, this Su-25 served with the Soviet 16th Air Army in Germany. The success of the aircraft has been limited, many potential operators preferring to buy supersonic fighters with a nominal ground attack capability.

Sukhoi **Su-25UB/UT/UTG 'Frogfoot-B'**

Development of a two-seat trainer version of the Su-25 was not accorded a high priority, since the basic single-seater was simple to fly, with benign handling characteristics. **VVS** Su-25 regiments therefore used Czech Aero L-39s for training and standardisation, and also for FAC duties. These aircraft have still not been entirely replaced by two-seat Su-25Us.

Two prototype trainers were converted from unfinished Su-25s at Tbilisi, under the designations **T-8-UB1** and **T-8-UB2**, making their maiden flights during 1985. After acceptance trials, the first prototype was flown to Ulan Ude to serve as a pattern aircraft. Production of the definitive **Su-25UB 'Frogfoot-B'** began in 1987, all aircraft produced there being decorated with the factory's bear badge.

The Su-25UB has forward fuselage slightly lengthened to accommodate the new stepped cockpits. These are covered by separate canopies and are divided by a sealed, armoured windscreen which prevents both cockpits depressurising if only one loses its integrity. The instructor is provided with a retractable periscope to improve his view directly forward on approach or on the ground. The tailfin is increased in height to compensate for the greater 'keel' area forward. The trainer retains all operational equipment and is fully combat-capable, although the weight and drag of the

second cockpit, and the slight reduction in fuel capacity, have an impact on performance.

Production of the Su-25UB ended in December 1991, after five Soviet Su-25 regiments had received their aircraft. Production also included about 16 **Su-25UBK** trainers for **Bulgaria**, **Czechoslovakia**, **Iraq** and **North Korea**. These aircraft lacked chaff/flare dispensers and were fitted with downgraded avionics.

The Su-25UB has also formed the basis of three more Su-25 sub-variants. The first of these was the **Su-25UT**, later redesignated **Su-28**. The prototype was a converted Su-25UB, with all armament and weapons systems removed, and it made its maiden flight on 6 August 1985. The aircraft was intended as a successor to the Czech Aero L-29 and L-39 in the pilot training role in both air force and DOSAAF service. It retained only two underwing hardpoints, to carry fuel tanks.

One prototype was painted in DOSAAF colours and participated in the 1988 DOSAAF aerobatic competition, pilot Yevgeni Frolov gaining a creditable third place. Although it offered some advantages over the L-39 (whose airframe life is already running out) the aircraft was unable to attract an order.

The basic Su-25 two-seater also served as the basis for the **Su-25UTG**, a dedicated carrier training aircraft (the G in the

suffix stands for Gak, or hook) for pilots destined to serve aboard the *Kuznetsov* (formerly *Tbilisi*). Development work began in 1987, and the prototype made its maiden flight in that same year. The airframe and undercarriage were considerably strengthened, and a heavy-duty arrester hook was mounted below the tailcone.

At one stage it was reported that a pre-production batch of 10 aircraft had been ordered, and these were constructed at Ulan Ude during 1989-90. Only the first was used for trials aboard the *Kuznetsov* flown

by Igor V. Botintsev and Alexander V. Krutov. It was also used for training test pilots involved in the Su-27K programme. One of the remainder crashed, and five were left at Saki (to be integrated into the **Ukrainian** forces), leaving four to be transferred to Severomorsk on the Kola Peninsula. This location has taken over from Saki as the **AV-MF**'s development centre. In March 1993, Sukhoi claimed that 10 Su-25UBs were being converted to a similar standard under the designation **Su-25UBP** (P for Palubnyi, or shipborne).

Finally, the Su-25UB served as the basis for the **Su-25T**, described separately.

SPECIFICATION

Sukhoi Su-25UB 'Frogfoot-B'
generally similar to the Sukhoi Su-25K 'Frogfoot-A' except in the following particulars:
Fuselage and tail: height 5.20 m (17 ft 0.75 in)

Below: Many Su-25UBs carry a bear badge on the nose. This is the emblem of the Ulan Ude factory which produced all two-seat Su-25s. This particular aircraft is armed with S-8 20-round 80-mm rocket pods. Plates on the wingtip fairings shield the pilot from the glare of the pop-down landing lights.

The Su-28 is a dedicated advanced trainer version of the Su-25UB. Whereas the heavier machine is fully armed and armoured and is used for conversion training, the Su-28's main role is intended to be advanced pilot training.

Left: The hook-equipped Su-25UTG is a dedicated carrier training variant of the two-seat 'Frogfoot'. Ten were built for trials (this one almost certainly the first) and have been augmented by a batch of similar Su-25UBPs. The aircraft may be converted to have a secondary attack role now that the MiG-29K seems unlikely to be procured for the carrier Kuznetsov.

Sukhoi **Su-25T** (no reporting name allocated)

The **Su-34** is an extensively upgraded and modernised derivative of the Su-25 'Frogfoot' and was originally designated **Su-25T**, the designation being changed to differentiate it from the older aircraft and thereby attract funding on the basis of being a 'new' project. The Su-34 designation is being reused to denote an advanced attack derivative of the Su-27 'Flanker'. The Su-25T designation is now used again by this advanced 'Frogfoot'.

Work on the new aircraft began in 1984, as Su-25 combat losses in Afghanistan were beginning to cause concern. The basic 'Frogfoot' was subjected to a host of modifications to improve survivability, but other problems, including lack of all-weather and night capability and insufficient range/endurance also needed to be addressed, and it was decided to design a new variant. The basic single-seat Su-25 lacked internal space, so the new variant was based on the airframe of the Su-25UB, using the rear cockpit and former internal gun and ammunition bay to house new avionics and extra fuel tanks. To camouflage the aircraft's true role, a dummy second cockpit was painted onto the prototypes. Three **T-8M** prototypes were converted from Su-25UB airframes, the first making its maiden flight on 17 August 1984 at Ulan Ude. The T-8Ms differed from Su-25UBs in having a GSL-30-6 30-mm cannon mounted below the centre fuselage, and some sources suggest that the new variant also had a slightly lengthened nose. The radar warning receiver

'spike' at the base of the fin was also deleted.

A pre-production batch of 10 aircraft was built under the designation **Su-25T**, the T standing for Tankovyi, or anti-tank. These aircraft were not all built to a completely common standard, but all feature a large (192-round) chaff/flare dispenser in a cylindrical fairing below the trailing edge of the rudder. The nose gear is offset to port and a variety of externally-mounted cannon have been fitted beside it, to starboard. The GSL-30-6 seems to have been abandoned and has been replaced by the Su-25's original twin-barrelled AO-17A 30-mm cannon, or by a single-barrelled weapon on some aircraft.

To give true night capability, the aircraft has a new avionics system, with a new Voskhod INAS and two digital computers. The nose is widened to accommodate an improved Schkval EO package, containing a new TV camera and laser designator, spot tracker and rangefinder. This can give a 23X magnification image of the target area. A variety of equipment pods can be carried under the belly, including a Mercury LLLTV/FLIR system or a low-light-level navigation system. An onboard electronic reconnaissance system allows hostile emissions to be detected, identified and located, increasing survivability and allowing the aircraft to undertake defence suppression missions. The aircraft has been offered for export under the designation **Su-25TK**, with Abu Dhabi targeted as one potential customer.

In March 1993, when it seemed as

One of three Su-25T prototypes converted from UB airframes. The second cockpit and gun/ammunition bays are used to house extra avionics and fuel tankage. An AO-17 cannon is scabbed on below the fuselage.

though the MiG-29K had not been selected for production, Sukhoi claimed to have received funding to develop a maritime strike aircraft based on the Su-25T, for service aboard the *Kuznetsov*. Designated **Su-25TP**, it reportedly combines the features of the Su-25UTG with the weapons system of the Su-25T. A prototype is reportedly under construction. During the same month, Sukhoi also announced a production order for a land-based Su-25T variant, redesignated **Su-25TM**, with Kinzhal podded MMW radar and a Khod FLIR targeting device (the latter replacing the original Mercury unit).

SPECIFICATION

Sukhoi Su-25TK
generally similar to the Su-25K 'Frogfoot' except in the following particulars:
Wing: span 14.52 m (47 ft 7.5 in)
Fuselage and tail: length 15.33 m (50 ft 3.5 in); height 5.20 m (13 ft 2.5 in)
Weights: maximum take-off 18600 kg (41,005 lb) Fuel and load: internal fuel 3840 kg (8,466 lb)
Range: combat radius with 2000-kg (4,409-lb) warload and two external fuel tanks 400 km (216 nm; 249 miles) on a lo-lo-lo profile, and 700 km (378 nm; 435 miles) on a hi-lo-hi profile

Sukhoi **Su-27 'Flanker'**

The **Su-27 'Flanker'** represents one of the jewels in the Soviet aerospace industry's crown. A modified version of the aircraft shattered 27 world records (taking most from a similarly modified example of its Western equivalent, the F-15 Eagle), and in countless displays the aircraft has demonstrated manoeuvres which no Western fighter can emulate, and has done so reliably and safely, at air show altitudes. The aircraft's reputation is nonetheless tarnished by doubts about its avionics, by doubts about its agility at operational weight, and by an early history of problems severe enough to require a total redesign.

Work on the **T-10** design began in 1969, when the Sukhoi OKB began work on a new interceptor for the IA-PVO, working closely with TSAGI, the MM Saturn engine design bureau and a number of research establishments. The design team was led by Yevgeny Ivanov, although Sukhoi himself took a close interest in the aircraft until his death in 1975. The requirement was for a highly manoeuvrable fighter with very long range, heavy armament and modern sensors. It was to be capable of intercepting low-flying NATO attack aircraft and high-level bombers, and to be able to meet agile fighters like the F-15 on equal terms.

In many ways, the Su-27 could be regarded as a scaled-up MiG-29, although Mikoyan and Sukhoi arrived at similar configurations because they were designing similar highly-agile fighters which were to be able to explore hitherto impossible parts of the flight envelope, and were relying on input from the same research institutes. The aircraft was thus designed around a highly-blended forebody and high-lift wing, with ogival leading-edge root extensions.

To maximise manoeuvrability, the T-10 was designed from the outset to be unstable, and therefore required a computer-controlled fly-by-wire control system at least in pitch. The OKB was able to draw on the experience it had accumulated during the T-4/Su-100 Mach 3 bomber programme, for which a FBW control system had been

designed. The first prototype T-10, powered by a pair of AL-21F-3 turbojets, made its maiden flight on 20 May 1977 in the hands of chief test pilot Vladimir Ilyushin. The provisional reporting name **'Ram-J'** allocated then was eventually replaced by the appellation **'Flanker-A'**. The first four prototypes (**T-10-1/-4**) were constructed at the bureau's own experimental shop in Moscow, and five more (**T-10-5, -6, -9, -10** and **-11**) were built at Komsomolsk-na-

Early production Su-27s had simple strakes on either side of the tail sting, rather than the box-like fairings which on later aircraft house chaff/flare dispensers. They also retain small anti-flutter weights on the leading edge of each tailfin.

Above: This Lipetsk-based Su-27 is fitted with wingtip Sorbitsiya ESM pods. 'Red 10' is seen diving on a ground target during a strafe attack, demonstrating the aircraft's secondary attack role. It sports a gaudy sharkmouth on each engine intake and carries a five-round 130-mm rocket pod under the starboard wing.

Below: Ukraine has about 60 Su-27s in service with at least two regiments: the 62nd IBAP at Bel'bek, as part of the new Air Defence Force's Southern Region, and the 831st IBAP at Mirgorod, which is part of the tactical air arm.

Above: This late-production Su-27 carries an individual aircraft excellence award on the nose, together with a series of small red stars. It is seen on approach to Chojna, once home to the 582nd IBAP and one of two Frontal Aviation 'Flanker' bases in Poland. The two-tone radome is noteworthy, the lighter colour denoting the extent of the Su-27's twist cassegrain antenna.

Amur. From **T-10-3** the aircraft were powered by Saturn (Lyul'ka) AL-31F turbofans, which gave about 12 per cent more thrust and much better specific fuel consumption.

The early flight development programme revealed serious problems. The second prototype was lost in a fatal crash, the aircraft weight escalated and fuel consumption proved higher than expected. Furthermore, the F-15 entered service, and it became clear that the T-10 as it was would be an inferior aircraft. Accordingly, the new designer general, Mikhail P. Simonov, supervised a total redesign. The **T-10-7** was completed as the first prototype of the new design, under the new designation **T-10S-1**, making its maiden flight on 20 April 1981. This was effectively a completely new aircraft, with a redesigned wing which had a straight, slatted leading edge and cropped wingtips incorporating missile launch rails. The latter also doubled as anti-flutter weights.

Ailerons were deleted, to be replaced by flaperons and differential tailerons, while the entire fuselage was redesigned, with a deeper spine and shallower nose. The mainwheel door airbrakes were replaced by a spine-mounted airbrake and the undercarriage was redesigned and repositioned. The nosewheel was moved aft to improve taxiing characteristics and to minimise foreign object ingestion on take-off or landing. The tailfins were moved outboard from the tops of the engine nacelles to booms which lay alongside them. These changes were sufficient to prompt NATO to allocate a new reporting name of **'Flanker-B'**.

The original T-10s were used in the flight test programme alongside the T-10S-1, and preparations were put in hand for series production. Before production could begin,

more problems had to be solved, the most serious being a wing fault which killed one pilot and nearly destroyed a second aircraft. Reducing the area of the leading-edge slats proved to be the answer.

The Su-27 finally began to enter operational service during the mid-1980s, although deliveries were at one stage held up by delays with the aircraft's advanced new radar. This led to completed but radarless Su-27s being stockpiled outside the Komsomolsk factory for several months. The earliest Su-27s delivered had a frameless rear canopy section and square-topped tailfins, but later aircraft added a frame behind the pilot's ejection seat headrest and cropped off the rear top corners of the fintips. Later still, prominent spikes on the fin leading edges (thought to be anti-flutter devices) were removed.

One interesting Su-27 sub-variant was the **P-42**. This had its radar and radome removed and replaced by ballast and a metal nosecone, and had ventral fins, fincaps and paint removed. The aircraft was powered by uprated AI-31F engines (designated R-32) and was used to set a series of time-to-height and other records, in the hands of Victor Pugachev, Nikolai Sadovnikov, Oleg Tsoi and Yevgeni Frolov. Because the lightened aircraft's brakes could not hold it against the full thrust of the more powerful R-32 engines, it had to be tethered to an armoured vehicle while it ran up to full power, before being released using an electronic locking device.

The standard Su-27 fighter is now in service with the Russian and Ukrainian air forces, and serves with Frontal Aviation as well as the old PVO air defence force. It is used primarily in the air-to-air role, although it can carry a range of freefall bombs and unguided rockets underwing, and the air-to-

ground role has been practised by some Su-27 units. Even in Frontal Aviation, however, the Su-27 is primarily used as an interceptor or escort fighter and not as a ground attack aircraft.

The Su-27 is equipped with an advanced pulse-Doppler radar, whose large antenna gives a long range, although poor signal processing means that only one target can be engaged at a time. The radar is backed up by a sophisticated EO complex which includes an IRST system and a collimated laser rangefinder. This allows the Su-27 to detect, track and engage a target without using radar. The Su-27 is also compatible with a helmet-mounted target designation system, facilitating the pilot's engagement of off-axis targets by cueing sensors or missile tracker heads onto a target which has not been boresighted.

WEAPON OPTIONS

The Su-27 has a total of 10 hardpoints that allow it to carry up to six R-27 (AA-10 'Alamo') and four AA-11 'Archer' air-to-air missiles, giving a remarkable degree of combat persistence. Missiles are backed up by a 30-mm GSh-30-1 cannon in the starboard wingroot, with 150 rounds of ammunition. In either the air-to-air or air-to-ground roles, the wingtip missile launch rails can be replaced by ECM pods.

OPERATORS

Su-27s were originally delivered to the integrated armed forces of the **former USSR**, but most have now been absorbed into **Russia**'s armed forces, the CIS having failed to keep central control of unified forces. The aircraft were originally ordered for the IA-PVO air defence force, but were also delivered to Frontal Aviation units. In 1994, approximately 200 serve with the **IA-PVO**, while a further 150 are in service with **Frontal Aviation**. Known users include the 234th 'Proskurovskii' Guards IAP at Kubinka, the 159th 'Novorossiisk' Guards IAP at Biesowice (formerly at Kluczewo, Poland), the 831st IAP at Mirogorod (Carpathian Military District), 54th IAP at Vainodo and 689th IAP at Nivenskoye (both Leningrad/St Petersburg MD). The 582nd IAP at Chojna, Poland, moved to Smolensk and disbanded at the end of 1992. Perhaps the best known Su-27s are the aircraft of the 234 'Proskurovskii' Guards Fighter Regiment based at Kubinka, near Moscow, which provides the 'Russian Knights' aerobatic team.

The break-up of the USSR left some Su-27 regiments on non-Russian territory, most such units then being absorbed by the new air arms of the states involved. The 62nd IAP at Bel'bek became part of the **Ukrainian air force**, and other Ukrainian Su-27

regiments were based at Zhitomir and Sevastopol. In 1994 Ukraine fielded a further Su-27 regiment at Mirgorod. Formerly assigned to the 24th Air Army, the 831st IAP now forms part of the 5th Air Army's tactical assets and retains its previous role of long-range fighter escort for Ukraine's Su-24 'Fencers'. In **Byelorussia**, Su-27s may serve with the former 61st IAP at Baranovidu. Since all Su-27 production is centered in Russia, spares support for these aircraft may be difficult, and many may be replaced by types which are easier to support locally.

The first true export customer for the Su-27 was **China**, ordering 24 aircraft which were delivered from August 1991, following a March 1991 contract signature. The aircraft were initially based on Hainan Island, but were then moved back to the mainland. A second similar batch is reportedly sought by China.

The sole export customer to date has been China, whose People's Liberation Army Air Force has taken delivery of 24 or 26 'Flankers'. They were delivered in a new medium grey scheme with an unusual 'cutout' in the lower part of the radome.

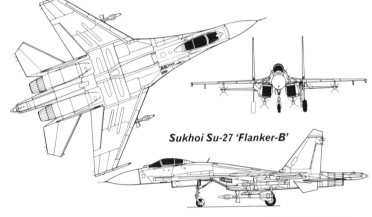

Sukhoi Su-27 'Flanker-B'

SPECIFICATION

Sukhoi Su-27 'Flanker-B'
Wing: span 14.70 m (48 ft 2.75 in); aspect ratio 5.6; wing area 46.50 m² (500.54 sq ft)
Fuselage and tail: length 21.90 m (71 ft 10 in) excluding probe; height 5.90 m (19 ft 4 in); tailplane

span 9.90 m (32 ft 6 in); wheel track 4.33 m (14 ft 2½ in); wheel base 5.88 m (19 ft 3.5 in)
Powerplant: two NPO Saturn (Lyul'ka) AL-31F turbofans each rated at 79.43 kN (17,857 lb) dry and 122.58 kN (27,557 lb st) with afterburning
Weights: empty 17700 kg (39,021 lb); normal take-off 23250 kg (51,257 lb); maximum take-off 33000 kg (72751 lb)
Fuel and load: normal internal fuel about 527 (11,618 lb); maximum internal fuel 9400 kg (20,723 lb); maximum ordnance 6000 kg (13,228 lb)
Speed: limiting Mach No. 2.35; maximum level speed

'clean' at 11000 m (36,090 ft) 2280 km/h (1230 kt; 1417 mph) and at sea level 1370 km/h (739 kt; 851 mph)
Range: at high-altitude 3680 km (1,986 nm; 2,287 miles); range at low-altitude 1370 km (739 nm; 851 miles)
Performance: maximum rate of climb at sea level 19800 m (64,960 ft) per minute; service ceiling 17700 m 58,071 ft); take-off run 450 m (1,476 ft) at maximum take-off weight; landing run 700 m (2,297 ft) at normal landing weight
g limits: +8

Sukhoi **Su-27UB 'Flanker-C'**

It is believed that no two-seat Su-27s based on the early 'Flanker-A' were produced, and that the prototype **Su-27UB**, designated **T-10U-1**, was based on the definitive production Su-27 'Flanker-B'. This aircraft reportedly made its maiden flight on 7 March 1985, piloted by Nikolai Sadovnikov. Series production of the Su-27UB began at Irkutsk in 1986, and deliveries began in 1987. Before the type became available in large numbers, Su-27 regiments used MiG-23UB 'Flogger', Su-17U 'Fitter' and MiG-29UB 'Fulcrum' two-seaters for conversion and continuation training.

The Su-27UB differs from the single-seater in having a lengthened forward fuselage with stepped tandem cockpits under a single canopy. The tailfins are increased in height and area, as is the airbrake. Due to a 740-kg (1,631-lb) increase in normal take-off weight and the increased drag caused by the new canopy, maximum speed is reduced by about 70 km/h (38 kt; 43 mph) at low level and 160 km/h (86 kt; 99 mph) at

height, while low-level range is reduced by 100 km (54 nm; 62 miles) and high-level range by 680 km (367 nm; 423 miles). Turn radius, rate of climb and take-off/landing distances are less affected.

Su-27UBs have also been used for a number of experimental programmes. Two-seat Su-27s conducted buddy refuelling trials using a centreline UPAZ refuelling pod, and made a number of extremely long distance flights, including a marathon 15-hour 42-minute, 13440-km (7,253-nm; 8,351-miles) sortie in 1987 flown by Sadovnikov and I. Votintsev. Other Su-27UBs have been used as airborne laboratories to support the

This Su-27UB 'Flanker-C' of the 234th 'Proskurovskii' Guards Fighter Regiment at Kubinka wears the striking colour scheme of the 'Russian Knights' aerobatic demonstration team. The front cockpit has been fitted with rails for an instrument flying training hood.

Gulfstream/Sukhoi SSBJ programme, and to test the vectoring nozzles under development for advanced versions of the Su-27.

SPECIFICATION

Sukhoi Su-27UB 'Flanker-C'
generally similar to the Sukhoi Su-27 'Flanker-B' except in the following particulars:

Fuselage and tail: height 6.36 m (20 ft 10.25 in)
Weights: normal take-off 23990 kg (52,888 lb)
Range: range at high altitude 3000 km (1,619 nm; 1,864 miles); range at low altitude 1270 km (685 nm; 789 miles)
Performance: maximum rate of climb at sea level 16200 m (53,150 ft) per minute; service ceilin 16700 m (54,790 ft); take-off run 580 m (1,903 ft) at maximum take-off weight; landing run 650 m (2,133 ft) at normal landing weight

Sukhoi Su-27K/Su-33

Development of the **Su-27K** was intended to produce a shipborne long-range interceptor to complement MiG-29Ks in air wings that would equip the Soviet Union's four new conventional aircraft-carriers. One carrier was never started, another (*Ulyanovsk*) was scrapped on the slipway, and *Varyag* (formerly *Riga*) remains incomplete and unlikely to enter Russian/CIS service, leaving only *Kuznetsov* in service with the **Russian navy**. This makes the provision of one dedicated carrierborne fighter (let alone two) an extremely expensive proposition, killing the original plan of having a navalised Su-27 as a kind of F-14-equivalent long-range interceptor plus a navalised MiG-29 as an F/A-18-equivalent shorter-range multi-role fighter. Although the logical decision would be to procure only the multi-role aircraft (especially since its intercept capability is identical, except in terms of range), the Su-27K still has a chance of snatching any order since the Sukhoi OKB appears to enjoy much greater political influence than its competitor.

Like the Su-27M/-35 (which is described separately), the Su-27K can trace its ancestry back to the **T-10-24**, the first Su-27 to be flown with canard foreplanes, which the Sukhoi OKB studied as a means of improving take-off performance and of reducing approach speed, as well as for improving agility. Navalising the Su-27 was a major task, and resulted in a host of modifications, most of which were applied to a series of at least seven prototypes.

The first of these, perhaps designated **T-10-37**, or perhaps **Su-27K-1**, (plus all subsequent Su-27Ks) was fitted with canard foreplanes and an arrester hook, and also had a retractable inflight-refuelling probe and the associated offset IRST. The prototype made its first flight on 17 August 1987, piloted by Victor G. Pugachev. The wing was initially unmodified, but eventually received a new, two-section double-slotted trailing-edge flap and drooping ailerons. No other Su-27 variant has ailerons, which confer better roll control on approach. Later prototypes had folding wings and even folding tailplanes, and were used in trials on land and aboard the *Tbilisi*, later renamed *Kuznetsov*. Victor Pugachev made the first arrested carrier shipboard landing in Soviet naval history in Su-27K '39', on 1 November 1989.

The Su-27K is based upon the airframe and weapons system of the basic Su-27, with the same radar and a virtually unchanged cockpit. It thus has minimal air-to-ground capability, unlike the competing MiG-29K, which is closely based on the airframe and systems of the multi-role MiG-29M. The Su-27K can carry a maximum ordnance load of 6500 kg (14,330 lb) and maximum take-off weight is reduced to 32000 kg (70,546 lb). Various air-to-surface weapons have been displayed under or beside statically displayed Su-27Ks, including the massive 250-km (135-nm; 155-mile) range Kh-41 Moskito ASM, the anti-radar Kh-31 and the smaller Zvezda Kh-35 ('Har-

poonski') ASM. The Su-27K is also the first 'Flanker' sub-type plumbed for the carriage of external fuel – in this case, a 1500-litre (396-US gal) centreline tank. It was widely believed that if an Su-27K were to be selected for production, it would be a hybrid aircraft more closely based upon the Su-35, and probably with vectoring nozzles. Such supposition was denied at Le Bourget in June 1993, when it was stated that the 20 **Su-33**s under construction at Komsomolsk on Amur were merely navalised ver-

sions of the basic interceptor Su-27, without multi-role capability or the flight control and weapons system improvements of the Su-35. 'Flanker' production at Komsomolsk was halted temporarily in early 1994, and there are reports that the more versatile MiG-29K may be put into production.

An Su-27K and a MiG-29K are seen together on the deck of the carrier **Kuznetsov.** *The Su-27K is optimised as an interceptor.*

This heavily armed **Su-27K** *carrying a centreline Kh-41 Moskito ASM and a full load of AAMs sits at Zhukovskii, with wings and tailplanes folded.*

Sukhoi Su-27K

Sukhoi Su-27P/PU/Su-30

The basic Su-27 interceptor and Su-27UB trainer produced a rash of derivatives which were publicly unveiled during the early 1990s. One such derivative was the **Su-27PU**, which at first glance seemed to differ very little from the Su-27UB trainer. Apart from provision of a retractable inflight-refuelling probe (also fitted to the Su-27K, Su-27KU/IB and Su-27M/Su-35), and with its IRST 'ball' offset to starboard to compensate, the aircraft is externally almost identical. Some analysts hypothesise that the radome is of different profile (perhaps the same as that fitted to the Su-27M/-35), suggesting that a new radar has been fitted. This was denied at the 1993 Paris Air Salon, where the aircraft's designer, Igor Emelianov, confirmed that the Su-30 retains the same

radar as the baseline Su-27 interceptor.

The aircraft was designed to meet a PVO requirement for a long-range, high-endurance interceptor that could secure Russia's enormous borders and provide air cover for naval forces. The requirement included a 10-hour endurance stipulation, necessitating provision for inflight refuelling, systems proved for 10 hour's continuous operation and identical twin cockpits housing two pilots, either of whom can assume command at any stage of the mission. Range of the aircraft is given as 3000 km (1,620 nm; 1,864 miles) with internal fuel, and 5200 km (2,808 nm; 3,231 miles) with inflight refuelling. Development funding was ensured by changing the designation to **Su-30** (existing aircraft projects being starved

of resources). The Su-30 has a new miniaturised navigation system, based on that fitted to Aeroflot's international airliners with a GPS and Loran, Omega and Mars navigation equipment. The prototype made its maiden flight on 30 December 1989 at Irkutsk, in the hands of Yevgeni Revunov. Since then, a small number of production Su-30s have been built, including a pair which was specially constructed to meet an order from the 'Test Pilots' aerobatic team. The latter aircraft were fitted with the IFR probe and navigation system, but lacked all combat equipment and military systems.

The aircraft is reportedly fully combat-capable and, with the addition of extra equipment in the rear cockpit, is also able to operate as a mini-AWACS and command post, operating in conjunction with up to four other aircraft (other Su-30s, Su-27 single-seat fighters, or Su-27Ps), directing or even automatically controlling them to the

most suitable target, and transferring information within the formation by datalink to build up the best possible tactical situation display. This is the same concept that has been pioneered by the MiG-31 'Foxhound'. In this role, the Su-30 carries a dedicated fighter controller in the back seat.

The single-seat **Su-27P** is a less well known aircraft. It is believed to have the same navigation system and increased endurance systems as the Su-30, but its single cockpit would make such capability difficult to exploit operationally. A number of stripped aircraft are operated by the 'Test Pilots' team, but the aircraft's service status is uncertain, and any redesignation must remain a matter of speculation.

The **Su-30MK** is an export Su-30 derivative for multi-role use with added ground-attack capability. The aircraft remains primarily a long-range interceptor, however, and comparisons with the F-15E have been

Above: One of the Su-30 prototypes refuels the T-10-37, a canard- and hook-equipped forerunner of the Su-27K that lacked folding wings, outboard ailerons and double-slotted flaps.

Right: This heavily armed aircraft is one of the demonstrators and development aircraft for the Su-30MK, the export version of the multi-role version of the original Su-30 interceptor. India has been mooted as a potential customer for the aircraft.

rejected. The Sukhoi OKB is eager to export the Su-30MK, whose flight test programme was reportedly completed in the early summer of 1993.

Sukhoi **Su-27IB/KU/Su-34**

A great deal of confusion exists even as to the proper designation of this two-seat Su-27 derivative. When the aircraft was displayed at Minsk-Maschulische (its first official unveiling) in a closed display for CIS leaders, an information board bore the designation **Su-27IB**. However, until the 1993 Paris air show this designation was consistently denied and the alternative designation **Su-27KU** was used instead.

This muddle over designation is more significant than being mere semantics, since the two designations represent two very different roles. The first sight of the aircraft was afforded in a TASS photo released in August 1991, showing it on approach to the carrier *Tbilisi*, although it seemed to lack arrester hook and folding wings (as was later confirmed). Side-by-side seating, giving pilot and instructor the same approach picture, is of obvious benefit for a carrier training aircraft, as is the strengthened undercarriage with twin nosewheels, and the newly revealed designation KU (Korabelnii Uchebno or, literally, shipborne trainer) would seem to support such a role, although the lack of arrester hook, wing and tailplane folding and the longer wheelbase would mitigate against naval use.

The IB designation (Istrebitel Bombardirovshchik or, literally, fighter-bomber) used at Minsk was supported by the aircraft's retractable inflight-refuelling probe (internal fuel would surely be adequate for carrier training) and (admittedly unlikely) load of bombs and air-to-surface missiles. With suitable sensors, the Su-27, with its excellent range and endurance, would make a commendable strike aircraft, and recent articles in the Russian press claim a titanium armoured cockpit, armoured glass and CRT displays. The intakes are also said to have been redesigned for higher speed at low

level and the aircraft is reportedly optimised for 'contour-hugging' flight.

It seems likely that the aircraft was originally developed as a two-seat carrier trainer but that changed circumstances have led to its consideration as a potential basis for an Su-24 replacement, and its use as a demonstrator for such an aircraft. This would explain the aircraft's lack of radar, IRST and sensors. The original KU designation may have been resurrected for political reasons.

Whatever the confusion over designation, the nickname 'Platypus' is universally recognised, leading from the flattened, slightly-upturned nose shape, whose chines make it reminiscent of the SR-71 nose. The Su-27IB might form the basis of EW and recce variants of the Su-27. The production version, designated **Su-34**, is of similar configuration but has tandem twin main-

wheels and an extended, raised and enlarged tail sting.

SPECIFICATION

Sukhoi Su-27IB
generally similar to the Sukhoi Su-27 'Flanker-B' except in the following particulars:

Powerplant: Two NPO Saturn (Lyul'ka, AL-31FM turbofans, each rated at 130.42 kN (29,320 lb st) with afterburning)
Weights: maximum take off 44,360 kg (97,795 lb)
Fuel and load: maximum ordnance 8,000 kg (17,636 lb)
Performance: service ceiling 17,000 m (55,755 ft)

Sukhoi Su-27IB/Su-34

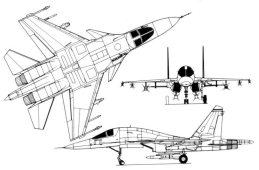

The Su-27IB was probably developed as a carrier-based training aircraft, but the design has since been revised slightly to meet the Russian air forces' requirement for an Su-24 replacement in the interdiction and strike roles. The production version will be the Su-34.

Sukhoi Su-27M/Su-35

In an atmosphere in which funding for existing aircraft projects was impossible, the Sukhoi OKB ensured continuing financial support for its advanced Su-27 derivative, initially designated **Su-27M**, by the simple expedient of redesignating it as **Su-35**. In contrast to Mikoyan's openness about its advanced MiG-29 derivatives, Sukhoi has remained remarkably tight-lipped about its Su-35 project. At Farnborough in September 1992, OKB designer general Simonov and project chief Nikolai Nikitin contradicted one another on several key questions when separately interviewed about the Su-35.

As far as can be ascertained, the project to develop an advanced version of the Su-27 was launched during the early 1980s, before the initial variant had entered service, with the primary aim of producing an aircraft with better dogfighting characteristics. A proof-of-concept aircraft with moving canard foreplanes, the **T-10-24**, first flew during 1982, and was the first of a confusing array of converted production aircraft used as testbeds, and newly built Su-27M 'prototypes'. Better agility (including higher Alpha limits and improved handling at high angles of attack) has reportedly been achieved through use of the

canards, and through provision of heavy internal fuel tanks in the tailfins.

The aircraft is equipped with a completely new flight control system, with four longitudinal channels and three transverse. The channel for the canard foreplane also functions as a redundant channel. To compensate for the canards, the tailfin area has also been increased on some Su-35 prototypes, and the new, square-topped tailfin will reportedly be incorporated on any production Su-35.

In addition to the aerodynamic and control system improvements, Sukhoi has been working on vectoring engine nozzles and on various avionics improvements. Simple two-dimensional vectoring nozzles (similar to those flown on the F-15 S/MTD) have been tested on at least one Zhukovskii-based Su-27UB, and are intended to be incorporated on any production Su-35 (if funding permits). Such nozzles could be retrofitted at a later date. A number of avionics improvements will definitely be incorporated in any production Su-35.

A new radar has been installed. Perhaps designated N-011, and probably similar in concept to the N-010 of the MiG-29M, it reportedly has a range of up to 400 km (248 miles) (or 200 km/124 miles against ground

targets) and can simultaneously track more than 15 targets, and engage up to six. The aircraft also has advanced datalink equipment allowing the kind of group operation practised by the MiG-31, whereby a formation leader can directly and automatically control his wingmen's aircraft, receiving radar and sensor inputs from (and automatically redistributing to) all formation aircraft, ground stations and AWACS aircraft.

A cryptic reference to 'radar tracking of multiple targets in free air or on the surface, at both forward or rear hemisphere' is believed to allude to the function of a dielectric radome in the tailcone, which is believed to house the antenna for a rear-facing search radar. In February 1993, at an international conference, Major General Vassily Alexandrov, head of the Russian Federation air force's Central Scientific and Research Institute, revealed that a rearward-facing air intercept radar was under development for the Su-35 to allow 'over-the-shoulder' missile shots.

In service, the Su-35 will be able to carry up to seven examples of the new Novator KS-172 AAM-L ultra-long-range missile. Originally revealed with a range of 300 km (186 miles), this has a new solid-propellant booster section (which adds 1.4 m/4.6 ft to the 6-m/19.7-ft long missile), increasing effective range to 400 km (248 miles). Fitted with an active radar seeker, the missile

also has inertial mid-course guidance and correction, and can be used at altitudes of up to 30000 m (98,425 ft)

The cockpit of the Su-35 features three large CRT MFD screens, each surrounded by 20 surprisingly crude input buttons, with a separate navigation display. No attempt seems to have been made to control these by HOTAS buttons, as in the MiG-29M. A sidestick controller was flown by a NIIAKM Su-27, but has not yet been incorporated in the Su-35. The new avionics give much better air-to-surface capability, conferring compatibility with a range of laser- (and perhaps TV-) guided air-to-ground weapons. Automatic terrain following is also possible. A retractable inflight-refuelling probe makes possible a further increase in the Su-27's already impressive radius of action.

Nikitin claims that the first of six Su-27M/Su-35 prototypes made its maiden flight on 28 June 1988, in the hands of Oleg Tsoi. In February 1993, Major General Alexander Yonov, director of operations and deputy chief of the Russian Federation air staff, stated that flight testing was complete and that production aircraft would enter operational service in the near future.

SPECIFICATION

Sukhoi Su-35
generally similar to the Sukhoi Su-27 'Flanker-B' except in the following particulars:
Wing: span 15.16 m (49 ft 8.75 in) over ESM pods
Fuselage and tail: length 22.183 m (72 ft 9 in) height 6.84 m (22 ft 5 in)
Powerplant: two NPO Saturn (Lyul'ka) AL-31FM turbofans, each rated at 130.42 kN (29,321 lb st) with afterburning
Weights: empty (40,564 lb); normal take-off 26000 kg (57,319 lb); maximum take-off 34000 kg (74,956 lb)
Load: maximum external load 8000 kg (17,637 lb)
Speed: maximum level speed 'clean' at 11000 m (36,089 ft) 2500 km/h (1,349 kt; 1,553 mph), and at sea level 1400 km/h (756 kt; 870 mph)
Range: at high-altitude with four AAMs 3500 km (1,889 nm; 2,175 miles); range at low-altitude with four AAMs 1450 km/h (783 nm; 901 miles); ferry range 4200 km (2,267 nm; 2610 miles); range with inflight refuelling in excess of 6800 km (3,670 nm; 4,225 miles)

The Su-35 is being aggressively marketed by the Sukhoi OKB, and prototypes have been painted in several eye-catching camouflage schemes.

Below: The Su-35 differs from the basic 'Flanker' in having a new radar, flight control system and airframe improvements. It also has tall square-topped fins.

MISSILE ARMAMENT
This Su-35 is armed with a pair of R-73s outboard, four R-77s and a trio of the new long-range AAM-L, a very long-range anti-AWACS weapon, whose range can be further extended by the addition of a separate booster.

RADOME
Since the new radar has a new flat plate antenna, instead of the old inverse cassegrain unit, the radome has been reshaped, becoming less bulged aft.

RADAR
The Su-35 has a new multi-mode radar, probably designated N-011, with significant air-to-ground capability. This may be related to the N-010 radar of the MiG 29M, itself a version of the Phazatron Zhuk (Beetle). More importantly, the radar has much improved processing capability, allowing up to 15 targets to be tracked simultaneously, and six to be engaged at ranges out to 362 km (195 nm; 225 miles).

POWERPLANTS
The Su-35 is powered by a pair of NPO Saturn (Lyul'ka) AL-31FM turbofans, each rated at 130.42 kN (29,320 lb) thrust with reheat. This is 7.85 kN (1,764 lb) more thrust than is produced by the standard aircraft's AL-31F, and compensates for the new type's increased weight. The AL-31FM may also have digital engine controls. The engine intakes do not seem to have been altered, so it may be assumed that the extra thrust is the result of higher operating temperatures (perhaps indicating a shorter life, or the use of advanced materials) and not greater mass flow.

COCKPIT
The Su-35 has a modern glass cockpit with three multi-function CRT displays. These mark a major improvement over the traditional 'steam-age' analog cockpit of the basic Su-27, but have traditional input buttons surrounding them rather than the throttle- and stick-mounted controls of those fitted to the MiG-29M.

Sukhoi Su-35 (Su-27M)

This aircraft is one of six Su-35 prototypes – probably the third, but said to have been the fifth to fly. Both Su-27M/Su-35s seen so far have carried 70-series codes, perhaps indicating the OKB designation T-10S-70. The Su-35 originated as the Su-27M and was designed as a follow-on to the basic Su-27, with better dogfighting characteristics (the primary goal according to its designer, Nikolai Feyodorevich Nikitin) and with better BVR combat and multi-role capability. Although the new type looks externally similar to the standard Su-27, it is in many respects an entirely new aircraft, with many new systems and some new structure.

ECM PODS
Wingtip ECM pods replaced missile launch rails on at least two Su-35 prototypes, and are usually illustrated in Sukhoi publicity material relating to the aircraft. The forward radome is reportedly a receiver, while that at the rear is a transmitter, rather than both being transmitters for front and rear hemisphere coverage, according to Sukhoi documents.

TAILCONE
The Su-35 has a reconfigured tailcone with a reshaped tip. This is a dielectric radome rather than the usual brake chute cover, perhaps tying in with oblique brochure references to rear hemisphere radar coverage, and 'over-the-shoulder' BVR missile capability.

FLIGHT CONTROL SYSTEMS
The Su-35 is controlled using a completely new digital fly-by-wire control system (the standard Su-27 uses FBW only in pitch). The system is quadruplex, using four channels in pitch and three in roll/yaw.

FINS
The Su-35 has new tailfins (each containing an auxiliary fuel tank), based on the taller fin of the Su-27UB but with the rudder extended downwards to the fin base, as it would be on the single-seat Su-27, and uncropped square tips.

Sukhoi Su-37

The **Su-37** was developed as a private-venture replacement for aircraft like the Su-25 'Frogfoot'. A single-seat fighter-bomber, the aircraft represented a major shift away from the dedicated ground attack concept embodied by the Su-25, perhaps reacting to the school of thought in the USSR which wanted to move towards greater use of multi-role aircraft and whose most prominent statesman was Colonel General Yevgeni Shaposhnikov, C-in-C of the Russian air forces and former MiG-21 pilot. The Su-37 is therefore fitted with an advanced multi-mode radar (probably the Zhuk, or the MiG-29M's similar N-010) and is compatible with the full range of Soviet air-to-air missiles. This radar reportedly gives automatic terrain-following capability and is augmented by an electro-optical complex which includes a laser rangefinder, an IRST and guidance for TV- and laser-guided missiles.

Details of the Su-37 first emerged during 1991, when the Yugoslav magazine *Aerosvet* published an artist's impression of the aircraft, illustrating a detailed but largely speculative article, which nevertheless revealed a great deal about the new design. Similar in configuration to the Dassault Rafale or Saab Gripen, with no tailplanes, a cropped delta wing and close-coupled canard foreplanes, the Su-37 combines excellent performance with some stealth characteristics and exceptional agility. Eighteen hardpoints are provided for up to 6000 kg (13,227 lb) of weapons, and a 30-mm cannon is reported to be buried in the starboard wingroot, although this has not been shown on models of the aircraft. Wing folding is provided to allow stowage in a restricted space.

A model of the aircraft was displayed at Dubai in 1992, and a model of the two-seat version was revealed in Moscow during the same year. Marketing of the aircraft has been at best sporadic, however. Enquiries about the aircraft at Farnborough in 1992 were met with feigned incomprehension or an old-style Soviet 'that is not interesting' type of answer. Interestingly, a handful of leaflets about the aircraft were accidentally released to the press. The break-up of Sukhoi and emergence of a new Sukhoi Attack Aircraft Division might lead to increased efforts to launch the aircraft, although a Russian/CIS order seems unlikely and progress is probably dependent on finding an overseas partner. The Sukhoi OKB has hinted at plans to fit a vectoring nozzle to further enhance manoeuvrability.

Swearingen (Fairchild) Merlin IIIA

Fairchild Aircraft Incorporated
PO Box 790490, San Antonio
TX 78279-0490, USA

In 1966 Swearingen began production of its Merlin II series of pressurised twin-turboprop executive transports. This continued from 1970 with the Merlin III that introduced revised tail surfaces, among other improvements. The **Merlin IIIA** introduced additional cabin windows and major system and flight deck improvements. Seating eight to 11 passengers, this version appealed to the **Belgian air force**, which purchased six in 1976, and the **Argentine army**, which acquired four the following year. Five of the Belgian aircraft are still in use with 21 Sm/Esc, while three of the Argentine aircraft remain.

In January 1981 Swearingen products were retitled under the Fairchild Swearingen banner, and subsequent developments, the stretched Merlin IV and Metro, are described under that manufacturer.

SPECIFICATION

Swearingen Merlin IIIA
Wing: span 46 ft 3 in (14.10 m); aspect ratio 7.71; area 277.5 sq ft (25.78 m²)
Fuselage and tail: length 42 ft 2 in (12.85 m); height 16 ft 9.5 in (5.12 m); tailplane span 15 ft 1.5 in (4.61 m); wheel track 15 ft 0 in (4.57 m); wheelbase 10 ft 7 in (3.23 m)
Powerplant: two Garrett AiResearch TPE331-3U-303G turboprops, each rated at 840 shp (626.5 kW)
Weights: empty equipped 7,400 lb (3356 kg);

Belgium's five Merlin IIIAs are used by 21 Smaldeel/Escadrille on staff transport duties.

maximum take-off 12,500 lb (5670 kg)
Fuel and load: internal fuel capacity 648 US gal (2452 litres)
Speed: maximum cruising speed at 16,000 ft (4875 m) 282 kt (325 mph; 523 km/h); economical cruising speed 250 kt (288 mph; 463 km/h)
Range: at maximum cruising speed 1,709 nm (1,968 miles; 3167 km); ferry range at economical cruising speed 2,483 nm (2,860 miles; 4,602 km)

Performance: maximum rate of climb at sea level 2,530 ft (770 m) per minute; service ceiling 28,900 ft (8810 m); take-off run 2,150 ft (655 m)

Transall C.160

Original Transport Allianz group consisted of Nord, VFW and HFB.
Transall now responsibility of Aérospatiale (France) and
DASA (Germany)

Originally conceived as a replacement for the Nord Noratlas, which equipped transport units of France's **Armée de l'Air** and West Germany's **Luftwaffe**, the C.160 was one of the first successful joint European aerospace ventures, being produced by a consortium of companies which was collectively known as the Transport Allianz group. Indeed, the name and designation chosen for the resulting machine reflected the origins of the project, for the initial quantity to be acquired was set at 160, comprising 50 **C.160F**s for France and 110 **C.160D**s for West Germany. Another possible explanation may be that the aircraft's wing area is 160 m². The **Transall** name was merely a contraction of Transport Allianz. Members of the original production group included Nord-Aviation, Hamburger Flugzeugbau (HFB) and Vereinigte Flugtechnische Werke (VFW), these joining forces at the beginning of 1959.

Three prototypes were built in all, one by each of the three major partners in this venture, and the first of these made a successful maiden flight on 25 February 1963. They were followed by six pre-production examples from May 1965, while production-configured C.160s began to emerge in the spring of 1967, deliveries getting under way soon afterwards; by the time manufacture ceased in 1972, a total of 169 had been built. In addition to the 160 supplied to the two principal partners, nine **C.160Z**s were sold to **South Africa**. The only other air arm to operate the original type is **Turkey**, which took delivery of 20 **C.160T** aircraft (former Luftwaffe examples) in the early 1970s.

Subsequently, at the end of the 1970s, it was decided to reopen the production line in France, that country's air force ordering 25 more examples under the designation **C.160NG** (Nouvelle Génération) which differ from their predecessors by virtue of additional fuel capacity and improved avionics. Range limitations have been partly resolved by the extra centre-section fuel tank, but the newest C.160s also feature inflight-refuelling capability in the form of a probe above the cockpit. Maximum payload is 16000 kg (35,275 lb), while 93 troops or 88 paratroops can be accommodated.

Four more C.160NGs were added in 1982, and production ended in 1985. Ten aircraft were completed with a hose-drum unit in the port undercarriage sponson for refuelling tactical aircraft, and five more have provision for the fitment of this feature so that they can be rapidly reconfigured as tankers. In 1994 the Transall fleet was engaged in an upgrade programme which adds defences against missile attacks and other improvements.

French Transalls serve in the transport role with ET 1/61 'Touraine' and ET 3/61 'Poitou' at Orléans, ET 1/64 'Béarn' and ET 2/64 'Anjou' at Evreux, CIET 340 at Toulouse, GAM 56 at Evreux, ETOM 58 'Guadeloupe' at Pointe-à-Pître, ETOM 52 'La Tontouta' at Tontouta, New Caledonia, ETOM 55 'Ouessant' at Dakar, Senegal, ETOM 88 at Djibouti and ETOM 50 'Réunion' at St Denis. Luftwaffe units are LTG 61 at Landsberg, LTG 62 at Wunsdorf and LTG 63 at Hohn. Turkish Transalls are based at Erkilet with 221 Filo, and the C.160Zs of South Africa have been recently retired.

Transall C.160

In addition to the two original manufacturing nations, the Transall is flown by Turkey (right). Germany operates three wings as its principal transport type.

SPECIFICATION

Transall C.160 (first generation)
Wing: span 40.00 m (131 ft 3 in); aspect ratio 10.0; area 160.10 m² (1,723.36 sq ft)
Fuselage and tail: length 32.40 m (106 ft 3.5 in); height 11.65 m (38 ft 5 in); tailplane span 14.50 m (47 ft 7 in); wheel track 5.10 m (16 ft 9 in); wheel base 10.48 m (34 ft 4.5 in)
Powerplant: two Rolls-Royce Tyne RTy.20 Mk 22 turboprops each rated at 6,100 ehp (4548 ekW)
Weights: empty equipped 28758 kg (63,400 lb); normal take-off 44200 kg (97,443 lb); maximum take-off 49100 kg (108,245 lb)
Fuel and load: internal fuel 16500 litres (4,359 US gal); external fuel none; maximum payload 16000 kg (35,273 lb)
Speed: maximum level speed 'clean' at 4500 m

(14,765 ft) 536 km/h (289 kt; 333 mph); maximum cruising speed at 5500 m (18,045 ft) 513 km/h (27 kt; 319 mph) and at 8000 m (26,245 ft) 495 km/h (267 kt; 308 mph)
Range: 4500 km (2,428 nm; 2,796 miles) with an 8000-kg (17,637-lb) payload or 1182 km (637 nm; 734 miles) with a 16000-kg (35,273-lb) payload
Performance: maximum rate of climb at sea level 440 m (1,444 ft) per minute; service ceiling 8500 m (27,885 ft); take-off run 795 m (2,608 ft) at maximum take-off weight; take-off distance to 35 ft (10.7 m) 1100 m (3,609 ft) at maximum take-off weight; landing distance from 50 ft (15 m) 640 m (2,100 ft) at normal landing weight; landing run 360 m (1,181 ft) at normal landing weight

The C.160NG is easily identified by the refuelling probe. It also features additional internal fuel capacity.

Transall **C.160 GABRIEL/ASTARTE**

The French air force Transport Command fleet of 77 C.160s (in 1994) includes six second-generation aircraft assigned to two forms of special duties. All were built as transports but underwent protracted conversion and testing before delivery. As replacements for eight Elint and jamming Nord N.2501 GABRIEL Noratlas variants, two aircraft were converted to **C.160 GABRIEL** (**C.160G**) and entered service with 11ᵉ Escadrille of 54ᵉ Escadron Electronique Tactique 'Dunkerque' at Metz in December 1988. Features include wingtip pods with UHF/DF blade antennas, a group of five large blade antennas on top of the forward fuselage, a blister fairing on each side of the rear fuselage, and a retractable dome, produced by Thomson-CSF, under the forward fuselage. Both have refuelling probes and a hose-drum unit in the port undercarriage pannier. In the lead-up to the

1991 Gulf War, missions were flown against Iraq by a C.160G based at Al Ahsa, Saudi Arabia. The aircraft flew another four sorties during hostilities.

Another electronic surveillance version, the **C.160SE**, was offered by the manufacturers in the early 1980s but received no orders. It was similar in concept to the C.160G, with equipment that included a retractable radome with 360° scan.

C.160H is the version of Transall adapted to carry Rockwell Collins TACAMO VLF radio transmission equipment, as also used by the US Navy's Boeing E-6A Hermes. This takes the form of a long trailing aerial that enables the aircraft to communicate with missile-armed nuclear submarines of the Force Océanique Stratégique without the need for them to surface. The aerial platform is known as **ASTARTE** (Avion STAtion Relais de Transmissions Excep-

Mounting a plethora of antennas, the GABRIEL is a Sigint-gathering platform used by EET 54.

tionelles – aircraft relay station for special transmissions) and is part of the overall RAMSES system (Réseau Amont Maillé Stratégique et de Survie – overhead strategic and survival link service). A new squadron, 59ᵉ Escadron Electronique 'Astarte', formed at Evreux on 1 January 1988 to operate the C.160Hs, the first of which had arrived a month or so previously. All four aircraft have refuelling probes and hoses.

Tupolev **Tu-4 'Bull'**

For an unlicensed copy of the wartime B-29 to appear in this book is remarkable, but it is the case that a handful may remain in occasional use in **China** as drone carriers and testbeds. Re-engined some years ago, with the same Zhuzhou WJ-6 turboprops as the Shaanxi Y-8, **Tupolev**

Tu-4s in the Chinese air force museum are reportedly regularly put back into service for particular trials.

Remarkably, a few Chinese Tu-4s are believed to serve still on military test duties. Note the turboprops.

Aviation Scientific-Technical Complex named after A.N. Tupolev
17 Naberejnaia Akademika Tupoleva
Moscow 11250, Russia

Tupolev **Tu-16/A/N/T 'Badger-A'**

Originally designated **'Aircraft N'** or **Tu-88**, the **'Badger'** was developed as a twin-jet medium bomber to complement the strategic Myasishchev M-4 and Tupolev Tu-95. The bomb bay was sized to accommodate the Soviet Union's largest bomb, the 9000-kg (20,000-lb) FAB-9000. This allowed the use of a fuselage shortened from, but closely based on, that of the Tu-85 (itself derived from the Tu-4/B-29). The central part of the fuselage was waisted to minimise cross-sectional area where the engines joined the fuselage, reducing drag considerably. The swept wing was based on that of the Tu-82, and incorporated huge integral fuel tanks. The wing proved too thin to accommodate the bogie

Illustrating the unique wingtip-to-wingtip method of refuelling other 'Badgers', a Tu-16N 'Badger-A' (background) passes fuel to a reconnaissance 'Badger-L'. Some 'Badger-A' tankers differ by having a fuselage HDU for refuelling other aircraft types.

undercarriage, which retracted into streamlined pods projecting from the trailing edge instead. Such pods became something of a Tupolev Design Bureau trademark.

The Tu-88 prototype made its maiden flight on 27 April 1952, powered by AM-3A engines, while the second AM-3M-engined prototype flew later the same year. Evalua-

tion against Ilyushin's conservative Il-46 only served to underline the Tu-88's remarkable performance, and it was ordered into production as the Tu-16. Nine were available for the 1954 May Day flypast, while 54 were in the 1955 Aviation Day flypast 15 months later. About 2,000 were built before production ceased, excluding manufacture

in China, where the aircraft is designated **Xian H-6** (described separately).

The production Tu-16 bomber dispensed with the pressurised tunnel between cockpit and rear gunner's compartment, necessitating the provision of separate entry hatches for the rear fuselage. The undernose radome for the Argon nav/bombing

Tupolev Tu-16/A/N/T 'Badger-A'

Virtually all surviving 'Badger-As' have been converted for special duties or as tankers. The Tu-16N is the dedicated refueller for the Tu-16 force.

radar was deepened slightly and the over-wing fences were lengthened. Several versions of the basic bomber were produced, including the **Tu-16A** nuclear bomber, and the navy's **Tu-16T**, which was equipped to carry four RAT-52 torpedoes or AMD-1000 mines, or up to 12 AMD-500 mines. The **Tu-16K Korvet** was equipped for SAR duties, with a radio-controlled lifeboat carried under the fuselage. None of these specialised variants remains in service, unlike the **Tu-16N**.

The Tu-16N was developed as a tanker for other Tu-16s, using a modernised ver-

sion of the wingtip-to-wingtip refuelling system used on the Tu-4 'Bull'. The tanker can be recognised externally by a wingtip extension, outboard of a pipe-like tube which projects aft from the trailing edge. It has a total transferable fuel load of 19000 kg (42,000 lb). A large white panel is often painted on the rear fuselage of the Tu-16N to help the pilot of the receiver aircraft keep station.

In addition to the Tu-16N, some 'Badger-As' have been converted as tankers for probe-equipped aircraft like the Tu-22 'Blinder', Tu-95 'Bear-G' and Tu-95MS 'Bear-H'. These aircraft have a hose/drogue

unit installed inside the former bomb bay, but may not be converted from Tu-16Ns and may not retain the wingtip-to-wingtip equipment needed to refuel other Tu-16s. The probe-and-drogue tankers have a total transferable fuel load of only 15000 kg (33,000 lb) because the HDU takes up room in the bomb bay usually occupied by fuel tanks. About 20 remain in **Russian air force** service, and another six are believed to remain in use with the former **AV-MF**.

Many redundant 'Badger-A' freefall bombers were also converted to serve as missile carriers, recce platforms or EW aircraft (described separately), and many examples of these remain in service. Other Tu-16 variants that retain the 'Badger-A' reporting name include the **Tu-16LL**, a dedicated engine testbed able to carry a variety of test engines on a semi-retractable cradle under the fuselage. About five may remain in use at Zhukhovskii. The 'Badger-A' reporting name also applies to a pair of slightly modified aircraft referred to as **Aircraft No. 14** and **Aircraft No. 16**. These set a number of world payload-to-height (rate of climb

with payload) and speed with payload records during February-October 1991. Aeroflot's **Tu-16G** crew trainers reverted to standard bomber configuration many years ago.

SPECIFICATION

Tupolev Tu-16 'Badger-A'
Wing: span 32.93 m (108 ft 0.5 in); aspect ratio 6.59; area 164.65 m² (1,772.34 sq ft)
Fuselage and tail: length 36.25 m (118 ft 11.25 in); height 14.00 m (45 ft 11.25 in); tailplane span 11.75 m (38 ft 6.5 in); wheel track 9.77 m (32 ft 0.75 in); wheel base 10.57 m (34 ft 8 in)
Powerplant: two MNPK 'Soyuz' (Mikulin) AM-3A turbojets each rated at 85.22 kN (19,158 lb st) dry or, in later aircraft, MNPK 'Soyuz' (Mikulin) AM-3M-500 each rated at 93.16 kN (20,944 lb st) dry
Weights: empty equipped 37200 kg (82,012 lb); normal take-off 75000 kg (165,347 lb); maximum take-off 75800 kg (167,110 lb)
Fuel and load: internal fuel 36600 kg (80,688 lb) plus provision for fuel in two underwing auxiliary tanks; maximum ordnance 9000 kg (19,841 lb)
Speed: maximum level speed 'clean' at 6000 m (19,685 ft) 992 km/h (535 kt; 616 mph); cruising speed at optimum altitude 850 km/h (460 kt; 530 mph)
Range: 5925 km (3,198 nm; 3,682 miles) with 3800-kg (8,377-lb) warload; combat radius 3150 km (1,700 nm; 1,957 miles)

Tupolev **Tu-16K/KS 'Badger-B/C/G'**

The first missile-carrying 'Badger' was the **Tu-16KS-1** (NATO **'Badger-B'**). This was little more than a 'Badger-A' airframe with a retractable missile guidance radome in the rear of the former bomb bay, and underwing pylons for the carriage of two KS-1 Komet III (NATO AS-1 'Kennel') I-band radar-guided anti-ship missiles with mid-course guidance provided by the Kobalt radar of the Tu-4K. None remains in use in their original configuration, although some

may have been converted as 'Badger-Gs'.

The **Tu-16K-10 'Badger-C'** was immediately recognisable by its broad, flat nose radome. This serves an I-band 'Puff Ball' radar associated with the K-10S (NATO AS-2 'Kipper') missile that the aircraft carried semi-recessed under the belly. About 100 aircraft (approximately 15 of which remain in service) were produced, and supplied to the Baltic, Black Sea, Northern and Pacific Fleets of the **AV-MF**. About 15 are

in service. 'Kipper' is now obsolete, and all 'Badger-Cs' have been converted to later standards or scrapped. Some were converted to carry the K-26 (AS-6 'Kingfish') missile underwing (retaining the capability to carry a centreline K-10) under the revised reporting name **'Badger-C Mod'** (possible Soviet designation **Tu-16K-10-26** or **Tu-16KM**). Normally only a single K-26 is carried, below the port wing. Some 'Badger-C Mods' may remain in use.

It has often been suggested that the **Tu-16K-11-16 'Badger-G'** was produced by conversion of redundant 'Badger-Bs', but this seems unlikely, since the normal bomb bay is retained, with no sign of the earlier aircraft's retractable guidance radome. Whatever its origins, the original 'Badger-G' was developed as a launch vehicle for the K-11/K-16 (AS-5 'Kelt') rocket-powered air-to-surface missile, entering service in 1968. Carried underwing, the 'Kelt' carried a 1000-kg (2,200-lb) warhead and had a range in excess of 320 km (200 miles) and a maxi-

Left: Egypt still operates about eight Tu-16K 'Badger-Gs' from Cairo-West. These are primarily used for anti-shipping duties, using the 'Kelt' missile.

mum speed of Mach 1.2. The missile followed a pre-programmed course, using its autopilot, but could accept course corrections from the launch aircraft before the active terminal homing phase.

To ensure the correct nose-up launch attitude, the 'Badger-G' is fitted with a simple sighting device on the nose glazing. This looks like an inverted 'T'. The original undernose Argon navigation and bombing radar of earlier Tu-16s is believed to have been replaced by the J-band target acquisition radar known to NATO as 'Short Horn'. This was housed in a slightly more bulged radome and had a range in excess of 200 km (125 miles). The Tu-16/'Short Horn'/'Kelt' combination proved devastatingly effective, and 'Badger-Gs' were exported to **Egypt** and **Iraq**, where about eight remain in service with each country, Iraq's force having been augmented by Chinese-built B-6Ds. Some Soviet 'Badger-Gs' were adapted as the **Tu-16K-26** to carry the AS-6 'Kingfish', usually (but not always) with 'Short Horn' removed and a new radar under the fuselage, adjacent to the air intakes. The NATO reporting name **'Badger-G Mod'** is applied to aircraft in this configuration. AS-6-equipped 'Badger-Gs' were first identified in 1977. About 30 remain in **VVS** service, with more in the **Ukraine**.

SPECIFICATION

Tupolev Tu-16 'Badger-G'
generally similar to the Tupolev Tu-16 'Badger-A' except in the following particulars
Wing: span 32.99 m (108 ft 3 in); aspect ratio 6.61
Fuselage and tail: length 36.80 m (118 ft 11.25 in); height 10.36 m (34 ft 0 in); wheel base 10.91 m (35 ft 9.5 in)
Powerplant: two MNPK 'Soyuz' (Mikulin) AM-3M-500 turbojets each rated at 93.16 kN (20,944 lb st)
Fuel and load: internal fuel 34360 kg (75,750 lb)
Speed: maximum level speed 'clean' at 6000 m (19,685 ft) 1050 km/h (566 kt; 652 mph)
Range: 7200 km (3,885 nm; 4,474 miles) with 3000-kg (6,614-lb) warload
Performance: service ceiling 15000 m (49,215 ft)

A few Tu-16K-10-26s remain in Russian navy service, equipped with the massive KSR-5/K-26 missile. This is available with either a large conventional charge or a tactical nuclear warhead.

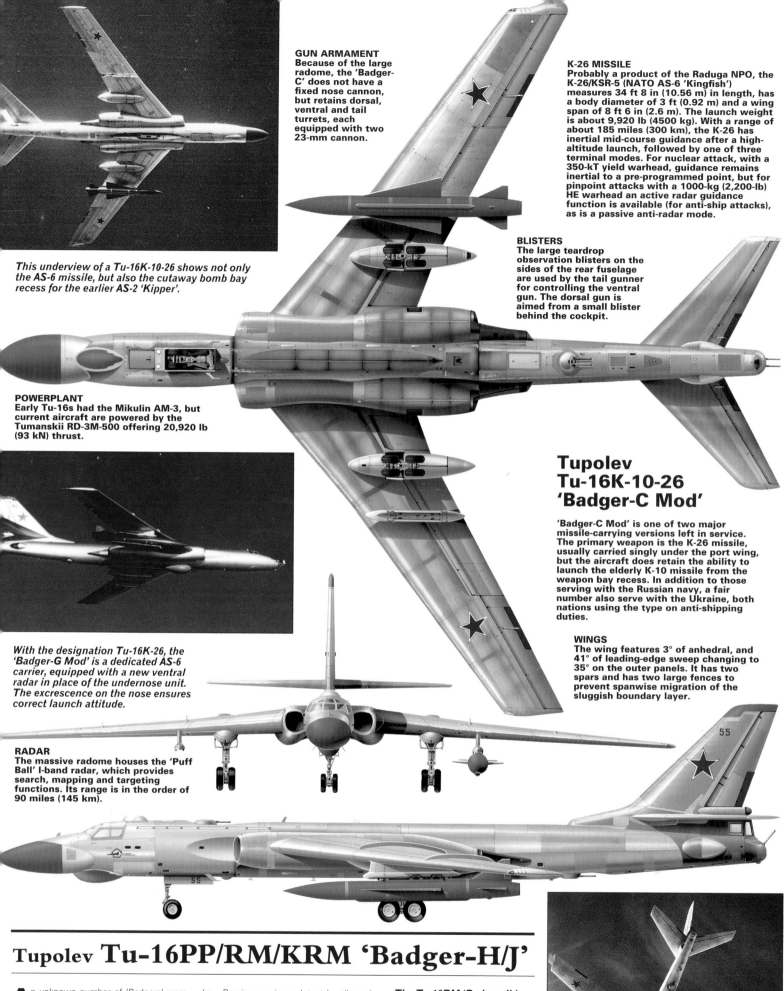

GUN ARMAMENT
Because of the large radome, the 'Badger-C' does not have a fixed nose cannon, but retains dorsal, ventral and tail turrets, each equipped with two 23-mm cannon.

K-26 MISSILE
Probably a product of the Raduga NPO, the K-26/KSR-5 (NATO AS-6 'Kingfish') measures 34 ft 8 in (10.56 m) in length, has a body diameter of 3 ft (0.92 m) and a wing span of 8 ft 6 in (2.6 m). The launch weight is about 9,920 lb (4500 kg). With a range of about 185 miles (300 km), the K-26 has inertial mid-course guidance after a high-altitude launch, followed by one of three terminal modes. For nuclear attack, with a 350-kT yield warhead, guidance remains inertial to a pre-programmed point, but for pinpoint attacks with a 1000-kg (2,200-lb) HE warhead an active radar guidance function is available (for anti-ship attacks), as is a passive anti-radar mode.

BLISTERS
The large teardrop observation blisters on the sides of the rear fuselage are used by the tail gunner for controlling the ventral gun. The dorsal gun is aimed from a small blister behind the cockpit.

This underview of a Tu-16K-10-26 shows not only the AS-6 missile, but also the cutaway bomb bay recess for the earlier AS-2 'Kipper'.

POWERPLANT
Early Tu-16s had the Mikulin AM-3, but current aircraft are powered by the Tumanskii RD-3M-500 offering 20,920 lb (93 kN) thrust.

Tupolev Tu-16K-10-26 'Badger-C Mod'

'Badger-C Mod' is one of two major missile-carrying versions left in service. The primary weapon is the K-26 missile, usually carried singly under the port wing, but the aircraft does retain the ability to launch the elderly K-10 missile from the weapon bay recess. In addition to those serving with the Russian navy, a fair number also serve with the Ukraine, both nations using the type on anti-shipping duties.

With the designation Tu-16K-26, the 'Badger-G Mod' is a dedicated AS-6 carrier, equipped with a new ventral radar in place of the undernose unit. The excrescence on the nose ensures correct launch attitude.

WINGS
The wing features 3° of anhedral, and 41° of leading-edge sweep changing to 35° on the outer panels. It has two spars and has two large fences to prevent spanwise migration of the sluggish boundary layer.

RADAR
The massive radome houses the 'Puff Ball' I-band radar, which provides search, mapping and targeting functions. Its range is in the order of 90 miles (145 km).

Tupolev **Tu-16PP/RM/KRM 'Badger-H/J'**

An unknown number of 'Badgers' were converted to serve as ECM escorts under the designation **Tu-16PP**, code-named **'Badger-H'** by NATO, carrying a chaff cutter and dispenser in the former bomb bay, dispensing chaff through three slightly swept chutes along the centreline. The aircraft carries up to 9000 kg (19,800 lb) of chaff in special containers in the bomb bay. Passive receivers detect hostile emissions, analyse threat priorities and cut strips of chaff to an appropriate length according to the frequency of the enemy signal. 'Badger-Hs' have a variety of antenna configurations, but most have a large hemispherical radome on the centreline, immediately aft of the former bomb bay.

The **Tu-16RM** sub-type is known to

The Tu-16RM 'Badger-J' is readily identified by the large canoe fairing under the belly. Surrounding the fairing are intakes and exhausts for the heat exchangers needed to cool the extensive amount of electronic equipment in the aircraft's former bomb bay.

The Tu-16PP 'Badger-H' is a chaff-laying platform, dispensing chaff through ports in the lower fuselage. A characteristic feature is the radome between the engine exhausts, with associated antennas.

the black boxes in the former bomb bay. The aircraft also has unique flat plate antennas on each wingtip.

An additional 'Badger-J' variant is the **Tu-16KRM**, which acts as a drone director for PVO targets. 'Badger-H' and 'Badger-J' serve with both the **Russian air force** and the former **AV-MF**.

SPECIFICATION

Tupolev Tu-16PP 'Badger-J'
generally similar to the Tupolev Tu-16 'Badger-A' except in the following particulars:
Powerplant: two MNPK 'Soyuz' (Mikulin) AM-3M-500 each rated at 93.16 kN (20,944 lb st)
Range: 5925 km (3,198 nm; 3,682 miles)

NATO as the **'Badger-J'**. An active ECM jammer, the 'Badger-J' has a distinctive ventral canoe fairing, housing radomes for the noise, spot, click and barrage jammers and covering the A- to I-bands. Ram air inlets alongside the canoe provide cooling air for

---

Tupolev **Tu-16 'Badger-D/E/F/K/L'**

Several recon Tu-16s display considerable differences from the standard variants. This aircraft appears to be a 'Badger-E', yet has the forward camera window of the 'K' or 'L'.

The first dedicated reconnaissance Tu-16 identified by NATO was the **Tu-16Ye 'Badger-D'**, an Elint conversion based on redundant 'Badger-C' airframes which retained that aircraft's distinctive broad, flattened nose radome. The chin radome was replaced by a slightly larger item, and three passive antenna blisters were added along the centreline, one large and two small. Crew complement was increased to eight or nine by equipment operators.

The **Tu-16R 'Badger-E'** was produced by converting redundant 'Badger-A' bombers, and is a dedicated reconnaissance aircraft with provision for a camera/sensor pallet inside the former bomb bay, and with two widely spaced passive receiver antennas under the fuselage. The **Tu-16P 'Badger-F'** is similar in appearance, but carries large equipment pods on its underwing pylons and sometimes has prominent blade antennas above and below the fuselage. The 'Badger-F' has been seen with a wide

variety of aerial and antenna configurations and is believed to be a dedicated maritime Elint platform. The Elint-tasked **Tu-16P 'Badger-K'** can be identified by its less widely spaced underfuselage teardrop fairings, which are also of equal size. The rearmost antenna is located just inside the area of the former bomb bay, leaving a long gap between it and the ventral gun turret. The aircraft has a row of tiny protuberances in the former bomb doors and usually has a camera window ahead of the port intake.

The **Tu-16P 'Badger-L'** reporting name is reserved for an updated maritime Elint or EW platform of configuration similar to the 'Badger-F', with underwing pylons carrying a variety of pods (including some similar to those carried by the 'Badger-F') and with the same unevenly-sized, widely-spaced underfuselage antennas as are carried by 'Badger-E' and '-F'. Differences include a thimble radome mounted in the transparent nosecone (designation becomes **Tu-16PM**)

Below: The giant radome for the 'Puff Ball' radar and ventral antenna radomes are the main identification features of the 'Badger-D'.

The 'Badger-F' was an early electronic reconnaissance variant, featuring wing pods.

WING PODS
Differing from those fitted to earlier Tu-16Ps, the wing pods carried by the Tu-16PM have cooling air inlets in the nose.

Tupolev Tu-16PM

Known to NATO as 'Badger-L', the Tu-16PM is the latest variant in a long line of electronic intelligence gatherers, but introduces a lengthened tailcone with EW equipment and a thimble radome on the nose. Only a handful of these conversions were undertaken, and the fleet exhibits several variations of antenna fit.

EQUIPMENT BAY
The weapon bay of the original 'Badger' was designed to accommodate huge bombs, and is the key to the aircraft's versatility. Large amounts of electronic equipment can be housed inside.

and an extended tailcone that replaces the rear gun turret, and is similar to the extended tailcone of the 'Bear-G'. This may house ECM equipment, or a trailing wire VLF antenna. About 80 reconnaissance and ECM Tu-16s are estimated to remain in former **AV-MF** service, alongside some 70 Tu-16N tankers and a handful of missile-carriers. The **Russian air force** operates only 15 Tu-16Rs (probably 'Badger-Fs' and '-Ls'); 15 Tu-16s also serve with **Byelorussia**, and 53 in **Ukraine** with the 260 HBAP at Stryy and the 251 HBAP at Belaya Tserkov.

SPECIFICATION

Tupolev Tu-16R 'Badger-D'
generally similar to the Tupolev Tu-16 'Badger-A' except in the following particulars:
Powerplant: two MNPK 'Soyuz' (Mikulin) AM-3M-500 turbojets each rated at 93.16 kN (20,944 lb st)
Range: 5925 km (3,198 nm; 3,682 miles)

Tupolev Tu-16R 'Badger-F'
generally similar to the Tupolev Tu-16 'Badger-A' except in the following particulars:

Powerplant: two MNPK 'Soyuz' (Mikulin) AM-3M-500 turbojets each rated at 93.16 kN (20,944 lb st)
Range: 5925 km (3,198 nm; 3,682 miles)

'Badger-K' is yet another Elint variant, identified by the equal size of its ventral radomes.

Tupolev **Tu-22 'Blinder'**

A Russian aviation journalist recently bemoaned the fact that while information on modern aircraft types like the MiG-29 and Tu-160 has been released for publication, many more elderly types are still top secret, and no information can be released. He referred specifically to the **Tu-22**, where "the number remaining in service is almost exceeded by examples in museums or raised on pedestals as gate guards."

Thus, any assessment of the Tu-22, and other same-generation Soviet aircraft, must rest partly on conjecture and informed guesswork. The original Tu-22 was developed to fly the missions of the Tu-16 'Badger', but with supersonic capability to give better penetration of sophisticated defences.

The Tupolev Design Bureau began working on high-speed supersonic bombers even before the Tu-16 'Badger' and Tu-95 'Bear' had flown, producing various designs, including the Tu-98 'Backfin'. The Tu-102 of 1957 shared a similar configuration, and was originally intended to be a multi-role aircraft, although it entered service only in its Tu-128/Tu-28 interceptor form.

The Tu-22 began life with the Bureau designation **'Aircraft Yu'** (the penultimate letter of the Cyrillic alphabet), and bore striking structural similarities to the Tu-98 and Tu-102, which in turn traced back their lineage to the Tu-16, the Tu-4 and the Boeing B-29. The Bureau designation **Tu-105** was later allocated, and the type was ordered into production under the Soviet military designation Tu-22. To add to the confusing profusion of designations and names, NATO's original reporting name of **'Beauty'** was judged 'too complimentary', and the less laudatory **'Blinder'** replaced it.

The first Tu-105 prototype is believed to have made its maiden flight during 1959, probably with Mikulin AM-3M engines, since the production Koliesov VD-7F engines were not ready. Little is known about the early flight test programme, beyond the

fact that it was conducted from Kazan. To reduce transonic drag, the Tu-22 conforms quite strictly to area-rule principles, with a waisted fuselage, engines mounted in pods above the rear fuselage, and the undercarriage carried in trailing-edge pods. The lip of each air intake forms a ring, which can be powered forward on take-off to expose an annular slot that functions as an auxiliary air intake. With little clearance between tail and runway on take-off and landing, a retractable tailskid is provided and, because of the likelihood of a tailscrape at high angles of attack, the consequent relatively high landing speed is compensated for by two massive braking parachutes. The three crew members sit in tandem, two using downward-firing ejection seats, with only the pilot in an upward-firing seat.

The first production version of the Tu-22 was disappointing, capable of about Mach 1.5, but with poor endurance and range capabilities. Basically a freefall bomber like the Tu-16 'Badger-A', its supersonic dash capability could not outweigh its inadequate radius of action. It was once believed that only a pre-production batch of **'Blinder-As'** was completed, but it now seems that the basic freefall bomber was procured in larger numbers, some still surviving as trainers and others probably having been converted to **Tu-22K 'Blinder-B'** standards, or as reconnaissance platforms or trainers.

The type made its public debut in July 1961, at the Tushino aviation display, when nine 'Blinder-As' and a single 'Blinder-B' made a flypast. By comparison with the earlier variant, the missile-carrying 'Blinder-B' had an enlarged undernose radome housing a 'Down Beat' missile guidance radar. Another feature is an overnose fairing housing a semi-retractable inflight-refuelling probe. This incorporates a triangular 'guard' on the lower surface, to prevent the refuelling drogue from damaging the nosecone. The same refuelling probe was probably

Tupolev Tu-22R 'Blinder-C'

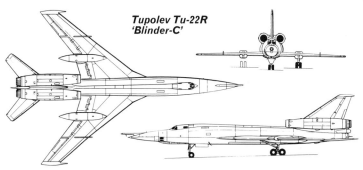

retrofitted to surviving 'Blinder-As'. The weapons bay doors were cut away to allow the AS-4 'Kitchen' ASM to be carried semi-recessed on the centreline, and improved defensive equipment and avionics were fitted in the landing gear pods and wingtip fairings. The AS-4 gave a measure of stand-off capability, and proved so successful that the missile was later adapted to the Tu-95

The Tu-22UB 'Blinder-D' trainer variant features a raised second cockpit aft of the normal flight deck.

'Bear'. When 22 Tu-22s flew over Moscow on Aviation Day (16 August) 1967, most were 'Blinder-Bs' with missiles and refuelling probes.

Two more variants of the original Tu-22

A pair of Tu-22K 'Blinder-Bs' demonstrates the carriage of the Kh-27 (AS-4 'Kitchen') missile, which nestles in a recess in the lower fuselage, formerly the bomb bay. The refuelling probe has a nosecone guard attached.

Tupolev Tu-22 'Blinder'

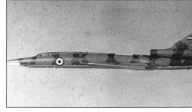

Above: Tu-22s were supplied to Iraq and Libya, the latter country operating this example. Libyan 'Blinders' saw action over Chad.

The Russian navy's main variant is the Tu-22R 'Blinder-C', used for maritime reconnaissance.

have been identified, both with the original 'Blinder-A'-type nose radome. The first of these is a dedicated reconnaissance version (possibly designated **Tu-22R**) with camera windows and dielectric panels in the nose and lower fuselage (**'Blinder-C'**), and the second is the **Tu-22UB** trainer (**'Blinder-D'**) with a raised cockpit for the instructor aft of the normal flight deck. There may be more than one version of the 'Blinder-C' operational, since different aircraft have different

camera and radome configurations, including an Elint-configured sub-variant sometimes reported as **Tu-22P 'Blinder-E'**. This has no optical sensors at all, and seems to be used purely in the electronic reconnaissance role. More recently, small numbers of Tu-22Rs have been seen with an unidentified pod below the nose, perhaps housing some kind of test equipment.

About 65 Tu-22s remain operational with **Russia**'s Long-Range Aviation, some 12 of these equipping one small regiment of the training centre at Ryazan, and about six reconnaissance-tasked Tu-22Rs are understood to equip one naval aviation regiment.

Fifty-five 'Blinders' serve with **Ukraine**, and 55 with **Byelorussia**. Tu-22s were also delivered to **Libya** (12) and **Iraq**. A handful remain operational in Libya, one of which bombed Tanzania during Libyan operations in support of Uganda. Another mounted a solo attack against N'Djamena airport, Chad, in February 1986, in retaliation for a French raid on Ouadi Doum: the 'Blinder' dropped four bombs from 16,500 ft (5030 m) at near supersonic speed, all hitting their target. Used during the long war with Iran, few of the Iraqi 'Blinders' are likely to have survived coalition attacks during Operation Desert Storm in 1991.

SPECIFICATION

Tupolev Tu-22 'Blinder-A'
Wing: span 23.75 m (77 ft 11 in)
Fuselage and tail: length 40.53 m (132 ft 11.7 in) excluding flight refuelling probe; height 10.67 m (35 ft 0 in); wheel track 8.72 m (28 ft 7.3 in); wheel base 13.73 m (45 ft 0 in)
Powerplant: two RKBM (Koliesov) VD-7M each turbojets rated at 156.90 kN (35,273 lb st) with afterburning
Weights: basic empty about 40000 kg (88,183 lb); maximum take-off about 83900 kg (184,965 lb)
Fuel and load: internal fuel about 36000 kg (79,365 lb); external fuel none; maximum ordnance 10000 kg (22,046 lb)
Speed: maximum level speed 'clean' at 12000 m (39,370 ft) 1480 km/h (800 kt; 920 mph) and at sea level 890 km/h (480 kt; 553 mph)
Range: ferry range 6500 km (3,508 nm; 4,039 miles); combat radius 3100 km (1,673 nm; 1,926 miles)
Performance: service ceiling 18300 m (60,040 ft); take-off run 2500 m (8,202 ft) at MTOW; landing run 1600 m (5,249 ft) at normal landing weight

Tupolev **Tu-22M 'Backfire'**

Initially known in the West as the Tu-26, it now seems that all 'Backfires' were actually known as **Tu-22M**s in Soviet service, and that the Tu-22M designation was not (as had once been thought) applied only to the initial 'converted' 'Blinders' ('Backfire-As'), and used by Brezhnev during the SALT-2 talks to confuse the West as to the

nature of what was called 'Backfire-B'.

It seems likely that the Tu-22M programme was launched at roughly the same time that the Su-7 was given a VG wing to become the Su-7IG (and later the Su-17). The two aircraft shared a very similar wing planform before conversion, and adopted a similar variable-geometry wing, with pivots

in roughly the same place, indicating that the same TsAGI-designed wing was used by both types. Some Western analysts have suggested that the Su-7IG was originally intended purely as an aerodynamic test vehicle for a scaled-down version of the Tu-22M wing, and that a VG wing was considered for an Su-7 derivative only as a result of these tests.

Whatever the truth, it seems that a decision was taken to fly the new wing at full scale, apparently using a radically converted

Tu-22 'Blinder' airframe (or possibly a batch of 14 'Blinder' airframes). Such reports as there are suggest that the initial **Tu-22M-1 'Backfire-A'** featured two new, larger engines in a bigger, box-section fuselage without area-ruling. These were fed by side-

A Tu-22M-3 taxis out in front of Il-76 command posts and a Tu-142LL testbed at Zhukhovskii. A set of auxiliary intakes supplements the main inlets at low speeds.

Right: The Tu-22M-2 featured simple intakes and a side-by-side twin-gun installation. The standard load was one 'Kitchen' under the belly.

Below: A large array of flaps, slats and spoilers combines with the sweeping wing to provide the Tu-22M-3 with excellent low-speed flying qualities.

mounted intakes forward of the wingroot, which were reminiscent of those fitted to the F-4 Phantom, with prominent variable intake ramps that doubled as splitter plates. The forward fuselage was unchanged, and the wings were given swinging outer panels. The latter were located outboard of the undercarriage pods, which seem to have been retained.

The very existence of any 'converted' 'Blinders' has been called into question recently, since an aircraft (coded '33') at Monino has been described as the prototype for the Tu-22M, and this has the standard 'Backfire-B' nose, undercarriage and intakes. It differs mainly in having a huge (brake-chute?) fairing on the trailing edge of the tailfin, displacing the gun turret and tail warning radar, and in having a large spike fairing projecting forward from the fintip. Soviet sources refer to an in-house Design Bureau designation of **Tu-126**, perhaps

explaining why the aircraft has been known as the **Tu-26**. There may still have been interim aircraft between the standard Tu-22 'Blinder' and this aircraft, of course.

It is believed that development began in about 1965, but no date or details are known concerning the first flight or flight test programme. NATO announced the existence of a variable-geometry Soviet bomber in 1969, and one was spotted on the ground at Kazan in July 1970. The production **Tu-22M-2 'Backfire-B'** is believed to have made its first flight in about 1975, and has always been said to have introduced a longer-span wing, a redesigned forward fuselage (with pilot and co-pilot sitting side-by-side, and with an extra crew member bringing the complement to four) and a revised undercarriage. This now retracts inboard, so that the six-wheeled undercarriage bogies fold inward to lie in the lower fuselage. These 'changes' are

thrown into doubt by the aircraft at Monino, although others are not.

Tail armament, for example, is increased by comparison with the older Tu-22, the single remotely-controlled GSh-23 twin 23-mm cannon in the tail being replaced by a pair of these weapons. The guidance/ranging radar for these weapons has been replaced by 'Fan Tail' equipment, since the original ogival radome has been replaced by a larger diameter 'drum'.

SALT limitations

During the abortive SALT-2 arms limitation talks, 'Backfire-Bs' had their nose-mounted refuelling probes removed to back up Brezhnev's contention that the aircraft was a medium bomber with no intercontinental capability, and were thus exempt from limitations proposed under the stillborn treaty. Initially, Tu-22Ms were usually seen carrying a single AS-4 'Kitchen' ASM

on the centreline, semi-recessed, but today a more usual load seems to be two of these potent missiles on underwing pylons. External stores racks for other types of weapon are often seen under the engine intake trunks. The 'Backfire' also has capacious internal bomb bays, capable of carrying an estimated 12000 kg (26,450 lb) of bombs.

In the later **Tu-22M-3 'Backfire-C'**, these bays can accommodate the rotary launchers for the RKV-500B (AS-16 'Kickback') SRAM, used mainly for defence suppression, with two more of these missiles under each wing. Defensive armament is reduced to a single GSh-23 twin-barrelled 23-mm tail cannon.

The new variant is distinguished by new wedge-type intakes similar to those fitted to the MiG-25, and has a recontoured, upturned nose. This may accommodate a new attack radar and TFR. The variant reportedly introduces new KKBM NK-25 turbofans that increase thrust by approximately 25 per cent. There is no external evidence of a refuelling probe, although this might merely mean that a low-drag fully-retractable probe has been fitted. The aircraft is believed to have entered service with the air force of the Black Sea Fleet during 1985, and has replaced the earlier 'Backfire-B' in production.

About 220 'Backfires' of different types are in service with **Russia**, 165 of them (and possibly more, following recent large-scale transfers of equipment from the air force to avoid infringing CSE limits) with the naval air forces.

Others Tu-22Ms serve with various Long-Range Aviation strategic regiments. Many of these are now concentrated within the Smolensk and Irkutsk air armies, having been withdrawn from the area west of the Urals to avoid being included in CSE-limited forces. Further 'Backfires' serve in **Byelorussia** (52) and in **Ukraine**, where 29 serve with the 185 HBAP at Poltava and the 260

With wings swept back, the Tu-22M-3 is capable of supersonic dashes during the attack phase of its mission. This aircraft carries racks for conventional bombs under the engine intakes.

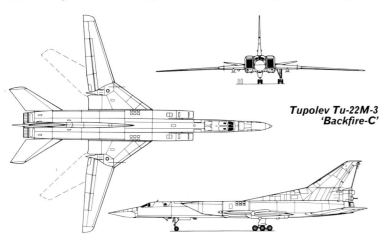

Tupolev Tu-22M-3 'Backfire-C'

Tupolev Tu-22M 'Backfire'

The Tu-22M-3 has an internal rotary launcher for carrying short-range nuclear missiles, but the massive Kh-22 is carried on wing pylons (as here). A combination of the two would be a typical nuclear load-out, using the short-range missiles primarily for defence suppression.

HBAP at Stryy. The exact locations of bomber regiments are unknown but, during 1989/90, the Tu-22Ms were said to be based at Machulische, Zhitomir, Neshun, Gomel and Baranovichi. Some carried unit insignia (a Tu-22M-3 wore a winged missile on its nose, for example) and some even carried Cyrillic characters spelling out BBC CCCP (VVS SSSR, or air forces of the USSR) on their intakes. Production is believed to continue at a rate of 30 per year, and may allow the final retirement of older aircraft (especially the Tu-22 and surviving Tu-16 bombers) in the near future.

A fully operational 'Backfire' is an extremely potent aircraft. With a substantial warload, which includes some of the latest and most lethal Soviet weapons, the Tu-22M can attack targets with deadly accuracy and an extremely heavy punch. Defensive systems are generously provided, with the 23-mm cannon providing a useful deterrent to enemy fighter pilots approaching within gun range, and extensive batteries of flares and chaff cartridges to 'spoof' enemy missiles. ECM and ECCM systems are also fitted, and some reports suggest that decoy

drones can be carried. With its wings fully swept back (to 65°), the Tu-22M is capable of a Mach 2 dash at high altitude, and of speeds up to Mach 0.9 at low level. The unrefuelled combat radius of the Tu-22M-2 'Backfire-B' is quoted as 4000 km (2,485 miles), and the radius of action of 'Backfire-C' may be even better. The recent termination of 'Blackjack' production has served to increase the importance of the 'Backfire' fleet. With only two squadrons of Tu-160s in service, the former Soviet air forces have only the Tu-95 'Bear' for long-range duties, and for penetration missions must rely on the Tu-22M to back up the handful of Tu-160s.

Severe spares shortages, reliability problems, and more recent problems in retaining trained air and ground crews render this significant bomber fleet much less effective than the overall number of airframes would suggest. Not only are engine failures and other major unserviceabilities common but, when an aircraft has been grounded for technical reasons, it will often stay grounded for up to six months. Training has deteriorated in both quality and quantity, with pilots 'chasing' an ever-dwindling number of

aircraft, and with severe fuel shortages severely rationing operational flying. Many problems have been laid squarely at the door of industry, where quality control is said to have declined markedly in recent years. Problems aside, the Tu-22M continues to play a vital role in the defence of the former Soviet Union, albeit now as part of the strategic forces nominally under the central control of the Commonwealth of Independent States. About 220 remain in service (and another 160 with the former AV-MF) and low-rate production may continue. The Tu-22M-3 has also been offered for export and may have been purchased by **Iran**.

WEAPON OPTIONS

Defensive armament of two (Tu-22M-2) or one (Tu-22M-3) GSh-23 23-mm cannon in remotely-operated tail turret. Two wing pylons and fuselage recess for the carriage of up to three Kh-22 (AS-4 'Kitchen') nuclear or conventional stand-off missiles. Alternative missile armament for Tu-22M-3 consists of six Kh-15P (AS-16 'Kickback') short-range nuclear missiles on internal rotary launcher with another four on two wing

pylons, or a combination of internal Kh-15P and external Kh-27. Conventional bomb load maximum of 24000 kg (52,910 lb), although 12000 kg (26,455 lb) more usual. Bombs of up to 3000 kg (6,614 lb) can be carried. Bomb racks under the intakes augment internal and wing pylon carriage.

SPECIFICATION

Tupolev Tu-22M-2 'Backfire-B'
Wing: span 34.30 m (112 ft 6.5 in) spread and 23.40 m (76 ft 9.25 in) swept; aspect ratio 6.92 spread; area 170.00 m² (1,829.92 sq ft) spread
Fuselage and tail: length 39.60 m (129 ft 11 in); height 10.80 m (35 ft 5.25 in)
Powerplant: probably two KKBM (Kuznetsov) NK-144 turbofans each rated at 196.13 kN (44,092 lb st) with afterburning
Weights: basic empty 54000 kg (119,048 lb); normal take-off 122000 kg (268,959 lb); maximum take-off 130000 kg (286,596 lb)
Fuel and load: internal fuel 57000 kg (125,661 lb); maximum ordnance 12000 kg (26,455 lb)
Speed: maximum level speed 'clean' at 11000 m (36,090 ft) 2125 km/h (1,146 kt; 1,320 mph) and at sea level 1100 km/h (594 kt; 684 mph)
Range: ferry range 12000 km (6,476 nm; 7,457 miles); combat radius 4000 km (2,159 nm; 2,486 miles)
Performance: service ceiling 18000 m (59,055 ft)

Tupolev Tu-22M-3 'Backfire-C'
generally similar to the Tupolev Tu-22M-2 'Backfire-B' except in the following particulars:
Powerplant: two KKBM (Kuznetsov) NK-25 turbofans each rated at 245.2 kN (55,115 lb st) with afterburning
Weights: maximum take-off 130000 kg (286,596 lb)
Fuel and load: external fuel none; maximum ordnance 12000 kg (26,455 lb)

Tupolev Tu-95/95M 'Bear-A'

Derived from the Tu-4 'Bull' and its enlarged and refined derivatives, the Tu-80 and Tu-85, the **Tu-95 'Bear'** was designed around the 12,000-shp (8952-kW) Kuznetsov NK-12M turboprop and slow-turning contra-rotating AV-60N airscrew, although the first aircraft flew on 12 November 1952 powered by four pusher-tractor tandem pairs of TV-2 turboprops. The immensely powerful NK-12M allowed jet-like speeds to be achieved (thus the need for swept wings and tailplane) but with much greater fuel economy, giving a genuine intercontinental range. In fact, the original 'Bear-A' is now estimated as having a range of 9,200 miles (14805 km) without inflight refuelling and while carrying a 25,000-lb (11340-kg) bomb load, with a cruising speed of Mach 0.67 (442 mph; 711 km/h). The maximum speed is Mach 0.82 (570 mph; 917 km/h) at 25,000 ft (7620 m) or Mach 0.78 (520 mph; 835 km/h) at 40,000 ft (12192 m). Later variants, with more powerful engines and cleaner airframes, can achieve higher speeds.

The basic **Tu-95M 'Bear-A'** was intro-

The 'Bear-A' was originally procured for the freefall nuclear bomber role, but the deterrent largely passed to missile-based systems many years ago. The bombers were mostly converted for other duties, although a handful remain in their original configuration for training purposes, some with sealed bomb bays.

duced into air force service in April 1956, as a freefall nuclear bomber with the air force designation **Tu-20**, featuring reverse pitch in place of a brake parachute. It relied on its speed and high-altitude capability to slip through enemy defences, with insurance provided in the form of five powered gun turrets in the tail and above and below the fuselage, operated by four gunners. The bomb bay was 14.2 m (46.6 ft) long. The dawn of the missile age brought with it an unacceptable degree of vulnerability, and an end to freefall bombing. Most 'Bear-As' were converted for other duties, mostly as missile-carrying 'Bear-Bs' and 'Bear-Cs'. The remainder were relegated to training duties.

To avoid being counted under START's limitations on strategic bombers, about a dozen surviving 'Bear-As' were converted to **Tu-95U** configuration, with sealed bomb bays and a broad red band painted around the rear fuselage. Most served with the Long-Range Aviation training centre at Ryazan. The unofficial reporting name **'Bear-T'** has been applied to these aircraft, most of which were withdrawn from use during 1991 and 1992 with the availability of other variants for training.

SPECIFICATION

Tupolev Tu-95 'Bear-A'
Wing: span 51.10 m (167 ft 7.75 in); aspect ratio 8.41; area 310.50 m² (3,342.30 sq ft)
Fuselage and tail: length 47.50 m (155 ft 10 in)

excluding flight refuelling probe and 49.50 m (162 ft 4.8 in) including flight refuelling probe; height 12.12 m (39 ft 9.2 in); tailplane span 14.90 m (48 ft 10.6 in); wheel track 12.95 m (42 ft 5.8 in); wheel base 15.85 m (52 ft 0 in)
Powerplant: four KKBM (Kuznetsov) NK-12MV turboprops each rated at 11033 ekW (14,795 ehp)
Weights: empty equipped 86000 kg (189,594 lb); normal take-off 154200 kg (339,947 lb); maximum take-off 188000 kg (414,469 lb)
Fuel and load: internal fuel 58500 kg (128,968 lb); external fuel none; maximum ordnance 20000 kg (44,092 lb)
Speed: maximum level speed 'clean' at 7600 m (24,935 ft) 925 km/h (500 kt; 575 mph); cruising speed at optimum altitude 708 km (382 kt; 440 mph)
Range: 14800 km (7,987 nm; 9,197 miles) with 11340-kg (25,000-lb) payload
Performance: climb to 5000 m (16,405 ft) in 13 minutes; service ceiling 13500 m (44,290 ft)

Tupolev Tu-95K 'Bear-B/C/G'

Improvements in SAM and interceptor technology during the late 1950s rendered traditional Soviet strategic bomber tactics unworkable. The use of freefall bombs was replaced by the use of stand-off missiles, and the 'Bear' was hastily modified to launch such weapons.

The first missile-carrying 'Bear' was the **Tu-95K-20 'Bear-B'**. Most Tu-95K-20s were produced by conversion of Tu-95Ms, and featured a broad, flat-bottomed radome under the nose and a dielectric panel following the normal nose contours above. The glazed nose was entirely faired over. The large undernose radome housed a 130-in (3.3-m) wide scanning antenna for the low I-band A-336Z 'Crown Drum' missile guidance radar. This was used in association with the Mikoyan-developed Kh-20 (AS-3 'Kangaroo') missile.

The Kh-20 was a turbojet-engined swept-wing missile weighing almost 25,000 lb (11340 kg) and carrying a 5,100-lb (2313-kg) 800-kT warhead. Launched from high altitude, the missile had a range estimated at about 400 miles (643 km) and had no terminal guidance. Once it was out of range of the launch aircraft (which could then turn away), the missile's autopilot simply flew a pre-programmed course to the target area. Some 'Bear-Bs' later received nose-mounted inflight-refuelling probes (**Tu-95KD**) and some may have been fitted with an Elint antenna on the starboard rear fuselage. Others may have been further upgraded to 'Bear-G' standards.

Some 'Bear-Bs' replaced by later missile carriers were relegated to training duties, and now serve with the former Long-Range Aviation's training centre at Ryazan. These aircraft do not have IFR probes fitted and the sides of the rear fuselage lack Elint antennas and other protuberances. They are now powered by 14,795-ehp (11037-kW) NK-12MV turboprops.

The **Tu-95KM 'Bear-C'** is believed to have been a new-build aircraft, and not a conversion from the 'Bear-A'. Intended as a missile carrier with a secondary multi-role capability, the aircraft was almost identical

Above: Most Tu-95KMs have since been modified or retired, although a few may remain on patrol duties.

Right: The Tu-95K-22 serves as a stand-off missile carrier. The wing pods are a notable feature, as is the solid ECM tailcone carried by most examples.

to late-series Tu-95K-20s in appearance, but had Elint antennas on each side of the rear fuselage, together with other reconnaissance sensors and equipment not normally fitted to 'Bear-Bs'. Many Tu-95KMs were upgraded to 'Bear-G' standards and it is unlikely that any remain operational in their original configuration.

The **Tu-95K-22 'Bear-G'** has a strong resemblance to the 'Bear-B' and 'Bear-C', although its broad flat nose radome differs in detail and accommodates an antenna for the 'Down Beat' radar associated with the Kh-22 (NATO AS-4 'Kitchen') missile. It was probably produced only by conversion of 'Bear-B' and 'Bear-C' airframes. The Tu-95K-22's AS-4 missiles are carried under the wingroots on pylons instead of semi-recessed under the belly. The rocket-powered AS-4 weighs about 13,000 lb (5897 kg) and is some 37 ft (11.3 m) long. It can be fit-

ted with a nuclear warhead of up to 350 kT or a smaller warhead and active radar terminal homing. Ranges vary from 270 miles (435 km) at high altitude to 190 miles (305 km) at low level.

The 'Bear-G' has a comprehensive defensive avionics suite, marked by the provision of a plethora of radomes and fairings. A thimble radome on the nose, between the undernose radome and the inflight-refuelling probe, is believed to be for a TFR, and small pylon-mounted pod-like ECM antennas are mounted below the lower fuselage in front of and behind the wing. Elint antennas are installed on the sides of the rear fuselage, and the aircraft has an extended tailcone,

with a distinctive external cable duct along the lower right rear fuselage running aft from below the Elint blister. The extended tailcone replaces the tail turret, and the dorsal turret is also removed, leaving only a single ventral turret for self-defence.

Most 'Bear-Gs' also carry an unidentified pod under each outer wing panel. These have a distinctive conical nose and may be ECM jamming pods, air sampling pods or chaff/flare dispensers. Forty-six serve with the Irkutsk Air Army at Ukrainka, perhaps alongside 15 earlier missile carriers. Three more are in storage at Belaya Tserkov, and there are more among the seven kept at Zhukhovskii for test duties.

Tupolev Tu-95MS 'Bear-H'

The production line at Taganrog reopened in 1983 to manufacture the 'Bear-F' and the **Tu-95MS 'Bear-H'**. The 'Bear-H' is a new strategic bomber version incorporating many features of the maritime Tu-142 airframe, and the latter aircraft's more powerful NK-12MV engines. Thus the Tu-95MS has the redesigned cockpit and slightly longer nose of the Tu-142M, and the same undercarriage (with its associated bulged undercarriage doors) and extended-chord rudder. Like the Tu-142M, the Tu-95MS lacks dorsal and ventral gun turrets, allowing the sighting blisters under the tailplanes to be removed. It does not have the 70-in (178-cm) forward fuselage plug of the maritime 'Bears', however, and retains the shorter fin and horizontal, undrooped refuelling probe of other bomber 'Bears'.

At first glance the nose of the Tu-95MS appears similar to that of the 'Bear-C' and 'Bear-G', but the resemblance is superficial. The deeper, shorter radome houses an unknown radar and has cable ducts running back from it on both sides of the fuselage. To port, this runs back almost to the tailfin,

An immaculate Tu-95MS 'Bear-H' tucks up its undercarriage after take-off. Something of a Tupolev trademark, the main bogies somersault through 90° as the gear retracts backwards, so that they lie flat in the rear of the extended engine nacelle.

and to starboard almost to the wing leading edge. Under the extreme rear fuselage the aircraft has a sensor/antenna package similar to that fitted to the 'Bear-F Mod IV'.

The Tu-95MS was developed specifically to carry the new RK-55 (AS-15 'Kent') cruise missile that also equips the Tu-160 'Blackjack'. Details of the RK-55 became available as a result of the INF treaty talks, from which it was learned that the missile is a turbofan-engined weapon with terrain comparison and inertial guidance. Weighing about 3,750 lb (1700 kg), the 26-ft (8-m) long weapon has a spread wingspan of

nearly 11 ft (3.3 m) and a range in excess of 2,175 miles (3500 km).

The 'Bear-H's' 7.5-m (24.6-ft) long weapons bay accommodates a rotary launcher for six of these missiles, and early aircraft, without underwing pylons, are designated **Tu-95MS-6 'Bear-H6'**. Three underwing pylons are fitted under each inner wing panel of later aircraft, the outboard pair

carrying three missiles and the other two single missiles. This brings the total number of missiles to 16 RK-55s, and changes the designation to **Tu-95MS-16 ('Bear-H16')**. For self-defence the Tu-95MS has only its rear gun turret. This is of entirely

Escorted by a Massachusetts ANG F-15A, a Tu-95MS probes US air defences. The variant is designed to launch cruise missile attacks from outside hostile air space.

new design, with a single twin-barrelled GSh-23L cannon in place of a pair of single-barrelled NR-23s.

The 'Bear-H' has now ceased production, but there are five examples at Belaya Tserkov in storage, and another two at the Kubyshev factory, in addition to those in service at Mozdok (22 MS16s) and Uzin (under the command of **Ukraine**) and Semi-palatinsk (Kazakhstan). The 40 aircraft (13 MS16s and 27 MS6s) at the latter base remain under control of **Russia**.

Tupolev **Tu-95RT/MR 'Bear-D/E'**

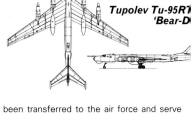

Tupolev Tu-95RT 'Bear-D'

T he **Tu-95RT 'Bear-D'** was first identified in 1967, and was a dedicated naval version converted from surplus Tu-95M 'Bear-As'. The new variant featured a new enlarged chin radome, and a much larger I-band search radar ('Big Bulge') in place of the former weapons bay. Another much smaller radome is located further aft. There are Elint blisters and other antennas on the fuselage. A handful of 'Bear-Ds' had their tail turrets removed and were fitted with a solid tailcone like that fitted to the 'Bear-G' or Tu-126 'Moss'. There are also stream-lined pods on the tips of the tailplanes, serving an unknown purpose. Some reports suggest that these accommodate a magnetic anomaly detector of some sort, but this would seem unlikely since the aircraft has no other ASW sensors or weapons.

It is believed that the Tu-95RT was developed as a mid-course missile guidance platform, acquiring targets for ship-, submarine- and air-launched missiles and sending guidance information to them before onboard terminal guidance could take over. It also has an important secondary maritime radar reconnaissance role, and often serves as an Elint and reconnaissance platform.

To extend range and endurance, the 'Bear-D' is fitted with a fixed inflight-refuelling probe above the nose. In April 1970 a

Tu-95RT took off from a base in the Kola Peninsula to participate in a Soviet naval exercise in the Iceland-Faroes gap, and then flew on south to Cuba. This marked the beginning of a 22-year cycle of deployments to Cuba by 'Bears', often with the big Tupolevs rumbling down the Eastern seaboard of the USA under escort by US fighters. Naval aviation 'Bears' have operated from a number of bases outside the USSR, including San Antonio de los Banos in Cuba, Conakry in Guinea, Belas in Angola, Okba ben Nafi in Libya and Cam Ranh Bay in Vietnam, as well as bases in Ethiopia and Mozambique.

Thirty-seven Tu-95RTs remaining in service were excluded from the 19 START negotiations on the basis that they were based at naval airfields and performed a purely naval role. About 15 were believed to remain in service with the **AV-MF** in 1994, fulfilling a maritime reconnaissance function now that most ship-launched missiles do not need mid-course guidance.

The **Tu-95MR 'Bear-E'** was also produced for the AV-MF by conversion of redundant Tu-95Ms, although a much

Right: A close-up reveals the reconnaissance camera pack in the weapons bay of the Tu-95MR.

smaller number (about 12) was produced. The aircraft is fitted with a slightly bulged removable reconnaissance pallet in the former bomb bay. This has seven camera windows set into it, three side-by-side pairs of windows forward with a single window further aft to starboard. It retains the 'Bear-A's' chin radome and has a smaller teardrop radome on the centreline just ahead of the wingroots. Elint blisters and what look like faired-over camera ports are mounted on the sides of the rear fuselage, and the aircraft is usually fitted with an inflight-refuelling probe. Some surviving Tu-95Rs have

been transferred to the air force and serve with the former Long-Range Aviation Training Centre at Ryazan. Red bands are painted around the rear fuselage for arms treaty verification purposes.

Above: The Tu-95RT was the most widely encountered 'Bear' variant due to its maritime reconnaissance brief. It was also used for missile guidance.

Below: Only a few Tu-95MRs were produced, these undertaking a long-range naval photo-reconnaissance role. Some Elint capability is incorporated.

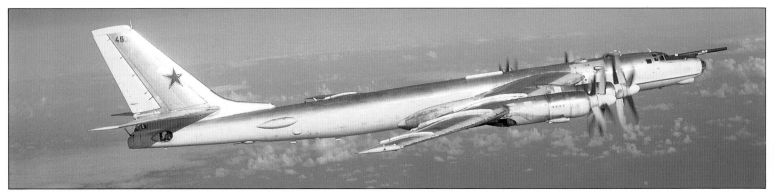

Tupolev Tu-128 'Fiddler'

The career of the world's largest interceptor is virtually at its end. A mere handful (if any) remain airworthy, having been replaced by MiG-31 'Foxhounds' and Su-27 'Flankers' in their primary role. Derived from the unsuccessful Tu-98 'Backfin' supersonic medium bomber prototype, the **Tu-128** (some reports suggest an alternative OKB designation of **Tu-102**) was developed into a long-range interceptor, flying in its new guise during 1959.

Developed to meet the threat posed by long-range stand-off missiles, the Tu-128 was armed with the enormous AA-5 'Ash' missile, and had a huge radar antenna in the nose. Two prototypes (**'Fiddler-A'**), with ventral fins, a large ventral fairing and two underwing missiles, made their public debut at Tushino in 1961. The production aircraft, without ventral bulge or fins, had four under-wing missiles, and was designated **'Fiddler-B'**. It made its debut at Domodedovo in 1967.

A dedicated trainer variant, with an extra cockpit in the nose, ahead of the usual cockpit, was reportedly designated **Tu-128M**.

The Tu-128 protected the frozen wastes of the Soviet Arctic. It is believed to be out of front-line service.

Tupolev Tu-134 'Crusty'

The **Tu-134 'Crusty'** was developed directly from the earlier Tu-124 'Cookpot', retaining the basic wing and fuselage, undercarriage and high-lift devices, but adopting a T-tail and rear-mounted engines, as well as incorporating slight increases in wingspan and fuselage length and an underfuselage airbrake to allow steeper approaches to be flown. It was originally designated **Tu-124A**, but was redesignated before the first flight in 1962. Production started in 1964 and the new 72-seater entered Aeroflot service in 1967. In 1970 the **Tu-134A** replaced the original aircraft on the production line. The new variant had a 2.1-m (6-ft 10-in) fuselage stretch and was fitted with an APU. The aircraft was re-engined with Soloviev D-30 Series II turbofans, and most Tu-134As also had a radar nose in place of the original variant's glazed navigator's position.

Primarily delivered to civilian customers, the Tu-134A serves with the air forces of **Angola**, **Czechoslovakia**, **Poland** and **Russia**, while Tu-134s serve with **Bulgaria** and Russia, mainly in the VIP transport role. Two aircraft previously based at Sperenburg in Germany carried extra communications antennas in their role as transports for the GSFG commander. Russia also has a handful of Tu-134s converted for bomber crew training duties. The **Tu-134BSh** is a dedicated bombardier trainer, and has a Tu-22M radar in the nose, with underwing pylons for the carriage of practice bombs. Consoles and radar bombsights for 12 students are provided in the cabin. These are used by fourth year students at the Higher Military School at Tambov. The **Tu-134UBL** (Uchebno-boevoi dla lotchikov, or trainer for pilots) has a similar external appearance, but is designed as a Tu-160 'Blackjack' crew trainer, with Tu-160 radar and avionics. It is primarily designed to train 'Blackjack' pilots, and simulates the bomber's handling characteristics (especially in the circuit and on take-off and landing) particularly well. Two entered service with the 184th Bomber Regiment at Priluki during early 1991.

There have been several special variants of the Tu-134, used for equipment tests or bomber training purposes. Fitted for the latter with Tu-160 radar is this Tu-134UBL.

SPECIFICATION

Tupolev Tu-134A 'Crusty'

Wing: span 29.00 m (95 ft 1.75 in); aspect ratio 6.6; area 127.30 m² (1,370.29 sq ft)

Fuselage and tail: length 37.10 m (121 ft 8.75 in); height 9.02 m (29 ft 7 in); tailplane span 9.20 m (30 ft 2 in); wheel track 9.45 m (31 ft 0 in); wheel base 13.93 m (45 ft 8.5 in)

Powerplant: two PNP 'Aviadvigatel' (Soloviev) D-30 II turbofans each rated at 66.68 kN (14,991 lb st)

Weights: operating empty 29000 kg (63,933 lb); maximum take-off 47000 kg (103,616 lb)

Fuel and load: internal fuel 16500 litres (4,359 US gal); external fuel none; maximum payload 8165 kg (18,000 lb)

Speed: maximum cruising speed at 8500 m (27,885 ft) 900 km/h (485 kt; 559 mph) or at 11000 m (36,090 ft) 870 km/h (470 kt; 541 mph); normal cruising speed at 11000 m (36,090 ft) 750 km/h (405 kt; 466 mph)

Tupolev Tu-134 'Crusty'

Range: 3500 km (1,889 nm; 2,175 miles) with a 4000-kg (8,818-lb) payload or 2000 km (1,079 nm; 1,243 miles) with an 8215-kg (18,111-lb) payload

Performance: service ceiling 11900 m (39,040 ft); balanced field length 2400 m (7,874 ft) at maximum take-off weight; balanced landing field length 2200 m (7,218 ft) at maximum landing weight; landing run 780 m (2,559 ft) at maximum landing weight

Tupolev Tu-142 'Bear-F'

The plentiful availability of 'Bear' airframes quickly led to the type's adoption by the **AV-MF** in the shape of the 'Bear-D' and 'Bear-E', which impressed their new operators with their performance, capacity and long range. The navy felt that it had only scratched the potential of the aircraft, and ordered Tupolev to develop a dedicated maritime reconnaissance and ASW variant, retaining the basic airframe but incorporating every necessary structural, aerodynamic and systems improvement. The wing is believed to have undergone a major redesign, although references to increased camber are believed to indicate the provision of new double-slotted flaps rather than a new wing section.

The wing is also strengthened for operation at higher all-up weights. The undercarriage is redesigned with larger tyres and more powerful brakes, and this necessitated the provision of bulged nosewheel doors and enlarged trailing edge fairings for the main undercarriage. A 70-in (178-cm) section was added to the fuselage ahead of the wing, and the rear pressure bulkhead

The Tu-142M3 'Bear-F Mod 4' is the current standard version of ASW aircraft, complete with antenna arrays under the nose and tail.

was moved aft to make possible major improvements to the crew accommodation and galley. To compensate for the increased forward fuselage length the trailing edge of the rudder was extended aft.

The weapons bays were completely redesigned, with a new rear bay for sonobuoys replacing the ventral turret, and with the main bay being divided into front and rear halves, covered by separate pairs of doors. These probably have a maximum capacity similar to the Tu-95's 25,000 lb (11340 kg) and are configured to carry anti-submarine torpedoes, depth charges, sonobuoys and SAR equipment, and possibly auxiliary fuel tanks. The 'Bear-F' also introduced a new ventral radome, slightly smaller than that fitted to 'Bear-D' and located further forward. The new radar operates at a higher frequency than 'Bear-D's' 'Big Bulge' (in J-band at about 21 gHz) and is optimised for overwater operation.

A second radome was mounted under the nose, in a longer and narrower radome than that fitted to the 'Bear-A', 'Bear-D' and 'Bear-E'. The aircraft had a remarkably clean fuselage, with tandem twin ADF blade antennas, but with no Elint blisters on the rear fuselage. It reintroduced streamlined pods on the tailplane tips similar to those seen on the Tu-95RT 'Bear-D'. If these fairings do accommodate a magnetic anomaly detector, it is probable that there is a galvanometer in each, their right/left symmetry cancelling out the magnetic influences of the airframe itself.

The resulting aircraft was given the designation **Tu-142** by the design bureau, emphasising the radical changes from the original air force Tu-95s. NATO allocated the reporting name **'Bear-F'**. Fifteen examples were built from 1970 before production changed to the modified **Tu-142A 'Bear-F Mod 1'**. Apart from minor changes to

429

Tupolev Tu-142 'Bear-F'

antennas and airscoops, the new aircraft had the undernose radome removed, and most also reverted to the smaller, standard trailing edge undercarriage fairings.

The basic Tu-142 was replaced on the production line by the **Tu-142M** that introduced major airframe changes. The forward fuselage was extended by a further 9 in (23 cm), and the cockpit was completely redesigned. Instead of sloping down to the windscreen, the roof of the flight deck continues straight forward, giving an extra 14 in (36 cm) of headroom at the front. This gives the pilots a better working environment and improves the view forward, which is also enhanced by the IFR probe being drooped downwards by 4°. The first Tu-142M sub-variant was given the reporting name

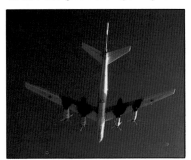

'**Bear-F Mod 2'** by NATO, and retained the same basic ASW systems as earlier 'Bear-Fs', with a small hemispherical thimble radome (perhaps for satellite communications) being the only notable addition to the antenna fit.

The addition of a new MAD in a spike-like fairing projecting aft from the tail, and an increased-length sonobuoy bay, resulted in the **Tu-142M2 'Bear-F Mod 3'** which entered service in about 1982. The latest sub-type is the **Tu-142M3 'Bear-F Mod 4'** which was identified in 1986. This was similar to the 'Bear-F Mod 3' but introduced a new undernose sensor package (probably including FLIR) and a new equipment package under the tail. The old gunner's sighting blisters below the tail were removed, and replaced by small blister fairings. There is a large cable duct or similar fairing running along the lower part of the port fuselage, from the cockpit almost back to the tailplane. A tiny 'pimple' radome on the nose may serve a TFR, or may have an ECM or EW function.

At least one converted 'Bear-F' has served as an engine testbed, under the designation **Tu-142LL**, with the test engine slung in a semi-retractable cradle under the centre-section. This aircraft is currently

From below, a 'Bear-F Mod 3' displays its tail-mounted MAD.

in open storage at Zhukhovskii. Between March and October 1988, eight Tu-142Ms were delivered to No. 312 Squadron of the **Indian Navy** at Dabolim. Often reported to be rebuilt or upgraded 'Bear-Fs', the Indian aircraft are to 'Bear-F Mod 3' standard, with the longer fuselage and taller cockpit of the Tu-142M, so this seems unlikely. India was the first, and so far the only, export customer for the 'Bear', but the 'Bear-F Mod 4' remains in low volume production, and further orders could follow.

India's eight Tu-142Ms serve with INAS 312 'Albatross'. The aircraft are to 'Bear-F Mod 3' standard.

SPECIFICATION

Tupolev Tu-142M 'Bear-F Mod 3'
Wing: span 51.10 m (167 ft 8 in); aspect ratio 8.39; area 311.10 m² (3,348.76 sq ft)

Fuselage and tail: length 49.50 m (162 ft 5 in); height 12.12 m (39 ft 9 in); tailplane span 14.90 m (48 ft 10.6 in); wheel track 12.95 m (42 ft 5.8 in); wheel base 15.85 m (52 ft 0 in)
Powerplant: four KKBM (Kuznetsov) NK-12MV turboprops each rated at 11033 ekW (14,795 ehp)
Weights: maximum take-off 185000 kg (407,848 lb)
Fuel and load: internal fuel 87000 kg (191,799 lb); external fuel none; maximum ordnance 11340 kg (25,000 lb)
Speed: maximum level speed 'clean' at 7620 m (25,000 ft) 925 km/h (500 kt; 575 mph); cruising speed at optimum altitude 711 km/h (384 kt; 442 mph)
Range: operational radius 6400 km (3,454 nm; 3,977 miles)

Tupolev **Tu-142MR 'Bear-J'**

The latest 'Bear' variant is known to NATO as '**Bear-J**' and was first identified in 1986. It is believed to be designated **Tu-142MR** and fulfils an airborne communications relay role, allowing national command authorities and strategic missile-carrying submarines to communicate with one another, like the Lockheed EC-130Q or Boeing E-6A. To fulfil this task the aircraft is equipped with an underfuselage winch pod for a trailing wire antenna (several kilometres long) and is liberally bedecked with blade and whip aerials. The underfuselage search radar has been removed. The aircraft also has an unidentified blister above the centre fuselage, and an unidentified spike projecting forward from the fintip. Coincidentally, the latter is similar in size and shape to the MAD that projects aft from the fintip of the 'Bear-F Mod 3' and 'Bear-F Mod 4'. Otherwise the aircraft is identical to the 'Bear-F Mod 4' and may have been produced by conversion. It is believed that the small number of conversions all serve with the **AV-MF**.

The Tu-142MR is obviously based on the 'Bear-F Mod 4', and is often seen with an ASW aircraft. However, it has a completely different mission equipment fit consisting of a varied array of communications antennas, including a bullet fairing projecting forward from the fin. Not visible in this view is the large ventral trailing wire aerial housing.

Tupolev **Tu-154 'Careless'**

The **Tu-154** tri-jet airliner was designed as a replacement for the Ilyushin Il-18 and Tu-104, and was required to couple good cruise performance and economy with 'hot-and-high' and short airstrip capability. Tupolev's response to the Aeroflot requirement was recognisably a scaled-up Tu-134, but had hydraulically-actuated leading-edge slats, triple-slotted trailing-edge slats, powered ailerons and four-section spoilers that augment the ailerons for roll control and act as lift dumpers and airbrakes. The fuselage was lengthened, and increased in diameter to allow six-abreast seating, allowing a maximum capacity of 167 passengers (128-158 is more normal). The third engine was located in the extreme rear fuselage, with an intake in the leading edge of the fin.

The prototype made its maiden flight on 4 October 1968 and the type entered service in February 1972. In 1975, the improved **Tu-154A** introduced a revised seating arrangement, additional emergency exits, increased fuel capacity and uprated engines, together with improved avionics. In 1977 the Tu-154A was superseded in production by the improved **Tu-154B**, and then by the **Tu-154B-2**. The **Tu-154S** is a dedicated freighter, with a freight door forward of the wing, and roller tracks inside the cabin. The aircraft is offered primarily as a conversion of existing Tu-154Bs, and it is not known whether any have been ordered or delivered.

Flight testing of the more radically modified **Tu-154M** began in 1982. This aircraft introduced new Kuznetsov D-30KU-154-II turbofans. Those mounted on the sides of the rear fuselage were in redesigned nacelles, similar to those fitted to the Il-62M, with similar clamshell thrust reversers. The APU had to be relocated to accommodate the centre engine. Other modifications included a redesigned tailplane, reduced size slats, enlarged spoilers and seating for up to 180 passengers (11 more than the standard aircraft).

Three Tu-154B-2s serve with the **Czech** Republic air force and three more with **North Korea**'s air force, and Tu-154Ms serve with **Poland** (two), and **Russia**.

SPECIFICATION

Tupolev Tu-154M 'Careless'
Wing: span 37.55 m (123 ft 2.5 in); aspect ratio 7.0; area 201.45 m² (2,168.46 sq ft)
Fuselage and tail: length 47.90 m (157 ft 1.75 in); height 11.40 m (37 ft 4.75 in); tailplane span 13.40 m (43 ft 11.5 in); wheel track 11.50 m (37 ft 9 in); wheel base 18.92 m (62 ft 1 in)
Powerplant: three PNPP 'Aviadvigatel' (Soloviev) turbofans D-30KU-154-II each rated at 103.95 kN (23,369 lb st)
Weights: operating empty 55300 kg (121,914 lb); maximum take-off 100000 kg (220,459 lb)
Fuel and load: internal fuel 39750 kg (87,632 lb); external fuel none; maximum payload 18000 kg (39,683 lb)

Speed: maximum cruising speed at 11900 m (39,040 ft) 950 km/h (389 kt; 590 mph)
Range: 6600 km (3,561 nm; 4,101 miles) with maximum fuel and a 5450-kg (12,015-lb) payload or 3740 km (2,018 nm; 2,324 miles) with maximum payload
Performance: take-off balanced field length 2500 m (8,202 ft) at maximum take-off weight; landing balanced field length 2500 m (8,202 ft) at normal landing weight

The Czech air force operates three Tu-154B-2s with its transport unit.

Tupolev **Tu-160 'Blackjack'**

The **Tu-160 'Blackjack'** is the largest bomber in the world, dwarfing the similar-looking American B-1B, and is the heaviest combat aircraft ever built. The Soviet bomber was heavily influenced by the original Rockwell B-1A, which first flew on 23 December 1974, but which was cancelled by President Carter in 1977. Originally designated **Product 70**, the Tu-160 made its maiden flight on 19 December 1981 at Zhukhovskii, in the hands of Boris Veremei. Spotted by an orbiting US spy satellite three weeks before its first flight, on 25 November 1981, the new aircraft received the reporting name **'Ram-P'** before being redesignated 'Blackjack'. Parked between a pair of Tu-144 'Chargers' the aircraft revealed many features in common with the American B-1, although comparison with the Tu-144 showed the Soviet aircraft to be very much bigger.

The B-1A was designed to penetrate enemy air defences at high level, relying on performance and a highly sophisticated ECM suite to get through. When the project was reborn as the cheaper, less complex B-1B, all thoughts of high-level penetration had been abandoned, and the less sophisticated aircraft was expected to use low-level flight (where it is limited to subsonic speeds) and a reduced radar cross-section to penetrate enemy defences. Back in the USSR there was no such cost-cutting exercise, and the Tu-160 remains committed to both low-level penetration (at transonic speeds) and high-level penetration at speeds of about Mach 1.9.

Variable geometry and full-span leading-edge slats and trailing-edge double-slotted flaps confer a useful combination of benign low-speed handling and high supersonic speed. Wing sweep is manually selected, with three settings: 20° for take-off and landing, 35° for cruise, and 65° for high-speed flight. The trailing edge of the inboard section of the flaps (immobilised when the wings are swept back) has no fuselage slot to retract into when the wing is swept, so instead folds upwards to be aligned with the aircraft centreline and thereby act as a fence. Some aircraft have a 'double-jointed' folding section which can fold up to be a fence at either 35° or 65°.

The Tu-160 has a crew of four, sitting in side-by-side pairs on Zvezda K-36D ejection seats. The crew enter the cockpit via a ladder in the rear part of the nose gear bay.

This unpainted Tu-160 is from the test base at Zhukhovskii. Visible under the nose is the camera fairing for visual aiming of weapons.

The pilot and co-pilot are provided with fighter-type control columns and, although the aircraft has a fly-by-wire control system, all cockpit displays are conventional analog instruments, with no MFDs, CRTs and no HUD. In front of the cockpit is the long pointed radome for the terrain-following and attack radar, with a fairing below it for the forward-looking TV camera used for visual weapon aiming. Intercontinental range is assured by the provision of a fully retractable inflight-refuelling probe.

The 'Blackjack's' offensive warload is carried in two tandem weapons bays in the belly. These are each normally equipped with a rotary carousel which can carry either six RK-55 (AS-15 'Kent') cruise missiles or 12 AS-16 'Kickback' 'SRAMskis'. The RK-55 has a range in excess of 3000 km (1,864 miles) and has a 200-kT nuclear warhead.

The development programme of the Tu-160 was extremely protracted, and at least one prototype is believed to have been lost. Series production was at Kazan and continued until January 1992, when President Yeltsin announced that no further strategic bombers would be built. In fact, it now seems that limited production will be reinstated, not least to replace aircraft lost to the Ukraine. Even after the aircraft entered service, problems continued to severely restrict operations. A shortage of basic flying equipment was a major irritation to aircrew, while a lack of ear defenders and antivibration boots for ground crew caused deafness in some men. Problems with the aircraft's ejection seats led to a situation in which seats could not be adjusted to individual crew members, and reliability of the aircraft, its engines and systems bordered on the unacceptable. Operations were supported by teams from the Kazan factory and the Tupolev OKB, which continued delivering aircraft before a common standard and configuration was agreed. Thus, wingspans, equipment fit, and intake configuration differs from aircraft to aircraft.

Eighteen of the 'Blackjacks' completed were delivered to the two squadrons of the 184th Heavy Bomber Regiment at Priluki beginning in May 1987. These were left at the Ukrainian base under Ukrainian command after the USSR split asunder, but are now reportedly to retransfer to **Russia** at an unspecified later date. The four newest aircraft, however, were delivered to Engels in the Saratov region of Russia, which was always intended to be the first 'Blackjack' base, Priluki being a temporary base pending the completion of construction work at Engels. At least six Tu-160s are at Zhukhovskii, in various states of repair, and these

include at least two 'flyers', one unpainted. These probably include the prototypes, and are used for trials and perhaps spares recovery. Plans exist to use the Tu-160 as a carrier for the Burlak space vehicle, in the same way that the United States' 'Pegasus' is launched by an L-1011 TriStar.

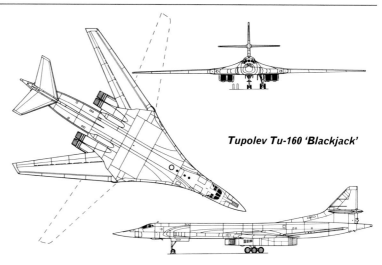

Tupolev Tu-160 'Blackjack'

SPECIFICATION

Tupolev Tu-160 'Blackjack-A'
Wing: span 55.70 m (182 ft 9 in) spread and 35.60 m (116 ft 9.75 in) swept; aspect ratio 8.56 spread and swept; area 360.00 m² (3,875.13 sq ft)
Fuselage and tail: length 54.10 m (177 ft 6 in); height 13.10 m (43 ft 0 in); tailplane span 13.25 m (43 ft 5.75 in); wheel track 5.40 m (17 ft 8.5 in); wheel base 17.88 m (58 ft 8 in)

Powerplant: four SSPE Trud (Kuznetsov) NK-321 turbofans each rated at 137.20 kN (30,843 lb st) dry and 245.16 kN (55,115 lb st) with afterburning
Weights: empty equipped 118000 kg (260,140 lb); normal take-off 267600 kg (589,947 lb); maximum take-off 275000 kg (606,261 lb)
Fuel and load: external fuel none; maximum ordnance about 16330 kg (36,000 lb)
Speed: maximum level speed 'clean' at 11000 m (36,090 ft) 2000 km/h (1,079 kt; 1,243 mph); long-range cruising speed at optimum altitude 850 km/h (460 kt; 528 mph)
Range: 14000 km (7,555 nm; 8,699 miles)

The Tu-160 is similar in configuration to the Rockwell B-1B, but is significantly larger. The main weapons are housed in a large bay on a rotary launcher.

UTVA-66

UTVA-SOUR Metalne Industrije, RO Fabrika Aviona
Jabucki Put bb
YU-26000 Pancevo, Serbia

A four-seater of classic high-wing, single-engined configuration, the **UTVA-66** is a descendant of the UTVA-56 which first appeared in 1959. After experience had been gained with the UTVA-60 in **Yugoslav air force** service, the improved -66 was flown in 1966 and introduced fixed leading-edge slats, a larger tail unit and strengthened undercarriage. Variants included the **UTVA-66H** floatplane, the **UTVA-66V** with underwing armament options, and the **UTVA-66AM** to carry two stretcher casualties. The remnants of the Yugoslav air force continue to fly some 25 of the 90 UTVA-66s originally received, for communications and 'hack' duties.

SPECIFICATION

UTVA-66
Wing: span 11.40 m (37 ft 5 in); aspect ratio 7.19; area 18.08 m² (194.50 sq ft)
Fuselage and tail: length 8.38 m (27 ft 6 in); height 3.20 m (10 ft 6 in); tailplane span 4.08 m (13 ft 4.5 in); wheel track 2.55 m (8 ft 4.25 in)
Powerplant: one Textron Lycoming GSO-480-B1J6 flat-six piston engine rated at 270 hp (201 kW)
Weights: empty equipped 1250 kg (2,756 lb); maximum take-off 1814 kg (4,000 lb)
Fuel and load: internal fuel 250 litres (66 US gal) plus provision for 200 litres (52.8 US gal) of auxiliary fuel in two wing tanks; external fuel none
Speed: maximum level speed 'clean' at optimum altitude 250 km/h (135 kt; 155 mph) or at sea level 230 km/h (124 kt; 143 mph); maximum cruising speed at optimum altitude 230 km/h (124 kt; 143 mph)
Range: 750 km (404 nm; 466 miles)
Performance: maximum rate of climb at sea level 270 m (885 ft) per minute; service ceiling 6700 m (21,980 ft); take-off run 187 m (614 ft) at maximum take-off weight; take-off distance to 15 m (50 ft) 352 m (1,155 ft) at maximum take-off weight; landing distance from 15 m (50 ft) 274 m (899 ft) at maximum landing weight; landing run 181 m (594 ft) at maximum landing weight

UTVA-75

The **UTVA-75** side-by-side two-seat conventional lightplane has been produced for civilian club and **JRV** use. First flown on 19 May 1976, the UTVA-75 has two wing fittings for the carriage of light weapon loads. At least 50 were delivered to serve at the Air Force College (VVG) at Mostar and the co-located Primary Flying Centre. Courses in both Air Force Academy establishments included 10 hours on the UTVA-75 for all pilots entering the air force.

Since the break-up of Yugoslavia, UTVA-75s have served with various air arms, including the **Croatian air force** and the **Bosnian republic**, the latter using the type as a light attack platform. The Serb-controlled **Yugoslav Air Force and Defence Force** operates UTVA-75s as aptitude trainers for prospective pilots with the 172nd Aviation Regiment at Podgorica.

SPECIFICATION

UTVA-75
Wing: span 9.73 m (31 ft 11 in); aspect ratio 6.5; area 14.63 m² (157.48 sq ft)
Fuselage and tail: length 7.11 m (23 ft 4 in); height 3.15 m (10 ft 4 in); tailplane span 3.80 m (12 ft 5.5 in); wheel track 2.58 m (8 ft 5.5 in); wheel base 1.93 m (6 ft 4 in)

Powerplant: one Textron Lycoming IO-360-B1F flat-four piston engine rated at 180 hp (134 kW)
Weights: empty equipped 685 kg (1,510 lb); maximum take-off 960 kg (2,116 lb)
Fuel and load: internal fuel 103 kg (227 lb); external fuel up to 153 kg (337 lb) in two 100-litre (26.4-US gal) drop tanks; maximum ordnance 200 kg (441 lb)
Speed: maximum level speed 'clean' at optimum altitude 215 km/h (116 kt; 133 mph); maximum cruising speed at optimum altitude 185 km/h (100 kt; 115 mph); economical cruising speed at optimum altitude 165 km/h (89 kt; 102 mph)
Range: ferry range 1,079 nm (1,242 miles; 2000 km); standard range 432 nm (497 miles; 800 km)
Performance: maximum rate of climb at sea level 270 m (886 ft) per minute; service ceiling 4000 m

This Bosnian republic UTVA-75 is fitted with light bomb racks.

(13,125 ft); take-off run 125 m (410 ft) at MTOW; take-off distance to 15 m (50 ft) 250 m (821 ft) at MTOW; landing distance from 15 m (50 ft) 340 m (1,115 ft) at normal landing weight
g limits: -3 to +6

Valmet **L-70 Miltrainer/Vinka**

Valmet Aviation Industries
Kuninkaankatu 30 (PO Box 11)
SF-33201 Tampere, Finland

The **Finnish air force** is the sole operator of the **Valmet L-70 Miltrainer**, to which it gives the name **Vinka** (Blast). A conventional low-wing lightplane of metal construction, the Vinka first flew on 1 July 1975, the prototype being designated **L-70X**. With two seats side-by-side under a large one-piece canopy, the L-70 was designed to be able to accommodate two additional seats behind the pilots, if required, for the liaison role. The name Miltrainer, proposed by the manufacturer, was appropriate, as provision was made on four wing hardpoints for up to 300 kg (660 lb) of weaponry such as gun pods, rockets or bombs. As a replacement for Saab Safirs in the training role, the L-70 was ordered by Suomen Ilmavoimat in 1978 and the first of the 30-aircraft batch flew in December 1979. Deliveries began on 13 October 1980 and were completed during 1982. The Vinkas serve primarily in the Kou1LLv training squadron at the Air Academy, Kauhava, to provide the initial 40 hours of primary flying for student pilots. One aircraft each is attached to the three fighter squadrons (HavLLv 11, 21 and 31) for liaison, and the type also serves at the Koelentue flight test unit at Kuorevesi.

SPECIFICATION

Valmet L-70 Miltrainer
Wing: span 9.63 m (31 ft 7.25 in); aspect ratio 6.62; area 14.00 m² (150.70 sq ft)
Fuselage and tail: length 7.50 m (24 ft 7.25 in); height 3.31 m (10 ft 10.25 in); wheel track 2.30 m (7 ft 6.5 in); wheel base 1.61 m (5 ft 3.5 in)
Powerplant: one Textron Lycoming AEIO-360-A1B6 flat-four piston engine rated at 200 hp (149 kW)
Weights: operating empty 767 kg (1,691 lb); normal take-off 1040 kg (2,293 lb) for aerobatic use or 1050 kg (2,315 lb) for utility use; maximum take-off 1250 kg (2,756 lb)
Fuel and load: internal fuel 170 litres (45 US gal); external fuel none; maximum ordnance 300 kg (661 lb)
Speed: never exceed speed 360 km/h (194 kt; 223 mph); maximum level speed 'clean' at sea level 235 km/h (127 kt; 146 mph); cruising speed at 1525 m (5,000 ft) 222 km/h (120 kt; 138 mph)
Range: standard range 950 km (512 nm; 590 miles)
Performance: maximum rate of climb at sea level 342 m (1,120 ft) per minute; service ceiling 5000 m (16,405 ft); take-off run 230 m (755 ft) at normal take-off weight; landing run 175 m (575 ft) at normal landing weight
g limits: -3 to +6 at aerobatic weight, -2.02 to +4.4 at utility take-off weight, and -1.8 to +3.3 at maximum take-off weight

Vinkas serve with the Finnish air force academy at Kauhava, and in pairs with liaison flights attached to front-line units.

Valmet **L-90TP Redigo**

After flying a prototype **L-80TP** as a slightly enlarged and turboprop-powered derivative of the L-70 Vinka, Valmet further developed the basic design to produce the **L-90TP Redigo**. As well as having an Allison 250 turboprop engine, this differed from the L-70 in having a retractable undercarriage and a revised wing. Prototype testing began on 1 July 1986, and a second prototype followed in 1987 with a Turbo-méca TP319 engine. Modifications to the tail unit were made before production was launched of a batch of 10 against an order placed by the **Finnish air force** in January 1989. Delivered in 1991/92, the Redigos supplement L-70 Vinkas in the training role with the air force academy at Kauhava. The Redigo has also been sold to **Mexico**.

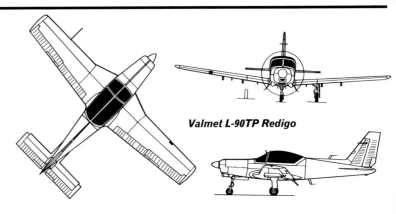

Valmet L-90TP Redigo

SPECIFICATION

Valmet L-90TP Redigo
Wing: span 10.60m (34 ft 9.25 in); aspect ratio 7.62; area 14.748 m² (158.75 sq ft)
Fuselage and tail: length 8.53 m (27 ft 11.75 in); height 3.20 m (10 ft 6 in); elevator span 3.684 m (12 ft 1 in); wheel track 3.367 m (11 ft 0.5 in); wheel base 2.112 m (6 ft 11.25 in)
Powerplant: one 500-shp (373-kW) Allison 250-B17F turboprop flat-rated at 420 shp (313 kW)
Weights: empty equipped 950 kg (2,094 lb); normal take-off 1350 kg (2,976 lb) for aerobatic use, or 1470 kg (3,241 lb) for utility use or 1600 kg (3,527 lb) for normal use; maximum take-off 1900 kg (4,189 lb)
Fuel and load: internal fuel 303 kg (668 lb); external fuel none; maximum ordnance 800 kg (1,764 lb)

Speed: never exceed speed 465 km/h (251 kt; 289 mph); maximum level speed 'clean' at optimum altitude 415 km/h (224 kt; 258 mph); maximum cruising speed at 2400 m (7,875 ft) 352 km/h (190 kt; 219 mph); economical cruising speed at 2400 m (7,875 ft) 312 km/h (168 kt; 194 mph)
Range: 1400 km (755 nm; 870 miles); endurance 6 hours 20 minutes
Performance: maximum rate of climb at sea level

540 m (1,771 ft) per minute; climb to 3000 m (9,845 ft) in 5 minutes and to 5000 m (16,405 ft) in 11 minutes; service ceiling 7620 m (25,000 ft); take-off run 240 m (788 ft) at normal take-off weight; take-off distance to 15 m (50 ft) 340 m (1,116 ft) at normal take-off weight; landing distance from 15 m (50 ft) 410 m (1,345 ft) at normal landing weight; landing run 240 m (788 ft) at normal landing weight without propeller reversal

---

VFW-Fokker **VFW-614**

VFW was merger of Focke-Wulf, Weser and Heinkel. It became equal trading partner with Fokker on 1 January 1969 although two divisions functioned separately. VFW's activities now grouped under the DASA banner.

The **Luftwaffe** was one of four customers for the uniquely configured **VFW-Fokker VFW-614**, designed as a short-haul airliner for the commercial market. Powered by two overwing-mounted turbofans, the VFW-614 first flew on 14 July 1971 and production ended in 1978 after 12 had been built. The Luftwaffe took delivery of its three aircraft in 1977/78 and put them into service with its special air missions squadron for VIP transportation (the Flugbereitschaftstaffel), with which they have remained based at Köln/Bonn.

The VFW-614 is remarkable for its unique layout. Three survive with the Luftwaffe's VIP unit.

area 64.00 m² (688.89 sq ft)
Fuselage and tail: length 20.60 m (67 ft 7 in); height 7.84 m (25 ft 8 in); tailplane span 9.00 m (29 ft 6¼ in); wheel track 3.90 m (12 ft 9½ in); wheelbase 7.02 m (23 ft 0¼ in)
Powerplant: two Rolls-Royce/SNECMA M45H Mk 501 turbofans each rated at 32.4 kN (7,280 lb) thrust
Weights: operating empty 12180 kg (26,850lb); maximum take-off 19950 kg (43,980 lb)
Fuel and load: internal fuel 6200 litres (1,363 Imp gal); standard seating for 40 plus two flight crew
Speed: maximum level speed 735 km/h (457 mph); never-exceed speed Mach 0.74; cruising speed at 7620 m (25,000 ft) 722 km/h (449 mph)
Range: with maximum fuel 2010 km (1,250 miles);

with 40 passengers 1205 km (748 miles)
Performance: maximum rate of climb at sea level 945 m (3,100 ft) per minute; service ceiling 7620 m

(25,000 ft); take-off distance to 10.7 m (35 ft) 956 m (3,135 ft); landing distance from 15 m (50 ft) 658 m (2,160 ft)

SPECIFICATION

VFW-Fokker VFW-614
Wing: span 21.50 m (70 ft 6½ in); aspect ratio 7.22;

Vickers **Viscount**

Several air forces found a use for the **Vickers Viscount** as a staff/VIP transport, mostly using aircraft acquired secondhand from the airlines. Such use is now dwindling, but the **Turkish air force** still has two **Series 700s** in 224 Filo (squadron) as part of the Etimesgut-based Transport Wing .Turkey's **Vickers Viscount 794s** were acquired from the nat-

ional airline and are powered by 1,740-shp (1299-kW) Rolls-Royce Dart 510 turboprops. One civil-registered **Viscount 781D** used by Zwartkop-based No. 44 Sqn of the South African Air Force was sold in late 1991, and one or two ex-civil **Series 810**s may still fly in military guise in the People's Republic of China. The last Viscount in UK DRA service at RAE Bedford was retired in 1993.

The aircraft of 224 Filo, Turkish air force, based at Erkilet, are believed to be the last military Viscounts. Three aircraft were transferred from the national airline, and two are still in service.

Vought **F-8E(FN) Crusader**

At the time of its entry into service, the **Vought F-8 Crusader** offered the US Navy an excellent fighter that was more than equal to its land-based counterparts. Successes in both Navy and Marine Corps hands during the Vietnam War enhanced its reputation. Out of service for some years with US forces (and with the Philippines, where a handful of F-8Hs were used for fighter duties), the Crusader continues to provide the French **Aéronavale** with its only dedicated fighter assets.

Designated **F-8E(FN)**, 42 were built for France, the (FN) differing from the standard multi-role **F-8E** by having blown flaps and other high-lift devices in order to operate from the small French carriers *Clémenceau* and *Foch*. Retaining the four Colt-Browning 20-mm cannon, the French Crusaders regularly carry MATRA Magic or R.530 air-to-air missiles in place of the Sidewinders previously carried by US aircraft. The multi-role capability is not practised, F-8E(FN)s being dedicated to the air defence of the carrier and its strike aircraft. The standard air wing has seven Crusaders.

The 19 survivors fly with Flottille 12F, shore-based at Landivisiau. Crusaders are expected to serve until replacement by the naval Rafale M in 1998. To keep the veterans relatively current, they are undergoing a minor upgrade programme which improves the navigation system and includes the addition of a missile warning system. In 1993 the first two upgraded machines were returned to the Aéronavale, with 15 to fol-

low through the improvement programme. This adds little to the combat capability of the type, which is woefully insufficient to protect the carrier group in the current climate. The lack of look-down radar, all-round visibility and lack of a true BVR missile are the main deficiencies, but on the Crusader's side is good manoeuvrability and the affection and loyalty of its pilots. In the US, Thunderbird Aviation and Rockwell use **F-8K**s and **RF-8G**s as test/chase aircraft.

SPECIFICATION

Vought F-8E(FN) Crusader
Wing: span 35 ft 8 in (10.87 m); width folded 22 ft 6 in (6.86 m); aspect ratio 3.63; area 350.00 sq ft (32.515 m²)
Fuselage and tail: length 54 ft 6 in (16.61 m); height 15 ft 9 in (4.80 m); tailplane span 19 ft 3.5 in (5.88 m); wheel track 9 ft 8 in (2.94 m)
Powerplant: one Pratt & Whitney J57-P-20A turbojet rated at 10,700 lb st (47.60 kN) dry and 18,000 lb st (80.07 kN) with afterburning
Weights: empty 19,925 lb (9038 kg); normal take-off 28,000 lb (12701 kg); maximum take-off 34,000 lb (15420 kg)
Fuel and load: internal fuel 1,400 US gal (5300 litres); external fuel none; maximum ordnance 5,000 lb (2268 kg)
Speed: maximum level speed 'clean' at 36,000 ft (10975 m) 986 kt (1,135 mph; 1827 km/h); cruising speed at 40,000 ft (12190 m) 486 kt (560 mph; 901 km/h)
Range: ferry range 1,216 nm (1,400 miles; 2253 km); combat radius 521 nm (600 miles; 966 km)

Performance: maximum rate of climb at sea level about 21,000 ft (6400 m) per minute; service ceiling 58,000 ft (17680 m)

The Crusader features a novel variable-incidence wing to lower the nose on approach.

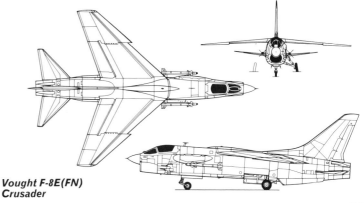

Vought F-8E(FN) Crusader

Westland (Aérospatiale) Gazelle

Westland Helicopters Ltd
Yeovil, Somerset, BA20 2YB
United Kingdom

In the mid-1960s, Sud Aviation began development of the **SA 340** to replace the Alouette II. The prototype **Gazelle** first flew on 7 April 1967 and retained a Turboméca Astazou IIN turboshaft and transmission similar to the SA 318C. In the renamed Aérospatiale group, the Gazelle sold well in civil and military markets. It was also developed and co-produced by Westland, with the SA 330 Puma and WG.13 Lynx, within the 1967 Anglo-French collaborative helicopter agreement. French-built Gazelles are described under Eurocopter.

In the **United Kingdom**, apart from a few civil sales, Gazelle military orders eventually totalled 282, comprising 212 **Army Air Corps AH.Mk 1**s (including at least 15 for the **Royal Marines**), 40 **Royal Navy HT.Mk 2**s and 30 **Royal Air Force HT.Mk 3**s. **SA 341B** Gazelle AH.Mk 1s entered AAC service with No. 660 Sqn at Soest, in the FRG, in July 1974, the last being delivered in March 1984. From 1977, 67 were upgraded to **SA 342** standard with 895-shp (668-kW) Astazou IIIN2 turboshafts and larger fenestron tail rotors, plus new radios, a tactical Doppler navigation system

and roof-mounted Ferranti AF532 gyro-stabilised periscopic sight, later with a bore-sighted laser-targeting system, for Lynx pathfinder/designation support. About 180 Gazelle AH.Mk 1s now serve alongside Lynxes with 16 UK AAC squadrons, and in flights in Belize, Berlin, Brüggen, Dhekelia, Nicosia in Cyprus, and Suffield in Canada. Some 29 RN **SA 341C** HT.Mk 2s are still operated, mainly for helicopter training by No. 705 Sqn at Culdrose. Approximately 20 Royal Marine AH.Mk 1s have been on establishment since December 1974 with 3 Commando Brigade Air Sqn at Yeovilton. The RAF operates some 20 **SA 341D**

Left: 3 Commando Brigade Air Squadron flies Gazelle AH.Mk 1s and Lynx to provide support for the Royal Marines. They are based at Yeovilton.

Right: A Gazelle from No. 670 Sqn, AAC.

HT.Mk 3 trainers with No. 2 FTS at Shawbury, plus four for VIP use with No. 32 Sqn from Northolt. A handful were briefly used by RAF Chinook squadrons as route-finders.

Nine Gazelle AH.Mk 1s of 3 CBAS and six initially unarmed Gazelles from No. 656 AAC Sqn underwent their operational baptism in the Falklands in April and May 1982 in support of their associated ground forces. The 3 CBAS Gazelles were hurriedly fitted with twin outrigger pods each containing six 68-mm (2.67-in) MATRA/SNEB air-to-ground

rockets, and a beam-mounted 7.62-mm (0.3-in) GP machine-gun.

SPECIFICATION

Westland (Aérospatiale) SA 341B Gazelle AH.Mk 1
generally similar to the Eurocopter SA 341F Gazelle except in the following particulars:
Powerplant: one Turboméca Astazou IIIN rated at 441 kW (592 shp)

Westland Lynx (Army versions)

Launched as part of the Anglo-French helicopter agreement of February 1967, the **Westland Lynx** is an extremely versatile machine. Its design is wholly of Westland origin, but the production of the type is shared in the ratio of 70/30 between the UK and France, in the form of the nationalised Aérospatiale (now Eurocopter) concern. One of the primary French responsibilities is the forged titanium hub, a one-piece structure for the four-bladed semi-rigid main rotor which is one of the most important features of the design.

All versions of the Lynx have advanced digital flight controls plus all-weather avionics, and no previous helicopter can equal the type for agility and all-weather single-crew operation. The origins of the design lie with the **WG.13** proposal, which was schemed in general-purpose naval and civilian applications. So versatile did the design appear that the concept was expanded to land-based tactical operations, in which the type's agility and performance would prove a very considerable asset. The first prototype of the Lynx flew on 21 March 1971, and the six prototypes were used exhaus-

The Lynx AH.Mk 7 is the British army's standard battlefield helicopter, equipped with TOW missiles, a roof-mounted sight and infra-red exhaust suppressors.

tively for all aspects of the certification programme, for trials and for record-breaking.

The second production model (following the naval HAS.Mk 2, which is described separately) was the **Lynx AH.Mk 1** battlefield helicopter for the **British army**. This first flew on 11 February 1977, and the type was cleared for service introduction at the end of 1977. Since that time, the Lynx has built up an enviable reputation as a versatile battlefield helicopter, being able to carry up to 12 troops in addition to a crew of two, or 907 kg (2,000 lb) of internal freight, or a slung load of 1361 kg (3,000 lb), or a wide assortment of weapons including eight TOW anti-tank missiles aimed with a stabilised sight mounted in the flight deck roof. The chief distinguishing feature of the land-based Lynx is its skid landing gear, the naval Lynx having wheeled tricycle landing gear.

A total of 113 Lynx AH.Mk 1s was built, and more than 100 are still in service with the Army Air Corps and Royal Marines. Nine Lynx **AH.Mk 5** aircraft were ordered, but only one example flew as such before the remainder of the order was switched to **Lynx AH.Mk 7** standard. This has the direction of rotation of the tail rotor reversed, uprated Gem 41 engines and a box-like IR shroud on the exhaust, in addition to improved electronics. Earlier AH.Mk 1s are being upgraded to this standard, or an interim **AH.Mk 1GT** standard without new

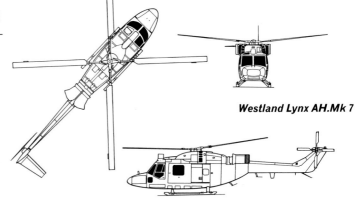

Westland Lynx AH.Mk 7

electronics, by RNAY Fleetlands. Eight AH.Mk 1s have also been converted to **AH.Mk 9** standard (described separately). The only overseas customer for the army Lynx was **Qatar**, which bought three for use with the police wing. These are now retired from service.

SPECIFICATION

Westland Lynx AH.Mk 1
Rotor system: main rotor diameter 42 ft 0 in (12.80 m); tail rotor diameter 7 ft 3 in (2.21 m); main rotor disc area 1,385.44 sq ft (128.71 m²); tail rotor disc area 41.28 sq ft (3.835 m²)
Fuselage and tail: length overall, rotors turning 49 ft 9 in (15.163 m) and fuselage 39 ft 6.75 in (12.06 m);

height overall 11 ft 6 in (3.504 m) with both rotors stationary, stabiliser span 5 ft 10 in (1.78 m); skid track 6 ft 8 in (2.032 m)
Powerplant: two Rolls-Royce Gem 2 turboshafts each rated at 900 shp (671 kW) or, in later helicopters, two Rolls-Royce Gem 41-2 each rated at 1,120 shp (835 kW); from 1987 the engines were upgraded to Gem 42-1 standard rated at 1,135 shp (846 kW)
Weights: manufacturer's empty 5,683 lb (2578 kg); manufacturer's basic 5,860 lb (2658 kg); operating empty 6,144 lb (2787 kg) in the troop transport role, or 6,772 lb (3072 kg) in the anti-tank role, or 6,532 lb (2963 kg) in the three-crew SAR role; maximum take-off 9,600 lb (4354 kg)
Fuel and load: internal fuel 214 Imp gal (257 US gal; 973 litres) plus provision for 47 Imp gal (56.4 US gal; 214 litres) of auxiliary fuel in a fuselage tank replaceable by 192 Imp gal (230.6 US gal; 873 litres) of ferry fuel in two fuselage tanks; external fuel none
Speed: maximum continuous cruising speed at optimum altitude 140 kt (161 mph; 259 km/h); economical cruising speed at optimum altitude 70 kt (81 mph; 130 km/h)
Range: 340 nm (392 miles; 630 km) with standard fuel; ferry range 724 nm (835 miles; 1342 km) with auxiliary fuel; typical range 292 nm (336 miles; 540 km) on a troop-carrying mission; endurance 3 hours
Performance: maximum rate of climb at sea level 2,480 ft (756 m) per minute; hovering ceiling 10,600 ft (3230 m) out of ground effect

Westland Lynx AH.Mk 7
generally similar to the Westland Lynx AH.Mk 1 except in the following particulars:
Fuselage and tail: height overall 12 ft 0 in (3.66 m) with rotors stationary
Powerplant: two Rolls-Royce Gem 41-1 turboshafts each rated at 1,120 shp (835 kW); from 1987 the engines were upgraded to Gem 42-1 standard rated at 1,135 shp (846 kW)
Weights: maximum take-off 10,750 lb (4876 kg)
Fuel and load: maximum ordnance about 1,210 lb (549 kg)

Westland Lynx AH.Mk 9

Features of the **Army Air Corps'** upgraded **Lynx AH.Mk 9**, including a nosewheel undercarriage instead of skids, and exhaust diffusers, were first shown by Westland at the 1988 Farnborough air show on the company demonstrator G-LYNX. The AAC is taking delivery of 24 AH.Mk 9s, including eight Lynx AH.Mk 7 conversions, the first new-build example (ZG884) of which flew on 20 July 1990 and was delivered by the year's end. Westland flew the 16th new-build AH.Mk 9 on 21 June 1992, and is continuing the Lynx AH.Mk 7 conversion programme.

The AH.Mk 9 consolidates all the AH.Mk 7 modifications incorporated in 107 AAC AH.Mk 1 conversions, comprising reversed-direction tail rotor, BERP main rotor blades and uprated gearbox, plus an 11,300-lb (5125-kg) maximum gross weight, secure speech transmission equipment, TACAN and improved IFF. Defence economies precluded the provision of TOW ATM capability, although this may follow if funds permit, using a modified weapons pylon made necessary by the new undercarriage.

In this form, the AH.Mk 9 is similar to Westland's **Battlefield Lynx** export project, apart from an extra fuel tank below the rear bench seat which increases total capacity by 375 lb (170 kg) to 2,088 lb (930 kg), and optional exhaust diffusion. Armament options can include GIAT 20-mm cannon pods, FN Herstal 7.62-mm machine-gun pods, rocket pods, and HOT or Hellfire ATGMs in place of the AH.Mk 9's TOW installation. Current production and Lynx conversions utilise Rolls-Royce Gem 42-1 turboshafts uprated to 1,135 shp (846 kW), although one aircraft was tested with the LHTEC 800 as the **Battlefield Lynx 800**.

No. 9 Regiment at Dishforth began Lynx AH.Mk 9 conversion in late 1991, No. 672 Squadron being the first operational AAC unit to re-equip (with 12 examples), followed by No. 664 Squadron, which began to replace its Lynx AH.Mk 1s in 1992. No. 673 Squadron received Lynx AH.Mk 9s in 1993. Some 150 Lynxes, including the 16 new-build AH.Mk 9s, remain in service in 1994 with the AAC, Royal Marines, MoD(PE) and Westland.

SPECIFICATION

Westland Lynx AH.Mk 9
generally similar to the Westland Lynx AH.Mk 1 except in the following particulars:
Rotor system: tail rotor diameter 7 ft 9 in (2.36 m); tail rotor disc area 47.17 sq ft (4.38 m²)
Fuselage and tail: length overall, rotors turning 50 ft 0 in (15.24 m) and with rotors folded 43 ft 5.25 in (13.24 m); height overall 12 ft 3 in (3.73 m) with tail rotor turning; stabiliser span 4 ft 4 in (1.32 m); wheel track 9 ft 2.25 in (2.80 m); wheel base 9 ft 11 in (3.02 m)

Powerplant: two Rolls-Royce Gem 42-1 turboshafts each rated at 1,135 shp (846 kW)
Weights: basic empty 7,006 lb (3178 kg); operating empty 8,707 lb (3949 kg) in the anti-tank role with TOW missiles, or 7,592 lb (3444 kg) in the reconnaissance role, or 7,707 lb (3496 kg) in the troop transport; maximum take-off 11,300 lb (5126 kg)
Fuel and load: maximum payload 3,000 lb (1361 kg)
Speed: maximum continuous cruising speed at optimum altitude 138 kt (159 mph; 256 km/h)

Range: typical range 370 nm (426 miles; 685 km) on a tactical transport mission; combat radius 25 nm (29 miles; 46 km) for a 2-hour patrol on an anti-tank mission

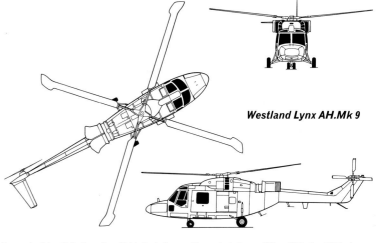

Westland Lynx AH.Mk 9

The wheeled undercarriage is the most notable AH.Mk 9 feature. Of greater significance is the BERP rotor with paddle tips, which improves high-speed performance.

Westland Lynx (Navy versions)

On technical grounds, the Westland Lynx is one of the foremost medium shipboard helicopters in the world, and from the original WG.13 concept (which formed part of the Anglo-French helicopter agreement of 1967) has come a series of uprated versions which not only bring in additional missions but also greatly enhanced capabilities. The original **Lynx HAS.Mk 2** for the Royal Navy was actually the first production variant to fly, in February 1976. Powered by two 559-kW (750-shp) Gem 2 engines, this has a gross weight of 4309 kg (9,500 lb), yet carries a crew of two (three in the ASW or SAR roles) plus all equipment for a wide range of shipboard missions including ASW, SAR, ASV (anti-surface vessel) search and strike, reconnaissance, troop transport (typically 10 troops), fire support, communication and fleet liaison, and VertRep duties.

Equipment of all these models includes a search radar, which in the 60 Lynx HAS.Mk 2s of the RN was the Ferranti Seaspray; the equivalent machines of the French Aéronavale have the OMERA-Segid ORB 31W. In the ASW search role other sensors can include Bendix or Alcatel dipping sonars or a Texas Instruments MAD. The basic Lynx has one of the world's most advanced flight control systems which, in conjunction with comprehensive navaids, makes possible precision flying in even the worst weather, as was amply proved during over 3,000 hours of combat operations off the Falklands in 1982. The campaign saw the operational combat debut of the new Sea Skua anti-ship missile. Although other missiles can be carried, the Sea Skua is the most effective in the world for this mission, and up to four can be fired and guided automatically by radar homing.

The Royal Navy received the first of 23 upgraded **HAS.Mk 3s** in March 1982, and converted its HAS.Mk 2s to this standard. Among the improved systems were Gem 41-1 engines. The **HAS.Mk 3ICE** designation covers a few aircraft with downgraded systems for utility work on the Antarctic patrol vessel HMS *Endurance*. Subsequently, seven HAS.Mk 3s were procured with secure speech facility and other upgrades (**HAS.Mk 3S**). Eighteen aircraft were upgraded to **HAS.Mk 3GM (Gulf Mod)** standard with improved cooling, and during Desert Storm were seen with infrared jammers and ALQ-167 ECM pods. The final Royal Navy version is that which adds a central tactical system and a flotation bag (**HAS.Mk 3CTS**). The definitive upgraded aircraft is the Lynx HAS.Mk 8/Super Lynx (described separately).

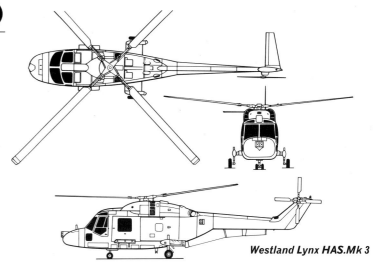

Westland Lynx HAS.Mk 3

The current standard RN version is the HAS.Mk 3, seen here armed with Sea Skua. There are several current mod states, the most recent being the Mk 3CTS with a RAMS 4000 central tactical system.

WEAPON OPTIONS

External pylons for the carriage of two torpedoes (Mk 44, 46 or Sting Ray), two Mk 11 depth charges or four Sea Skua anti-ship missiles. French aircraft have AS12 wire-guided missiles. Royal Navy aircraft can carry an FN HMP 0.50-in machine-gun for self-protection. ALQ-167 ECM pod also carried.

Westland Lynx (Navy versions)

Left: France bought a total of 40 Lynx for the Aéronavale, split between HAS.Mk 2(FN) and HAS.Mk 4(FN) models. They serve with Flottilles 31F and 34F, and with Escadrille 20S.

Right: German navy Lynx Mk 88s deploy aboard frigates to provide ASW coverage. They are shore-based at Nordholz.

SPECIFICATION

Westland Lynx HAS.Mk 2

Rotor system: main rotor diameter 42 ft 0 in (12.80 m); tail rotor diameter 7 ft 3 in (2.21 m); main rotor disc area 1,385.44 sq ft (128.71 m²); tail rotor disc area 41.28 sq ft (3.835 m²)

Fuselage and tail: length overall, rotors turning 49 ft 9 in (15.163 m), fuselage 39 ft 1.3 in (11.92 m), and with main rotor blades and tail folded 34 ft 10 in (10.618 m); height overall 11 ft 5 in (3.48 m) with rotors stationary; stabiliser span 5 ft 10 in (1.78 m); wheel track 9 ft 1.4 in (2.778 m); wheel base 9 ft 7.75 in (2.94 m)

Powerplant: two Rolls-Royce Gem 2 turboshafts each rated at 900 shp (671 kW) or, in later helicopters, two Rolls-Royce Gem 41-2 each rated at 1,120 shp (835 kW); from 1987 the engines were upgraded to Gem 42-1 standard rated at 1,135 shp (846 kW)

Weights: manufacturer's empty 6,040 lb (2740 kg); manufacturer's basic 6,680 lb (3030 kg); operating empty 7,370 lb (3343 kg) in the ASW role, or 7,224 lb (3277 kg) in the two-crew reconnaissance role, or 7,654 lb (3472 kg) in ASW classification and attack role, or 7,526 lb (3414 kg) in the ASV search and attack role with two crew and four Sea Skua missiles, or 7,531 lb (3416 kg) in the three-crew SAR role; maximum take-off 10,500 lb (4763 kg)

Fuel and load: internal fuel 214 Imp gal (257 US gal; 973 litres) plus provision for 47 Imp gal (56.4 US gal; 214 litres) of auxiliary fuel in a fuselage tank replaceable by 192 Imp gal (230.6 US gal; 873 litres) of ferry fuel in two fuselage tanks; external fuel none; maximum payload 3,000 lb (1361 kg)

Speed: maximum continuous cruising speed at optimum altitude 125 kt (144 mph; 232 km/h); economical cruising speed at optimum altitude 70 kt (81 mph; 130 km/h)

Range: ferry range 565 nm (651 miles; 1047 km) with auxiliary fuel; range 320 nm (368 miles; 593 km) with standard fuel; combat radius 96 nm (111 miles; 178 km) on a SAR mission with 11 survivors, or 50 nm (58 miles; 93 km) for a 65-minute ASW dunking sonar search and attack loiter, or for a 96-minute ASV loiter, or for a 120-minute ASW classification and attack loiter with two torpedoes, or for a 149-minute ASW anti-submarine strike loiter endurance 2.8 hours

Performance: maximum rate of climb at sea level 2,170 ft (661 m) per minute; hovering ceiling 8,450 ft (2575 m) out of ground effect

OPERATORS

All naval variants:

Argentina: two Mk 23s now sold, the remainder of the order embargoed after the Falklands War
Brazil: seven remaining of nine Mk 21s
Denmark: eight new Mk 80s, two Mk 23s from the embargoed Argentine order and one direct from Argentina. One new Mk 90. Remainder upgraded
France: 24 HAS.Mk 2(FN) and 13 HAS.Mk 4(FN), the latter with Gem 41 engines. 40 were delivered
Germany: 19 Mk 88s flying with MFG 3
Netherlands: purchased six utility Mk 25/UH-14A, 10 sonar-equipped Mk 27/SH-14B and eight MAD-equipped Mk 81/SH-14C Lynxes, the 22 survivors being converted to a common SH-14D standard with full ASW kit, RWRs, FLIR, GPS and uprated Gem Mk 42 engines, following the interim conversion of the SH-14Cs to SH-14B configuration
Nigeria: two remaining of three Mk 89s
Norway: five remaining of six Mk 86s
Portugal: three Mk 95 Super Lynx
South Korea: 12 Mk 99 Super Lynx
United Kingdom: purchased 60 HAS.Mk 2 and 31 HAS.Mk 3 for Royal Navy. 53 surviving Mk 2s upgraded to Mk 3 status. 65 Mk 3s being converted to HAS.Mk 8 standard

Westland **Lynx HAS.Mk 8/Super Lynx**

SPECIFICATION

Most of the 219 Westland WG.13 Lynx helicopters built for the Army Air Corps (128 AH.Mks 1-7) and the **Royal Navy** (91 HAS.Mks 2/3), excluding 11 prototypes, plus survivors of 26 French naval HAS.Mk 2(FN)s, are receiving new high-efficiency composite rotor blades through a £25 million MoD contract awarded to Westland in April 1991. This funds over 800 blades from Westland Engineering Composites with the RAE's record-breaking anhedralled and swept high-speed tips developed through the British Experimental Rotor Programme (BERP), plus over 100 similar blades for the Dutch navy's 22 SH-14s. These provide greater performance, speed and lift, as well as a higher fatigue life, and

A complete revision of the Royal Navy's existing Lynx fleet has resulted in the HAS.Mk 8, with BERP blades, GEC Sensors Sea Owl thermal imager and a repositioned GEC Ferranti Sea Spray radar. The onboard electronic suite is considerably revised.

are among the main upgrades for 65 RN Lynx HAS.Mk 3 to **HAS.Mk 8** standard.

This £200 million three-stage upgrade which followed the 1982 Falklands War parallels the AAC's AH.Mk 9, starting with installation of GEC Marconi AD3400 secure speech communications equipment. Second-stage integration is following in six trials Lynx HAS.Mk 3s of Racal's RAMS 4000-based automated and computerised central tactical management system.

Apart from the new BERP main rotor and reverse-direction tail rotor to improve yaw control at higher take-off weights of 11,300 lb (5125 kg) from the original 10,750 lb (4876 kg), third-stage Mk 8 changes include a nose-mounted GEC Sensors Sea Owl passive identification thermal imager turret, a rear-mounted CAE magnetic anomaly detector, INS and GPS satellite nav systems, Racal MIR-2 Orange Crop ESM and a Whittaker Yellow Veil ECM jamming pod. Defence cuts having deleted the 360° Ferranti Seaspray Mk 3 radar planned by the RN for its Mk 8s, the original 180° Seaspray Mk 1 being retained in a chin radome. As

well as detecting surface targets, Seaspray provides guidance for the Lynx's BAeD Sea Skua anti-ship missiles, as used in the 1991 Gulf War, or over-the-horizon targeting for the RN's frigate-launched MDC RGM-84D Block 1C Harpoon anti-ship missiles.

Originally equipped with three Lynx HAS.Mk 3CTS aircraft (ZF557, ZF563 and ZF558), with first- and second-stage upgrade equipment, No. 700L Squadron, the Lynx Operational Flight Trials Unit at Portland, received its first fully-equipped HAS.Mk 8s in mid-1992 when it combined with No. 815 Squadron.

Many Lynx Mk 8 features are incorporated in the export **Super Lynx**, which has been chosen by **Portugal** (five **Mk 95**s) and **South Korea** (12 **Mk 99**s). The Portuguese aircraft have 360° Allied Signal RDR 1500 search radar for service aboard 'Vasco da Gama'-class frigates, while the Korean aircraft are equipped with Sea Spray Mk 3 radar and Bendix AQS-18 dipping sonar for service aboard 'Sumner'- and 'Gearing'-class frigates. Neither has Sea Owl thermal imagers.

Westland Lynx HAS.Mk 8

generally similar to the Westland Lynx HAS.Mk 2 except in the following particulars:

Rotor system: tail rotor diameter 7 ft 9 in (2.36 m); tail rotor disc area 47.17 sq ft (4.38 m²)

Fuselage and tail: length overall, rotors turning 50 ft 0 in (15.24 m) and with main rotor blades and tail folded 35 ft 7.25 in (10.85 m); height overall 12 ft 0½ in (3.67 m) with tail rotor turning, and with main rotor blades and tail folded 10 ft 8 in (3.25 m); stabiliser span 4 ft 4 in (1.32 m); wheel track 9 ft 2¼ in (2.80 m); wheel base 9 ft 11 in (3.02 m)

Powerplant: two Rolls-Royce Gem 42-1 turboshafts each rated at 1,135 shp (846 kW)

Weights: basic empty 7,255 lb (3291 kg); operating empty 9,276 lb (4207 kg) in the ASW role, or 7,929 lb (3597 kg) in the surveillance and targeting role, or 9,373 lb (4252 kg) in ASV role with four Sea Skua missiles, or 8,064 lb (3658 kg) in the SAR role; maximum take-off 11,300 lb (5126 kg)

Range: combat radius 20 nm (23 miles; 37 km) for a 140-minute anti-submarine patrol with dunking sonar and one torpedo, or 148 nm (170 miles; 274 km) for an anti-ship point attack with four Sea Skua missiles, or 75 nm (86 miles; 139 km) for a 246-minute surveillance patrol

Above: Korea's 12 Super Lynx Mk 99s are in service with No. 627 Sqn. They are characterised by the lack of Sea Owl thermal imaging devices, but do have a dipping sonar, visible in the centre of the fuselage underside.

Westland Scout

In 1956 Saunders-Roe initiated design of a new light helicopter identified as the **P.531**, and began cutting metal on two prototypes in early 1958; both were flown that year, the first (G-APNU) on 20 July and the second (G-APNV) on 30 September. Following the acquisition of Saunders-Roe by Westland, it was this latter company which continued development, winning an order from the **Army Air Corps** for a pre-production batch of **P.531-2 Mk 1** aircraft. Evaluation, from August 1960, led to an initial production order in September 1960 for the **Westland Scout AH.Mk 1**, the first of these five-seat helicopters entering service in early 1963.

Scout AH.Mk 1 production for the UK Army Air Corps totalled 150, the last 30 or so survivors being retired in 1994. One aircraft was then still serving with the **Empire Test Pilot School** at Boscombe Down, and one with the AAC Historic Flight at Middle Wallop.

The Scout served the AAC faithfully until 1994, leaving this example with the ETPS at Boscombe as the only one in military service.

SPECIFICATION

Westland Scout AH.Mk 1
Rotor system: main rotor diameter 32 ft 3 in (9.83 m); tail rotor diameter 7 ft 6 in (2.29 m); main rotor disc area 816.86 sq ft (75.89 m²); tail rotor disc area 44.18 sq ft (4.10 m²)
Fuselage and tail: length overall, rotors turning 40 ft 4 in (12.29 m) and fuselage 30 ft 4 in (9.24 m); height overall 11 ft 8 in (3.56 m) with tail rotor turning, and 8 ft 11 in (2.72 m) to top of rotor head; skid track 8 ft

6 in (2.59 m)
Powerplant: one 1,050-shp (783-kW) Rolls-Royce (Bristol Siddeley) Nimbus Mk 101 or Mk 102 turboshaft derated to 685 shp (511 kW)
Weights: operating empty 3,232 lb (1465 kg); maximum take-off 5,300 lb (2404 kg)
Fuel and load: internal fuel 1,240 lb (562 kg); external fuel none; maximum ordnance 540 lb (245 kg) or maximum payload 1,500 lb (680 kg)

Speed: maximum level speed 'clean' at sea level 114 kt (131 mph; 211 km/h); maximum and economical cruising speed at optimum altitude 106 kt (122 mph; 196 km/h)
Range: 273 nm (314 miles; 505 km) with four passengers
Performance: maximum rate of climb at sea level 1,670 ft (510 m) per minute; service ceiling 13,400 ft (4085 m)

Westland Sea King

Amid-1960s agreement with Sikorsky for licence production of the S-61 resulted in four US-built examples (c/ns 61-393 to 396) being shipped to Westland as pattern aircraft. The first **Sea King** was a navalised SH-3D (allocated the serial G-ATYU/XV370), and was flown from Avonmouth docks on 11 October 1966. The other three (XV371-373) were used for British ASW systems trials for **Sea King HAS.Mk 1** (Specification HAS.261) development for the RN.

The first of 56 production HAS.Mk 1s (XV642-677/XV695-714) began flying on 7 May 1969, followed by 13 **HAS.Mk 2**s with uprated Rolls-Royce Gnome H.1400 turboshafts and six-bladed tail rotors from mid-1976, and the first 15 **HAR.Mk 3**s for RAF SAR roles from September 1977. Eight more HAS.Mk 2s from early 1979 included a prototype **HAS.Mk 5** ASW upgrade conversion, many of the earlier RN Sea Kings also being converted to **HAS.Mks 5/6** or **HAR.Mk 5** standards. New-build HAS.Mks 5 and 6 followed from mid-1980, eventually increasing overall RN ASW Sea King deliveries to 113. The HAS.Mk 5 introduced Thorn-EMI Sea Searcher radar in a large, flat-topped radome, Racal MIR-2 Orange Crop ESM, new sonobuoy dropping equipment and LAPADS acoustic processing. The cabin was enlarged to make room for the new equipment. The HAS.Mk 6 has a further enhanced ASW suite and reduced equipment weight, resulting in a 30-minute extension to endurance. The Orange Crop ESM system is raised to Orange Reaper standard, and the dunking depth of the sonar is increased from 245 ft (75 m) to 700 ft (213 m), among other improvements.

Three more HAR.Mk 3 SAR versions in 1985 brought RAF procurement to 19 (including one for ETPS at Boscombe Down in 1980) for three squadrons. Two SAR-tasked HAR.Mk 3s of No. 78 Sqn (based on the Falkland Islands) are equipped with chaff dispensers and RWRs. Another £50 million-plus early 1992 RAF order added six upgraded **HAR.Mk 3A**s, reopening Sea King production for more Wessex replacements.

Development of a non-amphibious Sea King variant as the Commando assault, tactical and general transport (described separately) began in mid-1971. The Royal Navy subsequently placed orders from 1979 for 41 **HC.Mk 4** Commando helicopters. Two **Mk 4X Sea Kings** (ZB506/ ZB507) were built by Westland as DRA avionics, rotor and systems test aircraft for EH.101 development, bringing overall UK service procurement of all variants to 175.

Although designated Commando Mk 3s, the aircraft of Qatar's No. 8 Anti-Surface Vessel Squadron have full Sea King systems and sponsons. Like Pakistani aircraft, they can carry Exocet anti-ship missiles.

Ten of the Royal Navy's Sea Kings serve with No. 849 Sqn in AEW.Mk 2A configuration. Searchwater radar is mounted on a swivelling strut, and is protected by an inflatable radome. The AEW system was also sold to Spain for its Sikorsky-built Sea Kings.

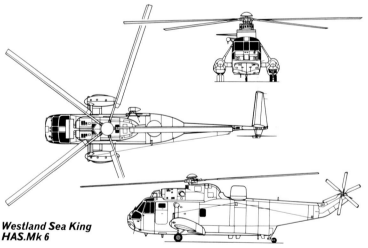

Westland has supplied 147 Sea Kings (and the related Commando) to overseas customers. German Sea Kings were converted from SAR to anti-ship roles from 1986 with Ferranti Seaspray Mk 3 radar and BAeD Sea Skua AShMs, which also arm Indian navy Mk 42Bs, while some Pakistani and Qatari Sea Kings/Commandos are equipped to launch Aérospatiale AM39 Exocet anti-ship missiles. The Indian navy's **Sea King Mk 42B**s are **Advanced Sea King**s, with 1,465-shp (1092-kW) Gnome H.1400-1T turboshafts, composite main and tail rotors, improved avionics and a take-off weight of 21,500 lb (9752 kg).

The Royal Navy's lack of airborne early-warning capability in the 1982 Falklands War resulted in the hurried conversion in May 1982 of two HAS Sea Kings (XV650 and 704) to **AEW.Mk 2A** standard with Thorn-EMI Searchwater radar and associated equipment, including anti-Exocet I-band jammers and Racal MIR-2 Orange Crop ESM. This involved fitting a large radome suspended to starboard of the cabin and swinging back through 90° for ground stowage. Both AEW.Mk 2A development aircraft began flying in July 1982, and were deployed in August on *Illustrious* for post-war Falklands service with No. 824 Sqn. Eight further Sea Kings were modified as AEW.Mk 2As and equipped No. 849 Sqn, the FAA's historic AEW unit, shore-based at RNAS Culdrose and in RN V/STOL carrier

Westland Sea King HAS.Mk 6

Westland Sea King

Left: The RAF operates the HAR.Mk 3 on dedicated SAR duties. Two serve in the Falklands, wearing a dark grey 'combat SAR' camouflage.

Right: India's Mk 42Bs are virtually to HAS.Mk 5 standard, and feature the square-topped fuselage radome for the Sea Searcher radar. They can launch the Sea Eagle anti-ship missile.

flights from 1 November 1984. Three similar radar systems were also sold to Spain in 1984 for AEW conversions of some of the AAA's Sikorsky SH-3H Sea Kings.

WEAPON OPTIONS

Up to four Mk 46, A244S or Sting Ray torpedoes can be carried externally, or four Mk 11 depth charges. The Sea King can also field BAe Sea Eagle or Exocet anti-ship missiles for anti-surface vessel duties. Pintle-mounted 7.62-mm GPMGs (general-purpose machine-guns) can be fitted in the starboard door.

SPECIFICATION

Westland Advanced Sea King

Rotor system: main rotor diameter 62 ft 0 in (18.90 m); tail rotor diameter 10 ft 4 in (3.16 m); main rotor disc area 3,019.07 sq ft (280.47 m²); tail rotor disc area 83.86 sq ft (7.79 m²)

Fuselage and tail: length overall, rotors turning 72 ft 8 in (22.15 m), fuselage 55 ft 10 in (17.02 m), with main rotor blades folded 57 ft 2 in (17.42 m) and with main rotor blades and tail pylon folded 47 ft 3 in (14.40 m);

height overall 16 ft 10 in (5.13 m) with rotors turning, 15 ft 11 in (4.85 m) with rotors stationary, and 15 ft 6 in (4.72 m) to top of rotor head; wheel track 13 ft 0 in (3.96 m); wheel base 23 ft 5 in (7.14 m)

Powerplant: two Rolls-Royce Gnome H.1400-1T turboshafts each rated at 1,660 shp (1238 kW) for take-off and 1,465 shp (1092 kW) for continuous running

Weights: basic empty 11,891 lb (5393 kg) with sponsons or 11,845 lb (5373 kg) without sponsons; empty equipped 16,377 lb (7428 kg) for the ASW role, or 16,689 lb (7570 kg) for the ASV role, or 17,143 lb (7776 kg) for the AEW role, or 13,760 lb (6241 kg) for the SAR role, or 12,594 lb (5712 kg) for the troop transport role, or 12,536 lb (5686 kg) for the freight role or 15,917 lb (7220 kg) for the VIP role; maximum take-off 21,500 lb (9752 kg)

Fuel and load: internal fuel 817 Imp gal (981 US gal; 3714 litres) plus provision for 190 Imp gal (228 US gal; 863 litres) of auxiliary fuel in a fuselage tank; external fuel none; maximum ordnance 2,500 lb (1134 kg)

Speed: never exceed speed at sea level 122 kt (140 mph; 226 km/h); maximum cruising speed at sea level 110 kt (126 mph; 204 km/h)

Range: ferry range 940 nm (1,082 miles; 1742 km) with auxiliary fuel; range 800 nm (921 miles; 1482 km) with standard fuel

Performance: maximum rate of climb at sea level

2,030 ft (619 m) per minute; service ceiling 4,000 ft (1220 m) with one engine out; hovering ceiling 6,500 ft (1980 m) in ground effect and 4,700 ft (1435 m) out of ground effect

Westland Sea King AEW.Mk 2A
generally similar to the Westland Advanced Sea King except in the following particulars:

Powerplant: two Rolls-Royce Gnome H.1400-1 turboshafts each rated at 1,660 shp (1238 kW)

Weights: maximum take-off 21,000 lb (9526 kg)

Speed: maximum cruising speed at optimum altitude 90 kt (104 mph; 167 km/h)

Performance: service ceiling 10,000 ft (3050 m)

OPERATORS

Export customers for all variants of Sea King are:

Australia: HAS.Mk 50/50As (12 delivered, seven remaining) serving with HS-817 at RAN Nowra in utility transport/ASW role

Belgium: five Mk 48s with 40 Sm/Esc at Coxyde on SAR duties

Egypt: five Commando Mk 1s, 17 Mk 2s, two VIP Mk 2Bs, four ECM Mk 2Es, six (five remaining) Sea King HAS.Mk 47s

Germany: 22 SAR/anti-ship Mk 41s serving with 1/MFG 5 at Kiel-Holtenau

India: 12 (eight remaining) Mk 42s and three Mk 42As for ASW with INAS 330 at Dabolim, 20 Mk 42Bs for ASW with INAS 336 at Cochin and six Mk 42Cs for assault transport with INAS 339 at Margar

Norway: 10 (eight remaining) Mk 43s, one Mk 43A and one Mk 43B for SAR with 330 Skvadron at Bodø, Banak, Ørland and Sola. Mk 43B features nose radar and FLIR, others being similarly upgraded

Pakistan: six ASW/ASV Mk 45s with No. 111 Sqn at PNS Mehran

Qatar: three Commando Mk 2As, one Mk 2C with No. 9 Squadron for assault/VIP transport, eight Mk 3s with No. 8 Squadron for anti-ship

United Kingdom (RN): deliveries were 56 HAS.Mk 1s, 21 HAS.Mk 2s, 40 HC.Mk 4s, 30 HAS.Mk 5s and five HAS.Mk 6s. Current force consists of 10 AEW.Mk 2As (No. 849 Sqn), 35 HC.Mk 4s (Nos 707, 772, 845 and 846 Sqns), five HAR.Mk 5s (No. 771 Sqn), 29 HAS. Mk 5s (Nos 706, 771 and 891 Sqns) and 41 HAS.Mk 6s (Nos 810, 814, 819 and 820 Sqns)

United Kingdom (RAF/MoD PE): 19 HAR.Mk 3s and six HAR.Mk 3As (on order) with Nos 22, 78 and 202 Sqns, headquartered at St Mawgan, Mount Pleasant and Boulmer, respectively. Two Mk 4Xs serve with DRA and one HC.Mk 4 with ETPS

Westland **Sea King HC.Mk 4/Commando**

Development of a non-amphibious transport version of the Sea King lacking flotation sponsons (but normally retaining flotation bags on the wheel hubs) and ASW equipment began in mid-1971, resulting in the **Westland Commando** assault, tactical and general transport. The aircraft was based on the Sea King HAS.Mk 2, with the same engines, gearbox and six-bladed tail rotors. In this form the helicopter could carry 7,500 lb (3402 kg) of equipment or 28 fully armed troops. No interest was expressed initially by the British armed forces, but a number of overseas customers placed orders. The first of these was the **Egyptian air force**, which received five **Commando Mk 1s (Sea King Mk 70s)** in early 1974, ordered by Saudi Arabia on its behalf. These aircraft were not, in fact, true Commandos, being based on the engine/airframe of the HAS.Mk 1 but with ASW equipment removed and provision for the carriage of troops or cargo. The Commando Mk 1s were

followed by 19 full-standard **Commando Mk 2s** based on the Sea King HAS.Mk 2. Two of the aircraft were fitted out as VIP transports and were designated **Commando Mk 2B**. All were delivered by February 1976. Four more aircraft, designated **Commando Mk 2E** and equipped for ECM operations with huge spherical radomes on the fuselage sides, were delivered during 1979-80. All but the Commando Mk 1s were fitted with intake dust filters.

Before Egypt took delivery of its Mk 2s, another customer for the aircraft was found. The **Qatar Emiri air force** bought four aircraft based on the Sea King HAS.Mk 2, delivered in 1975/76. Three (designated **Commando Mk 2A**) were 27-seat utility transports, while the fourth was a **VIP** transport designated **Commando Mk 2C**. Qatar later ordered a second batch of eight aircraft with the H.1400-IT engines of the Advanced Sea King, and equipped to carry Exocet ASMs, SURA or SNEB rockets or podded 0.5-in machine-guns. These **Com-**

mando Mk 3s, retaining Sea King-style undercarriage sponsons, were delivered from November 1982 to January 1984.

Royal Navy interest in the Commando began in 1978, when the aircraft was first considered as a potential 'off-the-shelf' replacement for the Wessex HU.Mk 5s then in use with the Commando ('Junglie') squadrons. Essentially a Commando Mk 2, the RN aircraft retained the Sea King name with the designation **HC.Mk 4**. An initial order for 15 was placed and the first made its maiden flight in November 1979. Further orders brought total HC.Mk 4 procurement to 41, one of these going to the ETPS at Boscombe Down, and another to the Aeroplane and Armament Experimental Establishment as a navigation and radio trials aircraft at the same base. Two basically similar **Sea King Mk 4Xs** were built by Westland for the RAE as avionics, rotor and systems test aircraft, and were extensively used for EH.101 development work. Over 50 RN Sea Kings of Nos 820, 824, 825, 826 and 846 Sqns played a prominent part in the 1982 Falklands War in the ASW, SAR, assault, transport, anti-ship missile decoy, and general fleet support roles, five being lost in action. One HC.Mk 4 was destroyed by its crew in Chile after landing an SAS surveillance party near the southern Argentine base at Punta Arenas. Sea King HC.Mk 4s of Nos 845, 846 and 848 Squadrons played a part in Operation Desert Storm, and aircraft from Nos 845 and 846 Squadrons were involved in humanitarian relief and UN support duties in Bosnia during 1993, the latter flying from RFA *Argus*.

Qatar's Commando Mk 2As serve with No. 9 Multi-Role Squadron, which also flies the Mk 2C VIP transport.

SPECIFICATION

Westland Commando Mk 2

Rotor system: main rotor diameter 62 ft 0 in (18.90 m); tail rotor diameter 10 ft 4 in (3.16 m); main rotor disc area 3,019.07 sq ft (280.47 m²); tail rotor disc area 83.86 sq ft (7.79 m²)

Fuselage and tail: length overall, rotors turning 72 ft 8 in (22.15 m), fuselage 55 ft 10 in (17.02 m); height overall 16 ft 10 in (5.13 m) with rotors turning, and to top of rotor head 15 ft 6 in (4.72 m); wheel track 13 ft 0 in (3.96 m); wheel base 23 ft 8 in (7.21 m)

Powerplant: two Rolls-Royce Gnome H.1400-1T turboshafts each rated at 1,660 shp (1238 kW) for take-off and 1,465 shp (1092 kW) for continuous running

Weights: operating empty 12,390 lb (5620 kg) with two crew; normal take-off 21,000 lb (9526 kg); maximum take-off 21,500 lb (9752 kg)

Fuel and load: internal fuel 817 Imp gal (981 US gal; 3714 litres) plus provision for 190 Imp gal (228 US gal; 863 litres) of auxiliary fuel in a fuselage tank; external fuel none; maximum payload 8,000 lb (3629 kg)

Speed: never exceed speed at sea level 122 kt (140 mph; 226 km/h); maximum cruising speed at sea level 109 kt (126 mph; 204 km/h)

Range: ferry range 940 nm (1,082 miles; 1742 km) with auxiliary fuel; range 800 nm (921 miles; 1482 km) with maximum standard fuel or 214 nm (246 miles; 396 km) with maximum payload

Performance: maximum rate of climb at sea level 2,030 ft (619 m) per minute; service ceiling 4,000 ft (1220 m) with one engine out; hovering ceiling 6,500 ft (1980 m) in ground effect

Westland Sea King HC.Mk 4

Westland Wasp

Simultaneously with its development of the Scout for service with the UK Army Air Corps, Westland began work to evolve from the same source (the Saunders-Roe P.531) a five-seat general-purpose helicopter optimised for operation to and from ships at sea. The Royal Navy ordered the type into production as the **Sea Scout HAS.Mk 1**, with two pre-production aircraft required for familiarisation. The first of these (XS463) was flown initially on 28 October 1962, by which time the aircraft's designation had been changed to **Wasp HAS.Mk 1**.

Westland produced a total of 133 Wasp HAS.Mk 1s, comprising 98 for the Royal Navy (these aircraft have been retired) and 35 Wasps built for export (for Brazil, the Netherlands, New Zealand and South Africa). The Wasp could carry a pair of Mk 44 ASW torpedoes, or a single Mk 46. A range of depth charges could be carried, or for surface attack two Aérospatiale AS12 wire-guided missiles (with roof-mounted sight). No sensors were fitted, the design of the Wasp being intended for rapid reaction to known threats.

New Zealand maintains seven Wasps in airworthy condition for service from 'Leander'-class frigates. Several non-flying airframes provide spares.

Current users are **Indonesia** (nine of 10 ex-Netherlands aircraft) operated by 400 Skwadron at Surabaya, **Malaysia** (six ex-RN aircraft operated by 499 Sqn at Lumut) and **New Zealand**, which has seven (of a total of 17 new and ex-RN deliveries) serving with No. 3 Sqn at Hobsonville.

SPECIFICATION

Westland Wasp HAS.Mk 1
Rotor system: main rotor diameter 32 ft 3 in (9.83 m); tail rotor diameter 7 ft 6 in (2.29 m); main rotor disc area 816.86 sq ft (75.89 m²); tail rotor disc area 44.18 sq ft (4.10 m²)
Fuselage and tail: length overall, rotors turning 40 ft 4 in (12.29 m) and fuselage 30 ft 4 in (9.24 m); height overall 11 ft 8 in (3.56 m) with tail rotor turning, and to top of rotor head 8 ft 11 in (2.72 m); wheel track 8 ft 0 in (2.44 m); wheel base 8 ft 0 in (2.44 m)
Powerplant: one 1,050-shp (783-kW) Rolls-Royce (Bristol Siddeley) Nimbus Mk 503 turboshaft derated to 710 shp (530 kW)
Weights: manufacturer's empty 3,452 lb (1566 kg); maximum take-off 5,500 lb (2495 kg)

Fuel and load: internal fuel 1,240 lb (562 kg); external fuel none; maximum ordnance 540 lb (245 kg) or maximum payload 1,500 lb (680 kg)
Speed: maximum level speed 'clean' at sea level 104 kt (120 mph; 193 km/h); maximum and economical cruising speed at optimum altitude 96 kt (111 mph; 179 km/h)
Range: 263 nm (303 miles; 488 km); typical range 235 nm (271 miles; 435 km) with four passengers
Performance: maximum rate of climb at sea level 1,440 ft (439 m) per minute; service ceiling 12,200 ft (3720 m); hovering ceiling 12,500 ft (3810 m) in ground effect and 8,800 ft (2680 m) out of ground effect

Westland Wessex

Turboshaft-powered versions of the Whirlwind had given Westland a good appreciation of the capability of a helicopter with such a powerplant, leading to licence negotiations with Sikorsky for manufacture of the S-58. Westland believed that its larger size, allied with a turboshaft powerplant, would make possible the development of an ASW aircraft combining the hunter and killer activities of the two-aircraft Whirlwind team, but such hopes proved to be premature. However, following receipt of a single S-58 sample aircraft from Sikorsky, Westland began by replacing its standard Wright R-1820 piston engine with an 820-kW (1,100-shp) Napier Gazelle NGa.11 turboshaft, with which it flew for the first time on 17 May 1957 to become the company's demonstrator (XL722).

Satisfactory testing led first to a Westland-built prototype (XL727) and two pre-production examples of what was to be named the **Westland Wessex**, all powered by the 1081-kW (1,450-shp) Napier Gazelle Mk 161, as was the initial production **Wessex HAS.Mk 1** helicopter, of which about 130 were built. These were used by the Royal Navy as 'hunter-killer' pairs in the ASW role, and by the Royal Marines as transports carrying up to 16 fully-equipped commandos. A similar **Wessex HC.Mk 2** for **Royal Air Force** deployment in ambulance, transport and utility roles featured an important difference in the introduction of two coupled Bristol Siddeley Gnome turboshafts, each rated at 1007 kW (1,350 shp), and interconnected so that in the event of an engine failure the remaining engine could continue to drive the rotors.

The Navy's next variant, the **HAS.Mk 3**, introduced the more powerful Napier Gazelle NGa.22 turboshaft and, more importantly, a new AFCS that allowed an entire

The RAF support helicopter fleet has adopted a two-tone green camouflage.

ASW search or strike mission, from lift-off to positioning for landing, to be flown automatically. Later versions included two **Wessex HCC.Mk 4** VIP transports (similar to the HC.Mk 2) for The Queen's Flight; the **Wessex HU.Mk 5** (similar to HC.Mk 2) troop-carrying assault helicopter for the Royal Marine Commandos; and a civil version of the HC.Mk 2, designated **Wessex Mk 60** and designed for use as 10-passenger civil transports, as an air ambulance with eight stretchers, two sitting casualties and a medical attendant, or to carry 15 survivors in a rescue operation.

The **Wessex HAS.Mk 31**, exported to the Royal Australian Navy, was similar to the HAS.Mk 1 except for a Napier Gazelle NGa.13/2 flat-rated at 1148 kW (1,540 shp); these were later given upgraded ASW systems and other improvements to become redesignated **HAS.Mk 31B**. Finally, versions of the HC.Mk 2 were built for Iran, Ghana and Brunei under the respective designations **Wessex Mk 52**, **Mk 53** and **Mk 54**. It is now over 35 years since the Westland-built Wessex prototype first flew, yet many of these multi-role helicopters continue to provide useful service.

The RAF is the sole current Wessex operator. Around 60 HC.Mk 2s are flown by No. 22 Sqn on SAR duties, No. 28 Sqn in Hong Kong, No. 60 Sqn at Benson and No. 72 Sqn in Northern Ireland. Aircraft of the latter two squadrons are often equipped with Nitesun searchlights, countermeasures and GPMGs mounted in the cabin door. The rotary-wing training unit at Shawbury, 2 FTS, also operates this variant. A pair of HCC.Mk 4s continues to serve with The

Right: The RAF's five HC.Mk 5Cs all serve with No. 84 Sqn at Akrotiri. These wear a blue band in recognition of their UN peacekeeping role in Cyprus. They are being replaced by HC.Mk 2s from mid-1994.

Queen's Flight at Benson, although they will transfer to Northolt as part of No. 32 Squadron in April 1995. No. 84 Sqn at Akrotiri operates five **HC.Mk 5C**s converted from ex-RN machines.

SPECIFICATION

Westland Wessex HC.Mk 2
Rotor system: main rotor diameter 56 ft 0 in (17.07 m); tail rotor diameter 9 ft 6 in (2.90 m); main rotor disc area 2,643.01 sq ft (228.81 m²); tail rotor disc area 70.88 sq ft (6.58 m²)
Fuselage and tail: length overall, rotors turning 65 ft 9 in (20.04 m) and fuselage 48 ft 4.5 in (14.74 m); height overall 16 ft 2 in (4.93 m) and 14 ft 5 in (4.39 m) to top of rotor head; wheel track 12 ft 0 in (3.66 m)

Powerplant: two Rolls-Royce (Bristol Siddeley) Gnome Mk 110/111 turboshafts each rated at 1,350 shp (1007 kW)
Weights: operating empty 8,304 lb (3767 kg); maximum take-off 13,500 lb (6123 kg)
Fuel and load: internal fuel 300 Imp gal (360 US gal; 1364 litres) plus provision for 200 Imp gal (240 US gal; 909 litres) of auxiliary fuel; external fuel none; maximum payload 4,000 lb (1814 kg)
Speed: maximum level speed at sea level 115 kt (132 mph; 212 km/h); maximum cruising speed at optimum altitude 105 kt (121 mph; 195 km/h)
Range: ferry range 560 nm (645 miles; 1040 km) with auxiliary fuel; range 415 nm (478 miles; 769 km) with standard fuel
Performance: maximum rate of climb at sea level 1,650 ft (503 m) per minute; hovering ceiling 4,000 ft (1220 m) out of ground effect

Left: The Wessex HC.Mk 2 is a regular sight in Britain's mountainous and coastal regions. They are being replaced in the search and rescue role by further procurement of Sea King HAR.Mk 3s.

Right: Helping to police the colony of Hong Kong until 1997 are the Wessex HC.Mk 2s of No. 28 Sqn, which fly from Sek Kong.

Westland WS-70

A single example of the Sikorsky S-70 (an S-70A-16) battlefield helicopter was imported into Britain after Westland acquired production rights from United Technologies, and flew initially in June 1986, powered by RTM 322 turboshafts. The first Westland-assembled **WS-70A** (Sikorsky **S-70A-19**) demonstrator was first flown on 1 April 1987. Equivalent to the US Army's **UH-60A Black Hawk**, it is powered by two 1,560-shp (1151-kW) General Electric T700-GE-701 turboshafts. An order for 88 **WS-70L**s was provisionally included in the Saudi Arabian Al Yamamah II (Peace Bird II) programme outlined in July 1988. The future of this order remains unclear, pending the completion of final contracts.

The single WS-70L has worn a number of paint schemes to attract customers with varying needs.

Xian H-6

Xian Aircraft Company
PO Box 140, Xian, Shaanxi 710000
People's Republic of China

As its most ambitious licence-building programme, in September 1957 the Chinese aircraft manufacturer acquired from the Soviet Union production rights to the Tupolev Tu-16 strategic medium bomber. It was decided that the aircraft would be built jointly by factories at Xian and Harbin. The first data reached **China** in February 1959, and were followed by two pattern aircraft together with one example of the Tu-16 disassembled and another in CKD (component knock-down) kit form. The first aircraft was reassembled at Harbin within 67 days, and was flown on 27 September 1959. Two years later, all work was transferred to what was to become the Xian Aircraft Manufacturing Company (XAC), work on production tooling commencing in 1964. The first completely Chinese-manufactured bomber flew as the **H-6A** on 24 December 1968.

The H-6A was powered by two 20,944-lb st (93.17-kN) Xian (XAE) WP8 turbojets, carried six crew members, featured a defensive armament of dorsal, ventral and tail twin-gun barbettes and, in its initial form, had a normal internal bomb load of 6,614 lb (3000 kg). The development of a maritime strike version, the **H-6D**, commenced in 1975, this flying in prototype form on 29 August 1981. The H-6D has a new undernose radome housing an unidentified target acquisition and missile guidance radar and provision for two C-601 anti-shipping missiles on underwing pylons, the maximum offensive load totalling 19,841 lb (9000 kg).

An impressive line-up of standard H-6 bombers rests at a People's Liberation Army Air Force base.

A dedicated nuclear bomber and a variant with a second-generation navigation and bombing system have also been produced. H-6s also serve as drone carriers, ECM platforms and engine testbeds.

Low-tempo production of the H-6 – averaging four aircraft annually – continued into the early 1990s, and in excess of 100 H-6s in various versions are reportedly currently serving with the People's Republic of China air force and navy. Four H-6Ds were exported to **Iraq** as **B-6D**s.

SPECIFICATION

Xian H-6 'Badger'
Wing: span 34.189 m (112 ft 2 in); aspect ratio 7.09; area 164.65 m² (1,772.34 sq ft)
Fuselage and tail: length 34.80 m (114 ft 2 in); height 10.355 m (33 ft 11.75 in); tailplane span 11.75 m (38 ft 6.5 in); wheel track 9.77 m (32 ft 0.75 in); wheel base 10.57 m (34 ft 8 in)
Powerplant: two Xian (XAE) Wopen-8 (Mikulin AM-3M-500) turbojets each rated at 93.16 kN (20,944 lb) thrust
Weights: empty equipped 38530 kg (84,943 lb); maximum take-off 75800 kg (167,110 lb)
Fuel and load: internal fuel 36600 kg (80,688 lb); external fuel none; maximum ordnance 9000 kg (19,841 lb) of bombs or 4880 kg (10,7598 kg) in the

form of two C-601 anti-ship missiles
Speed: maximum level speed 'clean' at 19,685 ft (6000 m) 992 km/h (535 kt; 616 mph); cruising speed at optimum altitude 786 km/h (424 kt; 488 mph) with two C-601 missiles
Range: 4300 km (2,320 nm; 2,672 miles); combat

radius 1,800 km (971 nm; 1,118 miles)
Performance: maximum rate of climb at sea level 2,513 ft (1140 m) per minute; service ceiling 39,370 ft (12000 m); take-off run 2100 m (6,890 ft) with maximum warload; landing run 1540 m (5,052 ft) at normal landing weight

Left: This H-6 is used for engine tests, complete with an icing rig in front of the intake.

Right: The large undernose radome and wing pylons identify the H-6D anti-ship variant.

Xian JH-7

Revealed publicly in model form at the 1988 Farnborough air show, the **JH-7** (Jianjiji Hongzhaji – fighter-bomber) is a high-performance interdictor and anti-ship aircraft with a maximum take-off weight in the 27500-kg (61,000-lb) class. The aircraft has a high-set anhedralled swept wing with a large dog-tooth notch at mid-span, sharply-swept tail surfaces with low-set tailplanes and two lateral intakes feeding side-by-side turbofans. A crew of two sits on tandem HTY-4 ejection seats. Offensive weapons (such as the C-801 anti-ship missile) and fuel tanks are carried on four underwing pylons, while for self-defence there are wingtip launch rails for AAMs and a nose-mounted 23-mm twin-barrelled cannon. A Chinese terrain-following radar is fitted.

The first prototype is believed to have flown in early 1989, powered by Xian WS9

An artists's impression shows the JH-7 in anti-ship form, with missiles on the inboard pylons and self-defence AAMs on wingtip launchers.

(licence-built Rolls-Royce Spey Mk 202) turbofans. Production aircraft are expected to feature a Liming engine of 138.3 kN (31,085 lb) afterburning thrust. Service entry was due for 1992-93, but this is likely to have slipped due to developmental problems. Variants for the **PLA air force** (interdictor) and **PLA navy** (maritime attack) may feature different avionics items.

Xian Y-7

The **Y-7** is essentially an unlicensed copy of the An-24 'Coke'. Development began in October 1966, and a design team was formed from engineers from Xian, Nanchang, Harbin and a collection of research institutes. The prototype made its maiden flight on 25 December 1970 and was certificated in July 1982. The aircraft entered service in early 1984, by which time production had switched to the improved **Y7-100**, developed by Hong Kong Aircraft Engineering Company. This was built to Western airworthiness standards, introduced Western avionics and was fitted with winglets. The

Chinese paratroops board Y7Hs for an air assault exercise. Up to 39 paratroops can be carried by each aircraft. The Chinese air force has about 20 Y7Hs in service.

Y7-200A is a derivative with Pratt & Whitney Canada PW124 turboprops and a Collins EFIS, while the **Y7-200B** is an indigenously powered version for the domestic market. Originally designated **Y-14-100**, the **Y7H-500** is a Chinese-built version of the An-26 'Curl', and features a rear-loading ramp. A handful of Y-7s and Y-7Hs are in military service, mostly with **China**, in both air force and navy service.

SPECIFICATION

Xian Y-7
Wing: span 29.20 m (95 ft 9.5 in); aspect ratio 11.37; area 74.98 m2 (807.10 sq ft)
Fuselage and tail: length 23.7 m (77 ft 9.5 in); height 8.55 m (28 ft 0.75 in); tailplane span 9.08 m (29 ft 9.5 in); wheel track 7.90 m (25 ft 11 in); wheel base 7.90 m (25 ft 11 in)
Powerplant: two Dongan (DEMC) Wojiang-5A-1

turboprops each rated at 2080 kW (2,790 shp) and one MNPK 'Soyuz' (Tumanskii) RU-19-300 turbojet (or Chinese-built equivalent) rated at 8.83 kN (1,984 lb st)
Weights: operating empty 14235 kg (31,382 lb); maximum take-off 21800 kg (48,060 lb)
Fuel and load: internal fuel 4790 kg (10,560 lb) plus provision for auxiliary fuel in four centre-section tanks; maximum payload 4700 kg (10,362 lb)
Speed: maximum level speed 'clean' at optimum altitude 518 km/h (280 kt; 322 mph); maximum cruising speed at 4000 m (13,125 ft) 478 km/h (258 kt;

297 mph); economical cruising speed at 6000 m (19,685 ft) 423 mph (228 kt; 263 mph)
Range: ferry range 2420 km (1,306 nm; 1,504 miles) with auxiliary fuel; range 1900 km (1,026 nm; 1,181 miles) with standard fuel, or 910 km (491 nm; 565 km) with maximum passenger payload
Performance: maximum rate of climb at sea level 458 m (1,504 ft) per minute; service ceiling 8750 m (28,705 ft); take-off run 1248 m (4,095 ft) at maximum take-off weight; landing run 620 m (2,035 ft) at normal landing weight

Yakovlev **Yak-11 'Moose'**

Moscow Machine-building Factory 'Skorost', named after A.S. Yakovlev
68 Leningradsky Prospekt
Moscow 125315, Russia

Derived directly from the wartime Yak-3 fighter, the **Yak-3UTI** tandem two-seat trainer first flew in 1945. Subsequently designated **Yak-11**, a slightly refined variant flew in 1946. Deliveries of an eventual 3,859 began in 1947, and 707 more were licence-built in Czechoslovakia as the **LET**

C-11. Sub-variants included the **Yak-11U**, which had a nosewheel undercarriage for training pilots destined for modern jets. Very widely exported, only a handful now survive in military service, probably in **Afghanistan**, **Mali**, **North Korea**, **Somalia**, **Vietnam** and **Yemen**.

SPECIFICATION

Yakovlev Yak-11 'Moose'
Wing: span 9.40 m (30 ft 10 in); aspect ratio 5.74; area 15.40 m2 (165.77 sq ft)
Fuselage and tail: length 8.50 m (27 ft 10.7 in);

height 3.28 m (10 ft 9 in)
Powerplant: one Shvetsov ASh-21 radial piston engine rated at 570 hp (425 kW)
Fuel and load: internal fuel 230 kg (507 lb); external fuel none; maximum ordnance 200 kg (440 lb)
Speed: maximum level speed 'clean' at 2500 m (8,200 ft) 465 km/h (251 kt; 289 mph)

Yakovlev **Yak-18 'Max'**

While the Yak-11 was intended as an advanced trainer, and was based on the wartime Yak-3 fighter, the **Yak-18** was intended primarily as a basic trainer and was derived from the pre-World War II Yak UT-2. Although the prototype had a fixed landing gear, subsequent aircraft had aft-retracting mainwheels and a fixed, castoring tailwheel. The 160-hp (119-kW) Shvetsov M-11FR radial engine was closely cowled, with distinct bulges over each of the five cylinders.

The **Yak-18U** introduced a tricycle undercarriage, with the nosewheel retracting aft and the mainwheels retracting forward. When retracted, half-wheels remained

exposed, giving the unusual possibility of a damage-free wheels-up landing if the propeller was stopped in the horizontal position. The aircraft also had a longer nose and increased dihedral on the outer wings. Heavier weight seriously degraded performance characteristics.

The **Yak-20** was powered by the more powerful 260-hp (194-kW) Ivchenko AI-14R engine in a long-chord smooth cowling, and featured structural strengthening, increased internal fuel capacity, a redesigned tail unit, a deeper canopy and improved avionics and systems. Later redesignated **Yak-18A**, it became the most widely used military train-

ing variant and served as the basis for the Chinese **Nanchang CJ-6**, which is described separately.

The **Yak-18P**, **Yak-18PM** and **Yak-18PS** were dedicated competition aerobatic machines, development of which led to the Yak-50 series. The **Yak-18T** was an extensively redesigned cabin version, with side-by-side seats for the pilots, and accommodation behind for passengers or cargo. Some of the latter may remain in military service with **Afghanistan**, **Mali**, **Mongolia**, **Romania** and **Vietnam**.

SPECIFICATION

Yakovlev Yak-18T
Wing: span 11.16 m (36 ft 7.25 in); aspect ratio 6.64;

area 18.75 m2 (201.83 sq ft)
Fuselage and tail: length 8.35 m (27 ft 4.75 in)
Powerplant: one VMKB (Vedeneyev) radial piston engine M-14P rated at 360 hp (269 kW)
Weights: empty 1200 kg (2,646 lb); normal take-off 1500 kg (3,307 lb); maximum take-off 1650 kg (3637 lb)
Fuel and load: internal fuel more than 150 kg (331 lb); external fuel none; ordnance none
Speed: maximum level speed 'clean' at optimum altitude 295 km/h (159 kt; 183 mph); maximum cruising speed at optimum altitude 250 km/h (135 kt; 155 mph)
Range: standard range 900 km (485 nm; 559 miles)
Performance: maximum rate of climb at sea level 300 m (984 ft) per minute; service ceiling 5500 m (18,045 ft); take-off run 330 m (1,085 ft) at maximum take-off weight; landing run 400 m (1,315 ft) at normal landing weight

Yakovlev **Yak-28 'Brewer'**

The **Yak-28** was a supersonic bomber developed from the Yak-25 and Yak-27, with similar configuration, but with increased wing and tailplane area and span, and with new 12,676-lb (56.4-kN) R-11AF-300 engines. The **Yak-28R 'Brewer-D'** was developed in 1963 as a dedicated tactical reconnaissance aircraft. A derivative was the **Yak-28PP 'Brewer-E'**, a dedicated ECM jammer designed to escort bombers and strike aircraft. The 'Brewer-E' could be externally distinguished by the replacement of its 'Short Horn' ventral radome with a broader, flatter, rectangular radome, and by the prominent cylindrical fairing projecting from the former bomb bay. Various other antennas, dielectric panels and heat ex-

The 'Brewer-E' was the last variant in front-line service, operating as an electronic warfare platform.

changer inlets and outlets proliferate, and the cannon seems to have been deleted. Rocket pods were frequently carried outboard of the underwing fuel tanks, perhaps indicating a secondary direct defence suppression role. Like late 'Brewer-Ds', the Yak-28PP has smaller, less heavily framed nose glazing, with a vertical aft edge.

Yak-28s were finally retired from the important Group of Soviet Forces in Germany during early 1989. A handful of 'Brewer-Ds' and 'Brewer-Es' may still remain in service in **Russia** and **Ukraine**.

No longer serving as front-line ECM-escort aircraft or reconnaissance platforms, these have probably been relegated to trials and

training roles. Most Yak-28s have now been replaced by dedicated Sukhoi Su-24 'Fencer' variants.

Yakovlev **Yak-38 'Forger'**

Development of a V/STOL fighter for the **Soviet** navy's new 'Kiev' class of aircraft-carriers began during the early 1960s. Intensive studies bore fruit in the shape of a number of **Yakovlev Yak-36 'Freehand'** research aircraft, with a bicycle undercarriage under the fuselage augmented by wingtip outriggers. The aircraft is believed to have been powered by a pair of 8,267-lb (36.78-kN) Koliesov engines, each with a rotating nozzle. These gave a tremendous thrust margin, and powerful autostabilisers gave a rock-steady hover, using reaction control 'puffer jets' in the tail, wingtips and at the tip of a long nose-probe.

Despite carrying UV-16-57 rocket pods at Domodyedovo, the Yak-36 was not an oper-

ational aircraft although it did lead directly to the Yak-38. This first flew in 1971 (reportedly as the **Yak-36MP**), and was first seen during trials of the *Kiev* in the Black Sea during 1975, and afterwards

Two Yak-38U two-seat trainers are usually deployed on each carrier. The Yak-38U features an unusual drooping nose and has a constant-section rear fuselage plug to compensate for the longer nose.

when the same vessel passed through the Bosphorus into the Mediterranean. Required by international treaty to declare details of the vessel's complement, the USSR described its new shipborne fighters as 'Yak-36s', leading to some confusion among Western analysts until 1984, when East European magazines began to use the type's correct Yak-38 designation.

Powered by a single 68-kN (15,300-lb st) Soyuz/Tumanskii R27V-300 turbojet with twin vectoring nozzles, the Yak-38 also has a pair of 30-kN (6,725-lb st) Koliesov/Rybinsk RD-36-35FVR lift jets mounted in tandem immediately aft of the cockpit. The vectoring nozzles are controlled by a separate lever, but this is linked to the throttle by a gate which limits nozzle movement angles

Yakovlev Yak-38 'Forger'

according to the throttle setting.

Up to four pylons can be fitted under the inboard sections of the wing, and these can carry a theoretical maximum weapon load of about 2000 kg (4,409 lb), although two pylons are normally left empty. Yak-38s have been seen armed with UV-16-57 and UV-32-57 rocket pods, R60 (AA-8 'Aphid') AAMs, bombs of up to 500 kg (1,102 lb), and various cannon pods. Auxiliary fuel tanks can be carried by some modernised and late production aircraft, which bear the designation **Yak-38M**.

The Yak-38's unique operating and handling characteristics made the construction of a two-seat trainer essential. The resulting **Yak-38U** has tandem cockpits under separate sideways-hinging canopies, with the longer nose having a pronounced 'droop'. A constant-section plug in the rear fuselage compensates for the longer nose, but fin area is not increased. The Yak-38U lacks underwing pylons, IR sensor and ranging radar, and thus has no combat capability.

Improvements during service included the provision of auxiliary blow-in doors in the sides of the main intakes, and fore-and-aft fences on each side of the upper fuselage intake for the lift jets. The basic colour scheme worn by these aircraft is also changing. The dark green anti-corrosion paint used on the undersides is retained, but the dark blue topsides are giving way to grey upper surfaces.

The Yak-38 has often been proposed as a land-based attack aircraft (like Britain's Harrier) and has been demonstrated operating from a lorry-towed take-off and landing platform. With the aircraft's wings folded, the platform folds up to become a trailer. During 1980/81 a handful of Yak-38s were deployed to Afghanistan for operational trials and evaluation against the Su-25. The Yak's limited payload and high accident rate made the result a foregone conclusion.

Production of the 'Forger' was limited to about 90 aircraft, and of these 37 are known to have been lost, resulting in 32 ejections (19 automatic) all of which were successful. When deployed, each carrier had a squadron with 12 single-seaters and two trainers. Reports that the Yak-38 has been retired from service or permanently withdrawn from deck operations are almost certainly premature since, although *Minsk* and *Novorossiysk* are being mothballed, another of the 'Kiev'-class carriers (*Gorshkov*, formerly *Baku*) remains in service and *Kiev* itself is under repair. Certainly the Yak-38's replacement, the Yak-141 'Freestyle', is nowhere near service entry, and the portion of the **AV-MF** which remains under Russian control is unlikely to be willing to give up its only operational shipborne strike fighter.

SPECIFICATION

Yakovlev Yak-38 'Forger-A'
Wing: span 7.32 m (24 ft 0.2 in); width folded 4.88 m (16 ft 0.1 in); aspect ratio 2.9; area 18.50 m² (199.14 sq ft)
Fuselage and tail: length 15.50 m (50 ft 10.3 in); height 4.37 m (14 ft 4 in); tailplane span 3.81 m (12 ft 6 in); wheel track 2.90 m (9 ft 6 in); wheel base 5.50 m (18 ft 0 in)
Powerplant: one MNPK 'Soyuz' (Tumanskii) R-27V-300 turbojet rated at 66.68 kN (14,991 lb st) and two RKBM (Koliesov) RD-36-35FVR lift jets each rated at 31.87 kN (7,175 lb st)
Weights: operating empty 7485 kg (16,501 lb) including pilot; normal take-off 11700 kg (25,794 lb) for vertical take-off; maximum take-off 13000 kg (28,660 lb) for short take-off
Fuel and load: internal fuel about 2900 litres (766 US gal); external fuel up to two 600-litre (158.5-US gal) drop tanks; maximum ordnance 2000 kg (4,409 lb)
Speed: maximum level speed 'clean' at 11000 m (36,090 ft) 1009 km/h (544 kt; 627 mph) and at sea level 978 km/h (528 kt; 608 mph)
Range: combat radius 370 km (200 nm; 230 miles) on a hi-lo-hi attack mission with maximum warload, or 240 km (130 nm; 150 miles) on a lo-lo-lo attack mission with maximum warload, or 185 km (100 nm; 115 miles) on a hi-hi-hi patrol mission with AAMs and drop tanks for a 75-minute loiter
Performance: maximum rate of climb at sea level 4500 m (14,764 ft) per minute; service ceiling 12000 m (39,370 ft)

Yakovlev **Yak-40 'Codling'**

The **Yak-40** was designed as a feederliner to replace the Lisunov Li-2 (the Soviet-built DC-3) and Il-14 in Aeroflot service. The prototype first flew on 21 October 1966. Good short-field performance was achieved by a lightly-loaded high-lift wing, and three powerful tail-mounted engines, which also kept cabin noise levels low. A hydraulically actuated ventral door with a built-in airstair allows passenger access without external steps, and an APU allows self-starting. Accommodating up to 32 passengers, the Yak-40 has become a popular military staff and VIP transport and serves with the air forces of **Bulgaria, Cambodia, Cuba, Ethiopia, Guinea Bissau, Laos, Poland, Syria, Vietnam,** **Yugoslavia** and **Zambia**. A proposed twin-fan Yak-40 conversion, the **Yak-40TL**, has not yet won any military orders.

SPECIFICATION

Yakovlev Yak-40 'Codling'
Wing: span 25.00 m (82 ft 0.25 in); aspect ratio 8.93; area 70.00 m² (753.50 sq ft)
Fuselage and tail: length 20.36 m (66 ft 9.5 in); height 6.40 m (21 ft 4 in); tailplane span 7.50 m (24 ft 7.25 in); wheel track 4.52 m (14 ft 10 in); wheel base 7.465 m (24 ft 6 in)
Powerplant: three ZMDB Progress (Ivchyenko) AI-25 turbofans each rated at 14.71 kN (3,307 lb st)
Weights: empty 8580 kg (18,916 lb); normal take-off

Poland's Yak-40s are operated by the 38th Special Transport Regiment based at Warsaw-Okecie. The unit has absorbed many aircraft from the national airline, LOT, into its fleet.

13150 kg (28,990 lb); maximum take-off 13700 kg (30,203 lb)
Fuel and load: internal fuel 3000 kg (6,614 lb); external fuel none; maximum payload 2790 kg (6,151 lb)
Speed: maximum level speed 'clean' at optimum altitude 600 km/h (324 kt; 373 mph); maximum cruising speed at optimum altitude 550 km/h (297 kt;

342 mph); economical cruising speed at optimum altitude 500 km/h (270 kt; 311 mph)
Range: 1600 km (863 nm; 994 miles)
Performance: take-off run 340 m (1,115 ft) at normal take-off weight or 360 m (1,181 ft) at maximum take-off weight; take-off distance to 15 m (50 ft) 1310 m (4,298 ft) at normal take-off weight or 450 m (1,476 ft) at MTOW; landing run 340 m (1,115 ft)

Yakovlev **Yak-42 'Clobber'**

Although sharing the same basic configuration as the Yak-40, the **Yak-42** 'Clobber' is an all-new design accommodating up to 120 passengers, and features a swept wing. The first prototype, with only 11° leading edge sweep, flew on 7 March 1975 and was followed by a second with 23° sweep, like the production aircraft. A number of Yak-42s serve as testbeds, including the **Yak-42E-LL** propfan development aircraft and the **Yak-42F**, which carries huge underwing equipment pods and is used for earth resources work and electro-optical research. A handful may be in use as military transports.

Yakovlev **Yak-44**

The status of the **Yak-44** is unknown. A twin turboprop aircraft, the Yak-44 is similar in appearance and concept to the US Navy's E-2C Hawkeye and may have been selected for service on the *Kuznetsov* after the An-74 'Madcap' was abandoned.

Yakovlev **Yak-50/52/53**

Derived from the Yak-18, the **Yak-50** was a single-seat competition aerobatic aircraft designed for the 1976 World Aerobatic Championship. A tricycle undercarriage two-seat training version, the **Yak-52**, was built by IAv Bacau in Romania (described separately under Aerostar), along with the similar (but single-seat) **Yak-53**. Yak-52s serve in large numbers with **Russia**'s paramilitary DOSAAF, which is administered by the CIS air force and is used as the basic flying training organisation for military and civilian pilots.

The **Yak-54** and **Yak-55** are two- and single-seat versions of a high-performance aerobatic design.

Yakovlev **Yak-41 'Freestyle'**

The **Yak-41** was developed as a supersonic replacement for the Yak-38 for service aboard the Soviet navy's 'Kiev'-class carriers. Development began during 1975. Spotted by a Western satellite at Zhukhovskii during the mid-1980s, the new (and still unflown) aircraft was assigned the reporting name **'Ram-T'** before the standard reporting name **'Freestyle'** was adopted in 1988. The first of two flying prototypes (in addition to two static test airframes) made its maiden flight in March 1989, in the hands of chief test pilot Andrei Sinitsin, under the bureau designation **Yak-141**. If it enters service, the designation **Yak-41** will be used.

The flight test programme progressed smoothly (apart from some early recirculation problems) until October 1991, when the second prototype, coded '77', was badly damaged in a landing accident on the *Gorshkov*. The rear fuselage suffered damage from an engine fire, and the forward fuselage was reportedly damaged when the pilot ejected. It was at one time suggested that it would be rebuilt as the prototype **Yak-41M**, but this was not funded.

The **Yak-141** is powered by a single 152-kN (34,150-lb st) Koptychenko R-79V-300 lift-cruise engine. The engine produces about 20 per cent less thrust in the hover mode. The main nozzle can be rotated

The remarkable Yak-141 has all the features of a modern supersonic fighter, yet incorporates V/STOL technology. Air defence and anti-shipping were the intended roles.

through 95° to give some forward thrust for braking or to move backwards in the hover. The main engine is augmented by a pair of 39-kN (8,767-lb) Rybinsk/Kuznetsov RD-41 (also quoted as RD-36) lift jets mounted in tandem, inclined about 15° aft. To facilitate the transition to forward flight, the nozzles can be vectored further aft to about 24°, and to give thrust braking can be angled forward to 2°. Retractable intake and exhaust doors are located above and below the fuselage immediately behind the cockpit.

A short take-off is achieved by rotating the nozzle of the main engine to 65° during the take-off roll, simultaneously increasing the thrust of the lift jets. An even shorter take-off roll (claimed as 5 m/16.4 ft) can be achieved by rotating the nozzle to 65° before take-off. Because afterburner is used during such short take-offs, runway surfaces can suffer heat damage. For this reason, steel matting is usually used in preference to a concrete runway.

The 'Freestyle's' controls are actuated by a triplex full-authority digital FBW control system with mechanical backup. Yakovlev claims that this gives a level of agility broadly comparable with that enjoyed by the MiG-29 but, in fact, manoeuvrability is considerably less impressive, although the main engine can be vectored in forward flight (VIFFed) to reduce turn radius or make

an unpredictable change in the plane of flight. Harrier operators have found VIFFing to be a valuable combat technique, although it does have the disadvantage of killing energy at an alarming rate, and must be used with caution.

The Yak-141 is claimed to have 'the same radar as the MiG-29', but whether this means the elderly N-019 of the basic 'Fulcrum' or the N-010 of the MiG-29M is uncertain. The aircraft also features a laser/TV target designator, a helmet-mounted sighting system, and avionics systems similar to the MiG-29 and Su-27. Four underwing weapons pylons are provided, all of them inboard of the wing fold, and a fifth pylon is provided under the centre fuselage. This can carry a 2000-litre (440-Imp gal) conformal fuel tank. Provision is made under the port side of the fuselage for a single GSh-30-1 30-mm cannon, with a 120-round ammunition tank.

Yakovlev began studies of a redesigned

Yak-141 following Operation Desert Storm, hoping to produce a land-based STOL fighter of the kind which might have been able to operate from Iraqi airfields even after coalition air attacks. This, it was hoped, would appeal to the Russian air force. The new version would have a new, more powerful version of the R-79 engine, a strengthened undercarriage and uprated brakes (to allow a shorter 120-m/394-ft landing run), and increased internal fuel capacity. The wing is redesigned to be trapezoidal in shape, similar to that of the YF-22, and the LERXes are extended forward to the intake lips. A wraparound windscreen and bubble canopy would also be added.

Funding difficulties have led Yakovlev to seek international partners for further development of all variants of the aircraft, discussing the project with Indian and South African aerospace companies, and perhaps with China and Abu Dhabi.

SPECIFICATION

Yakovlev Yak-141 'Freestyle'
Wing: span 10.10 m (33 ft 1.75 in); width folded 5.90 m (19 ft 4.25 in)
Fuselage and tail: length 18.30 m (60 ft 0 in); height 5.00 m (16 ft 5 in)
Powerplant: one MNPK 'Soyuz' R-79V-300 rated at 107.67 kN (24,206 lb st) dry and 152.00 kN (34,171 lb st) with afterburning, and two RKBM RD-41 each rated at 41.78 kN (9,392 lb st) dry
Weights: maximum take-off 19500 kg (42,989 lb) for short take-off
Fuel and load: maximum ordnance 2600 kg (5,732 lb)
Speed: maximum level speed 'clean' at 11000 m (36,090 ft) 1800 km/h (971 kt; 1,118 mph)
Range: 2100 km (1,133 nm; 1,305 miles) after STO with drop tanks or 1400 km (755 nm; 870 miles) after VTO with internal fuel
Performance: service ceiling more than 15000 m (49,215 ft)

Zlin 42/43

Zlin Aircraft Moravan Aeronautical Works
CR-765 81 Otrokovice
Czech Republic

Featuring side-by-side seating and a 180-hp (134-kW) Avia M 137AZ engine, the **Zlin Z 42** basic trainer first flew on 17 October 1967 and was adopted by the East German air force as its primary trainer. The **Z 43**, flown 10 December 1968, provided two additional seats behind the pilots and a 210-hp (157-kW) Avia M 337A engine. Small batches of Z 43s were acquired by East Germany and **Hungary**, and by the **Czechoslovakian air force** for liaison duties, and the type remains operational with the latter two. The **Zlin 142** and **143** are current production versions of the Z 42 and Z 43, with several variants available, including the **Zlin 242L** with Lycoming engine. The latter is operated by **Slovenia**.

Hungary operates four of the four-seat Zlin Z 43s on liaison duties. They serve with 2 Flight.

SPECIFICATION

Zlin 43
Wing: span 9.76 m (32 ft 0.2 in); area 14.50 m² (156.1 sq ft)

Fuselage and tail: length 7.75 m (25 ft 5 in); height 2.91 m (9 ft 6.5 in); tailplane span 3.00 m (9 ft 10 in); wheel track 2.44 m (8 ft); wheel base 1.75 m (5 ft 9 in)
Powerplant: one Avia M 337 AK piston engine rated at 210 hp (156.5 kW)
Weights: equipped 730 kg (1,609 lb); maximum take-off 1350 kg (2,976 lb)
Fuel and load: internal fuel 130 litres (28.5 Imp gal)
Speed: maximum level speed 'clean' at sea level 235 km/h (127 kt; 146 mph); cruising speed 210 km/h (113 kt; 130 mph)
Range: standard range 610 km (325 nm; 375 miles);

Performance: maximum rate of climb at sea level 330 m (1,082 ft) per minute; service ceiling 5000 m (16,405 ft); take-off run 220 m (722 ft) at normal take-off weight; take-off distance to 15 m (50 ft) 540 m

(1,772 ft) at maximum take-off weight; landing run 190 m (624 ft) at normal landing weight
g limits: -3.5 to +6 at aerobatic weight, -3 to +5 at normal take-off weight and -1.5 to +3.8 at MTOW

Zlin 326 and 526

The **Zlin Z 26** family was launched with a prototype first flight in 1947 and remained in production for some 30 years until 1980, with nearly 2,000 built. Successive variants ranged from the **Z 126** to the **Z 726**, the latter appearing in 1973, and included single-seat and tandem two-seat models, and versions with fixed or retractable undercarriages. Principal military users, of the **Z 326** and **Z 526** variants, included the air forces of **Czechoslovakia**, **Cuba**, **Egypt**, East Germany and **Mozambique**. Small-scale use continues with these air forces except in Germany, and possibly at the Air Force Academy in the former **Yugoslavia**, where the Z 526 has been used for liaison and recreational flying.

SPECIFICATION

Zlin 526 Trener-Master
Wing: span 10.60 m (34 ft 9 in); aspect ratio 7.26; area 15.45 m² (166.31 sq ft)
Fuselage and tail: length 7.80 m (25 ft 7 in); height 2.06 m (6 ft 9 in)
Powerplant: one Walter Minor 6-III piston engine rated at 160 hp (119 kW)
Weights: empty equipped 680 kg (1,499 lb); normal take-off 940 kg (2,072 lb) for aerobatics; maximum take-off 975 kg (2,150 lb)
Fuel and load: internal fuel 97 litres (25.6 US gal); external fuel up to two 68-litre (18-US gal) tip tanks; ordnance none
Speed: maximum level speed 'clean' at sea level

238 km/h (157 kt; 181 mph); cruising speed at optimum altitude 205 km/h (110 kt; 127 mph)
Range: ferry range 980 km (529 nm; 609 miles); standard range 580 km (313 nm; 360 miles)
Performance: maximum rate of climb at sea level 300 m (984 ft) per minute; service ceiling 5000 m

(16,405 ft); take-off run 230 m (755 ft) at normal take-off weight; landing run 135 m (443 ft) at normal landing weight

Egypt retains a few Zlin 326s for training and aerobatics.

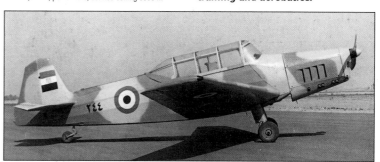

INDEX